TABLE OF CONTENTS

Repeater Listings

A TECHNOLOGY BREAKTHROUGH
New Advanced VX-8 Series GPS/APRS® Handheld Transceivers
Choose the Yaesu that meets your APRS® operating preferences in the field
Bluetooth®
50/144/(222)*/430 MHz
FM 5 W /AM 1 W (50 MHz) Triple Band Handheld
VX-8DR
(7.4 V 1,100 mAh Lithium Ion battery/FNB-101LI and battery charger/NC-86A included)
All-in-one Prestigious Tri-band Transceiver
Bluetooth® for hands-free Operation with optional accessories
Waterproof/Submersible IPX 7 rated - 3 ft for 30 minutes
144/430 MHz
FM 5 W Dual Band Handheld
VX-8GR
(7.4 V 1,100 mAh Lithium Ion battery/FNB-101LI and battery charger/NC-86A included)
144/430 MHz Dual Band Transceiver with GPS unit included
Built-in GPS Antenna - Waterproof
Wide Band Receive for 108-999 MHz (Cellular blocked - US Version)
Supports APRS® communication by the Built-in Worldwide Standard AX.25 Data TNC
The VX-8 series radios are compatible with the world wide standard APRS® (Automatic Packet reporting System) using the GPS system to locate and exchange position information.
• SmartBeaconing™ Function
• Memories to list 50 stations
• Memories to store 30 APRS® messages
• DIGI-PATH routing indication function
• 8 DIGI-PATH routing settings
• GPS Compass Display - "Heading Up" or "North Up"
• APRS® Symbol Icon pre-set function
• Clearly displayed APRS® Beacon Messages
• Selective Message Received indicated by Flashing LED
For the latest Yaesu news, visit us on the Internet:
http://www.yaesu.com
YAESU
The radio
YAESU USA
6125 Phyllis Drive,
Cypress, CA 90630
(714) 827-7600

FOREWORD

This new 42nd edition of the *ARRL Repeater Directory* contains information provided by frequency coordinators through early February 2013. These dedicated amateurs volunteer their services and strive to provide interference-free operation and we all appreciate their contributions. Without these coordinators, the *Repeater Directory* could not exist.

We depend on reader suggestions to improve each edition. It was reader feedback that brought the separate D-STAR and APCO 25 sections. Reader feedback also resulted in the EchoLink, IRLP and WIRES-II listings. If you have more suggestions for future *Directories*, please let us know. You can simply drop an e-mail message to **pubsfdbk@arrl.org.**

David Sumner, K1ZZ
Chief Executive Officer, ARRL

Newington, CT
February 2013

ANNUAL UPDATE INFORMATION

This edition of the *Repeater Directory* has been completely revised. Updates were received from all coordinators recognized by the National Frequency Coordinators' Council (NFCC) throughout the United States and Canada. In the few areas, noted throughout the book, served by a coordinator not recognized by the NFCC, information was provided by coordinating bodies seeking NFCC recognition.

FOREIGN LISTINGS

Listings outside the United States and Canada have been moved to ARRL's comprehensive reciprocal licensing Web site. ARRL welcomes thesubmission of additional foreign listings. Overseas travelers should refer to **www.arrl.org/international-regulatory**

InnovAntennas.us
Performance through Innovation
New For VHF!
Lightweight
OWL
(Optimized Wideband Low-impedance) Yagi
• Light weight for portable/backpacking
• 50 Ohm Closed Loop Direct Feed
• Great Pattern and Wide Bandwidth
• Stable Performance in All Weather
• Rear Mount Versions Available
Heavyweight
LFA-Q
(Loop Fed Array Quad) Yagi
• Full Wave Loops for High Gain
• EmComm Rugged, Because Failure is Not an Option!
• 50 Ohm Direct Feed
• Exceptional Pattern and Wide Bandwidth
• Models Available on 6 Meters through 70 cm
Info on our full line of HF, VHF and UHF antennas and equipment is at
www.InnovAntennas.us (North & South America) and www.InnovAntennas.com (Europe and ROW).
Toll Free: (US) 888-998-8541 - (UK) (0)800 0124 205

CHAPTER ONE

GENERAL INFORMATION

This chapter will address repeater operating practices, give you a few user notes, and discuss what to do if your repeater experiences jamming. A section listing CTCSS tone frequencies is also included for your information.

Repeater Operating Practices

The following suggestions will assist you in operating a repeater "like you've been doing it for years."

1) Monitor the repeater to become familiar with any peculiarities in its operation.

2) To initiate a contact simply indicate that you are on frequency. Various geographical areas have different practices on making yourself known, but, generally, "This is NUØX monitoring" will suffice. Please don't "ker-chunk" (key up without identifying yourself) the repeater "just to see if it's working."

3) Identify legally; you must identify at the end of a transmission or series of transmissions and at least once each 10 minutes during the communication.

4) Pause between transmissions. This allows other hams to use the repeater (someone may have an emergency). On most repeaters a pause is necessary to reset the timer.

5) Keep transmissions short and thoughtful. Your "monologue" may prevent someone with an emergency from using the repeater. If you talk long enough, you may actually time out the repeater. Your transmissions are being heard by many listeners, including non-hams with "public service band" monitors and scanners. Don't give a bad impression of our service.

6) Use simplex whenever possible. If you can complete your QSO on a direct frequency, there is no need to tie up the repeater and prevent others from using it.

7) Use the minimum amount of power necessary to maintain communications. This FCC regulation [97.313(a)] minimizes the possibility of accessing distant repeaters on the same frequency.

8) Don't break into a contact unless you have something to add. Interrupting is no more polite on the air than it is in person.

9) Repeaters are intended primarily to facilitate mobile operation. During the commuter rush hours, base stations should relinquish the repeater to mobile stations; some repeater groups have rules that specifically address this practice.

10) Many repeaters are equipped with autopatch facilities which, when properly accessed, connect the repeater to the telephone system to provide a public service. The FCC has liberalized Part 97.113 regarding business communications by amateurs. Amateur operators may not accept compensation for the use of their radios. Under certain conditions, however, the radio/autopatch can be utilized to make appointments and order items. This, though, is a decision that is made by the local repeater owner, so check with yours before making such calls. Autopatch facilities should never be used to avoid a toll call or where regular telephone service is available. Remember, autopatch privileges that are abused may be rescinded.

11) All repeaters are assembled and maintained at considerable expense and inconvenience. Usually an individual or group is responsible, and those who are regular users of a repeater should support the efforts of keeping the repeater on the air. Repeater owners may restrict individuals from using their machines, and the FCC expects users to comply with these restrictions. See Section 97.205(e) of the FCC's rules.

USER INFORMATION

Except where noted, repeaters are listed according to their Geographic Area (metropolitan area or county). There are, however, some state Frequency Coordinators who prefer to list their systems alphabetically by location.

This directory lists private (closed) repeater systems as well as open systems. Many private systems, including repeaters, remote bases, control and link channels are in properly coordinated operation on authorized frequencies but are not included in this directory. This is especially common on the 220 and MHz bands, commonly utilized for linking and/or remote control systems. Please consult your Frequency Coordinator for their recommendations for operating frequencies on new repeaters, remote bases or control links.

With an increase in the number of reports of repeater-to-repeater interference, the FCC is placing more emphasis on repeaters being coordinated. Repeater coordination is an example of voluntary self-regulation within the Amateur Service. Non-coordinated repeater operation may imply non-conformance with locally recognized band plans (eg, an unusual frequency split) or simply that the repeater trustee has not yet applied for, or received "official" recognition from the Frequency Coordinator. Known non-coordinated repeaters are indicated in this directory with a pound sign (#) in the Notes field. This symbol does not indicate anything about the relative merit of any particular repeater.

PLEASE NOTE: It is the responsibility of the TRUSTEE to provide the Frequency Coordinator with annual updates for inclusion in the *ARRL Repeater Directory*. Most coordination organizations have their own criteria for annual updates.

REPEATER-TO-REPEATER INTERFERENCE

In an effort to resolve repeater-to-repeater interference complaints, FCC has adopted the following rules. Where an amateur radio station in repeater or auxiliary operation causes harmful interference to the repeater or auxiliary operation of another amateur radio station, the two are equally and fully responsible for resolving the interference unless one station's operation is coordinated and the other's is not. In that case, the station engaged in the non-coordinated operation has primary responsibility to resolve the interference. See Sections 97.201 (c) and 97.205 (c) of the Commission's Rules.

REPEATER JAMMERS AND THE LOCAL INTERFERENCE COMMITTEE

Interference on VHF or UHF repeaters is primarily a local problem requiring local resolution. This kind of problem varies from non-existent in some parts of the country to extremely serious in others. The Amateur Auxiliary mechanism for dealing with any local amateur-to-amateur interference (primarily on VHF) is the local interference committee. The philosophy of the committee approach to solving this type of problem was provided in 1980 by the ARRL Interference Task Force. Many repeater groups have already successfully established local interference committees, some employing very sophisticated methods. The committee approach to solving this type of problem and Public Law 97-259 have proven most effective.

The Amateur Auxiliary incorporates this program of local interference committees into its comprehensive program of dealing with all types of amateur variations with the regulations. Since the ARRL Field Organization is the focus of Amateur Auxiliary involvement as recognized by agreement with FCC, the local interference committee now comes within the purview of the Section Manager's overall Amateur Auxiliary program. The local interference committee gains official standing through the Section Manager. It is, in effect, a "group appointment" of the Section Manager, for specific authorization to deal with local problems of amateur-to-amateur interference. Thus the local interference committee plays a crucially important role in the make-up of the Amateur Auxiliary.

For more information on local interference committees, Amateur Auxiliary and the ARRL Field Organization, contact your ARRL Section Manager, or the *Field and Educational Services Department* at ARRL HQ.

What follows is a discussion of some of the specialized features used in repeater listings in the Directory.

NOTES AND SPECIAL FEATURES

LOCATION — The city, town, or site at which a repeater is located.
OUTPUT — The output frequency in megahertz.
INPUT — The frequency offset (difference between input and output frequencies). Either a (+) or (–). A frequency printed in the input field indicates a "non-standard" offset.

Standard offsets by band:

29 MHz	- 100 kHz
52 MHz	- VARIOUS
144 MHz	- 600 kHz
222 MHz	- 1.6 MHz
440 MHz	- 5 MHz
902 MHz	- 12 MHz
1240 MHz	- 12 MHz

CALL — The call sign of the repeater.

NOTES — How the repeater may be accessed and other specialized features are indicated by the following abbreviations:

#	- Uncoordinated System
o	- Open system
Bi	- Bi-lingual system
c	- Closed, limited access system
LiTZ	- (Ltz) Long-Tone Zero. Used to alert users to an emergency in some areas of the country. A more in-depth discussion of LiTZ systems and their usage follows later in this chapter.
t	- Tone-Access (CTCSS tone) required to access the system.
TT	- Touch-Tone® access to specialized features
RB	- Remote Base (Auxiliary)
SNP	- Shared Non-Protected pair. In some areas there are repeater frequencies listed as SNP.

These frequencies are intended to provide spectrum for experimental repeaters, search and rescue operations, portable public service systems and to act as a holding place for repeaters awaiting coordination. Users of SNP frequencies do so under the following guidelines:

1) The frequencies are shared by all users.
2) Operators receive no protection from other co-channel users.
3) All systems use CTCSS or other approved method of limited access.
4) The frequency coordinator shall coordinate the CTCSS tones.

SPECIALIZED FEATURES:

a	- autopatch
(CA)	- closed autopatch
e	- emergency power
E-SUN	- solar power
E-WIND	- wind power
l	- linked or crossband system
p	- portable system
PKT	- digital/packet capability
r	- RACES affiliated
s	- ARES affiliated
x	- wide area coverage system
y	- RTTY/ASCII system
z	- direct access to law enforcement
WX	- weather net/weather usage
EXP	- experimental system

SPONSOR — The sponsor of the repeater. Plus (+) sign indicates the listed call plus additional calls sponsor the repeater.

NOTE: Listings of two CTCSS tones in the notes field indicates both the input and output are tone encoded.

LiTZ OVERVIEW

Mutual Assistance Procedures for VHF/UHF FM
Brief Overview for ARRL Repeater Directory
By: Paul Newland, AD7I
35 Barrister Lane
Middletown, NJ 07748
ad7i@arrl.net

Introduction

One of the great features of Amateur Radio is it gives hams the ability to provide mutual assistance to one another. There are two common procedures currently in place for mutual assistance on VHF/UHF FM frequencies. The first is "LiTZ," a DTMF (Touch-Tone) based all-call priority alerting system. The second is the "Wilderness Protocol".

LiTZ (i - added to make it easier to pronounce)

LiTZ is a simple method to indicate to others on an amateur VHF/UHF FM radio channel that you have an immediate need to communicate with someone, anyone, regarding a priority situation or condition.

LiTZ stands for LONG TONE ZERO. The LiTZ signal consists of transmitting DTMF (Touch-Tone) Zero for at least 3 seconds. After sending the LiTZ signal the operator announces by voice the kind of assistance that is needed. For example:
(5-seconds-DTMF-zero) "This is KA7BCD. I'm on Interstate 5 between mile posts 154 and 155. There's a 3 car auto accident in the southbound lane. Traffic has been completely blocked. It looks like paramedics will be needed for victims. Please respond if you can contact authorities for help. This is KA7BCD."

If your situation does not involve safety of life or property, try giving a general voice call before using LiTZ. Use LiTZ only when your voice calls go unanswered or the people who respond can't help you.

When you see the notation "LiTZ" for a repeater in this directory that means that it's highly likely that someone will receive and respond to LiTZ signals transmitted on the input frequency of the repeater. Please note, however, that if a CTCSS tone is needed to access that repeater you should transmit that CTCSS tone along with your LiTZ signal.

The type and nature of calls that justify the use of LiTZ may vary from repeater to repeater, just as other uses vary. Here are some general guidelines that may be suitable for most repeaters and simplex calling channels. Items with a star (*) should be acceptable on any frequency at any time.

LiTZ Use Guidelines

Event/Situation	*Waking Hours (0700-2200 LT)*	*Sleeping Hours (2200-0700 LT)*
Calling CQ	no	no
Calling a buddy	no	no
Weekly Test of LiTZ	yes	no
Club Message	yes	no
Need Driving Directions	yes	no
Report Drunk Driver	yes	yes
Car Break Down	yes	yes
Safety of Life or Property	yes	yes

For more information on LiTZ and LiTZ decoders refer to *QST* (Oct 92, page 82; Nov 92, pages 108-110; Dec 95, pages 25-31).

Wilderness Protocol

The Wilderness Protocol is a suggestion that those outside of repeater range should monitor standard simplex channels at specific times in case others have priority calls. The primary frequency is 146.52 MHz, with 52.525, 223.5 446.0 and 1294.5 MHz serving as secondary frequencies. This system was conceived to facilitate communications between hams that were hiking or backpacking in uninhabited areas, outside repeater range. However, the Wilderness Protocol should not be viewed as something just for hikers. It can (and should) be used by everyone anywhere repeater coverage is unavailable. The protocol only becomes effective when many people use it.

The Wilderness Protocol recommends that those stations able to do so should monitor the primary (and secondary, if possible) frequency every three hours starting at 7 AM, local time, for 5 minutes (7:00-7:05 AM, 10:00-10:05 AM, ..., 10:00-10:05 PM). Additionally, those stations that have sufficient power resources should monitor for 5 minutes starting at the top of every hour, or even continuously.

Priority transmissions should begin with the LiTZ signal. CQ-like calls (to see who is out there) should not take place until four minutes after the hour.

For more information on the Wilderness Protocol refer to *QST* (Feb 94, page 100; Apr 94, pages 109; May 94, pages 103-104.).

CTCSS AND DCS INFORMATION

The purpose of CTCSS (PL)™ is to reduce co-channel interference during band openings. CTCSS (PL)™ equipped repeaters respond only to signals having the sub-audible CTCSS tone required for that repeater. These repeaters do not retransmit distant signals without the required tone, and congestion is minimized.

The standard Electronic Industries Association (EIA) tones, in hertz, with their Motorola alphanumeric designators are as follows:

67.0 - XZ	97.4 - ZB	141.3 - 4A	210.7 - M2
69.3 - WZ	100.0 - 1Z	146.2 - 4B	218.1 - M3
71.9 - XA	103.5 - 1A	151.4 - 5Z	225.7 - M4
74.4 - WA	107.2 - 1B	156.7 - 5A	233.6 - M5
77.0 - XB	110.9 - 2Z	162.2 - 5B	241.8 - M6
79.7 - WB	114.8 - 2A	167.9 - 6Z	250.3 - M7
82.5 - YZ	118.8 - 2B	173.8 - 6A	
85.4 - YA	123.0 - 3Z	179.9 - 6B	
88.5 - YB	127.3 - 3A	186.2 - 7Z	
91.5 - ZZ	131.8 - 3B	192.8 - 7A	
94.8 - ZA	136.5 - 4Z	203.5 - M1	

Some systems use tones not listed in the EIA standard. Motorola designators have been assigned to the most commonly used of these tones: 206.5 (8Z), 229.1 (9Z), and 254.1 (0Z). Some newer amateur transceivers support additional tones of 159.8, 165.5, 171.3, 177.3, 183.5, 189.9, 196.6 and 199.5 hertz.

Some newer amateur gear supports Digital Code Squelch (DCS), a similar form of access control less susceptible to false triggering than CTCSS. DCS codes are designated by three digit numbers and are enabled in a manner similar to CTCSS tones.

Those wishing to use a CTCSS or DCS equipped system should check equipment specifications prior to purchase to ensure capability for the specified tone(s) or code(s).

CHAPTER TWO

BAND PLANS

This chapter will address band plans. These exist only as "traffic control" devices, allowing the most efficient use of limited spectrum space and varied amateur interests. The band plans published herein were developed by ARRL. Also discussed are the Line "A" restrictions, and a map delineating repeater offsets is provided.

Although the FCC rules set aside portions of some bands for specific modes, there's still a need to further organize our space among user groups by "gentlemen's agreements." These agreements, or band plans, usually emerge by consensus of the band occupants, and are sanctioned by a national body like ARRL. For further information on band planning, please contact your ARRL Division Director (see any issue of *QST*).

VHF-UHF BAND PLANS

When considering frequencies for use in conjunction with a proposed repeater, be certain that both the input and output fall within subbands authorized for repeater use, and do not extend past the subband edges. FCC regulation 97.205(b) defines frequencies which are currently available for repeater use.

For example, a 2-meter repeater on exactly 145.50 MHz would be "out-of-band," as the deviation will put the signal outside of the authorized band segment.

Packet-radio operations under automatic control should be guided by Section 97.109(d) of the FCC Rules.

Regional Frequency Coordination

The ARRL supports regional frequency coordination efforts by amateur groups. Band plans published in the ARRL Repeater Directory are recommendations based on a consensus as to good amateur operating practice on a nationwide basis. In some cases, however, local conditions may dictate a variation from the national band plan. In these cases, the written determination of the regional frequency coordinating body shall prevail and be considered good amateur operating practice in that region.

28.000-29.700 MHz

Please note that this bandplan is a general recommendation. Spectrum usage can be different depending upon local and regional coordination differences. Please check with your Frequency Coordinator for information.

28.000 – 28.070	CW
28.070 – 28.150	Data/CW
28.120 – 28.189	Packet/Data/CW
28.190 – 28.225	Foreign CW Beacons
28.200 – 28.300	Domestic CW Beacons (*)
28.300 – 29.300	Phone
28.680	SSTV
29.300 – 29.510	Satellites
29.510 – 29.590	Repeater Inputs
29.600	National FM Simplex Frequency
29.610 – 29.690	Repeater Outputs

*User note: In the United States, automatically controlled beacons may only operate on 28.2-28.3 MHz [97.203(d)].

In 1980, the ARRL Board of Directors adopted the following recommendations for CTCSS tones to be voluntarily incorporated by 10 meter repeaters:

Call Area	*Tones*	*Call Area*	*Tones*
W1	131.8/91.5	W7	162.2/110.9
W2	136.5/94.8	W8	167.9/114.8
W3	141.3/97.4	W9	173.8/118.8
W4	146.2/100.0	W0	179.9/123.0
W5	151.4/103.5	VE	127.3/88.5
W6	156.7/107.2		

The following band plan for 6 meters was adopted by the ARRL Board of Directors at its July, 1991 meeting.

50-54 MHz

Please note that this bandplan is a general recommendation. Spectrum usage can be different depending on location and regional coordination differences. Please check with your Frequency Coordinator for information.

50.0-50.1	CW, beacons	
50.060-50.080		beacon subband
50.1-50.3	SSB,CW	
50.10-50.125		DX window
50.125	SSB calling	
50.3-50.6	all modes	
50.4	AM calling frequency	
50.6-50.8	nonvoice communications	
50.62		digital (packet) calling
50.8-51.0	radio remote control (20-kHz channels)	
	NOTE: Activities above 51.10 MHz are set on 20-kHz-spaced "even channels"	
51.0-51.1	Pacific DX window	
51.5-51.6	simplex (6 channels)	
51.12-51.48	repeater inputs (19 channels)	
51.12-51.18		digital repeater inputs
51.62-51.98	repeater outputs (19 channels)	
51.62-51.68		digital repeater outputs
52.0-52.48	repeater inputs (except as noted; 23 channels)	
52.02, 52.04		FM simplex
52.2		TEST PAIR (input)

52.5-52.98	repeater output (except as noted; 23 channels)
52.525	primary FM simplex
52.54	secondary FM simplex
52.7	TEST PAIR (output)
53.0-53.48	repeater inputs (except as noted; 19 channels)
53.0	base FM simplex
53.02	simplex
53.1, 53.2, 53.3, 53.4	radio remote control
53.5-53.98	repeater outputs (except as noted; 19 channels)
53.5, 53.6 53.7, 53.8	radio remote control
53.52-53.9	simplex

Notes: The following packet radio frequency recommendations were adopted by the ARRL Board of Directors in July, 1987.

Duplex pairs to consider for local coordination for uses such as repeaters and meteor scatter:

50.62-51.62	50.68-51.68	50.76-51.76
50.64-51.64	50.72-51.72	50.78-51.78
50.66-51.66	50.74-51.74	

Where duplex packet radio stations are to be co-existed with voice repeaters, use high-in, low-out to provide maximum frequency separation from low-in, high-out voice repeaters.

144-148 MHz

Please note that this bandplan is a general recommendation. Spectrum usage can be different depending on location and regional coordination differences. Please check with your Frequency Coordinator for information.

144.00-144.05	EME (CW)
144.05-144.10	General CW and weak signals
144.10-144.20	EME and weak-signal SSB
144.200	SSB calling frequency
144.20-144.275	General SSB operation
144.275-144.300	Propagation beacons
144.30-144.50	OSCAR subband
144.50-144.60	Linear translator inputs
144.60-144.90	FM repeater inputs
144.90-145.10	Weak signal and FM simplex (145.01,03,05,07,09 are widely used for packet radio)
145.10-145.20	Linear translator outputs
145.20-145.50	FM repeater outputs
145.50-145.80	Miscellaneous and experimental modes
145.80-146.00	OSCAR subband
146.01-146.37	Repeater inputs
146.40-146.58	Simplex (*)
146.52	National Simplex Calling Frequency
146.61-147.39	Repeater outputs
147.42-147.57	Simplex (*)
147.60-147.99	Repeater inputs

NOTES: (*) Due to differences in regional coordination plans the simplex frequencies listed may be repeater inputs/ outputs as well. Please check with local coordinators for further information.

1) Automatic/unattended operations should be conducted on 145.01, 145.03, 145.05, 145.07 and 145.09 MHz.

a) 145.01 should be reserved for inter-LAN use.

b) Use of the remaining frequencies should be determined by local user groups.

2) Additional frequencies within the 2-meter band may be designated for packet radio use by local coordinators.

Footnotes

Specific VHF/UHF channels recommended above may not be available in all areas of the US.

Prior to regular packet radio use of any VHF/UHF channel, it is advisable to check with the local frequency coordinator. The decision as to how the available channels are to be used should be based on coordination between local packet radio users.

Some areas use 146.40-146.60 and 147.40-147.60 MHz for either simplex or repeater inputs and outputs.

States use differing channel spacings on the 146-148 MHz band. For further information on which states are currently utilizing which spacing structure see the Offset Map immediately following.

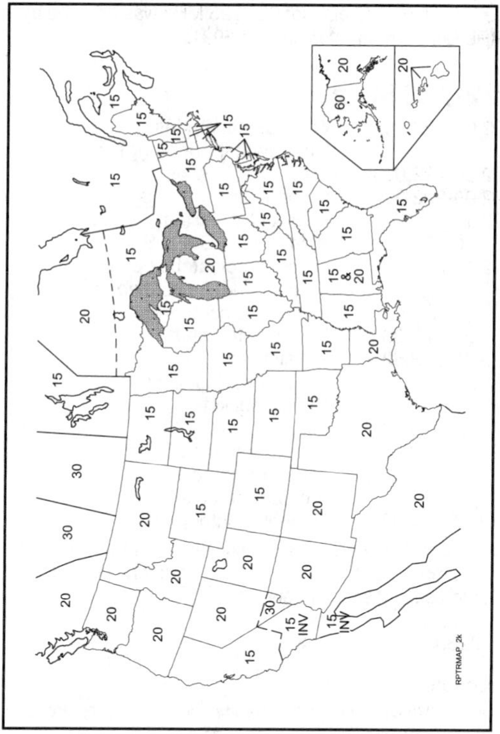

Note: This map shows channel spacing in the US and southern Canada. Spacing is in kHz unless otherwise specified. Please check with your Regional Frequency Coordinator for further information.

The following band plan for 222-225 MHz was adopted by the ARRL Board of Directors in July, 1991.

222-225 MHz

222.00-222.15	Weak signal modes (No repeater operating)
222.00-222.025	EME
222.05-222.060	Propagation beacons
222.1	SSB & CW Calling
222.10-222.150	Weak signal CW & SSB
222.15-222.25	Local coordinator's option: weak signal, ACSB, repeater inputs and control
222.25-223.38	FM repeater inputs only
223.40-223.52	FM simplex
223.50	Simplex calling
223.52-223.64	Digital, packet
223.64-223.70	Links, control
223.71-223.85	Local coordinator's option; FM simplex, packet, repeater outputs
223.85-224.98	Repeater outputs only

Notes: Candidate packet simplex channels shared with FM voice simplex. Check with your local fre-quency coordinator prior to use. Those channels are:

223.42	223.46
223.44	223.48

Footnotes

Specific VHF/UHF channels recommended above may not be available in all areas of the US.

Prior to regular packet radio use of any VHF/UHF channel, it is advisable to check with the local frequency coordinator. The decision as to how the available channels are to be used should be based on coordination between local packet radio users.

420-450 MHz

Please note that this bandplan is a general recommendation. Spectrum usage can be different depending on location and regional coordination differences. Please check with your Frequency Coordinator for information.

420.00-426.00	ATV repeater or simplex with 421.25 MHz video carrier, control links and experimental
426.00-432.00	ATV simplex with 427.25 MHz video carrier frequency
432.00-432.07	EME (Earth-Moon-Earth)
432.07-432.10	Weak signal CW
432.10	Calling frequency
432.10-432.30	Mixed-mode and weak-signal work
432.30-432.40	Propagation beacons
432.40-433.00	Mixed-mode and weak signal work
433.00-435.00	Auxiliary/repeater links
435.00-438.00	Satellite only (internationally)
438.00-444.00	ATV repeater input with 439.250-MHz video carrier frequency and repeater links
442.00-445.00	Repeater inputs and outputs (local option)
445.00-447.00	Shared by auxiliary and control links, repeaters and simplex (local option)
446.00	National simplex frequency
447.00-450.00	Repeater inputs and outputs (local option)

The following packet radio frequency recommendations were adopted by the ARRL Board of Directors in January, 1988.

1) 100-kHz bandwidth channels

430.05	430.35	430.65
430.15	430.45	430.85
430.25	430.55	430.95

2) 25-kHz bandwidth channels

431.025	441.000	441.050
440.975	441.025	441.075

Footnotes

Specific VHF/UHF channels recommended above may not be available in all areas of the US.

Prior to regular packet radio use of any VHF/UHF channel, it is advisable to check with the local frequency coordinator. The decision as to how the available channels are to be used should be based on coordination between local packet radio users.

Line A Restrictions

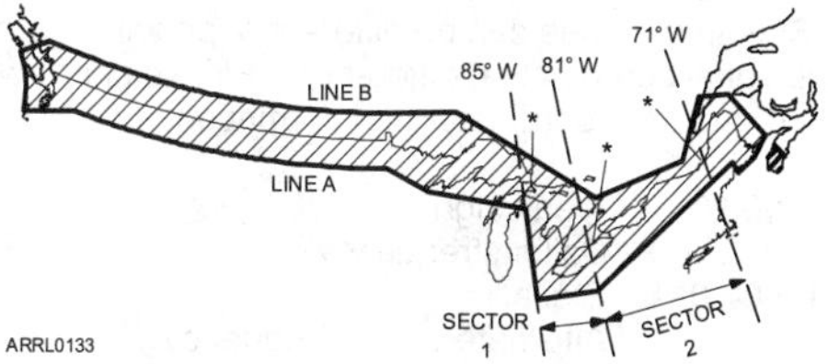

The band is shared by amateurs with government Radio Location Services (RADAR); amateurs must not interfere with these priority government stations. As part of WARC-79 proceedings, the 420-430 MHz portion of the band was removed from the Amateur Radio Service north of Line "A" (see figure).

In a later action, FCC allocated portions of the band 421-430 MHz to the Land Mobile Service within 50-mile radii centered on Buffalo, Detroit and Cleveland. Amateur stations south of Line "A" in the vicinities of these cities may continue to operate in the 421-430 MHz spectrum as long as they do not cause interference to land mobile or government radio-location users. Additionally, 50-watt PEP output power limitations apply to certain amateurs operating within circles of designated military installations in the US.
See 97.313(f).

902-928 MHz

Please note that this bandplan is a general recommendation. Spectrum usage can be different depending on location and regional coordination differences. Please check with your Frequency Coordinator for information.

902.0-903.0	Weak signal
902.1	Calling frequency
903.0-906.0	Digital
903.1	Alternate calling frequency
906.0-909.0	FM repeater inputs
909.0-915.0	Amateur TV
915.0-918.0	Digital
918.0-921.0	FM repeater outputs
921.0-927.0	Amateur TV
927.0-928.0	FM simplex and links

NOTE: A new bandplan is under development that reflects our need to avoid causing interference to AVM systems at 904-912 MHz and 918-926 MHz.

Notes: Adopted by the ARRL Board of Directors in July, 1989. The following packet radio frequency recommendations were adopted by the ARRL Board of Directors in January, 1988 as interim guidance. Two 3-MHz-bandwidth channels are recommended for 1.5 Mbit/s links. They are 903-906 MHz and 914-917 MHz with 10.7 MHz spacing.

Packet Footnotes

Specific VHF/UHF channels recommended above may not be available in all areas of the US.

Prior to regular packet radio use of any VHF/UHF channel, it is advisable to check with the local frequency coordinator. The decision as to how the available channels are to be used should be based on coordination between local packet radio users.

***Canadian amateurs note:** The Amateur Service will continue to have secondary status in the band 902-928 MHz throughout Canada, using any of the following emissions: N0N, A1A, A2A, A3A, A3E, C3F, F1A, F2A, F2B, F1C, F3E.*

Before operating in this band, Canadian amateur licensees are required to consult with their DOC District Office to ensure interference will not be caused to other services operating in the area as per Section 45 of the General Radio Regulations Part II, given in TRC 25.

Government of Canada shipborne radiolocation service is permitted within 150 km of the east and west coasts, Arctic Ocean, Hudson Bay, James Bay and up the St Lawrence River as far as Rimouski on precoordinated channels in the 902-928 MHz band.

Footnotes:

1) Extracts of FCC Rules & Regulations, 97.303(g)(1): No amateur station shall transmit from within the states of Colorado and Wyoming, bounded on the south by latitude 39 degrees North, on the north by latitude 42 degrees North, on the east by longitude 105 degrees West, and on the west by longitude 108 degrees West.(*)

(*) Waived July 2, 1990 to permit amateurs in the restricted areas to transmit in the following segments: 902.0-902.4, 902.6-904.4, 904.7-925.3, 925.7-927.3 and 927.7-928-MHz.

This band is allocated on a secondary basis to the Amateur Service subject to not causing harmful interference to, and not receiving protection from any interference due to the operation of, industrial, scientific and medical devices, automatic vehicle monitoring systems or government stations authorized in this band.

2) Coordinated frequency assignments are required.

3) ATV assignments should be made according to modulation type, e.g. VSB-ATV, SSB-ATV or combinations. Coordination of multiple users of a single channel in a local area can be achieved through isolation by means of cross-polarization and directional antennas.

4) Coordinated assignments at 100 kHz until allocations are filled, then assign 50 kHz until allocations are filled, before assigning 25 kHz channels.

5) Simplex services only; permanent users shall not be coordinated in this segment. High altitude repeaters or other unattended fixed operations are not permitted.

6) Voice and nonvoice operation.

7) Spread-spectrum requires FCC authorization.

8) Consult FCC (97.307) for allowable data rates and bandwidths.

The following band plan was adopted by the ARRL Board of Directors meeting in January, 1985.

1240-1300 MHz

Please note that this bandplan is a general recommendation. Spectrum usage can be different depending on location and regional coordination differences. Please check with your Frequency Coordinator for information.

1240-1246	ATV #1
1246-1248	Narrow-bandwidth FM point-to-point links and digital, duplex with 1258-1260.
1248-1252	Digital Communications
1252-1258	ATV #2
1258-1260	Narrow-bandwidth FM point-to-point links and digital, duplexed with 1246-1252
1260-1270	Satellite uplinks, experimental simplex ATV
1270-1276	Repeater inputs, FM and linear, paired with 1282-1288. (239 pairs, every 25 kHz, e.g. 1270.025, 050, etc.)
1271/1283	Non-coordinated test pair
1276-1282	ATV #3
1282-1288	Repeater outputs paired with 1270-1276
1288-1294	Wide band experimental, simplex ATV
1294-1295	Narrow band FM simplex, 25-kHz channels
1294.50	National FM Simplex calling
1295-1297	Narrow band weak signal (no FM)
1295-1295.80	STV, FAX, ACSSB experimental
1295.8-1296	Reserved for EME, CW expansion
1296-1296.05	EME exclusive
1296.07-1296.08	CW beacons

1296.1	CW/SSB calling frequency
1296.40-1296.60	Crossband linear translator input
1296.60-1296.80	Crossband linear translator output
1296.80-1297.00	Experimental beacons (exclusive)
1297-1300	Digital communication

Notes: The following packet radio frequency recommendations were adopted by the ARRL Board of Directors in January, 1988.

1) 2-MHz-bandwidth channels at:

1249.00	1251.00	1298.00

2) 100-kHz-bandwidth channels

1299.05	1299.45	1299.75
1299.15	1299.55	1299.85
1299.25	1299.65	1299.95
1299.35		

3) 25-kHz-bandwidth channels

1294.025	1294.125
1294.050	1294.150
1294.075	1294.175

1294.100 National packet simplex calling

Footnotes

1) Deleted

2) Coordinated assignments required

3) ATV assignments should be made according to modulation type (for example, VSB-ATV, SSB-ATV or combinations). Coordination of multiple users of a single channel in a local area can be achieved through isolation by means of cross polarization and directional antennas. DSB ATV may be used, but only when local and regional activity levels permit. The excess bandwidths from such users are secondary to the assigned services.

4) Coordinate assignments with 100-kHz channels, beginning at the lower end of the segment until allocations

are filled, then assign
50-kHz channels until allocations are filled before assigning 25-kHz channels.

5) Wide bandwidth experimental users are secondary to the satellite service and may be displaced upon the installation of any new satellites. Users are EIRP-limited to the noise floor of the satellites in service and may suffer interference from satellite uplinks.

6) Simplex services only: permanent users shall not be coordinated in this segment. High altitude repeaters or other unattended fixed operations are not permitted.

7) Voice and nonvoice operations.

8) Consult 47 CFR 97.307 for allowable data rates and bandwidths.

9) Provide guard bands at the higher frequency end of segments, as required, to avoid interference to ATV.

10) 1274.0-1274.2 and 1286.0-1286.2 MHz are optionally reserved for contiguous Linear Translators supporting multiple narrow bandwidth users. These may also be duplexed with other noncoordinated band segments.

The following band plan was adopted by the ARRL Board of Directors in January, 1991.

2300-2310 and 2390-2450 MHz

Please note that this bandplan is a general recommendation. Spectrum usage can be different depending on location and regional coordination differences. Please check with your Frequency Coordinator for information.

2300-2303	High-rate data
2303-2303.5	Packet radio
2303.5-2303.8	TTY, packet
2303.8-2303.9	Packet, TTY, CW, EME
2303.9-2304.1	CW, EME
2304.1-2304.2	CW, EME, SSB
2304.2-2304.3	SSB, SSTV, FAX, Packet, AM, AMTOR
2304.3-2304.32	Propagation beacon network
2304.32-2304.4	General propagation beacons
2304.4-2304.5	SSB, SSTV, ACSSB, FAX, Packet, AM, AMTOR experimental
2304.4	Calling frequency
2304.5-2304.7	Crossband linear translator input
2304.7-2304.9	Crossband linear translator output
2304.9-2305	Experimental beacons
2305-2305.2	FM simplex (25-kHz spacing)
2305.2	FM simplex calling frequency
2305.2-2306	FM simplex (25-kHz spacing)
2306-2309	FM repeaters (25-kHz) input
2309-2310	Control and auxiliary links
2390-2396	Fast-scan TV
2396-2399	High-rate data
2399-2399.5	Packet
2399.5-2400	Control and auxiliary links

2400-2403	Satellite
2403-2408	Satellite high-rate data
2408-2410	Satellite
2410-2413	FM repeaters (25-kHz spacing) output
2413-2418	High-rate data
2418-2430	Fast-scan TV
2430-2433	Satellite
2433-2438	Satellite high-rate data
2438-2450	Wideband FM, FSTV, FMTV, SS experimental

3300-3500 MHz

The following beacon subband was adopted by the ARRL Board of Directors in July, 1988.

3456.3-3456.4 Propagation beacons

5650-5925 MHZ

The following beacon subband was adopted by the ARRL Board of Directors in July, 1988.

5760.3-5760.4 Propagation beacons

10.000-10.500 GHZ

The following subband recommendation was adopted by the ARRL Board of Directors in January, 1987

10.368.1 GHz Narrow-band calling frequency

The following beacon subband was adopted by the ARRL Board of Directors in July, 1988.

10368.3-10368.4 Propagation beacons

CHAPTER THREE

REPEATER LISTINGS- COMMITTEES & COORDINATORS

Within the confines of this chapter you will find a description of repeater listing procedures, how and why repeaters are registered, and listings of Regional Frequency Coordinators. Also included for your information is a list of the ARRL Officers.

As you can imagine, many changes occur to the Frequency Coordinator's list during the course of the year. For the most current contact information of the Frequency Coordinator in your area, visit the ARRL Web site at: **www.arrl.org/nfcc**.

REPEATER LISTINGS

All repeater listings in the *Repeater Directory* are provided by regional frequency coordinators. Except for minor editorial changes and shuffling of field locations, all data appears exactly as it was submitted by the coordinator. If you notice any errors or omissions, please notify your frequency coordinator.

Repeater listings are accurate to the best of our ability; however, no guarantee of accuracy is made or implied. The listing of a repeater in the Repeater Directory does not imply that the listed repeater has any greater legal status than any other amateur station.

REPEATER REGISTRATION

Repeater registration and updates are necessary in order to compile a current and accurate *Repeater Directory*. In some cases the changes only involve the addition or deletion of a specialized feature—in other cases it may involve a frequency or location change. Your Frequency Coordinator is in charge of seeing to it that this updated information is provided to the *Repeater Directory* in a timely manner for publication.

Please note that all repeater registration is carried out through Frequency Coordinators.

ARRL Officers 2013

President
Kay C Craigie, N3KN
570 Brush Mountain Rd
Blacksburg, VA 24060
n3kn@arrl.org

First Vice President
Rick Roderick, K5UR
PO Box 1463
Little Rock, AR 72203
k5ur@arrl.org

Vice President
Bruce Frahm, KØBJ
1553 County Road T
Colby, KS 67701
k0bj@arrl.org

International Affairs Vice President
Jay Bellows, KØQB
1925 Bidwell St
West St Paul, MN 55118
k0qb@arrl.org

ARRL Headquarters
225 Main Street
Newington, CT
06111-1494
Phone: 860-594-0200
Fax: 860-594-0259
info@arrl.org

FREQUENCY COORDINATORS

The ARRL is not a Frequency Coordinator, nor does the ARRL "certify" coordinators. Frequency Coordinators are volunteers normally appointed by a coordinating body. The ARRL *Repeater Directory* reports only the fact of coordination or non-coordination as instructed by the coordinating body. Publication in the Repeater Directory does not constitute nor imply endorsement or recognition of the authority of such coordinators, as coordinators derive their authority from the voluntary participation of the entire amateur community in the areas they serve.

In some cases the person or group listed only compiles the information for listings in the Repeater Directory. In other cases the listed individual or group offers guidance but not coordination.

Frequency Coordinators keep extensive records of repeater input, output and control frequencies, including those not published in directories (at the owner's request). The coordinator will recommend frequencies for a proposed repeater in order to minimize interference with other repeaters and simplex operations. Therefore, anyone considering the installation of a repeater should check with the local frequency coordinator prior to such installation.

The following is a listing of groups or individuals for the United States and Canada who are active in Frequency Coordination and are acknowledged, by virtue of the recognition accorded them by the entire amateur community they serve, as the sole Frequency Coordinators in their respective jurisdictions.

ALABAMA

Alabama Repeater Council (ARC)
www.alabamarepeater council.org

Coordinator
Howard Grant, K4WWN
280 Martin Lane
Guntersville, AL 35976
coordinators@alabama repeatercouncil.org

President
Dave Drummond, W4MD
5001 Lakehurst Dr
Northport, AL 35473
coordinators@alabama repeatercouncil.org

ALASKA

www.alaskarepeaters.k17.net
Coordinator—South Central
Mel Bowns, KL7GG
23708 The Clearing
Eagle River, AK 99577
kl7gg@arrl.net

Coordinator—North, West, and Interior
Jerry Curry, KL7EDK
940 Vide Way
Fairbanks, AK 99712
jercurry@att.net

Coordinator—Panhandle
Jerry Prindle, KL7HFI
PO Box 210123
Auke Bay, AK 99821
kl7hfi@att.net

ARIZONA

Amateur Radio Council of Arizona (ARCA)
www.azfreqcoord.org

Chairman
Lance Halle, KW7LH
419 W. Cape Royal Ln
Phoenix, AZ 85029
602-902-6669
8AM-5PM MST M-F

6 meters (50 MHz)
Gary Duffield, WK7B
4102 W Paradise Ln
Phoenix, AZ 85053
602-843-7724

2 meters (144 MHz)
Rick Tannehill, W7RT
5410 W Diana Ave
Glendale, AZ 85302-4870
623-930-7507

222 MHz
Bill Jorden, K7KI
6861 Kenanna Pl
Tucson, AZ 85704
520-297-1666 (H)

420-440 MHz
Doug Pelley, WB7TUJ
PO Box 4355
Mesa, AZ 85211-4355
480-892-2929

440-450 MHz
Dennis Mills, WA7ZZT
Po Box 10416
Glendale, AZ 85318
623-934-4480

902 MHz
Walter Carter, WB4LDS
1715 W. Greenleaf Dr
Tucson, AZ 85746
520-741-0942 (H)

1200 MHz
Tom Sharp, WA9OXY
20619 N 21st St
Phoenix, AZ 85024-4411
602-569-6512 (H)
FAX 602-569-6599

2 GHz and Up
Troy Hall, WA7ELN
PO Box 899
Oracle, AZ 85623
520-896-2813 (H) evenings

Packet
George Strickroth, WA3PNT
13523 S. Hilltop Rd
Yuma, AZ 85365
928-341-0191

Database Coordinator
Dave Gorevin, N7OJZ
2310 E June St
Mesa, AZ 85213
480-890-0689

ARKANSAS

Arkansas Repeater Council (ARC)
www.arkansasrepeatercouncil.org

President
Mark Mullins, NN5NN
1 Foxboro Cir
Little Rock, AR 72209
nn5nn@ranch.cx

Coordinator
Bob King, W5LVB
217 Oak St
Hot Springs, AR 71901
w5lvb@arrl.net

CALIFORNIA—NORTHERN

Northern Amateur Relay Council of California (NARCC)
PO Box 8448
Santa Rosa, CA 95407-8448
www.narcc.org

CALIFORNIA—SOUTHERN

10 meters, 6 meters, 70 centimeters and above:
Southern California Repeater and Remote Base Association (SCRRBA)
PO Box 5967
Pasadena, CA 91117-5967
www.scrrba.org

2 meters
Two-Meter Area Spectrum Management Association
Attn: Technical Committee
358 S Main St #90
Orange, CA 92868-3834
www.tasma.org

Chairman
Bob Dingler, NO6B
PO Box 412
Walnut, CA 91788-0412
info@tasma.org

222 MHz
220 MHz Spectrum Management Association
Attn: 222 MHz Coordination Committee
21704 Devonshire St #220
Chatsworth, CA 91311-2949
www.220sma.org

Contact
Jim Fortney, K6IYK
PO Box 3419
Camarillo, CA 93011-3419
k6iyk@arrl.net

COLORADO

Colorado Council of Amateur Radio Clubs (CCARC)
PO Box 24244
Denver, CO 80224
www.ccarc.net

Chairman: Doug Sharp, K2AD **chairman@ccarc.net**

Vice Chairman: Jeff Ryan, KØRM, **k0rm@arrl.org**

Secretary: Phil Schechter, WØOJ; **secretary@ccarc.net**

Treasurer: Wayne Heinen, NØPOH, **n0poh@arrl.org**

Frequency Coordinator: Jim Reimer, ACØSO, **jgreimer@yahoo.com**

CONNECTICUT

Connecticut Spectrum Management Association (CSMA)
www.ctspectrum.com

Coordinator
Dana Underhill, KB1AEV
42 Douglas Dr
Enfield, CT 06082-2544
kb1aev@cox.net

DELAWARE

T-MARC—See Maryland

DISTRICT OF COLUMBIA

T-MARC—See Maryland

FLORIDA

Florida Repeater Council (FRC)
www.florida-repeaters.org

Database Manager
Dana Rodakis, K4LK
6280 Fairfield Ave South
St Petersburg, FL 33707-2323
coordinator@florida-repeaters.org

GEORGIA

Southeastern Repeater Association (SERA)
www.sera.org/ga.html

Director
Ron Johnson, WB4GWA
PO Box 306
Concord, GA 30206

Vice Director
John Davis, WB4QDX
201 Hanarry Dr
Lawrenceville, GA 30046

HAWAII

Hawaii State Repeater Advisory Council (HSRAC)
www.pdarrl.org/pacsec/HSRAC/index.html

Coordinator
Rick Ching, KH7O
PO Box 10868
Honolulu, HI 96816-2536
kh7o@arrl.net

IDAHO—SOUTHEAST

Southeast Idaho Coordination Committee (SEICC)

Coordinator
Rod Wilde, AB7OS
1061E 1100N
Shelley, ID 83274
ab7os@direcway.com

IDAHO—SOUTHWEST

Coordinator
Larry E. Smith, W7ZRQ
8106 Bobran St
Boise, ID 83709
larry.smith@idahoptv.org

IDAHO—PANHANDLE

IACC—See Eastern Washington

ILLINOIS

Illinois Repeater Association (IRA)
www.ilra.net

Coordinator
Aaron Collins, N9OZB
1338 S Arlington Hts Rd
Arlington Heights, IL 60085
collins@knowideas.com

INDIANA

Indiana Repeater Council
www.ircinc.org

Chairman
Dan Dahms, N9WNH
1320 E. Greenbriar Dr
Columbia City, IN 46725
260-503-4163
n9wnh@arrl.net

IRC Coordinator and
Database Admin
Charlie Sears, N9MEW
551 Mooreland Dr
New Whiteland, IN 46184
317-535-4829
n9mew@ircinc.org

Send Membership Applications, Renewals and Other Correspondence To:
Indiana Repeater Council Inc
PO Box 501642
New Castle, IN 46250

IOWA

Iowa Repeater Council (IRC)
www.iowarepeater.org

President
Chris Conklin, NØCF
126 Magnolia Dr
Cedar Falls, IA 50613

Coordinator
Dennis W. Crabb, WBØGGI
1306 4th Ave North
Denison, IA 51442-1413
dwcrabb@frontiernet.net

Secretary
Thomas G. Crabb, NØJLU
813 South 26th St
West Des Moines, IA 50265
tgcrabb.rphjd@juno.com

KANSAS

Kansas Amateur Repeater Council (KARC)
www.ksrepeater.com

Coordinator
Brian Short, KCØBS
12170 S Prairie Creek Pkwy
Olathe, KS 66061
kc0bs@arrl.net

KENTUCKY

Southeastern Repeater Association (SERA)
www.sera.org/ky.html

Director
Tim Osborne, K4TDO
PO Box 711
Hazard, KY 41702

LOUISIANA

Louisiana Council of Amateur Radio Clubs (LCARC)

Chair
Roger Farbe, N5NXL
12665 Roundsaville
Baton Rouge, LA 70818
n5nxl@bellsouth.net

Coordinator
Kevin Thomas, W5KGT
1573 Brownless Dr
Calhoun, LA 71225
lacoord@lacouncil.net

MAINE

(NESMC)
Apply for coordination online at **www.nesmc.org**, or you may apply by US mail:
New England Spectrum Management Council
PO Box 185
Berlin, MA 01503

10 Meter Coordinator
George Cleveland, WA1QGU
10m@nesmc.org

6 Meter Coordinator
George Cleveland, WA1QGU
6m@nesmc.org

2 Meter Coordinator
Bob DeMattia, K1IW
2m@nesmc.org

222 Coordinator
Bob Nelson, N1EUN
222@nesmc.org

440 Coordinator
Lou Harris, N1UEC
440@nesmc.org

902 and above Coordinator
Lew Collins, W1GXT
ghz@nesmc.org

MARYLAND

The Mid Atlantic Repeater Council (TMARC)
PO Box 1022
Savage, MD 20763-1022
www.tmarc.org

President
Dave Prestel, W8AJR
10160 Tanfield Ct
Ellicott City, MD 21042
w8ajr@arrl.net

MASSACHUSETTS

NESMC — See Maine

MICHIGAN—LOWER PENINSULA

Michigan Area Repeater Council (MARC)
2266 E Vermontville Hwy
Charlotte, MI 48813-8705
www.miarc.com

Coordinator
Phil Manor, W8IC
4865 Bates Dr
Warren, MI 48092-1991
w8ic@miarc.com

Database Manager
Dave Johnson, WD8DJB
2266 East Vermontville Hwy
Charlotte, MI 48813
wd8djb@mjarc.com

MICHIGAN—UPPER PENINSULA

Upper Peninsula Amateur Radio Repeater Association (UPARRA)
Coordinator
Noel Beardsley, K8NB
W7021 CR 356
Stephenson, MI 49887
k8nb@hotmail.com

MINNESOTA

Minnesota Repeater Council (MRC)
www.mrc.gen.mn.us

Coordinator
Jerry Dorf, NØFWG
601 Sunset Dr
Buffalo, MN 55313
jerryd@jerryd.net

MISSISSIPPI

Southeastern Repeater Association (SERA)
www.sera.org/ms.html

Coordinator
Steve Grantham, N5DWU
PO Box 127
Ellisville, MS 39437-0127
n5dwu@sera.org

MISSOURI

Missouri Repeater Council (MRC)
www.missourirepeater.org

Coordinator
Bryon Jeffers, KØBSJ
15585 Lovers Ln
Excelsior Springs, MO 64024
k0bsj@missourirepeater.org

Assistant Coordinators
Jeff Young, KB3HF
6 Long Beach Ct,
St Peters, MO 63376
kb3hf@missourirepeater.org

James Adkins, KØNHX
1004 SE Windstar Ct
Lee's Summit, MO 64081
kb0nhx@missourirepeater.org

MONTANA

Coordinator
Kenneth Kopp, KØPP
PO Box 848
Anaconda, MT 59711-0848
k0pp@arrl.net

NEBRASKA

Coordinator
John Gebuhr, WBØCMC
2349 North 64th St
Omaha, NE 68104
wb0cmc@radiks.net

NEVADA—SOUTHERN

Southern Nevada Repeater Council (SNRC)

President
Billy Smith, Jr, W7HMV
w7hmv@snrc.us

Coordinator
Nat Talpis, W7OQF
w7oqf@snrc.us

Treasurer
Frank Kostelac, N7ZEV
n7zev@snrc.us

Coordinator
Blayne Ence, KG7SS
kg7ss@snrc.us

Secretary
Steve Gebhard, WB9STH
wb9sth@snrc.us

Coordination requests to:
www.snrc.us
email: **info@snrc.us**

NEVADA—NORTHERN

Combined Amateur Relay
Council of Nevada (CARCON)
PO Box 71
Reno, NV 89504-0071
www.carcon.org

NEW HAMPSHIRE

NESMC—SEE MAINE

NEW JERSEY—All counties except Bergen, Essex, Hudson, Middlesex, Monmouth, Morris Passaic, Somerset and Union

Area Repeater Coordination
Council (ARCC)
PO Box 244
Bedminster, PA 18949
www.arcc-inc.org
info@arcc-inc.org

NEW JERSEY—Bergen, Essex, Hudson, Middlesex, Monmouth, Morris Passaic, Somerset and Union

Metropolitan Coordination
Association (MetroCor)
PO Box 107
New York, NY 10008-0107
www.qsl.net/metrocor
metrocor@qsl.net

NEW MEXICO

New Mexico Frequency
Coordination Committee
(NMFCC)
www.qsl.net/nmfcc

Chairman
Bill Kauffman, W5YEJ
1625 36th St SE
Rio Rancho, NM 87124
W5yej@arrl.net

NEW YORK—FAR NORTHERN

Saint Lawrence Valley
Repeater Council (SLVRC)
www.slvrc.org

NEW YORK—EASTERN AND CENTRAL UPSTATE

Upper New York Repeater
Council (UNYREPCO)
www.unyrepco.org

All correspondence to:
Upper New York Repeater
Council
PO Box 858
Vails Gate, NY 12584

NEW YORK—WESTERN

Western New York and
Southern Ontario Repeater
Council (WNYSORC)
PO Box 123
Athol Springs, NY 14010-0123
http://www.wnysorc.org

NEW YORK—NYC AND LONG ISLAND

Metropolitan Coordination Association (MetroCor)
PO Box 107
New York, NY 10008-0107
www.metrocor.net

President
Mario Sellitti, N2PVP
n2pvp@n2pvp.com

NORTH CAROLINA

Southeastern Repeater Association (SERA)
www.sera.org/nc.html

Director
Danny Hampton, K4ITL
5453 Rock Service Station Rd
Raleigh, NC 27603-9513
k4itl@sera.org

Coordinator
Frank A. Lynch, W4FAL
2528 Oakes Plantation Dr
Raleigh, NC 27610-9328
w4fal@sera.org

NORTH DAKOTA

Coordinator
Al Bennefeld, KØCGY
801 19th St South
Fargo, ND 58103
k0cgy@arrl.net

OHIO

Ohio Area Repeater Council (OARC)
www.oarc.com

Coordinator
Ken Bird, W8SMK
244 North Parkway Dr
Delaware, OH 43015-8788
w8smk@oarc.com

OKLAHOMA

Oklahoma Repeater Society, Inc. (ORSI)
PO Box 512
Owasso, OK 74055
www.qsl.net/orsi

Coordinator
Merlin Griffin, WB5SOM
wb5osm@hotmail.com

OREGON

Oregon Region Relay Council (ORRC)
PO Box 4402
Portland, OR 97208-4402
www.orrc.org

Chair
Daron Wilson, N7HQR
PO Box 4402
Portland, OR 97208-4402
541-270-5886
daron@wilson.org

PENNSYLVANIA—EASTERN

Area Repeater Coordination Council (ARCC)
PO Box 244
Plumsteadville, PA 18949
www.arcc-inc.org
info@arcc-inc.org

PENNSYLVANIA—WESTERN

Western Pennsylvania Repeater Council (WPRC)
10592 Perry Highway
PMB 173
Wexford, PA 15090
wprc@qsl.net
www.qsl.net/wprc

PUERTO RICO

Puerto Rico/Virgin Islands Volunteer Frequency Coordinators (PR/VI VFC)

Coordinator
Victor M. Madera, KP4PQ
PO Box 191917
San Juan, PR 00919
vmmadera@prtc.net

RHODE ISLAND

NESMC—See Maine

SOUTH CAROLINA

Southeastern Repeater Association (SERA)
www.sera.org/sc.html

Director and Coordinator
Roger Gregory, W4RWG
119 Royal Oak Dr,
Union, SC 29379

SOUTH DAKOTA

Coordinator
Richard L. Neish, WØSIR
Box 100
Chester, SD 57016-0100
neish@itctel.com

TENNESSEE

Southeastern Repeater Association (SERA)
www.sera.org/tn.html

Director and Coordinator
Randy Bennett, W4RFB
178 Bakers Chapel Rd
Medina, TN 38355

TEXAS

Texas VHF/FM Society (TVFS)
www.txvhffm.org

President
Rusty Herman, KB5R
116 S. Ave C
Humble, TX 77336
281-548-1500

State Frequency Coordination
Paul Baumgardner, W5PSB
12936 Honey Locust Cir
Euless, TX 76040
817-868-7663
coord@txvhffm.org

UTAH

Utah VHF Society (UVHFS)
www.ussc.com/~uvhfs

Coordinator
John Lloyd K7JL
2078 Kramer Dr
Sandy, UT 84092
lloyd@ussc.com

VERMONT

Vermont Independent Repeater Coordination Committee (VIRCC)
www.ranv.org/rptr.html

Mitchell Stern, W1SJ
PO Box 99
Essex, VT 05451
w1sj@arrl.net

VIRGINIA—SOUTH OF 38TH PARALLEL AND US 33

Southeastern Repeater Association (SERA)
www.sera.org/va.html

Coordinator—West
Mike Knight, K4IJ
4267 Prices Fork Rd
Blacksburg, VA 24060
k4ije@sera.org

Coordinator—East
Jim Campbell, K4YM
835 Meadow Dr
Tappahannock, VA 22550
k4ym@sera.org

Coordinator—Central
Jay Campbell, N4YMY
12085 Cheroy Woods Ct
Ashland, VA 23005
n4ymy@sera.org

VIRGINIA—NORTH OF 38TH PARALLEL AND US 33

T-MARC—See Maryland

WASHINGTON—EASTERN

Inland Amateur Coordination Council (IACC)
Coordinator
Doug Rider, KC7JC
19410 E. Buckeye Ave
Spokane Valley, WA 99027-9584
djr876@comcast.net

WASHINGTON—WESTERN

Western Washington Amateur Relay Association (WWARA)
PMB 243
16541 Redmond Way
Redmond WA 98052-4482
www.wwara.org
secretary@wwara.org

Chair
John Schurman, AA7UJ
12057 NE 97th St
Kirkland, WA 98033
aa7uj@aol.com

Vice Chair
Bob Lewis, W7AN
PO Box 10215
Bainbridge Island, WA 98110
w7an@arrl.net

Secretary
Mark McClain, N6OBY
10803 164th Place NE
Redmond, WA 98052
n6oby@prodigy.net

WEST VIRGINIA—EASTERN PANHANDLE

T-MARC—See Maryland

WEST VIRGINIA—ALL OTHER AREAS

Southeastern Repeater Association (SERA)
www.sera.org/wv.html

Director
H. Alex Hedrick, N8FWL
1021 Woodlawn Ave
Beckley, WV 25801-6431
n8fwl@sera.org

Vice Director
Richard Dillon, K8VE
PO Box 1177
Buckhannon, WV 26201-1777
k8ve@sera.org

Coordinator
Chris Hatcher, KC8AFH
PO Box 992
Beaver, WV 25813
kc8afh@sera.org

WISCONSIN

Wisconsin Association of Repeaters (WAR)
www.wi-repeaters.org

Chair
Gary Bargholz, N9UUR
8273 North 53rd St
Brown Deer, WI 53223
n9uur@wi-repeaters.org

Coordinator
Dave Karr, KA9FUR
S64 W24740 Susan St
Waukesha, WI 53189
ka9fur@wi-repeaters.org

WYOMING

Wyoming Council of Amateur Radio Clubs (WCARC)
www.breazile.com/ham

Chair
Greg Galka, N7GT
310 East Iowa
Cheyenne, WY 82009
galka6@bresnan.net

ALBERTA

Don Moman, VE6JY
PO Box 127
Lamont, AB T0B 2R0
ve6jy@3web.net

BRITISH COLUMBIA

British Columbia Amateur Radio Coordination Council (BCARCC)
www.bcarcc.org

Coordinator
George Merchant, VE7CHU
15021 Semiahmoo Place
Surrey, BC
Canada V4P 2K3
coordinator@bcarcc.org

MANITOBA

Coordinator
Tom Blair, VE4TOM
121 Miramar Rd
Winnipeg, MB R3R 1E4
tom1@mts.net

MARITIME PROVINCES

MARCAN Frequency
Coordinator
Ron MacKay, VE1AIC
Box 188
Cornwall, PEI C0A 1H0
ve1aic@rac.ca
ve1cra.no-ip.com_

NEWFOUNDLAND AND LABRADOR

VOARA
Ken Whalen, VO1ST
24 Wadland Crescent
St. John's, NF A1A 2J6
vo1st@rac.ca
www.avalon.nf.ca/~techline

ONTARIO—EAST AND NORTH

SLVRC—See Far Northern
New York

ONTARIO—SOUTHWEST

Western New York and
Southern Ontario Repeater
Council
647 View Lake Rd
Janetville, ON L0B 1K0
http://www.wynsorc.org

QUEBEC—WITHIN 50 km OF THE OTTAWA RIVER

SLVRC—See Far Northern
New York

QUEBEC—ALL OTHER AREAS

Radio Amateur du Quebec, Inc
(RAQI)
4545 ave Pierre du Coubertin,
CP1000
Montreal, QC H1V 3R2
www.raqi.ca
raqi@sympatico.ca

SASKATCHEWAN

Saskatchewan Amateur Radio
League (SARL)
Stan Ewert, VE5SC
7 Federal Dr
White City, SK S0G 5B0
sewert@sk.sympatico.ca

OTHER CANADIAN AREAS

Ken Oelke, VE6AFO
729 Harvest Hills Dr NE
Calgary, AB T3K 4R3
ve6afo@rac.ca

CHAPTER FOUR

REPEATER LINGO / HINTS

This chapter covers a basic course in "repeater-speak" and explains many of the terms heard on your local repeater.

REPEATER LINGO:

Definitions of the words and phrases commonly used on repeaters:

Autopatch - A device that interfaces the repeater system with the telephone system to extend ham communications over the telephone communications network.

Breaker - A ham who interjects his call sign during a QSO in an attempt to get a chance to communicate over a repeater.

Channel - The pair of frequencies (input and output) a repeater operates on.

Closed Repeater - A repeater whose use is limited to certain individuals. These are completely legal under FCC rules.

Control Operator - An individual ham designated to "control" the repeater, as required by FCC regulations.

COR - Carrier-Operated-Relay, a device that, upon sensing a received signal, turns on the repeater's transmitter to repeat the received signal.

Courtesy Tone - A short tone sounded after each repeater transmission to permit other stations to gain access to the repeater before the tone sounds.

Coverage - The geographical area in which the repeater may be used for communications.

CTCSS - Continuous Tone Coded Squelch System, a sub-audible tone system which operates the squelch (COR) of a repeater when the corresponding sub-audible tone is present on a transmitted signal. The squelch on a repeater which uses CTCSS will not activate if the improper CTCSS tone, or if no tone, is transmitted.

Crossband - Communications to another frequency band by means of a link interfaced with the repeater.

Desense - Degradation of receiver sensitivity caused by strong unwanted signals reaching the receiver front end.

Duplexer - A device that permits the use of one antenna for both transmitting and receiving with minimal degradation to either the incoming or outgoing signals.

Frequency Synthesis - A scheme of frequency generation in modern transceivers using digital techniques.

Full Quieting - Signal strength in excess of amount required to mask ambient noise.

Hand-Held - A portable FM transceiver that is small enough to use and carry in one hand.

Input - The frequency the repeater receiver is tuned to: The frequency that a repeater user transmits on.

Intermod - Interference caused by spurious signals generated by intermodulation distortion in a receiver front end or transmitter power amplifier stage.

Key-Up - Turning on a repeater by transmitting on its input frequency.

LiTZ - Long Tone Zero (LiTZ) Alerting system. Send DTMF zero (0) for at least three seconds to request emergency/urgent assistance.

Machine - The complete repeater system.

Mag-Mount - A mobile antenna with a magnetic base that permits quick installation and removal from the motor vehicle.

Offset - The spacing between a repeater's input and output.

Omnidirectional - An antenna system that radiates equally in all directions.

Output - The frequency the repeater transmits on; the frequency that a repeater user receives on.

Picket-Fencing - Rapid flutter on a mobile signal as it travels past an obstruction.

Polarization - The plane an antenna system operates in; most repeaters are vertically polarized.

Reverse Autopatch - A device that interfaces the repeater with the telephone system and permits users of the phone system to call the repeater and converse with on-the-air repeater users.

Reverse Split - A split-channel repeater operating in the opposite direction of the standard.

RPT/R - Abbreviation used after repeater call signs to indicate that the call sign is being used for repeater operation.

Simplex - Communication on one frequency, not via a repeater

Splinter Frequency - 2-meter repeater channel
15 kHz above or below the formerly standard 30 kHz-spaced channel.

Split Sites - The use of two locations for repeater operation (the receiver is at one site and the transmitter at another), and the two are linked by telephone or radio.

Squelch Tail - The noise burst that follows the short, unmodulated carrier following each repeater transmission.

Time-Out-Timer - A device that limits the length of a single repeater transmission (usually 3 minutes).

Tone Pad - A device that generates the standard telephone system tones used for controlling various repeater functions.

ARRL MESSAGE FORM INSTRUCTIONS

Every formal radiogram message originated and handled should contain the following four main components in the order given.

1. Preamble

The Preamble includes information used to prioritize and track the message and ensure its accuracy.

(A) Number. Assigned by the Station of Origin and never changed. Begin with 1 each month or year.

(B) Precedence. Determines the order in which traffic is passed. Assign each message a Precedence of R (Routine), W (Welfare), P (Priority) or EMERGENCY. See the guidelines on page 76.

(C) Handling Instructions (HX). Optional, used only if a specific need is present.

(D) Station of Origin. The call sign of the station originating (creating) the message.

(E) Check. The number of words or word groups in the text of the message. A word group is any group of one or more consecutive characters with no interrupting spaces.

(F) Place of Origin. The location (city and state) of the party for whom the message was created, and not necessarily the location of the Station of Origin.

(G) Time Filed. Optional, used only when the filing time has some importance relative to the Precedence, Handling Instructions or Text.

(H) Date. The date the message was filed. (If Time Filed is used, date and time must agree.)

2. Address

Name, address, city, state, ZIP and telephone number of the intended recipient, as complete as possible. Note that punctuation is not used in the Address section.

3. Text

The message information, limited to 25 words or less if possible. Normal punctuation characters are not used in the text. A question mark is sent as QUERY, while DASH is sent for a hyphen. The letter X is used as a period (but never after the last group of the text) and counts as a word when figuring the Check. The letter R is used in place of a decimal in mixed figure groups (example: 146R52 for 146.52).

4. Signature

The name of the party for whom the message was originated. May include additional information such as Amateur Radio call sign, title, address, phone number and so on.

Message Example

1. Preamble	1	R	HXG	W1AW	8	NEWINGTON CT	1830Z	JULY 1
	(A)	(B)	(C)	(D)	(E)	(F)	(G)	(H)

2. Address DONALD SMITH
164 EAST SIXTH AVE
NORTH RIVER CITY MO 00789
555 1234

3. Text HAPPY BIRTHDAY X SEE YOU SOON X LOVE

4. Signature DIANA

ARRL MESSAGE PRECEDENCES

EMERGENCY—Any message having life and death urgency to any person or group of persons, that is transmitted by Amateur Radio in the absence of regular commercial facilities. This includes official messages of welfare agencies during emergencies requesting supplies, materials or instructions vital to relief efforts for the stricken populace in emergency areas. On CW and digital modes, this designation will always be spelled out. *When in doubt, do not use this designation.*

PRIORITY—Abbreviated as P on CW and digital modes. This classification is for important messages having a specific time limit, official messages not covered in the emergency category, press dispatches and emergency-related traffic not of the utmost urgency.

WELFARE—Abbreviated as W on CW and digital modes. This classification refers to an inquiry about the health and welfare of an individual in the disaster area, or to an advisory from the disaster area that indicates all is well. Welfare traffic is handled only after all Emergency and Priority traffic is cleared. The Red Cross equivalent to an incoming Welfare message is DWI (Disaster Welfare Inquiry).

ROUTINE— Abbreviated as R on CW and digital modes. Most traffic in normal times will bear this designation. In disaster situations, traffic labeled Routine should be handled last, or not at all when circuits are busy with higher-precedence traffic.

ARRL MESSAGE HANDLING INSTRUCTIONS

Handling instructions (HX) convey special instructions to operators handling and delivering the message. The instruction is inserted in the message Preamble between the Precedence and the Station of Origin. Its use is optional with the originating stations, but once inserted it is mandatory with all relaying stations.

PROSIGN	INSTRUCTION
HXA	(Followed by number.) Collect landline delivery authorized by addressee within _____ miles. (If no number, authorization is unlimited.)
HXB	(Followed by number.) Cancel message if not delivered within ____ hours of filing time; service originating station.
HXC	Report date and time of delivery (TOD) to originating station.
HXD	Report to originating station the identity of station from which received, plus date and time. Report identity of station to which relayed, plus date and time, or if delivered report date, time and method of delivery.
HXE	Delivering station get reply from addressee, originate message back.
HXF	(Followed by number.) Hold delivery until _____ (date).
HXG	Delivery by mail or landline toll call not required. If toll or other expense involved, cancel message and service originating station.

ARRL NUMBERED RADIOGRAMS FOR POSSIBLE "RELIEF EMERGENCY USE"

Numbered radiograms are an efficient way to convey common messages. The letters ARL are inserted in the Preamble in the Check and in the text before spelled out numbers, which represent texts from this list. Note that some ARL texts include insertion of information.

Example: NR 1 W W1AW ARL 4 NEWINGTON CT DEC 25 DONALD R SMITH 164 EAST SIXTH AVE NORTH RIVER CITY MO PHONE 733 3968 BT ARL ONE ARL TWO BT DIANA AR.

ONE	Everyone safe here. Please don't worry.
TWO	Coming home as soon as possible.
THREE	Am in ____ hospital. Receiving excellent care and recovering fine.
FOUR	Only slight property damage here. Do not be concerned about disaster reports.
FIVE	Am moving to new location. Send no further mail or communication. Will inform you of new address when relocated.
SIX	Will contact you as soon as possible.
SEVEN	Please reply by Amateur Radio through the amateur delivering this message. This is a free public service.
EIGHT	Need additional _____ mobile or portable equipment for immediate emergency use.
NINE	Additional _____ radio operators needed to assist with emergency at this location.

TEN	Please contact ______. Advise to standby and provide further emergency information, instructions or assistance.
ELEVEN	Establish Amateur Radio emergency communications with ______ on _____ MHz.
TWELVE	Anxious to hear from you. No word in some time. Please contact me as soon as possible.
THIRTEEN	Medical emergency situation exists here.
FOURTEEN	Situation here becoming critical. Losses and damage from ____ increasing.
FIFTEEN	Please advise your condition and what help is needed.
SIXTEEN	Property damage very severe In this area.
SEVENTEEN	REACT communications services also available. Establish REACT communication with ______ on channel _____.
EIGHTEEN	Please contact me as soon as possible at _______.
NINETEEN	Request health and welfare report on ______(name, address, phone).
TWENTY	Temporarily stranded. Will need some assistance. Please contact me at _____.
TWENTY ONE	Search and Rescue assistance is needed by local authorities here. Advise availability.

TWENTY TWO	Need accurate information on the extent and type of conditions now existing at your location. Please furnish this information and reply without delay.
TWENTY THREE	Report at once the accessibility and best way to reach your location.
TWENTY FOUR	Evacuation of residents from this area urgently needed. Advise plans for help.
TWENTY FIVE	Furnish as soon as possible the weather conditions at your location.
TWENTY SIX	Help and care for evacuation of sick and injured from this location needed at once.

THE AMERICAN RADIO RELAY LEAGUE

RADIOGRAM

VIA AMATEUR RADIO

NUMBER	PRECEDENCE	HX	STATION OF ORIGIN	CHECK	PLACE OF ORIGIN	TIME FILED	DATE

TO

PHONE NUMBER

E-MAIL

THIS RADIO MESSAGE WAS RECEIVED AT

AMATEUR STATION ________ PHONE ________

NAME ________ E-MAIL ________

STREET ________

CITY, STATE, ZIP ________

	FROM	DATE	TIME		TO	DATE	TIME
REC'D				**SENT**			

THIS MESSAGE WAS HANDLED FREE OF CHARGE BY A LICENSED AMATEUR RADIO OPERATOR, WHOSE ADDRESS IS SHOWN IN THE BOX AT RIGHT ABOVE. AS SUCH MESSAGES ARE HANDLED SOLELY FOR THE PLEASURE OF OPERATING, NO COMPENSATION CAN BE ACCEPTED BY A "HAM" OPERATOR. A RETURN MESSAGE MAY BE FILED WITH THE "HAM" DELIVERING THIS MESSAGE TO YOU. FURTHER INFORMATION ON AMATEUR RADIO MAY BE OBTAINED FROM ARRL HEADQUARTERS, 225 MAIN STREET, NEWINGTON, CT 06111

THE AMERICAN RADIO RELAY LEAGUE, INC, IS THE NATIONAL MEMBERSHIP SOCIETY OF LICENSED RADIO AMATEURS AND THE PUBLISHER OF *QST* MAGAZINE. ONE OF ITS FUNCTIONS IS PROMOTION OF PUBLIC SERVICE COMMUNICATION AMONG AMATEUR OPERATORS. TO THAT END, THE LEAGUE HAS ORGANIZED THE NATIONAL TRAFFIC SYSTEM FOR DAILY NATIONWIDE MESSAGE HANDLING.

PRINTED IN USA

Disaster Welfare Message Form

Number	Precedence	HX	Station of Origin	Check	Place of Origin	Time Filed	Date

TO:

Telephone number:

Message Receipt or Delivery Information

Operator and station: ____________________

Sent to: ____________________

Delivered to: ____________________

Date: __________ Time: __________

(Circle not more than two standard texts from list below)

ARL ONE	Everyone safe here. Please don't worry.
ARL TWO	Coming home as soon as possible.
ARL THREE	Am in __________ hospital. Receiving excellent care and recovering fine.
ARL FOUR	Only slight property damage here. Do not be concerned about disaster reports.
ARL FIVE	Am moving to new location. Send no further mail or communications. Will inform you of new address when relocated.
ARL SIX	Will contact you as soon as possible.
ARL SIXTY FOUR	Arrived safely at ____________________

Time	Date	Telephone	Signature	Name

National Weather Service SKYWARN

In many areas local repeaters are used to conduct SKYWARN severe weather nets. In the ARRL Repeater Directory these nets are designated with the abbreviation WX (weather net/weather usage).

Severe weather nets play an important role in relaying information to National Weather Service (NWS) Weather Forecast Offices (WFOs). Amateurs who have completed NWS SKYWARN training play a key role in providing ground truth reports to NWS meteorologists. This information helps the NWS in issuing timely severe weather warnings to the public.

Reports submitted to your NWS WFO may be made via Amateur Radio, telephone or Internet. Here are some general guidelines for submitting a severe weather report:

- Follow the specific reporting guidelines for your area (available through your WFO)
- Remain calm, speak clearly, and do not exaggerate the facts
- If you are unsure of what you are seeing, make your report, but also express your uncertainty
- Your report should contain the following information

  WHO you are: trained spotter

  WHAT you have witnessed: the specific weather event

  WHEN the event occurred: NOT when you make your report

  WHERE the event occurred, (not necessarily your location) using well known roads or landmarks

Immediate, real-time reports are most helpful for warning operations, but delayed reports are also important, even days after an event. Delayed reports are used for climatological and verification purposes. Weather events should be reported according to the instructions provided by your local NWS office.

For more information contact your local WFO. You can find their information at **www.weather.gov**. Also consider reading Storm Spotting and Amateur Radio available through the ARRL. The NWS' Weather Spotter's Field Guide is available at **www.nws.noaa.gov/os/brochures/SGJune6-11.pdf**.

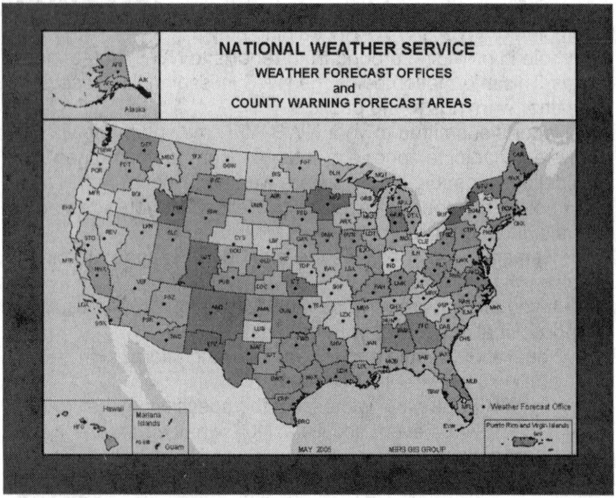

29.5-29.7 MHz

Location	*Output*	*Input*	*Notes*	*Call*	*Sponsor*
ALABAMA					
Foley	29.6600	–	O 118.8 TT(RACES)r	WB4GMQ	WB4GMQ
Tuscaloosa	29.6400	–	●x	KX4I	KX4I
ARKANSAS					
NORTHWEST					
Springdale	29.6400	–	Os	KE5LXK	NWAUHF
CALIFORNIA					
FREQUENCY USAGE - SOUTHERN CALIFORNIA					
So Cal	29.5000			SIMPLEX	
So Cal	29.6000			SIMPLEX	
NORCAL-CENTRAL COAST					
Santa Cruz	29.6600	–	O 156.7esx	K6HJU	IRCSLV
NORCAL-NORTH BAY					
Clear Lake	29.6800	–	O 156.7elx	NØEDS	NØEDS
NORCAL-SACRAMENTO VALLEY					
Auburn	29.6200	–	O 156.7x	N6NMZ	PARK
NORCAL-SAN JOAQUIN VALLEY					
Ahwahnee	29.6800	–	O 82.5ex	WB6NIL	WB6NIL
Copperopolis	29.6600	–	O 141.3elx	KG6TXA	SALAC
NORCAL-SOUTH BAY					
Los Altos	29.6400	–	O 156.7elx	KB6LED	KB6LED
San Jose	29.6200	–	O 127.3#l	KD6AOG	KD6AOG
NORCAL-TAHOE					
So Lake Tahoe	29.6800	–	O 156.7elx	W6SUV	W6SUV
SOCAL-#LA CENTRAL					
Arcadia	29.6600	–	107.2	K6TY	------------
Los Angeles	29.6200	–	107.2	NI8H	BHARC
SOCAL-#ORANGE					
Santiago Peak	29.6400	–	107.2	W6KRW	OC RACES
CONNECTICUT					
FREQUENCY USAGE					
Snp	29.6800	–	O		
FLORIDA					
EAST CENTRAL					
Cocoa	29.6400	–	O 103.5/103.5	N4LEM	N4LEM
NORTH CENTRAL					
Ocala	29.6800	–	OL(145.43)	KA2MBE	KA2MBE

Location	Output	Input	Notes	Call	Sponsor
NORTH EAST					
Tavares	29.6800	–	O 103.5/103.5 L(147)	WN4AMO	WN4AMO
NORTH WEST - TALLAHASSEE					
Tallahassee	29.6600	–	O 94.8/94.8 eL(444.8)SX	K4TLH	TARS
SOUTH EAST - MIAMI/FT LAUD					
Miami	29.6200	–	O 82.5/82.5 L(145.150 442.800 443.525 224.160) BI	WB4TWQ	WB4TWQ
GEORGIA					
Dalton	29.6800	–	O	N4BZJ	7.135 RPTR GRP
Monroe	29.6200	–	O	KQ4XL	KQ4XL
Warner Robins	29.6600	–	O	WR4MG	WR4MG
ILLINOIS					
CHICAGO					
Park Ridge	29.6600	–	107.2	WA9ORC	CFMC
DECATUR					
Decatur	29.6200	–	103.5e	K9HGX	CENOIS ARC
EAST CENTRAL					
Danville	29.6600	–	100.0 (CA)e	KC9USH	KC9USH
NORTHEAST					
Woodstock	29.6800	–	114.8	WB9YWX	WB9YWX
ROCKFORD					
Rockford	29.6200	–	118.8el	K9AMJ	K9AMJ
ST LOUIS					
Mascoutah	29.6800	–	I	AA9ME	AA9ME
Troy	29.6400	–	I	AA9MZ	AA9MZ
WEST CENTRAL					
Versailles	29.6800	–	103.5	KB9JVU	KB9JVU
INDIANA					
EAST CENTRAL					
Greens Fork	29.6600	–	O 110.9ers WX	K9APR	K9APR
INDIANAPOLIS					
Indianapolis	29.6400	–	O 127.3 (CA)el	N9ILS	N9ILS
NORTH CENTRAL					
South Bend	29.6800	–	O 131.8e	W9AMR	W9AMR
NORTHWEST					
Valparaiso	29.6400	–	O 131.8x	KB9KRI	Duneland
SOUTH CENTRAL					
Bedford	29.6800	–	O 136.5elr sWXx	N9UMJ	N9UMJ

Location	Output	Input	Notes	Call	Sponsor
KANSAS					
SOUTHEAST					
Parsons	29.6800	–	O 91.5/91.5 L(ECHOLINK#305758)	WØPIE	WØPIE
KENTUCKY					
Buckhorn Lake	29.6200	–	O	K4XYZ	K4XYZ
Ingle	29.6800	–	O 146.2/146.2e	AC4DM	AC4DM
Louisville	29.6400	–	O	KK4CZ	KK4CZ
MAINE					
PORTLAND/SOUTH COAST					
Lisbon Falls	29.6200	–	O(CA) E-SUN L(E517417 423344)sWX	W1LWT	Lee Trask
PORTLAND/YORK					
Windham	29.6800	–	O 173.8/173.8eL(444.9500)	N1FCU	N1FCU
MARYLAND					
WASHINGTON AREA					
Silver Spring	29.6600	–	O 141.3el	N3AUY	+KD3R
Silver Spring	29.6600	444.0250	O 156.7el	N3AUY	+KD3R
MASSACHUSETTS					
METROWEST					
Marlborough	29.6800	–	O 131.8/131.8x	W1MRA	MMRA
MICHIGAN					
LOWER PEN SOUTHEAST					
Ann Arbor	29.6400	–	O 114.8elx	WD8DPA	WD8DPA
MINNESOTA					
METRO					
Credit River	29.6200	–	O	NØKP	SCAN
MISSISSIPPI					
Bay Saint Louis	29.6400	–	O	KB5MPW	WQRZ
Byhalia	29.6800	–	O	N4DRL	N4DRL
Poplarville	29.6200	–	O	WA5WRE	WA5WRE
MONTANA					
SOUTH CENTRAL					
Bozeman	29.6200	–	Ol	KB7KB	BARBS

Location	Output	Input	Notes	Call	Sponsor
NEBRASKA					
OMAHA					
Bellevue	29.6400	–	Oe L(444.875)r	WBØQQK	WB0QQK
NEVADA					
E SIERRA/TAHOE					
SLake Tahoe	29.6800	–	O 156.7	W6SUV	W6SUV
NORTH CENTRAL					
Elko	29.6800	–	O 100	KE7LKO	WV3LMA
NEW HAMPSHIRE					
LAKES REGION					
Rochester	29.6600	–	O 131.8/131.8 L(224.78/53.030)	WM1P	MLP
NEW YORK					
BATH/HORNELL					
Hornell	29.6600	–	O 107.2/107.2	KD2WA	KD2WA
CATSKILLS NORTH					
Walton	29.6600	–	O 107.2	K2NK	K2NK
MID HUDSON					
Mahopac	29.6200	–	O 146.2#l	KQ2H	KQ2H
Mahopac	29.6600	–	O 74.4l	K2HR	ALIVE NETWORK A
Nyack	29.6400	–	O 114.8l	N2ACF	ROCKLAND REPEA
Wurtsburo	29.6200	–	O 146.2l	KQ2H	KQ2H
NEW YORK CITY - KINGS					
Brooklyn	29.6600	–	O 114.8 TT	WB2HWW	------------
NEW YORK CITY - MANHATTAN					
Manhattan	29.6200	–	146.2	KQ2H	------------
Manhattan	29.6800	–	O 136.5 TT eL(441.100)rsBI WX	N2HBA	PSARN
NIAGARA					
Buffalo	29.6800	–	O 107.2 L(BARRA)	AB2UK	BARRA
ROCHESTER					
Avon	29.6200	–	O	WR2AHL	GRIDD
Rochester	29.6800	–	O 123l	N2HJD	ROCHESTER RADIO
SYRACUSE					
Syracuse	29.6400	–	O 94.8/94.8 e	KD2SL	KD2SL
NORTH CAROLINA					
Angier	29.6400	–	O	NC4RA	NC4RA
Newport	29.6600	–	O	K4GRW	K4GRW
Rocky Mount	29.6600	–	O	N4JEH	N4JEH
Sparta	29.6400	–	O	WA4PXV	WA4PXV

Location	*Output*	*Input*	*Notes*	*Call*	*Sponsor*
Thomasville	29.6800	–	O	WW4DC	WW4FL
Youngsville	29.6200	–	O	WB4IUY	WB4IUY
OHIO					
CARROLL					
Malvern	29.6600	–	aelrz	K8NNC	CC ARES
LORAIN					
N Ridgeville	29.6200	–		W8HF	W8HF
LUCAS					
Toledo	29.6800	–	O	W8HHF	TMRA
MONTGOMERY					
Dayton	29.6400	–	O	WF8M	MVRFG
STARK					
Massillon	29.6400	–	O 103.5	W8NP	K8LK
WARREN					
Mason	29.6200	–	Ot	KD8C	FARA
OREGON					
PORTLAND METRO					
Portland	29.6800	–	O 162.2e	KR7IS	KR7IS
PENNSYLVANIA					
NORTHWEST					
Meadeville	29.6400	–	O	W3MIE	CrwfrdARS
PITTSBURGH					
Apollo	29.6800	447.8000	O 131.8ael rxz	N1RS	SARA
Apollo	29.6800	–	O 141.3ael rxz	N1RS	SARA
Pittsburgh Homestead	29.6200	–		WA3PBD	GatewayFMA
SOUTHWEST					
Indiana	29.6600	–	O	W3BMD	ICARC
YORK					
York	29.6800	–	O 123elrs	W3HZU	Keystone
PUERTO RICO					
N					
Aguas Buenas	29.6200	–	OE-SUN	KP4IA	------------
Corozal	29.6600	–	O	KP3AV	------------
W					
San Sebastian	29.6400	–	85.4	KP4IP	------------
SOUTH CAROLINA					
Sumter	29.6600	–	O	W4GL	SARA INC.
TENNESSEE					
Culleoka	29.6600	–	O	AG4TI	AG4TI

Location	*Output*	*Input*	*Notes*	*Call*	*Sponsor*
Gleason	29.6400	–	O	KA4BNI	KA4BNI
Greeneville	29.6600	–	O 118.8/118.8l	K4MFD	K4MFD
Springfield	29.6800	–	O	N8ITF	N8ITF
Tellico Plains	29.6800	–	O	KE4VQM	AJ4D
Union City	29.6600	–	O	WA4YGM	RARC
TEXAS					
Fort Worth	29.6600	–	O 192.8	W5DFW	DFW Remote Base A
Houston	29.6400	–	O 103.5el	WB5UGT	SALTGRASS
Rosehill	29.6800	–	O 123	K5SOH	------------
VIRGINIA					
Bluefield	29.6800	–	O	WZ8E	ARA-SOUTH
Fancy Gap	29.6600	–	O	KE4QOX	KE4QOX
Newport News	29.6000	29.6000	O	W4CM	NEWPORT NEWS A
Sterling	29.6800	–	O	KD4DN	KD4DN
WASHINGTON AREA					
Middleburg	29.6800	–	O 146.2e	KA4DCS	KA4DCS
WASHINGTON					
W WA - FREQUENCY USAGE					
	29.5200	29.5800		RPTR INPUTS (20KHZ SPACIN	
	29.6000			SIMPLEX	
	29.6000			CROSSBAND USE	
	29.6200	29.6800		RPTR OUTPUTS (20KHZ SPACI	
W WA - NORTH					
Mt Constitution	29.6800	–	O 110.9el	W7UMH	10/6/440 RPTR GRP
WEST VIRGINIA					
Beckley	29.6200	–	O	KA8OTX	KA4OTX
Beckley	29.6800	–	O	KE4QOX	KE4QOX
Berkeley Springs	29.6200	144.9900	O	KK3L	KK3L
Berkeley Springs	29.6200	–	O	KK3L	KK3L
Charleston	29.6400	–	O	WB8CQV	WB8CQV
Dry Fork	29.6400	–	O	WV8ZH	WV8ZH
Summersville	29.6600	–	O	KE4QOX	KE4QOX
WISCONSIN					
WAR					
Wausau	29.6400	–	O 114.8ael r	W9SM	WVRA
WYOMING					
NORTH WEST					
Cody	29.6800	–	O(CA)	KC7NP	KC7NP
SOUTH CENTRAL					
Rawlins	29.6400	–	Ol	KJ7AZ	KJ7AZ

Location	*Output*	*Input*	*Notes*	*Call*	*Sponsor*
ALBERTA					
HIGH RIVER					
Black Diamond	29.6900	29.5700	OI	VE6ERW	VE6ERW
NEWFOUNDLAND AND LABRADOR					
AVALON EAST					
St Johns	29.6200	–	TTIRB	VO1KEN	VO1ST
ONTARIO					
METRO TORONTO					
Uxbridge	29.6200	–	O 103.5e L(TFM IRLP)	VE3TFM	TFMCS
NATIONAL CAPITOL REGION					
Ottawa	29.6200	–	136.5/136.5 L(I 2210)x	VE3TST	VE3HXP
NORTHWESTERN ONTARIO					
Thunder Bay	29.6800	–	O#	VE3XFM	VE3OJ
QUEBEC					
Blainville Nord	29.5000	29.5000	O	VE2RNO	VE2THE
Gatineau	29.6800	–	O 173.8e	VE2REH	VE2ZVL
St-Calixte	28.1900	28.1900	O	VE2RVK	VE2VK
St-Calixte	29.6000	29.6000	141.3ex	VE2RVK	VE2VK
St-Calixte	29.6400	–	O 141.3	VE2RVK	VE2VK
St-Joseph du lac	29.6800	–	O	VE2RST	VE2GSB
OUTAOUAIS					
Gatineau	29.6800	–	173.8/173.8 (CA) L(I 2018)	VE2REH	ARAI

51-54 MHz

Location	*Output*	*Input*	*Notes*	*Call*	*Sponsor*
ALABAMA					
Bessemer	53.0900	52.0900	Oae L(ECHOLINK 371888) WXz	WB4YRJ	T.H.E. ARC
Birmingham	53.2500	52.2500	O	W4CUE	BARC
Calvert	53.7500	52.7500	O 123.0/123.0eWX	WX4MOB	WX4MOB
Decatur	53.3700	52.3700	O 203.5/203.5x	W9KOP	W9KOP
Gadsden	53.2700	52.2700	O 103.5/103.5	K4JMC	Gadsden ARC
Huntsville	53.2100	52.2100	O 100.0/100.0	W4XE	NARA
Mentone	53.1900	52.1900	O 114.8ex	W4OZK	W4OZK
Mobile	53.0300	52.0300	O 118.8	W4IAX	Mobile ARC
Montgomery	53.3500	52.3500	O 100.0	W4AP	MARC
Moulton	53.1700	52.1700	OelWX	N4IDX	Bankhead A
Pelham	53.7500	52.7500	100.0eWX	N4PHP	N4PHP
Russellville	53.1300	52.1300	O 103.5	KI4OKJ	PCRS
Salem Hill / Opelika	53.0100	52.0100	O 123.0/123.0e	KK4ICE	KK4ICE
Uriah	53.1300	52.1000	O	N4YYX	N4YYX
Vinemont	53.3300	52.3300	O	W4CFI	W4CFI
Warrior	53.0100	52.0100	O	N4CCQ	N4CCQ
ALASKA					
SOUTH CENTRAL					
Anchorage	52.8100	51.1100	OeRB	KA1NVZ	KA1NVZ
ARIZONA					
CENTRAL					
White Tanks	51.8600	51.3600	O 100lx	WK7B	WHITE TANKS
NORTH CENTRAL					
Mt Union	52.5600	52.0600	O 100x	N7NGM	MT UNION
NORTHWEST					
Kingman	51.9400	51.4400	O 100x	KA6NLS	Kingman
PHOENIX					
Pinal Mtn	53.1400	52.1400	O 100lx	WK7B	PINAL MTN
SOUTHEAST					
Heliograph Peak	53.0400	52.0400	O 141.3lx	K7EAR	HELIOGRAPH P
Mt Lemmon	53.7200	52.7200	O 136.5x	K7LHR	MT LEMMON

Location	*Output*	*Input*	*Notes*	*Call*	*Sponsor*
ARKANSAS					
CENTRAL					
Conway	53.2100	51.5100	O 114.8	W5AUU	W5AUU
Little Rock	52.8100	51.1100	O	W5DI	CAREN
Searcy/ C Hill	52.8300	51.1300	O 85.4ae	N5ZA	N5ZA
EAST CENTRAL					
Wynne	52.9500	51.9500	O 107.2ers WX	NØHNQ	N0HNQ
NORTH					
Harrison	53.0300	51.3300	Ol	WA9SSO	GathMtARC
Harrison	53.1500	52.1500	OeLITZx	WB5CYX	NAARS
NORTHWEST					
Decatur	51.9250	52.9250	O 114.8/114.8lx	N5UXE	N5UXE
Mountainburg	52.8700	52.1700	OWX	KC5MRE	KC5MRE
Springdale	53.0700	51.3700	Os	KE5LXK	NWAUHF
WEST					
Mena	52.9700	51.2700	O 100.0	W5HUM	Oua. ARA
WEST CENTRAL					
Mt Ida	52.9100	51.2100	O 100.0/100.0ex	KA5WPC	KA5WPC
Mt Magazine	53.1100	51.4100	O 131.8 WX	N5XMZ	N5XMZ
CALIFORNIA					
FREQUENCY USAGE - SOUTHERN CALIFORNIA					
So Cal	51.0200			DX	
So Cal	51.0400			DX	
So Cal	51.0600			DX	
So Cal	51.0800			DX	
So Cal	51.1000			DX	
So Cal	51.5000			SIMPLEX	
So Cal	51.5200			SIMPLEX	
So Cal	51.5400			SIMPLEX	
So Cal	51.5600			SIMPLEX	
So Cal	51.5800			SIMPLEX	
So Cal	51.6000			SIMPLEX	
So Cal	51.6200	51.1200		DIGITAL	
So Cal	51.6400	51.1400		DIGITAL	
So Cal	51.6600	51.1600		DIGITAL	
So Cal	51.6800	51.1800		DIGITAL	
So Cal	52.0200			SIMPLEX	
So Cal	52.0400			SIMPLEX	
So Cal	52.5250			SIMPLEX	
So Cal	52.5400			SIMPLEX	
So Cal	52.7000	52.2000		TESTPAIR	
So Cal	53.0000			SIMPLEX	
So Cal	53.0200			SIMPLEX	
So Cal	53.1000			RC	

Location	*Output*	*Input*	*Notes*	*Call*	*Sponsor*
So Cal	53.2000			RC	
So Cal	53.3000			RC	
So Cal	53.4000			RC	
So Cal	53.5000			RC	
So Cal	53.5200			SIMPLEX	
So Cal	53.6000			RC	
So Cal	53.7000			RC	
So Cal	53.8000			RC	
So Cal	53.9000			SIMPLEX	
NORCAL-CENTRAL COAST					
Ben Lomond	52.8000	–	○ 114.8esx	WR6AOK	SLVARC
Monterey	51.7600	–	●lrs	WE6R	WE6R
New Cuyama	52.6000	–	○ 82.5lx	WA6VPL	WA6VPL
Nipomo	52.5800	–	○ 82.5el	WA6VPL	WA6VPL
San Ardo	51.8200	–	○ 136.5#e	WR6VHF	CERT
NORCAL-EAST BAY					
Hayward	52.7600	–	○ 114.8ers	K6EAG	Hayward RC
Livermore	52.9000	–	○ 114.8#el x	K6LRG	L.A.R.G.E.
Oakland	53.7200	–	○ 118.8#el rs	W6EBW	East Bay M
Orinda	52.6800	–	○ 162.2erx	K6CHA	K6CHA
NORCAL-NORTH BAY					
Clear Lake	51.9600	–	○ 114.8elx	NØEDS	CDF/VIP
Guerneville	51.8000	–	○ 114.8#e	KM6XU	ChickenNet
Middletown	51.8400	–	○ 88.5#elx	AC6VJ	AC6VJ
Nacasio	52.8800	–	○ 114.8#e	KE6ORI	KE6ORI
Napa	51.7200	–	○ 114.8elx	N6TKW	NARC
NORCAL-NORTH COAST					
Scotia	51.8400	–	○ 114.8#a elx	N7HQZ	M.O.F.R.C.
Willits	51.7400	–	○ 114.8elr sx	K7WWA	K7WWA
NORCAL-NORTH EAST					
Mt Shasta City	52.7200	–	○ 110.9#lx	K6PRN	Patio RS
Redding	52.6600	–	○ 107.2ex	WR6TV	W6QWN
NORCAL-SACRAMENTO VALLEY					
Auburn	51.9000	–	○ 100elx	W7FAT	W7fat
El Dorado	52.5600	–	○ 107.2#rs x	W6OIU	HAWK
ElDoradoHills	52.8200	–	○ 110.9#a ex	WT6G	MEARA
Folsom	51.8600	–	○ 94.8elx	AB6LI	AB6LI
Foresthill	52.9800	–	○ 131.8#	N6ZQK	N6ZQK
Grass Valley	51.7000	–	○ 141.3el	W6WEE	W6WEE
Grass Valley	52.7200	–	○ 151.4ael rs	N1OES	CPRA
Grass Valley	52.7600	–	○ 131.8ex	KF6GLZ	N6ZN
Grassvalley	52.6000	–	○ 151.4rs	WD6AXM	WD6AXM

Location	Output	Input	Notes	Call	Sponsor
Magalia	51.9400	–	O 114.8#e	KC6USM	KC6USM
Mount Aukum	52.6400	–	O 88.5e	W6HMT	W6HMT
Pollock Pines	52.9800	–	O 141.3#	WB6DAX	WB6DAX
Quintette	52.7800	–	O 107.2els x	AG6AU	EDCARC
ShingleSprings	52.9000	–	O 100#	KG6HAT	KG6HAT
Vacaville	51.9800	–	O 114.8	WA6CAX	WA6CAX
Vacaville	52.7400	+	O 127.3#a elrsx	WV6F	WVA
Vacaville	52.8600	–	O 136.5	N6NMZ	N6NMZ
NORCAL-SAN JOAQUIN VALLEY					
Bakersfield	51.8800	–	O 114.8el	KG6KKV	KG6KKV
Bakersfield	51.9000	–	O 123el	K6ARN	KPARN
Bakersfield	52.6000	–	O 82.5#elx	KC6OVD	KC6OVD
Bakersfield	52.7800	–	O 82.5	W6LIE	KCCVARC
Coarsegold	52.7000	–	O 127.3e	W6HMH	W6HMH
Hanford	53.6600	–	O 77e	KC6QIT	KC6QIU
Modesto	51.8000	–	O 136.5esx	WD6EJF	SARA
New Idria	52.5800	–	O 82.5#lx	KC6OVD	KC6OVD
NORCAL-SOUTH BAY					
Los Gatos	51.9200	–	O 114.8elx	KU6V	KU6V
Palo Alto	52.6400	–	O 114.8elr sx	WA6FUL	WA6FUL
San Jose	52.5800	–	O 151.4ael s	W6PIY	WVARA
San Jose	52.6600	–	O 127.3#	KD6AOG	KD6AOG
San Jose	52.9400	–	O 100#	KG6HAT	KG6HAT
NORCAL-WEST BAY					
Menlo Park	51.7800	–	O 114.8lrx	KB7IP	NC6MLA
Redwood City	53.6800	–	O 114.8es	K6MPN	SCARES
Woodside	53.6400	–	●esx	N6ZX	KMARC
NORTH EAST					
Susanville	53.1000	52.1000	O 91.5	KE6NDG	KE6NDG
SOCAL-#KE,LA,OR,RIV,SBAR,SBER,VE					
Frazier Mtn	52.5600	52.1600	O	N6BKL	------------
SOCAL-#KERN					
El Paso Pk	52.7200	52.2200	82.5	W6NVY	------------
Shirley Peak	51.9800	51.4800	82.5	W6NVY	------------
SOCAL-#LA CENTRAL					
Arcadia	51.8600	51.3600	103.5	W6VIO	------------
Flint Peak	53.6800	53.1800	114.8	WA6MDJ	BHARC
Los Angeles	51.9000	51.4000	O	KC6MQL	------------
Los Angeles	53.6400	53.1400	100.0	WA6TFD	BHARC
Lukens	52.7400	52.2400	127.3	N6ENL	SCRN
Pico Rivera	52.6600	52.1600	O	WD6EZQ	------------
Wilson	52.5000	52.0000	O	W6ZOI	LARA
Wilson	52.8400	52.3400	94.8	WA6DVG	------------
SOCAL-#LA EAST					
Sunset	52.9000	52.4000	82.5	KB6MIP	------------

Location	*Output*	*Input*	*Notes*	*Call*	*Sponsor*
SOCAL-#LA NORTH					
Contractors PT	52.8600	52.3600	82.5	W6JW	------------
Oat Mtn	51.8000	51.3000	82.5	N6TCO	------------
Oat Mtn	51.8200	51.3200	82.5	W6NVY	------------
Santa Clarita	51.8600	51.3600	82.5	N6KNW	SCARC
SOCAL-#LA WEST					
Baldwin Hills	51.9200	51.4200	O	WA6MDJ	BHARC
Topanga Peak	52.5800	52.0800	O	KØJPK	------------
W Los Angeles	51.7800	51.2800	O	K6PYP	------------
Westchester	51.8800	51.3800	O	K6LH	------------
SOCAL-#LOMPOC					
Lompoc	51.8600	51.3600	O	WB6BGK	------------
Lompoc	52.8800	52.3800	82.5	WA6VPL	------------
SOCAL-#ONTARIO					
Chino Hills	51.7800	51.2800	O	WA6AJP	------------
SOCAL-#ORANGE					
Fullerton	51.7400	51.2400	Oel	N6ME	WARN
Orange	52.6400	52.1400	103.5	KB6CJZ	------------
Santiago Peak	52.6200	52.1200	103.5	W6KRW	OC RACES
SOCAL-#PALM SPRINGS					
Indio Hills	51.8400	51.3400	107.2	KA6GBJ	------------
SOCAL-#PALMDALE					
Hauser	51.9600	51.4600	82.5	W6NVY	------------
Lancaster	52.6800	52.1800	82.5	N6BCE	------------
Palmdale	52.6600	52.1600	O	WB6TTS	------------
SOCAL-#SAN BERNARDINO					
Green Vally LK	52.8800	52.3800	O	AA6PX	------------
Rimforest	52.9800	52.4800	103.5	KF6MZS	------------
Sky Forest	51.7600	51.2600	O	WA6BFH	------------
SOCAL-#SAN DIEGO					
Cuyamaca Peak	52.6000	52.1000	107.2	WA6ZZL	SD RACES
Palomar Mtn	52.6800	52.1800	107.2	W6NWG	PARC
Potrero	52.6600	52.1600	O	N6SXH	------------
San Diego	52.7800	52.2800	107.2	W6HDC	------------
SOCAL-#SANTA BARBARA					
Santa Barbara	52.9200	52.4200	88.5	K6BVA	SMUG
SOCAL-#THOUSAND OAKS					
Rasnow Pk	51.9400	51.4400	82.5	WB6RHQ	------------
SOCAL-#VENTURA					
Camarillo	51.8400	51.3400	82.5	WB6ZCO	------------
South Mtn	52.9800	52.4800	O	K6SMR	SMRA
SOCAL-KE,LA,OR,RIV,SBAR,SBER,VE					
Covers Area	52.9400	52.4400	●	W6+	------------
SOCAL-LA,OR,RIV,SBAR,SBER,SD,VE					
Covers Area	52.7200	52.2200	●	W6+	------------
Covers Area	52.7600	52.2600	●	W6+	------------
Covers Area	52.8000	52.3000	●	W6+	------------
SOCAL-LA,OR,RIV,SBER					
Covers Area	51.7200	51.2200	●	W6+	------------

Location	Output	Input	Notes	Call	Sponsor
SOCAL-LA,OR,RIV,SBER,SD					
Covers Area	52.8200	52.3200	●	W6+	------------
COLORADO					
FREQUENCY USAGE					
STATEWIDE	53.0700	52.0700			
COLORADO SPRINGS					
Colorado Springs	53.1300	51.4300	O 107.2e	KCØCVU	CMRG
DENVER METRO					
Denver	53.0500	52.0500	O 107.2/107.2ex	WØCRA	CRA
Denver	53.0900	52.0900	O 107.2/107.2e	WØTX	DRC
Denver	53.1900	52.1900	O 107.2/107.2l	WRØAEN	CARN
Idaho Springs	53.1500	51.4500	O 107.2x	NØPYY	DenPDEEB
NORTH FRONT RANGE					
Masonville	53.2700	52.2700	77/77 (CA)e rsWX	WØBFD	BFDARC
SOUTH CENTRAL					
Canon City	53.0300	52.0300	Oe	WBØWDF	WBØWDF
CONNECTICUT					
FREQUENCY USAGE					
Snp	53.5700	52.5700			
FAIRFIELD & SOUTHWEST					
Danbury	53.1300	52.1300	O 100.0/100.0	W1QI	CARA
HARTFORD & N CENTRAL					
Bolton	53.4500	52.4500	O 82.5/82.5 el	W1HDN	PVRA
Bristol	53.0500	52.0500	O 162.2/162.2e	WA1IXU	------------
E Hartland	53.1900	52.1900	162.2e	W1XOJ	YANKEE NET
Tolland	53.1500	52.1500	O 162.2/100.0e	W1GPO	------------
NEW HAVEN & S CENTRAL					
Guilford	53.7500	52.7500	110.9/110.9 e	NI1U	N1OFJ
Milford	53.2700	52.2700	77.0	KA1OYS	------------
NEW LONDON & SOUTHEAST					
Montville	53.4100	52.4100	O 156.7/156.7	K1IKE	K1IKE
New London	53.8500	52.8500	O 156.7/156.7	W1NLC	SCRAMS
DELAWARE					
NORTH					
New Castle	53.5700	52.5700	O 131.8e WX	ND3E	AMROS

Location	*Output*	*Input*	*Notes*	*Call*	*Sponsor*
FLORIDA					
CENTRAL - ORLANDO					
Eustis	53.2300	52.2300	O 103.5/103.5 (CA)e	KD4MBN	KD4MBN
EAST CENTRAL					
Cocoa	53.0700	52.0700	O 118.8/118.8	WB4OEZ	WB4OEZ
NORTH EAST					
Crescent City	53.7300	52.7300	Oe L(145.190) WX	KJ4UOP	KJ4UOP
Holly Hill	53.0500	52.0500	O 100/100e L(146 655 53.05 EC-50666)	KI4RF	KI4RF
Vero Beach	53.3300	52.3300	O 100/100	W4VRB	RATS
NORTH EAST - JACKSONVILLE					
Jacksonville	53.3300	52.3300	Oa(CA)er	W4RNG	Jax Range
Orange Park	53.1900	52.1900	O 100/100e L(EC-53190)	K4SIX	CC Sixers
St Augustine	53.2500	52.2500	Oe	KF4MX	KF4MX
NORTH WEST					
Marianna	53.0100	52.0100	Oe	W4BKD	Chipola AR
NORTH WEST - TALLAHASSEE					
Tallahassee	53.0300	52.0300	O 94.8/94.8 esx	K4TLH	TARS
SOUTH EAST - MIAMI/FT LAUD					
Hialeah	53.2100	52.2100	O 110.9/110.9a(CA)ersBlx	WB4IVM	WB4IVM
Miami	53.0300	52.0300	Oel	AC4XQ	AC4XQ
Miami	53.0500	52.0500	Oe	WB4TWQ	WB4TWQ
WEST CENTRAL					
Weeki Wachee	53.1300	52.1300	O 100/100a (CA)	KF4CIK	KF4CIK
WEST CENTRAL - TAMPA/ST PETE					
Brandon	51.6400	51.1400	O 141.3/141.3	W4HSO	STARC
GEORGIA					
Atlanta	53.1500	52.1500	O	KA5WZY	GPEARS/KA5W
Augusta	53.0300	52.0300	O	K4KNS	KR4XN
Biskey Mt	53.0500	52.0500	O	KC4JNN	NGAA
Brunswick	53.1100	52.1100	O	KG4PXG	KG4PXG
Clyattville	53.3900	52.3900	O	WR4SG	SOUTH GA RAD
Cochran	53.0100	52.0100	O	W4MAZ	W3LAP
Conley	53.6500	52.6500	O	N4MNA	N4MNA
Conyers	53.5500	52.5500	O	WB4JEH	------------
Crawford	53.3300	52.3300	O	KD4FVI	QRV ELECTRO
Dalton	53.1300	52.1300	O	N4BZJ	------------
Gray	53.4300	52.4300	O	AA4RI	AA4RI
Kingsland	51.9400	51.4400	O	KC5BMJ	KC5BMJ

Location	Output	Input	Notes	Call	Sponsor
Lake Park	53.8900	52.8900	O	WR4SG	KBØY
Lawrenceville	53.1100	52.1100	OesWX	W4GR	W4GR
Lula	53.8900	52.8900	O	WB4HJG	WB4HJG
Marietta	53.2100	52.2100	O	N1KDO	N1KDO
Mcintyre	53.7300	52.7300	O	KC4TVY	KF4CXL
Pine Log Mt	53.2900	52.2900	O	K4PLM	PINE LOG MT RPTR
Pine Log Mt	53.4500	52.4500	O	WD4OVN	KA4NNT
Roswell	53.0100	52.0100	O	W4OO	WA4YNZ
Summerville	53.7500	52.7500	O	K4PS	K4PS
Suwanee	53.8100	52.8100	O	KD4AKZ	KD4AKZ
Warm Springs	53.2300	52.2300	O	KD4BDB	N4UER
Warner Robins	53.7900	52.7900	O	WR4MG	MID GA RADIO ASS
Watkinsville	53.5700	52.5700	O	KD4AOZ	KD4AOZ
Watkinsville	53.7100	52.7100	O	KD4AOZ	KD4AOZ
Waycross	53.4100	52.4100	O	AE4PO	AE4PO
HAWAII					
HAWAII					
Glenwood	52.2000	51.2000	O 141.3a EXP	AH6GG	AH6GG
Hilo	51.8000	51.3000	O 100.0	WH6XM	WH6XM
OAHU					
Honolulu	53.0300	52.0300	O	WH6F	WH6F
IDAHO					
N ID - KELLOGG					
Wardner	52.8100	51.1100	136.5	N7SZY	N7SZY
N ID - LEWISTON					
Craig Mtn	53.3500	51.6500	O 100.0l	K7EI	K7EI
N ID - SPIRIT LAKE					
Spirit Lake	53.5900	51.8900	110.9	K7ZOX	K7ZOX
SOUTHEAST IDAHO					
Idaho Falls	52.2500	51.2500	O	AB7OS	------------
Idaho Falls	52.5500	51.5500	O	AB7OS	------------
SW ID					
Boise	52.7800	52.2800	O 123/123l	N7KNL	N7KNL
SW-ID					
Boise	52.6200	52.1200	O 100x	WA9WSJ	WA9WSJ
ILLINOIS					
CHICAGO					
Chicago	52.8100	51.1100	107.2	WA9ORC	CFMC
Chicago	52.8900	51.1900	131.8a	K9SAD	SADFAR
Chicago	53.3300	51.6300	100	W9GG	R-FAR
DECATUR					
Decatur	53.2300	51.5300	103.5e	K9HGX	CENOIS ARC
EAST CENTRAL					
Danville	52.9700	51.2700	88.5aes	NU9R	NU9R
Kansas	53.2900	51.5900	162.2	W9COD	W9COD

Location	*Output*	*Input*	*Notes*	*Call*	*Sponsor*
NORTH CENTRAL					
Marseilles	52.9300	51.2300	114.8elWX	KA9FER	KA9FER
Seneca	53.5400	53.0400	100	KF9NZ	KF9NZ
NORTHEAST					
Batavia	53.9100	52.2100	114.8el	W9XA	W9XA
Crystal Lake	52.9100	51.9100	114.8el	K9VI	K9QI
Dekalb	52.8500	51.1500	O 100.0	W9GG	R-FAR
Schaumburg	52.9500	51.9500	114.8el	N9KNS	MARC MOTO6
West Chicago	52.8700	51.1700	114.8alx	W9DMW	MOOSEFAR
ROCKFORD					
Rockford	53.0100	52.0100	118.8el	K9AMJ	K9AMJ
INDIANA					
EAST CENTRAL					
Glenwood	53.4300	52.4300	O 131.8e	WB9SBI	WB9SBI
Winchester	53.4100	52.4100	O 110.9	N9CZV	N9CZV
Yorktown	53.0700	52.0700	O	W9CSI	W9CSI
INDIANAPOLIS					
Danville	53.4500	52.4500	O 88.5aelr sx	WX9HC	HendrixARC
Indianapolis	52.7000	51.7000	Oel	K9IPL	IPL ARC
Indianapolis	53.0100	52.0100	Oer	K9TNW	HQ RC
NORTH CENTRAL					
Elkhart	53.1700	52.1700	O 131.8e WX	KC9GMH	KC9GMH
Kokomo	53.3900	52.3900	O 88.5es	W9NWN	W9NWN
South Bend	52.6200	52.1200	Oe	N9OCB	N9OCB
South Bend	53.8500	52.8500	O 131.8	N9JHQ	N9JHQ
NORTHEAST					
Columbia City	53.0500	52.0500	O 141.3ers WX	K9KOP	K9KOP
Columbia City	53.2700	52.2700	O 131.8ers WX	N9WNH	N9WNH
Huntington	53.1500	52.1500	O 131.8	WB9VLE	WB9VLE
SOUTH CENTRAL					
Nashville	53.0900	52.0900	OersWX	KA9SWI	KA9SWI
Paoli	53.6300	52.6300	OesWX	WB9FHP	WB9FHP
SOUTHEAST					
Brookville	53.3700	52.3700	O	N9HHM	N9HHM
SOUTHWEST					
Evansville	53.5500	52.5500	O 162.2elr sWXx	W9KXP	W9KXP
Jasonville	53.3100	52.3100	O 88.5	KC9AK	DuggerARC
WEST CENTRAL					
Cloverdale	53.7100	52.7100	O 88.5	N9XYY	N9XYY
Terre Haute	52.5250	52.9200	O	W9EQD	TerreHaute
West Lafayette	53.1900	52.1900	O 88.5e	W9YB	PurdueARC

Location	*Output*	*Input*	*Notes*	*Call*	*Sponsor*
IOWA					
CENTRAL					
Sheldahl	53.0900	51.3900	Oel	NØQFK	NØQFK
DES MOINES					
Gilman	53.0300	51.3300	151.4	NFØT	NFØT
Grimes	53.2500	51.5500	110.9ex	NØINX	WsideComm
WEST CENTRAL					
Mondamin	53.3900	51.6900	136.5aers	KØBVC	BVARC
KANSAS					
CENTRAL					
Hays	52.8500	51.1500	O	N7JYS	N7JYS
			131.8/131.8eL(IRLP#3917)		
KANSAS CITY METRO					
Kansas City	53.1300	52.1300	O 88.5/88.5	KØHAM	NEKSUN
			elrs		
Kansas City	53.8500	52.1500	O	WBØNSQ	WBØNSQ
Kansas City	53.8500	52.1500	O	WBØNSQ	WBØNSQ
Louisburg	53.1300	52.1300	O 88.5/88.5	KØHAM	NEKSUN
			elrs		
Shawnee Msn	53.1900	52.1900	Oe	KØGXL	SMMC
Shawnee Msn	53.1900	52.1900	Oe	KØGXL	SMMC
SOUTH CENTRAL					
Kechi	52.8300	51.1300	O	WBØNRV	------------
			156.7/156.7		
SOUTHEAST					
Parsons	53.7700	52.0700	O	WØPIE	WØPIE
			L(ECHOLINK#305758)		
Pittsburg	53.7900	52.0900	O 91.5/91.5	KØPKT	SLDDG
TOPEKA					
Topeka	52.9100	51.2100	O 88.5/88.5	KØHAM	NEKSUN
			elrs		
KENTUCKY					
Ashland	53.0100	52.0100	O	KC4QK	ASHLAND 24 REP.
Buckhorn Lake	53.7300	52.7300	O	K4XYZ	K4XYZ
Highland Heights	53.3300	52.3300	O	AD4CC	NKU & AD4CC
Highland Heights	53.7500	52.7500	O	W4YWH	W4YWH
LaGrange	53.9500	52.9500	O 88.5/88.5	WB4WSB	------------
Lawrenceburg	53.1300	52.1300	O	K4TG	K4TG
Louisville	52.0250	53.0250	O	WB4LBR	------------
Louisville	53.2900	52.2900	O	KF4UAQ	KF4UAQ
Louisville	53.4300	52.4300	O	N7BBW	FLOYD CO RACES
Middlesboro	51.7000	51.2000	O 100/100	WB4IVB	------------
Nancy	53.2700	52.2700	O 100/100e	AC4DM	AC4DM
Nicholasville	53.0900	52.0900	O	N4ALG	------------
Nicholasville	53.7100	52.7100	O	N4LG	JAWS WB4CWF
Stanton	53.8100	52.8100	O 100/100	WD4KNE	WD4KNE

Location	*Output*	*Input*	*Notes*	*Call*	*Sponsor*
Walton	53.8500	52.8500	O	KE4SHA	KE4SHA
Waynesburg	53.3900	52.3900	O 100/100e	AC4DM	AC4DM
Williamsburg	53.0700	52.0700	O	KB4PTJ	KB4PTJ
LOUISIANA					
REG 4 LAFAYETTE					
Morgan City	52.4500	51.4500	O 103.5/103.5	N5DVI	AADXA
REG 8 MONROE					
Columbia	53.2500	52.2500	O 94.8/94.8 aWX	KB5TLB	KB5TLB
West Monroe	53.6100	52.6100	O 94.8/94.8 aWX	KB5TLB	KB5TLB
REG 9 HAMMOND					
Hammond	53.0900	52.0900	O 107.2/107.2el	WB5ERM	WB5ERM
LaCombe	53.1300	52.1300	O 114.8e	K5OZ	K5OZ
MAINE					
AUGUSTA					
Litchfield	53.0500	52.0500	O 136.5/136.5x	K1AAM	K1AAM
CENTRAL/BANGOR					
Exeter	53.2900	52.2900	O 103.5	AA1PN	AA1PN
MID COAST					
Washington	53.5500	52.5500	O 91.5e	KC1CG	LMRG
NORTHWEST					
Hiram	53.3700	52.3700	O 136.5/136.5ex	K1AAM	K1AAM
Woodstock	53.0900	52.0900	O 136.5/100.0l	W1IMD	W1IMD
PORTLAND/YORK					
Harrison	53.5700	52.5700	O/151.4 (CA) E-WIND L(CLEOCAT)rWX	W1EMJ	jarc
Sanford	53.7100	52.7100	O 156.7/156.7aeL(PT-CCS NET) EXPx	N1KMA	CLEOSYS
So Berwick	53.0300	52.0300	O 131.8	WB1GGI	MLP
West Newfield	53.7100	52.7100	O 156.7/156.7aeL(PT-CCS NET) EXPx	N1KMA	CLEOSYS
MARYLAND					
BALTIMORE					
Catonsville	53.4700	52.4700	O 107.2	N3KTX	N3KTX
FREDERICK					
Frederick	53.7500	52.7500	O 100.0	N3IGM	N3IGM
NORTH CENTRAL					
Manchester	53.1900	52.1900	O	N3KZS	N3KZS
Westminster	53.0900	52.0900	O 107.2e	K3PZN	CCARC

Location	Output	Input	Notes	Call	Sponsor
NORTHEAST MD					
Jarrettsville	53.9300	52.9300	O	N3UR	N3UR
Port Deposit	53.8300	52.8300	O 94.8	WA3SFJ	CBRA
WASHINGTON AREA					
Ashton	53.2500	52.2500	O 100.0l	N3AGB	ARCS
Gaithersburg	53.2700	52.2700	O	KV3B	KV3B

MASSACHUSETTS

Location	Output	Input	Notes	Call	Sponsor
BERKSHIRES					
North Adams	53.2300	52.2300	O 162.2/162.2x	K1FFK	NOBARC
BOSTON METRO					
Boston	53.5500	52.5500	O 203.5/203.5e	KB1NZZ	CRN
Hopkinton	51.7400	51.2400	O 71.9/100.0elrsWXx	K1RJZ	CNHARC
CAPE & ISLANDS					
Barnstable	53.0100	52.0100	O 173.8/173.8e	N1YHS	N1YHS
CENTRAL					
Fitchburg	53.8300	52.8300	O 71.9/71.9 L(PT)	WB1EWS	WB1EWS
Oakham	53.6700	52.6700	O 123.0/100.0 E-SUN	KA1OXQ	KA1OXQ
Princeton	53.3100	52.3100	O 162.2+71.9/100.0ersWXx	WC1MA	MEMA
MERRIMACK VALLEY					
Pepperell	53.8900	52.8900	O 100.0/100.0ers	N1MNX	N1MNX
METROWEST					
Framingham	53.2700	52.2700	O 71.9/100.0 L(PT)x	WA1NVC	WA1NVC
Marlborough	53.8100	52.8100	O 71.9/71.9 L(PT)	W1BRI	MMRA
NORTH SHORE					
Danvers	53.8500	52.8500	O 71.9/71.9 ex	N1UEC	NSRA
PIONEER VALLEY					
Holyoke	53.3500	52.3500	O 71.9/71.9 x	AA1KK	KD1XP
Pelham	53.0900	52.0900	O 162.2/100.0	N1PAH	N1PAH
SOUTH SHORE					
Braintree	53.0300	52.0300	O CSQ/100.0	K1GUG	K1GUG
Braintree	53.3900	52.3900	O 71.9/71.9 e	AE1TH	B.E.M.A.
Norwell	53.3300	52.3300	O 71.9/71.9 eL(224.060)	KC1HO	KC1HO

Location	*Output*	*Input*	*Notes*	*Call*	*Sponsor*
MICHIGAN					
LOWER PEN NORTHEAST					
Roscommon	52.6400	52.1400	Olrs	WF8R	CRARC
Saginaw	51.8600	51.3600	Ors	K8DAC	SVARA
LOWER PEN NORTHWEST					
Big Rapids	52.8600	52.3600	O 94.8	KB8QOI	BRAARC
Glen Arbor	52.9200	52.4200	O 146.2l	WIØOK	IOOK
Kalkaska	52.8200	52.3200	Oe	W8KAL	W8KAL
Muskegon	52.8400	52.3400	O 94.8e	N8CUH	N8CUH
LOWER PEN SOUTHEAST					
Ann Arbor	51.7400	51.2400	O 88.5	W2PUT	W2PUT
Holly	53.7600	53.2600	O 151.4alx	W8FSM	W8FSM
Jackson	51.6200	51.1200	O 103.5	WD8PMD	WD8PMD
Lake Angelus	53.9400	53.4400	O 131.8e	NE9Y	NE9Y
Petersburg	52.7800	52.2800	OIWX	K8OF	K8OF
LOWER PEN SOUTHWEST					
Cedar Springs	52.7200	52.2200	O 136.5e	NW8J	NW8J
Decatur	52.9400	52.4400	O 94.8	KF8ZF	BASR
Grand Rapids	52.7600	52.2600	O 94.8al	W8DC	GRARA
Kalamazoo	51.7200	51.2200	O	K8KZO	SWMART
Lansing	52.9600	52.4600	●teWX	KD8PA	KD8PA
Ovid	51.9200	51.4200	OWX	WC8CLI	CCARA
Whitehall	52.8000	52.3000	O 94.8ers	K8COP	K8COP
UPPER PEN CENT					
Menominee	53.1100	51.4100	O 114.8e	AB9PJ	AB9PJ
MINNESOTA					
DULUTH					
Duluth	53.0500	52.0500	O	NØBZZ	NØBZZ
Duluth	53.1300	52.1300	O 103.5	KBØQYC	LSAC
Two Harbors	53.0200	52.0200	O 103.5	KBØTNB	LSAC
METRO					
Burnsville	53.3700	52.3700	O 100.0	WØBU	TCRC
Chaska	53.0300	52.0300	O	NØQNY	SMARTS
Credit River	53.3300	52.3300	O	NØKP	SCAN
Falcon Heights	53.1500	52.1500	O	WØYC	UOFM RC
Ramsey	53.5500	52.5500	O 114.8e	KØMSP	MIDWESTRA
NORTH CENTRAL					
Brainerd	53.1100	52.1100	O 123.0	WØUJ	BAARC
NORTH EAST					
Mahtowa	53.1700	52.1700	O 103.5	KBØTNB	LSAC
Virginia	53.1500	52.1500	O 103.5	KBØQYC	LSAC
NORTHCENTRAL					
Grand Rapids	53.2900	52.2900	O 146.2e	KBØCIM	KBOCIM
MISSISSIPPI					
Bay Saint Louis	53.6500	51.1400	O	KB5MPW	WQRZ
Byhalia	53.2700	52.2700	O	N4DRL	N4DRL

Location	*Output*	*Input*	*Notes*	*Call*	*Sponsor*
Ellisville	53.0100	52.0100	O	N5EKR	N5EKR
Jackson	53.4700	52.4700	O	W5PFC	W5PFC
Laurel	53.4500	52.4500	O	KC5PIA	KB5ZCX
Mendenhall	53.0500	52.0500	O	K5HYE	K5HYE
Nettleton	53.0500	52.0500	O	AB5MU	AB5MU

MISSOURI

CENTRAL					
Eldon	53.0500	51.3500	Ox	KCØKWL	------------
COLUMBIA/JEFF CITY					
Ashland	52.8900	51.1900	O 127.3/127.3a(CA)ex	KBØIRV	KBØIRV
EAST CENTRAL					
Union	52.8100	51.1100	O(CA)	WAØFYA	Zero Beaters ARC
NORTHWEST					
Amity	51.1300	52.8300	O 146.2x	KBØALL	KBØALL
SOUTHWEST					
Joplin	53.2500	51.5500	Oesx	KBØSTN	------------
Nixa	53.2700	51.5700	O 162.2/162.2ex	KØNXA	Nixa ARC
WEST CENTRAL					
Warrensburg	53.5500	51.8500	O	WØAU	WAARCI

MONTANA

SOUTH CENTRAL					
Bozeman	53.2900	51.5900	Ol	KB7KB	KB7KB
SOUTHEAST					
Billings	53.2900	51.5900	Ol	KF7FW	KF7FW
Worden	53.0500	52.0500	O	AE7V	AE7V
SOUTHWEST					
Anaconda	53.0300	52.0300	O 131.8	KB7IQO	KB7IQO
Helena	53.1100	51.4100	O	WR7HLN	WR7AGT

NEVADA

LAS VEGAS VALLEY					
Angel Peak	53.1900	52.1900	O 110.9	N9CZV	------------
Lo Potosi	53.0100	52.0100	O	WB6TNP	TRISTATE
NORTH CENTRAL					
Battle Mt	52.5250	52.7600	O	WA6TLW	WA6TLW
Elko	53.0100	52.0100	O 100	KE7LKO	WV3LMA
Elko	53.2500	52.2500	O 100l	W7LKO	N7EV
WEST CENTRAL					
New Washoe City	53.0000	53.0000	O 103.5l	NH7M	NH7M
Reno	51.8000	51.3000	O 110.9e	W7NV	W7PEB
Reno	52.6100	52.6100	Ol	WA6TLW	WA6TLW
Reno	52.9000	52.4000	O 107.2	KB6TDJ	KB6TDJ
Reno/Sparks	52.5800	52.0800	O 114.8	WA7DG	KK7SL
Sparks	52.8000	52.3000	O 123e	N7KP	N7KP

Location	*Output*	*Input*	*Notes*	*Call*	*Sponsor*
NEW HAMPSHIRE					
LAKES REGION					
Gilford	53.7700	52.7700	O 71.9/100.0 L(51.7400)rsx	K1RJZ	CNHARC
New Durham	53.2100	52.2100	O 88.5e L(PT-442.0500)	N1EUN	N1EUN
MERRIMACK VALLEY					
Brookline	53.4100	52.4100	O 127.3/127.3 L(N1IMO/N1IMN)s	N1IMO	N1IMO/N1IMN
Brookline	53.9300	52.9300	O 88.5/88.5 L(N1IMO/N1IMN)s	N1IMO	N1IMO/N1IMN
Derry	53.9700	52.9700	O 71.9+100.0/71.9aeL(FT 449.8750)sx	N1VQQ	N1VQQ
Goffstown	53.0700	52.0700	O 71.9151.4192.8/100.0ersWXx	W1DC	GEMOTO.com
Hudson	53.1300	52.1300	O 100.0/88.5	NE1B	RRA
Windham	53.6500	52.6500	O 71.9/100.0 L(442.6000)x	N1WPN	N1WPN
MONADNOCK REGION					
Keene	53.7300	52.7300	O 141.3/141.3	WA1ZYX	KA1QFA
NEW JERSEY					
ATLANTIC					
Egg Harbor	53.9100	52.9100	O 131.8lrs WX	W3BXW	BEARS
BERGEN					
Hackensack	53.3500	52.3500	O	W2MR	------------
CAMDEN					
Waterford Wks	52.6000	52.8400	O 131.8els RB WX	KA2PFL	------------
CUMBERLAND					
Rosenhayn	53.9500	52.9500	O 94.8e	KE2CK	------------
HUNTERDON					
Cherryville	53.2500	52.2500	O 146.2l	N3MSK	N3ODB
MIDDLESEX CO					
Monroe Twp	53.6700	52.6700	O 151.4lrs	W2CJA	CJRA
Monroe Twp	53.7100	52.7100	O 151.4/151.4 (CA)ersz	KA2CAF	CJRA
MONMOUTH CO					
Creamridge	53.4500	52.4500	O	N3IBX	CR-MRG
MORRIS CO					
Budd Lake	53.6700	52.6700	O 151.4lr	WS2V	------------
Lake Hopatcong	53.3900	52.3900	O 146.2a TTez	WR2M	WR2M-RC
Rockaway Twnshp	53.0100	52.0100	136.5	WA2SLR	------------

Location	Output	Input	Notes	Call	Sponsor
PASSAIC CO					
Little Falls	51.7200	51.2200	O 141.3/141.3eL(927.8000)r	W2VER	VRACES
SALEM					
Quinton	53.7100	52.7100	O 74.4e	N2KEJ	------------
SUSSEX					
Hopatcong Boro	53.3900	52.3900	Ot(CA)lRB	WR2M	WR2M RC
Vernon	51.7200	51.2200	O 136.5elrs	W2VER	VRACES
Vernon	51.7200	51.2200	O 136.5r	W2VER	Vern RACES

NEW MEXICO

Location	Output	Input	Notes	Call	Sponsor
NORTH CENTRAL					
La Cueva	53.2000	52.2000	O 107.2e	N9PGQ	N9PGQ
NORTHWEST					
Farmington	53.0100	52.0100	O 131.8	KB5ITS	KB5ITS
Farmington	53.8500	52.8500	O	NO3Y	NO3Y
SOUTH CENTRAL					
Alamogordo	53.4100	52.4100	O 100a	KA5BYL	KA5BYL
SOUTHEAST					
Hagerman	52.9400	52.4400	O 100.0/100.0e	W5GNB	W5GNB

NEW YORK

Location	Output	Input	Notes	Call	Sponsor
ADIRONDACKS/EAST					
Mineville	53.3500	52.3500	O 123elWXx	WA2LRE	ESSEX COUNTY RA
Plattsburgh	53.5900	52.5900	O 123.0elr	WA2LRE	Clin RACES
ALBANY/CAPITAL REGION					
Albany	53.4100	52.4100	O 100ex	W2GBO	W2GBO
Grafton	53.6300	52.6300	O	K2CBA	GURU
Grafton	53.8100	52.8100	Oe	K2RBR	K2RBR
AUBURN					
Auburn	53.0500	52.0500	O 71.9	K2INH	K2INH
BATH/HORNELL					
Hornell	51.6600	51.1600	O 107.2/107.2x	KD2WA	KD2WA
CATSKILLS/EAST					
Ashokan Rsvoir	51.7600	51.2600	O 103.5	N2NCP	N2NCP
Woodstock	53.1100	52.1100	O 77	N2WCY	N2WCY
CATSKILLS/NORTH					
Fleischmanns	53.4700	52.4700	O 107.2	WA2SEI	KNIGHT RIDERS
Schenevus	53.0300	52.0300	O 100e	KC2AWM	CTRC
Stamford	53.2700	52.2700	O 107.2e	K2NK	K2NK
ELMIRA/CORNING					
Elmira Heights	53.6900	52.6900	O	W2AC	W2AC
FRANKLIN					
Malone	53.1500	52.1500	/123.0l	WB2RYB	WB2RYB

Location	*Output*	*Input*	*Notes*	*Call*	*Sponsor*
LONG ISLAND - SUFFOLK CO					
Dix Hills	53.8500	52.8500	O 114.8e	W2RGM	------------
Mellville	53.1100	52.1100	O 107.2e L(447.950)	WB2CIK	Hilltop Gang
Yaphank	53.7900	52.7900	O 156.7s WXz	KA2RGI	------------
MID HUDSON					
Cragsmoor	53.3300	52.3300	O 100l	WB2BQW	NORTHEAST C
Harriman	53.1700	52.1700	O 136.5elx	W2AEE	COLUMBIA UNI
Mount Beacon	53.3100	52.3100	O 114.8e	K2ROB	MOUNT BEACO
Nyack	53.3700	52.3700	O 114.8l	N2ACF	ROCKLAND RE
NEW YORK CITY - KINGS					
Brooklyn	53.4100	52.4100	O 136.5e L(441.100)rsBI	N2ROW	PSARN
NIAGARA					
Colden	53.5700	52.5700	O 88.5e L(BARC) RB	W2IVB	BARC
Lancaster	53.1700	52.1700	O 107.2e L(LARC)	W2SO	LARC
Royalton	51.6400	51.1400	O 107.2 L(443.450) RB	KD2WA	------------
ROCHESTER					
Rochester	53.3300	52.3300	O 123aelrz	N2HJD	ROCHESTER R
Rochester	53.4300	52.4300	O	WR2AHL	W2HYP
Rochester	53.6300	52.6300	Olx	WR2AHL	GRIDD
SOUTHERN TIER					
Alma	53.0900	52.0900	O 88.5	KA2AJH	------------
Delevan	51.6200	51.1200	O 88.5e L(ILS IRLP ECHOLINK)	K2XZ	ILS
Limestone	53.3100	52.3100	O 127.3 L(442.750)	W3VG	------------
Sherman	53.6100	52.6100	O 127.3 L(442.75)	WB2EDV	------------
ST LAWRENCE					
Potsdam	53.1900	52.1900	O 151.4 EXP	KC2BEZ	------------
SYRACUSE					
Lafayette	53.6700	52.6700	O 103.5/103.5e	KD2SL	KD2SL
Syracuse	53.0100	52.0100	Oe	N2TUF	N2TUF

NORTH CAROLINA

Air Bellows Gap	53.7500	52.7500	O	WA4PXV	WA4PXV
Alexander	53.1900	52.1900	O	KG4LGY	KG4LGY
Asheville	53.2700	52.2700	O	WD4BQW	WD4BQW
Boone	53.7900	52.7900	Os	WA4NC	WA4NC
Claremont	53.8100	52.8100	O	WB4SRV	WB4SRV
Cleveland	53.9500	52.9500	O 100/100l	W4SNA	W4SNA

Location	Output	Input	Notes	Call	Sponsor
Durham	53.7500	52.7500	O	W4BAD	W4BAD
Fayetteville	53.8100	52.8100	O	K4MN	CAPE FEAR ARS
Gastonia	53.1100	52.1100	O	K4GNC	KC4YOT
Hatteras Island	53.0100	52.0100	O	K4OBX	W4HAT
Hendersonville	53.1300	52.1300	O	W4FOT	W4FOT
Lexington	53.7300	52.7300	O	W4PAR	HSMVHF SOCIETY
Marshall	53.4500	52.4500	O	K4MFD	K4MFD
Monroe	53.3700	52.3700	O	W4ZO	W4ZO
Morehead City	53.0900	52.0900	O 162.2/162.2e	KF4IXW	KF4IXW
Mt Airy	53.0700	52.0700	O	KD4FWS	KD4FWS
Raleigh	53.0300	52.0300	Oa(CA)	K4ITL	K4ITL
Robbinsville	53.7100	52.7100	O	NC4MO	NC4MO
Rocky Mount	53.0500	52.0500	O	N4JEH	N4JEH
Sauratown Mt	53.2100	52.2100	O	N4QLX	------------
Sophia	53.3500	52.3500	O	WR4BEG	BROADCAST PK7+R
Spruce Pine	53.0500	52.0500	O	WA4PXV	WA4PXV
Tarboro	53.1100	52.1100	O	K4SER	ROANOLE ARS
Thomasville	53.1700	52.1700	O	WW4DC	WW4FL
Williamston	53.3100	52.3100	O	K4SER	ROANOKE ARS
Wilmington	53.3300	52.3300	O	N4JDW	N4JDW
Wilmington	53.4300	52.4300	O	AD4DN	AD4DN
Youngsville	53.0700	52.0700	O	WB4IUY	5CRG

NORTH DAKOTA

Location	Output	Input	Notes	Call	Sponsor
N W CENTRAL					
Minot	53.4100	52.4100	O	KØAJW	SVARC
SE CENTRAL					
Cleveland	53.0100	52.0100	O	WØFX	NØHNM
SOUTHEAST					
Horace	52.9600	52.0600	O	WØZOK	WØZOK
SW-CENTRAL					
Bismarck	52.5250	52.5250	eL(444.220)	NØFAZ	NØFAZ

OHIO

Location	Output	Input	Notes	Call	Sponsor
ALLEN					
Lima	53.6300	52.6300	O 107.2e	KT8APR	LimaDARTS
BUTLER					
Middletown	51.6200	51.1200	●l	N8COZ	N8COZ
Middletown	53.2100	52.2100	O 77.0 TTel	W8JEU	Dial ARC
Middletown	53.3500	52.3500	O(CA)l	N8COZ	N8COZ
CLARK					
S Charleston	53.3900	52.3900	Oel	KB8GJG	KB8GJG
COLUMBIANA					
N Waterford	53.6300	52.6300	OeRB	KB8SHE	KB8SHE
New Franklin	51.6400	51.1400	O 107.2ex	NC8W	NC8W
Salem	53.0300	52.0300	O 88.5ael RB WXz	KB8MFV	KB8MFV

Location	*Output*	*Input*	*Notes*	*Call*	*Sponsor*
CUYAHOGA					
Brecksville	53.3100	52.3100		N8BHU	TCG
Cleveland	53.1100	52.1100	t	WA8WSO	WRRA
HighlandHills	53.2300	52.2300	O 136.5	WR8ABC	LEARA
Mayfield Hts	51.6200	51.1200	O	N8QBB	N8QBB
Shaker Hts	53.8300	52.8300	O	K8ZFR	CARS
ERIE					
Sandusky	53.3500	52.3500	O 107.2a (CA)elrWXx	W8LBZ	SREL
Vermillion	53.2900	52.2900	O 107.2a (CA)elrWXxz	KA8VDW	SREL
FRANKLIN					
Columbus	52.7000	52.9400	O 123.0al	W8RRJ	CORC
FULTON					
Wauseon	53.4100	52.4100	ae	KB8MDF	KB8MDF
GEAUGA					
Newbury	52.6800	52.9200	●x	WB8APD	SMART
GREENE					
Beavercreek	53.7300	52.7300	Ot	N8NPT	N8NPT
Fairborn	51.6600	51.1600	(CA)l	KI6SZ	KI6SZ
HAMILTON					
Cincinnati	53.1900	52.1900	114.8el	KD8TE	KD8TE
HANCOCK					
Findlay	53.3700	52.3700	O	WB8PBR	WB8PBR
JACKSON					
Ray	53.8100	52.8100	Ol	WB8LDB	WB8LDB
LORAIN					
Elyria	53.7700	52.7700	136.5e	WD8OCS	WD8OCS
MEDINA					
Brunswick	53.1900	52.1900		N8OVW	N8OVW
Leitchfield	51.6600	51.1600	e	W8EOC	M2M
MONTGOMERY					
Dayton	53.0300	52.0300	O	WF8M	MVRFG
Dayton	53.2900	52.2900	Oe	KB8CSL	KB8GDE
ROSS					
Chillicothe	53.2300	52.2300	O	KA8WWI	------------
STARK					
Canton	53.1300	52.1300	Olx	WØOZZ	WØOZZ
Canton	53.5700	52.5700	O 110.9	KB8MIB	KB8MIB
Massillon	53.0500	52.0500	O 136.5ae RBz	WA8GXM	WA8GXM
Uniontown	53.2500	52.2500	O	WD8BIW	WD8BIW
SUMMIT					
Akron	53.1700	52.1700	O 107.2e WXx	N8XPK	N8XPK
Norton	53.1500	52.1500		WB8UTW	WB8UTW
TRUMBULL					
Cortland	53.2100	52.2100	O 110.9	WA8ILI	KC8WY

Location	Output	Input	Notes	Call	Sponsor
VAN WERT					
Van Wert	51.6800	51.1800	O 156.7	N8IHP	N8IHP
VINTON					
Zaleski	53.2700	52.2700	O	KB8UIR	KB8UIR
WASHINGTON					
Marietta	53.1700	52.1700	O 141.3	N8OJ	W8JL
WAYNE					
Mt Eaton	53.3300	52.3300	100	KB8PXM	KB8PXM
West Salem	53.2700	52.2700	107.2	KE8X	KE8X
WOOD					
Perrysburg	53.6500	52.6500	Oa	KB8YVY	KA8WPC
OKLAHOMA					
NORTHWEST					
Buffalo	52.8100	51.1100	O 131.8/131.8 E-SUN E-WIND WXx	W5HFZ	GBARG
OKLAHOMA CITY METRO					
Bethany	53.0100	52.0100	O	KD5AHH	BOJIVE RAD
Oklahoma City	53.0500	52.0500	O 141.3/141.3 LITZ	KB5XM	KS5B
SOUTHEAST					
Broken Bow	53.0300	52.0300	O 100/100 E-SUNsWXx	KD5YQ	MCCURTAIN
OREGON					
CENTRAL WILLAMETTE VALLEY					
Oakridge	53.0700	51.3700	O 100e	W7ARD	W7ARD
Salem	52.9900	51.2900	O 100	WA7ABU	WA7ABU
COAST-NORTH					
Hebo	53.1100	51.4100	O 100e	KD7YPY	KD7YPY
COAST-SOUTH					
Myrtle Point	52.9300	51.2300	O 131.8e	KD7IOP	WA7JAW
NW OREGON & SW WASHINGTON					
Eugene/Monroe	53.0300	51.3300	O 100	W7ARD	W7ARD
Sandy	53.3500	51.6500	O 107.2el WX	KJ7IY	WORC
Timber	52.8500	51.1500	O 107.2	KR7IS	KR7IS
PORTLAND METRO					
Newberg	52.8300	51.1300	O 107.2el	KR7IS	WORC
Portland	53.0900	51.3900	O 107.2e	N7NLL	N7NLL
PENNSYLVANIA					
BEAVER					
New Galilee	51.7200	51.2200		KE3ED	KE3ED
BERKS					
Earlville	53.8700	52.8700	O 131.8	N3KZ	UPenn ARC
BRADFORD					
Towanda	53.4500	52.4500	O 82.5elrs RB BI WX	K3BM	Magic 45

Location	*Output*	*Input*	*Notes*	*Call*	*Sponsor*
BUCKS					
Almont	53.2300	52.2300	O 146.2rs	K3MFI	W Rockhill 6
Fairless Hills	53.0300	52.0300	O 131.8 (CA)rsRB WX	W3BXW	BEARS
Warminster	53.3700	52.3700	O 131.8 (CA)	K3MFI	WarmSix
CHESTER					
Valley Forge	53.4100	52.4100	O 131.8lRB	W3PHL	PARA Group
COLUMBIA					
Bloomsburg	53.1300	52.1300	O 131.8e RB	WB3DUC	------------
DAUPHIN					
Harrisburg	53.0100	52.0100	O 123l	W3ND	CPRA Inc
ERIE					
Albion	53.5500	52.5500	O 186.2l	WA3WYZ	WA3WYZ
LACKAWANNA					
Ransom	53.4300	52.4300	Otes	N3EVW	------------
LANCASTER					
Cornwall	53.8500	52.8500	O 114.8e	N3TJJ	L.R.T.S.
Holtwood	53.6300	52.6300	O 131.8l	WA3WPA	------------
LUZERNE					
Wilkes-Barre	53.8100	52.8100	O 82.5elrs WX	WB3FKQ	------------
MONROE					
Camelback Mtn	53.7900	52.7900	O 131.8	N3KZ	UPenn ARC
MONTGOMERY					
Eagleville	53.1100	52.1100	Ot(CA)ers	AA3E	Montco OEP
Schwenksville	51.9400	51.4400	O 88.5e	AA3RE	------------
NORTH CENTRAL					
Kane	53.4700	52.4700		WB3IGM	------------
Rockton	53.0700	52.0700	Or	N3HAO	N3HAO
NORTH CENTRAL 173.8					
Rockton	52.9000	52.4000	O 173.8	N5NWC	N5NWC
NORTHAMPTON					
Easton	51.8200	51.3200	O 88.5 WX	N3LWY	------------
Nazareth	51.7600	51.2600	O 151.4 (CA)elrsRB WX	W3OK	DLARC
North Bangor	53.8300	52.8300	O 131.8	KA2QEP	------------
Wind Gap	53.2900	52.2900	●t	N3MSK	------------
NORTHWEST					
Pleasantville	53.1500	52.1500		N3YEX	------------
Titusville	51.8200	51.3200	O	WB3KFO	WB3KFO
Vowinkel	51.7000	51.2000	186.2	N3GPM	N3GPM
PHILADELPHIA					
Philadelphia	53.8900	52.8900	O 131.8	N3KZ	UPenn ARC
PITTSBURGH					
Apollo	51.9000	51.4000	O 141.3ael rxz	N1RS	SARA
Bridgeville	51.9400	51.4400	O	N3WX	SHARC

Location	*Output*	*Input*	*Notes*	*Call*	*Sponsor*
Kilbuck Twp	53.2900	52.2900		WA3RSP	------------
Pittsburgh Homestead	51.7400	51.2400	O	WA3PBD	GtwyFM
SOUTHWEST					
Acme	51.7800	51.2800	O	N3QZU	LHVHFS
Finleyville	51.9800	51.4800	Oe	N3OVP	N3OVP
Mt Pleasant	51.9600	51.4600	O 141.3 (CA)elx	KA3JSD	KA3JSD
New Stanton	51.8400	51.3400	O 141.3	N3HOM	N3HOM
TIOGA					
Jackson Summit	53.7500	52.7500	O 167.9 LITZ	N3NXC	------------
WYOMING					
Mehoopany	53.3500	52.3500	O 131.8e	WA3PYI	------------
YORK					
York	53.9700	52.9700	O 123 (CA) el	W3HZU	Keystone

PUERTO RICO

Location	*Output*	*Input*	*Notes*	*Call*	*Sponsor*
E					
Luquillo	51.7200	51.2200	Oe	NP4ZB	------------
N					
Aguas Buenas	51.9800	51.4800	Oe	KP4IA	------------
Bayamón	51.6200	51.1200	● 136.5	WP3BM	------------
W					
Aguadilla	51.7400	51.2400		NP3LW	PR CW Club

RHODE ISLAND

Location	*Output*	*Input*	*Notes*	*Call*	*Sponsor*
EAST BAY					
Portsmouth	53.1700	52.1700	O 67.0/67.0 eL(FT 441.350)r	KA1RCI	KA1RCI
NORTHERN					
Greenville	53.8700	52.8700	O 146.2el WX	N1MIX	N1MIX

SOUTH CAROLINA

Location	*Output*	*Input*	*Notes*	*Call*	*Sponsor*
Gaffney	53.4700	52.4700	O	KF4BJO	KF4BJO
Greenville	53.4100	52.4100	O	KO4MZ	KO4MZ
Greenwood	53.4500	52.4500	O	W4JAK	------------
Leesville	53.2700	52.2700	O	N5CWH	N5CWH
Mountain Rest	53.5900	52.5900	O	KF4IWA	KF4IWA
Myrtle Beach	53.0500	52.0500	O	NE4SC	K4SHP
Pickens	53.3500	52.3500	O	AC4RZ	TRI COUNTY A R G
Sumter	53.7700	52.7700	O	W4GL	SARA INC.

TENNESSEE

Location	*Output*	*Input*	*Notes*	*Call*	*Sponsor*
Chattanooga	53.3500	52.3500	Oel	K4VCM	K4VCM
Clarksville	53.4100	52.4100	O	K4ORE	N3ORX

Location	*Output*	*Input*	*Notes*	*Call*	*Sponsor*
Cookeville	53.3100	52.3100	O	N4ECW	N4ECW
Dresden	53.1300	52.1300	O	KB4IBW	KB4IBW
Elizabethton	53.8900	52.8900	O 88.5/88.5	KN4E	KN4E
Gallatin	53.0500	52.0500	O	WA4BGK	WA4BGK
Knoxville	53.2500	52.2500	O	W4KEV	W4KEV
Knoxville	53.4700	52.4700	O	KB4REC	KB4REC
Knoxville	53.7700	52.7700	O	W4BBB	W4BBB
Laneview	53.7100	51.2000	O	KE4OVN	KE4OVN
Maryville	53.3700	52.3700	O	KC4PDQ	------------
Memphis	53.0100	52.0100	O	WB4KOG	WB4KOG
Memphis	53.4500	52.4500	O	W4EM	WA4KHN
Memphis	53.9300	52.9300	Or	W4GMM	W4GMM
Monteagle Mtn	53.4500	52.4500	O	NQ4Y	NQ4Y
Morristown	53.0300	52.0300	O	KF4FTD	KF4JOZ
Morristown	53.2300	52.2300	O	KQ4E	KQ4E
Mountain City	53.3300	52.3300	O	K4DHT	------------
Nashville	53.0100	52.0100	O	WA4BGK	------------
Oak Ridge	53.1100	52.1100	O	WD4GYN	WD4GYN
Tallassee	53.1500	52.1500	O	WB4GBI	WB4GBI

TEXAS

Location	*Output*	*Input*	*Notes*	*Call*	*Sponsor*
Abilene	53.0300	52.0300	O 167.9	NZ5V	------------
Amarillo	52.6500	51.6500	O 127.3	N5LUL	------------
Austin	53.6700	52.6700	O 103.5l	WB5PCV	------------
Beeville	53.6500	52.6500	O 107.2	KD5PXB	------------
Cedar Hill	53.1100	52.1100	O	W5AHN	------------
Channelview	53.1100	52.1100	O 141.3	WA5SIX	------------
Cut And Shoot	52.3900	51.3900	O 103.5e	W5WP	------------
Dallas	52.5900	51.5900	O 110.9	W5EBQ	------------
Edge	52.5500	51.5500	O 127.3	K5ENL	------------
El Paso	53.5500	52.5500	Ol	K5WPH	SCARC
Elmendorf	53.0900	52.0900	●	W5ROS	ROOST
Fort Worth	53.1500	52.1500	O 110.9	K5SXK	------------
Goldthwaite	53.0500	52.0500	O 88.5	K5AB	------------
Helotes	53.2900	52.2900	O 123	KB5ZPZ	------------
Houston	52.2500	51.2500	O 103.5 (CA)l	K5WH	COMPAQ ARC
Houston	52.6500	51.6500	O 156.7	N5TZ	------------
Houston	53.0500	52.0500	O 141.3	WB5UGT	SALT GRASS
Lufkin	53.3100	52.3100	O 141.3	N5CRW	------------
Lufkin	53.7100	52.7100	O 100	KD5TD	------------
Mesquite	52.7500	51.7500	O 110.9	AK5DX	------------
Midland	53.1100	52.1100	O(CA)elx	WB5RCD	WTX220ASN
Murphy	53.0300	52.0300	O	N5ROY	------------
Overton	53.1500	52.1500	Owx	N5VGQ	------------
Plano	53.6100	52.6100	O	N5TVN	------------
Rose Hill	53.2700	52.2700	O 123a	K5SOH	ALERT-HOU
San Angelo	53.6300	52.6300	O 88.5	N5SVK	------------
San Antonio	53.1300	52.1300	Oe	K5SUZ	SARO

Location	Output	Input	Notes	Call	Sponsor
San Antonio	53.1700	52.1700	O 88.5	WA5KBQ	------------
San Antonio	53.2100	52.2100	O 141.3	KB5BSU	------------
Tarzan	52.6500	51.6500	O 123	K5MSO	MIDLAND SO
Utopia	53.1500	52.1500	O 100l	W5FN	------------
Victoria	53.3700	52.3700	O 103.5	KC5WUA	------------
UTAH					
FREQUENCY USAGE					
Statewide	53.2100	52.2100	Ot	SHARED	
WASATCH FRONT					
Farmington	53.0100	52.0100	O 141.3x	K7DAV	------------
Murray	53.1100	52.1100	Oa(CA) L(448.125)	N7HIW	------------
Salt Lake	53.1500	52.1500	O 146.2 L(448.15)x	KI7DX	------------
VERMONT					
EAST CENTRAL					
Williamstown	53.8700	52.8700	O 100.0	N1IOE	N1IOE
VIRGIN ISLANDS					
St Thomas	51.7600	51.2600	O	KP2T	------------
VIRGINIA					
Alexandria	53.1300	52.1300	O	WA4CCF	------------
Alexandria	53.1300	52.1300	O	W4HFH	ALEXARC
Amelia	53.3900	52.3900	O	WB3R	WB3R
Amelia Courthse	53.1100	52.1100	O	KB4YKV	KB4YKV
Bedford	53.1500	52.1500	O	N4CH	N4CH
Bedford	53.7700	52.7700	O	N4TZE	N4TZE
Bluefield	53.3700	52.3700	O	N8RIG	N8RIG
Buckingham	53.2300	52.2300	O	K4YM	WW4GW
Bullrun	53.4500	52.4500	O	K8GP	DVMS
Centerville	52.4800	52.5800	O	KA4DCS	------------
Chesterfield	53.4300	52.4300	O	KD4SUU	KD4SUU
Fancy Gap	53.1900	52.1900	O	W4BAD	KG4GAI
Fancy Gap	53.2900	52.2900	O	WA4CQK	WA4CQK
Fancy Gap	53.3100	52.3100	O 100/100l	W4SNA	W4SNA
Gate City	53.2100	52.2100	O	N4WWB	SCOTT CO ARS
Gum Spring	53.0700	52.0700	O	KB4MIC	KB4MIC
Herndon	52.8200	52.6200	O	WD4KHP	ED KROM
Lexington	53.0100	52.0100	O	KI4ZR	ROCKBRIDGE ARC
Lynchburg	53.5700	52.5700	O	KE4KEH	KE4KEH
Newport News	53.2500	52.2500	O	KT4QW	KT4QW
Pearisburg	53.4700	52.4700	O	KE4JYN	DISMAL PEAK ARS
Portsmouth	53.8900	52.8900	O	W4POX	W4POX
Rice	53.1700	52.1700	O	KE4SFU	KE4SFU
Roanoke	53.0900	52.0900	O	WB8BON	WB8BON

Location	Output	Input	Notes	Call	Sponsor
Roanoke	53.2500	52.2500	O	N4CH	N4CH
Rocky Mt/ferrum	53.2700	52.2700	O	W4KZK	W4KZK
South Boston	53.6300	52.6300	O	W4HCH	W4HCH
Spotsylvania	51.8600	51.3600	O	W1ZFB	SPOTSYLVANIA
Vesta	53.4300	52.4300	O	KG4KUA	KE4JFV & KD4P
Vesta	53.4300	52.4300	O	N4GBO	N4GBO
White Top Mtn	53.6500	52.6500	O	KK4EJ	KK4EJ
FREDERICKSBURG					
Fredericksburg	51.8600	51.3600	O 127.3 (CA)el	W1ZFB	W1ZFB
Stafford	51.9000	51.4000	O(CA)er	K5JMP	K5JMP
FRONT ROYAL					
Front Royal	51.9400	51.4400	O 141.3 (CA)e	K4QJZ	K4QJZ
LURAY					
Fork Mountain	53.2300	52.2300	O	N3UR	N3UR
WASHINGTON AREA					
Alexandria	53.1300	52.1300	O 107.2	W4HFH	Alex RC
Ashburn	53.6100	52.6100	O	NV4FM	NVFMA
Bluemont	53.3700	52.3700	O 77.0el	K8GP	DVMS

WASHINGTON

Location	Output	Input	Notes	Call	Sponsor
W WA - FREQUENCY USAGE					
All Modes	50.3000	50.6000			
Crossband	52.5700	52.5700			
Cw Only	50.0000	50.1000			
Data	52.5900	52.7900			
Packet	50.6000	50.8000			
Radio Cntrl	50.8000	51.8000			
Rptr Inputs	51.1000	52.2900			
Rptr Outputs	52.8100	53.9900			
Shared	52.9900	51.2900			
Simplex	52.3100	52.5500			
Simplex	52.5250	52.5250			
Ssb	51.0000	51.1000			
Ssb, Cw	50.1000	50.3000			
E WA - ALMIRA					
NW of Almira	53.2100	51.5100	100.0	N7BHB	N7BHB
E WA - CENTRAL					
Saddle Mtn	52.9500	51.2500	100.0	N7BHB	N7BHB
E WA - COLVILLE					
Monumental	53.0900	51.3900	100.0l	WA7UOJ	WA7UOJ
E WA - PULLMAN					
Kamiak	53.7500	52.0500	100.0elr	N7ZUF	N7ZUF
E WA - RIVERSIDE					
Tunk Mtn	53.1100	51.4100	100.0	KK7EC	OCEMgt.
E WA - SPOKANE					
Mica Peak	53.2900	51.5900	O 100.0alx	K7LVB	WA7UOJ

Location	Output	Input	Notes	Call	Sponsor
PORTLAND METRO					
Vancouver	53.1300	51.4300	O 107.2e	KB7APU	KB7APU
SOUTHWEST WASHINGTON					
Camas	53.0500	51.3500	O	KD7DYR	KD7DYR
SW WASHINGTON					
Yacolt	52.9500	51.2500	O 94.8	W7AIA	W7AIA
W WA - NORTH					
Cultus Mtn	53.5900	51.8900	O 100e	K7OET	------------
Ferndale	53.2100	51.5100	O 103.5r	W7SSO	WHATCOM CO RAC
Lyman Hill	53.0900	51.5900	O 100e	W7UMH	5CECG
Sultan	53.3500	51.6500	O 100e	W7SKY	SKY VALLEY
W WA - NORTH COAST					
Blyn Mtn	53.3700	51.6700	O 100e	WR7V	------------
W WA - SEATTLE-TACOMA					
Bainbridge Island	53.4300	51.7300	O 100	W7NPC	BAINBRIDGE IS. AR
Baldi Mtn	53.3300	51.6300	O 100e	N7OEP	N7OEP
Buck Mtn	53.2900	51.5900	O 100e	W7FHZ	------------
Eatonville	53.4100	51.7100	O 100	W7PFR	GOBBLERS KNOB R
Everett	53.1300	51.4300	O 100e	KF7T	------------
Grass Mtn	53.8700	52.1700	O 100e	W7SIX	FRED BAKER
Issaquah	53.8300	52.1300	O 123.0	N9VW	------------
Lynnwood	53.2700	51.5700	O 100e	KG7PD	------------
North Bend	53.8500	52.1500	O 100	N9VW	------------
Olalla	53.2300	51.5300	O 103.5	K7PAG	------------
Redmond	53.0700	51.3000	O 100e	KC7IYE	------------
Seattle	53.2500	51.5500	O 100e	W7ACS	SEATTLE EM
Shoreline	53.2100	51.5100	O 100	NU7Z	------------
Snohomish	53.6500	51.9500	O 100e	W7QA	------------
Tacoma	53.1900	51.4900	O 100e	K7HW	------------
Tiger Mtn W	53.1500	51.4500	O 100e	K7CR	Channel 1 RPTR GR
University Place	53.0100	51.3100	O 100l	K7NP	U.P. RPTR
Vashon Island	53.7900	52.0900	O 103.5 (CA)e	K6AJV	------------
W WA - SOUTH					
Baw Faw Peak	52.9300	51.2300	O 100e	K7CH	K7CH
South Mtn	53.0300	51.3300	O 100l	K7CH	K7CH

WEST VIRGINIA

Location	Output	Input	Notes	Call	Sponsor
Alderson	53.1900	52.1900	O	WV8BD	BLACK DIAMOND A
Alderson	53.2300	52.2300	O	KE4QOX	KE4QOX
Beckley	53.1700	52.1700	O	N8FWL	N8FWL 222 RAD NT
Beckley	53.5900	52.5900	O	WB8YST	WB8YST
Belington	53.6500	52.6500	O	N8SCS	N8SCS
Charleston	53.6300	52.6300	O	WB8YST	WB8YST
Charleston	53.7500	52.7500	O	N8PEI	------------
Culloden	53.0300	52.0300	O	KC8POU	KC8POU
Elkins	53.0300	52.0300	O	WV8ZH	WV8ZH
Flatwoods	53.1100	52.1100	O	N8CQQ	N8ZVK

Location	*Output*	*Input*	*Notes*	*Call*	*Sponsor*
Gassaway	53.2100	52.2100	O	AB8WB	AB8WB
Grafton	53.4300	52.4300	O	WD8LNB	WD8LNB
Kenova	53.8700	52.8700	O	KC8PFI	KC8PFI
Lewisburg	53.3300	52.3300	O	KB8OUU	------------
Morgantown	53.4700	52.4700	O	W8CUL	WVU ARC - W8C
Mullens	53.0300	52.0300	O	KC8IT	KC8IT
Richwood	53.7100	52.7100	O	WB8YST	WB8YST
Shirley	53.3100	52.3100	O	KB8TJH	KB8TJH
Snowshoe	53.3300	52.3300	O	KC8CSE	KC8CSE
Sutton	53.0300	52.0500	O	W8LGB	W8LGB
BERKELEY SPRINGS					
Berkeley Springs	53.3500	52.3500	O 123.0e	W3VLG	W3VLG
WISCONSIN					
WAR					
Bayfield	53.0900	52.0900	O 110.9ers	KBØTNB	LSAC
Fitchburg	53.2300	52.2300	O 123.0aelrs	KA9VDU	KA9VDU
Holcombe	52.8100	51.1100	O 110.9ers	N9LIE	N9LIE
Madison	53.0700	52.0700	O 123.0aelrs	N9KAN	SWRG
Madison	53.1500	52.1500	O 123.0aelrs	WD8DAS	NERT
Milwaukee	53.0300	52.0300	O 127.3aes	W9DHI	WERA
Tomahawk	52.8300	51.1300	O 114.8aelr	N9MEA	N9MEA
Wausau	52.8900	51.1900	O 114.8aelr	W9SM	W.V.R.A.
WYOMING					
CENTRAL					
Lander	53.0300	52.0300	Ol	N7HYF	WYAME
Riverton	53.3500	51.6500	Ol	KB7PLA	KB7PLA
SOUTH CENTRAL					
Rawlins	53.9300	51.6900	Ol	KJ7AZ	KJ7AZ
SOUTH EAST					
Rock River	53.0300	52.0300	Ol	K7UWR	K7UWR
ALBERTA					
CALGARY					
Calgary	53.0300	52.0300	Oe	VE6RYC	CARA
Calgary	53.4100	52.4100	O 103.5	VE6ZV	VE6AKQ
CENTRAL WEST					
Limestone Mtn	52.6100	51.6100	Ol	VE6MTR	VE6CMM
EDMONTON					
Edmonton	53.0700	52.0700		VE6UFO	VE6UFO
Edmonton	53.4300	52.4300	Ol	VE6SSM	SARA

Location	Output	Input	Notes	Call	Sponsor
HIGH RIVER					
Black Diamond	53.5700	52.5700	Ol	VE6RPX	VE6ERW
KANANASKIS					
Fortress Mountain	53.5100	52.5100	O	VE6SHB	VE6SHB
LETHBRIDGE					
Lethbridge	53.4500	52.4500	O	VE6ZIX	VE6HDO
Red Cliff	53.0100	52.0100	O	VE6TEQ	VE6TEQ
MEDICINE HAT					
Medicine Hat	53.4700	52.4700	O	VE6MLD	VE6MLD
Red Cliff	53.0100	52.0100	O	VE6TEQ	VE6TEQ
BRITISH COLUMBIA					
FRASER VALLEY					
Abbotsford	52.8500	51.1500	100.0e	VE7RVA	FVARESS
GREATER VANCOUVER					
Anvil Island	52.9100	51.2100		VE7QRO	VE7LWB
Vancouver	52.8900	51.1900	#	VE7HCP	VE7HCP
SOUTH CENTRAL					
Vernon	52.0100	51.4100	110.9	VA7VMR	VE7OHM
VANC ISLAND SOUTH					
Victoria	52.8300	51.1300	100	VE7RSX	WARA
Victoria	52.9700	51.2700		VE7RFR	VE7DAT
MANITOBA					
WINNIPEG					
Winnipeg	53.4000	52.4000	O	VE4KOG	PMCStaff
NOVA SCOTIA					
GORE					
Gore	52.6200	51.6200	O	VE1OM	TPARC
HALIFAX					
Halifax	53.5500	52.5500	O 151.4el	VE1PSR	HARC
ONTARIO					
CENTRAL					
Edgar	53.0700	52.0700	Oe	VA3LSR	LSRA
Georgina	53.0900	520900.0000	O(CA)e	VA3PTX	------------
CENTRAL EAST					
Haliburton	53.0500	52.0500	O 162.2e RB	VE3ZHR	HARC
FRONTENAC/LENNOX-ADDINGTON					
Kingston	53.1300	52.1300		VE3KER	KARC
METRO TORONTO					
Ballantrae	53.1300	52.1300	O 103.5 (CA) L(443.275)	VA3PWR	------------
Brampton	53.1900	52.1900	OeWX	VE3PRC	PARC
Mississauga	53.2500	52.2500	O 103.5#	VE3MIS	MARC
Toronto	53.3500	52.3500	O 103.5e	VA3GTU	------------

Location	*Output*	*Input*	*Notes*	*Call*	*Sponsor*
Toronto	53.3900	52.3900	O 103.5	VE3ECT	TAG
NATIONAL CAPITOL REGION					
Ottawa	53.0300	52.0300	L(147.300/444.200)	VE3RVI	O6MIG
Ottawa	53.0900	52.0900	136.5/136.5 L(I 2210)x	VE3TST	VE3HXP
Ottawa	53.2300	52.2300	141.3/110.9	VA3LGP	VE3JGL
NORTHWESTERN ONTARIO					
Thunder bay	53.0300	52.0300		VA3OLA	------------
SOUTH					
Burlington	53.5900	52.5900	O 131.8	VE3BUO	------------
Carlisle	53.1100	52.1100	O 131.8 L(ERA)	VE3WIK	------------
Kitchener	53.3700	52.3700	O 131.8e L(ERA)	VE3SED	------------
SOUTHWEST					
Essex	53.0300	52.0300	O	VE3SMR	------------
Windsor	53.0500	52.0500	O 118.8	VE3RRR	WART
PRINCE EDWARD ISLAND					
CENTRAL					
Glen Valley	53.5900	52.5900	O	VY2SIX	VY2RU
QUEBEC					
Alma	53.2500	52.2500	O	VE2RYK	VE2AYK
Ange-Gardien	53.3100	52.3100	O 110.9ex	VE2REH	VE2ZVL
Blainville Nord	53.3100	52.3100	O	VE2RNO	VE2THE
Boucherville	53.1300	52.1300	O 103.5	VE2MRQ	VE2MRI
Gatineau	53.1100	52.1100	O 110.9e	VE2REH	VE2ZVL
Grand-Mere	53.1100	52.1100	O 141.3	VA2RTI	VE2JTR
Grenville	53.0100	52.0100	O 123e	VE2RCS	VE2HMA
St-Calixte	53.0700	52.0700	O 141.3x	VE2LED	VE2VK
St-Calixte	53.0700	52.0700	O 141.3	VE2RVK	VE2VK
St-Joseph du lac	53.0500	52.0500	O	VE2RST	VE2GDR
Ste-Marguerite	53.0900	52.0900	O	VE2RIX	VE2BPU
LAURENTIDES					
Lachute	53.0100	52.0100	I	VE2RCS	VE2HMA
OUTAOUAIS					
Gatineau	53.1100	52.1100	110.9/110.9 (CA) L(I 2018)	VE2REH	ARAI
PAPINEAU					
Ripon	53.3100	52.3100	110.9/110.9 (CA) L(I 2018)x	VE2REH	ARAI
SASKATCHEWAN					
SASKATOON					
Saskatoon	50.2100	51.5100	#	VE5FUN	MARS

Location	*Output*	*Input*	*Notes*	*Call*	*Sponsor*
SOUTHEAST					
Estevan	53.7300	52.7300	#	VA5EST	VE5AJ

YUKON TERRITORY					
YUKON					
Carcross	52.2000	52.7000	OI	VY1RMM	YARA

144-148 MHz

Location	Output	Input	Notes	Call	Sponsor
ALABAMA					
Albertville	145.1100	–	O 107.2 (CA)eWXx	KI4RYX	MCEARS
Alexander City	146.9600	–	O 88.5/88.5 l	WA4KIK	96 Radio Club
Andalusia	147.2600	+	O 100.0e WX	WC4M	South AL R
Anniston/Cheaha Mt	147.0900	+	O 131.800a eWXz	WB4GNA	CCARA
Anniston/Oak Mt	146.7800	–	OaelRB WXz	KG4EUD	Calhoun EMA
Arab	146.9200	–	O 77.0/77.0 elRBz	KE4Y	BMARA
Argo/Trussville	145.2600	–	O	K4YNZ	KE4ADV / D-STA
Ashland	147.2550	+	O 131.8ae WXz	KI4PSG	KI4PSG
Athens	145.1500	–	O 100.0/OR OFF/ARES (CA)eWXz	N4SEV	Limestone
Auburn	147.0600	–	O	KA4Y	KA4Y
Auburn	147.2400	+	O 156.7ae	K4RY	Auburn Uni
Auburn	147.3000	+	O 123.0/123.0elRB	W4HOD	HODARS
B,Ham /Shades Mt	147.1400	+	O 156.7/156.7e	WA4CYA	WA4CYA
Bald Rock	145.1300	–	O 103.5/RACESerRB WX	K4SCC	St Clair Ares/Rac
Barton	146.7600	–	O 100.0/100.0/ARES	WX4CC	CCARC
Bay Minette	145.4300	–	O 123.0el	KD4HYG	KD4HYG
Bessemer	145.1500	–	Oaez	WB4YRJ	T.H.E. Club
Birmingham	145.2300	–	O 203.5/203.5e	WB4TJX	UAB ARC
Birmingham	147.3400	+	O	W4RUM	W4RUM
Birmingham / Tuscaloosa	147.5800	146.4800	O	W4TTR	Tall Tower D-ST
Birmingham-East: Bald Rock	146.7600	–	O 114.8ae	KK4BSK	HC ARC
Birmingham-North: Springville	146.7600	–	O 103.5ae	KK4BSK	HC ARC
Birmingham-South: Pelham	146.7600	–	O 94.8ae	KK4BSK	HC ARC
Birmingham/ East Lake	146.7600	–	O 88.5ae	KK4BSK	HC ARC

ALABAMA

Location	*Output*	*Input*	*Notes*	*Call*	*Sponsor*
Birmingham/ Shades Mtn	146.8800	–	O 88.5/88.5 aeRB WX	W4CUE	B,ham ARC
Birmingham Ruffner	146.7600	–	O 88.5e	KK4BSK	HC ARC
Birmingham Tuscaloosa	145.3500	–	Ox	W4TTR	KX4I
Boaz	147.2000	+	O 123.0/123.0el	NA4SM	MCARC
Brent	145.3900	–	Oe	NU4A	Bibb Co
Brewton	146.9700	–	O#	WB4ARU	KT4CW
Butler	146.8500	–	O 210.7	KE4ROA	KE4WYK
Camden	147.3300	+	O 123.0/123.0	N5GEB	N5GEB
Carrollton	146.6850	–	O 77.0/77.0 TT(ARES)e	K4HDC	PICKENS CO EMA
Citronelle	147.2250	+	O 203.5/203.5	W4IAX	Mobile ARC
Citronelle	147.2250	+	O 203.5/203.5eWX	W4FRG	W4FRG
Clanton	145.1800	–	O	KF4LQK	AEMA ARC D-STAR
Clanton	147.1050	+	O 123.00 WX	WB4UQT	Clanton Am
Columbiana	147.3200	+	O 88.5/88.5	W4SHL	Shelby Co. ARC
Corner	147.1200	+	O 100.0/100.0e	KD4CIF	KD4CIF
Courtland	145.2500	–	O	W9KOP	W9KOP
Cullman	145.3100	–	O 100.0/ARES-LITZaer	N4TUN	CARC
Cullman	147.4150	146.4160	O 123.0	W4CFI	W4CFI
Decatur	145.2100	–	O/ARESel RB	N4VCN	N4VCN
Decatur	146.7200	–	Oe	W9KOP	W9KOP
Decatur	146.9800	–	O/RACESe rWX	W4ATD	DARC
Decatur/Brindlee Mt	147.0000	+	Oe	W4ATD	DARC
Demopolis	146.7900	–	OaelWX	N4QII	N4QII
Dixons Mills	147.0800	+	O 210.7/210.7	W4WTG	------------
Dothan	145.4300	–	O 186.2	WB4ZPI	WARC
Dothan	146.8500	–	O 186.200/186.200e	KE4GWW	------------
Dothan	147.1400	+	O 186.2/186.2	KC4JBF	KC4JBF
Dothan	147.3400	+	O ARES/RACESaerWXz	N4RNU	Houston Co
Elba / Victoria	146.7800	–	Oe	W4NQ	Troy ARC
Enterprise	145.3900	–	Oaez	KD4BWM	EEARA
Enterprise	147.2400	+	O 100.0/100.0aelz	WD4ROJ	EARS

Location	*Output*	*Input*	*Notes*	*Call*	*Sponsor*
Eufaula	147.2800	+	O 123.0/123.0	W4EUF	Eufaula ARC
Eutaw	145.3700	–	O 131.8e	WS4I	Druid City
Fayette	147.2000	+	O 110.9	N4DSS	N4DSS
Flagg Mountain	145.2700	–	O 88.5/88.5	KC4CM	KC4CM
Flint Ridge	146.8600	–	O(CA)elz	W4TH	W4TH
Florence	147.3200	+	O 123.0/123.0	K4NDL	------------
Foley	146.6850	–	O 82.5e	KI4ELU	KI4ELU
Fort Deposit	146.6700	–	O 103.5/103.5elWX	K4TNS	Butler Co. EMA
Friendship	147.2000	+	107.2e	KE4LTT	KE4LTT
Ft Payne	147.2700	+	O 100.0/ARESaelWXx	W4GBR	DeKalb ARC
Gadsden	145.4900	–	O 107.2/107.2	KI4FLY	KI4FLY
Gadsden	146.6700	–	O 100.0 (CA)e	K4BWR	K4BWR
Gadsden	146.8200	–	O 192.8/RACESaerRB WXz	K4VMV	Etowah EMA
Gadsden	147.1600	+	O 100.00/100.00aelWXz	K4JMC	Gadsden AR
Gaylesville	145.2500	–	110.9	K4JS	K4JS
Gaylesville	147.3200	+	O 100.0/100.0e	W4CCA	CCARC
Geneva County	145.2700	–	O 103.5/103.5 WX	W4GEN	GARS
Gold Hill	145.2300	–	O 123.0/123.0	KE4COL	KE4COL
Goodwater	145.3300	–	O 179.9e WX	K4YWE	Lake Martin ARC
Grove Hill	147.2800	+	O 210.8/210.8	AB4BR	Clark Co. ARC
Guntersville	147.3800	+	O 100.0/100.0	KCØONR	KCØONR
Hamilton	147.0200	+	O 123.0/123.0	KJ4I	KJ4I
Huntsville	145.2900	–	O 100.0ae	KK4AI	MARA
Huntsville	145.3300	–	O	W4ATV	NARA
Huntsville	145.3900	–	OTTe	WD4DNR	WD4DNR
Huntsville	145.4700	–	●CLOSED	W9KOP	W9KOP
Huntsville	147.1000	+	O 103.5ae	W4VM	W4VM
Huntsville	147.2400	+	O 82.5ael RB	KB4CRG	KB4CRG
Huntsville	147.3000	+	O 103.5a	W4QB	NADXC
Huntsville/ BrindleyMtn	147.1800	+	O 100.0 L(IRLP 4950)	WD4CPF	NARA
Huntsville MonteSano	145.2300	–	O 186.2/AICN L(RB) RB	W4XE	W4XE

Location	Output	Input	Notes	Call	Sponsor
Huntsville MonteSano	146.9400	–	O 100.0/ARESaesWX	N4HSV	NARA
Huntsville MonteSano	147.2200	+	O 136.5lr	W4HMC	Huntsville-Madison C
Huntsville MonteSano	147.5050	146.5050	O 123.0 (CA)	KC4HRX	KD4TFN
Irvington	145.1300	–	O 203.5/203.5	KD4NGA	ARMY COE
Jasper	146.6400	–	O 123.0/123.0eWX	WR4Y	Walker ARC
Jasper	146.9000	–	O	WB4ACN	WB4ACN
Jasper	147.2600	+	O	KI4GEA	KI4GEA
Jasper	147.3900	+	O 110.9/110.9eL(6-MTR) WX	W4WCA	Walker Co. ARES
Killen	146.6800	–	O 100.0ael z	WB4NQH	WB4NQH
Lanett	147.0000	+	O 141.300/141.300	K4DXZ	Chattahoochee Valley
Leesburg	147.0750	+	O 100.0e WXz	KB4AEA	Cheroke EMA
Leighton	145.4100	144.4100	100.0/100.0	W4ZZK	W4ZZK / N4RTR
Leighton	147.3400	+	O 100.0/100.0 (CA)	AC4EG	NAARC
Littleville	145.1300	–	Oae	WB4KKV	WB4BPS
Loxley	147.3900	+	118.8/118.8 ae	WB4GMQ	WB4GMQ
Marion	147.3600	+	O	N4EJF	Perry EMA
Millry	147.1800	+	O 114.8el	KF4ZLK	KF4ZLK
Mobile	146.8200	–	O 203.5l	W4IAX	Mobile ARC
Mobile	146.9400	–	O RACES/ARES (CA)eL(ECHOLINK) WX	WB4QEV	Mob Co EMA
Mobile	147.1500	+	Oe	WB4BXM	WB4BXM
Mobile	147.3450	+	O(CA)	W4IAX	MOBILE AMA
Mobile/Semmes	145.4700	–	O 123.0/123.0eWX	WX4MOB	WX4MOB
Monroeville	147.1600	+	O 167.9 (CA)e	WB4UFT	MARC
Montevallo	145.2900	–	OeRB	N4GEG	N4GEG
Montgomery	145.4900	–	O	N4QYL	N4QYL
Montgomery	146.8400	–	OeWX	W4AP	MARC
Montgomery	147.1800	+	O 123.0/RACESerWXx	W4AP	MARC
Moody	146.6200	–	O	KF4FVH	KF4FVH
Moulton	145.2700	–	O 107.2/ARES (CA)elsWX	KN4CI	Bankhead A
Moulton	146.9600	–	O(CA)elWX	N4IDX	Bankhead A
Moundville	147.2200	+	O 77.0/77.0	K4HDC	HDCP
Muscle Shoals	145.4100	–	203.5/AICNl WX	KF4MH	WB4NQ

Location	*Output*	*Input*	*Notes*	*Call*	*Sponsor*
Muscle Shoals	146.6100	–	Oae	W4JNB	MSARC
Nectar/ SkyballMtn	146.7000	–	O 203.5	W4BLT	Blount ARC
Ohatchee	147.0200	+	O 250.3e	WB4LYR	WB4LYR
Opelika	147.1200	+	Oe	W4LEE	East AL ARC
Opelika	147.1500	+	O 123.0/123.0	WX4LEE	Lee Co. EMA AR
Opelika	147.3750	+	OeWX	WX4LEE	EMA ARC
Opp	146.6400	–	O 100.0/100.0	W4ORC	Opp ARC
Ozark	146.9800	–	O 100.0/ARESe	KA4AFI	Dale ARES
Ozark	147.2100	+	O 100.0/100.0#e	WA4GIU	------------
Palmerdale	145.4500	–	O 100lRB	KE4QCY	WB4ZNQ
Pelham	146.9800	–	Oe	W4SHL	Shelby Co. ARC
Pell City	147.0200	+	O 131.8/131.8e	K4CVH	Coosa Valley HR
Perry County Courthouse	147.3600	+	O	N4EJF	Perry EMA
Phenix City	146.6100	–	OeWXz	W4CVY	Columbus ARC
Phenix City	146.7200	–	O 123.0e	WA4QHN	WA4QHN
Phenix City	146.8800	–	O 123.0/123.0	W4CVY	Columbus ARC
Phenix City	147.3200	+	123.0/ARES elrsWX	WX4RUS	Russell EMA
Pike Road	146.9000	–	O 67.0/67.0 eRB	W2YNE	W2YNE
Ranburne/ Turkey Heaven Mtn	146.8650	–	O 131.8	N4THM	Turkey Heaven
Red Bay / Vina	146.7900	–	O 103.5/103.5eL(I-LINK) WXx	NV4B	FCEMA
Roanoke	145.4300	–	O 141.3/141.3aelRB WXz	KA4KBX	PBI RC
Roanoke	147.2200	+	Ol	WD4KTY	WD4KTY
Roanoke	147.2700	+	O 141.3/141.3aelsLITZ WX	KA4KBX	KA4KBX
Robertsdale	147.0900	+	Oe	WB4EMA	Baldwin EM
Rogersville	146.7400	–	O 100.0/100.00e	KJ4LEL	ELRA KJ4LEL
Russellville	147.1600	+	OeWX	KE4ZIM	Franklin C
Russellville	147.2100	+	O	WX4FC	W4AQQ
Russellville	147.3600	+	O 103.5/103.5	WX4FC	FC EMA
Salem	146.9400	–	O 123.0e WX	WA4QHN	WA4QHN
Section	147.3600	+	O 123.0el WX	W4SBO	JCAR
Selma	146.7200	–	O 100.0e	N4KTX	N4KTX

Location	Output	Input	Notes	Call	Sponsor
Selma	147.0400	+	O 146.2 (CA)eWXz	KI4CNI	Dallas ARC
Sheffield	146.8800	–	103.5/103.5 eWX	KE4GOG	KE4GOG
Skipperville	147.0300	+	O 71.9/71.9 (CA)el	KD4KRP	KD4KRP
Smiths Station	145.3500	–	O 123.0/123.0eL(ECHOLINK)	KF4AEJ	KE4AEJ
Sylacauga	146.6550	–	O 123.0/123.0eWX	AF4FN	S.T.A.R.S.
Talladega	145.1600	–	OeEXP	N4WNL	EMA/TRAC
Talladega	145.3700	–	●e	N4ZDY	Sleeping G
Talladega	146.7400	–	O 131.8/131.8elWXz	N4WNL	EMA/TRAC
Talladega	146.8050	–	O 131.8/131.8eL(144/220/440) WXx	N4WNL	TRAC
Talladega	146.8050	–	O 131.8/131.8eWX	N4WNL	Talladega Radio ARC
Tecumseh Station	146.8500	–	O	W4RPO	W4RPO
Theodore	147.2000	+	O	N4LMZ	------------
Troy	146.8200	–	O 100.0 (CA)ez	W4NQ	Troy ARC
Tuscaloosa	145.1100	–	O 131.8el	WS4I	Druid City
Tuscaloosa	145.2100	–	O 103.5	W4UAL	Univ. of Alabama
Tuscaloosa	145.3500	–	●x	W4TTR	Tall Twr RC
Tuscaloosa	145.4700	–	● 203.5	KX4I	KX4I
Tuscaloosa	146.8200	–	O 118.8ae WXz	W4XI	Tuscal ARC
Tuscaloosa	146.9250	–	O 131.8e	WS4I	Druid City
Tuscaloosa	147.0600	–	● 179.9x	KX4I	KX4I
Tuscaloosa	147.2400	+	● 186.2/186.2a	KR4ET	W4MD / KX4I
Tuscaloosa	147.3000	+	131.8/RACESa(CA)erWX	W4WYN	West AL ARS
Tuscaloosa	147.5800	146.4800	●x	W4TTR	KX4I D-STAR
Uriah	145.1500	–	O	N4YYX	N4YYX
Vernon	145.4300	–	O 110.9/110.9	KI4QAH	KI4QAH
Vernon	146.6600	–	O 110.9/110.9lWX	W4WCA	Walker Co. ARES
Warrior	146.8400	–	O 156.7/156.7	WA4CYA	Hueytown Repeater A
Winfield	147.0400	+	O 192.8e	KT4JW	KC4RNF
York	147.0000	+	Oe	KE4ROA	Sumter ARC
NE					
Guntersville/ Douglas	145.1700	–	Oex	K4WWN	K4WWN

Location	Output	Input	Notes	Call	Sponsor
ALASKA					
INTERIOR					
Central/Circle	146.7000	–	103.5 E-SUN L(FAIRBANKS)x	AL7FQ	AL7FQ
Chena Dome	146.7900	–	O 103.5e E-SUN E-WINDlsx	KL7XO	AARC
Chicken	147.0900	+	O 103.5 E-SUNlx	KL7B	KL7B / NL7E
Denali Park	146.7600	–	Ol	KL7KC	ARCTIC ARC
Eagle	146.9400	–	O 103.5	KL7KC	KL7KC
Eielson AFB	147.1200	+	O 103.5	KL7KC	KL7KC
Fairbanks	146.8800	–	O 103.5ael x	KL7KC	ARCTIC ARC
Fairbanks	146.9400	–	Oa	KL7KC	ARCTIC ARC
Galena	146.7900	–	O 103.5	AL2J	Al2J
Manley	147.0300	+	O 103.5el	KL7KC	+KL7XO
Nenana	147.0600	+	O L(FAIRBANKS)	WL7TY	NARC
Northway	146.8200	–	103.5 L(FAIRBANKS)	KL7KC	ARCTIC ARC
SOUTH CENTRAL					
Anchorage	146.9400	–	O 100.0a TTez	KL7AA	AARC
Anchorage	147.3000	+	O 141.3ers	KL7ION	PARKA
Bethel	146.1000	+	O 114.8a TTe	AL7YK	BARK
Chugiak	147.1500	+	O 107.2 E-SUN E-WIND	KL5E	KL5E
Eagle River	145.4500	–	O 100.0 (CA) TTe	KL7GG	KL7GG
Elmendorf AFB	146.6700	–	O 103.5es	KL7AIR	EARS
Ft Richardson	147.1800	+	O 88.5ep	KL7USA	DHS&EM
Ft Richardson	147.3900	+	O 100.0 (CA) TTeRB	KL7GG	GG/ADES
Kodiak	146.8800	–	O 141.3es	AL7LQ	KARES
Kodiak	146.9400	–	O 103.5es	KL7JBV	Kodiak ARES
Mt Susitna	147.2700	+	O 103.5els	WL7CVG	AARC
Palmer	147.3300	+	O 103.5els	WL7CVF	AARC/ARES
Soldotna	146.8800	–	Oe	AL7LE	MARC
Wasilla	146.8500	–	O 103.5 TT e	KL7JFU	MARA
SOUTHCENTRAL					
Anchorage	145.1500	–	O 123x	KL7M	KL7M
Anchorage	146.7900	–	O 100.0l		CARA
Anchorage	146.8200	–	O 103.5l	WL7CWE	CARA
Wasilla	147.0000	+	Oe		AK Dstar group
Wasilla	147.2400	+	O 103.5	WL7CWE	CARA
SOUTHEAST					
Crystal Mt	147.3600	+	Oelx	W6SJJ	SARA

Location	Output	Input	Notes	Call	Sponsor
Haines-Mt Ripinski	147.0600	+	el	KL7GPG	JARC
Juneau-H Ridge	146.6400	–	Oael	KL7HFI	JARC
Juneau-Lena Point	147.0000	–	Oael	KL7PF	JARC
Juneau-Tramsite	146.8200	–	Oael	KL7PF	JARC
Ketchikan	146.7900	–	Oae	KL7ST	KARC
Mendenhall	147.3000	+	Oe	KL7IWC	ARES
Petersburg	146.9600	–	O(CA)	KL7FFP	PARC
Sitka	146.8200	–	O(CA)	KL7FFR	SITKA ARC
ARIZONA					
CENTRAL					
Black Canyon C	146.9000	–	O 118.8	KB7OCY	HENRY HURRASS
Mt Ord	146.9200	–	O 162.2aelx	W7MDY	ARIZONA REPEATE
Mt Ord	147.3600	+	O 162.2elx	W7MDY	ARIZONA REPEATE
Mt Union	147.2600	+	O 103.5ex	K7YCA	YAVAPAI COUNTY A
Pinal Peak	145.4100	–	O 141.3lx	K7EAR	EASTERN AZ AMAT
Pinal Peak	147.2000	+	O 162.2elx	W7ARA	ARIZONA REPEATE
Signal Peak	146.7400	–	O 162.2ex	WR7GC	GILA COUNTY EME
Towers Mtn	145.3700	–	O 162.2ex	W1OQ	NORTHLINK ASSCN.
Usery Pass	145.4900	–	O 107.2ex	KC7WYD	ROGER M LOPEZ III
Usery Pass	146.6600	–	O 162.2ex	WB7TUJ	HAROLD PIERSON
Usery Pass	147.0200	+	O 162.2elx	W7BSA	BSA EP 599
Wildflower Mtn	145.3500	–	O 162.2x	W7QHC	DAILY ARIZONA WE
EAST CENTRAL					
Heber	146.8000	–	O 162.2e	W7RIM	RIM COUNTRY AMA
S Mtn Alpine	145.2700	–	O 141.3lx	K7EAR	EASTERN ARIZONA
EASTERN					
Guthrie Peak	147.2800	+	O 141.3lx	K7EAR	EASTERN AZ AMAT
MESA					
Mesa	147.1200	+	O 162.2el	WB7TJD	SUPERSTITION A.R.
NORTH CENTRAL					
Bill Williams	146.7800	–	O 91.5elx	K7NAZ	BILL WILLIAMS MTN
Lake Havasu Ci	146.9600	–	O 162.2	W7DXJ	DOUG SPRENG
Mingus Mtn	145.2900	–	O 127.3ersx	K7YCA	YAVAPAI CO. ARES/
Mingus Mtn	147.0000	+	O 162.2elx	K7MRG	MINGUS MTN R.G. I
Mingus Mtn	147.2200	+	O 162.2elx	W7EI	VERDE VALLEY A.R.
Mt Elden	146.9800	–	O 162.2aex	W7ARA	ARIZONA REPEATE
Mt Elden	147.1400	+	O 162.2elx	W7ARA	ARIZONA REPEATE
Mt Ord	146.9600	–	O 141.3elx	WR7GC	MICHAEL O'DRISCO
Navajo Mtn	146.9600	–	Ox	W7WAC	WAYNE CHAPMAN
Prescott	145.3900	–	O	KC7TIL	STEVEN PEARSON
Prescott	146.8800	–	O 100	W7YRC	YAVAPAI ARC
Squaw Peak	147.1000	+	O 131.8x	KF6FM	SwRCC
Winslow	146.8400	–	O	N7RDZ	DONALD E SIEGMU

Location	*Output*	*Input*	*Notes*	*Call*	*Sponsor*
Winslow	147.3800	+	O 162.2	N7RDZ	DONALD E SIEG
NORTH WEST					
Kingman	145.1900	–	O 151.4	K7MPR	KD7MIA
Kingman	145.2100	–	O 151.4e	KD7MIA	KD7MIA
Kingman	146.9400	–	● 94.8lRBx	K7RLW	K7RLW
NORTHEASTERN					
Greens Peak	145.3100	–	O 110.9x	W7EH	KACHINA ARC
Greens Peak	146.6100	–	O 162.2elx	W7OTA	DON LETCHER
Greens Peak	146.7000	–	O 141.3lx	K7EAR	EASTERN AZ A
Greens Peak	146.7200	–	O 162.2elx	W7ARA	ARIZONA REPE
Holbrook	146.6800	–	O	KA7ARZ	NAVAJO CO AR
Porter Mtn	146.7600	–	O 162.2elx	W7OTA	DON W. LETCH
Roof Butte	145.2500	–	O 100elx	KB5ITS	BEN MCGAHA
Roof Butte	146.8200	–	O 100x	NM5SJ	SAN JUAN CO A
NORTHERN					
Jacob Lake	147.3000	+	O 100lx	N7YSE	KANAB ARC
Mormon Mt	145.2700	–	O 162.2x	KD7IC	JONATHAN P. K
Mt Elden	145.4500	–	O 103.5ae x	NO7AZ	JOHN LINDSEY
NORTHWEST					
Bullhead City	145.1700	–	O 131.8e	W7GAA	WESTERN ARIZ
Bullhead City	146.6400	–	O 123e	K3MK	FREEDOM NET
Bullhead City	147.3600	+	O 123.3	KD7MIA	WILLIAM SMITH
Chloride	146.7000	–	O 173.8e	N7NVR	GENE STAFFOR
Golden Valley	146.9400	–	O 123	K7MCH	MARK C. HERR
Golden Valley	147.1200	+	O 123el	N7FK	FRED KRICK - F
Hayden Peak	146.7600	–	O 131.8elx	N7SKO	WECOM, INC
Hopi Pt Grand	147.3200	+	Oex	WB6JAA	HARTLEY GARD
Hualapai Peak	147.2400	+	O 123x	K7MPR	MOHAVE AMAT
Kingman	147.2000	+	O 79.7e	KC8UQP	TIM BROWN
Mt Francis	147.2600	+	O 127.3ex	K7YCA	YAVAPAI CO. R
Potato Patch	146.8000	–	●t(CA)elx	N7DPS	NW-AZ REPEAT
Potato Patch	147.1600	+	O 131.8x	WB6RER	HUALAPAI ARC
Xmas Tree Pass	145.2700	–	O 131.8elx	N7SKO	WECOM INC
PAYSON					
Payson	146.9000	–	●t	KJ7K	R L GREEN
Payson	147.3900	+	O 100ae	N7TAR	TONTO AMATE
PHOENIX					
Bank One	146.8200	–	O 162.2	N1KQ	M.C.R.G. c/o JIM
Bell Butte	146.9800	–	O 100	AI7R	CITY OF TEMPE
Central Phx	146.6400	–	O 162.2ae	W7ARA	ARIZONA REPE
Chandler	145.4500	–	O 162.2ae	WW7CPU	INTEL AMATEU
Mesa	145.2100	–	●t(CA)el	KF7EUO	TIM OWEN
Mesa	145.3300	–	O 114.8e	WB7TUJ	BRIAN VIETRI
Mesa	146.7200	–	O 100ae	K7DAD	MERCURY AMA
Phoenix	145.1900	–	O 162.2	W7ATV	ARIZONA AMAT
Phoenix	145.2300	–	O 94.8	WK7B	GARY DUFFIEL
Phoenix	146.8000	–	O 100e	KD7LYO	MORGAN HOAG
Phoenix	147.0600	+	O 162.2e	W7UXZ	LEE WALTERS

ARIZONA

Location	*Output*	*Input*	*Notes*	*Call*	*Sponsor*
Phoenix	147.2800	+	O 162.2	WA7UID	MINGUS MTN REPE
Phoenix	147.3200	+	O	K5VT	CENTRAL AZ DX AS
Phoenix <Por>	145.1700	–	O 162.2el	W7ARA	ARIZONA REPEATE
Phoenix Metro	146.7000	–	O 162.2el	W7TBC	THUNDERBIRD AMA
Scottsdale	145.3100	–	O 91.5ae	KB6POQ	FRANK MAGARELLI
Scottsdale	147.1800	+	O 162.2e	WA7APE	SCOTTSDALE A.R.C
Scottsdale	147.3400	+	O 162.2ael	W7MOT	MOTOROLA AMATE
Scottsdale Air	146.7600	–	O 162.2e	W7ARA	ARIZONA REPEATE
Shaw Butte	146.8400	–	O 162.2ex	W7ATV	ARIZONA AMATEUR
Shaw Butte	147.2400	+	O 162.2ael	W7ARA	ARIZONA REPEATE
			x		
Sun City West	147.3000	+	O 162.2ae	NY7S	WEST VALLEY ARC
Tempe	145.2700	–	O	KB7KY	DAVE KNAPPENBE
Thompson Peak	147.0800	+	O 162.2ex	KG7UN	MARICOPA COUNT
Usery Mtn	146.8600	–	O 162.2elx	W7ARA	ARIZONA REPEATE
Usery Pass	145.4700	–	O 79.7ex	KE7JFH	FOUNTAIN HILLS A
White Tanks Mt	145.4300	–	O 100ex	N7SKT	HAROLD PIERSON
White Tanks Mt	147.3800	+	●tex	N7ULY	DOUG PELLEY
PINEDALE					
Pinedale	145.2300	–	O 110.9	KB7ZIH	PAUL CROOKSTON
SIERRA VISTA					
Sierra Vista	145.2300	–	● 94.8e	AD7BG	MARK CARNETT
Sierra Vista	147.3600	+	O 100ael	NØNBH	PAUL L. HERRMAN
SOUTH CENTRAL					
Casa Grande	146.7800	–	O 100l	N8UVV	DONALD J. DUFFY
Green Valley	145.4300	–	O	WB6TYP	WB6TYP c/o S.L. NA
Red Mtn/Patago	146.6400	–	Oex	W7JPI	W7JPI c/o LEO P SW
SOUTHEAST					
Duncan	146.9600	–	O	N5IA	MILT JENSEN, N5IA
Green Valley	145.2700	–	O 107.2	WE7GV	GREEN VALLEY A.R
Haystack Mt	145.3700	–	O 131.8x	K7SPV	SAN PEDRO VALLE
Heliograph Peak	146.8600	–	O 141.3elx	K7EAR	EAARS
Heliograph Peak	146.9000	–	O 141.3ex	K7EAR	EASTERN AZ AMAT
Juniper Flats	146.7600	–	O 162.2ex	K7RDG	COCHISE AMATEUR
Juniper Flats	147.0200	+	O 162.2elx	K7RDG	COCHISE AMATEUR
Mt Lemmon	147.1600	+	O 141.3ex	K7EAR	EASTERN AZ AMAT
Mule Mtn	147.0800	+	O 141.3elx	K7EAR	EASTERN ARIZONA
Vail	147.1200	+	O 100el	KF7FCQ	JOY BARTON
SOUTHERN					
Green Valley	145.2900	–	O 107.2ex	WE7GV	GREEN VALLEY AR
Keystone Peak	146.6200	–	O 156.7ael	WØHF	ORO VALLEY ARC
			x		
Mt Lemmon	145.2500	–	O 156.7ex	K7RST	RADIO SOCIETY OF
Mt Lemmon	145.3900	–	O 100elx	KG7KV	SPARC
Mt Lemmon	146.8800	–	O 110.9ex	N7OEM	TUCSON AMATEUR
Mt Lemmon	147.1400	+	O 127.3x	KA7SLW	LOMA GRIFFITH
SOUTHWEST					
Ajo Childs Mt	145.3100	–	O 100ex	W7AJO	AJO AMATEUR RADI
Cunningham Peak	147.0600	+	Ox	KR7AZ	DESERT WAVES AR

Location	*Output*	*Input*	*Notes*	*Call*	*Sponsor*
Gila Bend	145.2900	–	O 103.5e	K7PO	WARD WHEATO
Quartzsite	145.3100	–	O 162.2x	WB7FIK	CACTUS RADIO
Quartzsite	147.3600	+	O 107.2ex	K6TQM	COACHELLA VA
Telegraph Pass	146.7800	–	O 103.5el RBx	N7ACS	ACS GROUP FO
Yuma	146.6200	–	O 103.5e	N7ACS	YUMA AUX CO
TUCSON					
East Tucson	146.6600	–	O 110.9ae	W7GV	OLD PUEBLO R
Mt Lemmon	147.1000	+	O 100ex	KCØLL	DAVID BRANSO
Oro Valley	145.1900	–	O 156.7ael	WØHF	ORO VALLEY A
Oro Valley	147.2200	+	O 110.9e	W7GV	OLD PUEBLO R
S Tucson	147.3400	+	O 179.9el	W7SA	CATALINA RADI
Tucson	145.1700	–	O	KØDVH	STEVE ARENS
Tucson	145.2300	–	● 77e	NR7J	ROBERTO FER
Tucson	145.3300	–	O 127.3 (CA)	KA7LVX	KA7LVX c/o GIL
Tucson	145.4500	–	Oe	W7IBM	IBM A.R.C. (TIA
Tucson	146.6800	–	O 173.8	N7IQV	CITY OF TUCSO
Tucson	146.7000	–	O 127.3l	AC7IL	CARBA
Tucson	146.8000	–	O 156.7ael	K7RST	RADIO SOCIET
Tucson	146.8200	–	O 110.9e	W7GV	OLD PUEBLO R
Tucson	146.8500	–	Oe	AG7H	RON BATES
Tucson	146.9400	–	O 110.9	WD7F	BORDER AMAT
Tucson	146.9600	–	O 127.3	K7UAZ	U OF A AMATEU
Tucson	147.0000	+	O 110.9	N7OEM	PIMA CO EMER
Tucson	147.0400	+	O 123e	K7PCC	PANTANO CHRI
Tucson	147.3000	+	O 110.9e	N7OEM	TUCSON AMAT
WEST CENTRAL					
Black Peak	146.8500	–	O 162.2ex	WA7RAT	CAARA
Lk Havasu Cty	146.6400	–	O 156.7e	K7LHC	LONDON BRIDG
Smith Peak	146.6800	–	O 162.2elx	K7LKL	ARIZONA REPE
Wht Tanks Mtn	146.9400	–	O 162.2elx	W7EX	ARIZONA REPE
YUMA					
Potholes Hill	146.8400	–	O 88.5el	W7DIN	DESERT INTER
Yuma	146.8000	–	O 162.2el RB	N7ACS	YUMA COUNTY
Yuma	147.3000	+	O 162.2e	KD7GXW	MARK BUONO
ARKANSAS					
CENTRAL					
Alexander	145.2900	–	O 131.8/131.8e	N5YLE	N5YLE
Benton	146.6400	–	O 131.8elr sWX	N5CG	CAUHF
Benton	146.8050	–	O 114.8/114.8e	W5RHS	W5RHS
Benton	147.1200	+	O 114.8/114.8erWX	W5RHS	W5RHS
Cabot	147.1500	+	Oe	W5STR	KB5FOQ

Location	Output	Input	Notes	Call	Sponsor
Conway	145.2100	–	O 114.8l	W5AUU	FalkCoARC
Conway	146.6250	–	O 114.8	AE5GH	AE5GH
Conway	146.9700	–	O 114.8rsx	WB5NXJ	FalkCoARC
Conway	147.0300	+	O 114.8/114.8e	W5AUU	W5AUU
Hot Springs	145.2700	–	O	KE5SHR	KE5SHR
Hot Springs	146.7600	–	O 114.8/114.8es	WB5SPA	SpaARA
Hot Springs	146.8800	–	O 114.8/114.8eL(146.715-)rsWXx	W5LVB	W5LVB
Hot Springs	147.1800	+	O 114.8	WB5PIB	WB5PIB
Hot Springs Village	147.0150	+	O 114.8/114.8e	W5HSV	HSV ARC
Little Rock	145.1300	–	O 114.8ers	N5AT	ARES
Little Rock	145.1700	–	O 162.2e LITZ	N5UFO	N5UFO
Little Rock	145.4900	–	O 114.8elr sWX	N5CG	CAUHF
Little Rock	146.7300	–	O 141.3ex	WA5PGB	WA5OOY
Little Rock	146.7750	–	● 162.2el	N5CG	CAUHF
Little Rock	146.8500	–	Or	WA5LRU	UALR ARC
Little Rock	146.9400	–	O 114.8elr sWXx	W5DI	CAREN
Little Rock	147.0600	+	Oaelz	W5FD	CAREN
Little Rock	147.1350	+	O 114.8ex	W5DI	CAREN
Little Rock	147.3000	+	O 114.8ex	W5DI	CAREN
Malvern	145.1500	–	O 114.8 WX	W5RHS	W5RHS
Malvern	145.3100	–	88.5	KJ5YJ	MalvernARC
Malvern	147.3600	+	O 136.5ael z	W5BXJ	HSCAREN
Malvern	147.3900	+	O 136.5ae	W5BXJ	HSCAREN
Morrilton	145.3300	–	O 114.8el WX	N5CG	CAUHF
Pine Bluff	146.7000	–	OersWX	K5DAK	PinBlufARC
Pine Bluff	147.1650	+	Oes	N5RN	N5RN
Prattsville	145.1900	–	O 114.8e	KD5RTO	KD5RTO
Redfield	147.1950	+	O	N5KWH	PinBlufARC
Searcy	146.6550	–	Oe	AB5ER	NCAARC
Searcy	146.8950	–	O 85.4 (CA) l	N5ZA	N5ZA
Searcy	146.9250	–	O 94.8 (CA) e	KG5S	NCAARS
Searcy	147.3900	+	O 94.8e	AC5AV	WhiteCoARC
Sheridan	146.9850	–	O(CA)er	KB5ZES	GrantCoARC
Sherwood	147.2550	+	O 114.8el	N1RQ	N5QLC
Vilonia	145.4100	–	O 85.4e	NL7RQ	NL7RQ
White Hall	147.2400	+	Oaesz	K5DAK	PinBlufARC

Location	*Output*	*Input*	*Notes*	*Call*	*Sponsor*
EAST					
Forrest City	146.7600	–	O 100.0/100.0	KD5DF	KD5DF
Forrest City	147.3750	+	O 107.2ers WX	WA5CC	CrossCoARC
Gillette	146.7900	–	O 114.8l WX	N5CG	CAUHF
Helena	145.3900	–	O	WX5J	WX5J
Helena	146.6850	–	O 107.2ex	N5JLJ	N5JLJ
Marion	147.1500	+	O 103.5e	KI5XV	KI5XV
Wynne	145.3100	–	O 107.2	WB5LNG	WB5LNG
Wynne	146.8650	–	O 107.2ers WX	KD5NUB	KD5NUB
EAST CENTRAL					
Bald Knob	147.3150	–	O 114.8elx	WA5OOY	CAREN
Bradford	146.7450	–	O 107.2el RB WXx	W5BTM	W5BTM
Stuttgart	147.0000	–	Oers	KB5LN	KB5LN
NORTH					
Harrison	145.1500	–	O	KØJXI	KØJXI
Harrison	147.0000	–	O 103.5es LITZ WXx	WB5CYX	NAARS
Harrison	147.3150	+	O 103.5l	WA9SSO	GathMtARC
Mountain Home	146.8800	–	O 103.5/103.5 (CA)eL(442.300+)	K5OZK	OZARC
Mountain Home	147.0750	+	Oe	KC5RBO	OzARC
Mountain View	147.1800	+	Os	AD5TQ	AD5TQ
Yellville	147.2400	+	O 107.2e	W5YS	MarionCARC
NORTH CENTRAL					
Batesville	147.2250	+	O 107.2ers WXx	KD5HPK	KD5HPK
Batesville	147.2700	+	OelrsWXx	KD5AYE	BatsevilARC
Clinton	145.3700	–	O 114.8els WXx	W5DI	CAREN
Clinton	146.9100	–	O 114.8/114.8e	KD5GC	KD5GC
Fox	145.1100	–	O 110.9	NN5NN	NN5NN
Greers Ferry	147.3300	+	Ox	W5GFC	GFARC
Heber Springs	145.2300	145.2300	O	N5XUN	N5XUN
Heber Springs	145.4300	–	Oaez	KD5GFT	N5XUN
Jasper	146.6100	–	OeLITZ WX x	WB5CYX	NAARS
Jerusalem	145.4500	–	OeWXx	KC5WNU	ADARC
Mountain View	147.1200	+	O 100.0 (CA)elsWX	AA5EM	StonCoARC
NORTHEAST					
Blytheville	146.6700	–	O 107.2/107.2elrsWX	W5ENL	MissCoARA
Hardy	145.1900	–	Oe	W5SCR	SharpCoARC

ARKANSAS

Location	Output	Input	Notes	Call	Sponsor
Harrisburg	146.8350	–	O	N5OHO	PARC
Jonesboro	145.2900	–	OersWX	KC5TEL	RESPOND
Jonesboro	146.6100	–	OaeWX	W5JBR	JARC
Jonesboro	147.1650	+	O(CA)ers WX	N5MOT	N5MOT
Jonesboro	147.2100	+	Oe	K5CRS	K5CRS
Jonesboro	147.2400	+	O 107.2l	KØJXI	AISTC
Jonesboro	147.2850	+	O	KA5DRT	AISTC
Paragould	145.4700	–	O	W5BJR	GreenCoARS
Trumann	146.9550	–	O 107.2 (CA)el	NI5A	AISTC
Walnut Ridge	147.0450	+	OeWX	W5WRA	LawrCoARC
NORTHWEST					
Bella Vista	147.2550	+	Oe	KD5UFY	BVRG
Centerton	145.2900	–	O 110.9e	KD5DMT	BCRO
Clarksville	147.2850	+	O 114.8elr sWXx	W5OI	CAREN
Decatur	146.9250	–	O 114.8/114.8lx	N5UXE	N5UXE
Elkins	146.7000	–	O 110.9elr sWX	WC5AR/E	WashCoEOC
Fayetteville	147.0300	+	O 110.9ers WX	WC5AR/C	WashCoEOC
Fayetteville	147.1350	+	O 110.9e WX	W5YM	ARCUA
Holiday Island	146.8350	–	Oe	K5AA	LitSwitzARC
Lowell	147.2250	+	O 103.5/103.5ersWX	K5SRS	K5SRS
Mountainburg	145.4900	–	Oe	KC5GMG	KC5GMG
Ozone	147.0450	+	OE-SUNrs WX	K5OO	K5OO
Prairie Grove	146.7600	–	O 110.9elr sWX	WC5AR/W	WashCoEOC
Rogers	147.3750	+	OsWX	KE5LXK	NWAUHF
Rudy	147.1650	+	O 123.0ers WX	KD5ZMO	CCARC
Siloam Springs	146.6700	–	O 110.9ael WX	KC5YZI	SSARC
Springdale	146.8650	–	O	KE5LXK	NWAUHF
Springdale	146.9550	–	O 110.9ers WX	WC5AR/N	WashCoEOC
SOUTH					
El Dorado	146.7450	–	OlWX	KC5AUP	ARKLA
Magnolia	147.1050	+	Oarsz	KC5OAS	ClmbaCoARC
SOUTH CENTRAL					
Bearden	147.3300	+	O 100.0/100.0ersWX	N5IOZ	N5IOZ
Camden	146.9100	–	O 167.9e	WA5OWG	WA5OWG
Emerson	146.9550	–	O	N5PNB	N5PNB

Location	Output	Input	Notes	Call	Sponsor
SOUTHEAST					
Crossett	146.6100	–	O 127.3/127.3	WA5VSE	N5SEA
Huttig	146.6400	–	O 127.3	N5SEA	SEAARC
Monticello	147.2100	+	O 127.3/127.3 L(444.975)x	N5SEA	SEAARC
Star City	146.6700	–	O 114.8/114.8elWXx	W5DI	CAREN
SOUTHWEST					
Ashdown	147.3800	+	O 100.0 (CA)ersWX	KB5SSW	KB5SSW
Dequeen	147.0750	+	O 100.0lrs WXx	WA5LTA	SWARC
Dequeen	147.3150	–	O 100.0/100.0ersWX	N5THR	N5THR
Hope	146.6850	–	O 114.8sx	KC5FFN	H-N ARC
Nashville	147.0450	+	O 94.8/94.8 elsWX	N5THS	HEARClub
Willisville	146.6550	–	OsWXx	N5ZAY	ARKLA
WEST					
Athens	146.9250	–	O 100.0/100.0esx	KD5NUP	HowCoSAR
Fort Smith	145.4700	–	O 141.3e	KD5CCG	KD5CCG
Fort Smith	146.9400	–	O 88.5ers WXx	W5ANR	W5ANR
Fort Smith	146.9700	–	O 123.0ae LITZ	K3UNX	SPARKS
Hartford	146.8950	–	Oe	KC5JBX	KC5JBX
Mena	146.7900	–	O 100.0	W5HUM	Oua. ARA
Van Buren	145.1900	–	O	KC5YQB	KC5YQB
Van Buren	145.2300	–	OWX	KE5LTZ	KE5LTZ
WEST CENTRAL					
Alpine	147.2250	+	O 114.8ers WX	KD5ARC	DARC
Atkins	145.3900	–	O 107.2/107.2	W5VUB	W5VUB
Bismarck	147.2700	+	O 114.8el WX	W5DI	WA5OOY
Danville	147.0000	+	Oe	WB5UKW	WB5UKW
DeGray Lake	145.1100	–	O 88.5es WX	KD5ARC	DARC
Glenwood	146.8350	–	O 114.8	KC5EYQ	CaddoARC
Mount Ida	146.7150	–	O 127.3/127.3elsWXx	KA5WPC	KA5WPC
Mt Magazine	145.3500	–	O 151.4	N5XMZ	N5XMZ
Mt Magazine	147.0900	+	OWXx	W5MAG	MtMagARC
Okolona	145.3700	–	O 88.5ers WX	KD5ARC	DARC
Ola	147.2100	+	Oae	WA5YHN	WA5YHN

Location	Output	Input	Notes	Call	Sponsor
Russellville	146.8200	–	OersWX	K5PXP	ARVARF
WESTCENTRAL					
Lake Dardanelle	146.6850	–	O 141.3/141.3	WD5B	WD5B

CALIFORNIA

FREQUENCY USAGE - SOUTHERN CALIFORNIA

CAL	146.4300			ATV	
SO CAL	144.3450			ATV	
SO CAL	144.3900			APRS	
SO CAL	144.5050			RPTR_OUT	
SO CAL	144.8950			RPTR_OUT	
SO CAL	144.9100			XBND_RPT	
SO CAL	144.9300			PORT_OUT	
SO CAL	144.9500			RPTR_OUT	
SO CAL	144.9700			PACKET	
SO CAL	144.9850			RPTR_DIG_IN	
SO CAL	144.9950			RPTR_DIG_IN	
SO CAL	145.0050			RPTR_DIG_IN	
SO CAL	145.0150			RPTR_DIG_IN	
SO CAL	145.0300			PACKET	
SO CAL	145.0500			PACKET	
SO CAL	145.0700			PACKET	
SO CAL	145.0900			PACKET	
SO CAL	145.1050			RPTR_IN	
SO CAL	145.4950			RPTR_IN	
SO CAL	145.6300			PACKET	
SO CAL	145.6500			PACKET	
SO CAL	145.6700			PACKET	
SO CAL	145.6900			PACKET	
SO CAL	146.4000			RPTR_IN	
SO CAL	146.4150			RPTR_IN	
SO CAL	146.4600			RMT BASE	
SO CAL	146.4750			RPTR_IN	
SO CAL	146.4900			RPTR_IN	
SO CAL	146.5050			RPTR_IN	
SO CAL	146.5650			T_HUNTS	
SO CAL	147.4200			RPTR_OUT	
SO CAL	147.4350			RPTR_OUT	
SO CAL	147.4500			RPTR_OUT	
SO CAL	147.4950			RPTR_OUT	
SO CAL	147.5400			RPTR_DIG_OUT	
SO CAL	147.5500			RPTR_DIG_OUT	
SO CAL	147.5600			RPTR_DIG_OUT	
SO CAL	147.5700			RPTR_DIG_OUT	
SO CAL	147.5850			PORT_IN	
E SIERRA/TAHOE					
Truckee	146.6400	–	O 131.8l	W6SAR	W6SAR

Location	*Output*	*Input*	*Notes*	*Call*	*Sponsor*
EASTERN SIERRAS					
Benton	146.6700	–	○ 100	KA6HGI	KE6VVB
Bishop	146.9400	–	○	N6OV	K6BDI
IMPERIAL COUNTY					
Brawley	146.6700	–	○ 103.5a (CA)	N6LVR	ECRA
Brawley	147.1200	+	●t	WM6Z	ECRA
Glamis	146.8800	–	○ 162.2	WA6LAW	------------
Glamis	147.9900	–	●t	N6JAM	DRØNK
Yuma	146.7400	–	○e	WE7G	------------
INYO COUNTY					
Bishop	146.8200	–	○	K6PXF	------------
Bishop	146.9100	–	○el	W6IY	------------
Mazourka Peak	146.7600	–	○aE-SUN	K6RFO	LIARS/GRONK
Ridgecrest	147.2100	+	○E-SUN	K6RFO	LIARS/GRONK
Silver Peak	146.9400	–	○ 103.5e	W6IY	------------
Silver Peak	147.0600	+	○ 103.5e	W6IY	------------
KERN COUNTY					
Bird Spgs Pass	146.0850	+	○ 141.3el	KF6FM	SWRRC
El Paso Pk	147.0000	+	○ 107.2ae	WA6YBN	------------
El Paso Pk	147.0600	+	○ 107.2	W6IY	------------
Randsburg	145.3400	–	○ 100	WA6YBN	------------
Ridgecrest	146.6400	–	○er	WA6YBN	SARC
Ridgecrest	147.9750	–	○ 100el	WI6RE	WIN System
Tehachapi	147.0600	+	○ae	W6PVG	SSARS
LOS ANGELES COUNTY					
Baldwin Hills	146.9250	–	○ 114.8a (CA)	WA6TFD	BARC
Bel Air	147.0300	+	●ta(CA)e	K6LDO	BelAir RC
Castaic	145.2000	–	●t	KI6AIT	------------
Castro Peak	147.2250	+	○ 94.8a (CA)er	K6DCS	DCS TEN
Catalina	147.0900	+	○e	AA6DP	CARA
Contractor's Point	145.1200	–	●t	KC6PXL	LARMC
Contractor's Point	147.1200	+	○ 146.2	N6VGU	------------
Covina	145.2800	–	○ 141.3	KC6KUI	CARES
Diamond Bar	146.6400	–	○ 167.9a (CA)	W7BF	DBARS
Disappointment	145.3000	–	○ 100er	K6CPT	LACoDCS
Disappointment	147.2700	+	○ 100e	WA6ZTR	LACoDCS
Disappointment	147.3600	+	●tl	K6VGP	DARN
Duarte	146.0850	+	○ 110.9a (CA) E-SUN	KA6AMR	SGVRCRA
Duck Mtn	147.2400	+	○ 67	W6MEP	N6NMC
Frazier Park	147.7650	–	○e	K6VGA	------------
Glendale	146.0250	+	○ 136.5a (CA)e	WB6ZTY	CVARC
Grand Terrace	147.8850	–	○ 100l	AE6TV	AE6TV
Hauser Peak	146.7300	–	○ 100er	KE6KIS	------------

CALIFORNIA

Location	*Output*	*Input*	*Notes*	*Call*	*Sponsor*
Hollywood Hills	147.0750	+	O 100ae	KD6JTD	------------
Hollywood Hls	144.5050	+	●ta(CA)r	N6ACS	------------
Hollywood Hls	147.0000	+	●ta(CA)e	WB6BJM	------------
Johnstone Peak	144.9500	147.4050	●ta(CA)er	W6GLN	GlendoraPd
Johnstone Peak	146.8200	–	Oel	W6FNO	Edgwd ARS
La Mirada	146.6550	–	O 114.8a (CA)	KE6UPA	------------
Lancaster	146.6700	–	Oae	WB6RSM	------------
Littlerock	145.2000	–	O 114.8a (CA)el	KD6KTQ	------------
Littlerock	145.3800	–	O 151.4el	K6SRT	------------
Littlerock	147.0750	+	●t	KN6RW	------------
Littlerock	147.9150	–	Ot	KE6GUC	------------
Long Beach	146.1450	+	O 156.7	K6CHE	LB RA
Long Beach	146.7900	–	O 103.5	K6SYU	Anaheim AR
Long Beach	146.8050	–	●te	KE6HE	LBYachtCl
Los Angeles	147.1950	+	O 131.8	W6NVY	LAUSD ARA
Loyola Marymount University	147.8550	–	O 127.3	W6LMU	------------
Malibu	145.2600	–	O 100	N6FDR	------------
Monrovia	147.7650	–	O 131.8e	W6QFK	SGV ARC
Monterey Park	146.3550	+	O 71.9a (CA)e	KF6YLB	MPEC
Mt Lukens	145.4800	–	O 100	W6AM	SCA DXClb
Mt Lukens	146.6700	–	O 192.8a (CA)	KD6AFA	SSARO
Mt Lukens	147.1950	+	●t	W6NVY	LAUSD ARA
Mt Lukens	147.4950	146.4900	●tBI	NH2R	------------
Mt Wilson	147.3600	+	●tl	K6VGP	DARN
Oat Mtn	145.3400	–	O 131.8el	N7RDA	------------
Oat Mtn	147.7350	–	O 100	KB6C	MMRA
Oat Mtn	147.9450	–	O 136.5a (CA)	KF6JWT	HA ARC
Palmdale	146.7600	–	O 186.2	KC6ZQR	------------
Palmdale	146.7900	–	O 103.5	WA6YVL	------------
Palos Verdes	144.8950	+	O 186.2	KF6ZTY	MCRC
Palos Verdes	145.3800	–	O 100e	N6RBR	PVARC
Palos Verdes	146.2350	+	●ta(CA)e	KA6TSA	SCRAN
Palos Verdes	147.1950	+	O 100e	W6NVY	LAUSD ARA
Palos Verdes	147.3600	+	●tl	K6VGP	DARN
Palos Verdes	147.4200	146.4750	●t	AA6RJ	PARA-USA
Pasadena	145.1800	–	O 156.7	W6MPH	Telph ARC
Pasadena	147.1500	+	O 103.5	WR6JPL	JPL ARC
Pomona	146.0250	+	O 103.5a (CA)e	WB6RSK	------------
Redondo Beach	145.3200	–	O 114.8a (CA)e	W6TRW	SEA ARC
Rio Hondo Peak	146.7300	–	O 103.5	KØJPK	COLA
Rowland Heights	147.0300	+	O 100a (CA)lBI	N6XPG	------------

Location	*Output*	*Input*	*Notes*	*Call*	*Sponsor*
Saddle Peak	147.0000	+	●t	WB6BJM	HH RPT
San Clem Isl	147.1950	+	●tE-SUNr	K6JCC	SD RACES
Santa Clarita	146.7900	–	○ 123	W6JW	SCARC
Santa Clarita	146.9700	–	○ 123	W6JW	SCARC
Santa Monica	145.2800	–	○ 127.3	K6QN	------------
Sherman Oaks	145.2400	–	●ta(CA)	NK6S	Ham Watch
Sunset Ridge	145.4400	–	○ 136.5	N6USO	------------
Sunset Ridge	146.7000	–	●t	K4ELE	------------
Sunset Ridge	147.2100	+	○ 100	K6JSI	WinSystem
Table Mtn	145.2800	–	○ 131.8el	WR6AZN	GldstnARC
Tujunga	146.1600	+	○ 146.2	W6JAM	SSSS
Verdugo Peak	147.3000	+	●ta(CA)elr	WA6PPS	RAAVN
Verdugo Peak	147.3600	+	●tl	K6VGP	DARN
Whittier	146.1750	+	○el	W6GNS	RHARC
Woodland Hills	146.2650	+	○ 103.5	WA6AQQ	LittonARC
MONO COUNTY					
Mammoth Mountain	146.7300	–	○ 100r	NW6C	BARC
NORCAL-CENTRAL COAST					
Arroyo Grande	146.9400	–	○ 127.3ers	W6SLO	SLOECC
Arroyo Grande	147.0300	+	○ 127.3e	AE6HC	HVRA
Ben Lomond	147.1200	+	○ 94.8els	WR6AOK	SLVARC
Big Sur	146.9400	–	○ 94.8es	KI6PAU	KI6PAU
Boulder Creek	145.3500	–	○ 94.8e	KI6YDR	KI6YDR
Cambria	147.2700	+	○ 127.3#	KC6TOX	SLOECC
Felton	147.1800	+	○ 94.8elsx	W6WLS	W6WLS
Hollister	147.3150	+	○ 94.8els	N6SBC	SBC OES
Hollister	147.3150	+	○ 146.2es	N6SBC	SBC ARES
King City	145.3700	–	○ 100elrsx	N6SPD	N6SPD RG
Lompoc	147.1200	+	○ 131.8es	WA6VPL	WA6VPL
Los Osos	146.8600	–	○ 127.3ers	WB6MIA	SLOECC
Monterey	146.0850	+	●ers	WE6R	WE6R
Monterey	146.9700	–	○ 94.8ers	K6LY	NPSARC
Nipomo	147.9900	–	○ 127.3rs	WB6MIA	SLOECC
Paicines	146.6250	–	○ 94.8els	N6SBC	SBC ARES
Paso Robles	146.9800	–	○ 127.3els	W6YDZ	PRARC
Paso Robles	147.0600	+	○ 127.3ers	W6PRB	PRHS-ARC
Prunedale	146.9100	–	○ 94.8ers	W6OPI	W6OPI
Salinas	145.4100	–	○ 146.2#el	W6CER	CCARN
Salinas	145.4300	–	○ 94.8esx	N6SPD	N6SPD RG
Salinas	145.4700	–	○ 94.8ersx	K6JE	FPRA
Salinas	145.4900	–	○ 100l	W6RTF	W6RTF
Salinas	146.0850	+	○ 100#	KC6UDC	KC6UDC
Salinas	146.6550	–	○ 94.8#es	KI6FKX	KI6FKX
San Ardo	146.7300	–	○ 127.3elsx	W6FM	W6FM
San Simeon	146.6200	–	○ 127.3ersx	KD6EKH	SLOECC
SanLuisObispo	145.2900	–	●e	KC6WRD	FCC

Location	*Output*	*Input*	*Notes*	*Call*	*Sponsor*
SanLuisObispo	146.6700	–	O 127.3ersx	W6SLO	SLOECC
SanLuisObispo	146.7600	–	O 91.5aels	W6BHZ	CPARC
SanLuisObispo	146.8000	–	O 127.3#ersx	WB6FMC	WB6FMC
SanLuisObispo	147.3600	+	O 127.3ers	W6FM	W6FM
Santa Cruz	145.2500	–	O 100#s	W6PEK	W6PAD
Santa Cruz	146.7450	–	O 94.8ers	W6JWS	SLVARES
Santa Cruz	146.7900	–	O 94.8aelrs	K6BJ	SCCARC
Santa Cruz	146.8350	–	O 94.8ers	AE6KE	SC ARES
SantaMargarita	146.8350	–	O 127.3ersx	W6SLO	SLOECC
Templeton	146.8800	–	O 127.3elsx	W6YDZ	W6YDZ
Watsonville	145.1700	–	O 151.4#	W6UNI	W6UNI
Watsonville	145.3300	–	O 123#elsx	W6DNC	W6DNC
Watsonville	146.7000	–	O 94.8#e	NS6G	GOB/R
Watsonville	146.7750	–	O 123#a	KB6MET	KB6MET
Watsonville	147.0000	+	O 94.8ers	K6RMW	K6RMWK6GDI
Watsonville	147.9450	–	O 94.8elrs	KI6EH	SCCARC
NORCAL-EAST BAY					
Berkeley	145.2900	–	O 131.8x	K6GOD	K6GOD
Concord	145.3300	–	O 100ex	K6POU	MDRA
Concord	147.0600	+	O 100aersx	W6CX	MDARC
Concord	147.4500	–	O#elx	W6UUU	HORK
Concord	147.7350	–	O 107.2aelrsx	WA6HAM	CCRA
Danville	146.3550	+	O 100ers	K6SRM	SCCC RACES
Fremont	147.0150	+	O	WA6PWW	TRICO ARC
Fremont	147.4625	–	O#lx	W6TCP	W6TCP
Hayward	145.1300	–	O 127.3ers	K6EAG	Hayward RC
Hayward	145.2500	–	●DCSl	KQ6RC	KQ6RC
Hayward	146.9100	–	O 156.7#	KQ6YG	KQ6YG
Hayward	147.9750	–	O 162.2aelsx	KB6LED	KB6LED
Livermore	145.3500	–	O 100erx	AB6CR	LARK
Livermore	145.4300	–	O 100elrs	KO6PW	KO6PW
Livermore	146.7750	–	O 100ers	WA6YHJ	LLNLRC
Livermore	147.1200	+	O 100aer	AD6KV	LARK
Livermore	147.1500	+	O 110.9lrs	KB6FEC	AREA
Newark	146.0850	+	O 114.8	N3EL	P.A.R.E
Newark	146.2050	+	O 100	N1VLA	N1VLA
Oakland	146.6250	–	O 156.7#	W6MTF	W6MTF
Oakland	146.6700	–	O 85.4#erx	W6BUR	W6BUR
Oakland	146.8800	–	O 77aersx	WB6NDJ	ORCA
Oakland	147.2100	+	O 100ex	WB6TCS	WB6TCS

Location	*Output*	*Input*	*Notes*	*Call*	*Sponsor*
Orinda	145.4900	–	O 107.2aelrsx	WA6HAM	CCRA
Orinda	146.8500	–	O 114.8el	K6LNK	CARLA
Orinda	147.1050	+	O 77#es	K6ORI	Lamorinda
Pleasanton	147.0450	+	O 94.8elrsx	W6SRR	Sunol Ridg
San Leandro	147.0300	+	O 156.7#	WB6BDD	ACRC
San Leandro	147.2400	+	O 107.2er	W6RGG	NCCC
San Pablo	145.1100	–	O 82.5ers	WA6KQB	CCCC
San Ramon	145.4100	–	O 107.2aelrsx	WA6HAM	CCRA
Union City	146.6100	–	O 123elrs	KM6EF	GSARC
NORCAL-NORTH BAY					
Bodega Bay	146.6700	–	O 88.5lr	WA6M	WA6YGD
Clear Lake	147.6750	–	O 88.5ex	N1PPP	LCSOOESAA
Cloverdale	146.9700	–	O 103.5ls	KI6B	SMRS
Cobb	145.1500	–	O 103.5	KI6QCU	KI6QCU
Dillon Beach	146.8650	–	O 127.3l	KI6SUD	OceanMarin
Guerneville	146.9400	–	O 88.5els	KI6B	SMRS
Inverness	145.1700	–	O 88.5elrs	KI6B	SMRS
Kelseyville	146.7750	–	O 103.5#esx	N1PPP	Nice Amate
Middletown	145.3900	–	O 88.5el	AC6VJ	AC6VJ
Mill Valley	146.7000	–	O 179.9aerx	K6GWE	ACS
Napa	146.1150	+	O 127.3elrx	N6TKW	NARC
Napa	146.6550	–	O 88.5e	N6TKW	NARC
Napa	146.8200	–	O 100elrx	W6BYS	NARC
Napa	146.8200	–	O 151.4elrx	W6BYS	NARC
Napa	147.1800	+	O 151.4ersx	W6CO	SARS
Napa	147.1800	+	O 91.5elrs	W6CO	SARS
Novato	146.7750	–	O 110.9e	K6BW	HWA
Novato	147.3300	+	O 203.5erx	K6GWE	ACS
Petaluma	146.9100	–	O 88.5ersx	WB6TMS	SMRS
Pt Reyes Stn	145.4700	–	O 88.5elrs	WB6TMS	SMRS
San Rafael	147.3300	+	O 173.8er	K6GWE	ACS
Santa Rosa	145.1900	–	O 88.5#aers	K6CDF	CDF VIP
Santa Rosa	145.3500	–	O 88.5lrsx	WA6YGD	WA6YGD
Santa Rosa	146.7300	–	O 88.5erx	K6ACS	Sonoma ACS
Santa Rosa	146.7900	–	O 88.5er	KD6RC	KD6RC
Santa Rosa	146.8350	–	O 88.5es	KE6EAQ	SR ARES
Santa Rosa	147.3150	+	O 156.7es	W6SON	SCRA
Sebastopol	147.3150	+	O 88.5es	W6SON	SCRA
Sonoma	146.2050	+	O 88.5ers	AA6GV	AA6GV
Vallejo	145.3100	–	O 88.5	K6LI	NBARA

Location	*Output*	*Input*	*Notes*	*Call*	*Sponsor*
Windsor	146.9850	–	O 88.5	W6IBC	W6IBC
NORCAL-NORTH COAST					
Anchor Bay	147.2700	+	O 114.8elr	WA6RQX	SMRA
Anchor Bay	147.8250	–	O 103.5ael	W6ABR	ABARC
Cazadero	147.9750	–	O 88.5el	K6ACS	ACS
Covelo	147.2100	+	O 103.5ex	WB6TCS	WB6TCS
Crescent City	146.8800	–	O 136.5aes	W6HY	DNARC
Crescent City	147.0600	+	O 100l	K6JSI	WIN System
Crescent City	147.1800	+	O 136.5elsx	W6HY	DNARC
Dinsmore	146.9800	–	O 103.5#l	K6FWR	FWRA
Eureka	145.4700	–	O 103.5#	W6ZZK	HARA
Eureka	146.7000	–	O 103.5#l	K6FWR	FWRA
Fort Bragg	147.0300	+	O 103.5#	K6MHE	MCARA
Fortuna	147.0900	+	O 103.5x	KA6ROM	CDF/KA6ROM
Garberville	146.6100	–	O 103.5#lx	K6FWR	FWRA
Garberville	146.7900	–	O 103.5#	W6CLG	KE6WC
Garberville	146.7900	–	O 103.5#ael	W6HUM	SHARC
Garberville	147.1500	+	O 103.5lrx	KA6ROM	SMRS
Gualala	147.0000	+	O 114.8el	K6LNK	CARLA
Hopland	145.4700	–	O 103.5elr	WA6RQX	WA6RQX
Klamath	147.3900	+	O 103.5ex	KA6ROM	CDF/KA6ROM
Laytonville	145.4300	–	O 103.5elr	WA6RQX	WA6RQX
Laytonville	146.6550	–	O 103.5elrx	K7BUG	SMRS
Mendocino	146.8200	–	O 103.5e	WD6HDY	MCARC
Point Arena	146.6100	–	O 88.5el	W6ABR	ABARC
Scotia	145.1700	–	O 103.5elrsx	WB6TMS	SMRS
Scotia	146.7600	–	O 103.5#lx	K6FWR	FWRA
Sea Ranch	147.9450	–	O 88.5#ael	KI6HHA	TSRARA
Ukiah	146.9550	–	O 88.5elsx	AC6ET	SMRS
Ukiah	147.3900	+	O 103.5elr	WA6RQX	WA6RQX
Weott	147.3300	+	O 103.5ex	KM6TE	CDF/KA6ROM
Willits	145.1300	–	O 103.5ersx	K7WWA	K7WWA
Willits	147.1200	+	O 103.5aelrsx	K7WWA	K7WWA
Willow Creek	147.0000	+	O 103.5#lx	K6FWR	FWRA
NORCAL-NORTH EAST					
Belden	146.7000	–	O 110.9l	K6FHL	FOTHL
Burney	145.3500	–	O 107.2#erx	W6QWN	CARC
Burney	147.0300	+	O 103.5#	KI6WG	KI6WG
Chester	145.3700	–	O 123elrx	KF6CCP	KF6CCP
Dunsmuir	146.8200	–	O 100aelrx	K6SIS	SCARA
FallRiverMills	147.1200	+	O 103.5#	KI6WG	KI6WG

Location	*Output*	*Input*	*Notes*	*Call*	*Sponsor*
Happy Camp	146.9100	–	O 100aelrx	K6SIS	SCARA
Mt Shasta City	145.1100	–	O 123#elrx	KE6OUD	NCARRA
Mt Shasta City	146.6700	–	O 100#	KJ6RA	KJ6RA
Mt Shasta City	146.8800	–	O#	W6BML	MSARC
Quincy	145.4700	–	O 123ers	K6PLU	Plumas OES
Quincy	147.9450	–	O 123rs	AF6AP	AF6AP
Redding	145.1500	–	O 107.2s	W6STA	WO6P
Redding	146.7600	–	O 107.2#el x	WB6CAN	WB6CAN
Redding	147.0000	+	O 100#els x	K6MCA	Palo Cedro
Redding	147.0900	+	O 88.5s	NC6I	ARCA
Redding	147.2700	+	O 131.8el	KD6LOM	KD6LOM
Redding	147.3000	+	O 146.2#	K6NP	GBTPRC
Sierra City	145.1700	–	O 114.8	W7FEH	W7FEH
Weaverville	146.7300	–	O 85.4es	N6TKY	TCARC
Weaverville	146.9250	–	O 85.4esx	KF6OAH	TCARC
Yreka	146.7900	–	O 100aelrx	K6SIS	SCARA
Yreka	147.1200	+	O 136.5#a elsx	K7TVL	R.V.L.A.
NORCAL-SACRAMENTO VALLEY					
Auburn	145.2700	–	O 156.7	W6SAR	PCSAR
Auburn	145.3100	–	O 151.4elx	AB6LI	AB6LI
Auburn	145.4300	–	O 162.2ae s	W6EK	SFARC
Auburn	146.7600	–	O 136.5	N6NMZ	N6NMZ
Cameron Park	147.0300	+	O 77#aelrs x	N6RDE	N6RDE
Camino	147.8250	–	O 82.5aes x	AG6AU	EDCARC
Chico	145.2900	–	O 110.9er	W6SCR	Butte SCR
Chico	146.8500	–	O 110.9ae sx	W6RHC	GEARS
Chico	146.8950	–	O#lsx	K6CHO	AREA Repea
Chico	146.9400	–	O 123elx	W6ECE	W6ECE
Chico	147.3000	+	O 141.3e	K6NP	GBTPRC
Chico	147.3300	+	O 100elx	K6JSI	WIN System
Chico	147.9750	–	O 110.9elr sx	N6TZG	N6TZG
Davis	145.4500	–	O 203.5#e	K6JRB	UCDavis EO
Dobbins	147.0450	+	O 77ex	N6NMZ	CDF VIP
ElDoradoHills	145.3700	–	O 100#ael x	WT6G	WT6G
ElDoradoHills	147.1500	+	O 85.4#ael x	WT6G	MEARA
Elk Creek	147.1050	+	O 100ersx	N6YCK	N6YCK
Elk Grove	145.1100	–	O 103.5a	KE6OBO	KE6OBO
Fair Oaks	145.1300	–	O 162.2ex	WB6HEV	PARE
Fair Oaks	146.7900	–	O 100a	W6HIR	RAMS

Location	*Output*	*Input*	*Notes*	*Call*	*Sponsor*
Fiddletown	146.8800	–	O 156.7lrx	K6SCA	RMRG
Folsom	146.6100	–	O 136.5aelx	KS6HRP	SHARP
Foresthill	146.3550	+	O 94.8x	W6YDD	YDD 1.2
Foresthill	146.7450	–	O 156.7	W6SAR	PCSAR
Georgetown	146.6250	–	O 123elx	WB4YJT	NCAA
Grass Valley	145.3100	–	O 151.4e	KG6TZT	KG6TZT
Grass Valley	146.6250	–	O 151.4ex	WB4YJT	NCAA
Grass Valley	146.9250	–	O 71.9aelx	KI6FEO	KI6FEO
Grass Valley	147.0150	+	O 151.4esx	W6DD	NCARC
Grass Valley	147.2100	+	O 141.3#e	W6WEE	W6WEE
Grass Valley	147.2850	+	O 151.4ersx	W6DD	NCARC
Lincoln	147.3300	+	O 179.9e	K6PAC	WPARC
Maxwell	147.0450	+	O 156.7ex	N6NMZ	N6NMZ
N of Chico	145.3900	–	O 110.9ers	KI6PNB	KI6PNB
Oroville	146.6550	–	O 136.5elx	K6RCO	O.A.R.S.
Placerville	146.8050	–	O 123aelrsx	KA6GWY	KA6GWY
Placerville	147.2550	+	O 136.5#aes	N6QDY	C.A.R.U.N.
Plymouth	146.6700	–	O 156.7lrx	K6SCA	RMRG
Pollock Pines	146.8650	–	O 146.2ex	WA6BTH	P&F
Red Bluff	145.4500	–	O 88.5ersx	KF6KDD	CDF VIP
Redding	147.3000	+	O 123lx	K6JSI	WIN System
Redding Ca	145.2900	–	O 88.5#es	W6MAC	McCulley
Roseville	146.6400	–	O 156.7er	W6SAR	PCSAR
Roseville	147.3150	+	O 162.2ael	KD6PDD	HPRARC
Sacramento	145.1900	–	O 162.2ae	K6IS	NHRC
Sacramento	145.2300	–	O 162.2ae	KC6MHT	KC6MHT
Sacramento	145.2500	–	O 162.2x	N6NA	RCARCS
Sacramento	146.7000	–	●#l	K6INC	SCAN INT'L
Sacramento	146.9100	–	O 162.2er	W6AK	SARC
Sacramento	146.9850	–	O 94.8erx	AB6OP	AB6OP
Sacramento	147.3000	+	O 136.5ex	K6NP	GBTPRC
Sacramento	147.3900	+	●x	N6FR	WB6RVR
ShingleSprings	146.9400	–	O 136.5aelrx	N6RDE	N6RDE
Stonyford	146.1150	+	O 123elx	K6LNK	CARLA
Sutter	146.0850	+	O 127.3ersx	WD6AXM	YSARC
Tancred	147.2550	+	O 123ersx	N6QDY	V.E.R.A.
Vacaville	145.4700	–	O 127.3aelrsx	W6VVR	Western Va
Vacaville	146.6100	–	O 100#x	KS6HRP	SHARP
Vacaville	146.7450	–	●x	W6SAR	PCSAR
Vacaville	147.0000	–	O 136.5ex	K6MVR	MVRC
Vacaville	147.1950	+	O 123aelrsx	N6ICW	N6ICW

Location	*Output*	*Input*	*Notes*	*Call*	*Sponsor*
Vacaville	147.2700	+	O 77ex	W6AEX	SARO
Williams	146.7600	–	O 131.8ex	N6NMZ	N6NMZ
Woodland	146.9700	–	O 123esx	KE6YUV	BARK
Yuba City	145.2100	–	O 127.3l	N6IQY	N6IQY
Zamora	147.1950	+	O 123aelrs x	N6ICW	N6ICW
NORCAL-SAN JOAQUIN VALLEY					
Ahwahnee	147.8250	–	O 123aex	WB6NIL	WB6NIL
Angels Camp	145.1700	–	O 100aers x	N6FRG	FPRG/CARS,
Auberry	147.6750	–	O 141.3ael x	K6ARP	CARP
Bakersfield	145.1500	–	O 100ers	W6LIE	KCCVARC
Bakersfield	145.1900	–	O 141.3els x	KK6AC	KERN
Bakersfield	145.2100	–	O 100ers	KF6JOQ	KF6JOQ
Bakersfield	145.4100	–	O 103.5ae x	W6LI	KRVARC
Bakersfield	145.4900	–	O 186.2elr sx	KR6DK	KR6DK
Bakersfield	146.6700	–	O 100#	WA6CLS	BRS
Bakersfield	146.9100	–	O 100x	W6LIE	KCCVARC
Bakersfield	147.1500	+	O 100el	KG6KKV	KG6KKV
Bakersfield	147.2100	+	O 100#rs	K6RRS	Kern Count
Bakersfield	147.2700	+	O 94.8el	K6RET	K6RET
Bakersfield Ca	145.3500	–	O 67#elrsx	KR6DK	KR6DK
Clovis	147.2550	+	O 100#l	K6KDK	K6KDK
Clovis	147.3600	+	O 141.3#a ex	N6VQL	CVRC
Coalinga	147.3300	+	O 100#elrs x	N6DL	Kings ARC
Coarsegold	146.6400	–	O 127.3e	W6HMH	W6HMH
Columbia	147.9450	–	O 100aers x	W6FEJ	TCARES
Copperopolis	145.1500	–	O 141.3lx	KG6TXA	SALAC
Fiddletown	147.1650	+	O 107.2lrx	W6SF	KD6FVA
Fresno	145.2300	–	O 141.3elx	W6FSC	N6MTS
Fresno	145.4700	–	O 141.3ex	W7POR	FARA
Fresno	146.7750	–	O 141.3#a x	N6BYH	N6BYH
Fresno	146.7900	–	O 100elx	K6JSI	WIN System
Fresno	146.8200	–	O 141.3lx	KE6JZ	SJVARS
Fresno	146.8500	–	O 141.3sx	WQ6CWA	QCWA
Fresno	146.9400	–	O 141.3elx	W6TO	Fresno ARC
Fresno	147.1050	+	O 141.3ex	W7POR	W7POR
Fresno	147.1500	+	O 141.3#ar x	N6HEW	N6HEW
Fresno	147.1650	+	O 141.3#el x	N6VRC	CVRC

Location	*Output*	*Input*	*Notes*	*Call*	*Sponsor*
Groveland	145.3100	–	O 127.3	KF6OTM	WB6PHE
Hanford	145.1100	–	O 100aelrs	N6CVC	Kings ARC
Lake Isabella	145.4500	–	O 156.7es	KC6OCA	KC6OCA
Lemoore	145.2700	–	O 88.5l	WB6Y	WB6Y
Lemoore	146.2050	+	O 94.8#l	KM6OU	KM6OU
Lodi	147.0900	+	O 114.8elrx	WB6ASU	WB6ASU
Los Banos	146.9250	–	O 123e	K6TJS	AA6LB
Los Banos - Ea	147.2100	+	O 123el	K6TJS	K6TJS
Madera	146.7000	–	O 141.3erx	KD6FW	KD6FW
Mammoth	146.7300	–	O 100er	NW6C	BARC/CARS9
Manteca	145.3100	–	O 118.8	KF6NQR	KF6NQR
Manteca	146.9850	–	O 100aers	K6MAN	MARC
Mariposa	146.7450	–	O 146.2#aelx	W6PPM	MMU-VIP
Mariposa	146.7600	–	O 141.3lx	N6BYH	N6BYH
Mariposa	147.0300	+	O 100aelsx	W6BXN	TurlockARC
Meadow Lakes	145.2500	–	O 141.3e	KJ6CE	KJ6CE
Meadow Lakes	146.6100	–	Ox	WB6QDN	AARC
Merced	146.7450	–	O 123#aex	W6PPM	MMU-VIP
Moccasin	145.2900	–	O 100ers	K6DPB	TCARES
Modesto	145.1100	–	O 136.5es	WD6EJF	SARA
Modesto	145.3900	–	O 136.5elsx	WD6EJF	SARA
Modesto	146.3550	+	O 156.7aers	WA6OYF	WA6OYF
Oakhurst	147.1800	+	O 146.2ersx	W6WGZ	MCARC
Orange Cove	146.8950	–	O 107.2#e	KC6QIT	KC6QIU
Parkfield	147.2400	+	O 100elx	K6LLA	W6DCP
Patterson	146.7750	–	O 156.7elx	K6SCA	RMRG
Pine Grove	146.8350	–	O 100aex	K6ARC	ACARC
Pinecrest	147.9750	–	O 100ersx	K6TUO	TCARES
Pinehurst	147.3000	+	O 141.3ex	W6BLP	N6SGW
Pinehurst	147.7350	–	O 141.3#elx	N6VRC	CVRC
Porterville	146.6550	–	O 123rs	KE6DWX	PARA
Ripon	147.0150	+	O 114.8er	N5FDL	N5FDL
Selma	145.4300	–	O 100#e	K6KDK	K6KDK
Sonora	146.6250	–	O 136.5#ae	KJ6NRO	kj6nro
Soulsbyville	146.1150	+	O 100ersx	N6HUH	TCARES
Springville	145.3100	–	O 100ersx	KE6DWX	PARA
Stockton	145.2100	–	O 100erx	WA6SEK	WA6SEK
Stockton	146.9400	–	O 114.8#er	N5FDL	Calif Emer
Stockton	147.1050	+	O 67r	KN6KO	KN6KO
Tehachapi	146.7000	–	O 123e	W6SLZ	BVSET
Three Rivers	147.1950	+	O 156.7es	WA7HRG	WA7HRG

Location	*Output*	*Input*	*Notes*	*Call*	*Sponsor*
Tracy	146.6550	–	○ 100aelrs x	AB6CR	LLNL
Tracy	147.2100	+	○ 114.8er	N5FDL	N5FDL
Visalia	145.3300	–	○ 103.5elx	AB6BP	CVARC
Visalia	146.7300	–	○ 141.3#el x	KM6OR	TuleRptrGp
Visalia	146.7600	–	○ 141.3e	N6BYH	N6BYH
Visalia	146.8800	–	○ 103.5elr sx	WA6BAI	TCARC
Visalia	146.9700	–	○ 100ers	KE6DWX	PARA
Visalia	147.9450	–	○ 103.5#lx	AB6BP	CVARC
Westley	146.8950	–	○ 114.8erx	N5FDL	California
Westley	147.1200	+	○ 77elx	K6RDJ	WB6PBN
Yosemite	147.0000	+	○ 100aels x	W6BXN	TurlockARC
NORCAL-SOUTH BAY					
Los Gatos	145.4500	–	○ 100elrsx	K6FB	LCARC
LosAltosHills	146.7450	–	○ 110.9e	W6LAH	LAHEG
LosAltosHills	146.7450	–	●e	W6LAH	LAHEG
Milpitas	145.4300	–	○ 85.4elrs	W6MLP	MARES
Milpitas	147.9450	–	○ 77elsx	N6QDY	C.A.R.U.N.
Moffett Field	145.2500	–	○ 123rs	NA6MF	Ames ARC
Morgan Hill	147.3300	+	○ 103.5ae	K7DAA	MHARS
Morgan Hill	147.8250	–	○ 100aers	W6GGF	GVARC
Mountain View	145.2700	–	○ 100aelrs	W6ASH	SPECS RA
Palo Alto	145.2300	–	○ 100aers x	N6NFI	SPARK/SARS
Palo Alto	147.3600	+	○ 110.9esx	W6TI	NCDXC
Portola Valley	146.0850	+	○ 100#	WB5NVN	WB5NVN
San Jose	145.1900	–	○ 151.4#a e	WA2IBM	IBM ARC
San Jose	145.2100	–	○ 114.8#rs	KB6FEC	AREA
San Jose	145.3100	–	○ 162.2rs	KB6FEC	AREA
San Jose	146.1150	+	○ 100aers x	AA6BT	SVECS
San Jose	146.2050	+	○ 146.2	KI6AOZ	P.A.R.E
San Jose	146.3550	+	○ 127.3#	KD6AOG	KD6AOG
San Jose	146.6400	–	○ 162.2ex	WR6ABD	LPRC
San Jose	146.7600	–	○ 151.4alx	WB6OQS	SCVRS
San Jose	146.8200	–	○ 123	K6INC	SCAN INT'L
San Jose	146.8950	–	○ 110.9rs	KB6FEC	KB6FEC
San Jose	146.9700	–	●l	WA6INC	AD1U
San Jose	146.9850	–	○ 114.8aer	W6UU	SCCARA
San Jose	147.1500	+	●elx	WA6YCZ	BAYCOM
San Jose	147.1650	+	○ 100rs	KB6FEC	KB6FEC
San Jose	147.1650	+	○ 162.2ers	KB6FEC	KB6FEC
San Jose	147.2850	+	○ 103.5aer	KF6FWO	MARA
San Jose	147.3900	+	○ 151.4ael s	W6PIY	WVARA

Location	Output	Input	Notes	Call	Sponsor
San Jose	147.6750	–	O 162.2#	KB6FEC	KB6FEC
San Jose	147.8550	–	O 100ae	WA6TEM	WA6HNE
Saratoga	146.6550	–	O 114.8elr s	K6SA	SARA
Soledad	145.2100	–	●el	N6HU	KQ6RC
Sunnyvale	145.1700	–	O 94.8ers	K6GL	SNNYVLARES
NORCAL-TAHOE					
So Lake Tahoe	145.1500	–	O 123elrx	N6ICW	N6ICW
So Lake Tahoe	146.1150	+	O 192.8ael	W6SUV	W6SUV
So Lake Tahoe	146.8500	–	O 123ex	WA6EWV	TARA
So Lake Tahoe	147.2400	+	O 123ex	NR7A	TARA
South lake Tah	145.3500	–	O 110.9ael rs	KA6GWY	KA6GWY
Tahoe City	146.9400	–	O 100#	WA6FJS	Tahoe ARC
Truckee	145.1100	–	O 123elrx	K1BMW	WA6YOP
Truckee	145.3100	–	O 123#es	WA6FWU	WA6FWU
Truckee	146.6400	–	O 131.8elx	W6SAR	PCSAR
NORCAL-WEST BAY					
Belmont	147.0900	+	O 100es	WB6CKT	WB6CKT
Daly City	146.8350	–	O 123aelx	WD6INC	W1LLE
Half Moon Bay	147.2850	+	O 114.8#er s	WB6ASD	WB6ASD
La Honda	146.7300	–	O 114.8es	W6SCF	SC4ARC
Los Altos Hill	146.9400	–	O 123es	K6AIR	K6AIR
Pacifica	146.9250	–	O 114.8ael rsx	WA6TOW	CARC
Palo Alto	145.3900	–	O 100elsx	WW6BAY	Bay-Net
Pescadero	146.6250	–	O 114.8es	KE6MNJ	PMAC/South
Redwood City	146.8650	–	O 114.8ers x	KC6ULT	SM OES
San Francisco	145.1500	–	O 114.8ers x	W6PW	SFARC
San Francisco	146.7900	–	O 114.8elx	W6TP	GSPLRC
San Mateo	147.3000	+	O 100el	N6MPX	MSARC
Woodside	145.3700	–	O 107.2esx	N6ZX	KMARC
NORTH EAST					
Susanville	146.8350	–	O 91.5	K6LRC	K6ME
Susanville	146.8800	–	O 91.5e	K6LRC	K6ME
Susanville	146.9100	–	O 91.5e	K6LRC	K6ME
ORANGE COUNTY					
Anaheim	147.9150	–	O 136.5a (CA)e	K6NX	BoeingARC
Anaheim Hills	146.2650	+	O 136.5er	K6CF	APD RC
Brea	147.8850	–	O 103.5	W6BII	BeckmanARC
Costa Mesa	147.0600	+	●ta(CA)er	N6TVZ	MESAC
Disneyland	146.9400	–	O 131.8a (CA)	KE6FUZ	DsnylndRC
Easter Hill	145.1600	–	●ta(CA)e	KA6EEK	ALERT
Fountain Valley	145.2600	–	O 136.5er	WA6FV	FV RACES

Location	*Output*	*Input*	*Notes*	*Call*	*Sponsor*
Fountain Valley	145.2800	–	O 151.4e	W6CTR	SCIRA
Fullerton	145.4000	–	O 103.5el	N6ME	Wstrn ARA
Fullerton	146.7900	–	O 114.8	K6SYU	AARC
Fullerton	146.9700	–	O 136.5a (CA)e	K6QEH	RaytheonSy
Fullerton	147.9750	–	O 114.8a (CA)l	WD6DPY	------------
Huntington Bch	145.1400	–	●telr	KH6FL	HB RACES
Huntington Beach	147.4650	146.5050	O 103.5e	W6VLD	BEARS-HB
Laguna Beach	147.6450	–	O 110.9a (CA)er	K6SOA	SOARA
Laguna Hills	146.1600	+	O 110.9	KI6DB	LNACS
Laguna Woods	147.6150	–	O 136.5	W6LY	LW ARC
Lomas Peak	146.8950	–	O 136.5er	W6KRW	OC Races
Newport Beach	145.4200	–	O 136.5a (CA)er	WB6NLU	SOCAL
Orange	147.9750	–	O 114.8a (CA)l	WD6DPY	------------
Placentia	147.8550	–	O 100a (CA)e	WA6YNT	NrthropRC
San Clemente	146.0250	+	O 110.9a (CA)er	K6SOA	SOARA
Santiago Peak	145.1400	–	●ta(CA)elr	WD6AWP	HB RACES
Santiago Peak	145.1600	–	●ta(CA)e	KA6EEK	ALERT
Santiago Peak	145.2200	–	●ta(CA)	N6SLD	CLARA
Santiago Peak	146.9250	–	O 114.8	WA6TFD	BARC
Sierra Peak	146.6100	–	O 103.5elr	KD6DDM	KD6DDM
Sierra Peak	147.4500	146.4150	O 127.3/118.8	N6HOG	------------
Signal Peak	145.1600	–	●ter	KA6EEK	ALERT
Trabuco Canyon	145.2400	–	O 110.9a (CA)er	K6SOA	SOARA
RIVERSIDE COUNTY					
Anza	145.3400	–	O 107.2r	K6JM	ANZA RC
Anza	146.0850	+	O 107.2	WB6UBG	AVRC
Beaumont	147.9150	–	O 123r	W6CDF	------------
Blythe	147.0000	+	O 203.5el	KB6LJO	PARC
Cactus City	146.0250	+	O 107.2er	NR6P	CVARC
Canyon Lake	147.9150	–	O 100	KI6IGR	Canyon Lake CE
Chuckwalla Mtn	145.3800	–	O 162.2l	W6DRA	ZIA
Corona	147.2250	+	●t	W6CPD	CoronaPD
Desert Center	147.0300	+	O 107.2	KA6GBJ	------------
Granados Mt	146.1150	+	O 146.2	W6OY	GoldenSys
Hemet	144.5050	+	O 100er	W6COH	CityOfHemet
Hemet	145.4200	–	O 88.5er	N7OD	LeeDeFores
Idyllwild	146.8950	–	O 118.8e	KD6OI	MHRC
Lake Elsinore	146.7600	–	O 136.5	KI6ITV	------------
Menifee	147.9750	–	O 146.2er	KB9YIQ	City's OEM
Moreno Valley	146.6550	–	O 103.5er	AB6MV	MVARA

Location	Output	Input	Notes	Call	Sponsor
Norco Hills	147.0600	+	O 162.2	W6PWT	------------
Palm Springs	145.4800	–	O 107.2ae	W6DRA	DesertRA
Palm Springs	146.1600	+	●tr	KD6QLT	------------
Palm Springs Tram	145.2000	–	O 131.8elr	W6DRA	Desert Radio
Perris	146.6700	–	O 123a (CA)	WA6HYQ	------------
Rancho Mirage	146.9400	–	O 107.2e	WD6RAT	Dsrt RATS
Redlands	147.1800	+	O 88.5	W6LAR	RedlandsFD
Riverside	145.3600	–	●t	KQ6ZZ	------------
Riverside	146.8800	–	O 146.2a (CA)er	W6TJ	RCARA
Sun City	146.7000	–	O 103.5	KB6SSB	------------
Wildomar	145.4000	–	O 146.2	KI6ITV	------------
Wildomar	146.8050	–	O 100	W6GTR	GldTrngARC
SAN BERNARDINO COUNTY					
Barstow	145.2200	–	O 114.8	N6SLD	CLARA
Barstow	146.9700	–	Oa	WA6TST	Brstw ARC
Barstow	147.0300	+	Oa(CA)elr	WD6BNG	------------
Barstow	147.1800	+	Oa(CA)er	WA6TST	------------
Big Bear City	145.1800	–	O 100a (CA)	W6MPH	W6MPH
Big Bear Lake	147.3300	+	O 131.8ael	K6BB	BB ARC
Big Bear Lake	147.6450	–	O 103.5	KC6OKB	------------
Crestline	146.8500	–	O 146.2e	W6JBT	CBARC
Crestline	147.9450	–	O 123	K6JTH	K6SBC
Heaps Pk	145.2400	–	O 118.8e	K6LLU	Arwhd RG
Hesperia	147.8550	–	O 186.2	WW6Y	------------
Jobs Peak	146.9100	–	O 151.4el	W6CTR	SCIRA
Keller Peak	146.3850	+	O 146.2e	KE6TZG	KPRA
Loma Linda	147.7350	–	O 118.8a (CA)e	K6LLU	LLU ARC
Ludlow	147.8850	–	Oel	WA6TST	------------
Newberry Spgs	146.7000	–	Oel	WA6MTZ	------------
North Yucca Valley	147.7050	–	O 123elr	WB6CDF	WB6CDF.COM
Onyx Peak	145.1200	–	●t	K6SBC	------------
Onyx Peak	146.8200	–	Oel	W6FNO	Edgwd ARS
Running Sprgs	145.1200	–	O 131.8	WA6ISG	------------
Running Sprgs	147.6150	–	●t	N6NIK	HRAN
Running Springs	147.7050	–	●tel	KI6ZTP	------------
Sunset Ridge	145.4600	–	O 77	W6IER	IEARC
Trona	146.9700	–	O 123	K6YYJ	------------
Twntynine Plms	147.0600	+	O 136.5e	W6IF	MBRG
Upland	147.3000	+	O 123a (CA)e	WB6QHB	------------
Victorville	145.4200	–	●t	WW6Y	------------
Victorville	146.1150	+	O 91.5	K7GIL	------------
Victorville	146.9400	–	O 91.5a (CA)e	WA6EFW	------------

Location	*Output*	*Input*	*Notes*	*Call*	*Sponsor*
Victorville	147.1200	+	O 91.5a	WA6EFW	------------
Yucca Valley	146.1150	+	O 136.5	K6JB	------------
Yucca Valley	146.7900	–	O 136.5a (CA)e	W6BA	MARC
SAN DIEGO COUNTY					
Borrego Springs	147.8550	–	O 107.2	K7IKO	------------
Carlsbad	147.9150	–	●t	W6GK	CZB
Carmel Mountain Ranch	146.7900	–	O 107.2e	NG6ST	NorthGrum
Chula Vista	145.2600	–	O 107.2	KK6KD	------------
Chula Vista	146.0850	+	O 100e	K6QM	SOBARS
Chula Vista	147.0600	+	O 127.3a (CA)	KF6QNJ	Hltop ARC
Coronado	147.1800	+	O 110.9a (CA)e	W6SH	CERO ARES
Cuyamaca Pk	147.1950	+	●tr	K6JCC	SD RACES
El Cajon	146.3550	+	O 123	KN6NA	------------
Escondido	146.8800	–	O 107.2a (CA)el	N6WB	EARS
Fallbrook	146.1750	+	O 107.2ae	N6FQ	FallbrookARC
High Pass	145.2800	–	O 107.2	K6GAO	SANDRA
High Pass	147.9900	–	●tl	W6JAM	DRØNK
La Mesa	145.2400	–	O 131.8	WA6HYQ	------------
La Mesa	146.6700	–	●ta(CA)l	N6QWD	------------
La Mesa	147.4200	146.4750	O 107.2	WA6BGS	ECARC
La Mesa	147.7050	–	●ter	WD6APP	------------
Lyons Peak	146.2650	+	O 107.2e	W6SS	SANDRA
Lyons Peak	147.1950	+	●t	K6JCC	SD RACES
Mission Hills	145.3200	–	O 107.2	WD6APP	------------
Monument Peak	147.2400	+	O 103.5a (CA)el	KA6DAC	ECRA
Mt Helix	147.9150	–	O 107.2a (CA)e	K6GHM	------------
Mt Laguna	147.1500	+	O 107.2	WB6WLV	SANDRA
Mt Otay	145.3600	–	Ot	WB6WLV	SANDRA
Mt Otay	146.6400	–	O 107.2e	WB6WLV	SANDRA
Mt Otay	146.9100	–	O 107.2a (CA)el	KN6KM	SoBayRG
Mt Otay	146.9250	–	O 107.2	N6RSH	KN6KM
Mt Otay	147.2100	+	●t	N6VVY	FILAMARS
Mt Otay	147.9900	–	●tl	W6JAM	DRØNK
Mt San Miguel	145.1200	–	O 107.2	W6HDC	------------
Mt Woodson	145.1800	–	●t	W6HDC	------------
Palomar Mtn	145.4400	–	●ta(CA)l	N6NIK	HRAN
Palomar Mtn	146.7000	–	Ot	W6NWG	Palomar AR
Palomar Mtn	146.7300	–	O 107.2a (CA)e	W6NWG	Palomar AR
Palomar Mtn	147.0300	+	O 103.5e	K6RIF	ECRA
Palomar Mtn	147.0750	+	O 107.2a (CA)e	W6NWG	Palomar AR

Location	Output	Input	Notes	Call	Sponsor
Palomar Mtn	147.1300	+	O 107.2a (CA)el	W6NWG	Palomar AR
Palomar Mtn	147.1950	+	●t	K6JCC	SD RACES
Palomar Mtn	147.9900	–	●tl	W6JAM	DRØNK
Paradise Hills	145.4800	–	O 127.3a (CA)	W6JVA	------------
Point Loma	145.3800	–	O 107.2a (CA)e	KA4JSR	PLARC
Poway/Rosemont	147.1950	+	●t	K6JCC	SD RACES
Ramona	145.3000	–	O 88.5	KD6RSQ	------------
San Diego	146.1600	+	O 107.2	W6SS	------------
San Diego	147.7650	–	●t	AA6WS	------------
San Diego	147.8550	–	O 107.2a (CA)l	WA6ZMZ	SANDRA
San Diego	147.8850	–	O 107.2a (CA)	WA6AIL	SANDRA
San Diego	147.9450	–	O 107.2a (CA)	N6WYF	------------
Santee	147.9150	–	O 151.4	WA6OSB	------------
Stephenson Peak	147.9900	–	●t	N6JAM	DRØNK
Vista	146.9700	–	O 107.2a (CA)	KA3AJM	DesComNet
SAN LUIS OBISPO COUNTY					
Paso Robles	146.8800	–	O	W6YDZ	------------
SANTA BARBARA COUNTY					
Broadcast Pk	147.0000	+	O 131.8	WB6OBB	------------
Figueroa Mtn	147.2100	+	O 131.8a (CA)	K6SYV	SYVARRG
Gibralter Peak	146.7000	–	O 131.8	N6HYM	------------
Goleta	145.2400	–	O 131.8	K6TZ	SBARC
Guadalupe	146.1750	+	O 100	KA6BFB	------------
La Vigia Hill	146.7900	–	O 131.8aer	K6TZ	SBARC
Lompoc	145.3600	–	O 131.8r	WB6FLY	WSB_ARES
Lompoc	145.4200	–	Oa(CA)e	WA6YZV	Missn ARC
Lompoc	147.1200	+	O 131.8a (CA)	WA6VPL	LOMPOC ARC
Nipomo	146.9400	–	Oe	N6RAN	------------
Santa Barbara	145.4800	–	O 136.5	W6RFU	UCSB
Santa Barbara	147.0750	+	O 131.8	KG6TAT	------------
Santa Barbara	147.9450	–	O 131.8ae	WA6JFM	Gbrltr RA
Santa Maria	145.1400	–	O 131.8 E-SUN	KM6DF	Satellite ARC
Santa Maria	146.6400	–	O	N6UE	------------
Santa Maria	147.3000	+	O 131.8r	WB6FLY	NorSBCARES
Santa Maria	147.9150	–	O 103.5	W6NO	------------
Santa Ynez Peak	145.2000	–	O 131.8l	K6JSI	WIN System
Santa Ynez Pk	145.1800	–	O 131.8e	WA6COT	------------
Solvang	146.8950	–	Oe	N6JNS	------------
Sudden Peak	145.1200	–	O 100el	WA6VPL	WALA

Location	Output	Input	Notes	Call	Sponsor
SIERRA/TAHOE					
Truckee	145.3100	–	O 123	WA6FWU	WA6FWU
VENTURA COUNTY					
Camarillo	145.2800	–	O 100e	KN6OK	------------
Camarillo H'ght	147.9150	–	O 127.3r	WB6ZTQ	------------
Camarillo, Ventura County	147.9150	–	O 127.3	K6ERN	SMRA-ERN
Chatsworth Peak	147.1800	+	O 186.2el	KK6NJ	------------
Downtown Moorpark	145.2800	–	O 100el	W6WLW	Whitaker
Grissom Pt	146.8500	–	O 94.8a (CA)er	N6EVC	EVCRA
Newbury Park	146.6700	–	O 127.3e	N6JMI	Bozo ARN
Newbury Park	146.9400	–	●t	KE6TOI	------------
Newbury Park	147.8850	–	O 127.3a (CA)e	N6JMI	Bozo ARN
Ojai Valley	145.4000	–	OE-SUNr	N6FL	OJAI Vly ARC
Olivas Park Golf Course	147.7650	–	O 127.3r	K6ERN	SMRA-ERN
Oxnard	146.7300	–	●t	W6KGB	WOLF RN
Oxnard	146.9700	–	O 127.3a (CA)er	WB6YQN	LPMG
Red Mountain	146.8800	–	O 127.3a (CA)el	K6ERN	SMRA-ERN
San Fernando	146.9100	–	O 103.5er	W6IN	------------
SanBuenaventur	146.6100	–	O 127.3a (CA)	N3MBN	------------
Simi Valley	146.6400	–	O 127.3	WA6FGK	------------
Simi Valley	147.9300	–	O 127.3	K6ERN	SMRA-ERN
South Mtn	146.3850	+	O 127.3elr	WA6ZSN	SMRA-ERN
Thousand Oaks	145.3200	–	Oa(CA)e	WD8RCL	------------
Thousand Oaks	146.8050	–	O 127.3	KN6OK	------------
Thousand Oaks	147.1500	+	O 127.3	KØAKS	CHRS&VARS
Ventura	146.6550	–	O 131.8	WD5B	------------
Ventura	147.9750	–	O 127.3a (CA)e	N6VUY	------------

COLORADO

Location	Output	Input	Notes	Call	Sponsor
FREQUENCY USAGE					
STATEWIDE	145.1900	–			
STATEWIDE	145.2050	–			
STATEWIDE	146.7750	–			
STATEWIDE	146.8350	–			
STATEWIDE	146.8650	–			
STATEWIDE	147.1650	+			
STATEWIDE	147.3150	+			
BOULDER COUNTY					
Boulder	145.4600	–	O 107.2/107.2 (CA)e	WØCRA	CRA

Location	Output	Input	Notes	Call	Sponsor
Boulder	146.6100	–	O 100/100	WØDK	BARC
Boulder	146.7000	–	O 100 (CA) s	WØDK	BARC
Boulder	146.7300	–	O 91.5/91.5	KØDK	KØDK
Boulder	146.7600	–	O 100esx	WØIA	RMVHFS
Boulder	147.0300	+	100 (CA)x	WB2CBU	BUG
Longmont	147.2700	+	O 100 (CA) els	WØENO	LARC
CENTRAL					
Bailey	146.8950	–	O 100es	ABØPC	ParkCntyRC
Georgetown	147.2550	+	O 141.3/141.3el	KØIMT	JeffARES
Lake George	146.6850	–	O 107.2el	NXØG	MARC
Lake George	147.3600	+	O 107.2ex	KCØCVU	CMRG
COLORADO SPRINGS					
Colorado Springs	145.1300	–	O 123/123e lx	KBØVJJ	Colo Conn
Colorado Springs	145.1600	–	O 107.2/107.2 (CA)ex	WØCRA	CRA
Colorado Springs	145.2650	–	O 100/100 (CA)elrsWX	KBØSRJ	PPFMA
Colorado Springs	145.3750	–	Oelx	KCØCVU	CMRG
Colorado Springs	146.6250	–	O 123 (CA) elRB	KFØWF	ColoSprARA
Colorado Springs	146.7600	–	O 123 (CA) es	KCØCVU	CMRG
Colorado Springs	146.8500	–	O 103.5/103.5e	WØRSH	WØRSH
Colorado Springs	146.9100	–	O 151.4/151.4e	KØIRP	GGARC
Colorado Springs	146.9700	–	O 100/100 (CA)elrsWXx	KBØSRJ	PPFMA
Colorado Springs	147.1350	+	O 100e	AAØL	AAØL
Colorado Springs	147.1800	+	● 100 (CA) E-SUNx	AAØSP	AAØSP
Colorado Springs	147.3450	+	O 107.2 (CA)elx	KCØCVU	CMRG
Colorado Springs	147.3900	+	O 103.5/103.5e	WØMOG	WØMOG
Cripple Creek	147.0150	+	O 107.2el	NXØG	MARC
Woodland Park	145.4150	–	O 179.9 (CA)e	KAØWUC	MARC
Woodland Park	146.8200	–	O 107.2el	NXØG	MARC
DENVER METRO					
Aurora	145.4000	–	O 100aels	KBØUDD	CRRG
Como	147.0900	+	O 100/100e ls	ABØPC	ParkCntyRC
Conifer	147.1200	+	O 88.5ex	KCØIAD	ARA
Denver	145.1450	–	O 107.2/107.2esx	WØCRA	CRA

Location	*Output*	*Input*	*Notes*	*Call*	*Sponsor*
Denver	145.2200	–	O 103.5 (CA)ex	WNØEHE	RMRL
Denver	145.3100	–	O 123/123e lx	KBØVJJ	Colo Conn
Denver	145.3400	–	O 103.5e L(IRLP 3350)xz	NØPQV	RMRL
Denver	145.4300	–	O 103.5esx	WØMTZ	RMRL
Denver	145.4750	–	O 100e	NØJOQ	IRG
Denver	145.4900	–	O 100/100e l	WØTX	DRC
Denver	146.6400	–	O 100ex	WBØTUB	DRL
Denver	146.6700	–	O 100es	KBØUDD	CRRG
Denver	146.7150	–	OE-SUN	NØJXN	EARS
Denver	146.8800	–	O 100ex	WBØTUB	DRL
Denver	146.9400	–	O 103.5ex	WØWYX	RMRL
Denver	146.9850	–	O 100	KØFEZ	RADOPS EJ
Denver	147.2250	+	O 107.2/107.2 (CA)esx	WØCRA	CRA
Denver	147.3000	+	O 103.5x	NØPYY	DenPDEEB
Elizabeth	147.2100	+	O 100ael	K6AER	CRRG
Golden	145.2800	–	O 100 (CA) elrx	KEØSJ	IRG
Golden	147.1500	+	O 88.5a	WØCBI	ARA
Northglenn	147.0450	+	O 123e	KØML	NglennRA
EAST CENTRAL					
Flagler	146.8950	–	O 103.5z	KAØEFF	BigSndyARC
Genoa	147.0600	+	O 103.5	KAØEFF	BSARC
Leadville	147.2400	+	O 156.7/156.7sx	NØZSN	NØZSN
GRAND JUNCTION					
Grand Junction	145.1750	–	O 107.2ers WX	WØRRZ	WCARC
Grand Junction	145.2200	–	O 107.2	KEØTY	KEØTY
Grand Junction	145.3550	–	O 123elx	KBØVJJ	Colo Conn
Grand Junction	146.8200	–	107.2lx	KEØTY	KEØTY
Grand Junction	146.9400	–	O 107.2/107.2 (CA)elrsRB WX	WØRRZ	WCARC
Grand Junction	147.1050	+	Ot	WØSXI	WØSXI
Grand Junction	147.3900	+	O 107.2l	KEØTY	KEØTY
NORTH CENTRAL					
Hayden	146.6400	–	O 107.2/107.2s	ABØAA	KAØBSA
Kremmling	147.0750	+	O 123l	KBØVJJ	Colo Conn
Walden	145.1600	–	O 123l	KBØVJJ	Colo Conn
NORTH FRONT RANGE					
Estes Park	146.6850	–	O 123e L(IRLP 7268)	NØFH	EVARC
Fort Collins	145.1150	–	O 100ers WXx	WØUPS	NCARC

COLORADO CONNECTION

Connecting Colorado's Amateur Community

1	10,600'	145.310–	Denver/Boulder (Hub)*
2	13,600'	145.445–	Leadville*
3	12,600'	147.390+	Breckenridge* (new)
4	11,700'	147.285+	Salida
5	10,600'	146.850–	Glenwood Springs
6	10,300'	449.625–	Steamboat Springs
7	10,000'	145.355–	Grand Junction
8	9,800'	147.345+	Vail
9	9,500'	147.345+	Durango (pending)
10	9,300'	145.130–	Colorado Springs*
11	9,200'	147.075+	Kremmling
12	9,000'	145.160–	Walden
13	8,500'	147.270+	Meeker*
14	7,500'	146.970+	Craig*
15	4,700'	145.400–	Akron*

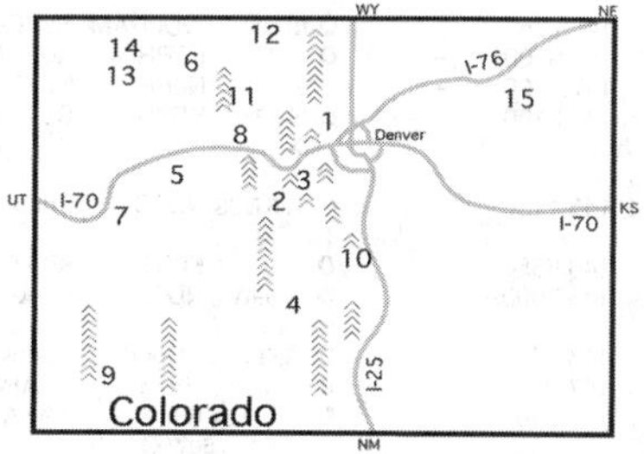

Colorado Connection Repeaters, Inc.
P.O. Box 22134, Denver, CO 80222

The KB0VJJ Repeaters
http://www.colcon.org/

Send SASE for info
kb0vjj@colcon.org

The Colorado Connection is a 501c3 non-profit corporation supported solely by donations. The system is open and fully linked. It requires a 123.0Hz tone on the input (* = tone available on output). National Traffic System net each evening 7:30pm. Before keying up, please allow the system to drop a few seconds after each proceed "k" signal.

COLORADO

Location	*Output*	*Input*	*Notes*	*Call*	*Sponsor*
Fort Collins	147.3600	+	O 100 (CA)	WØQEY	CSUARC
Ft Collins	146.6250	–	O 100/100el	WØUPS	NCARC
Greeley	146.8500	–	O 100/100lsWX	WØUPS	NCARC
Greeley	146.8500	–	O 100lsWX	WØUPS	NCARC
Greeley	147.0000	+	O 100/100 Z(911)	KCØKWD	WARS
Hudson	147.3300	+	O 100/100 (CA)	WØTX	DRC
Loveland	147.1950	+	O 100 (CA) es	WØLRA	LRA
NORTHEAST					
Akron	145.4000	–	O 123l	KBØVJJ	Colo Conn
Fort Morgan	147.3450	+	O 141.3/141.3	KCØOSG	KCØOSG
Holyoke	146.9550	–	Oe	NØJUN	PCARC
Peetz	145.3700	–	O 88.5/88.5 e	N5SXQ	N5SXQ
Sterling	145.2950	–	Oaex	WAØJTB	NECARA
Wray	146.7900	–	O	KØLMD	WH
NORTHWEST					
Craig	145.2650	–	O 107.2e	WDØHAM	NW Colo ARC
Craig	146.9700	–	O	NØPRG	NØPRG
Meeker	147.2700	+	Ote	NØPRG	NØPRG
Steamboat Springs	147.2100	+	O 107.2ls WX	KDØH	SSARC
PUEBLO					
Pueblo	145.1150	–	O 88.5 DCS e	NDØQ	PuebloHC
Pueblo	146.6550	–	O	KØST	KØST
Pueblo	146.7900	–	O 88.5eWX x	NDØQ	PuebloHC
Pueblo	146.8800	–	O 88.5ex	NDØQ	PuebloHC
Pueblo	147.0000	+	●	NEØZ	STARS
Pueblo	147.2400	+	O 103.5/103.5eWX	KJØT	TARA
Westcliffe	147.0600	+	O 103.5	KBØTUC	RGARC
SOUTH CENTRAL					
Canon City	145.4900	–	O 103.5ae s	WDØEKR	RGARC
Creede	146.9250	–	O 100e	KØIKN	CCRC
Cripple Creek	145.4600	–	O 67 E-SUN	WBØWDF	WBØWDF
La Veta	145.3550	–	O 100 E-SUNl	NØJPX	NØJPX
Salida	145.2950	–	O 107.2lx	KCØCVU	CMRG
Salida	147.2850	+	Otelx	KBØVJJ	Colo Conn
Walsenburg	146.7300	–	O 88.5 E-SUN	NDØQ	PuebloHC

Location	Output	Input	Notes	Call	Sponsor
SOUTHEAST					
La Junta	146.7000	–	OesWX	WØKEV	WØKEV
Lamar	146.6100	–	O 123/123l x	KCØHH	LAMAR ARC
Springfield	146.6400	–	O 118.8/118.8lx	KZØDEM	BCDEARC
Springfield	147.0900	+	O 118.8/118.8elx	KZØDEM	BCDEARC
Springfield	147.3300	+	O 118.8/118.8eWX	KZØDEM	BCDEARC
Trinidad	145.4300	–	O 107.2elx	KCØCVU	CMRG
Trinidad	147.3750	+	O 100/100e	KØBV	KØBV
Westcliffe	147.1050	+	O 118.8/118.8ersWX	KDØLXQ	KCØYWX
SOUTHWEST					
Cortez	146.7900	–	O 127.3	KD5LWU	KD5LWU
Cortez	147.1350	+		WØKCF	WØKCF
Durango	146.6700	–	O 100x	KØEP	DARC
Durango	146.7000	–	O 100a E-SUNx	KØEP	DARC
Durango	147.3450	+	O 123/123l	KBØVJJ	Colo Conn
Hesperus	145.3700	–	O 100/100e	KBØVIU	KBØVIU
Ignacio	147.1500	+	O 100/100e	KB5ITS	KB5ITS
Mancos	145.3250	–	O 100/100e x	KB5ITS	KB5ITS
Pagosa Springs	146.6100	–	O 123/123a eWX	NØJSP	DARC
Silverton	147.2700	+	O 127.3 E-SUNx	KB5ITT	KB5ITS
Silverton	147.3750	+	O 156.7 E-SUNx	KB5ITS	KB5ITS
WEST CENTRAL					
Breckenridge	146.7000	–	O 107.2/107.2eL(IRLP3972)	WBØQMR	GRARC
Breckenridge	146.7900	–	O 123elx	KBØVJJ	Colo Conn
Cedaredge	147.1950	+	OesWX	KØSX	CdrdgeRA
Cedaredge	147.3600	+	O 100	WØALC	WØALC
Glenwood Springs	146.8500	–	O 123elx	KBØVJJ	Colo Conn
Glenwood Springs	146.8800	–	O 107.2	KIØG	SCARC
Glenwood Springs	147.3000	+	O 107.2 E-SUNx	KØVQ	RFARC
Granby	146.8200	–	O 123/123 E-SUN	KAØYDW	GCARA
Gunnison	147.1200	+	OE-SUN	WBØQCL	GARC
Leadville	145.4450	–	O 123 E-SUNlx	KBØVJJ	Colo Conn
Montrose	146.7900	–	O 107.2/107.2e	KD5OPD	KCØUXX

Location	Output	Input	Notes	Call	Sponsor
Nathrop	146.7450	–	O 100 E-SUNs	WØLSD	CLARA
Paonia	147.3300	+	O 107.2/107.2	KIØMR	NFRA
Rifle	146.7600	–	O 107.2 E-SUN E-WIND	NØSWE	NØSWE
Rulison	147.1500	+	O 107.2/107.2 E-SUNl	KØRV	SCARC
Snowmass	146.6700	–	O 107.2lx	KØCL	SCARC
Vail	146.6100	–	Otx	KØEC	ECHO
Vail	147.3450	+	O 123elx	KBØVJJ	Colo Conn

CONNECTICUT

FREQUENCY USAGE

Location	Output	Input	Notes	Call	Sponsor
Snp	145.4300	–			

FAIRFIELD & SOUTHWEST

Location	Output	Input	Notes	Call	Sponsor
Bethel	147.0300	+	O	KA1KD	BEARS
Bridgeport	146.4450	147.4450	O 77.0e	WK1M	------------
Danbury	147.1200	+	O 141.3/141.3el	W1HDN	PVRA
Danbury	147.3000	–	O 100.0/100.0	W1QI	CARA
Fairfield	146.6250	–	O 100.0/100.0e	WB1CQO	------------
Fairfield	146.8950	–	O 77.0/77.0 e	N1MUC	N1LXV
New Canaan	146.7750	–	O 100.0/100.0ae	W1FSM	W1FSM
Newtown	145.2300	–	Oe	WA1SOV	PEARS
Norwalk	146.4750	147.4750	O 100.0/100.0 (CA)e	W1NLK	GNARC
Ridgefield	145.4700	–	O 100.0e	KR1COM	RCOM
Stamford	146.6550	–	O 100.0/100.0e	W1EE	SARA

HARTFORD & N CENTRAL

Location	Output	Input	Notes	Call	Sponsor
Bloomfield	146.8200	–	Oe	W1CWA	BlmfldARC
Bristol	145.3100	–	O 110.9	K1DII	------------
Bristol	146.6850	–	O 141.3/141.3er	W1DHT	CRBRC
Bristol	146.8800	–	Oel	K1DFS	ICRC
Burlington	147.1500	+	O 77.0e	N1JGR	ICRC
E Hartland	145.2300	–	Oe	K1YON	HartlandEM
Glastonbury	147.0900	+	O 110.9/110.9e	W1EDH	CT ARE SVC
Hartford	146.6400	–	O 141.3/141.3elz	W1HDN	PVRA
Hebron	145.4700	–	O	K1PTI	------------
Manchester	145.3300	–	O 88.5/88.5 e	WA1VOA	------------

Location	Output	Input	Notes	Call	Sponsor
Newington	145.4500	–	O 127.3/127.3e	W1AW	NARL
Somers	147.0000	+	O 127.3/127.3e	W1TOM	MTARA
Vernon	145.1100	–	O 77.0/77.0 e	W1BRS	BearsMAN
Vernon	145.4100	–	O 141.3/141.3el	W1HDN	PVRA
Vernon	146.7900	–	O 82.5/82.5 (CA)eWX	W1HDN	PVRA
Vernon	147.3450	+	O 77.0/77.0 el	KB1AEV	KB1AEV
W Hartford	146.7450	–	O 141.3/141.3	W1HDN	PVRA
Wethersfield	145.3500	–	Otae	KA1BQO	------------
Windsor	147.0450	+	O 88.5/88.5	N1SPI	N1TUP
LITCHFIELD & NORTHWEST					
Barkhamsted	147.2700	+	O 77.0/77.0 el	W1RWC	KB1AEV
New Milford	146.7300	–	O 77.0/77.0 el	NA1RA	NARA
Sharon	147.2850	+	O 77.0/77.0 el	WB1CEI	SBARC
Torrington	145.3700	–	O 77.0/77.0 el	KB1AEV	KB1AEV
Torrington	146.8500	–	O 141.3/141.3el	W1HDN	PVRA
Torrington	147.2400	+	O 141.3e	W1RWC	TorngtnCD
Winsted	147.3300	+	O 141.3/141.3e	W1EOO	Winsted CD
NEW HAVEN & S CENTRAL					
Ansonia	145.1900	–	O 77.0e	WK1M	------------
Ansonia	146.9850	–	O 141.3/141.3a	KD1BD	VLY ARA
East Haddam	147.0150	+	O 110.9	K1IKE	------------
East Haven	147.2550	+	O 110.9/110.9e	AA1VE	SCARA
Killingworth	145.2900	–	O 110.9/110.9aeWX	W1BCG	SARC
Milford	146.9250	–	Oaer	KB1CBD	MilfordARC
Milford	147.2250	+	O 77.0ae	WA1YQE	------------
Portland	147.0300	+	O 110.9/110.9	W1EDH	CT ARE SVC
Prospect	147.1800	+	O 141.3/141.3el	W1HDN	PVRA
Southington	145.1700	–	O 77.0/77.0	W1ECV	SARA
Wallingford	147.3600	+	O 162.2/162.2 LITZ	W1KKF	Meriden ARC
West Haven	146.6100	–	O 110.9/110.9e	W1GB	SCARA

Location	*Output*	*Input*	*Notes*	*Call*	*Sponsor*
West Haven	147.5050	146.5050	O 77.0/77.0 (CA)e	K1SOX	SPARC
Westbrook	146.7750	–	O 110.9e	W1BCG	SARC
NEW LONDON & SOUTHEAST					
Groton	146.6700	–	O 156.7a (CA)l	W1NLC	SCRAMS
Lebanon	147.3000	+	O 77.0ae	NA1RC	NatchARA
Ledyard	145.3900	–	O 156.7/156.7l	W1DX	AWASEC
New London	146.9700	–	O 156.7 (CA)	W1NLC	SCRAMS
Norwich	146.7300	–	O 156.7/156.7ae	N1NW	Rason
Salem	147.0600	+	O 156.7l	W1DX	AWASEC
WINDHAM & NORTHEAST					
Killingly	147.2250	+	O 156.7e	K1MUJ	ECARA
DELAWARE					
ALL					
SNP	145.1700	–	O		------------
DOVER					
Dover	146.7900	–	OA(*89)	N3YMS	N3YMS
Dover	146.9700	–	O 77.0	W3HZW	KentCoAR
Hazlettville	147.3000	+	O	N3YMS	K4CHE
NORTH					
Smyrna	146.6550	–	O 156.7ers	K3CRK	K3CRK
SOUTH					
Georgetown	145.3100	–	O	W3DR	STHS
Lewes	147.3300	+	O	W3LRS	LARS
Millsboro	147.0900	+	O 156.7e	KB3BHL	Sussex ARA
Seaford	145.2100	–	O 156.7a	W3TBG	NARC
Seaford	146.7150	–	O 156.7	N3KNT	N3YMS
WILMINGTON					
Newark	146.7000	–	O 131.8e	W3DRA	DRA
Wilmington	146.7300	–	O 131.8e	W3DRA	DRA
Wilmington	146.9550	–	Oae	WA3UYJ	DVARS
DISTRICT OF COLUMBIA					
ALL					
Snp	145.1700	–	O		------------
WASHINGTON AREA					
Washington	145.1100	–	Oaz	W3ETX	CCARS
Washington	145.1900	–	O 151.4	W3DOS	DOS ARC
Washington	147.0450	+	O	K3VOA	VOA ARC
FLORIDA					
CENTRAL					
Bartow	146.9850	–	O 127.3/127.3eL(444.625 444.950)rsWXx	WC4PEM	PCEM

Location	*Output*	*Input*	*Notes*	*Call*	*Sponsor*
Lake Wales	147.3300	+	O 127.3/127.3	K4LKW	LWRA
Lakeland	145.2700	–	O 127.3/127.3eL(444.300 145.130 443.350 E	WP3BC	WP3BC
Lakeland	146.6850	–	O 127.3/127.3a(CA)ers	K4LKL	LARC
Winter Haven	146.8650	–	O 127.3/127.3	KE4WDP	KE4WDP

CENTRAL - ORLANDO

Location	*Output*	*Input*	*Notes*	*Call*	*Sponsor*
Altamonte Springs	147.2850	+	O 103.5/103.5eL(442.975)	N4EH	LMARS
Apopka	147.0150	+	O 103.5/103.5a(CA)eL(146.760 443.275 146.	N4UMB	OARC
Bushnell	145.4900	–	O 123/123e rs	KI4DYE	SARESRG
Clermont	147.1800	+	O 127.3/127.3	KD4MBN	KD4MBN
DeLand	147.2400	+	O 123/123e r	W2DU	VEOC
DeLand	147.3150	+	Oe L(EC-80113)	WV4ARS	WESTVARS
Eustis	146.8950	–	O 103.5/103.5 (CA)eL(147.390 (APCO25) 147.	W4ALR	LCSO
Groveland	147.3450	+	O 103.5/103.5 (CA)eL(146.895 (APCO25) 147.	KD4MBN	LCPS
Kissimmee	147.2100	+	O 103.5/103.5a(CA)eL(444.4500. 927.7000 E	N4ARG	MFARRA
Lake Buena Vista	145.1100	–	O 103.5/103.5e	WD4WDW	DEARS
Longwood	147.1200	+	O 103.5/103.5e	N4LGH	N4LGH
Minneola	145.3900	–	Or	KB4NXE	Sugarloaf
Minneola	147.2250	+	O 103.5/103.5 (CA)ers	W4ALR	W4ALR
Orlando	145.1300	–	O 103.5/103.5a(CA)eL(443.325) RB	WD4IXD	WD4IXD
Orlando	145.4500	–	O 103.5/103.5	N4LRX	PARC
Orlando	146.7300	–	O 103.5/103.5ers	W4MCO	OCCA
Orlando	146.7600	–	O 103.5/103.5eL(443.275)	KB4UT	OARC
Orlando	147.0600	+	O 103.5/103.5	WD4MRR	CFRA
Orlando	147.3000	+	O 103.5/103.5 L(EC-632802)	WD4WDW	DEARS
Sanford	146.8050	–	O 103.5/103.5e	N4EH	LMARS
St Cloud	145.3500	–	O 103.5/103.5a(CA)eL(444.100 EC-458245)rs	KG4EOC	EOCARDS

Location	Output	Input	Notes	Call	Sponsor
St Cloud	146.7900	–	O t	W4SIE	OCRA
Sumterville	146.9250	–	O 123/123e rs	W4OE	SCEM
Tavares	145.3100	–	O 103.5/103.5ers	N4JTS	N4JTS
Tavares	147.3900	+	O 103.5/103.5eL(147.345 (APCO25) 146.895 (APCr	K4AUS	LCSO
Winter Park	147.1950	+	Oe L(EC-627152)	W4PLA	QCWA 45
DEEP SOUTH					
Key West	145.1300	–	O 114.8/114.8eL(145.430 145.230 145.310 443.650	KF4ZCL	KF4ZCL
Key West	145.1700	–	O 110.9/110.9a(CA) E-WIND L(145.230 145.370 44	N2GKG	N2GKG
Key West	145.3100	–	● 110.9/110.9rsBIx	W4HN	W4HN
Key West	146.9400	–	O 110.9/110.9e	W4LLO	FKARC
Marathon	147.1050	+	Oe	ND7K	ND7K
EAST CENTRAL					
Cocoa	145.1900	–	O 103.5/103.5	N4LEM	N4LEM
Cocoa	145.3700	–	O 156.7/156.7es	W2SDB	IRARC
Cocoa	147.3600	+	O	N4LEM	N4LEM
Ft Pierce	147.0150	+	O 107.2/107.2 A(* UP # DOWN)ersz	W4SLC	SLC EAR
Ft Pierce	147.2400	+	O 107.2/107.2aeWXxz	W4SLC	SLC EAR
Ft Pierce	147.3450	+	O 107.2/107.2 A(325) (CA)eL(444.800 IR-4545 EC-	W4AKH	FPARC
Melbourne	145.4700	–	O 107.2/107.2e	K4HRS	HIARC
Melbourne	146.6100	–	Oa(CA)ez	W4MLB	PCARS
Melbourne	146.8500	–	O 107.2/107.2a(CA)ez	W4MLB	PCARS
Melbourne	147.0000	–	O 167.9/167.9	K4YWC	K4YWC
Mims	146.6250	–	O 100.0/100.0es	KE4NUZ	KE4NUZ
Mims	146.7750	–	O	KD4HNW	TARC
Palm Bay	145.2500	–	O 82.5/82.5 eL(EC) BI	WW4AL	WW4AL
Palm Bay	146.7450	–	O 107.2/107.2aL(IR EC)	KI4HZP	KI4HZP
Palm Bay	146.8950	–	Oer	K4EOC	BEARS
Port St Lucie	146.9550	–	O 107.2/107.2eL(EC-17836)rsx	K4PSL	PSLARA
Rockledge	146.8800	–	O 107.2/107.2eL(EC-340944)s	W2SDB	IRARC

Location	*Output*	*Input*	*Notes*	*Call*	*Sponsor*
Rockledge	147.1350	+	Oers	K4EOC	BEARS
Titusville	145.4900	–	O 100.0/100.0esWX	WN3DHI	NBARC
Titusville	146.6700	–	O 103.5/103.5 E-SUN	WØLRC	WØLRC
Titusville	147.0750	+	O 107.2/107.2er	K4EOC	BEARS
Titusville	147.3300	+	O 107.2/107.2esWX	K4NBR	NBARC
Vero Beach	145.1300	–	O 107.2/107.2a(CA)rs	AB4AZ	TCRA
Vero Beach	145.3100	–	O 107.2/107.2ers	W4IRC	TCRA
Vero Beach	146.6400	–	O 107.2/107.2a(CA)ers	W4PHJ	TCRA
NORTH CENTRAL					
Anthony	146.9700	–	Oaex	KA4WJA	SCARS
Chiefland	147.3900	+	O 123/123a (CA)esx	W4DAK	DARK
Dunnellon	147.3600	+	O 127.3/127.3eL(443.250 EC-317403) WX(*55	KI4LOB	KI4LOB
Gainesville	146.6850	–	Oers	K4GNV	GARS
Gainesville	146.8200	–	O 123/123a (CA)ersx	K4GNV	GARS
Gainesville	146.9100	–	O 123/123a L(EC-258454)rz	W4DFU	GARC
Gainesville	146.9850	–	O 123/123e rsx	K4GNV	GARS
Gulf Hammock	147.3300	+	O 123/123e rs	KI4ZRI	LCEM
Hawthorne	147.1050	+	● 123/123a (CA)	K3YAN	K3YAN
Hines	146.7450	–	O 123/123	K4PRY	TCARC
Lake City	145.4900	–	Oersx	NF4CQ	CARS
Lake City	146.9400	–	O 123/123e	WA4ZFQ	WA4ZFQ
Lake City	147.1500	+	Oersx	NF4CQ	CARS
Live Oak	145.2700	–	O 123.0/123.0rsx	W1QBI	W1QBI
Macclenny	147.0900	+	O 127.3/127.3s	W4YIL	BCHRC
Ocala	145.1700	–	O 123/123e	KG4NXO	MCECT
Ocala	146.6100	–	O 123/123a erxz	K4GSO	SSARC
Ocala	147.2100	+	O 123/123 E-SUN E-WINDx	KI4MTN	KI4MTN
Old Town	146.7000	–	O 123/123e rs	WB4VBY	DARK
Starke	145.1500	–	O 127.3/127.3es	K4BAR	ARCBA

Location	Output	Input	Notes	Call	Sponsor
Summerfield	147.0300	+	O 123/123e x	KJ4AN	SCARESEOC
NORTH EAST					
Bunnell	145.4500	–	O 94.8/94.8 L(224.020 EC)	KB4JDE	KB4JDE
Bunnell	147.3000	+	O 123/123e rs	KB4RSY	FCES
Crescent City	145.1900	–	O 127.3/127.3eWX	KJ4UOP	KJ4UOP
Daytona Beach	147.3750	+	O 103.5/103.5e	N4ZKF	N4ZKF
DeBary	146.8350	–	O 103.5/103.5 L(EC-62180)	WD8JTJ	GOF
Espanola	146.7450	–	O 123/123e x	KD4QOF	FECA
Hollister	147.0600	+	O 123/123e rs	KF4CWI	PARC
Holly Hill	146.6550	–	O 103.5/103.5eL(444.175 53.05 EC-50666)	KI4RF	KI4RF
Keystone Heights	145.1300	–	OE-SUN	WB4EN	WB4EN
New Smyrna Beach	145.3300	–	O 127.3/127.3ers	K4BO	CWA
Orange City	147.0450	+	O 103.5/103.5eL(EC-369183)x	KW4LCB	KW4LCB
Palm Coast	145.4100	–	O 123/123e L(145.450 145.190) WX	KG4TCC	FECA
Palm Coast	145.4700	–	O 123/123a (CA)eL(EC-24216) WXx	KG4IDD	KG4IDD
Palm Coast	146.7150	–	O 123/123 A(123)eL(EC-130077)sWX	W4FPC	WA3QCV
Palm Coast	147.0750	+	O 123/123 A(123) L(EC-130077) WX	W4FPC	WA3QCV
San Mateo	146.7750	–	O 156.7/156.7e	W4OBB	W4OBB
Umatilla	146.8500	–	O 103.5/103.5 L(147)s	WN4AMO	WN4AMO
NORTH EAST - JACKSONVILLE					
Durbin	146.8050	–	O 127.3/127.3	KK4BD	KK4BD
Fernandina Beach	147.3600	+	O 127.3/127.3s	KC5LPA	KC5LPA
Hilliard	146.8350	–	O 127.3/127.3eL(EC-146835)s	W4NAS	NCARS
Jacksonville	146.6400	–	O 156.7/156.7a(CA)elrz	W4IJJ	W4IJJ
Jacksonville	146.7000	–	O 127.3/127.3aeL(444.400 145.370)sxz	W4IZ	NOFARS
Jacksonville	146.7600	–	Oa(CA)	W4RNG	Jax Range
Jacksonville	146.9550	–	O 131.8/131.8rs	AA4QI	AA4QI

Location	Output	Input	Notes	Call	Sponsor
Jacksonville	147.1350	+	O 127.3/127.3s	W4EMN	W4EMN
Jacksonville	147.3150	+	O 127.3/127.3	W4RNG	Jax Range
Jacksonville Beach	145.3500	–	O	KB4ARS	BARS
Keystone Heights	147.2250	+	O 156.7/156.7es	KI4UWC	CC ARES
Orange Park	146.9250	–	O 156.7/156.7es	KI4UWC	CC ARES
Orange Park	147.2550	+	O 103.5/103.5es	W4NEK	W4NEK
Ponte Vedra	147.0150	+	O 127.3/127.3es	KX4EOC	SJCARES
St Augustine	145.1700	–	O 107.2/107.2aer	AB4EY	AB4EY
St Augustine	145.2100	–	Oers	KX4EOC	SJCARES
St Augustine	146.6250	–	Oe	KF4MX	KF4MX
NORTH WEST					
Bonifay	145.1100	–	O 100/100 E-SUN RB	N4LMI	N4LMI
Bonifay	146.9100	–	O 100/100	KF4KQE	KF4KQE
Chipley	146.6250	–	O 103.5/103.5	N4PTW	N4PTW
Crawfordville	147.2550	+	O 94.8/94.8	KN4NN	KN4NN
DeFuniak Springs	147.2850	+	O 100/100ers	WF4X	WCARC
DeFuniak Springs	147.3750	+	O 100/100e	KJ4JAH	KJ4JAH
Freeport	145.2300	–	O 100/100 E-SUN L(147.2850 EC-564764)rs	WF4X	WCARC
Greensboro	147.3900	+	O 94.8/94.8 e	K4GFD	K4GFD
Lee	145.1900	–	O 123/123es	W4FAO	W4FAO
Marianna	146.6700	–	Oae	W4BKD	Chipola AR
Marianna	147.0450	+	O 123/123s	WX4EC	JCARES
Perry	145.3500	–	O 123/123e lx	K4PRY	K4III
Port St Joe	147.3000	+	O 103.5/103.5ers	W4WEB	GARS
Wacissa	147.0000	+	O 94.8/94.8 L(147.375)x	K4TLH	TARS
Wewahitchka	146.8650	–	O 100/100e	W4FFC	GARS
NORTH WEST - PENSACOLA					
Crestview	147.3600	+	O 100/100a esx	W4AAZ	NOARC
Eglin AFB	147.1200	+	O 100/100a	W4NN	EARS
Ft Walton Beach	146.6550	–	Oa(CA)	WD4CKU	WD4CKU
Ft Walton Beach	146.7900	–	O 100/100a	W4ZBB	PARC

Location	Output	Input	Notes	Call	Sponsor
Ft Walton Beach	147.0000	+	O 100/100a (CA)	W4RH	PARC
Gulf Breeze	147.0300	+	O 100/100e s	W4GMS	GB VFD
Milton	145.4900	–	O 100/100 E-SUN L(EC-424886)rsx	W4VIY	Milton ARC
Niceville	147.2250	+	Oae	W4ZBB	PARC
Pensacola	145.3500	–	O 100/100a (CA)s	KO4TT	KO4TT
Pensacola	145.4500	–	O 100/100e	WA4ECY	CSARC
Pensacola	146.8500	–	O 100/100e	WB4OQF	WB4OQF
Valparaiso	146.7300	–	Oae	K4DTV	TCARC
NORTH WEST - TALLAHASSEE					
Crawfordville	145.4500	–	O 94.8/94.8 E-SUNrs	K4WAK	SPARC
Havana	147.1650	+	O 94.8/94.8 es	W4EAF	W4EAF
Tallahassee	146.6550	–	O 94.8/94.8 aerx	AE4S	AE4S
Tallahassee	146.9100	–	O 94.8/94.8 aer	K4TLH	TARS
Tallahassee	147.0300	+	O 94.8/94.8 (CA)esx	K4TLH	TARS
SOUTH CENTRAL					
Arcadia	147.0750	+	O 100/100a eL(444.2)	W4MIN	DARC
Arcadia	147.1800	+	O 100/100 L(EC-213895)s	W4MIN	DARC
Avon Park	145.3300	–	O 100/100e sWX	W4HEM	HCEM
Clewiston	145.1400	–	O 103.5/103.5 L(EC)	WB4TWA	MRC
Clewiston	145.3500	–	O 127.3/127.3eL(443.525 442.800 444.500 29.620	WB4TWQ	KJ4GNM
Lake Placid	145.2100	–	O 100/100a esz	KE4WU	HCEOC
Okeechobee	147.0900	+	O 100/100e r	K4OKE	OARC
Okeechobee	147.1950	+	O 100/100	K4OKE	OARC
Sebring	147.2700	+	Oaerz	KE4WU	HCEOC
Wauchula	146.6250	–	O 127.3/127.3eL(442.325)rs	N4EMH	HARG
SOUTH EAST					
Belle Glade	147.1200	+	O 110.9/110.9eL(EC-147120)rx	AB4BE	BLRA
Boca Raton	145.2900	–	O 110.9/110.9ers	WB4QNX	BRARA
Boca Raton	146.8200	–	O 110.9/110.9a(CA)eWX	W4BUG	GCARA

Location	Output	Input	Notes	Call	Sponsor
Boca Raton	147.2550	+	O 123/123a (CA)ers	KC4GH	BRFD
Boca Raton	147.3900	+	O 110.9/110.9ersx	KS4VT	KS4VT
Boynton Beach	147.2250	+	O 107.2/107.2a(CA)eL(447.65)rsx	NR4P	NR4P
Delray Beach	147.0750	+	O 103.5/103.5eL(443.625)	W2GGI	W2GGI
Indiantown	146.7300	–	O 110.9/110.9ersxz	AG4BV	AG4BV
Palm Beach Gardens	145.1700	–	O 110.9/110.9ex	AG4BV	AG4BV
Palm Beach Gardens	145.4500	–	O 110.9/110.9 BI	AD4Y	AD4Y
Palm Beach Gardens	146.6250	–	O 110.9/110.9a(CA)ers	W4JUP	JTRG
Parkland	145.2700	–	O 110.9/110.9e	WR4AYC	WR4AYC RG
Riviera Beach	146.8800	–	O 110.9/110.9ers	W4PBC	PBCRACES
Royal Palm Beach	147.0450	+	O 110.9/110.9es	K4EEX	PWARC
Stuart	145.1500	–	O 107.2/107.2ers	WX4MC	MCARES
Stuart	146.9850	–	O 107.2/107.2 L(444.0000 927.6625)	K4NRG	NRG
Stuart	147.0600	+	O 107.2/107.2a(CA)e	K4ZK	MCARA
Wellington	147.2850	+	O 103.5/103.5erx	K4WRC	WRC
West Palm Beach	145.2300	–	O 110.9/110.9ersx	N4QPM	N4QPM
West Palm Beach	145.3900	–	O 110.9/110.9ers	W4PBC	PBCRACES
West Palm Beach	146.6700	–	O 110.9/110.9a(CA)ersx	WR4AKX	AREC RG
West Palm Beach	146.7150	–	O 110.9/110.9ersRBz	W4JUP	JTRG
West Palm Beach	147.1650	+	O 110.9/110.9ex	WA4FAP	WA4FAP
West Palm Beach	147.3150	+	O 110.9/110.9eL(EC-342177)rsx	N4KMM	N4KMM
West Palm Beach	147.3600	+	O 110.9/110.9ers	W4PBC	PBCRACES
SOUTH EAST - MIAMI/FT LAUD					
Aventura	147.2100	+	Oersx	K4PAL	PARC
Big Pine Key	145.2300	–	O 94.8/94.8 eL(145.370 145.230 146.700 145.170 442.	KC2CWC	KC2CWC
Cooper City	146.6850	–	O	WA4STJ	WA4STJ

FLORIDA

Location	*Output*	*Input*	*Notes*	*Call*	*Sponsor*
Coral Gables	147.2400	+	O 94.8/94.8	KD4BBM	KD4BBM
Coral Springs	145.1100	–	O 110.9/110.9eL(443.850 52.525 29.600 EC)	WR4AYC	WR4AYC RG
Coral Springs	146.6550	–	O 131.8/131.8 L(EC-301334)rsRBx	N2DUI	WA4EMJ
Cutler	146.8650	–	O 94.8/94.8 elBI	KD4WET	KD4WET
Deerfield Beach	147.1050	+	O 110.9/110.9	N4ZUW	N4ZUW
Ft Lauderdale	146.7900	–	O 88.5/88.5 esx	N4MOT	MARC
Ft Lauderdale	146.9100	–	O 110.9/110.9ersWXxZ(911)	W4AB	BARC
Ft Lauderdale	147.0300	+	O 103.5/103.5a(CA) TT(456) DCSeL(444.1)rRB BI x	W4RCC	W4RCC
Ft Lauderdale	147.3300	+	O 103.5/103.5	K4FK	SFDXA
Hialeah	145.2300	–	O 110.9/110.9	KC2CWC	KC2CWC
Hialeah	145.4900	–	O 110.9/110.9a(CA)ersBIx	WB4IVM	WB4IVM
Hialeah	146.7000	–	O 110.9/110.9	KC2CWC	KC2CWC
Hialeah	147.1200	+	O 110.9/110.9ersBIx	WB4IVM	WB4IVM
Hollywood	145.2100	–	O 103.5/103.5a(CA)el	AC4XQ	AC4XQ
Hollywood	147.1800	+	O 91.5/91.5 a(CA)e	WF2C	HMRH
Kendall	145.1700	–	O 141.3/141.3 L(145.230 146.700 444.500) RB BIx	KC2CWC	KJ4GNS
Miami	145.1300	–	OaBI	WD4RXD	RC de Cuba
Miami	145.1500	–	Oe	WB4TWQ	WB4TWQ
Miami	145.3100	–	● 110.9/110.9rsBIx	W4HN	W4HN
Miami	145.3300	–	OeBI	KB4AIL	KB4AIL
Miami	145.3500	–	O 114.8/114.8lRB BI	KE4RPC	KE4RPC
Miami	145.3900	–	O	AE4WE	AE4WE
Miami	145.4100	–	O 110.9/110.9 L(443.55)rsx	W4HN	W4HN
Miami	146.7300	–	Oa(CA) BI	WD4ARC	W4HN
Miami	146.8950	–	O 100/100l	AE4WE	AE4WE
Miami	146.9250	–	O 94.8/94.8 eL(443.925 927.525 444.275)rsx	KF4ACN	KF4ACN
Miami	146.9700	–	Oa(CA)ex	WD4FMQ	WD4FMQ
Miami	147.0900	+	Oex	W4ILQ	W4ILQ
Miami	147.1500	+	O 94.8/94.8	K4AG	K4AG
Miami	147.2700	+	O 146.2/146.2rsBIx	WD4ARC	ARC

Location	Output	Input	Notes	Call	Sponsor
Miami	147.3000	+	O 88.5/88.5 eL(442.525 927.025) BIx	KR4DQ	KR4DQ
Miami	147.3600	+	O 94.8/94.8 a(CA)I	K4AG	K4AG
Miami Beach	146.6400	–	O 103.5/103.5ez	W6BXQ	TCARS
Miramar	145.4700	–	OL(223.000 224.600 444.375 147.045 EC-268480)	KC4MNE	KC4MNE
North Miami Beach	146.8500	–	O 91.5/91.5 eL(442.250 147.375 443.825 IR-7740)rsx	WE4B	PARC
North Miami Beach	147.1350	+	O 127.3/127.3a(CA)	KC4MND	KC4MND
North Miami Beach	147.3750	+	O 114.8/114.8eL(442.250 146.850 443.825)rs	K4PAL	PARC
Plantation	146.7900	–	O 88.5/88.5 esx	W4MOT	MARC
Pompano Beach	146.6100	–	O 110.9/110.9a(CA)IWX	W4BUG	GCARA
Princeton	146.8350	–	O 94.8/94.8 eL(147.000 146.925 147.180 146.865 442.	KF4ACN	KF4ACN
Princeton	147.0000	–	Oa(CA)eIr	KI4GQO	DRC

SOUTH WEST

Location	Output	Input	Notes	Call	Sponsor
Marco Island	146.8500	–	O 141.3/141.3	K5MI	MIRC
Marco Island	146.9850	–	O 141.3/141.3	K5MI	MIRC
Naples	145.2700	–	O 136.5/136.5eL(EC-389568)	WB2QLP	ARASWF
Naples	146.6400	–	O 136.5/136.5x	WA3JGC	WA3JGC
Naples	146.6700	–	O 136.5/136.5e	WB2QLP	ARA of SWF

SOUTH WEST - FT MYERS

Location	Output	Input	Notes	Call	Sponsor
Cape Coral	145.4500	–	O 136.5/136.5	W4LAZ	W4LAZ
Cape Coral	147.2250	+	O 136.5/136.5e	W4LWZ	FMARC
Ft Myers	145.1700	–	O 136.5/136.5a(CA)eL(147.345)	KG4VDS	FMARC
Ft Myers	145.3900	–	O 136.5/136.5 L(444.725)	K4QCW	QCWA196
Ft Myers	146.8800	–	O 136.5/136.5	WX4L	WX4L
Ft Myers	147.1650	+	O 127.3/127.3ers	K4FPZ	LCEM
Ft Myers	147.3450	+	O 136.5/136.5a(CA)eL(145.17)	WG4K	FMARC
Lehigh Acres	147.2850	+	O 136.5/136.5rs	W1RP	FMARC

Location	Output	Input	Notes	Call	Sponsor
Lehigh Acres	147.3750	+	O 123/123e L(444.450 442.125 443.900)	N2FSU	N2FSU
Port Charlotte	146.9250	–	O 136.5/136.5	N4FOB	N4FOB
Port Charlotte	147.0150	+	O 136.5/136.5a(CA)e	KBØEVM	GRA
Port Charlotte	147.2550	+	O 136.5/136.5ersx	W4DUX	PRRA
Punta Gorda	146.6850	–	O 136.5/136.5rsx	KF4QWC	LCEM
Punta Gorda	146.7450	–	O 136.5/136.5aeL(444.975)rsWXxz	WX4E	CARS
WEST CENTRAL					
Brooksville	145.3700	–	Orx	W1LBV	W1LBV
Brooksville	146.7150	–	Oaersxz	K4BKV	HCARA
Dade City	146.8800	–	Or	K4EX	EPARS
Dade City	146.9100	–	O 146.2/146.2	KD4QLF	KD4QLF
Lecanto	146.7750	–	O 146.2/146.2es	W4CIT	CARL
Lecanto	146.9550	–	O 103.5/103.5ers	W4CRA	CCARC
New Port Richey	146.6700	–	O 103.5/103.5a(CA)eL(EC)rz	WA4GDN	GCARC
New Port Richey	147.1500	+	O 146.2/146.2esx	W4PEM	PCEM
Spring Hill	146.7600	–	O 123/123e sWX	KC4MTS	HCARES
Spring Hill	146.8050	–	O 123/123a esz	KF4IXU	SHARC
Spring Hill	147.0750	+	O 103.5/103.5e	N4TIA	N4TIA
Wesley Chapel	145.2500	–	O 88.5/88.5	WD4LWG	WD4LWG
Zephyrhills	145.1900	–	O 146.2/146.2	NI4M	NI4M
Zephyrhills	147.1350	+	Oer	W1PB	ZARC
WEST CENTRAL - SARASOTA					
Bradenton	145.1100	–	O 100/100 A(182)eL(EC-6420) Z(*911)	KJ3LR	KJ3LR
Bradenton	146.8200	–	O 100/100a (CA)erz	K4GG	MARC
Bradenton	146.9550	–	O 100/100e	K4BRC	BARC
Bradenton	147.1950	+	O 103.5/103.5 (CA)ers	KF4MBN	MC ARES/RACES
Englewood	146.7750	–	O 77/77	KØDGF	KØDGF
Englewood	146.8050	–	O 100/100e	W4AC	TARC
Laurel	145.1300	–	Oers	N4SER	SERC
Sarasota	145.3700	–	O 74.4/74.4 RB	WA2HCV	SSMART

Location	Output	Input	Notes	Call	Sponsor
Sarasota	146.7300	–	O 100/100a eL(147.12)rsx	N4SER	SERC
Sarasota	146.9100	–	O 100/100e L(EC)	W4IE	SARA
Sarasota	147.3000	+	O 141.3/141.3	KD4MZM	KD4MZM
Sarasota	147.3900	+	O 100/100e rsx	N4SER	SERC
Verna	145.4300	–	O 100/100e lrWX	NI4CE	WCFG
WEST CENTRAL - TAMPA/ST PETE					
Brandon	146.6100	–	O 141.3/141.3erz	W4HSO	STARC
Brandon	147.1650	+	O 136.5/136.5e	K4TN	BARS
Clearwater	145.2900	–	O 100/100e L(442.825 145.430 442.950 443.450 442.6	NI4CE	WCFG
Dunedin	146.7000	–	O 146.2/146.2	KE4EMC	KE4EMC
Land O' Lakes	145.3300	–	O 103.5/103.5	WA4GDN	GCARC
Largo	145.1700	–	O 156.7/156.7eL(443.400 442.800 442.400)rs	WE4COM	PCECG
Largo	146.9700	–	O 146.2/146.2 L(224.940 444.150 444.450 44	K4JMH	CARS
New Port Richey	145.1200	–	O 146.2/146.2	KK4HET	KK4HET
Redington Shores	147.0300	+	O 156.7/156.7eL(EC-155568)rsRB WX(70012)	WD4SCD	WD4SCD
Riverview	145.2100	–	O 77/77e L(443.725 EC-342674) WX(26)	KF4MM	KF4MM
St Petersburg	145.3100	–	O 103.5/103.5a(CA)eL(EC)	N4AAC	N4AAC
St Petersburg	145.3900	–	●l	KA9RIX	Homey HC
St Petersburg	147.1200	+	O 146.2/146.2e	KJ4ZWW	UPARC
St Petersburg	147.3150	+	Oa(CA)	N4BSA	PCRA
St Petersburg	147.3600	+	O 127.3/127.3	W4MRA	MRA
Sun City Center	147.0900	+	O 162.2/162.2a(CA)eL(EC-278318)	W4KPR	KPARC
Tampa	145.1500	–	O 146.2/146.2eL(EC-179273)	KP4PC	KP4PC
Tampa	145.4100	–	O 131.8/131.8x	WA4SWC	WA4SWC
Tampa	145.4500	–	OeL(443)rs	KK4AFB	DISCOM
Tampa	145.4900	–	O 88.5/88.5	W4EFK	W4EFK
Tampa	146.8350	–	O 131.8/131.8a(CA)eBI	KC4LSQ	TLRC

Location	*Output*	*Input*	*Notes*	*Call*	*Sponsor*
Tampa	146.9400	–	O 146.2/146.2rsx	NI4M	NI4M
Tampa	147.0000	+	O 107.2/107.2a(CA) DCS(35) E-SUN L(444.000 444	W4AQR	W4AQR
Tampa	147.1050	+	O 146.2/146.2a(CA)er	N4TP	TARCI
Tampa	147.2400	+	O 88.5/88.5	KD4HVC	USF REC
Tampa	147.3450	+	O 146.2/146.2	K4FEZ	Shriners
Valrico	146.7450	–	Oe L(EC-9697)	W7RRS	W7RRS

GEORGIA

Location	*Output*	*Input*	*Notes*	*Call*	*Sponsor*
435 Upper River Road	146.8050	–	O 77/77e	K4PDQ	K4PDQ
Adairsville	146.6850	–	O 167.9/167.9e	K4NGA	WB4AEG
Albany	145.1500	–	O	W4MM	ALBANY ARC INC.
Albany	146.7000	–	Os	W4MM	W4MM
Albany	146.7300	–	Os	W4MM	W4MM
Albany	146.8200	–	OesWX	W4MM	W4MM
Americus	147.2700	+	O	W4VIR	AMERICUS ARC
Ashburn	145.3500	–	O	N4OME	N4OME
Ashburn	147.2850	+	O 141.3/141.3s	W4PVW	W4PVW
Athens	146.7450	–	O	KD4QHB	ATHENS RADIO CLB
Athens	146.9550	–	O	KD4AOZ	KD4AOZ
Athens/crawfrd	147.3750	+	O	K4TQU	K4TQU
Atlanta	145.2900	–	O	W4IBM	IBM RADIO CLUB A
Atlanta	145.4100	–	O	W4PME	MATPARC
Atlanta	146.6400	–	O	WB4QGR	GALVIN RADIO CLU
Atlanta	146.6550	–	O	N4NFP	BSRG
Atlanta	146.8200	–	OsWX	W4DOC	W4DOC
Atlanta	146.9700	–	O 100/100	K4CLJ	K4CLJ
Atlanta	147.0300	+	O	W4NJQ	ATLANTA AIRPORT
Atlanta	147.1050	+	O	WB4RTH	WB4RTH
Atlanta	147.3450	+	O	N4NEQ	AMATEUR TV NETW
Augusta	145.1100	–	O	W4DV	AM R CLUB OF ATL
Augusta	145.2900	–	O	W4DV	W4DV
Augusta	145.3700	–	O	AA4UA	AA4UA
Augusta	145.4100	–	O	K4KNS	KR4XN
Augusta	145.4900	–	O	W4DV	ARC OF AUGUSTA
Augusta	146.9400	–	O	KG4HIQ	KG4HIQ
Augusta	146.9850	–	O	K4KNS	KR4XN
Augusta	147.1800	+	O	W4DV	W4DV
Austell	147.1950	+	O	K4JPD	PAULDING CO DX C
Baldwin	147.1800	+	O	WD4NHW	SPARC
Barnesville	147.2250	+	O	W8JI	W8JI

Location	Output	Input	Notes	Call	Sponsor
Black Rock Mt	147.3900	+	O	KE4SNT	KE4SNT
Blackshear	145.3700	–	O	KI4LDE	PIERCE CO EM
Blairsville	146.9550	–	O	W9QXW	------------
Blairsville	147.0900	+	O	WB3AYW	WB3AYW
Blairsville	147.2100	+	O	W4GNT	KI4DZY
Bogart	147.0000	+	O	W4EEE	OCONEE CTY A
Box Springs	146.7450	–	O 123/123	W4FIZ	COLUMBUS GA
Braselton	146.6250	–	O 127.3/127.3esWX	WX4TC	WX4TC
Brunswick	146.6850	–	O	KG4PXG	KG4PXG
Brunswick	146.7300	–	O	K4TVE	GWYNN CO CD
Butler	145.3100	–	O	KC4TVY	WB4OLL
Calhoun	146.7450	–	O	WB4QMJ	K4WOC
Carnesville	146.8950	–	O	N4VNI	N4VNI
Carrollton	146.6400	–	O	W4FWD	WEST GEORGI
Cedar Grove	147.1500	+	Ols	WA4FRI	WA4EHO
Cedartown	147.1200	+	Oe	W4CMA	W4CMA
Clarkesville	147.1200	+	O	K4HCA	K4HCA
Claxton	147.0750	+	O	W4CLA	W4CLA
Cleveland	146.9100	–	O 100/100e	K4GAR	K4RBM
Cochran	145.1100	–	OelsWX	WM4B	WM4B
Colbert	147.3000	+	O	KI4MHF	BUBBA RPT GR
Commerce	147.2250	+	O	NE4GA	NORTHEAST G
Concord	145.2500	–	O 110.9/110.9 WX	WB4GWA	WB4GWA
Conyers	145.2300	–	O	WB4JEH	------------
Conyers	146.6100	–	O	WB4JEH	------------
Conyers	147.2100	+	O	KF4GHF	CONYERS AR G
Cordele	145.4900	–	O	KA4WUJ	FLINT ARC
Covington	146.9250	–	O	WA4ASI	------------
Cumming	147.1500	+	O	WB4GQX	WB4GQX
Dahlonega	146.8350	+	O	N4KHQ	N4KHQ
Dallas	146.8950	+	O 77/77el WX	WD4LUQ	WD4LUQ
Dallas	146.9550	–	OersWX	WB4QOJ	WB4QOJ
Dalton	145.2300	–	O	W4DRC	DALTON ARC IN
Dalton	147.1350	+	O	N4BZJ	7.135 RPTR GR
Darien	146.6850	–	O	WA4EPK	WA4EPK
Darien	146.9850	–	O	KG4PXG	KG4PXG
Decatur	145.4500	–	O	W4BOC	W4BOC
Doerun	147.2250	+	O	KG4ABK	KG4ABK
Douglas	147.0450	+	O	KE4ZRT	DOUGLAS ARE
Douglas	147.1650	+	O	KE4ZRT	KK4ED
Douglas	147.3150	+	O	AD4EQ	AD4EQ
Douglasville	145.1100	–	O	W4SCR	SKINT CHESNU
Douglasville	147.3600	+	O	W4SCR	SKINT CHESNU
Dublin	147.3300	+	O 77/77	KD4IEZ	KD4IEZ
Dublin	147.3600	+	O	WA4HZX	KB4BKZ
Eastman	145.2100	–	O 103.5/103.5elsWX	KC4YNB	KC4YNB

GEORGIA

Location	*Output*	*Input*	*Notes*	*Call*	*Sponsor*
Eatonton	146.6550	–	O 186.2/186.2els	K4EGA	K4EGA
Eatonton	147.0900	+	O	KC4YHM	KC4YHM
Elberton	145.2100	–	O 118.8/118.8	KI4CCZ	KI4BST
Ellijay	145.1700	–	O	W4HHH	W4HHH
Ellijay	146.9850	–	O	KC4ZGN	KC4ZGN
Emerson	147.2400	+	O	AE4JO	ETOWAH VALLEY A
Fayetteville	145.2100	–	O 131.8/131.8elsWX	KK4GQ	KK4GQ
Fayetteville	146.6850	–	O 131.8/131.8s	KK4GQ	KK4GQ
Forsyth	147.3150	+	O	KI4KHO	AA4RI
Fort Valley	145.4700	–	O 82.5/82.5	KN4DS	KN4DS
Ga Tech	145.1500	–	O	W4AQL	GA TECH
Gainesville	145.3100	–	O 123/123esWX	W4TL	W4TL
Gainesville	146.6700	–	O 131.8/131.8esWX	W4ABP	W4ABP
Gainesville	147.0000	–	O	WA4NNO	W4GM
Glennville	146.7750	–	O	N4SFU	N4SFU
Gray	145.0400	146.4400	O	WR4DH	WM4F
Griffin	145.3900	–	O 110.9/110.9 WX	WB4GWA	WB4GWA
Griffin	146.9100	–	O	K4HYB	K4HYB
Guyton	146.7450	–	O	W4ECA	EFFINGHAM FIRE R
Hahira	145.2300	–	O	KO4QJ	KO4QJ
Hiawassee	146.8650	+	O	KI4ENN	KI4ENN
Hinesville	147.0150	+	O	KG4OGC	KD4HDQ
Irwinton	147.2400	+	O	WB4NFG	------------
Jackson	147.2850	+	O 131.8/131.8	WX4BCA	WX4BCA
Jasper	145.3700	–	O	KB4IZF	KB4IZF
Jasper	145.4300	–	O 107.2/107.2sWX	WB4NWS	WB4NWS
Jasper	146.7000	–	O 123/123	K4UFO	N3DAB
Jasper	146.8050	+	O	KC4AQS	KC4AQS
Jesup	145.1900	–	O	WA4EQL	------------
Jesup	145.4300	–	O	WA9RNZ	KA4PCZ
Jesup	146.8650	–	O	N4ZON	WAYNE CO. EMERG
Jesup	146.9250	–	O	N4PJR	N4PJR & N4RRO
Jesup	147.3450	+	O	N4PJR	N4PJR & N4RRO
Jonesboro	145.3300	–	O	WA4OGE	WA4OGE
Kibbee	146.8200	–	O 179.9/179.9	K4HVK	K4HVK
Kingsland	147.1950	+	O	N6EMA	CAMDEN CO EMA
Kingsland	147.2850	+	O	KC4WWU	KC4WWU
Lagrange	146.7000	–	O	AB4KE	KD4BWK
Lagrange	147.3300	+	O	WB4BXO	WB4BXO

Location	Output	Input	Notes	Call	Sponsor
Lake Park	147.1350	+	O	WR4SG	KBØY
Lavonia	146.7150	–	O 100/100	K4NVG	K4NVG
Lawrenceville	147.0750	+	OesWX	W4GR	W4GR
Lookout Mt	145.3500	–	O	W4GTA	W4GTA
Lookout Mt	146.7600	–	O	W4LAW	W4LAW
Macon	145.3700	–	O	KG4WVL	W4BKM
Macon	145.4300	–	O	AA4RI	AA4RI
Macon	146.7300	–	O	WA4DDI	WM4F
Macon	146.7750	–	O	WA4DDI	WA4DDI
Macon	147.0150	+	O	WX4EMA	KJ4PEO
Macon	147.0600	+	O	WA4DDI	WA4DDI
Madison	146.8650	–	O	WB4DKY	KC4GAV
Marietta	145.4900	–	O	W4LMA	LOCKHEED MA
Marietta	146.7300	–	O	N4YCI	KD4NC
Marietta	146.7750	–	O	N4NEQ	BIG SHANTY-IR
Marietta	146.8800	–	O	W4BTI	KENNEHOOCH
Mcdonough	146.7150	–	O	KI4FVI	KI4FVI
Milledgeville	146.7000	–	O	WB4DOJ	WB4DOJ
Milledgeville	147.1350	+	O	KE4UWJ	KE4UWJ
Monroe	147.2700	+	O 88.5/88.5 sWX	WE4RC	WE4RC
Montezuma	146.6400	–	O	K4FAR	AMERICUS ARA
Morganton	147.1650	+	O	N4NEQ	N4NEQ
Moultrie	146.7900	–	O	WD4KOW	COLQUITT CO
Moultrie	146.8950	–	O 89/89	KD4UTQ	KD4UTQ
Nashville	145.3100	–	O	KB4JF	KB4JF
Newnan	145.1300	–	O	K4SEX	B.GREMILLION
Newnan	146.7900	–	O	K4SEX	BGMRC
Newnan	147.1650	+	OelWX	N4OME	N4OME
Nickleville	145.1700	–	O	WR4SG	SGRA
Parrott	147.3600	+	O 173.8/173.8	WG4JOE	W4MM
Peach County	145.2900	–	OelsWX	AF1G	AF1G
Pembroke	147.1050	+	O	KF4DG	KF4DG
Perry	146.9550	–	O	WR4MG	MGRA
Perry	147.0150	+	O	KN4DS	KN4DS
Pine Mt	145.1900	–	O	WB4ULJ	WA4ULK
Quitman	146.8800	–	O	WA4NKL	WA4NKL
Riceboro	145.4700	–	O	KG4OGC	KD4HDQ
Ringgold	146.7150	–	O	W4ABZ	W4BAB
Rockledge	145.1500	–	O	KC4TVY	KC4TVY
Rome	145.3300	–	O	KI4KQH	FLOYD CO A.R.
Rome	146.9400	–	O	W4VO	NW GEORGIA A
Rome	147.3000	+	O	N4EBY	N4EBY
Roswell	147.0600	+	O	NF4GA	NF4GA
Sandersville	145.2700	–	O 77/77	KT4X	KT4X
Savannah	146.7000	–	O 100/100e s	W4LHS	W4LHS
Savannah	146.8500	–	O	K3SRC	AMERICAN RED

Location	Output	Input	Notes	Call	Sponsor
Savannah	146.8800	–	O	W4HBB	ARC OF SAVANNAH
Savannah	146.9700	–	O	W4HBB	ARC OF SAVANNAH
Savannah	147.2100	+	Os	W4LHS	W4LHS
Savannah	147.3300	+	O 203.5/203.5s	W4LHS	W4LHS
Snellville	147.2550	+	OesWX	W4GR	W4GR
St Simons Island	145.3300	–	O	N4XGI	N4XGI
Statesboro	147.3900	+	O	KF4DG	KF4DG
Stockbridge	145.1700	–	O	WA4DIW	CLAYTON ARES IN
Stone Mountain	146.7600	–	O	W4BOC	W4BOC
Summerville	147.2250	+	O	W4RLP	W4RLP
Sweat Mt	145.4700	–	O	NF4GA	NF4GA
Thomaston	147.3900	+	O	W4OHH	W4OHH
Thomasville	147.0600	+	O	W4UCJ	W4UCJ
Thomasville	147.1950	+	O	W4UCJ	W4UCJ
Toccoa	145.2500	–	O	K4TRS	TOCCOA A.R.S. IN
Toccoa	147.3300	+	O	N4DME	S.C.A.R.S (STEPH
Twin City	146.7150	–	O	N4SFU	N4SFU
Twin City	146.7900	–	O	N4SFU	N4SFU
Twin City	147.0000	+	O	N4SFU	N4SFU
Unadilla	146.7600	–	O	WR4MG	WR4MG
Valdosta	146.7600	–	O	W4VLD	VARC
Valdosta	147.0750	+	O	KC4VLJ	KC4VLJ
Vidalia	146.6250	–	O	K4HAO	FOUR RIVERS ARC
Vienna	147.3750	+	O	K4WDN	K4WDN
Villa Rica	147.1800	+	O	KB4TIW	VILLA RICA RADIO
Waleska	145.2700	–	O 100/100es	KG4VUB	KG4VUB
Waleska	147.0150	–	O 100/100	KI4GOM	KI4GOM
Warm Springs	146.9850	–	O	N4UER	N4UER
Warner Robins	146.6700	–	O 82.5/82.5 elsWX	WM4B	WM4B
Warner Robins	146.8500	–	O	WA4ORT	CEN.GA. ARC
Warner Robins	147.1800	+	O	WB4BDP	WB4BDP
Warner Robins	147.3000	+	O	WR4MG	MID GA RADIO ASS
Watkinsville	147.0450	+	O	KD4AOZ	KD4AOZ
Waycross	145.2700	–	O	AE4PO	AE4PO
Waycross	146.6400	–	O	AE4PO	OKEFENOKEE ARC
Waycross	147.2550	+	O	AE4PO	AE4PO
Waynesboro	145.2300	–	O	K4BR	K4BR
Wrens	147.1200	+	O	KT4N	AMERICUS ARA
Wrightsville	146.9400	–	O	WA4RVB	WA4RVB
Young Harris	147.2100	+	O	W4NGT	W6IZT

GUAM

Location	Output	Input	Notes	Call	Sponsor
Upper Tumon	146.9100	–	Oe	AH2G	MARC

Location	*Output*	*Input*	*Notes*	*Call*	*Sponsor*
HAWAII					
HAWAII					
Glenwood	145.3500	–	OelEXP	KD6QAI	KD6QAI
Hilo	145.3100	–	Opr	AH6JA	AH6JA
Hilo	146.6800	–	Oaelp	KH6EJ	BIARC
Hilo	147.1000	+	O	WH6HQ	WH6HQ
Hualalai	147.1600	+	Oaels	WH6DEW	KARS
Kamuela	146.9800	–	O#	KH6BI	KH6CQ
Kamuela	147.2400	+	Oes	KH6BI	KH6CQ
Kau	145.2900	–	O 100ael	WH6FC	WH6FC
Kau	146.9200	–	Oal	KH6EJ	BIARC
Keaau	147.2800	+	O	NH6HT	AH6HN
Kona	146.6600	–	O 100.0s	WH6FC	ARES
Kona	146.7000	–	O	NH6M	KARS
Kona	146.8600	–	Oel	KH7B	KARS
Kulani Cone	146.7600	–	Oael	KH6EJ	BIARC
Mauna Kea	146.7200	–	Oaex	KH6EJ	HSVOAD
Mauna Loa	146.8200	–	Oelx	KH6EJ	BIARC
Mauna Loa	147.0400	+	Oelrx	AH6JA	RACES
Naalehu	145.4100	–	Oe	KH6ANA	KH7MS
Naalehu	145.4900	–	O 100.0e	KH6TA	KH6TA
Pahoa	147.1400	+	Oelx	NH6P	W6YM
Pepeekeo	146.8800	–	Oael	KH6EJ	BIARC
Waimea	147.3200	+	O 100ael	NH7HI	KARS
Waimea	147.3800	+	OaelEXP	KH7T	KH7T
KAUAI					
Hanalei	147.1000	+	O	NH6HF	RACES
Kapaa	147.0800	+	O	NH6JC	RACES
Kapaa	147.3400	+	O 100e	KH6NN	KH6KWS
Lihue	147.0400	+	Oelrx	NH6HF	RACES
Lihue	147.1600	+	Oael	KH6E	KARC
LANAI					
Lanai City	146.7400	–	O	KH6HC	KH6HC
MAUI					
Haleakala	146.9400	–	O 110.9	KH6RS	MCDA
Haleakala	147.0200	+	O 103.5elr x	KH6HPZ	RACES
Haleakala	147.0800	+	O 107.2	NH6XO	STATE
Kahalui	147.1800	+	OaeRBz	AH6GR	AH6GR
Lahaina	146.6400	–	O/136.5az	AL4A	AL4A
Wailuku	146.7600	–	O 100.0aer z	KH6DT	MCDA
MOLOKAI					
Kualapuu	145.3700	–	Oe	W6KAG	W6KAG
OAHU					
Diamond Head	146.8200	–	O 88.5	KH6OCD	DEM
Diamond head	146.8800	–	OelWX	WH6CZB	DEM
Diamond head	147.0600	+	O/103.5elr x	AH6RH	RACES

Location	Output	Input	Notes	Call	Sponsor
Ewa	146.6000	–	Oe	WH6PD	WH6PD
Honolulu	145.2100	–	O	AH7HI	AH7HI
Honolulu	145.4700	–	ORB	WH6F	WH6F
Honolulu	146.7800	–	O	KH6WO	HARC
Honolulu	146.8400	–	O	KH6JUU	RAG
Honolulu	146.9200	–	O	WH6DIG	KH6MEI
Honolulu	146.9600	–	O	KH6JUU	RAG
Honolulu	146.9800	–	O 88.5el	KH6OCD	DEM
Honolulu	147.2200	+	O	KH6ICX	SFHARC
Honolulu	147.2800	+	O	KH6ICX	SFHARC
Honolulu	147.3000	+	●t	AH6CP	KARA
Honolulu	147.3400	+	Oe	WH7MN	WH7MN
Kaala	146.6800	–	O 107.2e	NH6XO	STATE
Kahaluu	147.1400	+	O	KH6BS	KH6BS
Kahuku	146.9800	–	O 88.5r	KH6OCD	DEM
Kailua	146.6600	–	Ol	WH6CZB	EARC
Kailua	147.0000	+	●l	WR6AVM	WR6AVM
Kaimuki	147.2600	+	O 103.5l	WR6AVM	WR6AVM
Kaimuki	147.3600	+	O	WH6ARC	RED CROSS
Kaneohe	145.1500	–	O 103.5	AH7HI	AH7HI
Leeward	145.1300	–	Oa	KH6OJ	Ohana ARC
Leeward	145.4300	–	O 77.0	KH7TK	AH7GK
Leeward	145.4900	–	O	KH7INC	KH6AZ
Leeward	146.7000	–	●#	KH7P	KH7P
Leeward	147.3200	+	O	AH6IH	AH6IH
Mauna Kapu	146.6200	–	O 103.5elx	KH7O	WR6AVM
Mauna Kapu	146.8000	–	Ol	WH6CZB	EARC
Mauna Kapu	147.1200	+	O(CA)eWX	KH6JPL	GTE ARC
North Shore	145.2900	–	Oae	KH6BYU	NEOARG
North Shore	146.6400	–	Oel	WH6CZB	EARC
North Shore	146.7600	–	O 100.0el	KH6OCD	DEM
North Shore	146.9000	–	O	KH6LJ	Ohana ARC
Round Top	147.1000	+	O	KH6MEI	KH6MEI
Waimanalo	145.2300	–	O(CA)e	WH6CXI	Ohana ARC
STATE					
STATE	144.5100	+	O	SNP	SNP
STATE	145.2500	–		SNP	SNP

IDAHO

Location	Output	Input	Notes	Call	Sponsor
FREQUENCY USAGE--IACC AREAS					
SNP	145.1300	–			
SNP	145.2900	–			
CENTRAL					
Stanley	147.1400	+	O 100l	AE6DX	WRARC
E IDAHO					
Salmon	146.9800	–	O	NQØO	Lemhi ARC
N ID - BONNERS FERRY					
Black Mtn	146.9600	–	O 123.0r	KE7ADU	KE7ADU
Bonners Ferry	147.0400	+	O	KE7MDQ	KE7MDQ

Location	Output	Input	Notes	Call	Sponsor
N ID - COEUR D ALENE					
Mica Peak Idaho	147.0800	+	O 100.0er	KC7ODP	KCOEM
Mica Pk Idaho	146.9800	–	O 100.0	K7ID	KARS
N ID - COTTONWOOD					
Cottonwood Butte	146.8400	–	O 100.0	KB7VOL	CPARC
N ID - EMERGENCY					
Boundary Co	147.1000	+		K7MNK	K7MNK
N ID - GRANGEVILLE					
Idaho Mtn	146.6800	–	100.0ae	KC7MGR	CPARC
N ID - KELLOGG					
Wardner Peak	146.9400	–	O 127.3	N7SZY	N7SZY
N ID - KOOSKIA					
Kamiah	146.6200	–	O 88.5e	KK3ARC	KK3ARC
N ID - LEWISTON					
Craig Mtn	146.9200	–	O 110.9l	K7EI	K7EI
Lewiston Hill	145.2100	–	● 192.8r	W7WWS	NPCEM
Lewiston Hill	146.8600	–	O 100.0	W7VJD	LCARC
N ID - MOSCOW					
Moscow	146.7000	–	Oe	WB7TBM	TARC
Moscow Mtn	146.8200	–	Olx	WA7HWD	NWTriSt
N ID - MULLAN					
Lookout Pass	147.0200	+	Ol	K7HPT	W7OE
N ID - OROFINO					
Orofino	145.4900	–	Oa	KC7VBT	CVARC
Peck	145.2100	–	206.5r	W7WWS	NPCEM
Wells Bench	146.7600	–	131.8e	K7NDX	CVARC
N ID - RATHDRUM					
Rathdrum	147.2200	+	O	N7ESU	N7ESU
N ID - SANDPOINT					
Sagle	145.2700	–	127.3r	AA7XM	AA7XM
Sagle	146.7800	–	100.0e	K7JEP	BCARC
Sandpoint Baldy	145.4900	–	107.2	KC7JLU	KC7JLU
Schweitzer Ski Hill	145.2300	–	Oel	N7JCT	BCEM
N ID - WALLACE					
Goose Hump	147.1800	+	O 110.9	KB7BYR	SCHRA
N NV, SW ID					
Jarbridge, NV	147.1600	+	O 100 E-SUN	KA7CVV	KA7CVV
NORTH					
Burley	145.2700	–	O 100.0e L(146.850)x	WA7FDR	------------
Burley	145.3300	–	O 123.0x	K7ACA	------------
Burley	147.0000	–	O 100x	KC7SNN	------------
Lava Hot Sp	146.8000	–	OA(80*/#)lx	AE7TA	BARC
S CENT					
Burley	145.2700	–	O 100.0e L(440)x	WA7FDR	WA7FDR
Burley	147.0000	–	O 100ex	KC7SNN	ISRA MHCH

Location	*Output*	*Input*	*Notes*	*Call*	*Sponsor*
Jerome	146.6600	–	Os	W7MVH	TF ARES
Ketchum	147.1800	+	Oel	N7ACB	WRARC
Twin Falls	146.7600	–	O(CA)e	KC7SNX	ISRA MVCh
SOUTH					
Burley	145.3300	–	O 123	K7ACA	MKR,LLC
SOUTH WEST					
Boise	146.8200	–	O 100	WR7ADL	W7OHM
Boise	146.8200	–	O 100e	WR7ADL	W7OHM
Mt Home	146.7000	–	O 107.2	WR7GEM	W7OHM
SOUTHEAST IDAHO					
Driggs	146.9400	–	O	K7ENE	MCCD
Grace	146.8000	–	O 88.5e	AE7TA	FCES
Howe	146.8500	–	O 100.0l	WA7FDR	ERARRA
Idaho Falls	146.6400	–	Oae	K7EFZ	ERARC
Idaho Falls	146.7400	–	O	K7EFZ	ERARC
Idaho Falls	147.1500	+	O	WA7KRP	WB7CCS
Pocatello	146.8200	–	O 100.0	N7LB	------------
Pocatello	147.0600	+	O	N7DN	PARC
Pocatello	147.3000	+	O	KA7MLM	------------
Rigby	146.7000	–	O	K7ENE	ERRS
Rigby	146.8800	–	O	K7ENE	ERRS
Roberts	146.7800	–	O	AB7OS	AB7OS
Roberts	147.0300	+	O	AB7OS	AB7OS
Sawtell	145.2300	–	O 100.0 L(W/PL 123.0)	WA7FDR	------------
Twin Falls	146.7600	–	O	KC7SNX	------------
SW					
Boise	147.3000	+		N7DJX	N7DJX
SW ID					
Star	147.2800	+	O	KA7EWN	KA7EWN
SW IDAHO					
Emmett	146.7400	–	O 100	W7RGC	W7RGC
Idaho City	145.3100	–	O 100	KA7ERV	BC ARES
Meridian	145.3500	–	O 100	W7LCD	LC ARC
Silver City	145.2300	–	O 100 DCS(174)l	WA7FDR	WA7FDR
SW- ID					
Ontario, OR	147.1000	+	O 100	K7OJI	TVRA
SW-ID					
Boise	145.2100	–	O	W7YFX	W7YFX
Boise	145.2500	–	O 100.0/100.0	K3ZFF	BCARC
Boise	146.8400	–	O 100.0 (CA)elxz	W7VOI	VOI ARC
Boise	146.9400	–	O 100.0elr sx	K7BSE	ISRA BOICH
Boise	147.2400	+	OE-SUNlrs WXx	W7VOI	VOI ARC
Boise	147.2600	+	O	AB7HP	HP ARC

Location	*Output*	*Input*	*Notes*	*Call*	*Sponsor*
Boise	147.3200	+	Oex	N7FYZ	N7FYZ
Caldwell	147.3600	+	O 100elx	K7TRH	CCEM
Emmett	147.2000	+	O(CA)x	K7WIR	WIARA
Homedale	146.9200	–	O	KB7AOF	KB7AOF
Marsing	146.8800	–	O 100/100.0elx	K7ZZL	DP ARC
Meridian	145.2900	–	O	W7VOI	VOI ARC
Weiser	145.3900	–	O 100.0aelx	K7OJI	TVARC
SW-ID, S EAST OR					
Huntington, OR	147.1200	+	O 100	K7OJI	TVRA
Nyssa, OR	147.2200	+	O	W7PAG	W7PAG
Vale, OR	146.7200	–	OE-SUN	W7PAG	W7PAG
W CENT ID					
Cascade	146.6200	–	Oelx	W7VOI	VOIARC
McCall	147.0200	+	O 100ex	KC7MCC	CIARC
ILLINOIS					
BLOOMINGTON					
Bloomington	146.7900	–	103.5sWX	WD9HRU	McLNCOARES
Bloomington	146.9400	–	103.5	W9AML	CIRC
Bloomington	147.1500	+	103.5	WD9FTV	WD9FTV
Bloomington	147.1950	+	97.4	W9NUP	W9NUP
Normal	147.0150	+	88.5e	NX9M	McLEANCOAR
CENTRAL					
Clinton	146.9850	–		KA9YPK	KA9YPK
Lincoln	145.3900	–	103.5rWX	N9EZJ	N9EJZ
Lincoln	147.3450	+	103.5	K9ZM	LOGAN ESDA
Nokomis	145.1500	–	88.5	N9TZ	W9COS
Pontiac	147.3900	+	127.3	WB9DUC	FARA
Sparland	147.1800	+	103.5	WB9NNS	WB9NNS
CHAMPAIGN					
Allerton	147.2850	+	146.2	K9LOF	K9LOF
Champaign	146.7600	–	162.2e	K9CU	TCARC
Urbana	147.0600	+	131.8e	K9CW	CCEMA
CHICAGO					
Chicago	145.1100	–	107.2	W9GN	UFDA
Chicago	146.7300	–	107.2 (CA)e	WB9RFQ	K9QKW
Chicago	146.7600	–	107.2 (CA)	WA9ORC	CFMC
Chicago	146.8500	–	100.0el	WA9DZO	M.A.P.S.
Chicago	146.8800	–	107.2 (CA)z	K9GFY	SARA
Chicago	147.1500	+	107.2sx	W9SRO	SRO/CFAR
Melrose Park	146.6700	–	107.2 (CA)lx	WB9AET	WAFAR
DECATUR					
Bement	145.4100	–	103.5eWX	K9IYP	PICO RAMS
Cadwell	145.1950	–	e	W9BIL	MARK
Cadwell	146.6550	–	162.2e	W9BIL	MARK
Decatur	146.7300	–	123.0z	K9HGX	CENOIS ARC

Location	Output	Input	Notes	Call	Sponsor
Decatur	147.1050	+	103.5	WA9RTI	MACONCOARC
EAST CENTRAL					
Charleston	145.3700	–	186.2e	KF9NB	KF9NB
Crescent City	147.0300	+	103.5eWX	AD9L	ICARC
Danville	146.8200	–	88.5s	W9MJL	VCARA
Kansas	147.3750	+	162.2	W9COD	W9COD
Loda	146.8500	–	179.9	W9NKX	IFARS
Martinsville	147.0300	+	O 107.2e	W9GWF	EIHC-W9GWF
Mattoon	145.3300	–	186.2	KF9NB	KF9NB
Mattoon	146.6250	–	107.2	KA9LRZ	UMRA
Oakwood	145.3100	–	162.2eLITZ	K9ADL	K9ADL
NORTH CENTRAL					
Dixon	146.9700	–	82.5ers	N9JWI	LEE CO. ES
Elizabeth	147.3300	+	250.3rsWX	W9SBA	NWIL EMA
Freeport	147.3000	+	88.5	N9WSQ	------------
Freeport	147.3900	+	114.8 (CA)e	KB9RNT	SCRA
Joliet	145.2500	–	156.7 (CA)	KB9LWY	KB9LWY
Joliet	146.8200	–	107.2e	W9OFR	WCARL
Joliet	147.3000	+	94.8 (CA)z	WD9AZK	MAVERICK A
Lasalle	146.8650	–	103.5ex	KB9LNK	CECIL JR.
Lasalle	146.8950	–	103.5x	KB9LNK	CECIL JR.
Leonore	147.1200	+	103.5 (CA)e x	W9MKS	SRRC
Malta	146.7300	–	100.0e	WA9CJN	KARC
Marseilles	146.7450	–	114.8elWX	KA9FER	KA9FER
Oregon	147.0450	+	67.0 (CA)e	KB9DBG	KB9DBG
Oregon	147.1650	+	146.2 (CA)e lrsWXz	N9ECQ	OGLE C OEM
Princeton	146.9550	–	103.5	WB9NTG	RCBARC
Roscoe	146.7750	–	100	W9USA	IHRS
Sterling	146.8500	–	114.8 (CA)	W9MEP	S/RF ARS
Utica	145.2900	–	103.5eWX	KC9CFU	TCARS
NORTHEAST					
Antioch	145.2900	–	107.2aelz	KA9VZD	STLIN ARC
Argonne	145.1900	–		W9ANL	ARGONNARC
Arlington Heig	146.9850	–	107.2a	WB9TAL	ARCOMLEAGU
Batavia	147.0600	+	103.5e	W9ZGP	NIARC INC
Batavia	147.2250	+		W9CEQ	FRRL
Blue Island	146.6400	–	107.2eWX	W9SRC	STARS
Bolingbrook	147.3300	+	107.2 (CA)e lWX	W9BBK	V BOLNGBRK
Chicago	145.3500	–	114.8	WA9TQS	WA9TQS
Crystal Lake	145.3300	–	107.2 (CA)e	N9HEP	N9HEP
Crystal Lake	146.6550	–	107.2	KB9WGV	KB9WGV
Downers Grove	145.4300	–	107.2 (CA)e l	W9DUP	DARC
East Dundee	145.2700	–	100.0s	W9DWP	W9DWP
Elburn	145.2700	–	107.2s	W9DWP	W9DWP
Elburn	147.2100	+	103.5	W9CEQ	FRRL, INC.

Location	*Output*	*Input*	*Notes*	*Call*	*Sponsor*
Elgin	146.7900	–	107.2 (CA)e	WR9ABQ	VARA
Elk Grove Vill	147.0150	+	107.2e	KB9L	EGDXA
Gilberts	146.9250	–	100.0 (CA)l WXx	WA9VGI	RATFAR
Glen Ellyn	145.3900	–	103.5 (CA)e z	W9CCU	WCRA
Glendale Heigh	145.1500	–	107.2aez	N9IRG	N9IRG
Glenview	147.0900	+	107.2 (CA)e z	W9AP	NORA
Gurnee	147.2400	+	127.3 (CA)e	W9MAB	GURNEE RG
Hazelcrest	146.8050	–	107.2e	WD9HSY	TRITOWN AR
Hinsdale	146.9700	–	107.2	K9ONA	SMCC
Kankakee	145.1300	–	107.2aes WX	W9AZ	KARS
Kankakee	146.9400	–	107.2a	W9AZ	KARS
Kankakee	147.1650	+	107.2a	WD9HSY	WD9HSY
Lake Villa	147.0300	+	107.2aelz	WB9RKD	WB9RKD
Libertyville	147.1800	+	127.3er	W9FUL	LAKE CO RA
Markham	147.1350	+	107.2	W9YPC	AREA
Mchenry	145.4100	–	107.2	KK9DX	ARROW
Morris	146.7150	–	94.8	KC9KKO	JP WATTERS
Morris	147.2700	+	107.2eWX	KB9SZK	GCARC
Naperville	145.1700	–	103.5	WA9WSL	IHARC
New Lenox	145.2100	–	107.2esWX	WB9IRL	WB9IRL
Niles	147.3150	+	107.2	W9FO	METRO ARC
Northbrook	147.3450	+	107.2e	NS9RC	NSRC
Schaumburg	145.2300	–	107.2 (CA)	K9IIK	SARC
Schaumburg	145.3700	–	107.2	K9SO	AMA
Schaumburg	146.7000	–	100.0 (CA)l	WB9PHK	STROKE
Schaumburg	147.2850	+	107.2 (CA)e lz	N9CXQ	NAPS
St Charles	145.4700	–	103.5e	KC9OEM	KCOEM
Union	146.6850	–	107.2	N9KHI	N9KHI
Westmont	145.4900	–	107.2aelr	WB9UGX	WSTMTESDA
Wheaton	145.3100	–	107.2	W9CCU	WCRA
Wheaton	147.3600	+	136.5l	W9BZW	NIDXA
Woodstock	146.8350	–	91.5erWX	K9ESV	MCEMA
Yorkville	147.3750	+	103.5s	N9FNS	N9FNS
NORTHWEST					
Moline	146.6400	–		WØBXR	DAVRC
Moline	146.9400	–		WØBXR	DAVRC
Morrison	145.2100	–	114.8 (CA)e	KA9QYS	S/RF ARS
Rock Island	146.7750	–	100.0ae	W9WRL	QCRG
Savanna	147.1350	+	e	N9FID	P.A.R.C.
Tampico	146.6250	–	114.8ae	N9ORQ	#NAME?
PEORIA					
Canton	147.2850	+	103.5 (CA)e z	K9ILS	FCARC
Dunlap	145.3700	–	156.7 (CA)e l	N9BBO	N9BBO

ILLINOIS

Location	*Output*	*Input*	*Notes*	*Call*	*Sponsor*
East Peoria	145.2700	–	103.5aez	KA9GCI	PEKIN RPTG
Kickapoo	146.9700	–	103.5ae	W9BFD	BFD RC
Metamora	147.2550	+	103.5aelrs WX	K9WRA	WCRA
Pekin	145.4500	–	103.5az	KA9GCI	PEKIN RPTG
Pekin	146.6700	–	103.5	W9TAZ	TCARS
Peoria	145.1050	–		W9PIA	PAARC
Peoria	146.7600	–	103.5e	W9UFF	HIFC
Peoria	146.8500	–	103.5aez	K9PEO	PAARC
Peoria	147.3300	+	103.5eWXx	WX9PIA	PALS
Tremont	146.9100	–	e	WA9DKO	TCEMA
Washington	147.0750	+	103.5 (CA)z	W9UVI	PAARC
ROCKFORD					
Belvidere	147.3750	+	100.0e	K9ORU	BRC
Mt Morris	145.1300	–	114.8ers WX	K9AMJ	K9AMJ
Mt Morris	147.1050	+	114.8l	K9AMJ	K9AMJ
Rockford	146.6100	–	114.8ae	W9AXD	RARA
Rockford	146.8050	–	114.8 (CA)e l	K9AMJ	K9AMJ
Rockford	147.0000	+	114.8	W9AXD	RARA
Rockford	147.1950	+	114.8eWX	K9RFD	RTG
Rockford	147.2550	+	114.8esWX x	WX9MCS	NIRA
SOUTH					
Alto Pass	146.8500	–	O 88.5e	K9GOX	MTAVARG
Ava	147.0900	+	88.5	W9RNM	SARA
Benton	146.8050	–	88.5eWX	KB9ADK	LEARS
Carbondale	146.7300	–	88.5	W9UIH	SIU ARC
Carbondale	147.1950	+	88.5e	KA9YGR	KA9YGR
Herald	147.3000	+	136.5elrs WXx	W9KXP	W9KXP
Herod	146.8800	–	88.5el	K9TSI	SCAN
Marion	145.1900	–	88.5	AA9ET	SCAN CLUB
Marion	146.6400	–	88.5 (CA)e	W9RNM	SARA
Metropolis	145.4500	–	● 103.5	N9XWP	N9XWP
Metropolis	147.2250	+	123.0aez	N9IBS	MAMA ARC
Olive Branch	147.2550	+	118.8e	K9IM	904 ARC
Tunnel Hill	147.3450	+	88.5e	W9WG	TRGHILARA
West Frankfort	147.0450	+	97.4e	AB9ST	AB9ST
SOUTH CENTRAL					
Effingham	146.8950	–	110.9e	K9UXZ	NTARC
Greenville	147.1650	+	103.5e	W9KXQ	OVARC
Mt Vernon	147.1350	+	88.5e	KB9KDE	ARCOM
Salem	147.2700	+	103.5ez	W9CWA	CWA
Tamaroa	146.9850	–	107.2	N9LUD	T.A.R.A.
SOUTHEAST					
Flora	146.7000	–	103.5esWX	KC9AGC	CCARC
Mt Carmel	146.9400	–	94.8aesWX z	AI9H	AI9H

Location	*Output*	*Input*	*Notes*	*Call*	*Sponsor*
Mt Carmel	147.2550	+	151.4ers WX	KC9MAK	WEMA RACES
Newton	145.4900	–	O 79.7e	K9ZN	JARS
Noble	146.7600	–	O 94.8e	K9QAT	OLNEY ARC
Robinson	147.3600	+	107.2esWX	WA9ISV	CCARC/IEMA
SPRINGFIELD					
Athens	147.0450	+	210.7elWX	WS9V	WS9V
Jacksonville	146.7750	–	103.5aez	K9JX	JARS
Pawnee	146.8050	–	94.8e	N9MAF	N9MAF
Springfield	146.6850	–	94.8	WA9KRL	WA9KRL
Springfield	147.3150	+	O 94.8	W9HJA	W9HJA
Springfield	147.3750	+	94.8	WA9KRL	WA9KRL
Taylorville	145.4300	–	79.7	N9FU	N9FU
Taylorville	146.8350	–	79.7	N9OGL	N9OGL
Taylorville	146.9550	–	79.7e	N9FU	CCARC
ST LOUIS					
Alton	145.1300	–	123.0esWX x	K9HAM	LCRC
Belleville	147.1200	+	127.3 (CA)z	K9GXU	ST CLAIR
Carlinville	145.2900	–	123	N9GGF	N9OWS
Carlyle	145.2500	–	103.5	K9XWX	K9XWX
Collinsville	146.7900	–	127.3ers WX	W9AIU	EGYPTN RC
Elsah	145.3100	–	79.7 (CA)e	N9YN	PRINCIPIA
Gillespie	146.6400	–	103.5	WB9QHK	MONTEMAC A
Gillespie	146.8200	–	103.5aez	WB9QHK	MONTEMAC A
Godfrey	145.2300	–	79.7aelz	K9HAM	LCRC
Godfrey	145.4700	–	123	N9GGF	N9OWS+
Granite City	145.4500	–	127.3e	KZ9G	KZ9G
Mascoutah	145.3900	–	l	AA9ME	AA9ME
Shiloh	145.1100	–	127.3eWXz	AA9RT	KB9VTP
Valmeyer	145.4300	–	127.3aeWX z	N9OMD	N9OMD
WEST CENTRAL					
Beardstown	146.7150	–	103.5	W9ACU	IVARC
Carthage	147.1050	+	103.5e	N9MTI	HCESDA
Dallas City	145.2500	–	151.4 (CA)e	KC9JIC	KC9JIC
Dallas City	145.3300	–	82.5 (CA)e	KC9JIC	KC9JIC
Galesburg	147.0000	–	103.5aelz	W9GFD	KNOXCARC
Galesburg	147.2100	+	107.2	KA9QMT	KNOX CO CD
Galva	145.4900	–	225.7eWX	AA9RO	AARO
Macomb	147.0600	+	103.5e	W9SSP	LEARC
Monmouth	146.6550	–	173.8	KD9J	KD9J
Pittsfield	147.2100	+	100.0es	WB9BUU	JW&DP RPTR
Pittsfield	147.2700	+	103.5	N9DO	N9DO
Quincy	146.8200	–	100.0l	WA9VGI	FISHNET
Quincy	146.9400	–	103.5eWX	W9AWE	WIARC
Quincy	147.0300	+	103.5eWX	W9AWE	WIARC
Quincy	147.1350	+	103.5	N9JI	N9JI

Location	Output	Input	Notes	Call	Sponsor
Quincy	147.1950	+		W9AWE	WIARC
Versailles	145.4300	–	103.5	KB9JVU	KB9JVU
INDIANA					
EAST CENTRAL					
Centerville	147.1800	+	O 82.5er WX	KB9SJZ	KB9SJZ
Chassis Ridge	145.1300	–	Oe	KB9BBA	TCRA
Connersville	146.7450	–	O(CA)e	KB9RVR	Fayette
Corydon	146.7750	–	O 103.5ers	WD9HMH	HarrEMA
Glenwood	146.6850	–	O 131.8e WX	WB9SBI	WB9SBI
Hartford City	146.6550	–	OersWX	K9VND	BARC
Marion	145.3100	–	O	WB9UCF	FisherBody
Marion	146.7900	–	O 131.8aer WXx	W9EBN	GrantARC
Marion	147.1950	+	O 131.8er WX	W9EBN	GrantARC
Muncie	146.7300	–	OlrsWX	WB9HXG	MuncieARC
New Castle	145.4500	–	OrsWX	N9EYG	N9EYG
New Castle	147.3600	+	O 82.5rs WX	N9WB	KB9BG/N9WB
Pennville	145.2100	–	O 100.0ers	WA9BFF	Jay ARC
Richmond	147.2700	+	O 131.8ae s	W1IDX	W1IDX
Rushville	147.0000	+	O 127.5r WX	K9PQP	E Ctrl Rpt
Winchester	147.3000	+	O 110.9	WD9EXZ	Ranpolph
INDIANAPOLIS					
Anderson	145.3900	–	O 151.4es	W9VCF	MCARC
Anderson	146.8200	–	O 110.9 (CA)eWX	W9OBH	AndersonRC
Anderson	147.0900	+	O 110.9er WX	KB9VE	AndersonRC
Belleville	147.0150	+	OesWX	K9PZ	HCARS
Danville	145.1300	–	O 88.5aelr sx	WX9HC	HendrixARC
Danville	147.1650	+	OrWX	K9LMK	K9LMK
Franklin	145.1100	–	O 103.5e	AA9YP	AA9YP
Greenfield	145.3300	–	OersWXx	W9ATG	HancockARC
Greenfield	147.1500	+	O	W9ATG	HancockARC
Greenwood	146.8350	–	O 151.4ers WX	WA9RDF	WA9RDF
Indianapolis	145.2100	–	O 100.0	NE9T	IndyMidARC
Indianapolis	145.3700	–	O 88.5 (CA)	W9GTA	MidAmRC
Indianapolis	146.6250	–	OsWX	W9IRA	Indy RA
Indianapolis	146.6700	–	O 88.5e	K9IPL	IPL ARC
Indianapolis	146.7000	–	Oes	W9IRA	Indy RA
Indianapolis	146.7600	–	O 151.4er WX	K9LPW	CentIN RA

Location	Output	Input	Notes	Call	Sponsor
Indianapolis	146.8800	–	O 88.5	W9RCA	RCA ARC
Indianapolis	146.9700	–	O 107.2el WX	W9ICE	ICE
Indianapolis	147.0750	+	O	KA9GIX	KA9GIX
Indianapolis	147.1200	+	OsWX	W9IRA	Indy RA
Indianapolis	147.2100	+	O 88.5ers	KC9JYA	Indpls EM
Indianapolis	147.3150	+	O 94.8el	K9DC	K9DC
Lebanon	147.1050	+	O 77.0 WX	N9HLL	N9HLL
Martinsville	147.0600	+	O 88.5es WX	K9PYI	MorganRA
Noblesville	145.1700	–	O 77.0elrs WX	N9EOC	HamCoARES
Plainfield	145.2900	–	O 88.5 (CA)	AB9D	AB9D
Shelbyville	145.4800	–	O	W9JUQ	BRV ARS
NORTH CENTRAL					
Culver	146.6700	–	O 131.8e WX	K9ZLQ	Mrshl ARC
Elkhart	145.2500	–	O 131.8el WX	KC9GMH	KC9GMH
Elkhart	145.4300	–	O 131.8 (CA)ersWXz	AA9DG	ElkhartCRA
Elkhart	146.6400	–	O 131.8ae	W9AMR	W9AMR
Frankfort	146.6100	–	OesWX	KC9HNP	ClintonARC
Frankfort	147.0450	+	O	N9SFA	N9SFA
Goshen	146.8950	–	O 131.8 (CA)e	K9TSM	GoshenARC
Kokomo	146.9100	–	OersWX	W9KRC	KRC
Kokomo	147.2400	+	O 88.5ers WX	W9KRC	KRC
Kokomo	147.3750	+	OersWX	W9KRC	KRC
Logansport	145.2300	–	Oes	W9VMW	CassARC
Logansport	145.3500	–	O	W9VMW	Cass ARC
Logansport	147.1800	+	O 77.0es	W9VMW	Cass ARC
Mishawaka	147.0900	+	O 131.8	N9GVU	N9GVU
Mishawaka	147.3300	+	O 131.8ae	W9AMR	W9AMR
Peru	147.3450	+	OrsWX	K9ZEV	Miami ARC
Plymouth	147.2850	+	O 131.8els WXx	K9WZ	K9WZ
Richvalley	146.9550	–	O 141.3e	WA9RRL	WA9RRL
Rochester	146.8050	–	O 131.8e WX	KB9WSL	FultonARC
South Bend	145.2900	–	O 131.8	N9OCB	N9OCB
South Bend	147.2250	+	O	W9AB	MARC
South Bend	147.3900	+	O 131.8rs WX	WB9AGX	StJoe EMA
Syracuse	146.9850	–	O 131.8rsx z	KB9AVO	KB9AVO
Wabash	147.0300	+	O 131.8er	KB9LDZ	WabashARC
Warsaw	145.1300	–	O 91.5es WX	KA9OHV	KA9OHV

Location	Output	Input	Notes	Call	Sponsor
NORTHEAST					
Angola	147.1050	+	O 131.8el WXx	W9LKI	W9LKI
Angola	147.1800	+	O 131.8el WXx	W9LKI	W9LKI
Angola	147.2100	+	O	AA9MU	AA9MU
Auburn	147.0150	+	OsWX	W9OU	NE In ARC
Berne	146.9700	–	O 97.4	KB9KYM	AdamsARC
Bluffton	145.4200	–	OelrsWX	AB9HP	AB9HP
Bluffton	147.0600	+	Oe	W9SR	W9SR
Columbia City	145.2700	–	O 131.8ers WX	WC9AR	WCARC
Decatur	145.4700	–	O 97.4ers WX	KB9KYM	AdamsARC
Fort Wayne	145.3300	–	Ol	W9FEZ	MizpahARC
Fort Wayne	146.7600	–	O 131.8e	W9TE	FWRC
Fort Wayne	146.8800	–	Oaers	W9INX	ACARTS
Fort Wayne	146.9100	–	O 131.8	W9TE	FWRC
Fort Wayne	146.9100	–	O 131.8	W9TE	FWRC
Fort Wayne	146.9400	–	Oa	W9TE	FWRC
Fort Wayne	147.1350	+	O 141.3el	N9VZJ	N9VZJ
Fort Wayne	147.1650	+	O 141.3el	N9VZJ	N9VZJ
Fort Wayne	147.2550	+	Oes	W9INX	ACARTS
Huntington	145.1500	–	O 141.3ers WXx	KB9UMI	KB9UMI
Huntington	146.6850	–	OeWX	K9HC	HCARS
Laotto	145.1100	–	O 141.3	KB9VTK	KB9VTK
Ligonier	147.1500	+	OersWX	N9BCP	21RptrGrp
Roanoke	146.6250	–	O 131.8	WB9VLE	WB9VLE
Spencerville	147.3600	+	O 131.8	WB9VLE	WB9VLE
Wolflake	147.2700	+	O 131.8e	N9MTF	N9MTF
NORTHWEST					
Cedar Lake	146.8350	–	O 131.8e	WB9VRG	WB9VRG
Crown Point	145.4500	–	O 131.8 WX	W9FXT	W9FXT
Crown Point	146.7000	–	O 131.8r WX	W9EMA	LakeEMA
Gary	146.6250	–	O 131.8e	W9SAL	W9SAL
Gary	146.9100	–	O 131.8e WXx	W9CTO	W9CTO
Hammond	147.0450	+	O 131.8el WX	KA9QJG	KA9QJG
Hammond	147.1950	+	O 131.8 (CA)elWX	W9FXT	IARA
Laporte	146.6100	–	O 131.8elr sWX	K9JSI	LaPorteARC
Merrillville	147.0000	+	O 131.8elr	W9LJ	LakeCoARC
Michigan City	146.9700	–	O 131.8	W9LY	MCARC
New Carlisle	146.8650	–	O 131.8s	AB9OZ	AB9OZ

INDIANA

Location	Output	Input	Notes	Call	Sponsor
St John	147.2400	+	O 131.8rs WX	W9LJ	LakeCoARC
Valparaiso	146.6850	–	O 199.5e WXx	N9IAA	N9IAA
Valparaiso	146.7750	–	O 131.8esx	K9PC	PorterARC
Valparaiso	147.0750	+	O 131.8rs WX	KI9EMA	Porter Emg
Valparaiso	147.1050	+	O 131.8es WXx	KB9KRI	Duneland
Winamac	145.4800	–	O 131.8ers WXx	KC9VBQ	KC9VBQ
SOUTH CENTRAL					
Bedford	145.3100	–	O 107.2er WX	W9QYQ	HoosrHills
Bedford	145.4900	–	O 103.5 (CA)e	AA9WR	AA9WR
Bedford	146.7300	–	O 107.2 (CA)erWX	W9QYQ	HoosrHills
Bedford	147.3450	+	O 107.2ae	KB9MXR	KB9MXR
Bloomington	146.6400	–	O 136.5 (CA)elrsWXxz	WB9TLH	WB9TLH
Bloomington	146.9400	–	O 136.5el	K9IU	K9IU
Columbus	146.7900	–	O 100.0ers WX	W9ALQ	CARC
Floyds Knob	146.7450	–	O 151.4er	WD9HMH	FloydAMA
Frenchtown	146.8200	–	O 103.5s	W9BGW	W9BGW
Leopold	145.1900	–	O 107.2elr sWXx	KC9OBN	PerryCty
Levenworth	147.0150	+	O 103.5e WX	WB4ROI	WB4ROI
Nashville	147.3000	+	O 136.5ers WX	KA9SWI	KA9SWI
Paoli	147.0450	+	O 103.5es WX	KB9OHY	Orange ARC
Salem	146.6550	–	O 103.5ers WX	KB9KPG	WashCoARC
Scottsburg	146.6100	–	O 103.5ers	WR9G	WR9G
Seymour	145.4300	–	O 103.5elr sWX	KC9JOY	KC9JOY
Seymour	147.1350	+	O 103.5e	KI9G	K9IG
SOUTHEAST					
Greensburg	146.9550	–	OersWX	N9LQP	DecaturARC
Lawrenceburg	147.2850	+	O 146.2ers WX	WA9BLA	LV ARC
Madison	145.1700	–	OesWX	W9EFU	Clifty ARS
Napoleon	146.8050	–	OerWX	KC9MBX	RipCoRA
SOUTHWEST					
Bloomfield	147.2400	+	O 103.5elr sWX	W9HD	W9HD

Location	Output	Input	Notes	Call	Sponsor
Boonville	147.0750	+	O 88.5er	WB9QVR	WarrickEMA
Chrisney	146.9100	–	Ors	KC9FTG	SpencerEOC
Dugger	146.7750	–	O 136.5	KC9AK	DuggerARC
Evansville	145.1100	–	O 107.2	AB9JT	AB9JT
Evansville	145.1500	–	O 107.2l WXx	KB9SGN	KB9SGN
Evansville	146.7900	–	O 88.5aelr sWXx	W9OG	TARS
Evansville	146.8350	–	O 136.5elr sWXx	W9KXP	W9KXP
Evansville	147.1050	+	Ol	W9MAR	MidwstARS
Evansville	147.1500	+	Oers	W9OG	TARS
Jasper	147.1950	+	O 107.2aer	KB9LHX	DuboisARC
Linton	145.1700	–	O 100.0	KA9JOK	KA9JOK
Linton	145.3900	–	O 118.8elr sWXx	KB9HIK	GreeneCo
Lynnville	145.2500	–	O 123.0elr sWX	W9KXP	W9KXP
Newburgh	145.4300	–	Oe	KA9VKO	KA9VKO
Petersburg	145.4500	–	Oel	WA9FGT	Petersburg
Princeton	145.4100	–	O 136.5ers WX	KB9NEJ	SoINMobEmg
Princeton	147.3900	+	O 131.8elr sWXx	W9KXP	W9KXP
Ridgeport	145.4700	–	O 136.5ael sWXx	KB9SIP	KB9TUN
Shoals	145.2100	–	Oae	KA9PSX	KA9PSX
Troy	146.9550	–	O 146.2elr sWXx	W9KXP	W9KXP
Vincennes	146.6700	–	O 91.5es WX	W9EOC	Old Post
Vincennes	146.9250	–	O 107.2al WXx	W9EAR	EARS
Washington	147.3150	+	O 107.2er WX	WA9IN	DaviessDHL
Winslow	147.0000	+	O 107.2ers WX	W9UL	PikeCoARC
WEST CENTRAL					
Center Point	145.4200	–	O 151.4elr sWXx	W9SKI	ClayEmg
Chalmers	147.2550	+	O 131.8es WX	KC9PQA	WhiteARS
Clinton	146.7150	–	O 151.4ers WX	W9COD	W9COD
Clinton	146.7450	–	O 177.3	NS9M	NS9M
Covington	145.4900	–	O 156.7el	W9ABH	BARC
Crawfordsville	146.8650	–	O 100.0	KB9GPB	SCRA
Crawfordsville	147.2250	+	O 88.5r	KB9GPB	MontRACES
Crawfordsville	147.2700	+	O	KC9QKL	Livewires

Location	Output	Input	Notes	Call	Sponsor
Foster	145.2700	–	O 88.5l	N9UWE	N9UWE
Gosport	146.8950	–	O 136.5aelsx	KB9SGN	K9TC
Greencastle	147.3300	+	O	WB9EOC	PutRACES
Rockville	146.7450	–	O	NS9M	NS9M
Spencer	146.9850	–	O 136.5es	KB9MZZ	OwenCoARA
Terre Haute	145.2300	–	OelrsWXx	W9SKI	Skywarn
Terre Haute	145.3500	–	Oe	NC9U	OtrCrkRC
Terre Haute	146.6850	–	O 151.4esWXx	K9IKQ	WVARA
Terre Haute	146.8050	–	Oers	K9HX	K9HX
Terre Haute	147.0900	+	OersWXx	WØDQJ	WØDQJ
Terre Haute	147.1500	+	O 151.4	W9EQD	TerreHaute
West Lafayette	146.7600	–	O 88.5els	W9YB	PurdueARC
West Lafayette	147.1350	+	O 88.5aesWX	WI9RES	WIRES

IOWA

Location	Output	Input	Notes	Call	Sponsor
BURLINGTON					
Burlington	146.7900	–	100.0aersz	WØLAC	IA-ILLARC
Burlington	147.3600	+	100.0e	WA6GUF	WA6GUF
Fort Madison	146.8650	–	100.0aersx	WFØRT	FtMadARC
Mt Pleasant	147.1650	+	156.7e	WBØVHB	MtPl ARC
Mt Pleasant	147.3900	+	OeWX	WØMME	MtPl ARC
CEDAR RAPIDS					
Cedar Rapids	145.1500	–	192.8 (CA)x	WØHUP	CRRA
Cedar Rapids	145.1900	–	192.8x	NØDX	EIDXA
Cedar Rapids	146.7450	–	192.8aersWX	WØGQ	CVARC
Cedar Rapids	147.0900	+	192.8 (CA)lx	WØHUP	CRRA+SEIT
Coralville	147.1500	+	192.8ex	WØFDA	CvilleRPT
Iowa City	145.2700	–	192.8aers	KDØMJV	J Co EIC
Iowa City	146.8500	–	192.8eWXx	WØJV	ICARC
Shellsburg	145.2900	–	770898ez	ACØOQ	ACØOQ
Van Horne	145.2300	–	● 141.3aersWXx	KDØDKS	BCEM
CENTRAL					
Ames	147.3750	+	114.8aelz	WØISU	CARC
Boone	146.8500	–	OaersWX	KBØTLM	BARK
Des Moines	145.3500	–	● 114.8aersx	KDØIAN	DMRAA
Fort Dodge	146.6850	–	110.9aersWX	KØRJV	WebCoEMA
Marshalltown	146.8800	–	141.3	KØMIW	CIRAS
Marshalltown	147.1350	+	141.3e	KØMIW	CIRAS
Mingo	146.6700	–	OaeWXx	WØAIX	WAØIHZ
Newton	147.0300	+	114.8aersWX	WØWML	NewtonARA

Location	*Output*	*Input*	*Notes*	*Call*	*Sponsor*
Perry	145.1900	–	710459aers	KDØNEB	HARC
Sheldahl	147.0750	+	210808aelrsWX	NØQFK	NØQFK
Stratford	146.6250	–	e	WØFS	WØFS
Webster City	147.0150	+	aersWX	KØKWO	HamCo ARA
COUNCIL BLUFFS					
Council Bluffs	146.8200	–	673095aers	KØSWI	SWIARC
Honey Creek	145.4100	–	97.4e	ABØVX	ABØVX
DAVENPORT					
Davenport	146.7000	–	aers	WØBXR	DvnprtRAC
Davenport	146.8800	–	192.8aersWX	WØBXR	DvnprtRAC
Muscatine	146.9100	–	e	KCØAQS	M ARC
DES MOINES					
Alleman	145.3100	–	509854el	WØTWR	WØTWR
Des Moines	145.2500	–	127.3	KØCSS	KØCSS
Des Moines	146.8200	–	114.8 (CA)elWX	WØKWM	CITS
Des Moines	147.3000	+	114.8	WAØQBP	WAØQBP
Indianola	146.6400	–	114.8aersWX	KDØFGV	WCEM
Johnston/Camp	146.7000	–	114.8elWXx	KCØMTI	KCØMTI
Johnston/Camp	147.1650	+	114.8el	KCØMTI	KCØMTI
Saylor TWP	145.3900	–	114.8aersz	KFØQI	STAR
Saylor TWP	146.8950	–	114.8aersWXz	KBØNFF	STAR
DUBUQUE					
Dubuque	147.2400	+	646395aersx	WØDBQ	GRARC
EAST CENTRAL					
Clinton	145.4300	–	100.0aersWX	WØCS	ClntnARC
Clinton	146.7300	–	94.8	KØEII	KØEII
Clinton	147.3150	–	114.8	KDØWY	KDØWY
Maquoketa	147.0600	+	x	KBØCAQ	MArea RGp
Monticello	147.1800	+	192.8e	NØXUS	NØXUS
MASON CITY					
Mason City	146.7600	–	103.5elWXx	WØMCW	NIARC
Mason City	147.1500	+		KØUXA	KØUXA
Mason City	147.3150	+	188447elWXx	KBØJBF	NIARC
NORTH CENTRAL					
Dumont	145.4300	–	136.5	NØRJJ	NØRJJ
Forest City	147.2700	+	e	WBØURC	W-H RS
Humboldt	147.1800	+	147180aers	KØHU	KØHU

IOWA

Location	Output	Input	Notes	Call	Sponsor
Humboldt	147.3900	+	O	KØHU	KØHU
NORTHEAST					
Cresco	146.9250	–	103.5 (CA)e WX	WØCYY	CrescoARC
Decorah	146.7750	–	Oe	NØOZG	NØOZG
Decorah	147.1650	+	123	KØNRA	NordicRA
Frankville	146.6700	–	103.5 (CA)e WX	KØRTF	KØRTF
Manchester	147.3000	+	Oex	WØII	DelCoARC
St Ansgar	147.1950	+	590155e	KCØVII	KCØVII
NORTHWEST					
Estherville	146.7000	–	Oaers	WØMDM	WØMDM
Paullina	147.1350	+	110.9	NØOYK	NØOYK
Perkins Corner	147.3000	+	110.9aers WX	WØVHQ	NIARC
Sheldon	145.3100	–	102345e	WØVHQ	NIARC
Spencer	146.8200	–	110.9eWXx	KGØCK	KGØCK
Spirit Lake	146.6100	–	350195aer sWXx	WØDOG	IGLARC
Storm Lake	146.7750	–	110.9el	WAØUZI	WAØUZI
SIOUX CITY					
LeMars	147.0150	+	110.9	KIØEO	KIØEO
LeMars	147.1950	+	110.9	KDØPMM	KDØPMM
Sioux City	146.9100	–	110.9aers WXx	KØAAR	91FunGp
Sioux City	146.9700	–	110.9ex	KØTFT	SARA
Sioux City	147.0600	+	110.9ex	KØTFT	SARA
Sioux City	147.2700	+	110.9	KCØDXD	KCØDXD
SOUTH CENTRAL					
Chariton	146.8350	–	123.0aelrs WXx	KBØAJ	S IA RA
Knoxville	147.1950	+	173.8aers	WØLWG	WØLWG
Melrose	146.7150	+	146.2 (CA)e x	NØWK	NØWK
Winterset	147.2700	+	114.8e	WAØO	WAØO
SOUTHEAST					
Fairfield	147.3300	+	OeWXx	KØBPR	F HS ARC
Keokuk	147.3000	+	146.2	WBØSBU	WBØSBU
Moravia	146.9250	–	146.2x	WØALO	WØALO
Oskaloosa	145.4900	–	146.2 (CA)e xz	KBØVXL	MhaskaARC
Ottumwa	146.6850	–	146.2	WAØDX	OARC
Washington	147.0450	+	343657e WX	WØARC	WAARC
SOUTHWEST					
Anita	147.3450	+	Oe	NØBKB	NØBKB
Atlantic	147.1500	+	● 151.4ael rsx	KØZQ	CassCoRA
Avoca	147.2550	+	151.4lx	NØDYB	------------

Location	Output	Input	Notes	Call	Sponsor
Bedford	147.1350	+	127.3aelrs WX	KAØRDE	TlrCoARA
Clearfield	147.2100	+	136.5aelrs WX	NØBKB	NØBKB
Creston	146.7900	–	107972aelr sx	KØCSQ	SW IA ARA
Glenwood	145.2900	–	**O**aelrsWX x	NØWKF	NØWKF
Greenfield	146.8650	–	146.2aelrs WX	NØBKB	NØBKB
Menlo	147.0450	+	114.8aelrs WX	NØBKB	NØBKB
Prescott	145.1500	–	127.3eWX	NØDTS	NØDTS
Red Oak	146.6550	–	509846aelr sWX	NØNHB	NØNHB
Thurman/Tabor	145.3900	–	36604aelrs WXx	WBØYLA	WBØYLA
WATERLOO					
Cedar Falls	146.6550	–	136.5	KMØK	CFARA
Fayette	147.3450	+	**O**aers	KDØBIJ	NEIaARES
Independence	145.3300	–	103.5e	KCØRMS	BCoARC
Waterloo	146.8200	–	136.54aers WXx	WØALO	WØALO
Waterloo	146.9400	–	136.5aers WXx	WØMG	NE IA RAA
WEST CENTRAL					
Audubon	147.1200	+	**O**elWX	WAØGUD	CnValARC
Carroll	146.8050	–	110.9el	KCØUIO	CCEM
Castana	145.4700	–	136.5aers	KØBVC	BVARC
Denison	147.0900	+	**O**aers	KØCNM	DenisonRA
Denison	147.3300	+	**O**	KCØLGI	------------
Manilla	147.2250	+	151.4elWX x	NØJRX	------------
Mondamin	145.1300	–	136.5aers WX	KØBVC	BVARC
Portsmouth	146.7450	–	136.5aers	KØBVC	BVARC
Sac City	146.9250	–	**O**a(CA)ers	WDØCLO	WDØCLO

KANSAS

Location	Output	Input	Notes	Call	Sponsor
CENTRAL					
Abilene	145.3300	–	**O**a(CA)er	KØAAC	DKCOEM
Chapman	145.2500	–	●a(CA)r	WAØLXV	NUØS
Great Bend	146.7600	–	**O**aer	KIØNN	------------
Hays	146.7900	–	**O**te L(IRLP#3917)	N7JYS	------------
Hays	147.0450	+	**O** 131.8/131.8eL(ECHOLINK ALLST)	N7JYS	N7JYS
Hays	147.1800	+	**O** 100/100a er	KCØPID	EllisCO

Location	*Output*	*Input*	*Notes*	*Call*	*Sponsor*
Hoisington	147.1350	+	O 88.5/88.5 elrs	KØHAM	NEKSUN
Junction City	146.8800	–	Oer	NØUZT	GC ARS
Lincoln	147.1950	+	Ol	KØMXJ	POST ROCK
Marion	147.0900	+	Oe L(ECHOLINK#241012)	KCØRVV	MCARC
McPherson	147.3300	+	Oe	WØTWU	McPhrsnRC
Russell	147.2850	+	Otelr	ABØUO	RUSSELL CO
Salina	146.7300	–	Oa(CA)er	NØKSC	NØKSC
Salina	147.0300	+	Oa(CA)er	WØCY	CKARC
Salina	147.2700	+	Oer	NØKSC	NØKSC
Smolan	146.6250	–	Ol	WDØGAH	WBØOPI
Wilson	146.9700	–	O 118.8/118.8	KØBHN	KØBHN
EAST CENTRAL					
Cadmus	146.8950	–	O	WAØSMG	WAØSMG
Emporia	145.3100	–	O 103.5/103.5	NØOFG	NØOFG
Emporia	146.9850	–	O 88.5/88.5 elr	KØHAM	EARS
Enterprise	145.1700	–	O	KE5MED	KE5MED
Garnett	146.8650	–	O	KØVEV	CHPPWARC
Matfield Green	147.0450	+	O 88.5/88.5 el	KØHAM	NEKSUN
Miller	147.3450	+	●a(CA)	KAØWOK	KAØWOK
Mound City	147.2850	+	Oer	WAØPPN	MnCrkARA
New Strawn	147.0750	+	O/91.5	NØMSA	------------
Osage City	146.9250	–	O 203.5/203.5	NØOFG	NØOFG
Ottawa	147.3900	+	Oe L(IRLP#7989)	WØQW	OttawaARA
Paola	147.3600	+	O(CA)er	WSØWA	WhtStWrls
KANSAS CITY METRO					
Basehor	145.3900	–	O 88.5/88.5 elrs	KØHAM	NEKSUN
Basehor	145.3900	–	O 88.5/88.5 elrs	KØHAM	NEKSUN
Blue Springs	147.0150	+	O 151/151e x	KBØVBN	BluSprRPTR
Excelsior Spgs	145.1900	–	O 107 RBx	KØBSJ	KØBSJ
Excelsior Spgs	147.3750	+	O 156/156e	KØESM	RayClay RC
Gladstone	145.4300	–	O	KDØFW	KCATVG
Holt	147.0450	+	O	NØTIX	NØTIX
Independence	145.3100	–	O 151er	KØEJC	EJCECS
Independence	145.3700	–	O	KØEJC	EJCECS
Independence	146.7300	–	Oaer	WØSHQ	ASCRA, Inc
Independence	147.0900	+	Oa(CA)elr	WØTOJ	IndFMARC
Kansas City	145.1300	–	Oa(CA)e	WAØNQA	ArtShrnRC
Kansas City	145.1300	–	Oa(CA)e	WAØNQA	ArtShrnRC

Location	*Output*	*Input*	*Notes*	*Call*	*Sponsor*
Kansas City	146.7900	–	O 107/107a (CA)es	WAØKHP	ClayCoARC
Kansas City	146.8200	–	Olrx	KCØARC	NEKSUN
Kansas City	146.9400	–	O 88.5/88.5 elrsZ(911)	KØHAM	NEKSUN
Kansas City	146.9400	–	O 88.5/88.5 elrsZ(911)	KØHAM	NEKSUN
Kansas City	146.9700	–	O 151/151x	WØWJB	WØWJB
Kansas City	147.1500	+	O 151.4/151.4er	WØLB	JyhwkARC
Kansas City	147.1500	+	O 151.4/151.4er	WØLB	JyhwkARC
Kansas City	147.2100	+	O 151.4/151.4er	WØKCK	WYCO EM
Kansas City	147.2100	+	O 151.4/151.4er	WØKCK	WYCO EMA
Kansas City	147.2700	+	Oa(CA)ex	WAØSMG	WAØSMG
Kansas City	147.3300	+	Oa(CA)er	WAØQFJ	TWA ARC
Kearney	147.3000	+	O 107	KØBSJ	KØBSJ
Lee's Summit	145.4100	–	Oa(CA)	WAØTEG	NEKSUN
Lee's Summit	146.7000	–	O 107/107e x	KCØSKY	KS SKY WRN
Lenexa	145.4900	–	O	KAØVVX	KISS ARC
Lenexa	145.4900	–	O	KAØVVX	KISS ARC
Liberty	145.1100	–	O	NØELK	NØELK
Louisburg	147.3150	+	O 88.5/88.5 eL(ECHOLINK#147315)rs	KØHAM	NEKSUN
Louisburg	147.3150	+	O 88.5/88.5 a(CA)elrs	KØHAM	NEXSUN
Olathe	145.4700	–	O 151.4/151.4a(CA)er	KØECS	JoCoECS
Olathe	145.4700	–	O 151.4/151.4a(CA)er	KØECS	JoCoECS
Olathe	147.2400	+	O 151.4/151.4a(CA)er	KAØFMZ	SFTARC
Olathe	147.2400	+	O 151.4/151.4ers	KAØFMZ	SFTARC
Overland Park	145.2900	–	O 151.4/151.4a(CA)er	WØERH	JCRAC
Overland Park	145.2900	–	O 151.4/151.4a(CA)er	WØERH	JCRAC
Overland Park	146.9100	–	O 151.4/151.4ers	WBØKKA	NEKSUN
Overland Park	146.9100	–	O 151.4/151.4a(CA)e	WBØKKA	NEKSUN
Raymore	147.1200	+	Oes	KCØJGA	SSARC
Raytown	145.1700	–	O 151/151e	KØGQ	Raytown AR
Shawnee	145.2100	–	Oa(CA)er	WBØHAC	SRACT
Shawnee Msn	145.2100	–	Oa(CA)er	WBØHAC	SRACT

Location	Output	Input	Notes	Call	Sponsor
Shawnee Msn	145.2300	–	Oa(CA)el	WBØRJQ	WBØRJQ
Smithville	146.6400	–	Osx	KCØIMO	NØVER
NORTH CENTRAL					
Beloit	145.3100	–	Oe	WAØCCW	SVRC
Clay Center	147.1650	+	O 162.2/162.2elr	NØUJQ	RVARC
Concordia	146.8650	–	Oelr	KØKSN	KNRC
Concordia	146.9250	–	Otelr	WBØSVM	NCK RC
Greenleaf	147.0600	+	Or	ACØI	BlueVlyRA
Lenora	146.8800	–	O	NØKOM	NTNCTYRUG
Minneapolis	147.2250	+	O 162.2/162.2aers	NØUJQ	K-Link
Norton	147.3000	+	Oe	KØENU	NrtnSgCrp
Osborne	147.3750	+	Otelr	NZØM	ORUG
Phillipsburg	147.1200	+	Oe	AAØHJ	AAØHJ
Smith Center	146.6100	–	O	NØLL	USCARC
NORTHEAST					
Effingham	146.6100	–	O 100/100a	KØDXY	ACARS
Hiawatha	147.1800	+	Ote	WAØW	HARC
Holton	146.7750	–	Oa(CA)e	AAØMM	JacksonARC
Lawrence	146.7600	–	Ot	WØUK	DCARC
Lawrence	147.0300	+	O 88.5/88.5 aer	NØAPJ	DG CO EP
Leavenworth	145.3300	–	Oe	NØKOA	WBØYNE
Leavenworth	147.0000	+	O 151.4/151.4a(CA)er	KSØLV	PKARC
Manhattan	145.4100	–	O	WØQQQ	KSU ARC
Manhattan	147.2550	+	O 88.5/88.5 ae	KSØMAN	MAARS
Marysville	147.2850	+	O	WØDOD	MCARC
Mission	147.1650	+	O 151.4/151.4elr	WBØKIA	WYCO RACES
Riley	146.6850	–	Otl	KCØNER	K-Link
Seneca	146.7150	–	Oer	KBØDEU	NMCOCD
Topeka	147.1950	+	O 88.5/88.5 el	KØHAM	NEKSUN
NORTHWEST					
Clay Center	145.1500	–	O 100/100 L(ECHOLINK#367513)	KD7QAS	------------
Colby	146.8200	–	O 156.7/156.7a(CA)er	NWØK	TARC
Goodland	147.0300	+	O 88.5/88.5 (CA) L(ECHOLINK#243285)	KSØGLD	SCARE
Norton	145.3500	–	Olr	WDØAVA	WDØAVA
Oberlin	145.1900	–	O	KBØDZB	TRI-STATE
SOUTH CENTRAL					
Anthony	146.6850	–	Oae	NØCR	NØCR
Arkansas City	147.0000	+	O 97.4/97.4 r	WAØJBW	CWLYCOARC

Location	*Output*	*Input*	*Notes*	*Call*	*Sponsor*
Beaumont	145.1300	–	O 156.7/156.7erLITZ	KSØKE	KARS
Hutchinson	146.6700	–	Oe	WBØEOC	ERCRC
Hutchinson	147.1200	+	Oa(CA)e L(ECHOLINK#105011)	WØWR	RCKARA
Kiowa	147.0150	+	Oaelr	KB5MDH	KDE-TV36
Kiowa	147.1800	+	O 103.5/103.5el	W5ALZ	GSPARC
Medicine Lodge	146.8800	–	Oer	KCØGEV	W5ALZ
Newton	145.1100	–	Oer	NØEVF	SKYWARN
Newton	146.6100	–	Ota(CA)er LITZ	WØBZN	NEWTON ARC
Pratt	146.7000	–	Oae	WBØOAO	WBØOAO
Wellington	146.6400	–	O 103.5/103.5	WAØQPY	WLNGTNARC
Wellington	147.2400	+	O	WAØZFE	WAØZFE
Winfield	145.1900	–	Orx	WAØJBW	CWCOARC
SOUTHEAST					
Chanute	145.3500	–	●t	NØWXG	NØWXG
Chanute	146.7450	–	O 100/100r	AIØE	CAARC
Chanute	147.1050	+	O 91.5/91.5	KZØV	------------
Coffeyville	146.6100	–	O 91.5/91.5 e	WRØCV	COFYVLARC
Coffeyville	147.3000	+	O 91.5/91.5	NUØB	C A R C
Fort Scott	146.7150	–	O 91.5/91.5	KBØSWH	------------
Gas	147.3750	+	O/179.9	WIØLA	IARC
Humboldt	147.1800	+	O	WBØSHN	WBØSHN
Independence	145.4900	–	O 91.5/91.5	NØID	IARC
Independence	147.0150	+	O 100/100	NØID	IARC
Parsons	145.2500	–	O 91.5/91.5 a(CA) L(ECHOLINK#305758)	WØPIE	WØPIE
Parsons	146.6850	–	O 91.5/91.5 e	AAØPK	PAARC
Pittsburg	146.9400	–	O 91.5/91.5 a(CA)e	KØPRO	PRO
Pittsburg	147.2400	+	O 91.5/91.5 a(CA)	KØPRO	PRO
Sedan	146.9550	–	Oalr	WXØEK	CQ EM
SOUTHWEST					
Dodge City	146.6100	–	O 67/67er	KØBAI	KØBAI
Dodge City	147.0300	+	O 123/123a eL(ECHOLINK)r	KUØL	KUØL
Dodge City	147.1650	+	O 88.5/88.5 ers	KØHAM	NEKSUN
Garden City	146.9100	–	O 141.3/141.3e	WØGCK	SNDHILSARC
Hugoton	147.2400	+	Oe	WØQS	SPARK
Lakin	146.9850	–	O 156.7/156.7e	NØOMC	NØOMC

Location	Output	Input	Notes	Call	Sponsor
Liberal	145.1500	–	O 88.5/88.5 l	WØKKS	SPARK
Liberal	146.8050	–	O 103.5/103.5ae	WØKKS	SPARK
Plains	147.1800	+	O	WKØDX	WKØDX
Sublette	147.3000	+	Oa(CA)	NØDRB	NØDRB/CRO
Ulysses	147.0600	+	Oe	KØECT	SKECT
TOPEKA					
Canton	145.2900	–	O 186.2/186.2ae	KCØIFO	------------
Carbondale	147.3000	+	O 88.5/88.5 e	KBØWTH	------------
Hoyt	145.2700	–	O 88.5/88.5 er	WØCET	KVARC
Meriden	146.8350	–	Oer	NØLFN	BARCBADS
Overbrook	146.8050	–	Oe	WDØDDG	WDØDDG
St Marys	146.9550	–	O 88.5/88.5 elrs	KØHAM	NEKSUN
Topeka	145.4500	–	O 88.5/88.5 aer	WØCET	KVARC
Topeka	146.6700	–	O 88.5/88.5 aeL(ECHOLINK#157350)r	WAØVRS	911 Top
WEST CENTRAL					
Scott City	146.7000	–	Oe	KØEQH	SNDHILSARC
Syracuse	146.7750	–	Oe	KAØTAO	KAØTAO
WICHITA					
Derby	145.4700	–	O 156.7/156.7 L(ECHOLINK#44447)	KCØSOK	ALRERC
Derby	146.6400	–	Ote	KDØHNB	------------
Derby	146.8500	–	O 103.5/103.5elrWX	WØUUS	WARC
El Dorado	147.1500	+	O	WØRGB	FlntHlsRC
El Dorado	147.2100	+	O 100/100e	KØFAO	KARS
Goddard	147.0600	+	O 156.7/156.7 L(ECHOLINK#350393)	WFØA	ALRERC
Haysville	145.4100	–	Oa(CA)er	KAØRT	KAØRT
Haysville	147.1050	+	Oa(CA)er	KAØRT	KAØRT
Hutchinson	146.8200	–	O 103.5/103.5er	WØKA	WARC
Mulvane	146.7150	–	O 100/100e	NØKTA	MLVANEARC
Valley Center	147.3900	+	Or	KØFFR	KØFFR
Wichita	145.2700	–	Ote L(ECHOLINK#358668)	WØVFW	VFW3115
Wichita	145.4500	–	O 103.5/103.5er	NØJWY	NØJWY
Wichita	146.7900	–	O/103.5e	WØSOE	WARC
Wichita	146.8950	–	Oa	KCØAHN	BEARS
Wichita	146.9400	–	Oa(CA)er	WAØRJE	TECNICHAT

Location	Output	Input	Notes	Call	Sponsor
KENTUCKY					
Agnes	145.4500	–	O	W4RRA	W4XXA
Allen	147.3000	+	O	K4ICN	K4ICN
Artemus	147.3900	+	O	N4INT	N4INT
Ashland	146.9400	–	O 107.2/107.2	KG4DVE	KG4DVE
Ashland	147.2400	+	O	KC4QK	ASHLAND 24 RP
Auburn	145.4500	–	O	W6ZP	W6ZP
Bardstown	145.4700	–	O 151.4/151.4e	KB4KY	KB4KY
Beaver Dam	145.1700	–	Oers	KI4HEC	KI4HEC
Benton	145.3900	–	O 118.8/118.8e	KI4HUS	N4STW
Bowling Green	147.1650	+	O	W4WSM	------------
Bowling Green	147.3300	+	O 107.2/107.2e	KY4BG	KY4BG
Brooks	146.7000	–	O 79.7/79.7 esWX	KY4KY	KY4KY
Buckhorn Lake	147.3750	+	O	K4XYZ	K4XYZ
Buffalo	147.2550	+	O 77/77	W4LJM	W4LJM
Buttonsberry	146.7300	–	O 82.5/82.5	KY4MA	NU4O
Cane Valley	146.6400	–	O	WA4UXJ	CENTRAL KY A
Cerulean	147.1950	+	O 136.5/136.5e	KY4KEN	KY4KEN
Cloverport	147.3750	+	O	K4DJF	K4DJF
Columbia	147.1950	+	O	KY4TF	------------
Corbin	146.6100	–	Oe	WD4KWV	WD4KWV
Covington	145.4100	–	O	WR8CRA	CINCINNATTI R
Covington	147.3900	+	O	WR8CRA	CINCINNATI RE
Crestwood	147.3900	+	O	KY4OC	OLDHAM COUN
Danville	145.3100	–	O 100/100es	W4CDA	W4CDA
Dawson Springs	146.7750	–	O	KF4CWK	KF4CWK
Dewdrop	147.0300	+	O	KD4DZE	KD4DZE
Dixon	145.3500	–	Oes	AJ4SI	------------
Edgewood	147.2550	+	O	K4CO	K4CO
Elizabethtown	145.3500	–	O 103.5/103.5esWX	WX4HC	------------
Elizabethtown	146.9800	–	O	W4BEJ	LINCOLN TRAIL
Flemingsburg	146.9550	–	O	KF4BRO	GREATER MAS
Frankfort	147.1050	+	O	K4TG	K4TG
Georgetown	146.6850	–	O	KF4NTQ	GEO-SCOTT CO
Georgetown	147.6750	–	O	N4CO	GEORGETOWN
Glasgow	146.9400	–	O	KY4X	MCARC INC
Grayson	146.7000	–	O	KD4DZE	KD4DZE
Grethel	147.0450	+	O	KJ4VF	KJ4VF
Halls Gap	146.7900	–	O	AG4TY	------------
Hamlin	147.2400	+	O 91.5/91.5	W4GZ	K4MSU

KENTUCKY

Location	Output	Input	Notes	Call	Sponsor
Hardin	146.9850	–	O 123/123	KN4CG	JCRA
Harlan	147.1050	+	O 103.5/103.5esWX	KK4KCQ	------------
Hawesville	146.7150	–	O	KY4HC	KY4HC
Hazard	146.6700	–	O 103.5/103.5elsWX	KY4MT	KY4MT
Henderson	145.4900	–	O 103.5/103.5	W4KVK	W4KVK
Henderson	146.9700	–	Oe	WA4GDU	WA4GDU
Highland Heights	146.7900	–	O	W4YWH	W4YWH
Highland Heights	146.8950	–	O	K4CO	K4CO
Hopkinsville	147.0300	+	O 103.5/103.5e	KD4ULE	KD4ULE
Hueysville	145.4700	–	O	K4NLT	KF4ZTB
Irvine	146.8200	–	O	W4CMR	CHESTNUT MTN RP
Irvine	147.0150	+	O 100/100e	AD4RT	KY4LD
Jackson	147.2700	+	O 103.5/103.5elsWX	K4TDO	------------
LaGrange	147.2100	+	O 88.5/88.5	WB4WSB	------------
Lawrenceburg	145.1100	–	O	KYLAW	K4TG
Lawrenceburg	146.8350	–	O	K4TG	K4TG
Leitchfield	147.2250	+	O 179.9/179.9e	KY4RCE	------------
Lexington	145.2500	–	O	AD4YJ	AD4YJ
Lexington	146.7600	–	O	K4KJQ	BLUEGRASS ARS
Lexington	146.9400	–	O 88.5/88.5 es	KY4K	KY4K
Lexington	147.1200	+	O	K4UKH	------------
Lexington	147.1650	+	O	WA4HBM	BLUEGRASS ARS
London	147.2850	+	O	KC4ZFH	KC4ZFH
Louisa	147.3900	+	O 127.3/127.3elsWX	WA4SWF	WA4SWF
Louisville	145.1300	–	O	N4UL	N4UL
Louisville	145.1500	–	O	KG4CCW	KG4CCW
Louisville	145.4100	–	O 151.4/151.4	KK4CZ	KK4CZ
Louisville	146.8800	–	O	W4PF	W4PF
Louisville	147.0300	+	O	W4PJZ	LVL & JEF EMERG
Louisville	147.0700	+	O	N4MRM	N4MRM
Louisville	147.1200	+	O	KA4KMT	KA4MKT
Louisville	147.1800	+	O	W4CN	W4CN
Louisville	147.2700	+	O	WB4EJK	WB4EJK
Louisville	147.3600	+	O	KQ9Z	KQ9Z&K9BAW
Lynch	147.2100	+	O 103.5/103.5	K4BKR	------------
Madisonville	146.6100	–	O	KC4FRA	HOPKINS CO ARA
Madisonville	147.0900	+	O	KC4FIE	KC4FIE
Magnolia	146.6700	–	O	WA4FOB	------------
Manchester	146.9250	–	O 79.7/79.7 elWX	KG4LKY	KG4LKY

Location	Output	Input	Notes	Call	Sponsor
Marion	147.2850	+	O 100/100e	KA4FGA	------------
Mayfield	145.1100	–	O 179.9/179.9	WA6LDV	KF4GCD
Maysville	145.4700	–	O	KF4BRO	GMCARA
Mckee	147.0600	+	O	W4CPT	W4CPT
Middlesboro	146.7750	–	O	KA4WZX	KA4WZX
Millard	146.7450	–	O	KD4RTR	------------
Monticello	145.1500	–	O 100/100e	AC4DM	AC4DM
Monticello	146.9950	–	O	WB9SHH	WB9SHH
Morehead	145.1300	–	O	KJ4VF	KJ4VF
Morehead	146.9100	–	O	K4GFY	K4GFY
Morgantown	146.6550	–	O	W4WSM	W4WSM
Mt Sterling	147.3300	+	O	KI4CAZ	GATEWAY ARC
MtVernon	146.7150	–	O 100/100e rs	KF4OFT	KF4OFT
Munfordville	146.8950	–	O	KY4X	KY4X
Murray	146.9400	–	O 91.5/91.5 eWX	K4MSU	K4MSU
Nicholasville	145.4900	–	O	WB4CWF	WB4RZD
Owensboro	145.3300	–	O	KI4JXN	KI4JXN
Owensboro	146.6850	–	O	N4WJS	N4WJS
Owensboro	146.8650	–	O 82.5/82.5	KY4K	------------
Owensboro	147.2100	+	O	K4HY	OARC
Owingsville	147.0750	+	O	N4TLP	CAVE RUN ARC
Paducah	146.7600	–	O	K4CUW	K4CUW
Paducah	147.0600	+	O	W4NJA	PARA
Paducah	147.1200	+	O 179.9/179.9e	KD4DVI	KD4DVI
Paintsville	145.2700	–	O 127.3/127.3elsWX	N4KJU	KY4ARC
Paintsville	147.2250	+	O 127.3/127.3esWX	KY4ARC	KY4ARC
Phelps	147.0900	+	O	N4MWA	N4MVY
Pikeville	145.1500	–	O	KY4BP	ARCS
Pikeville	146.8500	–	O	KM4IV	MARK L SMITH
Pineville	146.6400	–	O	WA4YZY	MARC
Pleasent Ridge	145.2700	–	O	KD4BOH	------------
Powderly	146.7450	–	Oe	KA4HHW	KF4DKJ
Princeton	145.2300	–	O 179.9/179.9es	W4KBL	W4KBL
Radcliff	146.9250	–	O	W4BEJ	LTARC
Radcliff	147.1500	+	O 103.5/103.5esWX	WX4HC	WX4HC
Richmond	145.3700	–	O 192.8/192.8a(CA)ers	KE4YVD	KE4YVD
Richmond	146.8650	–	O 192.8/192.8ers	KM4EOC	------------
Russell Springs	146.9550	–	O	N4SQV	N4SQV
Russell Springs	147.0750	+	O	KV4D	KV4D

Location	*Output*	*Input*	*Notes*	*Call*	*Sponsor*
Salyersville	145.1900	–	O	KB4SQI	KB4SQI
Salyersville	146.6250	–	O	KY4CM	------------
			127.3/127.3elsWX		
Sandy Hook	147.1350	+	O	KD4DZE	KD4DZE
Scottsville	145.2500	–	O	KJ4GL	KJ4GL
Shelbyville	147.0000	+	O	KE4LR	STUBBLEFIELD REP
Somerset	146.8800	–	O 77/77e	AC4DM	AC4DM
Springfield	147.3000	+	O	WA4SJH	J. MURRAY WALKE
St Charles	147.2700	+	O	KE4AIE	KE4AIE
Stanton	145.2900	–	O	N4VOS	------------
Tompkinsville	146.7750	–	O	KJ4OG	------------
Union City	146.7000	–	O	WA4YGM	------------
Uniontown	145.2900	–	Oe	KJ4HNC	------------
Vanceburg	146.7750	–	O	AE4SK	AE4SK
Versailles	145.3300	–	O	KY4WC	KY4WC
Walton	147.3750	+	O	K4CO	------------
Westview	147.0600	+	O	KY3O	------------
			136.5/136.5		
Whitesburg	145.3500	–	O	KK4WH	------------
			186.2/186.2elsWX		
Williamsburg	147.0000	+	O	KG4M	STUBBLEFIELD RPT
Winchester	145.4300	–	O	KF4CBT	KF4CBT
Winchester	147.1200	+	O	WB4ASZ	WB4ASZ
Winchester	147.1950	+	O	KJ4VF	------------

LOUISIANA

REG 1 NEW ORLEANS

Belle Chasse	146.8950	–	O 114.8e	KA5EZQ	PPOEP
			L(444.175)rs		
Marrero	146.9400	–	O 114.8ers	W5ABD	WARC
Marrero	147.1500	+	O 127.3	N5SC	N5SC
			(CA)ers		
Metairie	145.3900	–	O 114.8e	W5GAD	JARC
Metairie	145.4700	–	O 114.8	W5GAD	JARC
Metairie	146.8200	–	O 114.8	N5OZG	N5OZG
Metairie	147.3600	+	●	W5RU	DDXA
New Orleans	146.7750	–	O 114.8esx	W5MCC	SELCOM
New Orleans	146.8600	–	O	W5MCC	SELCOM
			114.8/114.8 (CA)er		
New Orleans	146.9600	–	O 114.8	W5UNO	UNOE
New Orleans	147.0300	+	O 114.8esx	W5MCC	SELCOM
New Orleans	147.1200	+	O 114.8e	N5OZG	N5OZG
New Orleans	147.1950	+	Oae	KE5WWX	KE5WWX
New Orleans	147.2400	+	O 114.8e	W5GAD	JARC
			L(444.000)		
Port Shulphur	146.6550	–	O 114.8e	KA5EZQ	PPOEP
			L(444.075)rs		

REG 2 BATON ROUGE

Baton Rouge	145.2300	–	O	W5GQ	WAFB-TV-E
			107.2/107.2 (CA)elx		

Location	*Output*	*Input*	*Notes*	*Call*	*Sponsor*
Baton Rouge	145.4500	–	O aez	WA5TQA	OMIK-BR
Baton Rouge	145.4900	–	O aelx	KD5SL	RASC
Baton Rouge	146.7900	–	O 107.2e	W5GIX	BR ARC
Baton Rouge	146.9400	–	O 107.2er	KD5CQB	EBRP OEP
Baton Rouge	147.2550	+	O	N5NXL	BRRG
Baton Rouge	147.3450	+	O 100ael	W5DOW	Dow ARC
Fordoche	147.1800	+	O ersx	KE5WQB	F-RACES
Gonzales	145.3100	–	O 10.2 L(444.025)	K5ARC	ASCN ARC
Gonzales	146.9850	–	O e	K5ARC	ASCN ARC
Gonzales	147.2250	+	O 107.2e	K5ARC	ASCN ARC
Holden	146.7300	–	O 107.2e	W5LRS	LARS
REG 3 THIBODAUX					
Destrehan	146.8050	–	O e	WB5MUI	Plantation
Dularge/Theriot	147.3000	+	O e	W5YL	THBDX ARC
Thibodaux	145.2100	–	O ae	WD5IWT	WD5CFM+
Thibodaux	147.3900	+	O ael	W5YL	THBDX ARC
REG 4 LAFAYETTE					
Abbeville	147.0600	+	O	KC5Z	VARC
Berwick	146.7450	–	O 103.5/103.5a	N5BOD	N5BOD
Carencro	145.2900	–	O	KE5KUL	DRCC
Crowley	147.2400	–	O 127.3 (CA)e	K5ET	TV 10 RG
Duson	147.0400	+	O 103.5/103.5e	W5EXI	ACDN ARA
Franklin	147.1200	+	O aer	N5BOD	ST MRY CD
Lafayette	145.3700	–	O 103.5/103.5e	KF5VH	LRA
Lafayette	146.8200	–	O 103.5/103.5ae	W5DDL	ACDN ARA
Morgan City	146.9100	–	O aer	N5BOD	ST MRY CD
New Iberia	145.4100	–	O 103.5es	K5BLV	ADXA
New Iberia	146.6800	–	O 103.5/103.5aer	K5ARA	IBR PR OEP
Opelousas	147.1500	+	O 103.5/103.5 BI	W5OPL	OPLS AARC
REG 5 LAKE CHARLES					
DeRidder	146.8500	–	O 203.5	N5BDD	W LA ARS
Kinder	146.9250	–	O 203.5 E-SUN	W5ELM	W5ELM
Lake Charles	145.2100	–	O 103.5	W5BII	SWLARC
Lake Charles	146.7300	–	O 173.8/173.8ae	W5BII	SWLARC
Sulphur	145.3500	–	O 103.5/103.5 (CA)e	W5BII	SWLARC
REG 6 ALEXANDRIA					
Alexandria	147.3300	–	O 173.8ael rZ(911)	KC5ZJY	ARCCLA

Location	*Output*	*Input*	*Notes*	*Call*	*Sponsor*
Ashland	147.2100	+	●ex	KC5UCV	KC5UCV
Jena	147.1050	+	O 173.8x	KE5KT	KE5KT
Leesville	145.3100	–	O 173.8 (CA)elz	W5LSV	WCLARC
Leesville	147.3900	+	O 203.5	W5TMP	WCLARC
Many	146.8050	–	OeWX	KC5UCV	KC5UCV
Many	147.2800	–	O 173.8aels	K5MNY	ARCS
Moreauville	145.1300	–	O 173.8e	KA5KON	AVOY OEP
Natchitoches	146.8800	–	O 173.8aer	WA5BWX	WA5BWX-CD
Pineville	146.6400	–	● 173.8 (CA)e	AB5IS	AB5IS
Pineville	147.3750	+	O 173.8els	KD5DFL	CL-ARES
Winnfield	147.0600	+	O 173.8esx	KE5IXL	WPARES
REG 7 SHREVEPORT					
Bossier	147.1500	+	O 186.2elr sWXz	K5BMO	B.M.O.
Coushatta	145.2700	–	O 186.2 (CA)er	K5EYG	RRARA
Haughton	147.2400	+	O 123e	KC5UCV	KC5UCV
Mansfield	146.9400	–	Oaer	KC5XR	UNTD R AC
Minden	147.3000	+	O 186.2a	N5RD	MARA
Shreveport	145.1100	–	O 186.2 (CA)eWX	N5FJ	S.A.R.A.
Shreveport	145.4100	–	O 186.2e	KC5OKA	ARK LA TX
Shreveport	145.4300	–	Oal	KB5PKW	MARA
Shreveport	146.6700	–	O 186.2e WXx	N5SHV	ARCOS
Shreveport	146.7000	–	O 186.2er	K5SAR	SARA
Shreveport	146.7600	–	O 186.2ae	N5SHV	ARCOS
Shreveport	146.8200	–	O 186.2 (CA)e	K5SAR	S.A.R.A
Springhill	146.7300	–	Oa	W5KJN	SPHL ARC
Springhill	147.1650	+	OWX	AF5P	ARKLA ARA
REG 8 MONROE					
Bastrop	146.9250	–	O 127.3e	NE5WX	NE5WX
Bernice	145.3300	–	O 127.3	W5JC	W5JC
Bernice	147.0750	+	O 127.3	W5JC	W5JC
Columbia	147.0150	+	Otex	K5NOE	K5NOE
Farmerville	145.2300	–	Oers	KA5JNL	UP-ARES
Holly Ridge	145.3500	–	O 127.3elr sWXx	W5KGT	W5KGT
Jonesboro	146.7900	–	Os	WB5NIN	JAARO
Kilbourne	146.7750	–	O	KJ5NQ	KJ5NQ
Monroe	146.8500	–	Oersx	N5DMX	N5DMX
Rayville	145.4900	–	O	WA5KNV	Beouf R RA
Ruston	145.1900	–	O 94.8ael LITZx	N5WLG	N5WLG
Ruston	147.1200	+	O 94.8es	WC5K	PHARA

Location	Output	Input	Notes	Call	Sponsor
West Monroe	145.4500	–	O 127.3els	W5KGT	W5KGT
West Monroe	147.1350	+	O 127.3ael rsLITZ WXxZ(911)	W5KGT	W5KGT
West Monroe	147.3750	+	O 127.3	KB5TLB	KB5TLB
REG 9 HAMMOND					
Hammond	145.1300	–	O 107.2/107.2e	WB5NET	SELARC
Hammond	147.0000	–	O 107.2/107.2 (CA)ez	WB5NET	SELARC
LaCombe	145.2900	–	O	K5OZ	Ozone ARC
LaCombe	146.6200	–	O 114.8l	W5MCC	SELCOM
LaCombe	146.6400	–	O 114.8l	N5UK	N5UK
LaCombe	147.2700	–	O 114.8/114.8e	W5SLA	Ozone ARC
Madisonville	147.3750	+	O 107.2e	W5NJJ	NLAKE ARC+
Mandeville	146.7150	–	O 107.2/107.2 (CA)e	W5NJJ	NLAKE ARC+
Pine	145.4300	–	O 107.2/107.2e	WA5ARC	WARC
STATEWIDE					
Shared	145.1700	–	#		------------
MAINE					
AROOSTOOK COUNTY					
Allagash	146.7150	–	O 100.0 E-SUN	N1FG	SJVARA
Fort Fairfield	147.3900	+	OL(RF)	KB1JVP	KB1JVP
Fort Kent	146.6400	–	O 100 E-SUNx	N1FG	SJVARA
Frenchville	147.3300	+	O 103.5	N1FCV	N1FCV
Madawaska	146.8200	–	O 179.9e	KB1NLQ	PChasse
Merrill	145.1700	–	O 123e L(KQ1L 147.000) WXx	KB1JVP	KB1JVP
North Wade	146.7300	–	Oe	K1FS	AARA
AUGUSTA					
Augusta	146.6700	–	O 100ae L(KQ1L LINK SYSTEM)rsWX	KQ1L	KQ1L
Augusta	146.7900	–	● 157.6er WX	KQ1L	KCEMA
Belgrade Lakes	145.3900	–	O 100e L(E15061 443.200)sWXx	W1PIG	KenebecARS
Gardiner	147.2550	+	O 114.8 (CA)eL(MT. WASHINGTON N.H.)s	KB1RAI	Late Night
Kents Hill	147.0000	+	O 100e L(449.275)rsWX	W1PIG	KARS
Litchfield	146.7000	–	O 100e L(KQ1L LINK SYSTEM)rsWXx	N1ITR	N1ITR/KQ1L
Waterville	146.9250	–	O 100e L(KQ1L)r	KQ1L	KQ1L

MAINE

Location	Output	Input	Notes	Call	Sponsor
Winslow	146.7600	–	O 103.5	KD1MM	KD1MM
CENTRAL/BANGOR					
Bangor	145.4500	–	O 67eps	WA1RES	PnbCtyARES
Beaver Cove	147.2550	+	O 131.8e	W3VNE	SDHiggins
Brownville	147.1050	+	O 103.5ex	N1BUG	N1BUG
Dixmont	146.8500	–	O 100e L(KQ1L LINK SYSTEM)rsWXx	KQ1L	KQ1L
East Holden	146.9400	–	O 100e	N1ME	PSARC
East Millinocket	146.7450	–	O 100 L(145.250 + 449.275)	KA1EKS	KA1EKS
Hampden	147.3000	+	O 100 (CA) eWX	W1GEE	W1GEE
Lincoln	147.0000	+	O 100 L(KQ1L LINK SYSTEM)	KQ1L	KQ1L
Millinocket	145.2500	–	O 100 L(146.745 + 449.275)	KA1EKS	KA1EKS
Milo	147.2100	+	O 71.9	KC1AU	PARC
Orono	145.4700	–	O 71.9	W1YA	U ME ARC
Springfield	147.3750	+	O 100ex	WA1ZJL	WA1ZJL
MID-COAST					
Belfast	147.1650	+	O 136.5eprs	W1EMA	WCARA
Ellsworth	146.9100	–	O 151.4ersx	KB1NEB	HC EMCOMM
Hope	147.2400	+	O	WA1ZDA	WA1ZDA
Hulls Cove	147.0300	+	O 100e	W1TU	EAWA
Knox	145.4100	–	OeL(D*V)rs	W1EMA	WCARA
Knox	147.2700	+	O 136.5ers	W1EMA	WCARA
Palermo	145.2700	–	O 100e L(145.390 OR 449.275)rsWXx	W1PIG	KARS
Rockland	147.0600	+	O 91.5 (CA) eL(W1PBR/R WASHINGTON)rsx	W1PBR	PBay RACES
Rockport-Ragged Mtn	146.8200	–	O 100e L(KQ1L LINK SYSTEM)rsWXx	KQ1L	KQ1L
Washington	145.4900	–	O 91.5 (CA) eL(WZ1J BRUNSWICK)rsx	KC1CG	KC1CG
Washington	147.0600	+	O 91.5 (CA) eL(W1PBR/R ROCKLAND)rsx	W1PBR	PBay RACES
NORTHWEST					
Buckfield-Strkd Mtn	146.8800	–	O 100e L(KQ1L LINK SYSTEM)rsWXx	KQ1L	KQ1L
Farmington	147.1800	+	O 123	W1BHR	KY1C
Hiram	147.0150	+	O 103.5ex	K1AAM	K1AAM
Madison	146.7300	–	O 91.5es	KA1C	KA1C
New Sharon	145.3500	–	O 100e L(KQ1L MAINE NETWORK)rsWXx	N1UGR	KQ1L
Norway	147.1200	+	O 136.5ers	W1OCA	OCARES
Rumford	146.9100	–	O 100ex	N1BBK	N1BBK
Skowhegan	147.3450	+	O	KA1ZGC	KA1ZGC

Location	Output	Input	Notes	Call	Sponsor
Sugarloaf Mtn	146.9700	–	O 100e	KQ1L	KQ1L
			L(KQ1L LINK SYSTEM)rsWXx		
PORTLAND/SOUTH COAST					
Acton	145.2100	–	O 156.7	N1KMA	CLEOSYS
			L(CCS NETWORK)		
Alfred	145.4100	–	O 103.5aer	WJ1L	RACES
Arundel	146.9250	–	O 103.5	W6BZ	N East ARC
			(CA)eL(WATERBORO 444.600)r		
Auburn	146.6100	–	O 88.5e	W1NPP	AARC
Biddeford	147.1500	+	O 79.7	KA1JWM	KA1JWM
Brunswick	147.1350	+	O 103.5	WZ1J	G.R.U.
			(CA)eL(444.9)x		
Brunswick	147.2100	+	O 100aepr	KS1R	MARA
			sx		
Cornish	145.2100	–	O 156.7ae	N1KMA	CLEOSYS
			L(CCS SYSTEM) EXPx		
Falmouth	146.7300	–	O 100	W1KVI	PAWA
Falmouth	147.0900	+	O 100aes	W1QUI	W1QUI
			WXx		
Gray	147.0450	+	O 103.5e	K1MV	RRRA
Livermore Falls	147.2250	+	O 123	W1BHR	BHRG
Naples	146.8350	–	103.5x	K1AAM	K1AAM
Poland Spring	147.3150	+	O 103.5x	K1AAM	K1AAM
Portland	147.3600	+	O#	K1SA	COORDEXP
Saco	146.7750	–	O	WA1GTT	WA1GTT
Sanford	145.2100	–	O 156.7ae	N1KMA	CLEOSYS
			L(CCS SYSTEM)x		
Sanford	146.8050	–	O	N1KMA	CLEOSYS
			156.7/146.2aeL(DMR D*V CCS SYSTEM)x		
Sanford	147.1800	+	O 88.5/100	K1PHF	KQ1L
			eL(D*V DMR KQ1L NETWORK)x		
Waldoboro	147.3900	+	O 179.9	K1NYY	K1NYY
			(CA)		
Wales	145.2900	–	O 100e	W1PIG	KARS
			L(145.390 449.275 145.270 443.200)sWXx		
Waterboro	147.2700	+	O 103.5e	W1CKD	PRG
			L(444.6) WXx		
West Newfield	146.6700	–	O 146.2e	N1KMA	CLEOSYS
			L(D*V CCS NETWORK) EXPx		
WASHINGTON COUNTY					
Calais	145.1700	–	Oes	W1LH	R Holst
Cooper	146.6100	–	O 114.8	WB5NKJ	WB5NKJ
Cooper	146.9850	–	● 179.9es	W1LH	CMRG
			WXx		
Cooper	147.3300	+	O 118.8s	W1LH	W1LH
			WX		
Marshfield	146.7750	–	O 192.8	K1HF	K1HF
			E-SUN		
Topsfield	146.6700	–	O 100	K1HHC	COORDEXP
			L(KQ1L LINK SYSTEM)		

Location	Output	Input	Notes	Call	Sponsor
MARYLAND					
ALL					
SNP	145.1700	–	O		------------
ANNAPOLIS					
Davidsonville	147.1050	+	O 107.2aez	W3VPR	AARC
Millersville	146.8050	–	O 107.2aerZ(911)	W3CU	MMARC
BALTIMORE					
Baltimore	147.0300	+	O(CA)elWX	WB3DZO	BRATS
Baltimore	147.3450	+	O 127.3	N3HIA	N3HIA
Cockeysville	145.1900	–	O 110.9	K3NXU	Boumi AR
Columbia	147.1350	+	O 156.7er	K3CUJ	Col. ARA
Cooksville	147.3900	+	O 156.7ersWX	K3CUJ	Col. ARA
Curtis Bay	147.0750	+	O 107.2 (CA)elrsWX	W3VPR	AARC
E Baltimore	147.2400	+	Ol	W3PGA	Aero ARC
Jessup	146.7600	–	O 107.2l	WA3DZD	MFMA
Jessup	146.7600	223.1600	O 107.2l	WA3DZD	MFMA
Jessup	146.7600	449.0000	O 107.2l	WA3DZD	MFMA
Towson	146.6700	–	O 107.2aelr	W3FT	BARC
CENTRAL MD					
Damascus	145.2500	–	O 146.2l	N3VNG	KK3L
CUMBERLAND					
Cumberland	145.4500	–	O 123.0elrsWX	W3YMW	Mtn ARC
Cumberland	147.1050	+	O 192.8	WX3M	WX3M
FREDERICK					
Frederick	146.6400	–	O 156.7	K3ERM	FARC
Frederick	146.7300	–	O 141.3e	W3ICF	FARG
Frederick	147.0600	+	O 123.0 (CA)elrWX	K3MAD	MADXRA
Thurmont	147.1950	+	O 179.9	N3EJT	N3EJT
HAGERSTOWN					
Clear Spring	147.3450	+	O 123.0	K3MAD	MADXRA
Hagerstown	146.9400	–	Oar	W3CWC	AnttmRA
Hagerstown	147.0900	+	Oer	W3CWC	AnttmRA
Hagerstown	147.3750	+	Or	K3UMV	K3UMV
NORTH CENTRAL					
Manchester	146.8950	–	Ol	N3KZS	N3KZS
Sykesville	147.2850	+	O	K3PZN	CCARC
Westminster	145.4100	–	O 114.8aelrz	K3PZN	CCARC
NORTH EASTERN SHORE					
Centerville	146.9400	–	O 107.2l	N8ADN	K.I. ARC
Worton	147.3750	+	O 156.7 (CA)ersWX	K3ARS	Kent ARS

Location	Output	Input	Notes	Call	Sponsor
NORTHEAST MD					
Bel Air	146.7750	–	O 146.2aer	WBØEGR	HarfdCoRACES
Bel Air	147.1200	+	O	N3EKQ	N3EKQ
Charlestown	145.4700	–	O 107.2 (CA)rz	N3RCN	N3RCN
Port Deposit	146.8500	–	O 107.2 L(53.83)	WA3SFJ	CBRA
Shawsville	145.3300	–	O	K3HT	W3EHT
SOUTH EASTERN SHORE					
Easton	147.0450	+	O 156.7er Z(911)	K3EMD	EARS
Ocean City	147.0150	+	O 156.7a	N3KZS	Tri-Co A
Princess Anne	146.6250	–	O 156.7ar	KA3MRX	SCARES
Salisbury	146.8200	–	O 156.7ae	WA3ROW	DARC
Salisbury	146.9250	–	O 156.7erz	W3PRO	PROS
SOUTHERN MD					
Blossom Point	146.8500	–	Oe	W3BPT	BPARC
Brandywine	147.1500	+	O 114.8els WX	W3SMR	SMARC
Hollywood	147.1950	+	O 156.7er	N3PX	SPARC
Hughesville	145.3900	–	O 186.2e	W3ZO	W7UH
Lexington Park	146.6400	–	O 146.2ae z	K3HKI	StMary'sCoARA
Prince Frederick	145.3500	–	O 156.7ael	N3NO	CARC
Sunderland	146.9850	–	O 156.7er	K3CAL	Calvert ARA
WASHINGTON AREA					
Adelphi	145.3700	–	Oe	W3ARL	HDL ARC
Ashton	147.0000	–	O 156.7a	K3WX	ARCS
Bethesda	145.2900	–	O 156.7e	K3YGG	NIHRAC
Bladensburg	146.6100	–	O(CA)er	K3GMR	GMRA
College Park	145.4900	–	OA(*911)z	W3EAX	U of Md ARC
Germantown	147.2700	+	O 156.7 L(P25 NAC 293)	WA3KOK	NERA
Greenbelt	146.8350	–	Oe	WA3NAN	Goddard ARC
Greenbelt	146.8800	–	O(CA)er	W3GMR	GMRA
Jessup	146.7600	–	O 107.2l	WA3DZD	MFMA
Jessup	146.7600	223.1600	O 107.2l	WA3DZD	MFMA
Jessup	146.7600	449.0000	O 107.2l	WA3DZD	MFMA
Lanham	145.2300	–	O 110.9	K3ERA	PGCERA
Laurel	145.4300	–	O 114.8es	K3MRC	DCMARC
Rockville	146.9550	–	O(CA)er	KV3B	MARC
Silver Spring	147.1800	+	O 156.7ar	KA3LAO	Tri-Co A
Silver Spring	147.2250	+	O 156.7ael	WB3GXW	WB3GXW
WESTERN MD					
Frostburg	147.2400	+	O 123.0l	KK3L	KK3L
Lonaconing	147.3150	+	O 118.8e	N3JJK	N3JJK
Midland	146.8800	–	O 123.0/141.3ars	W3YMW	Mtn ARC
Oakland	146.8050	–	O 123.0arz	KB8NUF	GCARES

Location	Output	Input	Notes	Call	Sponsor
MASSACHUSETTS					
BLACKSTONE VALLEY					
Medway	147.0600	+	O 100 L(224.66)	W1KG	W1KG
Mendon	146.6100	–	O 146.2 (CA) L(MMRA)	AE1C	MMRA
BOSTON METRO					
Belmont	145.4300	–	O 67	W1MRA	MMRA
Boston	145.2100	–	O 100e	KB1BEM	KB1BEM
Boston	145.2300	–	O 88.5esx	W1BOS	BARC
Boston	145.3100	–	O 123e	W1KBN	NUWireless
Brookline	146.8200	–	O 146.2 E-SUN E-WIND L(MMRA)	K5TEC	MMRA
Brookline	146.9850	–	O 88.5/118.8x	W1FCC	BrklineARC
Burlington	146.7150	–	O 146.2 (CA)eL(MMRA)r	KC1US	MMRA
Newton	147.3600	+	O 67 L(E117424)	W1LJO	MDLSX ARC
Quincy	146.6700	–	O 146.2 (CA) L(MMRA)	W1BRI	MMRA
Wakefield	147.0750	+	O 151.4e	WA1RHN	WA1RHN
Waltham	146.6400	–	O 136.5 L(P25:NAC293 E490278)	W1MHL	WalthamARA
BOSTON SOUTH					
Attleboro	147.1950	+	O 127.3ers WXx	K1SMH	SMHARC
Canton	146.7450	–	O 146.2 L(E375668 I4632)	K1BFD	EMARG
Foxborough	147.0150	+	O 67	KB1CYO	NWS
Norwood	147.2100	+	O 100	W1JLI	NARC/NEMA
Sharon	146.8650	–	O 103.5rsx	K1CNX	S EMA
Taunton	145.2800	–	OL(NXDN)	WG1U	KA1DTA
Taunton	147.1350	+	O 67rsx	KA1GG	PAWA
Walpole	146.8950	–	O 123eWX	K1HRV	EMA
Wrentham	147.0900	+	O 146.2e L(E222792 I4751)x	K1LBG	K1LBG
CAPE AND ISLANDS					
Barnstable	146.7300	–	O 67e L(E402289)	W1SGL	CC & IARA
Dennis	146.9550	–	O 88.5e L(E20024)rsWX	K1PBO	BARC
Falmouth	146.6550	–	O 88.5 (CA) eL(NEWTON GPO REPEATER)prs	K1RK	FARA
Falmouth	147.3750	+	O 110.9ers	N1YHS	N1YHS
Nantucket	145.3100	–	O 107.2e	W1UF	W1UF
North Eastham	145.2700	–	ODCS(445)	N1BX	N1BX
Truro	147.2550	+	O 67e L(E403358)	WA1YFV	PARC

Location	Output	Input	Notes	Call	Sponsor
West Tisbury	147.3450	+	O 88.5e L(E 242147)rs	KB1QL	MVRC
CENTRAL					
Athol	147.3900	+	O 100	N1WW	M.A.R.S.
Clinton	146.6550	–	O 74.4 (CA) er	N1ZUZ	CEMA
Fitchburg	145.4500	–	O 74.4 (CA) er	W1GZ	MARA
Fitchburg	147.3150	+	O 100 (CA) eL(224.34/442.95/53.93)px	WB1EWS	WB1EWS
Gardner	145.3700	–	O 136.5e L(I8581)rsWXx	W1GCD	GardnerOEM
Oxford	147.2550	+	O 88.5	K1AOI	K1AOI
Paxton	146.9700	–	O 114.8ex	W1BIM	CMARA
Warren	147.2100	+	O 88.5rs	K1QVR	QVARC
Worcester	145.3100	–	O 100a L(449.025)	W1WPI	WPIWA
Worcester	146.9250	–	O 100	W1YK	WPIWA
FRANKLIN COUNTY					
Deerfield	145.1300	–	O 173.8	KB1NTK	AB1RS
Leyden	146.9850	–	O 136.5ers WXx	KB1BSS	FCARC
Orange	146.6250	–	O 110.9	NA1P	NQRA
South Deerfield	147.1650	+	O 118.8e	N1PMA	N1PMA
MERRIMACK VALLEY					
Andover	146.8350	–	O 94.8ers	KB1PTZ	Tn Andover
Billerica	147.1200	+	O 103.5	W1DC	1200 ARC
Haverhill	145.3500	–	O 136.5 (CA)e	KT1S	KT1S
North Andover	145.2900	–	O 167.9 (CA)e	KA1LFD	ECAT
Pepperell	147.3450	+	O 100ers	N1MNX	N1MNX
Westford	145.3300	–	OL(D*V)	WB1GOF	PART
Westford	146.9550	–	O 74.4e L(E380799)rsWXx	WB1GOF	PART
METROWEST					
Concord	145.1100	–	O 110.9e	N1CON	CWA
Framingham	147.1500	+	O 100 L(E506576 I4355 448.025)	W1FY	FARA
Harvard	145.4100	–	O 74.4arsx	W1DVC	Harvard RA
Holliston	145.1400	–	OL(D*V)	W1DSR	DigitalARC
Holliston	147.3750	+	OL(DMR)	W1NGS	DigitalARC
Marlborough	147.2400	+	O 71.9/110.9ers	WA1NPN	TH Group
Marlborough	147.2700	+	O 146.2 (CA)eL(MMRA MRO NET)	W1MRA	MMRA
Southborough	145.2700	–	O L(DMR:CC7)	W1EMC	EMC ARC
Wellesley	147.0300	+	O 123 L(COLOCATED 444.600)	W1TKZ	WellslyARS

Location	Output	Input	Notes	Call	Sponsor
Weston	146.7900	–	O 146.2 (CA) L(MMRA)r	N1BE	MMRA
NORTH SHORE					
Beverly	147.3900	+	O 131.8er	WA1PNW	Beverly CD
Danvers	145.4700	–	O 136.5 (CA) L(E314375 I4427)rs	NS1RA	NSRA
Gloucester	145.1300	–	O 107.2ae L(EW1GLO-R)x	W1GLO	CAARA
Ipswich	145.4900	–	O 131.8ers WX	W1IEM	Ipswich EM
Lynn	145.3300	–	O 88.5 (CA) L(E20908)	W1DVG	W1DVG
Lynn	147.0150	+	● 88.5 (CA) L(E20908)	W1DVG	W1DVG
Salem	146.8800	–	O 118.8e	NS1RA	NSRA
Saugus	146.9100	–	O 123 (CA) er	K1SVP	E.M.F.r.a.
Topsfield	147.2850	+	O 100e	W1VYI	ECRA
West Newbury	146.6250	–	O 131.8 (CA)ersx	K1KKM	PRA
SOUTH COAST					
Dartmouth	145.2200	–	OL(D*V)	K1RFI	SEMARG
Dartmouth	147.0000	+	O 67ae L(E4343 I4347)rx	W1AEC	SEMARA
Fairhaven	145.4900	–	O 67ae L(E4611 I4617)sWXx	W1SMA	SCMARG
Fall River	145.1500	–	O 123e L(E668385)rs	WA1DGW	BCRA
Fall River	145.4200	–	OL(D*V)	K1RFI	SEMARG
Fall River	146.8050	–	O 67 (CA)e	NN1D	SEMARG
New Bedford	145.1100	–	O 67 L(E4254 I4245)	NB1MA	LAARA
Swansea	145.3200	–	Oe L(NXDN)	KC1JET	PAWA
SOUTH SHORE					
Bridgewater	147.1800	+	O 67 (CA)e L(E451971 I4388) WXx	W1MV	MARA
Norwell	145.2500	–	O 77e L(D*V)	W1QWT	W1QWT
Norwell	145.3900	–	O 67e L(NXDN I4320 443.600 RMTBASE)r	AC1M	NS1N
Plymouth	146.6850	–	O 82.5er WX	N1ZIZ	G.A.R.S.
Plymouth	147.3150	+	O 67e L(NXDN)x	WG1U	WG1U
West Bridgewater	146.7750	–	ODCS(244) eL(WESTBORO MA 448.775)x	W1WNS	W1WNS
Weymouth	147.3000	+	O 67er	N1BGT	SSRA
Whitman	147.2250	+	O 67 (CA)e L(E484193 I8691)r	WA1NPO	WhitmanARC

Location	*Output*	*Input*	*Notes*	*Call*	*Sponsor*
SPRINGFIELD/PIONEER VALLEY					
Agawam	146.6700	–	O 127.3 L(I4322)s	W1TOM	MTARA
Feeding Hills	145.1500	–	OeL(D*V)x	W1KK	W1KK
Holyoke	146.7150	–	O 100e	K1ZJH	K1ZJH
Holyoke	146.9400	–	O 127.3 L(147.000 MTARA REPEATER)sx	W1TOM	MTARA
Monson	147.1050	+	O 162.2	W1OBQ	NYNES
Westfield	147.0750	+	O 88.5	W1JWN	GWMRC
THE BERKSHIRES					
Egremont	145.2500	–	O 114.8x	WB2BQW	NE. Conn.
Great Barrington	145.2700	–	O 136.5e WX	KA1OA	NoBARC
Lenox	145.2900	–	O 77e L(E264386)x	WA1WMG	PiveroComm
Mt Greylock	145.2100	–	O 77e L(E264386)rx	WA1WMG	PiveroComm
Mt Greylock	146.9100	–	O 162.2e L(PL:10*=DEFEAT 11*=ENABLE) WXx	K1FFK	NoBARC
North Adams	145.4900	–	O 100	KC1EB	KC1EB
Pittsfield	147.0300	+	O 162.2e	K1FFK	NoBARC
MICHIGAN					
LOWER PEN NORTHEAST					
Alpena	145.4900	–	O 100rsWX	WB8ZIR	N8BIT-8BIT RPT
Alpena	146.7600	–	O 88.5e	K8PA	TBARC
Bad Axe	145.4700	–	OWX	N8LFR	LHARC
Bad Axe	146.8800	–	Oe	KA8PZP	Thumb ARC
Bay City	145.3100	–	O 131.8ers WX	N8BBR	BARC
Bay City	147.3600	+	OaelrsWX	N8BBR	BARC
Caro	146.6600	–	O 141.3ers WX	KC8CNN	TCARA
Caro	146.8200	–	OaesWXz	WA8CKT	WA8CKT
Cheboygan	146.7400	–	O 103.5ex	W8IPQ	CCARA
Gaylord	147.1200	+	O 151.4ers WXx	WD8DX	N8JCN
Harrisville	147.0400	+	O 123aers WXz	W8HUF	Alcona County E
Hemlock	145.3300	–	O 88.5	K8DO	K8DO
Lewiston	145.1900	–	●tl	W8YUC	RARG
Mackinaw City	145.1100	–	O 103.5r	W8AGB	CCECPSCO
Midland	147.0000	+	O 103.5a DCSersWX	W8KEA	MARC
Mio	145.3500	–	Oe	WT8G	AVARC
Oscoda	145.2300	–	O 100	WD8RNO	WD8RNO
Pleasant Valley	146.7200	–	O 103.5ex	KB8ZGU	CMARA
Rogers City	147.0200	+	O 103.5	WB8TQZ	Presque Isle Cou
Roscommon	145.4500	–	Ors	WF8R	CRARA

Location	Output	Input	Notes	Call	Sponsor
Rose City	145.1100	–	O 156.7s WXz	W8DMI	W8DMI
Saginaw	147.2400	+	O 103.5ars WX	K8DAC	SVARA
Sandusky	146.8600	–	OesWX	W8AX	Thumb ARC
Sterling	147.0600	+	O 103.5e	K8WBR	N8CJM
West Branch	145.4100	–	O 91.5l	W8YUC	RARG
West Branch	146.9400	–	O 103.5ers	K8OAR	OARS
LOWER PEN NORTHWEST					
Benzonia	147.0400	+	O 114.8alr s	W8BNZ	Benzie ARC
Big Rapids	145.2900	–	O 94.8ael WXxz	W8IRA	IRA
Big Rapids	146.7400	–	OaersWXx	KB8QOI	BRAARC
Cadillac	146.9800	–	O(CA)exz	K8CAD	WEXARC
Cadillac	147.1600	+	O 103.5ael WXxz	W8IRA	IRA
East Jordan	147.2800	+	O 103.5ers WX	W8COL	COLARC
Farwell	147.2000	+	O 103.5r	KA8DCJ	KA8DCJ
Fremont	146.9200	–	O 94.8aers WX	KC8MSE	NCRG
Gaylord	146.8200	–	O 118.8 (CA)ersWXxz	NM8RC	TOMARC
Gladwin	147.1800	+	O 173.8e	W8GDW	GAARC
Grayling	145.1300	–	O 107.2e	N8AHZ	ARAHH
Hart	146.6400	–	O 94.8elrs WX	N8UKH	OCARES
Holton	147.3200	+	O 94.8ers WXz	WD8MKG	WD8MKG
Kalkaska	147.3000	+	O 123e	AA8ZV	AA8ZV
Lake City	145.2100	–	O	KG8QY	Rat Pack
Lake Leelanau	146.9200	–	O 114.8	N8JKV	N8JKV
Leland	145.3900	–	O 103.5ars	W8SGR	LRA&CARC
Ludington	145.3100	–	O 94.8ael WXxz	W8IRA	IRA
Ludington	145.4700	–	O 103.5e WX	K8DXF	K8DXF
Ludington	146.6200	–	O 94.8ae	WB8ERN	WB8ERN
Mackinaw City	146.8400	–	O 103.5ael WXxz	W8IRA	IRA
Mancelona	147.3800	+	O 107.2el	K8WQK	K8WQK
Manistee	145.1700	–	O 94.8	KB8BIT	KB8BIT
Manistee	146.7800	–	O 94.8e	W8GJX	Western Mich. Repea
Moorestown	146.9600	–	O 103.5 (CA)e	KA8ABM	KA8ABM
Mt Pleasant	145.1500	–	O 103.5ael WXxz	W8IRA	IRA
New Era	147.2200	+	●tDCSepr sWX	AB8AZ	AB8AZ

Location	*Output*	*Input*	*Notes*	*Call*	*Sponsor*
Peshawbestown	146.6600	–	●trs	W8QPO	Leelanau Repeat
Stutsmanville	146.6800	–	O 110.9e WXx	W8GQN	SAARC
Traverse City	145.1500	–	O 114.8ael WXxz	W8IRA	IRA
Traverse City	145.2700	–	O 114.8el	W8TVC	NMARC / IOOK
Traverse City	146.8600	–	O 114.8rs	W8TCM	CARC
Traverse City	147.1000	+	O 100rsWX x	K8HIB	K8HIB
Traverse City	147.3400	+	O 114.8	KJ4KFJ	KJ4KFJ
Vanderbilt	145.2900	–	O 103.5ael WXxz	W8IRA	IRA
Walkerville	145.4300	–	O 94.8	NW8J	NW8J
White Cloud	145.4500	–	O 94.8e	KB8IFE	KB8IFE
LOWER PEN SOUTHEAST					
Adrian	145.3700	–	O 85.4es WX	W8TQE	Adrian ARC
Ann Arbor	145.2300	–	O 100e	W8UM	U of M ARC
Ann Arbor	146.7400	–	O 107.2ex	WB8UPM	WB8UPM
Ann Arbor	146.9600	–	O 100es	W8PGW	Arrow ARC
Burton	147.3800	+	O 88.5el	N8NE	FAIR
Chelsea	145.4500	–	O 100es WX	WD8IEL	CARC
Clarkston	146.8400	–	O 100 (CA) ersWX	K8NWD	CRA
Dearborn	145.2700	–	O 100 (CA) e	K8UTT	Ford ARL
Dearborn	147.1600	+	O 100 (CA) ersWX	WR8DAR	N8DJP
Detroit	145.1100	–	●te	W8DET	DM&KC
Detroit	145.2100	–	O 123 DCS x	WW8GM	GMARC
Detroit	145.3300	–	O 100ers WX	WR8DAR	RADAR
Detroit	146.7600	–	O 100as WXx	KE8HR	SpiritARC
Durand	145.2900	–	O 100lrs WX	N8IES	N8IES
Fenton	146.7800	–	O 67 (CA) WXx	W8VHB	FAARA
Flint	147.1000	+	O 100 (CA) elrsWXz	KC8KGZ	Michigan Speciali
Flint	147.2600	+	O 100lrs	KC8KGZ	Michigan Speciali
Flint	147.3400	+	O 100	W8ACW	GCRC
Fort Gratiot	146.8000	–	O 100lrs WXx	K8ARC	ARCARS
Garden City	146.8600	–	O 100 (CA) elrs	KK8GC	GCRA
Grosse Point Woods	146.7400	–	O 100	K8BYI	SEMARA

Location	*Output*	*Input*	*Notes*	*Call*	*Sponsor*
Howell	146.6800	–	O 162.2aelrsWX	W8LRK	LARK
Lapeer	146.6200	–	O 100 (CA) ersWXxz	W8LAP	LCARA
Livonia	145.3500	–	O 100el	K8UNS	LARC
Manchester	146.9800	–	O 100es	WD8IEL	CARC
Milford	146.9000	–	O 100ers WX	W8OAK	Oakland Co EmerMg
Monroe	145.3100	–	OersWX	W8YZ	MEMRA
Monroe	146.7200	–	O 100 (CA)l rsWXz	K8RPT	River Raisin Repeater
Mt Clemens	147.2000	+	O 100ers WX	WA8MAC	MCEM
Northville	145.1700	–	O 100elrs WX	KA8SPW	KA8SPW
Oak Park	146.6400	–	O 100arsx z	W8HP	DART
Owosso	147.0200	+	O 100 (CA) ersWX	N8DVH	N8DVH
Paw Paw	147.2000	+	O 94.8	W8GDS	W8GDS
Port Huron	146.7200	–	O 110.9ers WX	WD8DUV	PHART
Port Huron	147.3000	+	OersWXx	K8DD	PHART
Rankin	145.1900	–	●tl	W8YUC	RARG
Roseville	147.2200	+	Ol	N8EDV	N8EDV
Royal Oak Twp	147.1400	+	O 100ax	N8KD	SMART
South Lyon	147.0400	+	O 110.9e	K8VJ	SLARA
Sterling Heights	147.0800	+	O 100e	N8LC	LCARC
Utica	147.1800	+	O 100 DCS e	K8UO	USECA
Waterford	145.4300	–	O 100 (CA) elWX	W8JIM	W8JIM
White Lake	145.4900	–	O 67 (CA)el rsWXxz	N8BIT	8BITRG
Wyandotte	147.2400	+	O 100	WY8DOT	DARES
Ypsilanti	146.9200	–	O 100lrs WXx	K8RUR	I 94 ARC
LOWER PEN SOUTHWEST					
Allegan	147.2400	+	O 94.8ers WX	AC8RC	ACARC
Alma	145.3700	–	O 100as WXz	KC8MUV	Alma Repeater Club
Bangor	147.3600	+	O 94.8ers WXx	K8BRC	BRARC
Battle Creek	145.1500	–	O 94.8ael WXxz	W8IRA	IRA
Battle Creek	146.6600	–	O 94.8aez	W8DF	SMARS
Berrien Springs	145.3700	–	O(CA)x	W8YKS	DOCRG
Cassopolis	146.9200	–	O 156.7ers WX	N8VPZ	N8VPZ

Location	*Output*	*Input*	*Notes*	*Call*	*Sponsor*
Cedar Springs	146.8800	–	O 141.3e	NW8J	NW8J
Centreville	145.3100	–	O 94.8lrs WX	KC8AAF	ARPSA
Charlotte	147.0800	+	O 103.5ers WX	K8CHR	ECARC
Coldwater	147.3000	+	O 100ers WX	WD8KAF	BCARC
Dowagiac	145.2100	–	O 94.8rWX	KU8Y	KU8Y
Grand Haven	145.4900	–	O 94.8ls WX	W8CSO	North Ottawa Am
Grand Rapids	145.1100	–	O 94.8ers	NW8J	Kent Co Emerge
Grand Rapids	145.2300	–	O 94.8	W8USA	Michigan Amateu
Grand Rapids	145.4100	–	O 94.8ers WX	K8WM	541 Inc
Grand Rapids	146.7600	–	O 94.8e	W8DC	GRARA
Grand Rapids	147.1600	+	O 94.8ael WXxz	W8IRA	IRA
Grand Rapids	147.2600	+	O 94.8al	W8DC	GRARA
Holland	146.5000	147.5000	O 94.8	K8DAA	HARC
Holland	147.0600	+	O 94.8ers WX	K8DAA	HARC
Jackson	145.4700	–	O 114.8 (CA)lx	KA8HDY	KA8HDY
Jackson	146.8800	–	O 114.8ars WXz	W8JXN	CARS
Jackson	147.3600	+	O 100aers	KA8HDY	CARS
Jonesville	147.0600	+	O 151.4ers WX	KC8QVX	HCARC
Kalamazoo	145.1700	–	O 94.8e	N8FYZ	N8DXB
Kalamazoo	147.0000	+	O 94.8 (CA) erWX	W8VY	KARC
Kalamazoo	147.0400	+	O 94.8 (CA)	K8KZO	SWMART
Lansing	146.7000	–	O 107.2aers	WB8CQM	LCDRA
Lansing	146.9400	–	O 100ers	WB8CQM	LCDRA
Lansing	147.2800	+	O 107.2	KB8LCY	KB8LCY
Lowell	145.2700	–	O 94.8as WXxz	W8LRC	Lowell Amateur
Mattawan	146.5000	147.5000	O 94.8rs WX	W8GDS	W8GDS
Muskegon	145.3300	–	O 94.8ael WXxz	W8IRA	IRA
Muskegon	146.8200	–	O 94.8rWX	K8WNJ	MCES
Muskegon	146.9400	–	O 94.8e	W8ZHO	MAARC
Muskegon	147.3800	+	O 94.8	KE8LZ	N8UKF
Niles	147.1800	+	O 94.8es WX	KC8BRS	Four Flags ARC
Okemos	145.3900	–	O 100ers WXx	WB8CQM	LCDRA

MICHIGAN

Location	Output	Input	Notes	Call	Sponsor
Portland	145.1300	–	O 94.8	N8ZMT	Ionia ARES
Saranac	146.5000	147.5000	O 94.8	N8MRC	N8MRC
Saugatuck	146.9600	–	O 94.8	AC8GN	AC8GN
Sister Lakes	146.8200	–	O 88.5lrs WX	W8MAI	Blossomland Amateur
St Joseph	145.4700	–	O 94.8ael WXxz	W8IRA	IRA
St Joseph	146.7200	–	O 131.8rs	KB8VIM	SCRA/BARA
Whitehall	146.5000	147.5000	O 127.3ers WX	W8WPD	W-M ES
Whitehall	146.6800	–	O 94.8ers WX	K8COP	K8COP
UPPER PEN CENT					
Escanaba	145.1300	–	Oe	KB9BQX	KB9BQX
Escanaba	147.1500	+	O 100.0e	W8JRT	DCARS
Gladstone	147.2400	+	O 107.2	N8DP	N8DP
Gwinn	146.6400	–	O 100.0l	N8RRZ	HARA
Iron Mountain	146.8500	–	OaeWX	WA8FXQ	MichACon
Ishpeming	146.9100	–	Oe	K8LOD	HARA
Marquette	146.9700	–	Oe	KE8IL	MrquttRA
Marquette	147.2700	+	O 100.0el	KG8YT	HARA
Menominee	147.0000	+	O 107.2e	W8PIF	M&MARC
Munising	145.4100	–	O 100.0lz	KC8BAN	AlgerARC
Republic	146.8200	–	O 100.0e	KBØP	HARA
Republic	147.0900	+	OE-SUN E-WIND	NZ8U	CUPRA
Trenary	147.0300	+	O 100.0e	W8FYZ	TRA
UPPER PEN EAST					
Cooks	146.7000	–	O 110.9rs	WA8WG	WA8WG
Deer Park	147.0900	+	O 114.8e	W8NBY	LARS
Drummond Island	147.3600	–	O 110.9e	W8ON	EARS
Grand Marais	147.1950	+	O 100.0lz	KC8BAN	AlgerARC
Manistique	146.7900	–	O	W8NI	MARA
Newberry	146.6100	–	O	W8NBY	LARS
Pickford	146.6400	–	Oe	W8EUP	EUPAR
SaultSte Marie	147.1050	+	Oe	KB8SKC	KB8SKC
SaultSte Marie	147.2100	+	O 107.2e	W8EUP	EUPAR
Strongs	147.3300	+	Oe	W8EUP	EUPAR
UPPER PEN WEST					
Bessemer	146.7600	–	Oe	K8ATX	BlkJckRA
Calumet	147.3150	+	O 100.0ae z	K8MDH	KewCoRA
Gaastra	145.1700	–	O 107.2e	N8LVQ	IRARC
Hancock	146.8800	–	O 100.0ae	W8CDZ	CCRAA
Houghton	147.3900	+	O 100.0	N8WAV	N8WAV
Ironwood	146.8050	–	O 110.9e	K9MLD	K9MLD
Winona	146.7300	–	Oe	W8UXG	SARA

Location	Output	Input	Notes	Call	Sponsor
MINNESOTA					
CENTRAL					
Avon	147.1050	+	O 85.4ae WX	KØSTC	STEARNS
Becker	147.3450	+	O 85.4	KØOS	+KBØRRN
Cambridge	146.6400	–	O 146.2e	WRØP	ICSES
Collegeville	147.0150	+	O 100.0x	WØSV	STCLOUDRC
Crown	145.2100	–	O 114.8	NØGEF	NOGEF
Darwin	146.6850	–	O 146.2	WØCRC	CRARC
Elk River	146.9700	–	O	KØCJD	ELKRVRRA
Foley	147.0750	+	O 85.4es WX	KBØPXT	BCEM
Hutchinson	147.3750	+	O 146.2 WX	KBØWJP	CITYOFHUT
Little Falls	147.1350	+	O 123.0e	WØREA	LARA
Long Prairie	146.6550	–	Oe	KCØTAF	TODDCTYES
Maple Lake	145.2300	–	O 114.8	WØEQO	HANDIHAM
Milaca	145.3500	–	O 141.3	WBØMPE	WBØMPE
Paynesville	145.2700	–	O	WDØDEH	PAYNSRA
Sauk Centre	147.2550	+	O	WØALX	RUNEARC
St Cloud	146.8350	–	O 85.4eWX	NØOYQ	NØOYQ
St Cloud	146.9400	–	O 100.0a	WØSV	STCLDARC
Wyoming	146.8950	–	O 82.5	NØVOW	NØVOW
DULUTH					
Duluth	145.3100	–	O 110.9	NØEO	SVAMATRS
Duluth	145.4100	–	Oe	KCØHXC	NØBZZ
Duluth	145.4500	–	O 103.5e	KCØRTX	KCØRTX
Duluth	146.9400	–	Oae	WØGKP	AROWHDRC
Duluth	147.0600	+	O 110.9a	KCØIPA	LSAC
Duluth	147.1800	+	O 103.5e	KAØTMW	KAØTMW
Proctor	147.3300	+	O 151.4	NØBZZ	LSAC
EAST CENTRAL					
Carlton	146.7900	–	O 103.5e	KCØRTX	KCØRTX
Forest Lake	146.7300	–	O 114.8	KØHPY	KØHPY
Isle	146.6100	–	O 141.3	WBØSYO	WBØSYO
Mahtowa	147.0000	–	O 103.5e	WØGKP	MOOSELKRA
Ogilvie	147.2400	+	O 146.2el WX	KDØCI	KCEMO
Rush City	145.3300	–	O 146.2e	KØECM	ECMARC
METRO					
Blaine	146.6700	–	O 114.8ae	WØYFZ	ANOKACRC
Bloomington	147.0900	+	O(CA)e	KDØCL	ARAB
Burnsville	147.2100	+	O 100.0ae WXx	WØBU	TCRC
Carver	147.1650	+	O 107.2ae	WBØRMK	SMARTS
Cottage Grove	147.1800	+	O 74.4s	KSØJ	SEMARC
Eden Prairie	146.8800	–	O	WAØVLL	SWRPTRASN
Edina	145.4300	–	O 127.3e	WCØHC	HC RACES
Gem Lake	145.2300	–	O 94.8	KØLAV	KØLAV

MINNESOTA

Location	Output	Input	Notes	Call	Sponsor
Golden Valley	146.8200	–	O 127.3 (CA)e	WØPZT	HC SHERIFF
Hampton	147.3600	+	O 136.5e	KØJTA	KØJTA
Inver Grove	146.9850	–	O	WØCGM	SARCASM
Little Canada	146.9250	–	O 127.3a	KBØUPW	RAMCOES
Maple Plain	147.0000	+	O 114.8 (CA) WX	KØLTC	RARC
Maplewood	146.9250	–	O 127.3	KBØUPW	RAMCOES
Maplewood	147.1200	+	Oe	WØMR	MINING ARC
Minneapolis	145.1100	–	O	NØTL	TWINSLAN
Minneapolis	146.7000	–	O 127.3e	WCØHC	HC RACES
Minneapolis	147.0300	+	O	WBØMPE	WBØMPE
Minneapolis	147.1500	+	O 114.8	WØYC	UOFM RC
Minneapolis	147.2700	+	O 114.8	WBØZKB	WBØZKB
Minnetonka	145.4500	–	Oel	NØBVE	MHRA
New Brighton	145.2900	–	O 114.8	NØFKM	NØFKM
Oakdale	146.8500	–	O(CA) WXx	WDØHWT	MARA
Plymouth	146.7000	–	O 118.8e	WCØHC	HENNRACES
Ramsey	145.3700	–	O 118.8e	KØMSP	MIDWESTRA
Richfield	145.3900	–	O 103.5e	WBØPWQ	RICHPSAF
St Louis Park	146.7600	–	Oe	WØEF	TCFMCLUB
St Paul	145.1700	–	O 100.0	NØGOI	KØGOI
St Paul	145.3100	–	Oa	KØAGF	STPAULRC
Stillwater	147.0600	+	O 114.8s	WØJH	SARA
West St Paul	147.3900	+	O 77.0r	WØDCA	DCEC
NORTH CENTRAL					
Aitkin	146.8050	–	O 156.7	KCØQXC	ACRC
Aitkin	147.3600	+	O 203.5l	NØBZZ	L.S.A.C.
Bemidji	145.4500	–	Oe	KBØMM	TURTLRVRH
Bemidji	146.7300	–	Oa	WØBJI	PBARC
Brainerd	145.1300	–	O	WØUJ	BAARC
Brainerd	147.2250	+	OaeWX	WØUJ	BAARC
Crosslake	147.0300	+	O	WØUJ	BAARC
Grand Rapids	146.8800	–	O 123.0ae	KØGPZ	NLARC
Grand Rapids	147.0750	+	Oel	KØGPZ	NLARC
Hibbing	147.1200	+	OrsWX	WØHRF	WØHRF
International	146.9700	–	Oe	KØHKZ	KØHKZ
Lengby	147.2700	+	Oel	WØBJI	PBARC
Outing	145.4300	–	O 127.3	WRØG	WRØG
Park Rapids	147.3900	+	Oe	KØNLC	CWARC
Pequot Lakes	147.0900	+	O 123.0	WØREA	BRNLKARA
NORTH EAST					
Cloquet	146.6700	–	Oa	WAØGWI	WAØGWI
Coleraine	147.1650	+	O 114.8	KBØQYC	LSAC
Cook	147.3600	+	O 162.2l	NØBZZ	L.S.A.C.
Deer River	147.2550	+	O 103.5	KD6FFN	KD6FFN
Ely	146.6400	–	O 151.4e	NØOIW	LSAC
Giese	146.8650	–	O 146.2e	KBØQYC	LSAC
Grand Marais	146.7300	–	O 151.4 (CA)el	WØBBN	BWARC

Location	Output	Input	Notes	Call	Sponsor
Grand Marais	146.8950	–	O 151.4 (CA)e	WØBBN	BWARC
Grand Marias	147.3600	+	O 114.8l	NØBZZ	LSAC
Grand Portage	146.6550	–	O 151.4el	WØBBN	BWARC
Isabella	147.3000	+	O 114.8e	KBØQYC	KGØQR
Knife River	147.1350	+	O 103.5	KCØRTX	KCØRTX
Silver Bay	147.0900	+	O 114.8	NØBZZ	LSAC
Tofte	146.8650	–	O 151.4el	WØBBN	BWARC
Wales	147.2700	+	O 103.5e	WBØDGK	LSAC
NORTH WEST					
Barnsville	147.0600	+	O 123.0lx	KCØSD	KCØSD
Detroit Lakes	147.1950	+	Oe	WØEMZ	DETLKSARC
Karlstad	145.4700	–	O 77.0	KAØNWV	KAØNMV
Karlstad	146.6550	–	O 127.3	KAØNWV	KAØNWV
Park Rapids	147.3000	+	O	KØGUV	KØGUV
Sebeka	147.3300	+	O	KØJO	WADENARC
Thief River Falls	146.8500	–	OeWX	WBØWTI	WBØWTI
NORTHCENTRAL					
Cohasset	146.9850	–	O 118.8e	KBØCIM	KBOCIM
NORTHEAST					
Aurora	147.2400	+	O 156.7	NØBZZ	NØBZZ
Virginia	147.0600	+	O 103.5e	KBØQYC	LSAC
NORTHWEST					
Angle Inlet	147.2100	+	O 123.0ers WX	NØMHO	LOWRA
Detroit Lakes	146.7750	–	O	NØIZZ	NØIZZ
Moorhead	145.3500	–	O 123.0el	WØILO	WØILO
SOUTH CENTRAL					
Blue Earth	147.0000	+	Os	KØUSR	BLUERTHCD
Fairmont	146.6400	–	O	KØSXR	FAIRMTRC
Faribault	145.1900	–	O 100.0	NØZR	NØZR
Le Sueur	146.6100	–	O 136.5a	WBØERN	WBØERN
Mankato	147.0450	+	O 136.5ae	WØWCL	MARC
Mankato	147.2400	+	O 136.5 WX	WØWCL	MARC
New Ulm	146.8050	–	O 151.4	NØVQA	NØVQA
Sleepy Eye	147.3300	+	O 100.0	KØMTW	NEWULMARC
St Peter	147.1350	+	O 100.0	WQØA	SCAN
Waseca	146.7150	–	O 141.3e WX	KBØUJL	WCEM
Waseca	146.9400	–	OeWX	WAØCJU	VARS
SOUTH EAST					
Austin	145.4700	–	O 100.0	WØAZR	AUSTINRC
Austin	146.7300	–	O 100.0ae z	WØAZR	AARC
Faribault	146.7900	–	O 100.0ae	WBØNKX	WBØNKX
Glenville	146.8800	–	O 100.0	WAØRAX	ALBLEARC
La Crescent	146.9700	–	O 131.8ae WX	WR9ARC	RVRLNDARC

Location	*Output*	*Input*	*Notes*	*Call*	*Sponsor*
Northfield	146.6550	–	O 136.5e	NØOTL	CCRC
Owatonna	145.4900	–	O 100.0ers WX	KØHNY	OSCAR
Owatonna	147.1050	+	O 100.0ael	WBØVAJ	WBØVAK
Red Wing	147.3000	+	O	KCØLXM	HIWATVATC
Rochester	146.6250	–	O 100.0	WØMXW	ROCHARC
Rochester	146.8200	–	O 100.0ae	WØMXW	ROCHARC
Rochester	147.2550	+	O 100.0es WX	WØEAS	OEOC
Spring Valley	147.0150	+	O 110.9e	NØZOD	SPGVLYEMS
Wabasha	146.7450	–	O 136.5e	WAØUNB	WAØUNB
Winona	146.6400	–	Oae	WØNE	WINONARC
Winona	147.1500	+	Oe	WDØHAD	+OTHERS
Winona	147.2850	+	O 100.0e	NØPDD	NØQZU
SOUTH WEST					
Marshall	147.1950	+	O	WØBMJ	MARSHALRC
Pipestone	147.0750	+	O 141.3es WX	WØDRK	NPRRC
Redwood Falls	146.8650	–	O 141.3ae z	KBØCGJ	REDWARA
Tracy	147.1500	+	O 141.3es WX	WØDRK	NPRRC
Verdi	145.1100	–	O 146.2	KAØBWS	KAØBWS
Windom	147.2550	+	O 141.3es WX	WØDRK	NPRRC
Worthington	146.6700	–	O 141.3e WX	KØQBI	WORTHTARC
SOUTHEAST					
Glenville	146.6850	–	O 100.0ae	NXØP	NXØP
WEST CENTRAL					
Alexandria	146.7900	–	Oe	WØALX	RUNESTNRC
Fergus Falls	146.6400	–	Oae	KØQIK	LKREGARC
Madison	146.7300	–	O 146.2els WXx	KØLQP	WC MN ARC
Montevideo	147.1200	+	O 146.2e	NYØI	WCMARC
Ulen	146.6850	–	Oa	WØQQK	WØQQK
Willmar	145.2300	–	O 91.5	KCØUEA	RIDGEWATER
Willmar	146.9100	–	OeWXx	WØSW	WILLEAR
Willmar	147.0300	–	Oe	WØSW	WILLEAR

MISSISSIPPI

Abbeville	145.4700	–	O	WB5VYH	WB5VYH
Aberdeen	147.2700	+	O	WB5USN	MONROE CO ARC
Ackerman	147.1200	+	O	NO5N	------------
Amory	146.9400	–	O	KB5DWX	N MONROE CO RPT
Amory	147.0900	+	O	KB5DSN	------------
Batesville	146.6100	–	O	KM5WX	KM5WX
Bay St Louis	146.7000	–	O	KB5MPW	WQRZ

Location	*Output*	*Input*	*Notes*	*Call*	*Sponsor*
Bay St Louis	146.8500	–	O	KØVNO	------------
Bay St Louis	147.3000	+	O	KB5MPW	HANCOCK CO A
Biloxi	146.7300	–	O	W5SGL	MISS. COAST A
Biloxi	146.7900	–	O	K5TYP	KEESLER ARC
Booneville	145.1900	–	O	K5YD	BOONEVILLE R
Booneville	147.1500	+	O	KI5WI	------------
Brandon	145.1700	–	O	K5RKN	KD5RWF
Brandon	147.3450	+	O	K5RKN	KD5RWF
Bude	146.8500	–	O	W5WQ	SW MS ARC
Byhalia	145.3300	–	O	N4DRL	N4DRL
Byhalia	145.3500	–	O	W5GWD	W5GWD
Byhalia	147.2250	+	O	N4DRL	N4DRL
Chatawa	145.3100	–	O	WB5GOJ	WB5GOJ
Chunky	147.3900	+	O	W5PPB	W5PPB
Cleveland	146.7750	–	O	KD5YTB	------------
Cleveland	147.2850	+	O	N5LRL	------------
Collins	146.9850	–	O	N5LRQ	------------
Columbia	147.1950	+	O	N5YNY	N5YNY
Columbia	147.2850	+	O	N5LJC	N5LJC
Columbus	145.4300	–	O	KA5LVU	------------
Columbus	146.6250	–	O	KC5ULN	KC5ULN
Columbus	147.0000	+	O	KC5ULN	KC5ULN
Corinth	145.3900	–	O	WF5D	------------
Corinth	146.9250	–	O	WB5CON	ACARES
Corinth	147.0000	–	O	K5UFH	K5UFH
Corinth	147.2850	+	O	K5WHB	CRA
Corinth	147.3450	+	O	KJ5CO	KJ5CO
D'iberville	145.4100	–	O	KC5IF	KC5IF
D'iberville	147.2250	+	O	W5OXA	------------
Ellisville	144.5500	+	O	W5NRU	AA5SG
Ellisville	145.2300	–	O	W5NRU	AA5SG
Ellisville	146.8350	+	O	N5DWU	------------
Ellisville	146.8650	+	O	W5NRU	AA5SG/N5HOA
Ellisville	146.9550	–	O	N5EKR	N5EKR
French Camp	147.2250	+	O	W5BJT	W5BJT
Fulton	145.4500	–	O	WX5P	WX5P
Gloster	145.4300	–	O	KX5E	ONARC
Greenville	146.8200	–	O	WA5MBA	------------
Greenville	147.3450	+	O	KG5SF	KG5SF
Greenville	147.3450	+	O	N5PS	N5PS
Greenwood	146.7150	–	O	KA5TQY	------------
Grenada	146.7000	–	O	W5LV	W5LV
Gulfport	145.3300	–	O	KK5RK	HARRISON CO
Gulfport	147.3750	+	O	KA5VFU	------------
Guntown	147.0750	+	O	W5NEM	W5NEM
Hattiesburg	145.1500	–	O	W5NRU	AA5SG
Hattiesburg	145.1900	–	O	W5CJR	W5CJR
Hattiesburg	145.3700	–	O	K5IJX	K5IJX
Hattiesburg	146.7750	–	O	W5CJR	W5CJR

Location	*Output*	*Input*	*Notes*	*Call*	*Sponsor*
Hattiesburg	147.3150	+	O	KD5MIS	KD5MIS
Hattiesburg	147.3600	+	O	W5CJR	HATTIESBURG ARC
Hernando	145.3700	–	O	N5PYQ	SRA
Hernando	146.9100	–	O	W5GWD	W5GWD
Hernando	147.2250	+	O	KD5VMV	KD5VMV
Horn Lake	145.2700	–	O	N5NBG	REDNECKS
Houston	146.8950	–	O	KD5YBU	KD5YBU
Isola	146.9550	–	O	KC5OB	KC5OB
Iuka	146.8500	–	O	W5TCR	W5TCR
Jackson	145.3900	–	O	KB5KGE	------------
Jackson	146.7600	–	O	W5AXQ	JARC INC
Jackson	146.8800	–	O	K5QNE	JARC INC.
Jackson	146.9400	–	O	KA5SBK	KA5SBK
Jackson	147.0000	+	O	W5IQ	W5IQ
Jackson	147.0750	+	O	NC5Y	NC5Y
Kiln	145.3300	–	O	K5DMC	K5DMC
Kiln	145.3300	–	O	K5XXV	WEST COASTAL MS
Kosciusko	146.8500	–	O	KB5ZEA	MID-MS ARC
Laurel	146.6100	–	O	W5LAR	LAUREL ARC
Laurel	147.0300	–	O	WV5D	WV5D
Laurel	147.2550	+	O	KC5RC	JONES CO ARC
Leakesville	147.0000	+	O	KE5WGF	GREENE CO EM CO
Louisville	147.3600	+	O	KC5QGC	WINSTON CO ARC
Lucedale	146.9100	–	O	WA5JZL	WA5JZL
Lucedale	147.1200	+	O	N5LRQ	N5LRQ
Madison	146.6400	–	O	K5XU	JARC INC
Magee	146.8200	–	O	KA5LNY	SIMPSON CO ARC
Magee	147.3000	+	O	KA5LNY	KA5LNY
Mccomb	146.9400	–	O	W5WQ	SW MS ARC
Mchenry	147.3300	+	O	KK5RK	HARRISON CO CD
Mclain	145.2300	–	O	KC5QYG	KC5QYG
Meridian	145.4100	–	O	N5DWU	EARS
Meridian	146.6550	–	O	KC5ZZH	KC5ZZH
Meridian	146.7000	–	O	W5FQ	MERIDIAN ARC
Meridian	146.9700	–	O	NO5C	LAUDERDALE REP
Monticello	147.0150	+	O	N5JHK	N5JHK
Mooreville	146.6400	–	O	WB5NAY	------------
Morton	145.1100	–	O	W5PES	W5PES
Morton	147.0450	+	O	KB5LCL	------------
Natchez	146.6850	–	O	W5KHB	W5KHB
Natchez	146.7450	–	O	K5SVC	K5SVC
Natchez	146.9100	–	O	K5OCM	OLD NATCHEZ ARC
Natchez	146.9100	–	O	K5OCM	K5OCM
Natchez	147.3600	+	O	K5SVC	K5SVC
New Albany	145.2300	–	O	KC5VZI	KC5VZI
New Albany	146.6700	–	O	W5UBG	NEMARC
New Albany	146.7450	–	O	KC5VZI	------------
New Hebron	147.0900	+	O	N5MRS	N5MRS
Ocean Springs	147.0300	+	O	W5LDD	W5LDD

Location	*Output*	*Input*	*Notes*	*Call*	*Sponsor*
Okolona	145.1100	–	O	KC5NIX	------------
Olive Branch	147.2550	+	O	KD5CKP	KD5CKP
Oxford	145.2900	–	O	KC5KLW	------------
Oxford	147.3300	+	O	W5LAF	W5LAF
Pascagoula	146.8800	–	O	KE5SJ	KE5SJ
Pascagoula	146.9700	–	O	N5PH	N5PH
Pascagoula	146.9700	–	O	N5OS	N5OS
Pearl	147.1500	+	O	KF5IZ	------------
Pelahatchie	145.3900	–	O	W5PPB	W5PPB
Pelahatchie	147.2400	+	O	W5PPB	W5PPB
Perkinston	145.1700	–	O	K5GVR	K5GVR
Perkinston	147.1650	+	O	K5GVR	K5GVR
Petal	145.1700	–	O	N5DWU	N5DWU/N5HOA
Philadelphia	147.3300	+	O	N5EPP	NESHOBA ARC
Picayune	145.1500	–	O	KE5LT	KE5LT
Picayune	147.1800	+	O	K5LFP	PEARL RIVER C
Pontotoc	147.3800	+	O	WB5NAY	------------
Poplarville	145.1500	–	O	K5PRC	K5PRC
Poplarville	145.2100	–	O	W5PMS	------------
Poplarville	145.4100	–	O	N5LRQ	N5LRQ
Port Gibson	146.6250	–	O	KE5WO	KE5WO
Purvis	146.6700	–	O	KB5ZCX	KB5ZCX
Richton	145.4900	–	O	N5DWU	EARS
Richton	147.0600	+	O	N5OCF	N5OCF
Rose Hill	145.1300	–	O	N5LRQ	------------
Saltillo	146.8350	–	O	KD5YBE	KD5YBE
Senatobia	146.9850	–	O	KB5DMT	------------
Sharon	145.4500	–	O	W5PPB	W5PPB
Silver Creek	147.1950	+	O	W5JVK	------------
Southaven	145.4500	–	O	WB4KOG	WA4KOG
Starkville	146.7300	–	O	KD5GVU	MAGNOLIA ARC
Starkville	146.8050	–	O	KF5C	------------
Stennis Space Cen	147.2100	+	O	N5GJB	N5GJB
Sumner	147.0900	+	O	WB5FXH	WB4FXH
Sumrall	147.1950	+	O	KA5FYW	SUMRALL ARC
Taylorsville	146.8950	+	O	W5NRU	AA5SG/N5HOA
Tupelo	145.4900	–	O	N5VGK	------------
Tupelo	147.2400	+	O	KK5K	TUPELO ARA
Union	147.2100	+	O	N5SPJ	ECMARC
Union	147.2400	+	O	K5SZN	K5SZN
Utica	145.3500	–	O	N5ZMZ	N5ZMZ
Utica	146.7300	–	O	KC5TGT	KC5TGT
Utica	147.3450	+	O	N5ZMZ	N5ZMZ
Vancleave	145.1100	–	O	W5WA	W5WA
Vancleave	147.0000	–	O	KE5TL	KE5TL
Vicksburg	145.2900	–	O	KD5CQX	LESTER GRANT
Vicksburg	145.4100	–	O	W5WAF	W5WAF
Vicksburg	146.8050	–	O	K5IMT	K5IMT

Location	Output	Input	Notes	Call	Sponsor
Vicksburg	147.2700	+	O	K5ZRO	VICKSBURG ARC
Vossburg	145.4700	–	O	N5DWU	EARS
Vossburg	146.9250	–	O	N5DWU	------------
Vossburg	147.1350	+	O	KB5UIX	KB5UIX
Water Valley	147.0000	–	O	N5DXM	TRI-LAKE HNDCP A
Waynesboro	145.2100	–	O	W5SAR	W5SAR
Waynesboro	146.9250	–	O	KI5WK	KI5WK & WD5IMP
Waynesboro	147.1050	+	O	W5SAR	W5SAR
Waynesboro	147.3150	+	O	N5DWU	N5DWU/N5HOA
West Point	146.7900	–	O	KO5S	------------
West Point	147.1800	+	O	KD5RZQ	CLAY CO ARS
Wiggins	145.2700	–	O	N5UDK	N5UDK
Winona	146.9700	–	O	N5EYM	N5EYM
Yazoo City	147.2250	+	O	KE5YES	KINGS DAUDNERS

MISSOURI

Location	Output	Input	Notes	Call	Sponsor
BRANSON					
Branson	145.3100	–	O 186.2el	WØDLR	WØACE
Branson	147.1500	+	Os	NA9X	TriLks ARC
Branson	147.1950	+	Oes	NA9X	TriLks ARC
CAPE GIRARDEAU					
Cape Girardeau	146.6100	–	Oa	WØQMF	WBØTYV
Cape Girardeau	146.6850	–	O 100x	WØQMF	SEARC
Cape Girardeau	146.9400	–	O	WBØTYV	WBØTYV
CENTRAL					
Boonville	147.3600	+	O	WØBRC	BnvilleRC
Brinktown	146.8950	–	Ox	NØGYE	NØGYE
Eldon	146.6250	–	O 131.8s	AAØNC	NSARC
Eldon	147.2700	+	● 123/123	NØQVO	------------
Fulton	147.3150	+	OE-SUN E-WINDr	KCØMV	C.A.R.L.
Gainesville	145.2900	–	Oe	KFØBA	------------
Hermitage	147.2550	+	Oer	KBØAL	OlHickARC
Laurie	146.7300	–	Oes	NØZS	LkOzksARC
Laurie	146.9550	–	O 192.8a (CA)elx	KAØRFO	KRMS
Marshall	147.1650	+	O 127.3a	WBØWMM	IndFtHARC
Mexico	147.2550	+	Olsx	AAØRC	AudrainARC
Moberly	147.0900	+	O 127.3/127.3	KØMOB	TriCtARC
Paris	146.8350	–	Oe	NØSYL	NØSYL
Sedalia	147.0300	–	O 179.9/179.9ers	WAØSDO	SPARK
Stover	147.3900	+	O	KBØQWQ	------------
Warsaw	146.9250	–	O 107.2/107.2e	KDØCNC	KDØCNC
Warsaw	147.0750	+	O 146.2	KIØIP	KIØIP
Warsaw	147.3000	+	Oa(CA)	KCØRDO	TwnLkesARC
Windsor	147.1950	+	O 107.2/107.2p	KØUG	KØUG

Location	Output	Input	Notes	Call	Sponsor
COLUMBIA/JEFF CITY					
Ashland	146.6850	–	O 77a(CA) ers	WØDQJ	WØDQJ
Columbia	146.6100	–	O 127.3/127.3a(CA) L(441.7)	K4CHS	------------
Columbia	146.7600	–	O 127.3/127.3asx	KØSI	CMRA
Jefferson City	146.8650	–	O 127.3elr sx	KCØCZI	KCØCZI
Jefferson City	147.0000	–	O 127.3/127.3es	KØETY	MidMO ARC
Linn	145.3900	–	O 127.3/127.3ex	KMØHP	MULEBARN
EAST CENTRAL					
De Soto	146.7000	–	O	KØMGU	SHO-ME
De Soto	146.8800	–	Oa	KØMGU	KØMGU
Hermann	146.7450	–	Oae	KBØTZG	------------
Hermann	147.1350	+	OerWX	KBØWCY	KBØWCY
Hillsboro	147.0750	+	O 141.3a (CA)l	KBØTLL	JeffCoARC
Imperial	147.1050	+	O 141.3 L(446.95)	KBØTLL	JeffCoARC
Sullivan	145.1500	–	Ol	KØCSM	SARC
Sullivan	146.8050	–	Oe	KCØDBS	SARC
Warrenton	147.0450	+	O 141.3s	KAØCWU	KAØCWU
Warrenton	147.3300	+	O 123/123e r	WAØEMA	WCEMA
Washington	147.1800	+	Ox	WAØFYA	WAØFYA
Washington	147.2400	+	O 141.3/141.3a(CA)erx	WAØFYA	ZBARC
JOPLIN					
Duneweg	147.2100	+	O 91.5/91.5 ersx	WØIN	JoplinARC
Joplin	145.3500	–	O 91.5/91.5 x	NØARM	NØARM
Joplin	147.0000	+	Oe	WBØIYC	WBØIYC
KANSAS CITY METRO					
Blue Springs	147.0150	+	O 151.4/151.4ex	KBØVBN	BluSprRPTR
Excelsior Spgs	145.1900	–	O 107.2 RB x	KØBSJ	KØBSJ
Excelsior Spgs	147.3750	+	O 156.7/156.7e	KØESM	RayClay RC
Gladstone	145.4300	–	O	KDØFW	KCATVG
Holt	147.0450	+	O	NØTIX	NØTIX
Independence	145.3100	–	O 151.4er	KØEJC	EJCECS
Independence	145.3700	–	O	KØEJC	EJCECS
Independence	146.7300	–	Oaer	WØSHQ	ASCRA, Inc
Independence	147.0900	+	Oa(CA)elr	WØTOJ	IndFMARC

Location	*Output*	*Input*	*Notes*	*Call*	*Sponsor*
Kansas City	146.7900	–	O	WAØKHP	ClayCoARC
			107.2/107.2a(CA)es		
Kansas City	146.8200	–	Olrx	KCØARC	NEKSUN
Kansas City	146.9700	–	O	WØWJB	WØWJB
			151.4/151.4x		
Kansas City	147.2700	+	Oa(CA)ex	WAØSMG	WAØSMG
Kansas City	147.3300	+	Oa(CA)er	WAØQFJ	TWA ARC
Kearney	147.3000	+	O 107.2	KØBSJ	KØBSJ
Lee's Summit	145.4100	–	Oa(CA)	WAØTEG	NEKSUN
Lee's Summit	146.7000	–	O	KCØSKY	KS SKY WRN
			107.2/107.2ex		
Liberty	145.1100	–	O	NØELK	NØELK
Raymore	147.1200	+	Oes	KCØJGA	SSARC
Raytown	145.1700	–	O	KØGQ	Raytown ARC
			151.4/151.4e		
Smithville	146.6400	–	Osx	KCØIMO	NØVER
NORTHEAST					
Brookfield	147.3450	+	Oa(CA)	WØCIT	WØTH
Eolia	145.1900	–	Oelr	KAØEJQ	KAØEJQ
Glenwood	145.1100	–	O	KDØIZE	Sch-Co-RA
			103.5/103.5		
Hannibal	146.6250	–	O 103.5er	WØKEM	HannibARC
Hannibal	146.8800	–	O 103.5er	WØKEM	HannibARC
Kirksville	145.1300	–	Oex	WØCBL	NEMOARC
Lancaster	145.3300	–	O 100el	KEØBX	OLRG
Macon	146.8050	–	Oer	NØPR	MARC
Madison	146.9850	–	O 110.9e	NØSYL	NØSYL
Monroe City	146.7000	–	Oel	KAØEJQ	KAØEJQ
NORTHWEST					
Amity	147.3900	+	O 146.2	KBØALL	------------
Chillicothe	147.2250	+	Ol	KØMPT	GHARC
Grant City	147.0600	+	O	WBØUJF	RWElliott
Guilford	146.6850	–	O	NØOEV	NØOEV
Osborn	145.1500	–	O 107.2	KBØUDL	------------
			L(442.675) WXx		
Plattsburg	146.8950	–	O 114.8e	KCØQLU	KCØQLU
			L(444.925+ PL 100.0)sRB		
Tarkio	145.3500	–	O	NØNHB	NØNHB
			146.2/146.2l		
Trenton	146.9550	–	Oes	KBØRPJ	NC Mo ARC
ROLLA					
Rolla	145.4500	–	O	WØEEE	UMR ARC
			110.9/110.9a(CA)l		
Rolla	146.7900	–	O 88.5els	WØGS	RollaRARS
SOUTH CENTRAL					
Ava	146.6250	–	O 110.9els	NØRFI	DouglasCoEMA
Bunker	147.2700	+	O 156.7	KDØIM	------------
			(CA)		
Cuba	147.3450	+	O	KDØJOX	AAØGB
			110.9/110.9		

Location	*Output*	*Input*	*Notes*	*Call*	*Sponsor*
Eminence	145.3100	–	O 100/100 E-SUNs	KNØD	CRARC
Gainesville	147.3900	+	O 110.9/110.9erx	WBØJJJ	ARCO
Grove Spgs	147.3750	+	O 88.5/88.5 e	K5HEZ	K5HEZ
Houston	147.1350	+	O 100a (CA)e	KBØMPO	------------
Lebanon	145.4700	–	O 88.5/88.5 es	KØLH	LebanonARC
Lebanon	146.7000	–	O 88.5/88.5 e	KØLH	LebanonARC
Mansfield	147.0900	+	O 162.2/162.2el	K5HEZ	K5HEZ
Mountain Grove	147.2850	+	Oae	KGØLF	KGØLF
Prescott	146.8500	–	Oe	NØKBC	OMRG
Rolla	147.2100	+	O 88.5/88.5 L(146.79)	WB9KHR	WB9KHR
Salem	146.6550	–	Oer	WBØNRP	WBØNRP
Thayer	146.8050	–	O	WBØLLS	OrgnCoARC
Van Buren	146.8650	–	O 100/100	NØIBV	NØIBV
Viburnum	147.3000	+	O 110.9/110.9	NØWNC	NØWNC
West Plains	145.2500	–	O 110.9/110.9s	KDØAIZ	HoCoARC
West Plains	146.9400	–	O 110.9ex	WØHCA	HoCoARC
SOUTHEAST					
Benton	146.7900	–	O	NØGK	CrlRDgARC
Bloomfield	147.3300	+	O 100/100e x	KMØHP	MULE BARN
Dexter	147.0000	–	O 100	NØGK	CR ARC
Dexter	147.1500	+	O 100	NØDAN	------------
Farmington	147.0300	+	O 100e	KØEOR	EtnOzkARC
Ironton	146.8350	–	O 100/100	ABØTL	------------
Kennett	147.1950	+	O	KCØLAT	BARC
Kennett/Hayti	146.9850	–	O 100/100e WX	KBØUFL	BARC
New Madrid	146.9250	–	O	KBØUFL	BARC
Piedmont	147.3750	+	O 100/100e rx	NØQAQ	W.C. ARC
Poplar Bluff	145.3500	–	O 100a (CA)	ABØJW	SEMOARA
Poplar Bluff	146.9100	–	O 100/100e rx	KMØHP	Mulebarn
Potosi	146.7150	–	O 88.5/88.5	NØVOJ	NØVOJ
Potosi	147.1950	+	O 141.3/141.3	NØWNC	NØWNC
St Genevieve	146.6250	–	O 100/100r s	KØQOD	St GenCoARC

MISSOURI

Location	Output	Input	Notes	Call	Sponsor
SOUTHWEST					
Aurora	146.9700	–	OE-SUNrx	WØOAR	OzarkARS
Bolivar	147.0600	+	O 107.2els	WBØLVR	LksAraARA
Buffalo	147.1800	+	Oa(CA)e	K9HOI	BARK
Cape Fair	145.4100	–	O/162.2e	KØJPK	SC C.E.R.T.
Carthage	146.8800	–	O	WØLF	CARC
Caulfield	145.1700	–	Oe	KBØRPA	Cld9RptC
Elkhead	146.9250	–	● 162.2	KØDCA	DouglasCoARES
Highlandville	145.2300	–	O 162.2ers	WA6JGM	CC ARS
Kimberling Cty	147.3450	+	O 162.2ae s	KØEI	KmbrlnARC
Lamar	147.2400	+	O 91.5/91.5 x	KØPRO	pr
Marshfield	146.8650	–	O 156.7	KØNI	------------
Neosho	146.8050	–	O 127.3/127.3es	KCØNJZ	SW ARG
Nevada	147.1350	+	Oes	WBØNYD	N.A.R.C.
Nixa	145.2700	–	O 162.2/162.2elx	KØNXA	Nixa ARC
Pineville	147.0750	+	O 162.2es	WB6ARF	McDonaldCoEMA
Shell Knob	145.2100	–	O 162.2sx	ACØJK	TableRock ARC
Walnut Grove	147.3300	+	O 162.2	AKØC	------------
SPRINGFIELD					
Republic	146.8200	–	O 162.2e	KØEAR	EARS
Rogersville	147.1200	+	●	KBØE	SARA
Springfield	145.3300	–	O 156.7	KCØDBU	BSAPost30
Springfield	145.4300	–	O 136.5/85.4 A(*)ex	KAØFKF	MSU ARC
Springfield	145.4900	–	O 136.5/136.5elrsRB WXx	NØNWS	------------
Springfield	146.6400	–	O 179.9erx	WØEBE	SW MO ARC
Springfield	146.9100	–	O 162.2elr x	WØEBE	SW MO ARC
Springfield	147.0150	+	O 162.2/162.2ex	KØNXA	Nixa ARC
Springfield	147.2250	+	O 162.2/162.2elrsx	WØPM	------------
ST JOSEPH					
St Joseph	146.7450	–	O	WBØHNO	------------
St Joseph	146.8500	–	O 100/100e r	WØNH	MOValARC
ST LOUIS METRO					
Bridgeton	146.7300	–	O 141.3a (CA)e	WØKE	NWAR/EAsn
Clayton	146.9400	–	O 141.3ers LITZ WX	KBØMWG	SLSRC
Crystal City	146.7750	–	O 100x	KØTPX	TwnCtyARC
Des Peres	146.9100	–	O 141.3/141.3a(CA)e	NØTYZ	SLSRC

Location	*Output*	*Input*	*Notes*	*Call*	*Sponsor*
Ferguson	147.0000	–	O 107.2/107.2	WAØWKI	FVCC ARC
Harvester	145.4900	–	O 141.3/141.3ersLITZ	WØECA	ARESRACES
Kirkwood	147.1500	+	●/141.3a (CA)e	KBØZRI	TelemRC
O'Fallon	145.4100	–	O/141.3e	KØRBR	RBARC
O'Fallon	146.6700	–	O/141.3e WX	WBØHSI	StChasARC
Olivette	146.8500	–	O 141.3a (CA)ers	WØSRC	SLSRC
St Charles	145.3300	–	Oes	KOØA	StChasARC
St Charles	145.3700	–	O 88.5/88.5 a(CA)el	KJØA	KJØA
St Louis	145.1700	–	●a(CA)e	KØKYZ	KØKYZ
St Louis	145.2100	–	O 123a (CA)elx	WBØQXW	#NAME?
St Louis	145.2700	–	O 123/123a (CA)	KA9HNT	XEEARC
St Louis	145.3500	–	O 123erx	KAØYXU	------------
St Louis	146.6100	–	Oa(CA)elr	KCØTPS	CARS
St Louis	146.7600	–	O 141.3 (CA)es	W9AIU	EgyptnRC
St Louis	146.9250	–	O 192.8/192.8 L(444.55)	KØAMC	AMARC
St Louis	146.9700	–	O 141.3ers WX	WØFF	SLSRC
St Louis	147.0000	–	O 141.3/141.3	KØDO	MonsantARA
St Louis	147.0600	+	O 141.3/141.3a(CA)e	WØMA	BEARS-STL
St Louis	147.2250	+	Oe	NØFLC	NØFLC
St Louis	147.2850	+	Oa(CA)	WØQEV	WashUARC
St Louis	147.3600	+	O/141.3a (CA)ex	KØDO	MonsantARA
St Louis	147.3900	+	O 100/100e I	WØSLW	44405RPTR

WEST CENTRAL

Appleton City	146.8500	–	O 107.2/107.2	WA9QME	WA9QME
Butler	147.2250	+	Ox	KBØPSG	KBØPSG
Carrollton	146.6550	–	O 94.8esx	NØSAX	NØSAX
Concordia	146.7750	–	O 156.7	AAØIY	KCØBQB
Nevada	145.4500	–	O 91.5x	WØHL	WØHL
Warrensburg	146.8800	–	O 107.2esx	WØAU	WAARCI

MONTANA

CENTRAL

Lewistown	146.9600	–	O 100.0	K7VH	K7EC

Location	Output	Input	Notes	Call	Sponsor
EAST CENTRAL					
Fallon	147.1600	+	O 100.0	K7HWK	SEMARC
Glendive	146.7600	–	Oelx	W7DXQ	LYARC
Miles City	146.9200	–	O 100.0	K7HWK	SEMARC
Sidney	147.3800	+	Ol	W7DXQ	LYARC
NORTH CENTRAL					
Chester	146.6400	–	O	KD7JZ	Mt. Royal Rptr Soc
Cut Bank	146.7000	–	O 103.5el	K7HR	K7HR
Cut Bank	146.8200	–	O 100.0	K7JAQ	HARK
Cut Bank	147.2000	+	O	KE7QIP	KE7QIP
Great Falls	146.6800	–	O 100.0	AA7GS	MRLA
Great Falls	146.7400	–	O 100.0elx	W7ECA	GFAARC
Great Falls	147.0800	+	Ol	WR7MT	MRLA
Great Falls	147.1200	+	O 100.0lx	W7ECA	GFAARC
Great Falls	147.2400	+	O	AA7GS	AA7GS
Great Falls	147.3000	+	Oez	W7ECA	GFAARC
Great Falls	147.3600	+	O 100.0	W7GMC	W7GMC
Havre	146.9100	–	O 100.0	W7HAV	HI-LINE ARC
Millegan	146.9800	–	O 100.0	N7SEE	N7SEE
Vaughn	147.1400	+	O 100.0	KD7WIZ	KD7WIZ
Zortman	147.2600	+	O 100.0	W7ECA	GFAARC
NORTHEAST					
Fort Peck	146.8400	–	O 100.0	WX7GGW	Valley RC
Plentywood	146.6600	–	Ol	KB7QWG	KB7QWG
Plentywood	147.3000	+	Ol	KB7QWG	KB7QWG
Plentywood	147.3400	+	O 100.0l	KD7ZEB	Sheridan County
Whitetail	147.1000	+	O	W7WZW	NLARG
NORTHWEST					
Bigfork	145.3300	–	O	KE7JI	KE7JI
Bigfork	146.6200	–	O 100.0ael RBxz	KA5LXG	FVRG
Eureka	145.3900	–	O 100.0	WR7DW	WR7DW
Eureka	145.4300	–	O 100.0	K7EUR	Tobacco Valley ARC
Eureka	146.8200	–	O 100.0	WR7DW	WR7DW
Eureka	147.2800	+	O	WR7DW	WR7DW
Eureka	147.3200	+	O 100.0	K7BIR	K7BIR
Eureka	147.3400	+	O 100.0ael RBxz	KC7CUE	FVRG
Happy's Inn	145.3100	–	O 100.0ael RBxz	KB7TPD	FVRG
Lakeside	146.7400	–	O 100.0l	KA7G	NMRG
Lakeside	146.7600	–	O 100.0l	K7LYY	FVARC
Lakeside	146.8600	–	O 100.0	W7ZKA	W7ZKA
Lakeside	147.1600	+	O 123.0	KA7G	KA7G
Lakeside	147.1800	+	O 100.0	K7LYY	FVARC
Libby	146.8400	–	O 100.0r	K7LBY	LCARG
Lookout Pass	147.0200	+	O	K7HPT	W7OE
Noxon	145.3300	–	O	KD7OCP	KD7OCP
Plains	146.6400	–	O 103.5	W7GET	W7GET

Location	*Output*	*Input*	*Notes*	*Call*	*Sponsor*
Plains	147.1400	+	O 103.5l	K7KTR	K7KTR
Polson	145.3500	–	O 100.0ael RBxz	W7CMA	FVRG
Polson	145.4300	–	O	KD7YVU	KD7YVU
Ronan	146.7000	–	O 162.2	KC7MRQ	KC7MRQ
Thompson Falls	146.6800	–	O 100.0	W7GET	W7GET
Whitefish	145.2700	–	O 100.0ael RBxz	KO8N	FVRG
Whitefish	147.2600	+	O 100.0 E-SUN	WR7DW	WR7DW
Whitefish	147.3800	+	O 100.0l	K7LYY	FVARC
Yaak	147.0000	+	O	W3YAK	N3AAW
SOUTH CENTRAL					
Big Sky	146.8200	–	O 82.5 E-SUN	W7LR	ERA
Bozeman	145.2500	–	O 107.2l	KB7KB	BARBS
Bozeman	146.8800	–	O 100.0ael x	W7YB	ERA
Bozeman	147.1800	+	O 100.0elx	WR7MT	MRLA
West Yellowstone	145.2300	–	O 100.0l	WA7FDR	WA7FDR
West Yellowstone	146.7200	–	O 100.0	KL7JGS	KL7JGS
SOUTHEAST					
Big Timber	146.7000	–	O	WA7KQO	WA7KQO
Billings	146.8000	–	O 100.0	KF7TQX	KF7TQX
Billings	147.0400	+	O 100.0 E-SUN	KA7MHP	KA7MHP
Billings	147.0800	+	O 100.0elx	WR7MT	MRLA
Billings	147.2000	+	O 100.0	N7YHE	N7YHE
Billings	147.2400	+	O 100.0	K7EFA	YRC
Billings	147.3000	+	O 100.0l	K7EFA	YRC
Billings	147.3600	+	O 100.0	K7EFA	YRC
Forsyth	147.2000	+	O 100.0	KC7BOB	KC7BOB
Greycliff	147.2800	+	O 100.0elx	WR7MT	MRLA
Joliet	147.1400	+	O	KF7SN	BARC
Park City	147.1000	+	O	N7YHE	N7YHE
Pompey's Pillar	147.1800	+	Ol	WR7MT	MRLA
Red Lodge	147.0000	+	Oe	WB7RIS	BARC
Roundup	145.4100	–	O 100.0el	K7EFA	YRC
SOUTHWEST					
Anaconda	147.0200	+	O 107.2	KB7IQO	KB7IQO
Anaconda	147.0800	+	O 107.2l	KØPP	AARC
Butte	146.6800	–	O	N7SKI	N7SKI
Butte	146.9400	–	O 100.0aer	W7ROE	BARC
Dillon	146.7600	–	O 107.2l	K7IMM	DARC
Drummond	146.7400	–	O 146.2	W7KNT	W7KNT
Helena	145.4500	–	O 100.0el WXx	WR7MT	MRLA
Helena	147.1000	+	O 100.0	WR7HLN	WR7AGT
Helena	147.2200	+	O 100.0	W7TCK	CCARC

Location	*Output*	*Input*	*Notes*	*Call*	*Sponsor*
Helena	147.3200	+	O 100.0l	W7MRI	W7MRI
Philipsburg	147.1600	+	O 107.2l	KA7NBR	AARC
Salmon, ID	146.9800	–	O	KE7NYR	LARC
Three Forks	147.3800	+	O 100.0elx	WR7MT	MRLA
Townsend	145.3100	–	O 100.0	KE7ZVK	KE7ZVK
Wisdom	147.0600	+	O 107.2l	N7YET	DARC
STATEWIDE APRS					
Statewide APRS	144.3900	–	O		------------
STATEWIDE EMERGENCY					
Statewide Emergency	145.4700	–	O		------------
WEST CENTRAL					
Frenchtown	146.8400	–	O 146.2	N7DWB	N7DWB
Hamilton	146.7200	–	O 186.2l	W7FTX	BARC
Hamilton	146.7800	–	O 151.4e	AE7OD	AE7OD
Lolo	146.9600	–	O 88.5l	W7PX	HARC
Missoula	146.8000	–	O 88.5	W7PX	HARC
Missoula	146.9000	–	O 88.5al	W7PX	HARC
Missoula	146.9200	–	O 100.0	WR7HLN	WR7AGT
Missoula	147.0000	+	O(CA)	NZ7S	NZ7S
Missoula	147.0400	+	O 88.5e	W7PX	HARC
Missoula	147.1200	+	O 103.5	W7GET	W7GET
Stevensville	145.2300	–	O 151.4s	W7FTX	Ravalli County ARES
Stevensville	146.6600	–	O 88.5	KE7WR	KE7WR
Stevensville	147.3200	+	O 151.4l	KD7HP	KD7HP
Stevensville	147.3600	+	O 146.2	KK7GV	KK7GV

NEBRASKA

Location	*Output*	*Input*	*Notes*	*Call*	*Sponsor*
CENTRAL					
Burwell	147.0900	+	Oe	WØEJL	------------
Waco	147.2700	+	Oels	WAØHOU	Blue valley ARC
COLUMBUS					
Columbus	146.6400	–	Oae	KAØS	Pawnee ARC
Columbus	146.7750	–	O(CA)es	NØRHM	PLATTE CO.
Columbus	146.9950	–	Oe	WAØCOL	PAWNEE ARC
EAST					
Nickerson	145.2650	–	Oe	KDØPGV	KDØPGV
FREMONT					
Fremont	146.6700	–	Ol	KDØEFC	KDØEFC
Fremont	147.1050	+	Oes	KFØMS	KFØMS
GRAND ISLAND					
Grand Island	145.4150	–	O	WØCUO	NE STATE FAIR
HASTINGS					
Hastings	145.1300	–	Ols	WØWWV	ARAN
KEARNEY					
Kearney	145.2350	–	Oes	KCØWZL	BUFFALO CO.
Kearney	145.2950	–	Os	WBØYIG	M.A.R.C.
Kearney	146.6250	–	Oes	WØKY	M.A.R.C.

Location	Output	Input	Notes	Call	Sponsor
LEXINGTON					
Lexington	147.1350	+	Oe	WØSOK	HARA
LINCOLN					
Lincoln	145.1900	–	Oes	NØFER	------------
Lincoln	146.7600	–	Oes	KØKKV	LARC
Lincoln	147.1950	+	O(CA)ez	KØSIL	KØSIL
Lincoln	147.2400	+	Oes	NØFER	------------
Lincoln	147.3300	+	Oes	WØMAO	NE. EMA
NORFOLK					
Neligh	146.8350	–	O	KBØTRU	BUZZARDS RO
Norfolk	146.7300	–	O 131.8 (CA)ez	WØOFK	EVARC
Wayne	147.0300	+	Oe	NØZQR	WAYNE ARA
NORTH CENT					
O'Neill	146.6100	–	O	KBØGRP	------------
Spencer	147.3300	+	O	KCØHMN	KCØHMN
Valentine	147.2100	+	O	KAØWJW	KAØWJW
NORTH EAST					
Sioux City (IA)	146.9700	–	O 110.9/110.9	KØTFT	SARA
NORTH WEST					
Alliance	147.0150	+	O 100/100	N2VHZ	N2VHZ
OMAHA					
Bellevue	145.1150	–	Oes	WBØQQK	WB0QQK
Bellevue	147.3900	+	Oes	WØWYV	BELLEVUE ARC
Omaha	145.3700	–	Oel	NØOFQ	EWETAN ARC
Omaha	145.4500	–	Oel	KØBOY	K0BOY
Omaha	146.9400	–	O/131.8es	KØUSA	AKSARBEN A
Omaha	147.0000	–	O/131.8ael	WBØCMC	WBØCMC
Omaha	147.3000	+	●e	WAØWTL	WA0WTL
Omaha	147.3600	+	Oe	KØBOY	K0BOY
Omaha (E)	147.0000	+	O/131.8ael	WBØCMC	WBØCMC
SCOTTSBLUFF					
Scottsbluff	145.4750	–	Oaes	WDØBQM	RWMC
SOUTH CENT					
Alma	145.2050	–	Ols	KAØRCZ	------------
Heartwell	146.8200	–	Oels	WØWWV	ARAN
Loomis	146.8950	–	Oes	KØPCA	PCEMA
Nelson	147.2100	+	Oels	WØWWV	ARAN
SOUTH EAST					
Beatrice	145.3400	–	Os	KCØMLT	------------
Fairbury	147.1200	+	Oaels	WBØRMO	JCARS
Falls City	147.3150	+	Oes	KBØFVP	KBØFVP
Humboldt	147.0750	+	Oels	WBØYLA	WBØYLA
Shubert	147.3150	+	Oes	KBØFVP	KBØFVP
Wilber	146.9850	–	O 100.0/100.0aes	NØYNC	Saline EMA
SOUTH WEST					
Cambridge	146.9700	–	Oe	KAØTDT	Camb. 2M Club

Location	Output	Input	Notes	Call	Sponsor
McCook	147.2700	+	Oe	KØTAJ	McCOOK ARA
Ogallala	146.7600	–	Oe	KBØSOL	TRAILS END
WEST					
North Platte	146.7000	–	Oes	NEØNP	KØKDC
North Platte	146.8350	–	Oes	KØKDC	KØKDC
North Platte	146.9400	–	Oe	NØUGO	NØUGO
North Platte	147.3300	+	Oe	NØIQ	------------

NEVADA

Location	Output	Input	Notes	Call	Sponsor
CENTRAL					
Dyer	147.0600	+	Oe	W7WOW	W7WOW
Tonopah	145.3300	–	O 151.4l	WA6MNM	WA6MNM
Tonopah	146.6400	–	O 123e	WB5KLJ	WB5KLJ
Warm Springs	146.8500	–	O	WB7WTS	WB7WTS
E SIERRA/TAHOE					
Glenbrook	146.7000	–	O 123	N3KD	N3KD
Lake Tahoe	147.2400	+	Oe	NR7A	WA6EWV
S Lake Tahoe	146.1150	+	O 203.5	WA6SUV	W6SUV
EAST CENTRAL					
Ely	145.3500	–	Ol	WB7WTS	WB7WTS
Ely	146.6100	–	Olx	WB7WTS	WB7WTS
Ely	146.8800	–	O 114.8l	WB7WTS	WB7WTS
Eureka	147.0600	+	O	WB7WTS	WB7WTS
Eureka	147.0600	+	O 114.8	WB7WTS	WB7WTS
Lund	147.1800	+	O 114.8lx	WB7WTS	WB7WTS
Pioche	147.2400	+	O 100l	K7NKH	K7NKH
LAS VEGAS VALLEY					
Angel Peak	145.3700	–	O 123/123	N7ARR	NARRI - IRLP
Angel Peak	147.1800	+	ODCS(244) L(CC ARES/RACES)rs	N7SGV	CC ARES/RACES
Apex Mtn	147.0600	+	O 100/100	KC7TMC	Nellis RAC
Black Mountain	146.7300	–	O	KD8S	QST
Black Mtn	145.3900	–	O 100/100	NK2V	FARS
Henderson	145.4200	–	O 100/100e L(447.675)x	K7FED	------------
Henderson	146.6400	–	O	W6JCY	------------
Henderson	146.9700	–	O 100/100	KE7MWY	------------
Hi Potosi Mtn	146.7900	–	O 100/100 L(449.9750)	KB6XN	------------
Hi Potosi Mtn	146.8800	–	O 100/100	WA7HXO	LVRA
Las Vegas	145.2500	–	O 100	K6JSI	WINS System
Las Vegas	145.3500	–	O 100/100	N7LD	ALLSTAR
Las Vegas	145.3500	–	O 100/100	WR7NV	Nevada ARC
Las Vegas	146.6700	–	O 136.5/136.5	WA7CYC	------------
Las Vegas	146.9400	–	O 100/100	K7UGE	LVRAC
Las Vegas	147.0000	+	O 123/123	N7ARR	NARRI IRLP
Las Vegas	147.0300	+	O 100/100	WB6EGR	ALLSTAR
Las Vegas	147.0900	+	O 100/100	N7OK	SDARC

Location	*Output*	*Input*	*Notes*	*Call*	*Sponsor*
Las Vegas	147.2700	+	O	KC7DB	MARA
North Las Vegas	145.4600	–	O 100/100e rs	N7RNR	------------
Red Mtn	145.1100	–	O 100/100	WA7HXO	LVRA
LINCOLN COUNTY					
Highland Peak	145.2200	–	O 100/100	WA7HXO	LVRA
Pioche	147.1200	+	O 123/123	W7AOR IRLP	---------
Utah Hill	146.8200	–	O 100/100	W7KVS	------------
NEVADA SUPER LINK					
Battle Mt	146.7900	–	Olx	WA6TLW	WA6TLW
Carlin	146.9400	–	O 100l	KE7LKO	WB7BTS
Elko	147.3300	+	O 100	W7YDX	W7YDX
Ely	146.6100	–	Olx	WB7WTS	WB7WTS
Eureka	147.0600	+	O 114.8	WB7WTS	WB7WTS
Hawthorne	146.7900	–	O 192.8lx	WA6TLW	WA6TLW
Wells/Wendover	146.7900	–	O 156.7lx	WA7MOC	WA7MOC
Winnemucca	146.8650	–	O 146.2lx	WB7WTS	WA6TLW
NORTH CENTRAL					
Battle Mountain	146.7600	–	O 100e	KE7LKO	WV3LMA
Battle Mt	146.7900	–	Olx	WA6TLW	WA6TLW
Battle Mt	146.9100	–	O 100l	W7LKO	N7EV
Carlin	146.9400	–	O 100l	KE7LKO	WB7BTS
Elko	147.2100	+	O 100lx	W7LKO	N7EV
Elko	147.3300	+	O 100	W7YDX	W7YDX
Jarbidge	146.7000	–	O 100	KA7CVV	KA7CVV
Jarbidge	146.7600	–	O 100l	KA7CVV	KA7CVV
Spring Creek	146.7450	–	● 127.3	NB9E	NB9E
Valmy	147.1050	+	O 100	KF7UTO	KF7UTO
Winnemucca	146.6400	–	O 100l	W7LKO	W7LKO
Winnemucca	146.7300	–	O 88.5	WO7I	WO7I
Winnemucca	146.8650	–	O 146.2lx	WB7WTS	WA6TLW
Winnemucca	146.9850	–	O 100el	KF7UTO	KF7IYC
Winnemucca	147.0900	+	O 100e	W7TKO	W7TKO
NORTH EAST					
Contact	146.8500	–	O 192.8l	KA7CVV	KA7CVV
Jackpot	147.2700	+	O 100l	W7GK	W7GK
Wells/Wendover	146.7900	–	O 156.7lx	WA7MOC	WA7MOC
NORTH LAS VEGAS VALLEY					
Beacon Hill	145.3000	–	ODCS(244) L(CC ARES/RACES)rs	N7SGV	CC ARES/RACE
Glendale	147.3900	+	O	W7MZV	------------
NORTH WEST					
Empire	146.6550	–	O	KS2R	KS2R
Gerlach	145.2300	–	O 123l	KD7YIM	KD7YIM
Gerlach	146.7000	–	O 100	KD6KAC	KD6KAC
NVLLRC					
Carson City	145.2700	–	● 141.3	KC7STW	KC7STW
NYE COUNTY					
Beatty	145.6400	–	O	AC7EL	------------

NEVADA

Location	Output	Input	Notes	Call	Sponsor
Montezuma Peak	146.6400	–	O	WB7WTS	------------
Pahrump	145.1300	–	O 100/100	W7NYE	ARES
Pahrump	145.6200	–	O 100/100	W7NYE	------------
Pahrump	146.8500	–	O 173.8/173.8	AD7DP	------------
Pahrump	146.9100	–	O 123/123	N7ARR	NARRI - IRLP
Schader Peak	145.6200	–	O	AC7EL	------------
Tonopah	146.6400	–	O 123/123	N7ARR	NARRI - IRLP
PORTABLE					
Gerlach	147.0000	+	O 100p	KD6THY	KD6THY
Portable Repeat	145.3100	–	O 123p	NK7W	NK7W
Portable Repeat	147.0000	–	O 123ep	W7TA	K7JN
SOUTH					
Las Vegas	147.1050	+	O 146.2	WØJAY	WØJAY
SOUTH CENTRAL					
Wellington	146.8800	–	O 123e	KD7NHC	KD7NHC
SOUTHERN CLARK COUNTY					
Laughlin	147.1800	+	O 127.3/127.3 L(CC ARES/RACES)rs	N7SGV	CC ARES/RACES
WEST					
Rocky Point NV	146.9600	–	Ox	WA7BWF	EARC
WEST CENTRAL					
Carcon City	147.2700	+	O 123el	W7DI	K7VC
Carson City	145.2400	–	Oe	KB7MF	KB7MF
Carson City	145.2700	–	● 141.3	KC7STW	KC7STW
Carson City	146.8200	–	O 123lx	WA7DG	N7LPT
Dayton	147.1050	+	O 123	K7DNV	K7DNV
Fallon	145.3100	–	O 123	NK7W	NK7W
Fallon	145.3500	–	O 123el	KE6QK	KE6QK
Fallon	147.0900	+	O 123	KF7ETH	KF7ETH
Fernley	147.3600	+	O 123l	N7PLQ	N7PLQ
Hawthorne	146.7900	–	O 192.8lx	WA6TLW	WA6TLW
Hawthorne	147.1200	+	● 114.8l	KB7PPG	KB7PPG
Lovelock	145.3100	–	O 123	KE7INV	KE7INV
Lovelock	146.9250	–	O 123el	W7TA	K7JN
Minden	145.4300	–	O 141.3	KB7PDF	KC7PAO
Minden	147.2700	+	O 123	W7DI	K7VC
Minden	147.3300	+	O 123	NV7CV	WA6EYD
New Washoe City	145.4100	–	O 97.4	NH7M	NH7M
Reno	145.1500	–	O 123	KD7DTN	KD7DTN
Reno	145.2100	–	O 123l	W7RHC	W7NIK
Reno	145.2900	–	O 123e	W7UNR	NS9E
Reno	145.3100	–	O 110.9e	W7RHC	KE7DZZ
Reno	145.3700	–	Ol	W7UIZ	W7UIZ
Reno	145.3900	–	O	W7UIZ	W7UIZ
Reno	145.4500	–	O 123	K7AN	W7FD
Reno	145.4900	–	O 123	W6JA	W7AB
Reno	146.6100	–	O 123l	W7TA	K7JN
Reno	146.6700	–	O 110.9el	W7RHC	W7NIK

Location	Output	Input	Notes	Call	Sponsor
Reno	146.7300	–	O 123	K7RDO	W7FD
Reno	146.7600	–	O 123	WA7SIX	W7URL
Reno	146.8650	–	O 103.5	KK7RON	KK7RON
Reno	146.8650	–	O 103.5	KK7RON	KK7RON
Reno	146.9400	–	O 131	N7VXB	N7YPZ
Reno	147.1200	+	O 123e	KE7R	NN7B
Reno	147.1500	+	O 123el	WA7DG	KK7SL
Reno	147.2100	+	O 123l	WA7DG	KK7SL
Reno	147.3000	+	O 123elx	WA7DG	KK7SL
Reno	147.3900	+	O 100e	W7TA	K7JN
Reno/Sparks	145.4700	–	O 123	WA7UEK	W1BUS
Reno/Sparks	147.0300	+	O 123e	WA7DG	KK7SL
Reno/Sparks	147.0900	+	O 100	KK7RON	KK7RON
Silver Springs	146.9700	–	O 103.5l	KE6QK	KE6QK
Sparks	145.2300	–	O	N7KP	N7KP
Sparks	146.8200	–	O 146.2	WA6TLW	WA6TLW
Sparks	146.8950	–	O 123	KA7ZAU	KA7ZAU
Sparks	147.0600	+	O 123	N7PLQ	N7PLQ
Topaz Lake	146.7150	–	O 203.5e	W6SUV	W6SUV
WHITE PINE COUNTY					
Ely	147.1800	+	O 114.8/114.8 L(SALT LAKE CITY)	WB7WTS	------------
NEW HAMPSHIRE					
DARTMOUTH/LAKE SUNAPEE					
Charlestown	146.9250	–	O 118.8	NX1DX	NX1DX
Claremont	147.2850	+	O 103.5es	KU1R	SCARG
Etna	147.1500	+	O 110.9e	W1UWS	CVFMA
Hanover	145.3300	–	O 100e L(E363356)sx	W1FN	TSRC
New London	145.2500	–	O 88.5e L(147.285 CLAREMONT NH)	W1VN	K1JY/SCARG
New London	147.1200	+	O 136.5eps	WA1ZCN	NHARES
Unity	147.1800	+	O 123e L(KA1BBG NH 2 METER NETWORK)x	KA1BBG	KA1BBG
GREAT NORTH WOODS					
Berlin	145.1100	–	O 100	N1ZGK	SCI
Clarksville	146.7150	–	O 100e L(MT. WASHINGTON 224.86)rs	W1COS	CoosCyARES
Colebrook	147.3000	+	O 110.9e L(I4494 (I THINK))	W1HJF	LMRAPP
Groveton	147.3150	+	O 100 L(NNH REPEATER NETWORK)s	N1PCE	N1PCE
LAKES REGION					
Alton	146.8650	–	O 88.5	K1JEK	K1JEK
Franklin	147.3000	+	O 88.5es	W1JY	CNHARC
Gilford	146.9850	–	O 123e L(E147390)sWXx	W1JY	CNHARC

Location	*Output*	*Input*	*Notes*	*Call*	*Sponsor*
Moultonborough	145.3100	–	O 88.5 L(N1IMO-N1IMN)	N1TZE	N1TZE
Moultonborough	147.2550	+	O 156.7 (CA) E-SUN E-WIND L(E147255)px	W1RLM	LksRgn ARC
Moultonborough	147.3900	+	O 123es WX	W1JY	CNHARC
Ossipee	147.0300	+	O 88.5e	W1BST	LRRA
Pittsfield	146.7900	–	O 88.5 L(N1IMO-N1IMN)sx	N1IMO	N1IMO
West Ossipee	147.0750	+	O 100e L(D*V) EXPx	K1LTM	Whittier
MERRIMACK VALLEY					
Bedford	146.6850	–	O 141.3es	N1QC	GSARA
Bow	147.3300	+	O 141.3	N1SM	N1SM
Bow Center	145.1700	–	O 131.8x	K1OX	K1OX
Chester	145.1900	–	O 100x	K1OX	K1OX
Concord	146.9400	–	O 114.8	W1ALE	W1ALE
Concord	147.2250	+	O 100	KA1OKQ	KA1OKQ
Deerfield	147.0000	–	O 100	W1SRA	Saddlbk RA
Derry	145.3100	–	O L(DMR-MARC)	K1QVC	SNHDStrGrp
Derry	146.7450	–	O 114.8e L(E501047)	NM1D	NM1D
Derry	146.8500	–	O 85.4 (CA) ex	K1CA	IntrStRS
East Derry	147.2100	+	107.2e L(KC2LT)x	KC2LT	KC2LT
Goffstown	145.4800	–	OL(D*V)	NE1DV	EWARN
Goffstown	147.1350	+	O 100e L(E600646)sx	W1AKS	NHRADIO
Henniker	146.8950	–	O 100ers	K1BKE	CVRC
Hollis	146.7300	–	O 88.5e L(N1IMO-N1IMN)s	N1IMO	N1IMO
Hudson	145.2600	–	O L(DMR-MARC)	K1MOT	MARC-NE
Hudson	147.1050	+	O 88.5 L(E15837)	NE1B	RRA
Nashua	147.0450	+	O 100e	WW1Y	WW1Y
New Boston	147.3750	+	O 88.5	W1VTP	GSARA
Northwood	146.7000	–	O 88.5e L(E232623)x	K1JEK	K1JEK
Salem	145.3200	–	OL(D*V)	K1HRO	K1HRO ARC
Salem	147.1650	+	O 136.5	NY1Z	MtMRH RS
MONADNOCK REGION					
Gilsum	147.3600	+	O 123e L(KA1BBG NH 2 METER NETWORK)	KA1BBG	KA1BBG
Greenfield	147.0600	+	O 123e L(KA1BBG NH 2 METER NETWORK)x	KA1BBG	KA1BBG
Keene	146.8050	–	O 100 (CA) eL(440 MHZ LINKING)s	K1TQY	ChsCntyDXA

Location	*Output*	*Input*	*Notes*	*Call*	*Sponsor*
Peterborough	147.1950	+	O 88.5e L(N1IMO-N1IMN)sx	N1IMO	N1IMO
Rindge	146.7750	–	O 123 L(KA1BBG NH 2 METER NETWORK)	KA1BBG	KA1BBG
Walpole	147.0300	+	O 100e	K1PH	K1PH
Winchester	146.8650	–	O 100e L(K1TQY)	N1NCI	CCDX ARC
SEACOAST					
Hampton	145.4400	–	OeL(D*V)	K1HBR	HBAR
Kensington	145.1500	–	O 127.3 E-SUNs	W1WQM	PCARC
Kensington	145.4000	–	OL(D*V)	KB1TIX	SeacoastDA
Madbury	145.3800	–	OL(D*V IRCDDB)	N1HIT	NE-RDS
Seabrook	146.6100	–	O 141.3r	WA1NH	WA1NH
WHITE MOUNTAINS					
Cannon Mountain	145.4300	–	O 114.8e WXx	K1EME	LARK
Littleton	147.3450	+	O 114.8	K1EME	LARK
Mt Washington	146.6550	–	O 100ers	W1NH	WA1WOK
North Conway	145.4500	–	O 100s	W1MWV	WhtMtnARC
Whitefield	145.3700	–	O 114.8 L(NNH REPEATER NETWORK)s	N1PCE	N1PCE

NEW JERSEY

Location	*Output*	*Input*	*Notes*	*Call*	*Sponsor*
ATLANTIC					
Absecon	147.2100	+	O 123 (CA) eRB	N2HQX	DVRC
Brigantine	146.7150	–	O 91.5eWX	KA2OOR	------------
Buena	146.8050	–	O 118.8	KE2CK	KC2YWJ
Egg Harbor	146.6400	–	O 131.8elr sRB WX	W3BXW	BEARS
Egg Harbor Twp	146.7450	–	O 146.2 (CA)erWX	K2BR	SCARA
Galloway Twp	147.1650	+	O 91.5eWX	KD2AFX	ACURA
W Atlantic City	146.9850	–	O 146.2 (CA)e	W2HRW	SPARC
BERGEN					
North Arlington	147.2100	+	O 088.5e	K2DCG	------------
BERGEN CO					
Alpine	146.9550	–	O 141.3a TT	K2ETN	CRRC
Fair Lawn	145.4700	–	O 107.2	W2NPT	Fair Lawn ARC
Fort Lee	145.4500	–	O 100.0r	W2MPX	METROPLX
Paramus	146.7900	–	O 141.3	W2AKR	BCFMA
BURLINGTON					
Chatsworth	145.4700	–	O 127.3elr s	KC2QVT	BURLCO OEM
Medford Twp	145.2900	–	O 91.5 (CA) e	K2AA	SJRA

Location	Output	Input	Notes	Call	Sponsor
Robbinsville	147.0750	+	O 71.9 (CA) elr	KX2D	Robbinsvil
Westampton	147.1500	+	O 127.3 (CA)elrsWX	KC2QVT	BURLCO OEM
Willingboro	146.9250	–	O 131.8 (CA)e	WB2YGO	WARG Inc.
CAMDEN					
Blackwood	146.8950	–	O 192.8ers WX	K2EOC	CCOEM
Camden	146.8200	–	O 131.8es	W3PHL	PARA Group
Cherry Hill	145.3700	–	O 91.5 (CA) e	NJ2CH	CH OEM
Pine Hill	146.8650	–	O 131.8 (CA)el	K2UK	CCAPRA
Runnemede	147.2250	+	O 192.8e	WA2WUN	------------
Waterford Wks	145.2100	–	O 71.9e EXP	W2FLY	------------
Waterford Wks	147.3450	+	O 127.3er WX	WA3BXW	SNJ-ARES
Winslow	145.1500	–	O 91.5e	K2AX	JTRA
CAPE MAY					
Avalon	147.1200	+	O 203.5e WX	KC2KAX	ECLWA
Cape May Ct Hse	146.6100	–	O 88.5	N2CMC	CMCARC
Cape May Ct Hse	147.2400	+	O 146.2ers	W2CMC	------------
Ocean City	147.2850	+	O 156.7 (CA)elrRB LITZ WX	W3PS	METRO-COMM
Wildwood	145.4500	–	O 167.9er	KA3LKM	------------
CUMBERLAND					
Bridgeton	147.2550	+	O 179.9 (CA)ersWX	KC2TXB	Cum.Co.OEM
Vineland	145.4900	–	O 179.9eBI	WA2WUN	------------
ESSEX CO					
Livingston	146.5950	147.5950	O 100.0ez	NE2S	SBARC
Newark	145.3500	–	O 107.2 BI	W2JDS	------------
Newark	147.2250	+	O 141.3 L(440.500)	K2MFF	NJIT
North Caldwell	147.1800	+	O 151.4	W2JT	NJDXA
West Orange	146.4150	147.4150	O 85.4 (CA) eL(224.480)rsLITZz	WA2JSB	WORA
West Orange	147.2850	+	O 141.3/141.3 (CA)elrsLITZ WXz	WA2HYO	NJRA
GLOUCESTER					
Monroe Twp	145.3900	–	O 91.5rs	K2DX	+WC2K
Pitman	147.1800	+	O 131.8 (CA)rs	W2MMD	GCARC
HUNTERDON					
Cherryville	147.3750	+	O 151.4ae	WB2NQV	W2CRA
Holland Twp	146.8500	–	O 151.4ae LITZ	WA2GWA	K2PM

ADVANCED SPECIALTIES INC.
New Jersey's Communications Store
YAESU The radio
ALINCO
AMATEUR RADIO'S VALUE LEADER
Authorized Dealer
ALINCO • TYT • COMET • MALDOL • MFJ
UNIDEN • ANLI • YAESU • ANYTONE • BAOFENG
Yaesu FT-7900R Dual Band mobile
Anytone AT-5888UV DualBand Mobile Radio
VX-8DR Quadband Submersible HT
FT-857D HF, 6M, 2M, 70 CM
Uniden Home Patrol Digital TouchScreen Scanner
FT-2900R 75W 2M Mobile
Closed Sunday & Monday
Orders/Quotes
1-800-926-9HAM ▪ (201)-VHF-2067
114 Essex Street ▪ Lodi, NJ 07644
Big Online Catalog at:
www.advancedspecialties.net
AMATEUR RADIO – SCANNERS – BOOKS – ANTENNAS
MOUNTS – FILTERS
ACCESSORIES AND MORE!
MasterCard
VISA
DISCOVER

NEW JERSEY

Location	*Output*	*Input*	*Notes*	*Call*	*Sponsor*
Mt Kipp	147.0150	+	O 151.4 (CA)elrWX	WB2NQV	W2CRA
MERCER					
Allentown	147.1050	+	● 123 (CA)	K2UQ	Allentown
Lawrenceville	146.4600	147.4600	O 131.8	N2RE	SarnoffRC
West Trenton	146.6700	–	O 131.8 (CA)ersWX	W2ZQ	DVRA
MIDDLESEX CO					
Old Bridge	147.1200	+	O 162.2/162.2 (CA)elrsz	W2CJA	PSARN
Sayreville	146.7600	–	O 156.7/156.7 (CA)eL(443.200)rsLITZ	K2GE	RBRA
MONMOUTH CO					
Creamridge	147.2400	+	O 131.8 (CA)er	N2DRM	CR-MRG
Ellisdale	145.4500	–	O 131.8e	K2NI	HRG
Middletown	145.4850	–	O 151.4 (CA)er	N2DR	MT RACES OEM
Ocean Twp	147.0450	+	O 67.0 (CA) ersLITZ WX	WB2ABT	MCRA
Wall Twp	145.1100	–	O 127.3es	N2MO	OMARC
Wall Twp	146.7750	–	Oe	N2CTD	WALL OEM
MORRIS					
Lake Hopatcong	145.1800	–	OTT	NJ2MC	------------
MORRIS CO					
Boonton	147.0300	+	O 151.4/151.4e	W2TW	WARC
Butler	147.1350	+	O 141.3elr sRB WX	WB2FTX	ButlrRACES
Long Valley	147.0300	+	O 141.3/141.3ers	N2GS	CWRACES
Morris Twp	146.8950	–	O 151.4/151.4 (CA)erWX	WS2Q	MORISOEM
Roxbury	146.9850	–	O 131.8 (CA)e	K2RF	SARA
OCEAN					
Lakehurst	145.1700	–	O 131.8ers	N2IFP	CrmRdgRG
Lakewood	146.9550	–	O 103.5e	W2RAP	EARS
Manahawkin	146.8350	–	O 127.3 (CA)ers	N2OO	835UserGrp
Toms River	146.4450	147.4450	O 131.8ae sWX	KC2GUM	O.C.R.G.
Toms River	146.6550	–	O 127.3 RB WX	WA2JWR	HCARC
Toms River	146.9100	–	O 127.3eBI	W2DOR	JSARS
Tuckerton	146.7000	–	O 192.8ers	N2NF	------------
PASSAIC CO					
Little Falls	146.9250	–	O 151.4/151.4er	W2VER	VRACES

Location	*Output*	*Input*	*Notes*	*Call*	*Sponsor*
Passaic	147.3450	+	O 067.0/067.0 (CA) TTersRB WX(845)	KC2MDA	TECNJ
Wanaque	146.4900	147.4900	a	WA2SNA	RAMPOARC
Wanaque	146.7000	–	O 141.3 (CA) TT(1070)ersLITZ WXz	W2PQG	10-70 RA
Wayne	145.2100	–	O 141.3e	W2GT	Partyline Net
West Patterson	146.6100	–	151.4	W2FCL	LND ROVERS A
SALEM					
Pennsville	146.6250	–	O 131.8 (CA)er	N2KEJ	S.C.R.A.
SOMERSET CO					
Green Brook	146.6250	–	O 141.3	W2QW	RVRC
Green Brook	146.9400	–	O 141.3/141.3 (CA)ers	K2ETS	ETS OF NJ
Hillsboro	147.1350	+	O 151.4/151.4ersz	K2NJ	WJDXG
Martinsville	147.2850	+	O 141.3e	W2NJR	NJRA
SUSSEX					
Newton	147.2100	+	O 151.4rs	W2LV	SCARC
Newton	147.3000	+	O 151.4 (CA)elrs	W2LV	SCARC
Newton	147.3300	+	O 151.4rs	W2LV	SCARC
Vernon	146.9250	–	O 151.4er WX	W2VER	Vern RACES
UNION CO					
Elizabeth	145.4100	–	O 107.2 RB BI	W2JDS	------------
Murray Hill	147.2550	+	O 141.3 (CA)rsWX	W2LI	TRI-CNTYARA
Roselle Park	146.6850	–	O 123.0/123.0 (CA)er	WA2ZDN	------------
Springfield	147.5050	146.5050	O 123.0 (CA) TTerz	WA2BAT	SPFD EMRC
WARREN					
Columbia	146.4750	147.4750	O 110.9e	WB2NMI	------------
Washington	146.8200	–	O 110.9r	W2SJT	PJARC
NEW MEXICO					
ALBUQUERQUE					
Albuquerque	145.1300	–	O 162.2e L(145.160)rs	K5BIQ	BC-OEM
Albuquerque	145.3300	–	O 100.0e L(444.0)x	W5CSY	ARCC
Albuquerque	146.7200	–	O 100.0/127.3ex	K5CQH	K5CQH
Albuquerque	146.9000	–	O 67.0e L(147.0600)x	K5FIQ	URFMSI
Albuquerque	146.9200	–	O 67eBI	KF5ERC	------------
Albuquerque	147.3200	+	O 100.0 (CA)	K5LXP	K5LXP

NEW MEXICO

Location	Output	Input	Notes	Call	Sponsor
Albuquerque	147.3600	+	Oe	KB5XE	KB5XE
Rio Rancho	145.3700	–	O 162.2e	NM5HD	High Desert ARC
Rio Rancho	147.1000	+	O 100.0e L(443.000)rsRB	NM5RR	SCARES
Sandia Crest	147.3800	+	O 162.2e L(442.1000)x	KB5GAS	ABQ Gas Balloon
Tijeras	145.1500	–	O 100.0e L(145.130)rs	K5BIQ	BC-OEM
ARES/RACES NET					
Abiquiu	147.0400	+	O 141.3ers	NM5EM	NMEMA ARC
Caprock	145.2500	–	O 141.3ers	NM5EM	NMEMA ARC
Cloudcroft	145.3700	–	O 156.7ers	NM5EM	NMEMA ARC
Clovis	145.3700	–	O 141.3ers	NM5EM	NMEMA ARC
Corona	145.1150	–	O 141.3ers	NM5EM	NMEMA ARC
Cuba	145.1750	–	O 141.3ers	NM5EM	NMEMA ARC
Davenport	147.3200	+	O 141.3ers	NM5EM	NMEMA ARC
Des Moines	145.1750	–	O 141.3ers	NM5EM	NMEMA ARC
Eagle Nest	147.0400	+	O 141.3ers	NM5EM	NMEMA ARC
Grants	146.9800	–	O 141.3ers	NM5EM	NMEMA ARC
Reserve	147.3400	+	O 141.3ers	NM5EM	NMEMA ARC
Santa Fe	147.0200	+	O 141.3ers	NM5EM	NMEMA ARC
Santa Rosa	147.0400	+	O 141.3ers	NM5EM	NMEMA ARC
Silver City	145.1450	–	O 141.3ers	NM5EM	NMEMA ARC
Socorro	145.1750	–	O 141.3ers	NM5EM	NMEMA ARC
Tres Piedras	145.1750	–	O 141.3ers	NM5EM	NMEMA ARC
Truth or Consequences	145.1300	–	O 141.3ers	NM5EM	NMEMA ARC
Wagon Mound	145.3700	–	O 141.3ers	NM5EM	NMEMA ARC
CENTRAL					
Belen	146.7000	–	O 100.0ers	KC5OUR	Val.CoARA
Belen	146.9600	–	O 100.0 (CA)elxZ(123)	K5URR	URFMSI
Clines Corners	147.0600	+	O 67.0 (CA) eL(146.9000) Z(123)	K5FIQ	URFMSI
La Madera	147.0800	+	O 100.0/100.0ers	NM5SC	SCARES
Los Lunas	145.3900	–	O 85.4ers	NM5LL	LLARA
Los Lunas	145.4900	–	O 85.4 (CA) elrsx	NM5LL	LLARA
Socorro	146.6800	–	O 100.0/123.0aexz	W5AQA	Soc. ARA
Socorro	147.1600	+	O 100.0ae prs	W5AQA	SocorroARA
EAST CENTRAL					
Clovis	147.2400	+	O 67.0ers	KA5B	ENM ARC
Clovis	147.3200	+	O 71.9/71.9 e	WS5D	WS5D
Portales	146.8200	–	O 67.0e	N5HXL	Greyhound ARC
Portales	147.0000	+	O 67.0es	W5OMU	W5OMU

Location	*Output*	*Input*	*Notes*	*Call*	*Sponsor*
Redlake	146.8400	–	O 67.0ers	KE5RUE	Greyhound ARC
MEGA-LINK					
Alamogordo	145.3500	–	O 67.0 (CA) elxZ(123)	NM5ML	Mega-Link
Albuquerque	145.2900	–	O 100.0 (CA)elxZ(123)	NM5ML	Mega-Link
Bloomfield	147.2800	+	O 67.0 (CA) elxZ(123)	NM5ML	Mega-Link
Clovis	147.2800	+	O 67.0 (CA) elxZ(123)	NM5ML	Mega-Link
Conchas Dam	147.3600	+	O 100.0 (CA)elxZ(123)	NM5ML	Mega-Link
Corona	147.2800	+	O 100.0 (CA)elxZ(123)	NM5ML	Mega-Link
Cuba	147.2400	+	O 67.0 (CA) elxZ(123)	NM5ML	Mega-Link
Datil-Davenport	147.0400	+	O 100.0 (CA)elrsxZ(123)	NM5ML	Mega-Link
Datil-Luera Peak	147.1400	+	O 100.0 (CA)elxZ(123)	NM5ML	Mega-Link
Deming	147.0200	+	O 100.0 (CA)lxZ(123)	NM5ML	Mega-Link
Ft Sumner	147.1400	+	O 100.0 (CA)elxZ(123)	KB5ZFA	Mega-Link
Gallup	147.2200	+	O 67.0 (CA) elxZ(123)	NM5ML	Mega-Link
Grants	146.6600	–	O 100.0 (CA)elxZ(123)	NM5ML	Mega-Link
Las Cruces	147.1800	+	O 100.0 (CA)elxZ(123)	NM5ML	Mega-Link
Las Vegas	147.2600	+	O 67.0 (CA) E-SUNlxZ(123)	NM5ML	Mega-Link
Maljamar	147.1400	+	O 67.0 (CA) elxZ(123)	NM5ML	Mega-Link
Raton	147.2800	+	O 100.0 (CA)elxZ(123)	NM5ML	Mega-Link
Reserve	147.3600	+	O 67.0 (CA) lxZ(123)	NM5ML	Mega-Link
Roswell	146.6600	–	O 67.0 (CA) lsxZ(123)	NM5ML	Mega-Link
Roswell	147.2600	+	O 100.0 (CA)lxZ(123)	NM5ML	Mega-Link
Silver City	145.1150	–	O 100.0/100.0 (CA)lxZ(123)	NM5ML	Mega-Link
Socorro	147.2400	+	O 100.0 (CA)elxZ(123)	NM5ML	Mega-Link
T or C	147.2600	+	O 100.0 (CA)elxZ(123)	NM5ML	Mega-Link
Taos Ski Valley	147.1400	+	O 67/67 (CA)lrsx	NM5ML	Mega-Link

Location	Output	Input	Notes	Call	Sponsor
Tijeras	147.4400	147.4400	O 100.0 (CA)lZ(123)	NM5ML	Mega-Link
Tres Piedras	147.2200	+	O 100.0 (CA)elxZ(123)	NM5ML	Mega-Link
Tucumcari	147.2200	+	O 100.0 (CA)elxZ(123)	NM5ML	Mega-Link
Wagon Mound	147.2000	+	O 67.0/67.0 (CA)elrsZ(123)	NM5ML	Mega-Link
NORTH CENTRAL					
Angel Fire	147.3400	+	Oex	N5LEM	Taos ARC
Chama	147.0800	+	O 162.2 E-SUN L(146.82)	W5SF	SFARC
Embudo	147.1800	+	O	K5PEY	------------
La Cueva	145.4100	–	O 100.0/100.0eLITZ	W5HO	------------
La Cueva	146.8400	–	O 107.2elx	N9PGQ	------------
Las Vegas	145.4500	–	Oe	KB5WEZ	KB5WEZ
Las Vegas	147.3000	+	O 162.2elx	W5SF/ELK	SFARC
Las Vegas	147.3800	+	Oe	KB5ENM	ALOST RS
Los Alamos	145.1900	–	O 100 (CA) es	KD5CUC	SFARC
Los Alamos	146.8800	–	O	W5PDO	LAARC
Red River	145.3900	–	O/100.0e	KF5ORU	Taos ARC
Taos	147.1200	+	Oelx	W5TYL	Taos ARC
Tres Piedras	146.7600	–	O 67.0ex	KD5CHU	HiVly ARC
NORTH EAST					
Des Moines	146.8500	–	O 100.0ex	N5BOP	SGRC
Raton	145.4900	–	O 100/100 TTeLITZ WX	NØDRC	------------
NORTH WEST					
Aztec	146.7400	–	O 100.0 (CA)eL(146.85)	NM5SJ	SJC EMCOMM
Blanco	147.1000	+	O 100.0	KB5ITS	KB5ITS
Bloomfield	146.9200	–	O 100.0 (CA) L(146.85)	NM5SJ	SJC EMCOMM
Farmington	146.7600	–	O 100.0 (CA)e	KB5ITS	KB5ITS
Farmington	146.8500	–	O 100.0 (CA) L(TOTAH ARC)	NM5SJ	SJC EMCOMM
Farmington	147.0000	+	O 100.0ae	KB5ITS	KB5ITS
Lybrook	145.4900	–	O 100.0 (CA) L(146.85)	NM5SJ	SJC EMCOMM
Navajo Dam	147.3600	+	O 100.0/100.0e	KB5ITS	------------
Tank Mountain	146.8800	–	O 100.0e	KB5ITS	KB5ITS
SANTA FE					
Santa Fe	146.8200	–	O 162.2ae x	W5SF/TES	SFARC
Santa Fe	147.2000	+	O 162.2e	W5SF/SVH	SFARC

Location	*Output*	*Input*	*Notes*	*Call*	*Sponsor*
SOUTH CENTRAL					
Alamogordo	146.8000	–	O 100.0e	K5LRW	Alamo ARC
Alamogordo	146.8600	–	O 100.0/100.0e	N6CID	------------
Alamogordo	146.9000	–	O 77.0a	KC5OWL	------------
Benson Ridge	145.2300	–	O 123.0lx	K5BEN	JPARA
Benson Ridge	145.2700	–	O 162.2	K5KKO	ELP Dig Int Gp
Capitan	146.6100	–	OE-SUNx	KB5ZFA	------------
Cloudcroft	146.9600	–	O 100.0e L(147.34)rsRBx	KE5MIQ	SMRC
Cloudcroft	147.2200	+	O 100.0/100.0eL(147.34)rsx	KE5MIQ	SMRC
Cloudcroft	147.3400	+	O 100.0/100.0eL(147.22)rsx	KE5MIQ	SMRC
High Rolls	147.0000	+	O 141.3/141.3 E-SUNrs	W5AKU	------------
Las Cruces	146.6400	–	O 100.0 (CA)e	N5BL	MVRC
Las Cruces	146.7800	–	Oe	N5IAC	------------
Las Cruces	147.3800	+	O 100.0a TT	W7DXX	------------
Ruidoso	145.4500	–	O 100.0/100.0eL(146.92)	KR5NM	SBARC
Ruidoso	146.7400	–	O 100.0e L(443.825)rsWX	K5FBK	------------
Ruidoso	146.9200	–	O 100.0/100.0eL(145.45)	KR5NM	SBARC
Ruidoso	146.9800	–	O 100.0/100.0 (CA)eE-SUN L(145.31)rsRB WX	K5RIC	ARC
T or C	146.7600	–	O 100.0 (CA)ex	N5BL	MVRC
Tularosa	147.0800	+	O 100.0e	W5TWY	------------
SOUTH EAST					
Caprock	147.1800	+	Oex	KB5ZFA	------------
Carlsbad	146.8800	–	Ors	W5TD	------------
Carlsbad	147.2800	+	O 123.0e L(442.4500)sRB LITZx	K5CNM	Eddy Co ARES/S
Hobbs	147.2200	+	O 173.8e	K5INW	------------
Hope	147.3800	+	O 123.0e L(442.4500)sRB LITZx	K5CNM	Eddy Co ARES/S
Jal	147.1000	+	O	N5SVI	N5SVI
Loving	147.3600	+	O 123.0e L(442.4500)sRB LITZx	K5CNM	Eddy Co ARES/S
Queen	147.3000	+	O 123.0e L(442.4500)sRB LITZx	K5CNM	Eddy Co ARES/S
Roswell	146.6400	–	OTTe	N5MMI	NMMI ARC
Roswell	146.9400	–	O(CA)rs	W5TD	------------
Roswell	147.3200	+	O 162.2/162.2e	W5GNB	W5GNB

Location	*Output*	*Input*	*Notes*	*Call*	*Sponsor*
Tatum	146.7000	–	O	AH2AZ	------------
			127.3/127.3#L(147.22)x		
SOUTH WEST					
Columbus	145.4300	–	O 88.5rs	W5DAR	DARC
Deming	146.8200	–	Oex	W5DAR	DARC
Deming	147.0800	+	O	W5JX	------------
Deming	147.1200	+	O 88.5/88.5	K5UPS	K5UPS
			E-SUN		
Jacks Peak	145.1700	–	O 100.0e	N5IA	N5IA
			L(MEGALINK)		
Jacks Peak	145.2100	–	O 141.3	N5IA	JPARA
			L(EAARS)		
Jacks Peak	145.2500	–	O 88.5x	WB5QHS	JPARA
Little Florida Mtns	147.0400	+	O 127.3	N5IA	N5IA
			L(147.06)		
Little Florida Mtns	147.0600	+	O 127.3	N5IA	N5IA
			L(147.04)		
Reserve	147.3800	+	O 103.5#	K7QCW	CCARS
Silver City	146.9800	–	O 103.5	K5GAR	Gila ARS
			(CA)elsx		
STATEWIDE					
Statewide	147.1600	+	Oprs		ARES/SAR
WEST CENTRAL					
Gallup	147.2600	+	O 100.0rs	KC5WDV	KC5WDV
Grants	146.6400	–	O(CA)e	K5URR	URFMSI
			L(146.7400)xZ(123)		
Grants	146.9400	–	O 100.0	K5URR	URFMSI
			(CA)elxZ(123)		
Grants	147.1800	+	O 100.0	WB5EKP	CARCUS
Zuni	145.4300	–	O 162.2	WA5SOX	MCARES
			(CA)x		

NEW YORK

Location	*Output*	*Input*	*Notes*	*Call*	*Sponsor*
ADIRONDACKS EAST					
Blue Mtn	145.4900	–	O 123lx	N2JKG	RACES
Lake Placid	147.3000	+	O 100.0	N2NGK	N2NGK
Long Lake	146.6400	–	●	KCZZO	Bear Bait Radio Club
			162.2/162.2ex		
Lyon Mtn	147.2850	+	O 123.0e	W2UXC	ChmpVlyRC
Mineville	147.2550	+	O 123elr	WA2LRE	Essx RACES
			WX		
Plattsburgh	147.1500	+	O 123.0e	W2UXC	ChmpVlyRC
Saranac Lake	147.0300	+	O 100.0	W2WIZ	Red Cross
Speculator	147.1650	+	Oer	KA2VHF	Hmltn ARC
Whiteface Mtn	145.1100	–	O 123.0elr	N2JKG	Clin RACES
			x		
ALBANY/CAPITAL REGION					
Albany	145.1900	–	O 103.5e	K2CT	ALBANY AMATEUR
Albany	147.1200	+	Oer	K2ALB	Albany County ACES

Location	*Output*	*Input*	*Notes*	*Call*	*Sponsor*
Albany	147.3750	+	O 100	KA2QYE	KA2QYE
Averill Park	145.3700	–	O 127.3l	W1GRM	W1GRM
Columbia	146.6700	–	O 100	N2JVE	N2JVE
Delmar	146.6400	–	Or	W2VJB	BethRACES
East Galway	147.3600	+	O	N2FEP	N2FEP
Fonda	147.1950	+	O 156.7erz	KC2AUO	MOHAWK VALL
Galway	147.2400	+	O 100e L(147.00)r	K2DLL	Saratoga County
Glenville	146.7900	–	O 100	W2IR	Schenectady Mu
Gloversville	146.7000	–	Oar	K2JJI	TRYON AMATE
Grafton	145.2500	–	O 100 (CA) e	WB2BQW	NORTHEAST C
Grafton	145.3100	–	O	K2CBA	GURU
Grafton	147.1800	+	O(CA)elrsz	K2REN	RENSSELAER A
Hoosick Falls	147.3450	+	Oer	K2RBR	K2RBR
Middle Grove	145.4300	–	O 156.7	WB2BGI	WB2BGI
Rensselaer	147.3300	+	O 146.2	WB2HZT	WB2HZT
Schenectady	147.0600	+	Oaer	K2AE	SCHENECTADY
Schenectady	147.3000	+	Oa	WA2AFD	WA2AFD
Troy	145.1700	–	OelrsWX	N2TY	TROY AMATEU
Troy	145.3300	–	Olr	K2RBR	NiMo ARC
Troy	146.7600	–	O 103.5elr s	K2REN	RENSSELAER A
Troy	146.8200	–	O(CA)l	W2SZ	RPI AMATEUR
Troy	146.9400	–	Oael	W2GBO	Tel Pionrs
Troy	147.2700	+	O 100elrs	KG2BH	CohEddy Ct
AUBURN					
Auburn	145.2300	–	O 71.9aep sxz	W2QYT	W2QYT
Auburn	147.0000	+	O 71.9aep xz	W2QYT	W2QYT
Auburn	147.2700	+	O 71.9aer	K2RSY	CayugaEMO
Moravia	146.6700	–	O 151.4ers WXx	AK2K	AK2K
Seneca Falls	145.1300	–	Ol	N2POH	Sen ARES
Skaneateles	147.1950	+	O 82.5e	WB2FOF	WB2FOF
BATH/HORNELL					
Alfred	146.9550	–	Oe	K2BVD	ALFRED RADIO
Arkport	147.0450	+	O 110.9elr	KC2FSW	Keuka LARA
Bath	145.1900	–	Oael	KB2WXV	KEUKA LAKE A
Bath	146.8050	–	OelWXx	N2HLT	N2HLT
Groveland	147.0300	+	O	W2COP	W2COP
Jasper	147.3300	+	Ol	KC2JLQ	Keuka LARA
Naples	146.9250	–	Ol	NO2W	Telcourier
Prattsburg	147.2400	+	O 110.9l	K1NXG	N2PA MtnGp
Springwater	146.7600	–	O(CA)elz	WA2DHB	Lvgstn ARS
BINGHAMTON					
Bing Airport	146.8650	–	O 146.2r WX	WA2QEL	Susquehanna Va

Location	Output	Input	Notes	Call	Sponsor
Binghamton	145.4700	–	O	W2EWM	W2EWM
Binghamton	146.7300	–	O 100ex	K2TDV	K2TDV
Binghamton	146.8200	–	O 146.2 WXx	WA2QEL	Susquehanna Valley
Binghamton	147.0750	+	OeWXx	K2VQ	K2VQ
Binghamton	147.3900	+	Ot#	W2OW	BINGHAMTON AMR
Endicott	145.3900	–	O 123 EXP	N2YR	W.A.G.
Endicott	147.2550	+	O 100 (CA) e	WA2VCS	N2ZOJ
Hancock	147.3450	+	O 146.2r WX	WA2QEL	Susquehanna Valley
Owego	146.7600	–	OWX	W2VDX	TIGARS
Vestal	147.1200	+	O 100l	K2ZG	K2ZG
CANANDAIGUA					
Bristol	145.1100	–	O 110.9l	WR2AHL	GRIDD
Canandaigua	146.8200	–	O 110.9ers WXx	K2BWK	SQUAW ISLAND AM
Farmington	145.4100	–	O 110.9	N2HJD	N2HJD
Geneva	147.0900	+	O 110.9er	W2ONT	ONTARIO COUNTY
Hemlock	147.3750	+	O	K2BWK	SQUAW ISLAND AR
South Bristol	145.4500	–	O 110.9er	W2ONT	ONTARIO COUNTY
CATSKILLS EAST					
Cairo	146.7450	–	O 210.7e	KB2DYB	KB2DYB
Cairo	147.0900	+	O(CA)ersz	N2SQW	GRN CTY RC
Hunter	145.1500	–	O	WB2UYR	Mtntop ARA
Jewett	145.4500	–	O	W1EQX	W1EQX
Krumville	146.7450	–	O 123es	KC2BYY	RIDGE TOP AMATE
Roxbury	146.9850	–	Oe	K2AGF	Mrgrtvl RC
CATSKILLS NORTH					
Cherry Valley	145.3500	–	O 167.9e	NC2C	OTSEGO COUNTY A
Cobleskill	146.6100	–	O 123ar	WA2ZWM	SCHOHARIE COUNT
Cooperstown	146.6400	–	Oer	NC2C	OTSEGO COUNTY A
Delhi	146.7450	–	Oersz	K2NK	Del Cty ES
Oneonta	146.8500	–	O 167.9 (CA)ersWXxz	W2SEU	OARC
Stamford	145.2300	–	Orsx	W2SEU	W2SEU
Walton	145.2500	–	O 100rLITZ WXz	WB2BQW	NORTHEAST CONN
Walton	146.9550	–	O 127.3ers z	K2NK	Walton RA
Walton	147.3150	+	Oer	W2LZ	WALTON RADIO AS
CORTLAND/ITHACA					
Burlington	146.7150	–	O 167.9r	W2EES	W2EES
Cortland	145.4900	–	O 151.4ae z	KB2LUV	SKYLINE AMATEUR
Cortland	147.0300	+	O	WA2VAM	FngrLksRA
Cortland	147.1800	+	O 71.9e	K2IWR	SKYLINE AMATEUR
Cortland	147.2250	+	O/71.9	KB2FAF	KB2FAF
Ithaca	146.6100	–	Oaez	W2CXM	CORNELL UNIV AM

Location	*Output*	*Input*	*Notes*	*Call*	*Sponsor*
Ithaca	146.8950	–	○ 107.2ex	K2ZG	K2ZG
Ithaca	146.9400	–	○ 103.5	KC1RM	KC1RM
Ithaca	146.9700	–	○ 103.5ae sWXxz	AF2A	TOMPKINS COU
Norwich	146.6850	–	○	W2RME	CHENANGO VA
ELMIRA/CORNING					
Corning	147.0150	+	○(CA)elz	N2IED	CARA
Elmira	146.7000	–	○l	W2ZJ	ELMIRA AMATE
Elmira	147.3600	+	○aelrsWX xz	N3AQ	ROOKIES
FRANKLIN					
Malone	147.0900	+	a(CA)	NG2C	------------
Malone	147.2250	+	151.4/151.4l	WB2RYB	------------
Saranac lake	145.3100	–	127.3	W2TLR	TLARC
Tupper lake	147.3300	+	100.0 L(449.700)x	KA2DRE	Greater Adironda
LONG ISLAND - NASSAU CO					
Mineola	146.6400	–	●telr	W2EJ	PLAZA RPTR
Plainview	146.8050	–	○ 136.5 (CA)lsRB WX	WB2WAK	NC ARES
Plainview	147.1350	+	○ 136.5 (CA)rsRB	WB2CYN	PHNX ARTS
Plainview	147.3300	+	○ 114.8/114.8 DCS(023)eL(927.1125)	N2BBO	------------
LONG ISLAND - SUFFOLK CO					
Bethpage	146.7450	146.1460	○ 136.5	WA2LQO	Grumman ARC
Dix Hills	147.0750	+	○ 136.5el BI	W2RGM	------------
Hauppauge	145.3300	–	○ 136.5ers	WA2LQO	Grumman ARC
Hauppauge	145.4300	–	○ 136.5 L(443.425)	W2LRC	LARKFIELD AR
Holbrook	145.4100	–	○ 136.5/136.5eL(927.1125) RB	N2BBO	------------
Holbrook	147.3900	+	○ 136.5/136.5eL(927.1125) RB	N2BBO	------------
Huntington	147.2100	+	○ 136.5 (CA)eL(443.675)rs	WR2ABA	LARKFIELD AR
Huntington	147.2850	+	● 97.4/167.9	KB2AKH	------------
Islip	147.3450	+	○ 100.0 (CA)rs	K2IRG	ISLIP RG
Manorville	145.3700	–	○ 136.5 (CA)eL(442.3)rs	N2NFI	PARC
Middle Island	146.8200	–	○ 151.4/151.4eL(449.7353)r	W2OQI	------------
N Babylon	147.2550	+	○ 136.5 (CA)elrsZ(911)	KB2UR	SSARC
N Lindenhurst	146.6850	–	○ 110.9/110.9eL(INTERNET)rsWXx	W2GSB	GSBARC

Location	Output	Input	Notes	Call	Sponsor
Port Jefferson	145.1500	–	O 136.5 (CA)el	W2RC	RCARC
Rocky Point	146.5950	147.5950	O 136.5 RB WX	N2FXE	------------
Selden	146.7150	–	● 136.5a (CA)el	WA2UMD	------------
Selden	146.7600	–	O 136.5e L(52.8&448.825)	WA2VNV	SBRA
Selden	147.3750	+	136.5 (CA)e	WB2NHO	LIMARC
Setauket	146.9400	–	O 136.5elr	WB2MOT	MST ARC
Southhampton	147.1950	+	O 136.5 (CA)esWX	WA2UEG	EARS
Yaphank	145.2100	–	O 136.5 (CA)ers	W2DQ	SCRC
LOWER HUDSON - WESTCHESTER					
Chappaqua	145.1100	–	O 123.0/123.0 (CA)ers	N2FMC	NWARA
New Rochelle	147.0400	+	O 192.8z	N2ZTE	SWRA
Vallhalla	147.0600	+	O 114.8 (CA)ersx	WB2ZII	WECA
Yonkers	146.8650	–	O 110.9 (CA)er	W2YRC	YNKRS ARC
Yorktown Hts	146.9400	–	O 123.0aer	WA2TOW	YCDARC/MSARC
Yorktown Hts	147.0150	+	O 114.8 (CA)er	WB2IXR	NWARA
MID HUDSON					
Carmel	145.1300	–	O 136.5r	K2PUT	PUTNAM EMERGEN
Harriman	147.1050	+	O 114.8l	N2JTI	ROCKLAND REPEA
Highland	147.0450	+	O 100es	N2OXV	MOUNT BEACON A
Hudson	147.2100	+	Oes	K2RVW	Rip Van Winkle Amat
Kingston	147.2550	+	O 77erz	WA2MJM	OVERLOOK MTN A
Lake Peekskill	146.6700	–	O 156.7 (CA)es	W2NYW	PEEKSKILL CORTLA
Liberty	147.1350	+	O 94.8l	KC2AXO	SOUTHERN CATSKI
Mahopac	145.3900	–	O 74.4	NY4Z	ALIVE NETWORK A
Middletown	146.7600	–	O 100ers WXx	WA2VDX	WA2VDX
Middletown	147.0750	+	O 88.5ae	KD2ANX	ORANGE COUNTY
Middletown	147.3900	+	O 123lx	WA2ZPX	WA2ZPX
Millbrook	146.8950	–	O 100el	N2EYH	MOUNT BEACON A
Mount Beacon	146.9700	–	O 100 (CA) esWXx	KC2DAA	MOUNT BEACON A
New Windsor	146.9400	–	O 88.5/88.5 e	KD2ANX	ORANGE COUNTY
New Windsor	147.1500	+	O 88.5/88.5 e	KD2ANX	Orange County Repe
Nyack	145.1700	–	O 114.8l	N2JTI	ROCKLAND REPEA
Nyack	147.1650	+	O 114.8 (CA)elsx	K2CIB	ROCKLAND REPEA

Location	Output	Input	Notes	Call	Sponsor
Pearl River	146.8350	–	O 141.3	N2HDW	StatelineRA
Washingtonville	145.2500	–	O 100el	WB2BQW	NORTHEAST CONN
West Point	146.7300	–	O#r	W2KGY	USMA AMATEUR RA
MONROE COUNTY					
Churchville	145.2100	–	O 110.9	N2EPO	------------
NEW YORK CITY - KINGS					
Brooklyn	145.2300	–	O 114.8/114.8es	WA2JNF	------------
Brooklyn	146.7300	–	O 88.5es	KB2NQT	KCRC
NEW YORK CITY - MANHATTAN					
Manhattan	145.2900	–	O 094.8/094.8 TTlRB	K2HR	Alive Net
Manhattan	147.1500	+	O 123.0/123.0z	N2JDW	Manh RS
Manhattan	147.1950	+	O 136.5	W2ML	------------
Manhattan	147.2700	+	O 141.3 (CA)elRB WX	W2ABC	BEARS
New York	147.3600	+	O 107.2er	WA2ZLB	MAARC
NEW YORK CITY - NEW YORK					
Manhattan	145.2700	–	O 136.5es	KC2PXT	HOSARC
NEW YORK CITY - QUEENS					
Flushing	147.0900	+	● 114.8/82.5 (CA) DCSeZ(911)	K2HAM	ELECHSTR VHFC
Glen Oaks	146.8500	–	O 136.5 (CA)e	W2VL	LIMARC
NEW YORK CITY - STATEN ISLAND					
Staten Island	146.4300	147.4300	O 136.5/136.5e	KC2RA	KCRA
Staten Island	147.3150	+	Ot(CA)ez	WA2RXQ	------------
NIAGARA					
Boston	146.9100	–	O(CA)e L(BARRA)rsWXxz	W2EUP	BARRA
Buffalo	146.8650	+	O 151.4 L(443.525)	WB2ECR	------------
Buffalo	147.3900	+	O 88.5 L(ECHOLINK)	W2DXA	WNYDXA
Colden	145.3100	–	O 88.5e L(BARC) RB	W2IVB	BARC
Colden	147.0900	+	O 107.2e	WB2ELW	STARS
Kenmore	147.0000	+	O 107.2	N2YDM	BARRA
Lancaster	147.2550	+	O 107.2e L(LARC IRLP) WX	W2SO	LARC
Lancaster	147.3600	+	O 107.2e	W2GUT	------------
Lewiston	146.7750	–	O 107.2e	WB2NCR	RACES
Lockport	146.8200	–	O 107.2 (CA)e	W2RUI	LARA
North Tonawanda	146.9550	–	O 151.4 (CA)e	W2SEX	ARATS
Wheatfield	146.7300	–	O 107.2	K2ILH	BARRA

Location	Output	Input	Notes	Call	Sponsor
OSWEGO/FULTON					
Fulton	145.3300	–	Oalr	KW2M	NiMo ARC
Fulton	147.1500	+	O 103.5r	N2GIV	NiMo ARC
Oswego	146.8500	–	O 123er	K2QQY	OswegoCEMO
ROCHESTER					
Fairport	146.6100	–	O 110.9 (CA)esz	W2COP	FLARES
Fairport	147.1350	+	O(CA)ep	WB2SSJ	WB2SSJ
Mendon	146.9250	–	O 110.9alr z	N2HJD	ROCHESTER R
Rochester	145.2900	–	Oaelxz	KE2MK	XEROX AMATE
Rochester	146.6550	–	O 110.9l	WR2AHL	BARRA
Rochester	146.7150	–	O	W2KZD	W2KZD
Rochester	146.7900	–	Oa	K2SA	Genesee RA
Rochester	146.8800	–	O 110.9 (CA)elrsz	K2RRA	ROCHESTER R
Rochester	147.3000	+	O	WB2TRC	WB2TRC
SOUTHERN TIER					
Alma	147.2100	+	O 123.0el WX	KA2AJH	------------
Bemus Point	145.2900	–	O 127.3	WA2LPB	STAN
Delevan	145.3900	–	O	K2XZ	------------
Frewsburg	146.7900	–	O	W2DRZ	------------
Jamestown	145.3300	–	O 127.3	KS2D	------------
Jamestown	146.9400	–	O 127.3ae L(445.225)	K2LUC	CCAFMA
Limestone	146.8500	–	O 127.3	W3VG	------------
Pomfret	146.6250	–	O 127.3 (CA)ex	W2SB	NCARC
Ripley	145.4700	–	O 127.3e	K2OAD	------------
ST LAWRENCE					
Fine	147.1350	+		WA2NAN	Oswegatchie Vall
Ogdensburg	147.1650	+		N2MX	N2MX
Parishville	147.3900	+	151.4	W2LCA	NCARC
Potsdam	146.8950	–	151.4 L(443.350) Z(*911)	K2CC	CUARC
Russell	146.9250	–	A(*+9/#)r	KA2JXI	SLVRA
SYRACUSE					
Cazenovia	147.0750	+	O 97.4e	N2LZI	James I McHerro
Jamesville	145.1500	–	O 123eRB	KB2SWA	KB2SWA
Lafayette	145.3500	–	O	WW2N	WW2N
Phoenix	147.3450	+	O	W2ZC	SALT CITY DX A
Pompey	146.7750	–	O 151.4	W2CNY	Onondaga Count
Saquoit	145.2100	–	O 71.9eWX	N2CNY	CNY Amateur Ra
Sentinel Hgts	145.3100	–	O 151.4ex	KB2RES	KB2RES
Syracuse	145.2700	–	Oe	W1MVV	W1MVV
Syracuse	145.4300	–	O 141.3l	K2SDD	K2SDD
Syracuse	146.6250	–	O 103.5 (CA)	N2PYK	N2PYK

NEW YORK

Location	Output	Input	Notes	Call	Sponsor
Syracuse	146.6400	–	O 103.5epz	W2JST	W2JST
Syracuse	146.9100	–	O 103.5z	W2CM	LARC
Syracuse	147.1050	+	Oarz	K2JVL	K2JVL
Syracuse	147.2100	+	O 103.5 (CA)	N2VZD	LARC
Syracuse	147.3000	+	Oerz	N2ACO	OndgaRACES
Syracuse	147.3900	+	O 151.4lr	K2BFH	NiMo ARC
TIOGA					
Candor	147.3000	+	O 91.5/91.5 e	K2OQ	CAROUSEL RADIO
Owego	147.3900	+	O 91.5/91.5 e	K2OQ	CAROUSEL RADIO
UPPER HUDSON					
Glens Falls	146.7750	–	OeWX	KA5VVI	SoAdRG
Lake George	146.7300	–	O 100r	KT2M	Warr RACES
North Creek	147.1350	+	O 123r	KT2M	Warr RACES
Saratoga Spr	147.0000	–	O 91.5/91.5 eL(147.240)r	K2DLL	Saratoga County RA
UTICA/ROME					
Boonville	146.6550	–	Oe	KC2NBU	BRVRA
Ilion	145.1100	–	O 167.9 (CA)ersWX	N2ZWO	HERKIMER COUNTY
Ilion	146.8050	–		KB3BIU	KB3BIU
Kirkland	147.2400	+	O 71.9/71.9	KA2FWN	K1DCC
Mohawk	147.0900	+	O	W2JIT	Deerfld RA
Norway	147.0450	+	O 167.9ers WX	N2ZWO	HERKIMER COUNTY
Rome	146.8800	–	O 71.9/71.9 eL(ECHOLINK)sWXx	W2OFQ	ROME RADIO CLUB
Rome	147.2850	+	O(CA)	WA2ZXS	416 COMBAT SUPP
Utica	145.4500	–	O	W2JIT	Deerfld RA
Utica	146.7600	–	O	W2JIT	Deerfld RA
Utica	146.9700	–	O	WB2FAW	RACOM
Verona	145.1700	–	Oae	KA2NIL	KA2NIL
WATERTOWN					
Lowville	146.9550	–	O 156.7aer	W2RHM	BLACK RIVER VALL
Watertown	146.7000	–	O 151.4ez	WB2OOY	WB2OOY
Watertown	147.2550	+	O 151.4ars WXxz	N2KFJ	CANAMARA
Watertown	147.3750	+	Ol	K2BFH	NiMo ARC
WATKINS GLEN					
Branchport	146.9850	–	O 110.9	N2LSJ	N2LSJ
Penn Yan	145.2500	–	O 100	N2HLT	N2HLT
Penn Yan	145.3700	–	Oelrsx	WA2UKX	WA2UKX
Penn Yan	146.8350	–	O	KE2BV	KE2BV
Watkins Glen	147.1650	+	Olr	KA2IFE	KA2IFE

Location	*Output*	*Input*	*Notes*	*Call*	*Sponsor*
WAYNE/NEWARK					
Clyde	145.4700	–	O	KA2NDW	KA2NDW
Newark	146.7450	–	O	WA2AAZ	DRUMLINS AMA
Sodus	146.6850	–	Oaer	WB2QKO	Wyn RACES
WEST					
Albion	145.2700	–	O 141.3	WA2DQL	OCARC
Batavia	147.2850	+	O 141.3 (CA)e	W2SO	LARC
Gainsville	145.4900	–	O 88.5e L(ILS IRLP ECHOLINK)	WB2JPQ	ILS
Wethersfield	145.1700	–	O 110.9e L(BARRA) RBx	K2ISO	BARRA
Wethersfield	145.4500	–	O 141.3e WX	N2FQN	------------
Wethersfield	146.6400	–	O 88.5	K2XZ	------------
Wethersfield	147.1050	+	O 141.3	N2FQN	------------
Wethersfield	147.3150	+	O 141.3e L(443.625)	WA2CAM	------------

NORTH CAROLINA

Location	*Output*	*Input*	*Notes*	*Call*	*Sponsor*
Ahoskie	145.1300	–	O 131.8/131.8l	WB4YNF	WB4YNF
Ahoskie	146.9100	–	O	KG4GEJ	FRANKLIN ARC
Albemarle	146.9850	–	O	K4OGB	STANLY COUNT
Albemarle	147.2100	+	O	KD4ADL	KD4ADL
Andsn Mt	145.1700	–	OerWX	K4CCR	K4CCR
Apex	147.0750	+	O 118.8/118.8e	KJ4ZPE	KJ4ZPE
Asheville	146.8350	–	O	WB4PLA	WB4PLA
Asheville	146.9100	–	O	W4MOE	W.CAROLINA A
Asheville	147.1800	+	O	KF4TLA	KF4TLA
Bakersville	145.3100	–	O 123/123e s	KK4MAR	KK4MAR
Bath	146.9550	–	O 82.5es	K4BCH	Pamlico ARC
Benson	146.9700	–	O	KD4BJD	JARS
Bethel	147.3750	+	O	KD4EAD	KD4EAD
Boone	147.3600	+	O	WA4J	WATAUGA ARC
Brevard	147.1350	+	O	K4HXZ	TRANSYLVANIA
Broadway	147.1050	+	O 82.5/82.5 el	K4ITL	WB4UBU
Burgaw	146.9400	–	O	K4CTY	4-CTY ARC
Burlington	145.3200	–	O	AK4EG	AI4UE
Burlington	146.6700	–	O	K4EG	K4EG
Burnsville	146.9550	–	O	KD4WAR	KD4WAR
Burnsville	147.3750	+	O	KD4WAR	KD4WAR
Butner	146.9400	–	O	WA4IZG	FALLS LAKE AR
Canton	146.8050	+	O	KI4GMA	W4DJB
Carthage	147.2400	+	O	NC4ML	MOORE COUNT

Location	*Output*	*Input*	*Notes*	*Call*	*Sponsor*
Chapel Hill	147.1350	+	O 82.5/82.5 el	K4ITL	WB4UBU
Charlotte	145.1400	–	O	KI4WXS	KI4WXS
Charlotte	145.2300	–	O	W4BFB	MECKLENBURG AR
Charlotte	145.2900	–	O	W4BFB	MECKLENBURG AR
Charlotte	145.3500	–	O	WA4AOS	------------
Charlotte	146.9400	–	O	W4BFB	MECKLENBURG AR
Charlotte	147.0600	–	O	W4CQ	CHARLOTTE AR CO
Charlotte	147.2700	+	O	W4CQ	CHARLOTTE ARC
Cherry Lane	145.2700	–	ODCSl	KK4UTT	KK4UTT
Cherry Mtn	147.2400	+	O	KG4JIA	KG4JIA
China Grove	145.4100	–	O	N4UH	KQ1E
Clayton	147.3900	+	O	WB4IUY	TEARA
Cleveland	146.7300	–	O 94.8/94.8	KU4PT	KU4PT
Clinton	146.7900	–	O	W4TLP	SAMPSON CO ARS
Coinjock	145.2900	–	O	WN3X	CARES
Columbia	146.8350	–	O	KX4NC	COLUMBIA EMER R
Concord	146.6550	–	O	K4CEB	CABARRUS ARS
Dobson	146.9250	–	O 100/100s WX	W4DCA	W4DCA
Dunn	146.7000	–	O	W4PEQ	W4PEQ
Durham	145.3700	–	O	W4BAD	W4BAD
Durham	145.4500	–	O	WR4AGC	DURHAM FM ASSN
Durham	146.9850	–	O	KB4WGA	KB4WGA
Durham	147.3600	+	O	W4REG	MID-STATE AM REP
Elizabeth City	146.6550	–	O	WA4VTX	TAARS
Elizabethtown	145.2500	–	O	W4MKD	W4MKD
Elizabethtown	146.9850	–	O	N4DBM	N4DBM
Elm City	145.1500	–	O	K2IMO	K2IMO
Englehard	146.7150	–	O	K4OBX	W4HAT
Farmville	145.2700	–	O	K4ROK	PITT CO ARES
Fayetteville	146.9100	–	O	K4MN	CAPE FEAR ARS
Fayetteville	147.3300	+	O	WA4FLR	CAPE FEAR A.R.S.
Forest City	146.6700	–	O	K4OI	K4OI
Gastonia	146.8050	–	O	K4GNC	GAARC
Gastonia	147.1200	+	O	N4GAS	GCARS
Gibsonville	145.4900	–	O	WB4IKY	WB4IKY
Goldsboro	146.8500	–	O	K4CYP	WAYNE CO ARA
Graham	147.3750	+	O	K4GWH	K4GWH
Grantsboro	145.2300	–	O 85.4/85.4 e	KF4IXW	KF4IXW
Greensboro	145.1500	–	Oa(CA)es	W4GSO	W4GSO
Greensboro	146.7600	–	O	K4GWH	K4GWH
Greenville	145.3500	–	O	WD4JPQ	PITT CTY REP ASS
Greenville	147.0900	+	O	W4GDF	GREENVILLE REP A
Hatteras Island	145.1500	–	O	K4OBX	W4HAT
Hatteras Island	146.6250	–	O	K4OBX	W4HAT
Hayesville	147.0900	+	O 100/100s	KG4GPJ	KG4GPJ
Hendersonville	145.2700	–	O	WA4KNI	WA4KNI

Location	*Output*	*Input*	*Notes*	*Call*	*Sponsor*
Hendersonville	146.6400	–	O	WB4YAO	W4FOT
Hendersonville	147.1050	+	O	WA4KNI	WA4KNI
Hendersonville	147.2550	+	O	WA4KNI	WA4KNI
Hertford	147.3300	+	O	WA4VTX	TAARS
Hickory	145.4900	–	O	KF4LUC	KF4LUC
Hickory	146.8500	–	O	WA4DSZ	UNIFOUR ARC
High Point	145.2900	–	O	NC4AR	NC4AR
High Point	147.1650	+	O	W4UA	HPARC
Hillsborough	147.2250	+	O	WR4AGC	DURHAM FM AS
Holden Beach	146.7750	–	O	W4ZU	W4ZU
Hope Mills	146.8350	+	O	W4KMU	W4IDR
Jacksonville	145.1900	–	O 88.5/88.5	WD4FVO	WD4FVO
Jacksonville	147.0000	–	O 88.5/88.5	NC4OC	NC4OC
Jefferson	147.3000	+	Oa(CA)es WX	W4YSB	W4YSB
Jefferson	147.3000	+	O	W4YSB	ASHE CO ARC
Kannapolis	147.3000	+	O	N4JEX	W1WBT
Kill Devil Hills	145.1100	–	O	W4PCN	OUTERBANKS
Kinston	145.4700	–	O 88.5/88.5 a(CA)e	W4OIX	W4OIX
Laurinburg	146.6250	–	O	KI4RR	SCOTLAND CTY
Lawndale	147.0450	+	O	NA4CC	NA4CC (CCARS)
Lenoir	146.6250	–	O 94.8/94.8 es	N4NIN	N4LNR
Lenoir	147.3300	+	O	KN4K	HIBRITEN REPT
Level Cross	147.2550	+	O 82.5/82.5 el	K4ITL	K4ITL
Lexington	145.3100	–	O	N4LEX	HSMVHF SOC
Lexington	146.9100	–	O	W4PAR	HSMVHF SOC
Locust	147.3900	+	O	WA4CHZ	BENTON BLALO
Lumberton	145.1500	–	O	W4LBT	ROBESON CO A
Lumberton	147.0450	+	O	W4LBT	ROBESON CO A
Lumberton	147.1650	+	O	KD4PBK	------------
Lumberton	147.3600	+	O	W4LBT	ROBESON CO A
Madison	147.3450	+	O	N4IV	RC ARC
Malmo	147.0600	+	O	K4MAL	TELEPATCH
Marion	146.9850	–	Oa(CA)es WX	WD4PVE	WD4PVE
Millers Creek	146.7150	–	O	N4GGN	N4GGN
Monroe	145.3900	–	O	NC4UC	UNION CTY AR
Moravian Falls	147.2250	+	O	N1KKD	N1KKD
Morehead City	146.8050	–	O	KD4RAA	KD4RAA RPT G
Morg/Walker Top	146.7450	–	O	KC4QPR	KC4QPR
Morganton	145.2100	–	O	K4OLC	K4OLC/KI4VIV
Morganton	147.1500	+	O	W4YIU	W.PIEDMONT A
Mount Airy	145.3300	–	O	N4VRD	N4VRD
Mount Gilead	147.0900	+	O	KI4DH	KI4DH
Mt Airy	145.1300	–	O	N4VL	BRIARPATCH A
Mt Mitchell	145.1900	–	O	N2GE	N2GE

Location	*Output*	*Input*	*Notes*	*Call*	*Sponsor*
Mt Pisgah	146.7600	–	O	N2GE	N2GE
N Wilkesboro	145.3700	–	O 94.8/94.8 e	W4FAR	W4FAR
Nashville	145.2900	–	O	WA4WPD	WA4WPD
New Bern	146.6100	–	O	W4EWN	NEW BERN ARC
Newport	145.4500	–	O	K4GRW	KD4KTO
Newton	147.0750	+	O 88.5/88.5 a(CA)r	K4CCR	K4CCR
Oriental	147.2100	+	O	W4SLH	W4SLH
Oxford	145.1700	–	O	W4BAD	W4BAD
Powells Point	146.9400	–	O	W4PCN	OUTER BANKS RPT
Raeford	145.4300	–	O	KG4HDV	KG4HDV
Raleigh	145.1900	–	O	K4GWH	K4GWH
Raleigh	145.2100	–	O 82.5/82.5 el	K4ITL	PCRN
Raleigh	145.4900	–	O	W4BWC	CAPITAL ARS
Raleigh	146.6100	–	O	WB4TOP	W4FMN
Raleigh	146.6400	–	O	W4DW	RALEIGH ARS
Raleigh	146.7750	–	O	KD4RAA	KD4RAA REP GR/N
Raleigh	146.8800	–	OelsWX	WB4TQD	WB4TQD
Raleigh	147.0150	+	O	KAØGMY	KAØGMY
Raleigh	147.2700	+	O	AK4H	JARS (JOHNSTON)
Red Springs	147.3000	+	O	W4MZP	W4MZP
Reidsville	146.8500	–	O	N4IV	RC ARC
Reidsville	147.0300	+	O	W4BJF	ROCKINGHAM CO R
Riegelwood	145.1700	–	O 88.5/88.5 eWX	N4JDW	------------
Roanoke Rapids	146.7450	–	O	N4WFU	N4WFU
Roanoke Rapids	147.0300	+	O	KB4DJT	ROANOKE VALLEY
Roanoke Rapids	147.1500	+	O	K4ITL	PCRN
Robbinsville	145.1100	–	O	N4GSM	SMOKY MTNS A.R.
Rockingham	146.9550	–	O	K4RNC	------------
Rocky Mount	147.1200	+	O	WR4RM	WR4RM
Rocky Mount	147.3450	+	O 91.5/91.5 e	K4ITL	K4ITL
Rolesville	147.3150	+	O	KF4HFQ	FCARC
Rtp	145.1300	–	O	W4RNC	RALEIGH ARS
Salisbury	146.7750	–	O	KG4WAD	KG4WAD
Sanford	147.5050	146.5050	O	KE4DSU	------------
Sauratown Mt	145.4700	–	O	W4NC	FORSYTH ARC
Sauratown Mt	146.7900	–	O	KG4ASL	TRIAD ARA
Shallotte	145.3700	–	O	K4PPD	BRUNSWICH CTY A
Shallotte	147.3150	+	O	K4PPD	BRUNSWICK CO AR
Shelby	145.0800	146.4800	O	W4NYR	SHELBY ARC
Shelby	146.8800	–	O	W4NYR	SHELBY ARC
Shelby	147.3450	+	O	W4NYR	SHELBY ARC
Sparta	145.4300	–	O	K4QFQ	PIED COAST REP N
Statesville	146.6850	–	O	W4SNC	W4SNC
Swansboro	146.7600	–	O	KB2XI	KB2XI

Location	*Output*	*Input*	*Notes*	*Call*	*Sponsor*
Sylva	147.3450	+	O	KF4DTL	KF4DTL
Taylorsville	147.1950	+	O	W4ERT	ALEXANDER AR
Thomasville	146.8350	+	O	KB4BPV	KC4KUL
Thomasville	146.8650	+	O 88.5/88.5 I	KD4LHP	KD4LHP
Thomasville	147.0000	+	O	WW4DC	WW4FL
Trenton	145.3100	–	O 82.5/82.5 elWX	WB4TQD	WB4TQD
Tryon	147.2850	+	O	W4RCW	W4RCW
Waxhaw	146.8650	+	O	K4WBT	WBT ARC
Waynesville	147.3900	+	O	N4DTR	N4DTR
Whiteville	147.2100	+	O	W4WVL	COLUMBUS CT
Williamston	145.4100	–	O	K4SER	ROANOKE ARS
Wilmington	146.6700	–	O	AD4DN	AD4DN
Wilmington	146.7300	–	O	N4ILM	WILMINGTON V
Wilmington	146.8200	–	O	N4ILM	WILMINGTON V
Wilmington	146.8950	–	O	N2QEW	N2QEW
Wilmington	147.1350	+	O	WA4US	WA4US
Wilmington	147.1800	+	O	AC4RC	AZALEA COAST
Wilmington	147.3450	+	O 82.5/82.5 el	K4ITL	N4ILM
Wilson	146.7600	–	O 131.8/131.8	WA4WAR	WA4WAR
Winston-salem	146.6400	–	O	W4NC	FORSYTH ARC
Yadkinville	147.0150	–	O	N4YSB	------------
Youngsville	145.3900	–	O 82.5/82.5 el	WB4TQD	WB4TQD

NORTH DAKOTA

FREQUENCY USAGE					
Eastern ND	145.2300	–		SNP	
Western ND	145.4700	–		SNP	
N E CENTRAL					
Devils Lake	146.8800	–	Oae L(SUPLK 338)	WDØFFQ	RCARC
Harlow	147.0150	+	123.0	KFØHR	KFØHR
Lakota	146.8200	–	Oe	KAØFIN	KØPVG
Maddock	147.2400	+	O 141.3e L(SUPLK 623)	KFØHR	BCARC
Rugby	147.0600	–	Oe	NØGUY	------------
St John	146.8500	–	O	VE4IHF	TMARC
N W CENTRAL					
Kenmare	147.3600	+	O 100.0e	KØAJW	SVARC
Minot	146.9700	–	O	KØAJW	SVARC
Minot	147.2700	+	Oa L(SUPLK 646)	KØAJW	SVARC
NORHTWEST					
Williston	147.2100	+	O	KØWSN	WBARC

Location	*Output*	*Input*	*Notes*	*Call*	*Sponsor*
NORTHEAST					
Cavalier	147.1500	+	**O**al	NØCAV	PCARC
Grand Forks	146.9400	–	**O**e	WAØJXT	FORXARC
Grand Forks	147.0300	–	**O**(CA)	WAØLPV	Forx UG
Langdon	146.7900	–	**O**	KAØBKO	KAØBKO
Mayville	146.9100	–	**O**	WØKZU	GRARC
NORTHWEST					
Stanley	146.6100	–	**O**	KØWSN	WBARC
S E CENTRAL					
Carrington	146.6700	–	**O**e	KRØW	HN ARC
			L(SUPLK 227)		
Cleveland	147.1800	+	**O**ae	WØFX	JARC
Jamestown			L(SUPLK 526)		
S W CENTRAL					
Bismarck	146.8500	–	**O** 107.2e	WØZRT	CDARC
Bismarck	147.3900	+	**O**el	WØZRT	CDARC
Glen Ullin	147.3000	+	**O**	KD7RDD	KD7RDD
			162.2/162.2		
Hannover	145.4300	–	**O**	WØZRT	CDARC
			L(SUPLK 426)		
Mandan	146.9400	–	**O**ae	WØZRT	CDARC
			L(SUPLK 247)		
SOUTHEAST					
Fargo	145.4900	–	**O** 82.5el	KBØIXM	KBØIXM
Fargo	146.9700	–	**O**TT	WØRRW	Ernie Ande
Fargo	147.0900	+	**O**	WØHSC	NDSU ARS
Grandin	146.7600	–	**O**x	KCØKAE	Red River
Horace	146.7150	–	**O**	WØZOK	WØZOK
Lisbon	147.0000	–	**O**el	NØBQY	NØBQY
Wahpeton	147.3750	+	**O**ae	WØEND	TRARC
Wheatland	147.2550	+	**O** 123.0els	WØILO	RRRA
SOUTHWEST					
Bowman	145.3100	–	**O**e	KBØDYA	SLARC
			L(SUPLK 269)		
Dickinson	146.8200	–	**O**ae	KØND	TRARC
			L(SUPLK 342)		
Killdeer	146.6400	–	**O**e	KØND	TRARC
			L(SUPLK 545)		
Sentinel Butte	146.7300	–	**O**e	KØND	TRARC
			L(SUPLK 736)		

OHIO

Location	*Output*	*Input*	*Notes*	*Call*	*Sponsor*
ADAMS					
Cherry Fork	147.0000	+	**O** 94.8 (CA) e	K8GE	DforestRC
Peebles	145.1700	–	**O**(CA)e	KJ8I	KJ8I
Wrightsville	147.1800	+	**O** 118.8	KF8RC	N8XGP
ALLEN					
Lima	145.1700	–	**O**ae	N8GCH	ShawneeRA

Location	Output	Input	Notes	Call	Sponsor
Lima	145.3700	–	O 107.2e	KT8APR	LimaDARTS
Lima	146.6700	–	Oaez	WB8ULC	NWOhioARC
Lima	146.7450	–	O 100.0er WX	W8AOH	ALLEN EMA
Lima	146.9400	–	Ot	W8EQ	LAARC
Lima	147.0300	+	Ote	K8TCF	OttawaVRA
ASHLAND					
Ashland	146.7450	–	O 71.9	W3YXS	AshlndARC
Polk	145.1300	–	O 110.9	N8SIW	N8SIW
Widowville	147.1050	+	O 71.9ae WX	N8IHI	AAARC
ASHTABULA					
Conneaut	147.3900	+	O 131.8ae	W8BHZ	ConntARC
Jefferson	146.7150	–	O 141.3ae	K8CY	Ash.CoARC
Orwell	146.6550	–		KF8YF	KF8YF
ATHENS					
Athens	145.1500	–	O(CA)e	W8UKE	AthensARA
Athens	146.6250	–	Oae	K8TUT	K8TUT
Athens	146.7300	–	O	K8TUT	K8TUT
Athens	147.1500	+	O	KC8AAV	SCARF
Jacksonville	147.2250	+	O	KC8QDQ	KC8QDQ
AUGLAIZE					
St Marys	146.8050	–	O 107.2	W8GZ	W8GZ
St Marys	147.3300	+	O 107.2el	K8QYL	Rsvr ARA
Uniopolis	145.3900	–	O 107.2a	KC8KVO	ACARES
BELMONT					
Barnesville	146.6400	–	Ot	WB8WJT	WB8WJT
St Clarsville	145.2100	–	Oe	W8GBH	EOAWA
BROWN					
Georgetown	146.7300	–	O 162.2ae z	N1DJS	K8YGV
BUTLER					
Fairfield	145.2300	–	O	W8PRH	FARA
Fairfield	145.3900	–	Oa	W8PRH	FARA
Fairfield	147.0300	+	O 123.0	WB8CRS	Cinci FMC
Hamilton	146.9700	–	O 118.8	W8CCI	BVHFAssoc
Hamilton	147.0000	+		W8WRK	BCARA
Hamilton	147.3300	+	O 118.8	W8CCI	BVHFAssoc
Middletown	146.6100	–	O 77.0 TTel	W8BLV	Dial ARC
Middletown	146.7150	–	●t	N8COZ	N8COZ
Middletown	147.3150	+	O 77.0 TTel	W8JEU	Dial ARC
Oxford	145.2100	–	O 118.8	W8CCI	BVHFAssoc
CARROLL					
Carrollton	145.4300	–	O 192.8e	NC8W	NC8W
Carrollton	145.4700	–	O 79.7es WXxz	N8YDF	CCARC
Malvern	147.0750	+	Oael	K8VPJ	K8VPJ
CHAMPAIGN					
Urbana	146.9550	–	O 100.0e	K8VOR	WD8XX

Location	Output	Input	Notes	Call	Sponsor
Urbana	147.3750	+	O 100.0ae sWX	WB8UCD	WB8UCD
CLARK					
Springfield	145.3100	–	Oe	W8OG	CLARA
Springfield	145.4500	–	(CA)	K8IRA	IndepndRA
Springfield	146.7300	–	O 77.0 (CA) e	W8OG	CLARA
Springfield	147.2250	+	●t(CA)elx	KA8HMJ	KA8HMJ
CLERMONT					
Bethel	147.2250	+	O 118.8a TTe	WB8NJS	BARA
Felicity	146.6550	–	Oar	W8EMA	CCEMA
Owensville	147.3450	+	O 123.0	W8MRC	MilfordRC
CLINTON					
Blanchester	145.2500	–	O 162.2a	KB8CWC	KB8CWC
Wilmington	147.1200	+	O 123.0el WXz	WB8ZZR	ClintonRA
COLUMBIANA					
E Liverpool	146.7000	–	O 162.2 (CA)eWX	K8BLP	TrianglRC
E Palestine	146.7750	–	Oe	W8GMM	EPARC
Lisbon	146.8050	–	OaeLITZ WX	K8GQB	LAARA
Salem	147.2550	+	O(CA)eWX	KA8OEB	KA8OEB
Salem	147.2850	+	O 88.5ael RB WXz	KB8MFV	KB8MFV
COSHOCTON					
Coshocton	145.2300	–	Oaez	KE8XM	#NAME?
Keene	147.0450	+	O	W8CCA	CCARA
CRAWFORD					
Bucyrus	147.1650	+	88.5aeWX	W8DZN	W8DZN
Galion	146.8500	–	71.9	W8BAE	NCORA
CUYAHOGA					
Cleveland	146.7600	–	O 110.9e	WR8ABC	LEARA
Cleveland	146.8800	–	Oael	WR8ABC	LEARA
Cleveland	147.1950	+	O(CA)el	NA8SA	NGARC
Euclid	145.2100	–	O 110.9	N8CHM	N8CHM
N Royalton	145.1500	–	O 110.9e	K8KRG	NOARS
NorthRoyalton	147.3600	+	Ot	W8DXA	NOH DXAsn
Parma	145.3100	–	O 110.9elz	WD8CHK	WoodchkRC
Parma	145.4100	–	O 110.9 (CA)lRB	KB8WLW	KB8RST
Parma	145.4300	–	O 186.2el	N8SO	N8SO
Parma	146.7300	–	Otsx	W8CZW	WR RA
Parma	146.8200	–	O 110.9e	K8ZFR	C.A.R.S.
South Euclid	146.7900	–	Ot(CA)elz	N8APU	HERO
DARKE					
Greenville	146.7900	–	OaeWX	N8OBE	TCARA

Location	Output	Input	Notes	Call	Sponsor
DEFIANCE					
Defiance	147.0900	+	O(CA)e	K8VON	DCARC
DELAWARE					
Delaware	145.1700	–	O 8825elpr	W8SMK	W8SMK
Delaware	145.1900	–	O	N8DCA	DelCoARES
Delaware	145.2900	–	O 123.0e	KA8IWB	KA8IWB
ERIE					
Berlin Height	146.8050	–	O 110.9e	WB8LLY	Firelands
Sandusky	146.6550	–	O 110.9 (CA)el	W8LBZ	SREL
FAIRFIELD					
Lancaster	146.7000	–	O 94.8ael	K8QIK	LanFarARC
Lancaster	147.0300	+	O 71.9ael	K8QIK	LanFarARC
FAYETTE					
Greenfield	146.6850	–	O(CA)e	N8OOB	N8OOB
Washington CH	147.2700	+	O 77.0 (CA) e	N8EMZ	FayetteRA
FRANKLIN					
Columbus	145.1100	–	O(CA)elx	WC8OH	WCOARA
Columbus	145.2700	–	O 82.5e	WA8PYR	WA8PYR
Columbus	145.4300	–	O 123.0ael z	N8PVC	CCRA
Columbus	146.6700	–	O 131.8 (CA)e	W8ZPF	LUCENT TC
Columbus	146.7600	–	O 123.0a WX	W8RXX	CORC
Columbus	146.8050	–	Ot	WB8LAP	MARK
Columbus	146.9700	–	O 123.0al	W8RRJ	CORC
Columbus	147.0600	+	O 94.8	K8DDG	C OH ARES
Columbus	147.0900	+	O 94.8l	K8DDG	C OH ARES
Columbus	147.1500	+	O	W8CQK	Battel RC
Columbus	147.2100	+	O	N8OIF	CCRA
Columbus	147.2400	+	O 179.9ael z	K8DRE	CCRA
Grove City	145.2300	–	Oel	WB8MMR	WB8MMR
Reynoldsburg	146.9100	–	71.9	W8FEH	W8FEH
FULTON					
Archbold	145.4100	–	O 8866ael pr	WD8IEJ	WD8IEJ
Delta	147.2850	+	O 4479lpr	K8LI	K8LI
Wauseon	147.1950	+	O	K8BXQ	FultonARC
GALLIA					
Gallipolis	147.0600	+	O 74.4 (CA)	KC8ZAB	MOVARC
GEAUGA					
Bainbridge	146.8500	–	O 110.9	W8LYD	ClevQCWA
BainbridgeTwp	147.0600	+	O 110.9	WR8ANN	CVRA
Chardon	146.9400	–	O 110.9e	W8DES	GCEMA
Montville	145.3300	–	●	N8XUA	N8XUA
Newbury	147.0150	+	Oer	W8OKE	NORMA

Location	*Output*	*Input*	*Notes*	*Call*	*Sponsor*
GREENE					
Bellbrook	146.9100	–	Oae	W8GCA	GCARES
Bellbrook	147.0450	+	Oe	W8DGN	BARC
Fairborn	145.4100	–	O 118.8e	K8FBN	UpVlyARC
Xenia	147.1650	+	O(CA)e	N8JFA	XeniaARN
GUERNSEY					
Cambridge	146.8500	–	O 91.5ael	W8VP	CARA
Cambridge	147.0000	+	O 91.5e	KB8ZMI	KB8ZMI
HAMILTON					
Cincinnati	145.1900	–	Oaelrxz	W8PRH	FARA
Cincinnati	145.2700	–	O(CA)er	W8DZ	GCARA
Cincinnati	145.3100	–	O	N8SIM	CinMilARC
Cincinnati	145.3700	–	Oer	K8YOJ	HCARPSC
Cincinnati	145.4500	–	Oae	K8ORW	OcasaraUC
Cincinnati	146.6250	–	O 123.0er	K8SCH	OhKyInARS
Cincinnati	146.6700	–	O 123.0123.0 (CA)elprz	K8SCH	OhKyInARS
Cincinnati	146.7000	–	O 123.0	WR8CRA	CRA
Cincinnati	146.7600	–	O	WR8CRA	CRA
Cincinnati	146.8500	–	O 123.0	K8YOJ	HCARPSC
Cincinnati	146.8800	–	123.0elWX x	WB8CRS	Cinci FMC
Cincinnati	146.9250	–	O 123.0 (CA)er	K8SCH	OhKyInARS
Cincinnati	147.0600	+	(CA)	W8YX	Unv-Cinci
Cincinnati	147.0900	+	O 123.0ae	WR8CRA	CRA
Cincinnati	147.2400	+	O 123.0	W8VND	QueenCyEN
Cincinnati	147.3000	+	O	WD8NVI	OMIKEA
HANCOCK					
Findlay	147.0450	+	O 100.0	KA8HHW	FndlyARTS
Findlay	147.1500	+	O 88.5ae	W8FT	FRC
HARDIN					
Kenton	146.6250	–	O	W8VMV	KentonARC
HARRISON					
Cadiz	146.6550	–	Oa	WB8FPN	HARC
HENRY					
Napoleon	147.2250	+	Oe	K8TII	HCARC
Napoleon	147.3150	+	Oe	K8TII	HenryCoRC
HIGHLAND					
Hillsboro	146.7450	–	O(CA)e	WA8KFB	HlsboroRC
Hillsboro	147.2100	+	100.0 (CA)e WX	K8HO	HilandARA
HOCKING					
Logan	147.3450	+	Oe	K8LGN	H.V.A.R.C
HOLMES					
Millersburg	146.6700	–	O 71.9e	KD8QGQ	Holmes RA
HURON					
Clarksfield	147.3150	+	O 71.9lp	AL7OP	AL7OP
Willard	146.8650	–	110.9aer	AC8AP	HuronEMA

Location	Output	Input	Notes	Call	Sponsor
JACKSON					
Jackson	146.7900	–	O 167.9	WA8YUL	JacksonRC
Jackson	146.8950	–	167.9aez	K8ZUA	KB8EGI
Ray	147.0150	+	O 100.0	KD8EAD	WO8Z
JEFFERSON					
Steubenville	147.0600	+	O 114.8 TT e	WD8IIJ	SWARC
KNOX					
Mount Vernon	146.7900	–	O 71.9 (CA)	K8EEN	MtVernRC
LAKE					
Mentor	147.1650	+	Oez	N8BC	LCARA
Mentor	147.2550	+	O	WB8PHI	WB8PHI
Mentor-O-T-Lk	145.1100	–	O 110.9 (CA)lWX	KF8YK	KF8YK
Painesville	147.2100	+	O 110.9ael z	N8BC	LCARA
Painesville	147.3450	+	Oael	N8GAK	N8GAK
LAWRENCE					
Chesapeake	146.7150	–	O 103.5e	W8SOE	SoOHARA
Willow Wood	146.6100	–	e	W8SOE	SOARA
LICKING					
Alexandria	145.4700	–	Oaez	KC8EVM	KC8EVM
Amsterdam	146.8350	–	O 91.5e	KB8ZMI	KB8ZMI
Jersey	147.3300	+	O 8094lpr	W8NBA	CORC
Newark	145.3700	–	O(CA)	WD8RVK	WD8RVK
Newark	146.8800	–	O(CA)e	W8WRP	NARA
LOGAN					
Bellefontaine	147.0000	+	O 100.0871 aTTel	W8FTV	CLARC
Lakeview	145.1300	–	O	KA8CHH	KA8QIX
LORAIN					
Amherst	146.6250	–	lpWX	WD8OCS	WA8WUU
Amherst	147.2250	+	Ot(CA)	W8TRT	WARS
Elyria	145.2300	–	O 110.9e	W8HF	W8HF
Elyria	146.7000	–	O 110.9	K8KRG	NOARS
Elyria	147.1500	+	O 110.9ael RB WXz	KC8BED	LCARA
Lorain	147.0000	+	O 91.5ae WX	N8VUB	N8RBI
S Amherst	145.4700	–	O 110.9 (CA)eRB	WD8CXB	SARA
LUCAS					
Oregon	147.3750	+	OaeWX	W8RZM	ToledoRAC
Toledo	146.6100	–	O 103.5e	K8ALB	GTARA
Toledo	146.9400	–	O 103.5	W8RZM	ToledoRAC
Toledo	147.1200	+	O 103.5e	K8ALB	GTARA
Toledo	147.2700	+	O 103.5123 aTTez	W8HHF	TMRA
Toledo	147.3450	+	O 103.5e	WJ8E	WJ8E

Location	Output	Input	Notes	Call	Sponsor
MADISON					
London	147.2850	+	O 82.5es	KE8RV	MARC
MAHONING					
Beloit	146.8650	–	Oae	KB8MFV	KB8MFV
Canfield	145.2700	–	O 110.9aelz	KD8DWV	KD8ED
Youngstown	146.7450	–	O 110.9 (CA) WX	W8QLY	MVARA
Youngstown	146.9100	–	O	W8IZC	W8IZC
Youngstown	147.0000	+	Oael	KB8N	KB8N
Youngstown	147.3150	+	156.7a	K8TKA	TONRC
Youngstown	147.3750	+	Oaez	W8RAJ	W8RAJ
MARION					
Marion	146.8950	–	O 71.9aTTe	WW8MRN	MARC
Marion	147.3000	+	O 250.3aTTe	WW8MRN	MARC
MEDINA					
Brunswick	145.2900	–	110.9 (CA)	K8SCI	N.C.A.R.C
Brunswick	147.0300	+	131.8	W8EOC	M2M
Medina	145.1900	–	110.9el	W8HAC	HAofCLEV
Medina	147.0300	+	O 141.3 (CA)ez	W8EOC	M2M
Wadsworth	146.6850	–	O 110.9aTTelRBxz	WA8DBW	WA8DBW
MEIGS					
Pomeroy	146.8650	–	88.5er	KC8LOE	MeigsCoAR
Pomeroy	147.0450	+	O 67.0r	KC8KPD	BBARC
MERCER					
Coldwater	145.2500	–	O 107.2 WX	W8MCA	MCARES
MIAMI					
Piqua	147.2100	+	Oaer	W8SWS	Piqua ARC
Tipp City	147.2400	+	O	KD8KID	84/24FMA
Troy	145.2300	–	O 100.0 (CA)e	W8FW	MiamiCoRC
MONROE					
Hannibal	147.2400	+	Oe	WB8CSW	MDARC
MONTGOMERY					
Dayton	145.1100	–	O 67.0 (CA) elx	WC8OH	WCOARA
Dayton	146.6400	–	OaeWX	K8MCA	MoCoARES
Dayton	146.8200	–	O 77.0e	WA8PLZ	MWA
Dayton	146.9400	–	O 123.0a	W8BI	DARA
Dayton	146.9850	–	O 123.0l	WF8M	MVRFG
Dayton	147.1350	+	O(CA)z	WB8SMC	FaroutARC
Dayton	147.3600	+	O 77.0e	WA8PLZ	MWA
Kettering	147.0750	+	Oe	W8KMC	KMCN
Miamisburg	145.3300	–	O(CA)e	W8DYY	MoundARA

Location	Output	Input	Notes	Call	Sponsor
Miamisburg	146.7750	–	O 77.0	W6CDR	W6CDR
Miamisburg	147.0150	+	O 77.0	W8NCI	W8NCI
Miamisburg	147.1950	+	O(CA)eWX	W8DYY	MoundARA
MORGAN					
McConnelsvill	147.1950	+	O	WB8VQV	WB8VQV
MORROW					
Mt Gilead	146.7750	–	O 107.2a	WN7C	WN7C
MUSKINGUM					
Philo	146.6100	–	O 74.4	W8ZZV	Znsvl ARC
Zanesville	147.0750	+	O 91.5e	KB8ZMI	KB8ZMI
NOBLE					
Caldwell	147.2850	+	O 91.5	NC8OH	NOBLECoAR
OTTAWA					
Oak Harbor	147.0750	+	O 100.0e	K8VXH	OttawaARC
PAULDING					
Paulding	146.8650	–	O	WB8EHJ	WB8EHJ
PERRY					
New Lexington	146.8200	–	O 100.0e	KB8ZMI	KB8ZMI
PICKAWAY					
Circleville	147.1800	+	O	KD8HIJ	PICWYARES
PORTAGE					
Kent	146.8950	–	O 110.9aer WX	K8IV	N8KW
Ravenna	145.3900	–	Oae	KB8ZHP	PortageRC
PREBLE					
Eaton	145.4700	–	O(CA)e	K8YR	PrebleARA
PUTNAM					
Ottawa	146.7150	–	Oaez	W8MCB	Ottawa RC
RICHLAND					
Mansfield	145.3300	–	Ote	W8NDB	RC-Mnsfld
Mansfield	146.9400	–	O 71.9aez	K8RT	IARC, INC
Mansfield	147.3600	+	O 4412ael pr	K8HF	INTERCITY
ROSS					
Bourneville	146.9250	–	O(CA)e	W8BAP	SciotoARC
Chillicothe	146.8500	–	O 74.4e	W8BAP	SciotoARC
SANDUSKY					
Clyde	145.3500	–	O 110.9a (CA)elrWXz	NF8E	ClydeARS
Fremont	145.2500	–	O 186.2	W8NCK	SVARC
Fremont	145.4900	–	O 107.2ers WX	N8SCA	SCARES
Fremont	146.9100	–	●	KC8EPF	KC8EPF
SCIOTO					
Portsmouth	145.4500	–	O 136.5aer RB WX	W8KKC	SCARES
Portsmouth	147.3600	+	O 136.5	KC8BBU	KC8BBU
South Webster	145.3900	–	O 136.5	N8QA	Portsm RC

Location	Output	Input	Notes	Call	Sponsor
SENECA					
Bascom	145.1500	–	O 107.2	KB8EOC	SenCoEMA
Bascom	145.4500	–	O 107.2ael rWX	W8ID	W8ID
Bascom	146.6850	–	WXx	N8VWZ	N8VWZ
Republic	147.2550	+	O 107.2	KC8RCI	WD8NFQ
SHELBY					
Maplewood	146.8350	–	156.7aeWX	K8ZUK	SCARES
Sidney	147.3450	+	O 107.2el	W8AK	W8AK
STARK					
Alliance	145.3700	–	Oaez	W8LKY	AARC
Canton	145.1100	–	O 110.9lx	WØOZZ	WØOZZ
Canton	145.4900	–	O	W8TUY	W8TUY
Canton	146.7900	–	Oae	W8AL	CantonARC
Canton	147.1200	+	OaelrsWX z	WD8AYE	#NAME?
Massillon	146.9550	–	O 110.9ep z	WB8HHP	WB8HHP
Massillon	147.1800	+	O 110.9a TTex	W8NP	MARC
Uniontown	145.4500	–	O	WD8BIW	WD8BIW
SUMMIT					
Akron	145.1700	–	O	W8UPD	UofAKRON
Akron	146.6100	–	O 110.9	W8CTT	P.A.R.F.
Akron	146.6400	–	Oae	WB8DJP	Cmnty ARS
Akron	146.9850	–	O	WA8UXP	GoodYrARC
Akron	147.1350	+	alz	W8CTT	P.A.R.F.
Akron	147.3000	+	O	WB8HFZ	Cmnty ARS
Akron	147.3300	+	Ot	WB8CXO	AKCOM
Barberton	147.0900	+	O	WB8OVQ	WB8OVQ
Cuyahoga Fall	147.2400	+	Ot	WD8MJS	IndepndRA
Cuyahoga Fall	147.2700	+	O 110.9e	W8VPV	CFRC
Hudson	145.2500	–	Otae	K8KSW	K8KSW
TRUMBULL					
Cortland	147.1050	+	O 114.8ael prz	N8GZE	N8GZE
Newton Falls	147.2250	+	OeWX	N8VPR	N8VPR
Vienna	147.0450	+	O 141.3	W8FBE	W8FBE
Warren	146.8350	–	O 131.8	N8DOD	N8DOD
Warren	146.9700	–	O 100.0ae WX	W8VTD	WarrenARA
TUSCARAWAS					
New Philadelp	146.9250	–	O 71.9er	W8ZX	TUSCO ARC
Stone Creek	146.7300	–	O 71.9er	W8ZX	TUSCO ARC
UNION					
Marysville	145.3500	–	O 127.3	N8IG	UNION EMA
Marysville	147.3900	+	O	N8YRF	N8YRF
VAN WERT					
Delphos	147.1200	+	Oa	W8YEK	TRI-CoARC

Location	Output	Input	Notes	Call	Sponsor
Middlepoint	146.8500	–	O	W8FY	VWARC
Van Wert	146.7000	–	●(CA)	W8FY	VWARC
VINTON					
McArthur	147.1050	+	O 88.5aer	W8VCO	VCARC
Wellston	147.3750	+	91.5l	N8OJ	W8JL
WARREN					
ClearcreekTwp	145.4300	–	O 88.5ez	WB8ART	CtrvilARS
Franklin	145.2900	–	O 118.8 (CA)r	WB8ZVL	WB8ZVL
Lebanon	146.8650	–	O 118.8a (CA)elr	WC8EMA	WarrenEMA
Mason	145.1300	–	Oe	W8BRQ	MasonRC
Springboro	145.4900	–	O 77.0el	W8CYE	DRAKE ARC
WASHINGTON					
Belpre	147.3150	+	O 103.5	KI8JK	KI8JK
Constitution	146.7450	–	114.8aeWX	W8TAP	WTAP
Constitution	146.9700	–	O(CA)	N8NBL	PARK
Marietta	145.3300	–	141.3aRB	W8JL	KC8GF
Marietta	146.8050	–	O 118.8	KI8JK	KI8JK
Marietta	146.8800	–	O 91.5aez	W8HH	MARC
WAYNE					
Doylestown	147.3900	+	O 114.8el WX	W8WKY	SlvrckARA
Orrville	146.7150	–	OTT	KD8SQ	OARS
Wooster	147.2100	+	O 88.54781 (CA) TTe	W8WOO	WARC
Wooster	147.3450	+	110.9	WB8VPG	WB8VPG
WILLIAMS					
Bryan	146.8200	–	Oaelpz	KA8OFE	Wms ARC
WOOD					
Bowling Green	145.1500	–	●	KD8BTI	K5EYP
Bowling Green	146.7900	–	O 103.5	KD8BTI	WCARES
Bowling Green	147.1800	+	O 67.0e	K8TIH	WoodCoARC
Perrysburg	146.8350	–	Oa	KB8YVY	KA8WPC
WYANDOT					
Upper Sandsky	147.2100	+	107.2e	KE8PX	KE8PX

OKLAHOMA

Location	Output	Input	Notes	Call	Sponsor
ANTLERS					
Antlers	145.4900	–	Ot	KI5KC	TAAG
LAWTON					
Lawton	146.8050	–	OtE-SUN	N5PYD	N5PYD
LAWTON/ALTUS					
Altus	145.3900	–	O 141.3/141.3 E-SUNx	W5KS	LFSARC
Cyril	147.0450	+	O 123/123	KB5LLI	SWIRA
Grandfield	147.2550	+	O 192.8/192.8	KB5LLI	SWIRA
Headrick	146.6400	–	OBI	WD5BBN	WD5BBN

Location	Output	Input	Notes	Call	Sponsor
Lawton	145.1700	–	OtBI WX	KC5AVY	KC5AVY
Lawton	145.4300	–	OtE-SUN	K5VHF	K5VHF
Lawton	146.9100	–	O 173.8/173.8 E-SUN	W5KS	LFSARC
Lawton	147.3300	+	Ot	WX5LAW	LIRA
Lawton	147.3600	+	OtE-SUN WXx	W5KS	LFSARC
Lawton	147.3900	+	● 192.8/192.8 E-SUN	AB5J	F. PHILLIP
NORTHEAST					
Bartlesville	145.1500	–	O 88.5/88.5	KB5KZS	KB5KZS
Bartlesville	146.6550	–	O 88.5/88.5 E-SUN	W5NS	BARC
Bartlesville	146.7600	–	O 88.5/88.5 E-SUN WX	W5NS	BARC
Blackwell	145.3100	–	Ot	KD5MTT	OIDAR
Chandler	147.3600	+	O 192.8/192.8	KP2CP	RASS
Chouteau	145.1300	–	OE-SUN	K5LEE	------------
Mounds	146.7750	–	OtE-SUN	WB5NJU	775 GROUP
Mounds	147.1200	+	O 88.5/88.5 E-SUN	KD5DRW	KD5DRW
Muskogee	146.7450	–	O 88.5/88.5 E-WIND	KK5I	MUSKOGE RC
Muskogee	146.8500	–	Ot	KK5I	MUSKOGE RC
Muskogee	147.3300	+	O 88.5/88.5	WA5VMS	WA5VMS
Nowata	145.3700	–	OtE-SUN	N5ZZX	NOWATA H.C
Pawhuska	147.2700	+	O 88.5/88.5 E-SUN	N5ZQW	270 GROUP
Perry	146.8650	–	O 141.3/141.3 WX	KF5RDI	HAM SPOTTE
Ponca City	145.2300	–	O 123/123 WX	WB5MRE	WB5MRE
Ponca City	146.7300	–	Ot	N5PC	KAY CTY AR
Ponca City	146.9700	–	OtLITZ	W5HZZ	KAY CTY AR
Preston	145.3300	–	O 88.5/88.5	W5KO	W5KO
Preston	147.2250	+	O 88.5/88.5 WXx	WX5OKM	OCSA
Pryor	147.0600	+	O 88.5/88.5 E-SUN WXx	WB5Y	WB5Y
Rose	146.9850	–	O 110.9/110.9	KC5DBH	KC5DBH
Stillwater	145.3500	–	O 107.2/107.2 E-SUN WXx	K5SRC	SWO ARC
Stillwater	146.7150	–	Ot	W5YJ	OSU ARC
Stillwater	147.2550	+	O 107.2/107.2 E-SUN	K5FVL	K5FVL
Tahlequah	147.2400	+	OtE-SUN WX	N5ROX	EMERG. NET

Location	*Output*	*Input*	*Notes*	*Call*	*Sponsor*
Vinita	146.7300	–	O 88.5/88.5	KC5VVT	NORA
Vinita	147.3600	+	O 88.5/88.5 E-SUN	KC5VVT	NORA
Winchester	147.1500	+	O 88.5/88.5	N5LW	N5LW
NORTHWEST					
Arapaho	145.1900	–	O 123/123 E-SUN WXx	KE5RRK	CUSTER CTY
Buffalo	145.1300	–	O 131.8/131.8 E-SUN E-WIND WXx	W5HFZ	GBARG
Buffalo	147.1200	+	O 203.5/203.5	W5GPR	GPARC
Catesby	145.1700	–	O 131.8/131.8 E-SUN E-WINDsWXx	W5HFZ	GBARG
Cheyenne	147.2250	+	O 114.8/114.8	NØGB	NØGB
Elk City	146.7600	–	Ot	KA5BSA	WCENOK ARC
Enid	145.2900	–	O 141.3/141.3	W5HTK	ENID ARC
Enid	146.9400	–	Ot	WA5NYX	------------
Enid	147.1500	+	O	W5HTK	------------
Enid	147.3750	+	OtDCS	N5LWT	NW
Fairview	145.4500	–	OtE-SUN	WK5V	MCARA
Fairview	147.0750	+	OtE-SUN	WK5V	WK5V
Guthrie	147.1050	+	OtE-SUN	KA5EOS	KA5EOS
Guymon	147.1500	+	O 88.5/88.5 E-SUN WXx	N5DFQ	DBARC
Kingfisher	146.6400	–	O 100/100 E-SUNrWX	W5GLD	W5GLD
Seward	145.1700	–	O 123/123a E-SUN	KA5LSU	KF5AQR
Sharon	147.0000	+	O 100/100s WXx	N5WO	WX WATCH
Sharon	147.3600	+	O 88.5/88.5 E-SUN WX	N5WO	WX WATCH
Texhoma	147.3750	+	● 100/100 E-SUN	K5TSI	K5TSI
Vining	147.3000	+	O 103.5/103.5 E-SUN WXx	KCØGEV	GSPARC
Watonga	146.7450	–	O 88.5/88.5	N5WO	WX WATCH
Woodward	145.3900	–	O 103.5/103.5 E-SUNsWXx	W5OKT	TSARG
Woodward	146.6250	–	O 103.5/103.5 E-SUNsx	K5GUD	K5GUD
Woodward	146.7300	–	O 203.5/203.5 E-SUN	W5GPR	GPARC
OKLAHOMA CITY METRO					
Calumet	146.6100	–	OtE-SUN E-WIND	KD5YUL	WHEATSTRAW
Choctaw	147.0900	+	O 141.3/141.3	W5RGT	CHOCTAW AR

Location	Output	Input	Notes	Call	Sponsor
Del City	146.7000	–	O 103.5/103.5	W5DEL	DEL CITY A
Edmond	145.2100	–	O 131.8/131.8 E-SUN	K5CPT	COLE
Edmond	145.2700	–	O 100/100 E-SUNx	W5BIV	W5BIV
Edmond	146.7900	–	O 100/100	W5RLW	W5RLW
Edmond	147.0300	+	O 167.9/167.9 E-SUN	WD5AII	EDMOND ARC
Edmond	147.1350	+	O 79.7/79.7 E-SUN	K5EOK	EARS
Edmond	147.1800	+	O 203.5/203.5 E-SUN	WA5A	WA5A
Elreno	147.2400	+	O 141.3/141.3	W5ELR	ERARC
Newalla	145.1500	–	O 114.8/114.8	K5UV	K5UV
Norman	146.8800	–	OtE-SUN	N5MS	OUARC
Norman	147.0600	+	O 141.3/141.3eWX	W5NOR	SCARS
Oklahoma City	145.2500	–	O 141.3/141.3ar	KS5B	KS5B
Oklahoma City	145.3300	–	O/100	WN5J	WN5J
Oklahoma City	145.3700	–	O 141.3/141.3	KK5FM	KK5FM
Oklahoma City	145.4100	–	O 141.3/141.3sBI WXx	WX5OKC	ODCEM
Oklahoma City	145.4900	–	O 131.8/131.8	KD5AHH	BOJIVE RN
Oklahoma City	146.6700	–	O 141.3/141.3 E-SUN	W5PAA	MMACARC
Oklahoma City	146.7600	–	O 141.3/141.3 E-SUN	AE5GS	AE5GS
Oklahoma City	146.8200	–	O 151.4/151.4e	W5MEL	OCAPA
Oklahoma City	146.8500	–	O 141.3/141.3 E-SUN LITZ	W5PAA	MMACARC
Oklahoma City	146.9250	–	O 141.3/141.3 E-SUN	W5PAA	MMACARC
Oklahoma City	146.9850	–	O 141.3/141.3 LITZ	W5PAA	MMACARC
Oklahoma City	147.2100	+	O 141.3/141.3 E-SUN	W5MEL	OCAPA
PANHANDLE					
Forgan	147.3900	+	Ot	N5AKN	N5AKN
SOUTHEAST					
Ada	145.2700	–	O 141.3/141.3 E-SUN	KE5GLC	PCARC
Ada	147.2850	+	O 114.8/114.8 E-SUN	WB5NBA	ASA ARC

OKLAHOMA

Location	*Output*	*Input*	*Notes*	*Call*	*Sponsor*
Ada	147.2850	+	O 114.8/114.8 E-SUN	WB5NBA	ADA ARC
Antlers	147.2400	+	OtE-SUN	KD5DAR	KD5DAR
Atoka	145.4300	–	O 114.8/114.8 E-SUNrsx	WB5VUE	ATOKA E M
Big Cedar	147.3750	+	O 123/123	AB5CP	N5JMG
Broken Bow	147.1350	+	O 67/67 E-SUNsWXx	KD5ABB	MCCURTAIN
Cavanal Mtn	146.6400	–	● 88.5/88.5 E-SUNsWXx	W5ANR	FSAARC
Clayton	146.7300	–	O 114.8/114.8	KM5VK	KM5VK
Coleman	147.1650	+	O 131.8/131.8	WG5B	WG5B
Daisy	145.2100	–	O 100/100 WXx	W5CUQ	PCARC
Durant	146.9850	–	O 118.8/118.8 E-SUN WXx	K5BQG	DURANT BR
Durant	147.3900	+	O 118.8/118.8e	K5KIE	D.A.R.A,
Enterprise	146.6850	–	O	KB1HSZ	LEARC
Enterprise	147.2700	+	OtWXx	N5JMG	N5JMG
Honobia	145.1500	+	O 114.8/114.8 E-SUN E-WIND	KM5SB	KM5SB
Hugo	146.6100	–	O 114.8/114.8 E-SUN	KB5JTR	KARC
Liberty	145.1100	–	O 114.8/114.8 E-SUN WXx	W5JWT	W5JWT ET A
McAlester	145.3700	–	O 71.9/71.9 E-SUN	W5CUQ	PCARC
Mt Sycamore	145.4100	–	O 88.5/88.5 sWXx	N5NHU	LEFLORE EM
Nashoba	145.2900	–	O 162.2/162.2 E-SUN E-WIND	KM5VK	KM5VK
Nashoba	145.3300	–	O 162.2/162.2 E-SUN E-WIND EXP WX	KM5VK	KM5VK
Near Davis	146.8650	–	O 192.8/192.8	K5CPT	KN6UG
Seminole	147.0150	+	O	WJ5F	WJ5F
Seminole	147.1950	+	O	WJ5F	WJ5F
Shawnee	145.3900	–	OtE-SUN LITZ	W5SXA	PCARC
Soper	145.1700	–	O 114.8/114.8	KM5SB	------------
Tecumseh	145.2900	–	O 141.3/141.3	K5DOK	K5DOK
Tecumseh	146.6250	–	O 131.8/131.8 LITZ	KD5WAV	K5DOK
Velma	147.2250	+	O 123/123	KC5JCO	KD5JCO

Location	Output	Input	Notes	Call	Sponsor
SOUTHEST					
Durant	147.2550	+	O 114.8/114.8	K5CGE	K5CGE
SOUTHWEST					
Alfalfa	145.1100	–	ODCS(712) WX	K5GSM	K5GSM
Altus	146.7900	–	O 100/100 E-SUN	WX5ASA	ALTUS SKYW
Altus	147.2850	+	O 100/100 BI	WB5KRH	SOKRA
Anadarko	147.2700	+	OtE-SUNx	WX5LAW	SPARS/LIRA
Arbuckle Mtns	145.2300	–	● 179.9/179.9 E-SUNsWXx	WG5B	WG5B
Ardmore	146.9700	–	O 131.8/131.8 LITZ	W5BLW	SOARESSS
Blanchard	145.4700	–	O 141.3/141.3	WA7WNM	KS5B
Chichasha	145.1300	–	Ot	WAØAQO	CARS
Chickasha	145.2300	–	O 141.3/141.3 LITZ	WK5S	LFSARC
Clinton	147.3000	+	O 127.3/127.3 E-SUN	KE5FBW	------------
Cyrill	147.0000	+	Oe	KB5LLI	SWIRA
Davis	145.4500	–	O 100/100a	KC5TDG	KC5TDG
Davis	147.0750	+	Ot	KB5LLI	SWIRA
Davis	147.1500	+	O 131.8/131.8	WG5B	WG5B
Duncan	146.7300	–	OtE-SUN	WD5IYF	CTARC
Duncan	147.3000	+	O 123/123 WX	KB5LLI	SWIRA
Elmore City	146.7450	–	O 141.3/141.3sWX	KB5LLI	SWIIRA
Granite	146.7150	–	OWX	KB5LLI	S.W.I.R.A
Granite	146.9850	–	O 156.7/156.7 DCS(293) E-SUN	K5XTL	K5XTL
Hobart	146.8950	146.3950	O 100/100 E-SUN	KD5WVL	HOBART ARE
Lawton	147.1800	+	Ot	WX5LAW	LIRA
Lone Grove	146.7900	–	OtWX	W5BLW	SOARESSS
Mangum	147.3450	+	Ot	W5KRG	ALTUS SKYW
Marietta	146.8350	–	O 131.8/131.8	KF5JFZ	LCMMC
Marlow	146.9550	–	Ote	K5UM	MARLOW ARC
Newcastle	147.3150	+	O 151.4/151.4 LITZ	K5CPT	L & M RADI
Waurika	145.2900	–	O 123/123	W5KS	LFSARC
TULSA METRO					
Broken Arrow	146.9100	–	O 88.5/88.5	W5DRZ	BAARC
Claremore	147.0900	+	OtE-SUN LITZ	N5FEE	RCWA

Location	Output	Input	Notes	Call	Sponsor
Liberty Mounds	145.2300	–	O 88.5/88.5 E-SUN	N5XBE	N5XBE
Mannford	147.0450	+	O 88.5/88.5	W5IAS	TULSA ARC
Owasso	146.7000	–	Ot	K5LAD	K5LAD
Sapulpa	145.4300	–	O 88.5/88.5 E-SUNx	KE5OKT	CCARES
Tulsa	145.1100	–	O 88.5/88.5 E-SUNsWXx	W5IAS	TULSA ARC
Tulsa	145.1700	–	Ot	N5NNF	AAARC
Tulsa	146.8050	–	O 88.5/88.5 e	WA5LVT	TRO INC
Tulsa	146.8800	–	O 88.5/88.5 esWXx	WA5LVT	TRO INC
Tulsa	147.0000	+	Ot	K5JME	AM AIR ARC
Tulsa	147.1800	+	O 88.5/88.5	W5IAS	TULSA ARC
Tulsa	147.2850	+	O 88.5/88.5 LITZ	KC5TJT	KC5TJT
Tulsa	147.3900	+	OtE-SUN	WB5NJU	39 GROUP
West Tulsa	145.2700	–	OtE-SUN	N5FWX	N5FWX

OREGON

Location	Output	Input	Notes	Call	Sponsor
CENTRAL EAST OREGON					
Bend	147.0400	+	O 100elz	K7RPT	ARRG
CENTRAL WILLAMETTE VALLEY					
Albany	146.6100	–	O 167.9e	KA7ENW	ELRA
Blue River	145.3700	–	O 100 (CA) elz	W7EUG	LCSARO
Brownsville	147.2600	+	O 100	W7EXH	W7EXH
Central Point	145.4100	–	O 100aez	KB7QMV	KB7QMV
Chemult	145.4700	–	O 162.2e	WA7TYD	WA7TYD
Corvallis	146.7800	–	OeLITZ	K7CVO	BCARES
Corvallis	146.8200	–	O	WA7TUV	MPRA
Eugene	145.1700	–	O 100e	W7EXH	W7EXH
Eugene	145.4500	–	O 123ae	W7ARD	W7ARD
Lebanon	147.2000	+	O 167.9e	KA7ENW	ELRA
Lyons	147.0600	+	O 123e	W1ARK	W1ARK
Salem	145.2900	–	Oelsx	WA7ABU	WA7ABU
Salem	145.3500	–	O 186.2 (CA)e	K7MRR	EHFERG
Springfield	146.7400	–	O 100e	WA7FQD	EARS
CENTRAL-EAST					
Bend	146.7000	–	O 162.2e	W7JVO	HIDARG
Bend	146.9400	–	O 162.2e	W7JVO	HIDARG
Bend	147.3600	+	Oae	KB7LNR	KB7LNR
Fossil	147.2400	+	O	KB7LNR	KB7LNR
Mitchell	147.1800	+	O 162.2e	W7JVO	HIDARG
Sisters	146.9000	–	O 123e	W7DUX	W7DUX
Sun River	146.6400	–	O 162.2ae	WA7TYD	WA7TYD
Terrebonne	147.0600	+	O 162.2e	W7JVO	HIDARG

Location	*Output*	*Input*	*Notes*	*Call*	*Sponsor*
Warm Springs	145.1100	–	O 162.2e	KB7LNR	KB7LNR
COAST-CENTRAL					
Florence	146.8000	–	O 100e	W7FLO	OCERI
Lincoln City	147.0600	+	O 118.8el	N7HQR	OCRG
COAST-NORTH					
Astoria	146.6600	–	O 118.8ae z	KD7UDX	KD7UDX
Tillamook	147.2200	+	O 100e	W7LI	MHRG
Tillamook	147.2600	+	O 162.2e	N7QFT	N7QFT
COAST-SOUTH					
Brookings	146.9600	–	O 88.5e	KLØHH	KLØHH
Coos Bay	147.1000	+	O 146.2e	W7OC	SWORA
Coos Bay	147.2800	+	O 146.2ae z	W7OC	SWORA
Coos Bay	147.3800	+	O 146.2e	W7OC	SWORA
Gold Beach	146.7400	–	O 88.5e	K7SEG	K7SEG
Myrtle Point	145.1900	–	O 146.2e	W7OC	SWORA
Myrtle Point	146.9200	–	O 100e	W7EXH	W7EXH
North Bend	145.4100	–	O 103.5	K6TC	K6RGC
Reedsport	147.1800	+	O 146.2	W7OC	SWORA
COLUMBIA RIVER GORGE					
Hood River	147.1000	+	O 100e	KF7LN	KF7LN
LOWER COLUMBIA					
Rainier	147.2000	+	O 127.3e	K7PP	K7PP
NORTH CENTRAL					
Sisters	147.3400	+	O 100e	W7EXH	W7EXH
The Dalles	146.7400	–	O 100	KC7LDD	KC7LLD
NORTH EAST OREGON					
Baker City	145.2700	–	O 110.9ae z	W7NYW	W7NYW
Baker City	147.0600	+	O 110.9ae z	W7NYW	N/A
Huntington	147.1200	+	O 100 (CA) el	K7OJI	TVRA
La Grande	145.1500	–	O 110.9 (CA)	W7NYW	EOARS
Ontario	147.1000	+	O 100 (CA) el	K7OJI	TVRA
Weiser	145.3900	–	O 100 (CA) el	K7OJI	TVRA
NORTH WILLAMETTE VALLEY					
Forest Grove	147.3200	+	O 100 (CA) e	K7RPT	ARRG
Newberg	145.4900	–	Oe	K7FM	K7FM
North Plains	145.4500	–	Oe	KE7DC	WA7ZNZ
Oregon City	145.2100	–	O 110.9e	WB7QFD	WB7QFD
Timberline	147.1200	+	O 100el	K7RPT	ARRG
NORTHEAST					
Fort Rock	145.1500	–	O 162.2e	WA7TYD	WA7TYD

Location	Output	Input	Notes	Call	Sponsor
La Grande	146.9800	–	O 100e	W4PJS	W4PJS
NW OREGON & SW WASHINGTON					
Beaver Creek	146.9200	–	O 107.2e	AH6LE	AH6LE
Colton	146.9600	–	Oaz	W7OTV	W7OTV
Mill City	145.1900	–	O 100es	WA7ABU	WA7ABU
Newberg	145.4700	–	O 107.2el	KR7IS	WORC
Portland	145.3100	–	O 123e	W7EXH	W7EXH
Portland	146.8000	–	O 107.2ael sWX	KJ7IY	WORC
Portland	146.9800	–	O 123e	W7EXH	W7EXH
Sandy	145.4300	–	O 107.2ael sWX	KJ7IY	WORC
Timber	145.2700	–	O 107.2ael sWX	KJ7IY	WORC
OREGON COAST-CENTRAL					
Tillamook	147.1600	+	O 118.8e	W7HH	W7GC
OREGON COAST-SOUTH					
Coquille	146.6100	–	O 110.9e	K7CCH	K7CCH
Port Orford	147.2000	+	O 118.8e	K7POH	POARC
PORTLAND METRO					
Aloha	147.3600	+	O 107.2e	WC7EOC	N7QQU
Portland	145.2300	–	O(CA)e	K7LJ	K7LJ
Portland	145.3900	–	O 100 (CA) elz	K7LJ	K7LJ
Portland	146.7000	–	O 100e	KD7TFZ	KD7TFZ
Portland	146.8400	–	Oe	W7LT	PARC
Portland	146.9400	–	Oe	W7LT	PARC
Portland	147.0400	+	O 100 (CA) ez	K7RPT	ARRG
Portland	147.2800	+	O 167.9e	WB7QIW	HARC
Scholls	145.1100	–	O	KB7PSM	IRRA
Scholls	146.9000	–	O(CA)elz	K7WWG	K7WWG
SOUTH CENTRAL					
Ashland	146.6200	–	O 100e	W9PCI	W9PCI
Central Point	147.3800	+	O 131.8e	KL7VK	KL7VK
Chemult	147.1400	+	O 100e	W7EXH	W7EXH
Keno	147.3200	+	O 118.8e	KE7CSD	KBRA
Lakeview	147.3400	+	O 100e	KE7QP	KE7QP
Wolf Creek	145.2900	–	O 123e	K7TVL	RVLA
Wolf Creek	146.8400	–	O 77el	W7EXH	W7EXH
Wolf Creek	147.3400	+	O 136.5e	WB6YQP	JARS
SOUTH CENTRAL OREGON					
Medford	147.0000	+	O 123eWX	K7RVM	K7RVM
SOUTH WILLAMETTE VALLEY					
Blue River	145.1100	–	O 100e	W7EXH	W7EXH
Dorena	145.2300	–	Oe	W7EXH	W7EXH
Eugene	145.3100	–	O	W7EXH	W7EXH
Eugene	146.8800	–	Oe	WJ7S	BHRA
Eugene	147.0800	+	O 100 (CA) e	W7CQZ	W7CQZ

Location	*Output*	*Input*	*Notes*	*Call*	*Sponsor*
Eugene	147.2600	+	O 100el	W7EXH	W7EXH
Eugene	147.3600	+	O	W7EXH	W7EXH
Junction City	146.6800	–	O 100e	W7WTQ	LCSARO
Oakridge	146.9800	–	Oe	W7EXH	W7EXH
Saginaw	146.7600	–	Oe	W7EXH	W7EXH
SOUTHEAST					
Burns	147.3000	+	O 162.2e	W7JVO	HIDARG
Glide	145.4300	–	O 82.5e	WA7BWT	N/A
Hampton	147.2000	+	O 162.2e	W7JVO	HIDARG
Huntington	145.1700	–	O 110.9e	W7NYW	EOARS
Juntura	147.2800	+	O 162.2e	W7JVO	HIDARG
Silver Lake	146.8000	–	O 173.8e	KE7QP	KE7QP
Vale	146.7200	–	O 103.5	W7PAG	W7PAG
SOUTHWEST					
Agness	147.0400	+	O 88.5e	WA7JAW	WA7JAW
Ashland	147.2600	+	O 123es LITZ WX	WX7MFR	NWSJAWS
Cave Junction	145.4900	–	O 136.5e	WB6YQP	WA6YSM
Glide	147.2400	+	O 136.5e	WA7BWT	WA7BWT
Grants Pass	145.1500	–	● 162.2e	N7EZY	KA7YZI
Grants Pass	146.6400	–	Oaez	K7LIX	SOARC
Grants Pass	147.2200	+	Oe	WA6OTP	WA6OTP
Grants Pass	147.3000	+	O 100e	K7LIX	SOARC
Jacksonville	145.3300	–	Oe	W9PCI	W9PCI
Lakeview	145.3100	–	O 100	KE7QP	KE7QP
Medford	147.0200	+	O 100	K7RPT	ARRG
Medford	147.0600	+	O(CA)e	K7FH	WB7RQG
Port Orford	146.8600	–	O 123el	K7TVL	K7TVL
Rogue River	146.7600	–	Oe	WB6YQP	JARS
Roseburg	145.2100	–	O 136.5e	WA6RHK	RED CROSS
Roseburg	146.9000	–	O 100aez	KC7TLY	UVARC
Ruch	146.7200	–	O 131.8e	KL7VK	KL7VK
STATEWIDE					
Corvallis	145.1300	–	O 100e	K7TVL	K7TVL

PENNSYLVANIA

FREQUENCY USAGE - ALL WPA SECTION	
APRS	144.3900
APRS	145.7900
D-STAR VOICE SX	145.6700
FM VOICE SX	145.5100
FM VOICE SX	145.5300
FM VOICE SX	145.5500
FM VOICE SX	145.5700
FM VOICE SX	145.5900
FM VOICE SX	145.6100
FM VOICE SX	145.6300
FM VOICE SX	145.6500

Location	Output	Input	Notes	Call	Sponsor
FM VOICE SX	146.5200				
FM VOICE SX	146.5350				
FM VOICE SX	146.5500				
FM VOICE SX	146.5650				
FM VOICE SX	146.5800				
FM VOICE SX	146.5950				
FM VOICE SX	147.5250				
FM VOICE SX	147.5400				
FM VOICE SX	147.5550				
FM VOICE SX	147.5700				
FM VOICE SX	147.5850				
Packet	144.9100				
Packet	144.9300				
Packet	144.9500				
Packet	144.9700				
Packet	144.9900				
Packet	145.0100				
Packet	145.0300				
Packet	145.0500				
Packet	145.0700				
Packet	145.0900				
Packet	145.6900				
Packet	145.7100				
Packet	145.7300				
Packet	145.7500				
Packet	145.7700				
Repeater Input	147.4150				
Repeater Input	147.4300				
Repeater Input	147.4450				
Repeater Input	147.4600				
Repeater Input	147.4750				
Repeater Input	147.4900				
Repeater Input	147.5050				
Repeater Output	146.4150				
Repeater Output	146.4300				
Repeater Output	146.4450				
Repeater Output	146.4600				
Repeater Output	146.4750				
Repeater Output	146.4900				
Repeater Output	146.5050				
ADAMS					
Gettysburg	145.3500	–	O 103.5 (CA)er	W3KGN	ACARS
ALTOONA 123.0					
Altoona	146.6100	–	O 123.0ae z	W3QZF	HARC
Altoona	146.8200	–	O 123.0ae z	W3QW	HARC
New Germany	145.2100	–	O(CA)elrz	KC3DES	CCDES

Location	Output	Input	Notes	Call	Sponsor
BEAVER 131.8					
Beaver	146.8500	–	Oer	N3TN	TAARA
Beaver	147.1350	+	Oer	N3TN	TAARA
Beaver	147.1650	+	O 100.0r	N3CYR	N3CYR
Beaver Falls	145.3100	–	O 100.0aelrz	W3SGJ	B.V.A.R.A.
Industry	146.4150	147.4150	O(CA)e	N3CYR	RESCUE40
BERKS					
Pine Grove	145.1700	–	O 110.9el	AA3RG	A.A.R.G.
Pine Grove	146.6400	–	O 82.5 (CA) ersWX	AA3RG	A.A.R.G.
Pottstown	147.2100	+	O 131.8 (CA)er	K3ZMC	P.A.R.T.
Reading	145.4900	–	O 114.8ae	K3TI	DDXA
Reading	146.9100	–	O 131.8e	W3BN	RDGRADIOCL
Reading	147.1800	+	O 110.9 (CA)ersWX	WB3FPL	BerksCoEMA
BRADFORD					
Seeley	146.7900	–	O 179.9e WX	N3YCT	------------
Towanda	147.2850	+	O 82.5ers RB LITZ WX	K3ABC	NTRG
BUCKS					
Doylestown	145.3500	–	O 131.8 (CA)erWX	WA3EPA	WRC ARC
Fairless Hills	147.3000	+	O 131.8elrsRB WX	W3BXW	BEARS
Hilltown	145.3300	–	O 131.8 (CA)e	W3HJ	HiPointRA
Hilltown	147.3900	+	O 100 (CA) e	W3HJ	CBRA
Perkasie	145.3100	–	O 131.8 (CA)e	W3AI	RF Hill ARC
Southampton	146.7900	–	O 131.8 (CA)rs	W3SK	PWA
Upper Bucks	146.8050	–	O 127.3 RB	N3ITN	------------
Warminster	147.0900	+	O 131.8 (CA)elrs	K3DN	WARC
Warrington	147.0000	+	Oe	WA3ZID	------------
CARBON					
Jim Thorpe	147.2550	+	O 162.2 (CA)ers	W3HA	CARC
CENTRAL 173.8/123.0					
Huntingdon	145.3100	–	Oel	W3WIV	LTRA
Huntingdon	146.7000	–	O	W3VI	------------
Lewistown	145.1900	–		W3MCC	W3MCC
Lewistown	146.9100	–	O	K3DNA	JVARC
Philipsburg	146.4300	147.4300	173.8	W3PHB	PARA
Philipsburg	146.6400	–		W3PHB	PARA

Location	*Output*	*Input*	*Notes*	*Call*	*Sponsor*
State College	145.4500	–	Oael	K3CR	PSARC
State College	146.7600	–	Oael	W3GA	NtnyRC
State College	146.8500	–	Ol	W3YA	NtnyRC
CHESTER					
Paoli	145.1300	–	O 131.8 (CA)ers	WB3JOE	MidAtlARC
Parkesburg	146.9850	+	O 94.8aers RB	WA3GMS	------------
Valley Forge	146.7600	–	O 131.8 (CA)l	W3PHL	PARA Group
West Chester	146.9400	–	O 131.8els LITZ	W3EOC	PARA/CCAR
COLUMBIA					
Berwick	147.2250	+	O 203.5 (CA)ersWX	KB3BJO	CMARC
Bloomsburg	147.1200	+	O 131.8 (CA)elWX	WB3DUC	WB3DUC
CUMBERLAND					
Mt Holly	145.4300	–	O 67ersWX	N3TWT	SMRA
DAUPHIN					
Ellendale	147.0750	+	O 123ers	KB3NIA	HRAC
Harrisburg	145.1100	–	O 131.8er	W3ND	CPRA Inc.
Harrisburg	145.2100	–	O 123e	WB3EYB	------------
Harrisburg	145.2700	–	O 74.4l	W3WAN	WAN-RS
Harrisburg	145.2900	–	O 123r	W3ND	CPRA Inc.
Harrisburg	145.4700	–	O 123 (CA) erWX	W3ND	CPRA Inc.
Harrisburg	146.7600	–	O 100 (CA) es	W3UU	HRAC
Harrisburg	147.3750	+	O 123	W3ND	CPRA Inc.
Steelton	147.3000	+	O 100e	N3NJB	HBG REACT
DELAWARE					
Darby	147.3600	+	O 131.8 (CA)esRB	W3UER	DCARA
Media	145.2300	–	O 131.8a	W3AWA	Mobl 6ers
Newtown Square	147.0600	+	O 131.8 (CA)esWX	WB3JOE	MidAtlARC
Newtown Square	147.1950	+	O 100 (CA) elWX	W3DI	MNARC
ERIE 186.2					
Cherry Hill	146.7600	–	Oaelx	WA3USH	+WYZ
Corry	147.0900	+	O	W3YXE	RAC
Erie	146.6100	–	O 186.2elr s	W3GV	RAErie
Erie	146.6400	–	O(CA)elz	KA3MJN	KA3MJN
Erie	147.2700	+	Oae	N3APP	N3APP
Union City	146.7300	–	●a	WA3PGL	WA3PGL
Waterford	146.8200	–	O 186.2elr s	W3GV	RAErie

Location	Output	Input	Notes	Call	Sponsor
JOHNSTOWN 123.0					
Hastings	146.7750	–	O	KA3ZYC	CRC
Johnstown	145.3900	–	Oer	N3YFO	N3YFO
Johnstown	146.9400	–	O(CA)erz	WA3WGN	CRC
Johnstown	147.3750	+	O(CA)lRBz	N3LZX	N3LZX
Mineral Point	147.0600	+	O 123.0	K3WS	K3WS
N Cambria	146.6550	–	O	KE3DR	KE3DR
JUNIATA					
Tuscarora Mtn	147.0450	+	O 146.2ae WX	K3TAR	T.A.R.A.
LACKAWANNA					
Scranton	146.8350	–	O 127.3el LITZ	KB3BIU	BgmU RS
Scranton	146.9400	–	O(CA)ers WX	K3CSG	SPARK
LANCASTER					
Cornwall	145.3900	–	O 118.8e	W3AD	L.R.T.S.
Ephrata	145.4500	–	O 100 (CA) eRB BI LITZ WX	W3XP	EphrataARS
Holtwood	146.7450	–	O 114.8e	KX3B	------------
Lancaster	145.3100	–	O 118.8elr sWX	N3FYI	RVARG
Lancaster	147.0150	+	O 118.8ael rsWX	W3RRR	R.R.R.A.
Manheim	145.2300	–	O 118.8aer sWX	K3IR	SPARC Inc.
LEBANON					
Cornwall	147.1050	+	O 141.3lRB	N3KYR	SVARC
Grantville	147.1650	+	O 82.5ers	K3LV	------------
Lebanon	146.8800	–	O 74.4l	W3WAN	WAN-RS
Lebanon	147.2400	+	O 82.5es WX	W3BFD	LVSRA
Lebanon	147.3150	+	O 82.5 (CA) ers	K3LV	LVSRA
Newmanstown	147.2850	+	O 131.8 (CA)e	N3SWH	SPARK
LEHIGH					
Allentown	146.9400	–	O 71.9ers LITZ WX	W3OI	LVARC
Allentown	147.1350	+	O 71.9 (CA) ersBI WX	W3OI	LVARC
Allentown	147.2250	+	O 151.4 (CA)	WA3VHL	------------
LUZERNE					
Berwick	145.1300	–	O 77 (CA)r s	NQ3G	B.A.R.S.
Bunker Hill	145.4500	–	Oe	K3YTL	Murgas ARC
Hanover Twp	147.3300	+	O 88.5 (CA) e	WA3CPW	------------

Location	Output	Input	Notes	Call	Sponsor
Hazleton	146.6700	–	O 103.5 (CA)	W3OHX	A.R.A.
Hazleton	147.0300	+	O 103.5e	K3BS	A.R.A.
Hunlock Creek	146.8050	–	O 94.8 (CA) e	AD3L	JMRA
Wilkes-Barre	146.4600	147.4600	O 100ae WX	N3FCK	------------
Wilkes-Barre	146.6100	–	O 82.5elrs WX	WB3FKQ	------------
LYCOMING					
Huntersville	145.4500	–	O 167.9ers LITZ WX	KB3DXU	LycCoEMA
Montoursville	145.4900	–	O 167.9	KB3HLL	B.E.R.A.
Trout Run	145.1500	–	O 167.9ers LITZ WX	KB3DXU	LycCoEMA
Waterville	145.3500	–	O 167.9ers LITZ WX	KB3DXU	LycCoEMA
Williamsport	145.3300	–	O 167.9ers LITZ WX	KB3DXU	LycCoEMA
Williamsport	146.7300	–	Oael	W3AVK	WestBranch
Williamsport	147.0900	+	O 167.9 (CA)el	KB3HLL	B.E.R.A.
Williamsport	147.3000	+	O 151.4 (CA)elrsRB WX	W3AHS	MARC
MONROE					
Jackson Twp	145.2300	–	O 77elWX	W3WAN	WAN-RS
Tannersville	146.8650	–	OersRB	N3SEI	MCOES
MONTGOMERY					
Eagleville	146.8350	–	O 88.5 (CA) ers	AA3E	Montco OEP
Hatfield	147.3300	+	O(CA)el	WA3RYQ	H.A.R.A.
Horsham	147.1650	+	O 162.2	K3JJO	DELMONT R.C.
Meadowbrook	146.7150	–	O 131.8 (CA)eWX	WA3UTI	HRH-ARC
Souderton	145.1900	–	O 131.8 (CA)ers	N3ZA	TARA
MONTOUR					
Liberty Twp	145.2900	–	Oe	WA2JOC	MCEMA
NORTH CENTRAL 173.8					
Bradford	147.2400	+	O	KD3OH	KD3OH
Coudersport	146.6850	–		N3PC	HARC
Coudersport	146.8800	–		K3CC	------------
Emporium	146.8050	–	O(CA)	N3FYD	CCARC
Emporium	147.1800	+	O(CA)e	WA3WPS	CCARC
Galeton	147.3450	+	O(CA)	KB3EAR	NTRS
James City	146.7300	–		WB3IGM	WB3IGM
Lock Haven	147.3600	+	Oelr	K3KR	K3KR
Ridgway	147.0000	+	O	N3NIA	WA8RZR
Ridgway	147.2850	+		N3NWL	N3NWL

Location	*Output*	*Input*	*Notes*	*Call*	*Sponsor*
Rockton	147.3150	+	173.8	N3QC	QCARC
Rockton	147.3900	+	**O**r	KE3DR	N5NWC
Sigel	147.1050	+		N3JGT	JCEMA
Smethport	147.3000	+	**O**er	N3LLR	N3LLR
Ulysses	145.4300	–	**O**(CA)r	KB3HJC	PCEMA
NORTHAMPTON					
Bethlehem	146.7750	–	**O** 136.5 (CA)	K3LPR	------------
Lehigh Valley	146.6550	–	**O** 136.5el	N3LWY	------------
Nazareth	145.1100	–	**O** 151.4ers	W3OK	DLARCNCEMA
Nazareth	146.7000	–	**O** 151.4 (CA)elrsRB LITZ WX	W3OK	DLARC
NORTHUMBERLAND					
Milton	146.9850	–	**O**(CA)eWX	WA3AMI	Milton ARC
Sunbury	147.2700	+	**O** 100 (CA) ersWX	K3ARR	SVARC
NORTHWEST 186.2					
Clarion	146.8650	–		N3GPM	KE3EI
Edinboro	146.9850	–		KB3PSL	------------
Erie	146.4300	147.4300	**O**l	KE3JP	KE3JP
Franklin	145.2300	–	**O**aelz	W3ZIC	FVM&KC
Greenville	146.4450	147.4450	**O**	KE3JP	KE3JP
Guys Mills	147.0300	+	**O**	W3MIE	CARS
Marienville	146.8950	–		N2EVA	N2EVA
Meadville	145.1300	–	**O**elr	W3MIE	CfdARS
Meadville	147.2100	+	**O**aerz	N3PYJ	N3PYJ
Pleasantville	147.1200	+	**O**alrz	W3ZIC	FVM&KC
Springboro	146.4600	147.4600	100.0el	KF8YF	KF8YF
Tionesta	145.4900	–	e	KE3EI	------------
Union City	146.7000	–	**O**e	WA3UC	WA3UC
Vowinkel	147.0750	+	110.9	N3UOH	N3UOH
Warren	145.1100	–	**O**er	W3GFD	WC RACES
Warren	146.7600	–	**O** 88.5e	KB3KOP	CCAFMA
Waterford	145.4300	–		KE3JP	KE3JP
Youngsville	146.9700	–	**O**e	W3YZR	CCAFMA
PERRY					
Newville	146.4600	147.4600	**O** 67ers	N3TWT	SMRA Inc.
PHILADELPHIA					
Center City	146.6850	–	**O** 146.2 (CA)ls	WM3PEN	HARC
Philadelphia	145.2700	–	**O** 131.8 (CA)e	W3PVI	ChSixARC
Philadelphia	145.4100	–	**O** 127.3 (CA)e	KD3WT	Schuylkill
Roxborough	147.0300	+	**O** 91.5 (CA) el	W3QV	Phil-Mont
PIKE					
Dingmans Ferry	145.3300	–	**O** 141.3 (CA)e	AA2HA	------------

Location	Output	Input	Notes	Call	Sponsor
Schahola	145.3500	–	O 100elrs WX	K3TSA	TSARA
PITTSBURGH 131.8					
Apollo	146.9700	–	O 131.8aer xz	N1RS	SARA
Bridgeville	145.1300	–	O(CA)	KS3R	SHARC
Carnegie	147.0300	+	Oe	W3KWH	SCARC
Clinton	147.2100	+	O 100.0a E-SUNlz	K3KEM	K3KEM
Derry	146.4900	147.4900	O 131.8ael x	N1RS	SARA
Gibsonia	145.2900	–	(CA)el	WA3UQD	WA3UQD
Irwin	147.1200	+	O 131.8 (CA)	W3OC	TRARC
Jeanette	146.9250	–	Oe	W3NDP	IwnARA
Mt Lebanon	146.9550	–	O	N3SH	WASH
New Kensington	145.3700	–	Ot(CA)e	WA3WOM	WA3WOM
New Kensington	146.4900	147.4900	O 131.8ael x	N1RS	SARA
New Kensington	146.6400	–	O 131.8ae	K3MJW	Skyview
Pittsburgh Baldwin	145.3300	–	O	K3EOC	ACES
Pittsburgh/Carrick	146.6100	–	Oaelz	W3PGH	GPVHFS
Pittsburgh Hazelwood	145.4700	–	Oaex	WA3PBD	GtwyFM
Pittsburgh Homestead	146.7300	–	Oaex	WA3PBD	GtwyFM
Pittsburgh/N Hills	147.0900	+	O 88.5 (CA) er	W3EXW	NHARC-RPT
Pittsburgh Oakland	146.8800	–	O 88.5 (CA) er	W3EXW	NHARC-RPT
Washington	147.3450	+		W3PLP	W3PLP
West Mifflin	145.2500	–	O(CA)el	AB3PJ	------------
SCHUYLKILL					
Delano	145.3700	–	Ot(CA)e WX	W3EEK	SARA
SNYDER					
Selinsgrove	147.1800	+	O 100 (CA) rsWX	NR3U	SVARC
SOMERSET 123.0					
Central City	146.6250	–	O 123.0 (CA)lz	WR3AJL	Wj8G
Meyersdale	145.2700	–	O(CA)lz	KQ3M	AHRA
Seven Springs	146.8350	–	O 123.0lrxz	W3WGX	AHRA
Somerset	147.1950	+	Oaerz	K3SMT	SARC
SOUTH CENTRAL 123.0					
Bedford	145.4900	–	O	K3NQT	BCARS
Blue Knob	147.1500	+	Oaelx	KB3KWD	BKRA
Fort Loudon	147.2250	+	O	N3NRI	N3NRI

PENNSYLVANIA

Location	*Output*	*Input*	*Notes*	*Call*	*Sponsor*
McConnellsburg	145.2500	–	Ol	KB3UAG	------------
Upper Strasburg	147.1200	+	O	W3ACH	CVARC
SOUTHWEST 131.8					
Acme	146.6700	–	Oaerz	WA3TVG	LHVHFS
Bentleyville	147.2700	+	O	N3QWW	N3QWW
California	145.1100	–	Oae	KA3FLU	------------
Connellsville	145.1700	–		WB3JNP	WB3JNP
Connellsville	146.8950	–	Oer	W3NAV	CCRC
Derry	145.1500	–	O 131.8a TTer	W3CRC	CRARC
Greensburg	147.1800	+	O(CA) TTe	W3LWW	FARC
Indiana	146.9100	–	O	W3BMD	ICARC
Monongahela	147.2250	+	O(CA)	KA3BFI	MARC, Inc
Mt Pleasant	147.0150	+	O(CA)elx	KA3JSD	KA3JSD
Uniontown	147.0450	+	Oax	W3PIE	UARC
Uniontown	147.2550	+	O	W3PIE	UARC
Washington	145.4900	–	O	W3CYO	W3CYO
Washington	146.7900	–	Oa	K3PSP	K3PSP
Waynesburg	146.4300	147.4300	O 131.8e	N3GC	GCARA
SULLIVAN					
Laporte	145.3100	–	O 167.9el	N3XXH	EndlessMtn
Laporte	146.9250	–	O 82.5 (CA) ersRB LITZ WX	W3NOD	SCESARA
SUSQUEHANNA					
Elk Mountain	145.4300	–	O 77	N3KZ	UPenn ARC
Montrose	147.2400	+	O 107.2e	KB3YFX	Susq Cty
Montrose	147.3750	+	O 77	N3KZ	UPenn ARC
Silver Lake	145.2900	–	O 131.8 (CA)els	N3HPY	B&B
Susquehanna	145.2500	–	O 100aels	WB2BQW	------------
TIOGA					
Bloss Mt	145.2700	–	O 127.3er RB WX	NR3K	PAGCRG
Blossburg	146.9100	–	O 127.3ers WX	N3FE	------------
Dutch Hill	147.0600	+	O 127.3aer WX	NR3K	PAGCRG
Tioga	146.6250	–	O 131.8 (CA)l	KB3EAR	N.T.R.S
UNION					
Lewisburg	146.6250	–	O 110.9elr sRB WX	K3FLT	Milton ARC
WAYNE					
Waymart	146.6550	–	O 146.2ae BI WX	WB3KGD	------------
WEST CENTRAL 131.8/186.2					
Butler	147.3000	+	Or	N3LEZ	------------
Butler	147.3600	+	O(CA)e	W3UDX	BCARA
Cowansville	146.5050	147.5050	O 131.8elr x	N1RS	SARA

Location	*Output*	*Input*	*Notes*	*Call*	*Sponsor*
Fombell	146.4750	147.4750		N3ZJM	N3ZJM
Independance	145.4500	–	O	KA3IRT	KA3IRT
Kittanning	145.4100	–	O	K3TTK	FAWA
Leechburg	147.3300	+	Oer	WA3JVG	WA3JVG
Mercer	146.6850	–		W8IZC	------------
New Castle	146.6250	–	O	WA3VRD	B.DeSANZO
New Castle	147.1950	+	Oaelz	N3ETV	N3ETV
Parker	145.1900	–	Oalr	W3ZIC	FVM&KC
Punxsutawney	146.7150	–	O(CA)el	N5NWC	PAARC
Sharon	145.3500	–	Oaelrxz	W3LIF	MercerCARC
Warrendale	147.2400	+	Oe	K3SAL	BCFMA
WYOMING					
Mehoopany	147.2100	+	O 141.3e	WA3PYI	------------
YORK					
Hanover	147.3300	+	O 123ers WX	W3MUM	PMRC Inc
Red Lion	146.8650	–	O 123elWX	W3ZGD	Hilltopers
Reesers Summit	146.7900	–	O 114.8e RB	KAØJQO	------------
Shrewsbury	146.7000	–	O 123es	K3AE	SoPaCommGp
York	146.9250	–	O 74.4el	W3WAN	WAN-RS
York	146.9700	–	O 123 (CA) elrsLITZ WX	W3HZU	Keystone

PUERTO RICO

Location	*Output*	*Input*	*Notes*	*Call*	*Sponsor*
E					
Canovanas	147.1700	+	O	KP4FCC	------------
Ceiba	147.2700	–	O 88.5	KP4FGL	------------
Fajardo	145.1900	–	O	KP3AB	------------
Fajardo	145.2500	–	● 88.5	WP3CB	------------
Fajardo	145.3500	–	O	KP3AB	------------
Fajardo	145.3500	+		KP3AB	CRAN
Fajardo	146.6900	–	Oae	NP3H	CEC
Las Piedras	146.6500	–	Oe	KP4PF	EARCLUB
Las Piedras	146.8900	–	O	KP4JF	PREAHR-NV+
Maricao	147.0700	+	O	WP4CPV	------------
Rio Grande	146.9900	–	O	NP3H	------------
Rio Grande	147.3100	+	● 88.5	NP3EF	------------
Rio Grande	147.3500	+	O	NP3EF	ERGRP
San Lorenzo	147.0300	+	O	WP4LTR	SAMGRP
Yabucoa	145.3300	–	O	WP4BV	------------
Yabucoa	147.1900	+	O	KP4MCR	------------
N					
Aguas Buenas	145.3700	–	O	KP4IA	------------
Aguas Buenas	146.7300	–	O 118.8	KP3AB	------------
Aguas Buenas	146.8500	–	O 127.3a (CA)eBlxz	KP4CK	[PRARL]
Bayamon	145.1500	–	O	KP4ILG	------------
Bayamon	145.3100	–	●	WP4F	------------

PUERTO RICO

Location	*Output*	*Input*	*Notes*	*Call*	*Sponsor*
Bayamon	146.7300	–	○	KP3AB	------------
Ciales	145.3500	–	○	KP3AB	------------
Corozal	146.6100	–	○#	WP4ENA	------------
Corozal	146.6700	–	●a(CA)e	KP4DH	------------
Corozal	146.7100	–	○	KP4DEU	------------
Corozal	146.8300	–	○	KP4FRA	[FRA/1]
Corozal	147.3300	+	○e	KP3AJ	------------
Guaynabo	145.2300	–	○ 77	WP4OCD	------------
Gurabo	145.1700	–	● 136.5	WP4WC	------------
Gurabo	145.2100	–	○	WP3Z	------------
Gurabo	146.7900	–	○	WP4WC	------------
Gurabo	146.8700	–	○	WP4SE	------------
Gurabo	147.3700	+	○	KP4QW	------------
Lares	146.7900	–	●	KP4ARN	------------
Naranjito	147.0100	+	○	WP4FHR	ARG
Naranjito	147.2300	+	●	WP4NPC	POL
San Juan	147.3900	+		KP4FAK	------------
Toa Baja	145.2700	–		WP3ZQ	------------
Utuado	145.4300	–	○	KP4BOL	------------
S					
Adjuntas	145.4500	–	○	KP4ST	------------
Adjuntas	146.9300	–	○	KP4FRA	[FRA/2]
Barranquitas	145.4100	–	○Blx	KP4RF	------------
Barranquitas	145.4900	–	○	KP4LP	MOLINO
Cayey	145.1100	–	○	KP4CR	------------
Cayey	145.1300	–	○	WP4MXB	------------
Cayey	146.7700	–	○ 100.0	KP3AB	------------
Cayey	147.0900	+	○x	KP4ID	[{NV}PRARC]
Jayuya	146.7500	–	○	WP4NPG	LTRGp.
Jayuya	146.9900	–	○	NP3H	CEC.
Jayuya	147.1500	+	○	WP4IFU	ARG
Jayuya	147.2100	+	○	KP4CAR	------------
Orocovis	145.3900	–	○	KP4OG	------------
Ponce	147.3900	+		KP4JLQ	------------
Villalba	145.1900	–	○	KP3AB	------------
Villalba	145.2900	–	○	NP4A	------------
Villalba	147.0500	+	○ex	WP4AZT	------------
Yauco	145.3500	–	○	KP3AB	------------
Yauco	145.4700	–	○	WP4MJP	------------
Yauco	147.3500	+	○	NP4FL	------------
W					
Aguada	145.3300	–	○	NP4WX	------------
Aguada	146.7700	–	○	KP3AB	------------
Aguada	147.0300	+	I	WP4S	RAA
Maricao	147.1300	+	● 100.0e	KP4IP	------------
Maricao	147.2300	+	● 146.2	WP4CPV	CRG
Quebradillas	146.8700	–	●	WP3OF	------------
San Sebastian	147.2900	+	○ 123	WP4HVS	PepinoRG

Location	Output	Input	Notes	Call	Sponsor
RHODE ISLAND					
EAST BAY					
Bristol	145.3300	–	O 94.8	K1CW	K1CW
Newport	146.8800	–	O 100 (CA) e	WC1R	WC1R
Portsmouth	145.3000	–	OL(D*V)	W1AAD	NCRC
Portsmouth	145.4500	–	O 100es	W1SYE	NwptCntyRC
Portsmouth	147.0750	+	O 67 (CA)e L(E524799 RCI NETWORK)rsx	KA1RCI	NBARC
Portsmouth	147.1200	+	O 173.8e	K1WEW	SubSig ARC
NORTHERN					
Coventry	145.2100	–	O 192.8e	N1JL	N1JL
Coventry	145.3700	–	O 67e L(RMT BASE)	N1JBC	N1JBC
Cranston	146.7000	–	Oe	K1CR	K1CR
Cranston	147.1050	+	O 103.5es	W1PHR	PHARRG
Cumberland	146.6250	–	O 146.2ers	N1RWW	K1TSR
Cumberland	146.9400	–	O 67esWX x	AA1PL	RIAFMRS
East Providence	147.3300	+	O 173.8e L(E147330 I4907)s	W1AQ	W1AQ
Foster	146.9100	–	O 67 (CA)e L(E524799 RCI NETWORK)rsx	KA1RCI	NBARC
Johnston	145.1900	–	O 67 (CA)e L(E524799 RCI NETWORK)rsx	KA1RCI	NBARC
Johnston	146.8350	–	● 192.8e	WA1QCA	WA1QCA
Lincoln	145.1700	–	O 67e L(E524799 RCI NETWORK)x	KA1RCI	NBARC
Lincoln	146.4600	147.4600	O 67 (CA)e L(E524799 RCI NETWORK)prsx	KA1RCI	NBARC
North Scituate	146.7600	–	O 67esWX x	AA1PL	RIAFMRS
West Warwick	145.1300	–	O 77e	W1RI	JARCORI
West Warwick	145.3500	–	O 100 L(E524799 RCI NETWORK)	N1BS	N1BS
West Warwick	147.0450	+	O 141.3 L(D*V)	W1HDN	PVRA
SOUTH COUNTY					
Exeter	146.9850	–	O 67 (CA)e L(E524799 RCI NETWORK)rsx	KA1RCI	NBARC
Exeter	147.1650	+	O 67e	N1VDJ	N1VDJ
Saunderstown	146.7150	–	O 67	K1NQG	FARC
Westerly	147.2400	+	O 100e L(449.675/446.575/147.27/448.425)x	N1LMA	N1LMA
Westerly	147.3900	+	O 67 (CA)e L(E524799 RCI NETWORK)rsx	KA1RCI	NBARC
SOUTH CAROLINA					
Aiken	145.3500	–	O 156.7/156.7	N2ZZ	N2ZZ

Location	Output	Input	Notes	Call	Sponsor
Aiken	147.2850	+	O	N4ADM	N4ADM
Anderson	146.9700	–	Oers	N4AW	Anderson Radio Club
Anderson/SAS MT	146.7900	–	Ox	N4AW	Anderson Radio Club
Awendaw	146.7600	–	O 123.0/123.0 TT(*31)elrs	WR4SC	SCHEART.US
Aynor	146.7150	–	O 162.2/162.2 TT(*30)elrs	WR4SC	SCHEART.US
Bamberg	145.3300	–	O	WA4DFP	WA4DFP
Barnwell	147.0300	+	O	KK4BQ	Salkahatchie ARC
Batesburg Leesville	147.2550	+	O 123/123e	W4RRC	Ridge Amateur Radio
Beaufort	145.1300	–	Oes	W4BFT	Beaufort RAG
Beech Island	147.3450	+	O 91.5/91.5 TT(*42)elrs	WR4SC	SCHEART.US
Charleston	145.2500	–	O 123.0/123.0	W4HRS	HEART
Charleston	145.4100	–	O	WA4USN	Charleston ARC
Charleston	145.4500	–	O 123.0/123.0	W4HRS	HEART
Charleston	146.7300	–	O 123.0/123.0	W4HRS	HEART
Charleston	146.7900	–	O	WA4USN	Charleston ARC
Charleston	146.9400	–	O	WA4USN	Charleston ARC
Charleston	147.1050	+	O 123.0/123.0 TT(*33)elrs	WR4SC	SCHEART.US
Charleston	147.3900	+	O 123.0/123.0	W4HRS	HEART
Cheraw	147.1350	+	O	K4CCC	Chesterfield County A
Chester	146.6250	–	O	KF4SXO	CHESTER CTY ARS
Clemson	145.4500	–	O	WD4EOG	Clemson University A
Columbia	146.7150	–	O 91.5/91.5 TT(*32)elrs	WR4SC	SCHEART.US
Columbia	147.3300	+	O 156.7/156.7ers	W4CAE	Columbia ARC
Columbia	147.3600	+	O 100.0/100.0e	WZ4O	WZ40
Conway	147.2400	+	O	NE4SC	Beach & Inland Grou
Dillon	146.7450	–	O 82.5/82.5 TT(*82)elrsx	W4PDE	Greater Pee Dee RS/
Dorchester	147.1800	+	O 123.0/123.0	W4HNK	W4HNK
Edgefield	146.8500	–	O 91.5/91.5 es	KK4NUQ	Edgefield ARC/ SCH
Elloree	146.6100	–	O	KC4WIF	KC4WIF
Florence	146.6850	–	O 91.5/91.5 TT(*35)elrs	WR4SC	SCHEART.US
Florence	146.8500	–	O	W4ULH	FLORENCE ARC
Florence	146.9700	–	O 167.9/167.7a(CA)e	W4GEY	W4GEY

Location	*Output*	*Input*	*Notes*	*Call*	*Sponsor*
Florence	147.1950	+	O 123/123e lWX	W4APE	PALS - Palmetto
Florence	147.2850	+	O	NE4SC	Beach & Inland
Fort Mill	145.1100	–	O	K4YS	SUGAR CREEK
Fort Mill	147.1800	+	O	W4DXA	CAROLINA DX A
Ft Jackson	146.7750	–	O 156.7/156.7ers	W4CAE	Columbia ARC
Gaffney	145.2500	–	O	KG4JIA	KG4JIA
Georgetown	146.7000	–	O 123.0/123.0	W4HRS	HEART
Georgetown	147.3750	+	O	NE4SC	Beach & Inland
Greeleyville	145.2300	–	O 123/123e l	KG4AQH	PALS - Palmetto
Greenville	145.3700	–	O 123/123 TT(*37)elrs	WR4SC	SCHEART.US
Greenville	146.6100	–	O	W4NYK	BLUE RIDGE AR
Greenville	146.8200	–	O	W4NYK	BLUE RIDGE AR
Greenville	146.9400	–	O	W4IQQ	GREER ARC
Greenwood	145.1300	–	O	W4JAK	W4JAK
Greenwood	147.1650	+	O	W4GWD	GREENWOOD A
Hilton Head	145.3100	–	O 100.0/100.0	W4IAR	Islanders Amateu
Hilton Head	147.2400	+	O	W4IAR	Islanders Amateu
Kingstree	145.3100	–	O	NE4SC	Beach & Inland
Lancaster	146.7000	–	O 123.0/123.0	W4PAX	LANCASTER CO
Leesville	146.6550	–	O	N5CWH	N5CWH
Lexington	147.3900	+	O 156.7/156.7	KA4FEC	KA4FEC
Little Mt	147.2100	+	O 156.7/156.7e	K4AVU	MID-CAROLINA
Little River	146.8650	–	O	KF4VGX	KF4VGX
Lucknow	146.9250	–	O 123/123e lWX	W4APE	PALS - Palmetto
Marion	147.0000	–	O 91.5/91.5	KO4L	KO4L
Moncks Corner	145.4900	–	O 103.5/103.5	W4HRS	HEART
Moncks Corner	147.1500	+	O 91.5/91.5 ers	WD4NUN	Berkley County A
Moncks Corner	147.2100	+	O	KB4VFD	KB4VFD
Mountain Rest	147.0300	–	O	KJ4YLP	------------
Mullins	145.4700	–	O 123/123e lWX	W4APE	PALS - Palmetto
Murrels Inlet	146.8050	–	O 85.4/85.4 TT(*46)el	W4GS	Grand Strand AR
Myrtle Beach	145.1100	–	O 85.4/85.4	W4GS	GRAND STRAN
Myrtle Beach	145.2900	–	O 85.4/85.4	W4GS	Grand Strand AR
Myrtle Beach	146.6550	–	O	NE4SC	Beach & Inland
Myrtle Beach	147.0900	+	O	NE4SC	Beach & Inland

Location	Output	Input	Notes	Call	Sponsor
Myrtle Beach	147.1200	+	O 85.4/85.4	W4GS	GRAND STRAND AR
Myrtle Beach	147.2850	+	O	N4JTH	N4JTH
N Augusta	146.7300	–	O	K4NAB	N.AUGUSTA/BELVE
Nixonville	147.0300	+	O 123/123	NE4SC	Beach & Inland Grou
Orangeburg	146.8050	–	O	KJ4QLH	Edisto ARC
Orangeburg	146.8800	–	O 123/123 TT(*39)elrs	WR4SC	SCHEART.US
Orangeburg	147.0900	+	O	KJ4QLH	KJ4QLH
Pageland	146.8950	–	O 123/123e lWX	W4APE	PALS - Palmetto Ama
Pickens	146.7000	–	O	WT4F	FOOTHILLS ARC
Pickens	147.0000	–	O	WB4YXZ	PICKENS RADIO GR
Pine Ridge	146.9550	–	O	KD4BMX	KD4BMX
Rock Hill	147.0300	–	O 88.5/88.5 TT(*40)elrs	K4YTZ	York County ARC/ S
Russelleville	147.3000	+	O 162.2/162.2	KK4B	------------
Saluda	146.9100	–	O	W4DEW	W4DEW
Savannah River	145.4500	–	O	W4ZKM	US DEPT OF ENER
Sececa	145.2900	–	O 162.2/162.2e	K4WD	Keowee Toxaway AR
Simpsonville	146.7300	–	O	WA4UKX	WA4UKX
Six Mile	145.1700	–	O 162.2/162.2	KK4SM	Tri County Amateru R
Smoaks	145.2100	–	O	KG4LAP	KG4LAP
Spartanburg	147.0900	+	O 162.2/162.2 TT(*47)elrs	WR4SC	SCHEART.US
Spartanburg	147.3150	+	O	K4JLA	Spartanburg ARC
St George	146.8350	–	O 103.5/103.5	K4ILT	------------
St George	147.0450	+	O 103.5/103.5el	K4ILT	------------
St Matthews	146.6700	–	O 156.7/156.7x	AD4U	AD4U
Summerville	146.9850	–	O	W1GRE	W1GRE
Summerville	147.2700	+	O	W4ANK	W4ANK
Sumter	146.6400	–	O	W4GL	SUMTER ARA
Sumter	147.0150	+	O 156.7/156.7 TT(*44)el	W4GL	SUMTER ARA/ SCH
Union	145.1500	–	O	K4USC	Union County ARC
Union	146.6850	–	O	K4USC	Union County ARC
Wallace	145.4900	–	O 123.0/123.0elWX	W4APE	PALS - Palmetto Ama
Walterboro	145.3900	–	O	KG4BZN	KG4BZN
Walterboro	147.1350	+	O	KG4BZN	LOW CTY. REP SYS
Wedgefield	145.4300	–	O	WB4BZA	Wateree Amateur Ra
White Hall	146.9100	–	O 156.7/156.7ex	WA4SJS	COASTAL ARA
Whitehall	146.7150	–	O 123.0/123.0 TT(*34)elrs	WR4SC	SCHEART.US

Location	Output	Input	Notes	Call	Sponsor
SOUTH DAKOTA					
FREQUENCY USAGE					
Statewide	145.2300	–		SNP (PRI)	
Statewide	145.4700	–		SNP (SEC)	
CENTRAL					
Huron	147.0900	+	O	KØOH	KØOH
Mitchell	146.6400	–	O 146.2ae	WØZSJ	MARC
Murdo	147.3000	+	O 146.2 L(SDLINK)x	AAØCT	SDARC
Phillip	147.3750	+	O 146.2e L(SDLINK)	NØOMP	SDARC
Pierre	145.3500	–	O 146.2a	KDØS	PARC
Pierre	146.7300	–	O 146.2 L(SDLINK)	WØCQN	SDARC
Reliance	146.9400	–	O 146.2e L(SDLINK)x	NØNPO	MB ARC
Wessington Spr	147.3450	+	O 146.2 L(SDLINK)x	AAØF	SDARC
E					
Toronto	146.7750	–	O 146.2 L(SD LINK SYSTEM)	KCØOVC	SDARC
EAST CENTRAL					
Brookings	146.9400	–	O 110.9a	WØBXO	BR ARC
Flandreau	146.9850	–	146.2	KØTGA	KØTGA
NE					
Crandall	146.7900	–	O 146.2 L(SD LINK SYSTEM)	NØAHL	SDARC
NORTH CENTRAL					
Aberdeen	146.9100	–	O 146.2el	WBØJZZ	HubCtyARC
Aberdeen	147.0300	+	O 146.2 L(GL LINK)	WBØTPF	WB0TPF
Bowdle	147.1200	+	O 146.2 L(GL LINK)	NØAHL	GLARA
Mobridge	147.2100	+	Oe L(GL LINK)	WØYMB	MARC
Redfield	147.1500	+	O	WDØBIA	S ARC
NORTHEAST					
Britton	146.6100	–	Ol	NØSHL	TRAC
Garden City	146.6700	–	O 146.2 L(SDLINK)	WDØFKC	GCRA
Gary	145.3900	+	O	KØTY	KØTY
Pierpont	147.3300	+	O 146.2 L(GL LINK)	WØJOZ	GLARA
Sisseton	146.8800	–	Oe	WAØBZD	WAØBZD
Watertown	146.8500	–	O(CA)e	WØWTN	LARC
NW					
Reva	147.1500	+	Oe	KDØKMT	KDØKMT
SOUTHEAST					
Beresford	147.2400	+	O 141.3	KAØVHV	PD ARC

Location	Output	Input	Notes	Call	Sponsor
Humboldt	147.2850	+	O 146.2	NØLCL	SDARC
			L(SDLINK)x		
Sioux Falls	146.8950	–	O 146.2e	WØZWY	SEARC
Tabor	147.3150	+	Oe	KCØTOW	KCØTOW
Vermillion	147.3750	+	O 146.2l	WØMMQ	PD ARC
Yankton	146.8500	–	O 146.2	WØOJY	PD ARC
SOUTHWEST					
Custer	146.8500	–	Olx	KCØBXH	Northern Hills-ARC
Custer	147.0900	+	O 146.2e	WN6QJN	WN6QJN
Hot Springs	146.7000	–	Oe	KØHS	HS ARC
WEST					
New Underwood	146.9700	–	114.8#	KA1OTT	KA1OTT
WEST CENTRAL					
Lead	146.9700	–	146.2/146.2	KCØBXH	Northern Hills ARC
			L(449.200)		
Lead/Terry Peak	146.7600	–	O 146.2lx	KBØBXH	Northern Hills-ARC
Rapid City	146.9400	–	Ol	WØBLK	BlkHlsARC
Rapid City	147.2400	+	Oe	KBØBUT	KBØBUT
Terry Peak	147.0300	+	O 146.2	WBØJEK	SDARC
			L(SDLINK)		

TENNESSEE

Location	Output	Input	Notes	Call	Sponsor
Alamo	147.1350	+	O	K4WWV	STARNET
Allons	147.0450	+	O	KG4NPF	N2UP
Allons	147.0450	+	O	KG4NPF	W4WGM
Altamont	146.6550	–	O	KF4TNP	KF4TNP
			167.9/167.9		
Arnold AFB	147.1950	+	O	N4HAP	WARC
Athens	145.1500	–	O	KG4FZR	KG4FZR
Athens	147.0600	–	O	KG4FZR	KC4KUZ
Benton	145.4500	–	O	K4AJM	------------
Blountville	147.0000	+	O	W4CBX	W4FXO
Bluff City	146.7000	–	O	KE4CCB	KE4CCB
Bolivar	147.0450	+	O	KI4LFV	KI4LFV
Bristol	146.6700	–	O	W4UD	BRIS ARS/SUL CTY
Brownsville	146.6550	–	O	KI4BXI	KI4BXI
Camden	145.4900	–	O	KF4ZGK	TN VALLEY ARC
Carthage	145.4100	–	O	AG4QK	AG4QK
Carthage	146.6850	–	O	WT4X	WT4X
Chattanooga	145.1300	–	O	K4CMY	K4CMY
Chattanooga	145.3900	–	Oes	W4AM	W4AM
Chattanooga	146.6100	–	O	W4AM	W4AM
			107.2/107.2esWX		
Chattanooga	146.7900	–	Oa(CA)e	K4VCM	K4VCM
Clarksville	146.9250	–	O	K4ORE	CLARKSVILLE OPE
Cleveland	146.9250	–	Oa(CA)ers	W4GZX	CLEVELAND ARC
Cleveland	147.1050	+	O	KD4NEC	KD4NEC
Cleveland	147.1800	+	O	WD4DES	WD4DES

Location	*Output*	*Input*	*Notes*	*Call*	*Sponsor*
Cleveland	147.3750	+	O	KA4ELN	KA4ELN
Coker Creek	146.8200	–	O	K4EZK	K4EZK
Collegedale	147.0000	+	O	KA6UHV	KA6UHV
Collierville	145.3300	–	O	WT4E	WT4E
Columbia	147.1200	+	O	W4GGM	W4GGM
			127.3/127.3		
Cookeville	145.1100	–	O	KK4TD	UCARS/KK4TD
Cookeville	145.2700	–	O	N4ECW	N4ECW
Cookeville	145.4300	–	O	WA4UCE	ARS OF TTU
Cookeville	147.2100	+	O	W4HPL	COOKEVILLE R
Covington	145.4900	–	O	KE4ZBI	KE4ZBI
Cross Plains	147.3450	+	O	AF4TZ	AF4TZ
Crossville	146.8050	–	O	W4EYJ	CUMBERLAND
Crossville	146.8650	–	O	W8EYU	W8EYU
Crossville	147.3450	+	O	WM4RB	WE4MB
Cumberland	145.3300	–	O	N4FOX	N4FOX
Furnace			114.8/114.8		
Dandridge	146.8950	–	O	WD4EGD	WD4EGD
Dayton	147.3900	+	O	K4DPD	RHEA CO ARS I
Dellrose	147.1350	+	O	N4AZY	W4VM
Dover	145.2500	–	O	KR4WG	KR4WG
Dover	145.4100	–	O	N4VIH	WD4DBJ
Dresden	145.1500	–	O	KB4IBW	KB4IBW
Dresden	145.4700	–	O	KA4BNI	KA4BNI
Dyersburg	145.1900	–	O	K4DYR	K4DYR
Dyersburg	146.7450	–	O	W4MV	W4MV
Eaton	145.1900	–	O	K4DYR	K4DYR
Elizabethon	145.1100	–	O	WM4T	WM4T
Elizabethon	145.2900	–	O	KF4ZQA	CARTER COUN
Erwin	147.1650	+	Oa(CA)es	KC4DSY	KC4DSY
Fayetteville	147.0300	+	O	W4BV	KA4WOG
Franklin	145.1500	–	O	WC4EOC	K4COM
Gadsden	145.4300	–	O	WF4Q	WF4Q
Gallatin	145.3900	–	O	W4LKZ	W4LKZ
			114.8/114.8elrsWX		
Gallatin	147.2400	+	O	W4LKZ	SUMNER CO RA
Gallatin	147.2700	+	OlrsWX	WD4BKY	W4LKZ
Gallatin	147.3000	+	O	W4CAT	CATS
Gatlinburg	146.8500	–	O	WA4KJH	------------
Gatlingburg	147.1950	+	O	W4KEV	W4KEV
Georgetown	145.3100	–	OersWX	WM4RB	WM4RB
Greenbrier	147.0750	+	O	WQ4E	WQ4E
Greeneville	145.1500	–	O	K4MFD	K4MFD
			118.8/118.8		
Greeneville	145.3900	–	O	W4WC	W4WC
Greeneville	145.4100	–	O	KI4OTQ	KI4OTQ
Greeneville	147.0600	+	O	N4FV	N4FV
Greenfield	145.3500	–	O	KE4OVN	KE4OVN
Henderson	147.1050	+	O	W4FHU	FREED HARDE

TENNESSEE

Location	Output	Input	Notes	Call	Sponsor
Hohenwald	146.8950	–	O	K4TTC	TTC-ARCH
Holstn Mt	146.7600	–	O	K4JP	KD4DH
Huntingdon	146.8350	–	O	KF4ZGK	TN VALLEY ARC
Jackson	145.1700	–	O	WF4Q	WF4Q
Jackson	145.3100	–	O	KF4SC	WF4Q
Jackson	146.7750	–	O	WF4Q	WF4Q
Jackson	147.2100	+	O	WF4Q	WF4Q
Jackson	147.2700	+	O	WBØTMC	WBØTMC
Jamestown	147.0900	+	O	KI4KIL	FENTRESS C ARC
Jasper	145.1900	–	O	KD4XV	SEQUACHEE VAL.A
Johnson City	146.7900	–	O	W4ABR	JCARA (JOHNSON C
Johnson City	147.2700	+	O	K4LNS	K4LNS
			103.5/103.5e		
Jonesborough	147.1200	+	O	K4DWQ	K4DWQ
Joyner	147.1500	+	O	K4EAJ	K4EAJ
Knoxville	145.1700	–	O	WB4GBI	WB4GBI
Knoxville	145.2100	–	O	W4BBB	RACK
Knoxville	145.3700	–	O	W4KEV	W4KEV
Knoxville	145.4300	–	O	WB4YLC	KERBELA ARS
Knoxville	145.4700	–	O	WB4GBI	WB4GBI
Knoxville	146.6250	–	O	WB4GBI	WB4GBI
Knoxville	146.7300	–	O	WB4GBI	WB4GBI
Knoxville	146.9100	–	O	KC4ROG	------------
Knoxville	146.9400	–	O	WB4GBI	WB4GBI
Knoxville	147.0000	–	O	KD4CWB	KD4CWB
Knoxville	147.0750	+	O	WB4GBI	WB4GBI
Knoxville	147.3000	+	O	W4BBB	RACK
Lafayette	145.3100	–	O	KC4ECD	KC4ECD
Lafollette	145.1300	–	O	KA4OAK	KA4OAK
Lafollette	146.6700	–	O	K4BGW	W4TZG
Lafollette	147.3600	+	O	KA4OAK	KA4OAK
Laverne	145.2300	–	O	W4CAT	CATS
			114.8/114.8elsWX		
Lawrenceburg	146.6550	–	O	KG4LUY	W4RDM
Lebanon	147.1050	+	O	W4LYR	WILSON AMATEUR
Leipers Frk	145.1300	–	O	WC4EOC	K4COM
Lexington	147.0750	+	O	WF4Q	WF4Q
Livingston	146.7150	–	O	KG4NPF	KG4NPF
Lynchburg	145.4500	–	O	KF4TNP	KF4TNP
			127.3/127.3e		
Manchester	146.7000	–	O	K4EGC	AF4JJ
			114.8/114.8 E-SUNs		
Martin	146.6250	–	O	W4UTM	UT-MARTIN ARC
Maryville	145.2700	–	O	KF4VDX	KF4VDX
Maryville	146.6550	–	O	W4OLB	SMOKY MTN ARC
Maryville	146.6850	–	O	K4DSZ	------------
Maynardville	145.2300	–	O	KB4KIE	KB4KIE
Maynardville	145.2300	–	O	W4KEV	W4KEV
Mcewen	147.2250	+	O	NO4Q	NO4Q
			114.8/114.8		

Location	*Output*	*Input*	*Notes*	*Call*	*Sponsor*
McMinnville	146.9700	–	O	WD4MWQ	WD4MWQ
Medina	146.9700	–	O	WT4WA	KJ4CLS
Memphis	145.2100	–	O	W4EM	W4EM
Memphis	145.2500	–	O	N4ER	N4ER
Memphis	145.4100	–	O	K5FE	K5FE
Memphis	146.6400	–	O	K4DTM	K4DTM
Memphis	146.7300	–	O	N4GMT	N4GMT
Memphis	146.8200	–	O	W4BS	DELTA ARC
Memphis	146.8500	–	O	WB4KOG	WA4KOG
Memphis	146.8800	–	O	WB4KOG	WA4KOG
Memphis	147.0300	+	O	W4EM	W4EM
Memphis	147.0600	+	O	WA4MQQ	WA4MQQ
Memphis	147.0900	+	Oer	W4GMM	W4GMM
Memphis	147.1200	+	O	N4WAH	N4WAH
Memphis	147.3000	+	O	N4GMT	N4GMT
Memphis	147.3600	+	O	W4BS	DELTA ARC
Middlesboro	146.7750	–	O	KA4OAK	KA4OAK
Monteagle Mtn	145.4100	–	O	NQ4Y	NQ4Y
Mooresburg	147.1350	+	O	KE4KQI	KJ4TKV
			114.8/114.8lsWX		
Morgan County	147.3300	+	O	WD4ORB	MCARC
Morristown	145.4500	–	O	KQ4E	KQ4E
Morristown	147.0300	+	O	W2IQ	LAKEWAY ARC
Morristown	147.2250	+	O	WB4OAH	WB4OAH
Morristown	147.3900	+	O	KQ4E	KQ4E
Moscow	145.1100	–	O	WA4MJM	KF4OID
Mountain City	145.4700	–	O	W4MCT	JOHNSON CTY
			103.5/103.5		
Mountain City	146.6100	–	O	K4DHT	KJ4HB
Murfreesboro	145.1700	–	O	KU4B	KU4B
			114.8/114.8esWX		
Nashville	145.1100	–	O	W4RFR	KF4ZIS
Nashville	145.2100	–	O	WC4EOC	K4COM
Nashville	145.4700	–	O	N4ARK	N4ARK
Nashville	146.6100	–	O	WA4PCD	WA4PCD
Nashville	146.6400	–	O	AF4TZ	RPT SOC OF MI
Nashville	146.6700	–	O	AF4TZ	RPT SOC OF MI
Nashville	146.7600	–	O	WA4PCD	N.R.A.
Nashville	146.7900	–	O	W4SQE	MUSIC CITY AR
Nashville	146.8500	–	O	W4AY	SOTS
Nashville	146.8800	–	O	WA4PCD	N.R.A.
Nashville	146.9550	–	OelsWX	W4CAT	W4CAT
Nashville	146.9850	–	O	KC4PRD	KC4PRD
Nashville	147.0150	+	O	AF4TZ	CRAN
			114.8/114.8		
Nashville	147.1500	+	O	WA4PCD	N.R.A.
Nashville	147.3150	+	O	N4ARK	N4ARK
Newport	147.0900	+	O	KG4LHC	KG4LDK
			203.5/203.5		

TENNESSEE

Location	*Output*	*Input*	*Notes*	*Call*	*Sponsor*
Nolensville	145.3500	–	O	WD4JYD	------------
Oak Ridge	146.8800	–	O	W4SKH	OAK RIDGE ARC
Oak Ridge	146.9700	–	O	W4SKH	OAK RIDGE ARC
Oakfield	147.3900	+	O	WA4BJY	WA4BJY
Oakland	146.9400	–	O	WB4KOG	WA4KOG
Oneida	145.3500	–	O 77/77l	KB4PNG	KB4PNG
Paris	145.2700	–	O	N4ZKR	HENRY CO EMA
Paris	147.1650	+	O	KC4YLL	N4TZV
Paris	147.3300	+	O	N4ZKR	N4ZKR
Paris	147.3600	+	O	KJ4ISZ	HENRY CO REPT A
Petros	147.2550	+	O	KJ4SI	KJ4SI
Phildelphia	145.2500	–	O	W4YJ	W4YF
Pikeville	147.2850	+	O	KF4JPU	KF4JPU
Piperton	145.1300	–	O	WA4MJM	WA4MJM
Pulaski	146.8050	–	O 114.8/114.8l	KF4TNP	KF4TNP
Pulaski	147.3300	+	O	WD4RBJ	WD4RBJ
Puryear	147.1650	+	O	WA4CEX	RIDGE REP ASSN I
Ridgetop	145.2900	–	O	K4DXC	MTDARC INC.
Ripley	145.2300	–	O	KE4NTL	------------
Rockwood	147.0150	+	O	KE4RX	RCARC
Rockwood	147.1200	+	O	K4EAJ	MORGAN CO ARC
Rogersville	147.3150	+	O	KD4HZN	KD4HZN
Saltillo	146.7150	–	O	KB4JUB	SALTILLO ARES
Sardis	147.1950	+	O	AF4OQ	AF4OQ
Savannah	146.7000	–	O 131.8/131.8e	KA4ESF	KA4ESF
Selmer	146.8050	–	O	KA4BNI	MCNAIRY CO EMER
Shelbyville	147.0600	+	O	KI4NJJ	KI4NJJ
Shiloh	145.2900	–	O	WF4Q	WF4Q
Short Mtn	145.4900	–	O 114.8/114.8	KU4B	KU4B
Sneedville	147.2400	+	O 114.8/114.8lsWX	KE4KQI	KI4YWW
Sparta	147.1650	+	O	KR4BT	K44BT & TRI-CTY
Telford	146.9250	–	O	K4DHT	------------
Tellico Plains	147.3150	+	O	KE4VQM	KE4VQM
Trenton	146.8650	–	O	KN4KP	GIBSON CTY EMS
Union City	146.7000	–	O	WA4YGM	WA4YGM
Union City	147.0150	+	O	WF4Q	WF4Q
Walland	145.3300	–	O	AC4JF	AC4JF
Wartburg	146.7450	–	O	AA4YQ	AA4YQ
Watertown	146.7300	–	O	K4EHL	K4EHL
Watertown	146.8350	–	O	W4LYR	W4LYR
White Bluff	147.3750	+	OeWX	KG4HDZ	KG4HDZ
Williston	147.1800	+	O	WB4KOG	WB4LHD
Winchester	146.8200	–	O	W4UOT	MTARS
Woodbury	146.9100	–	O	W4YXA	SHORT MTN.REP C

Location	Output	Input	Notes	Call	Sponsor
TEXAS					
Abernathy	146.7600	–	O 179.9l	WB5BRY	CRRC
Abilene	145.3500	–	O 110.9ae	KC5PPI	AAHTC
Abilene	145.4900	–	O 88.5	KI5ZS	------------
Abilene	146.7600	–	O 146.2 (CA)e	KC5OLO	KCARC
Abilene	146.8000	–	O 88.5 (CA) e	W5TNJ	AARC
Abilene	146.9600	–	O 146.2e	KC5OLO	KCARC
Allen	147.1800	+	O 107.2 (CA) WX	WD5ERD	PARK
Alpine	145.2300	–	O 146.2	AD5BB	BIGBENDARC
Alpine	146.7200	–	Oel	AD5BB	BIGBENDARC
Alvarado	147.2200	+	O 110.9e	K5AEC	TX ADVENT EM
Alvin	145.1100	–	O 123	KA5QDG	------------
Alvin	145.2100	–	O 167.9	K5PLD	PEARLAND ARC
Alvin	145.2500	–	O 141.3	KA9JLM	AARC
Alvin	146.7400	–	O 123	KA5QDG	HAMS
Amarillo	146.7400	–	O 88.5	N5ZLU	SWL SYSTEM
Amarillo	146.9200	–	Oel	N5LTZ	CRI
Amarillo	146.9400	–	O 88.5	W5WX	PARC
Amarillo	147.3400	+	O 88.5	W5WX	PARC
Anahuac	145.3300	–	O 123e	KK5XQ	CCOEM
Angleton	147.1800	+	O 141.3els	N9QXT	BCARES
Angleton	147.3400	+	O 103.5l WX	WB5UGT	SALTGRASS
Anhalt	145.1300	–	O 131.8l	W5DK	------------
Archer City	146.8400	–	O 192.8ar	W5GPO	WF VHF ARC
Arlington	146.8600	–	O 110.9 (CA)	WD5DBB	MCR GROUP
Arlington	147.1400	+	O 110.9 (CA)	K5SLD	AARC
Athens	147.2200	+	O 136.5e WX	K5EPH	AARC
Atlanta	145.2500	–	O 123	K5JRK	------------
Atlanta	146.9800	–	Oa	K5HCM	RACC
Aubrey	145.2600	–	O 100	K5RNB	------------
Austin	145.1700	–	O 88.5 (CA)	KB5HTB	------------
Austin	145.2100	–	O 97.4e	KA9LAY	------------
Austin	146.6100	–	O 103.5e	WB5PCV	------------
Austin	146.6800	–	O 123	KE5ZW	------------
Austin	146.7800	–	O 107.2e	W5KA	AARC
Austin	146.8400	–	O 103.5	W5WXW	------------
Austin	146.8600	–	●	NØGSZ	------------
Austin	146.8800	–	O 100a	W5KA	AARC
Austin	146.9000	–	Oael	W3MRC	3M ARC
Austin	146.9400	–	O 107.2	W5KA	AARC
Austin	147.1800	+	O(CA)	W5HS	------------
Austin	147.3600	+	O 131.8e	WA5VTV	------------

Location	Output	Input	Notes	Call	Sponsor
Azle	147.1600	+	O 110.9	WB5IDM	------------
Baird	147.2600	+	O 88.5l	KK5MV	------------
Baird	147.3000	+	O 146.2a	KF5YZ	------------
Ballinger	147.3200	+	O	W5YP	RCARC
Bangs	147.0000	+	O 94.8e	KB5ZVV	------------
Bastrop	147.3400	+	O 100	NA6M	------------
Bay City	146.7200	–	O 146.2e	W5WTM	MCARC
Bayside	147.2000	+	O 107.2	AD5TD	------------
Baytown	145.3100	–	O 167.9el	N5JNN	------------
Baytown	146.7800	–	O 123e	K5BAY	BAARC
Beaumont	146.7000	–	O 107.2e	W5RIN	BARC
Beaumont	146.7600	–	O 107.2l	W5GNX	BEARC
Beaumont	147.3000	+	O 103.5	W5XOM	EMERC
Beaumont	147.3400	+	O 118.8l	W5RIN	BARC
Bedias	147.1200	+	O 123	NQ5D	------------
Beeville	147.3000	+	O 103.5	KC5DYC	------------
Belton	146.7200	–	O 88.5l	NU5D	------------
Belton	147.3000	+	O 123	W5AMK	Dorn
Big Bend	146.8200	–	O 146.2elr	AD5BB	BIGBENDARC
Big Spring	146.8200	–	O 88.5 (CA)	W5AW	BSARC
Big Spring	147.0400	+	O 88.5el	KE5PL	WTXC
Boerne	145.1900	–	O 88.5	KB5TX	KARS
Boerne	146.6400	–	O 88.5	KB5TX	KARS
Bonham	145.4700	–	Oa	K5FRC	FCRC
Borger	147.0600	+	O	WA5CSF	NWTARC
Bowie	145.3900	–	O 192.8 (CA)	W5QT	MONTAGE ARS
Boyd	146.9800	–	Oa	K5JEJ	------------
Brackettville	146.8800	–	O 127.3	KD5HAM	BARS
Brady	146.6200	–	O 114.8 (CA)l	AA5JM	------------
Brady	146.9000	–	O 162.2ael	KC5EZZ	------------
Brenham	145.3900	–	O 103.5	W5AUM	BRENHAM ARC
Brenham	147.2600	+	O 103.5	W5AUM	Brenham ARC
Bridge City	145.4700	–	O 103.5a	W5SSV	JCARC
Brookston	146.7000	–	O 114.8	KD5HIS	------------
Brownfield	146.8000	–	O 162.2a	KA5BQG	TCARC
Brownfield	147.3400	+	O 162.2l	WA5OEO	------------
Brownsville	147.0400	+	O 114.8els WX	W5RGV	STARS
Brownwood	146.8200	–	●	WB5FXD	------------
Brownwood	146.9400	–	O 94.8ae	K5BWD	BWDARC
Bruceville	147.2400	+	O 97.4	W5NCD	------------
Bryan	146.6200	–	O 88.5	KZ5M	------------
Buffalo	145.4500	–	O 146.2 WX	W5VSD	LCARC
Buffalo	147.2800	+	O 146.2ls WX	W5UOK	------------
Buna	145.3900	–	O 118.8	W5JAS	LAREAARC

Location	*Output*	*Input*	*Notes*	*Call*	*Sponsor*
Burkburnett	146.7000	–	O 192.8e	W5DAD	------------
Burkburnett	146.8800	–	O 192.8ae WX	KD5INN	------------
Burnet	145.2900	–	O 114.8	KB5YKJ	------------
Burnet	146.6600	–	O 88.5	K5HLA	HGLD LKE
Cameron	147.0200	+	O 123eWX	KE5URD	MCARES
Carlton	145.2700	–	O 110.9er WX	W5GKY	------------
Carrollton	145.2100	–	O 110.9ers	N5MJQ	METROARC
Carrollton	146.6100	–	O 110.9	K5ZYZ	NORTH DALLAS
Carrollton	147.3200	+	●	K5MOT	MOTOROLA AR
Carthage	146.7200	–	O	KA5HSA	------------
Carthage	147.1800	+	O 123aes	WA5PC	PANOLA COUN
Castroville	146.8000	–	O 162.2	K5YDE	------------
Castroville	147.2000	+	O 162.2	KD5DX	MCARC
Cat Spring	145.4100	–	O 100el	W5SFA	SFARC
Cat Spring	146.8800	–	O 203.5x	WR5AAA	HRRC
Cedar Hill	147.0600	+	O 110.9 (CA)e	W5WB	SWDCARC
Cedar Hill	147.2600	+	O(CA)	W5AHN	------------
Cedar Hill	147.3200	+	●	K5MOT	MOTOROLA AR
Cedar Park	145.3700	–	O 103.5	KC5WLF	HAMBUDSARC
Cedar Park	146.9800	–	O 103.5	W2MN	------------
Cedar Park	147.1200	+	O 103.5	W2MN	------------
Celina	146.9000	–	O	K5XG	------------
Centerville	145.2100	–	●	K3WIV	------------
Centerville	147.3000	+	O 114.8 E-SUN	KDØRW	------------
Childress	146.9600	–	O	N5OX	------------
Chita	145.3500	–	O 131.8	W5IOU	ULLWA
Chocolate Bayou	145.3900	–	O 103.5	KA5QDG	HAMS
Clarksville	147.2000	+	O 186.2	KA5BCR	RRCA
Clear Lake	146.8600	–	O 100ael	K5HOU	CLARC
Cleveland	146.9000	–	Oae	N5AK	SHARK
Clifton	147.1800	+	O 123ex	W5BCR	BCRA
Clute	145.3500	–	O 103.5l	WB5UGT	------------
Coldspring	147.1600	+	O 103.5e	WB5HZM	LLRR
Coleman	146.9800	–	O 94.8ae	N5RMO	CARC
College Station	146.6800	–	O 88.5 (CA) e	W5BCS	BARC
College Station	146.8200	–	O 88.5	W5AC	TAMUARC
Columbus	147.1400	+	O 103.5	W5SFA	SFARC
Comanche	146.6800	–	O 94.8s	KC5QHO	CARC
Conroe	147.0200	+	O 136.5	N5PJY	CARE
Conroe	147.1400	+	O 136.5e	N5KWN	------------
Copperas Cove	147.2600	+	O 88.5 E-SUNx	K5CRA	CRA
Corinth	145.1700	–	O 110.9 WX	W5FKN	LTARC

Location	*Output*	*Input*	*Notes*	*Call*	*Sponsor*
Corpus Christi	146.8200	–	○ 107.2	N5CRP	STARC
Corpus Christi	146.8400	–	○ 88.5	N5IUT	------------
Corpus Christi	146.8800	–	○ 107.2ae	N5CRP	STARC
Corpus Christi	147.0600	+	○ 107.2e WX	WA5MPA	------------
Corpus Christi	147.1000	+	○ 107.2ae WX	W5DCH	W5DCH
Corsicana	145.2900	–	○ 146.2els WX	KD5OXM	NARC
Corsicana	147.3400	+	○rWX	K5NEM	Navarro County EM
Crockett	145.3100	–	○ 103.5	W5DLC	HCARC
Crockett	146.7000	–	○ 123ae	WA5EC	HCARC
Crosbyton	147.1600	+	○ 179.9l	WB5BRY	CRC
Dallas	145.1300	–	○rs	W5FC	Dallas ARC
Dallas	145.1900	–	○ 110.9 (CA)	KA5CTN	------------
Dallas	145.4300	–	○ 110.9	K5DM	TEXINSARC
Dallas	146.6400	–	○ 118.8	K5AHT	RECA
Dallas	146.7000	–	○ 110.9e	W5EBQ	------------
Dallas	146.8200	–	○	N5IUF	TRUSTEE
Dallas	146.8800	–	○ 110.9 (CA)r	W5FC	DARC
Dallas	146.9600	–	○ 110.9 (CA)r	K5JD	------------
Del Rio	146.8200	–	○ 127.3	KD5HAM	BARS
Denton	146.9200	–	○ 110.9 (CA)	W5NGU	DCARC
Devers	146.9800	–	○ 103.5	N5FJX	HAMS
Devine	146.8800	–	○ 141.3	WB5LJZ	------------
Donna	146.7400	–	○ 114.8a	KC5YFP	------------
Doss	147.1600	+	○ 162.2ael	W5RP	HOTROCS
Dripping Springs	146.7400	–	○ 162.2	KA5AMP	------------
Eagle Pass	146.6400	–	○ 100	N5UMJ	------------
Eastland	145.3500	–	○a	KA5BNO	------------
Eddy	145.3100	–	○ 123eWX x	N5ZXJ	------------
Eddy	147.1400	+	○ 123eWX	W5BEC	BELL COUNTY EOC
Eden	147.3900	+	○ 114.8 (CA)l	KD5FUN	------------
Edinburg	146.7600	–	○ 114.8ls WX	W5RGV	STARS
El Paso	145.1100	–	●	W5ELP	WTX Dig RC
El Paso	145.3300	–	○ 67l	K5BEN	JPARA
El Paso	145.4100	–	○ 88.5	WX5ELP	EP SKYWARN
El Paso	146.7000	–	○ 114.8al	K5ELP	WTRA
El Paso	146.8800	–	○s	K5ELP	WTRA
El Paso	147.0600	+	●	KJ5EO	El Paso Races
El Paso	147.1000	+	●	KJ5EO	El Paso Races
El Paso	147.1400	+	○	NM5ML	MEGA LINK

Location	*Output*	*Input*	*Notes*	*Call*	*Sponsor*
El Paso	147.2000	+	O 67a	K5ELP	WTRA
El Paso	147.2400	+	O 162.2	K5WPH	SCARC
El Paso	147.2800	+	O 67l	KD6CUB	------------
El Paso	147.3200	+	O 162.2	K5KKO	EPDIG
El Paso	147.3600	+	●	KE5OIB	------------
Eldorado	146.7200	–	O 100elWX	KC5EZZ	------------
			x		
Eldorado	147.2600	+	O	W5AHN	------------
Elmendorf	145.2100	–	O 162.2e	W5CRS	------------
Elmendorf	146.8600	–	O 123 (CA)	W5ROS	ROOST
Emory	146.9200	–	O 88.5es	W5ENT	RAINS ARA
Fabens	147.9800	–	O 162.2	W5PDC	------------
Fairfield	145.1100	–	O 146.2	WB5YJL	NAVARRO ARC
Florence	147.3800	+	O 100	K5AB	------------
Flower Mound	145.2300	–	O 110.9es	N5ERS	ERS
Fort Davis	146.6200	–	O 146.2elr	AD5BB	BIGBEND ARC
Fort Davis	147.3600	+	O	W5CDM	------------
Fort Stockton	145.3700	–	O 88.5	KB5GLA	------------
Fort Stockton	146.6800	–	O 88.5l	N5SOR	WTC
Fort Stockton	146.9200	–	O 146.2	AD5BB	BIGBEND ARC
			E-SUN		
Fort Worth	145.1100	–	O 110.9	K5FTW	FWTXVHFFM
Fort Worth	145.2500	–	O 192.8	KD5HOG	------------
Fort Worth	145.3300	–	O 110.9	W5NRV	Next Generation
Fort Worth	146.6800	–	O 110.9	W5URH	------------
Fort Worth	146.7600	–	O 110.9	K5FTW	FWTX VHFFM
Fort Worth	146.8000	–	O 110.9	W5URH	------------
Fort Worth	146.8400	–	O 110.9	W5SH	FWKCCL
Fort Worth	146.9400	–	O 110.9r	K5FTW	FWTX VHFFM
Fort Worth	147.2800	+	O 110.9	W5SJZ	LMRARC
			(CA)		
Franklin	146.9600	–	O 85.4es	W5KVN	------------
Fredericksburg	146.7600	–	O 162.2	W5FJD	------------
Freeport	147.3800	+	O 110.9el	KA5VZM	BCARS
Freer	146.7200	–	O 77	KB5ZXD	CACTUS PATCH
Fritch	147.3000	+	Ol	WA5CSF	NWTXRC
Gainesville	145.2900	–	O 100a	K5AGG	------------
Gainesville	147.3400	+	O 100ae	WB5FHI	CCARRA
Galveston	146.6800	–	O 103.5e	WB5BMB	UTMB/ECG
Galveston	147.0200	+	O	N5ZUA	------------
Galveston	147.0400	+	●	WB5BMB	------------
Garland	146.6600	–	O 110.9	K5QHD	GARC
Garland	147.2400	+	O 110.9	K5QBM	RSARC
			(CA)e		
Gatesville	146.9600	–	O(CA)e	N5DDR	------------
Geneva	146.7400	–	O 118.8e	K5TBR	TBARC
			WX		
George West	146.9800	–	O 107.2	K5YFL	Live Oak County
Georgetown	146.6400	–	O 162.2e	N5TT	WCARC

TEXAS

Location	*Output*	*Input*	*Notes*	*Call*	*Sponsor*
Georgetown	147.0800	+	O 100el	NA6M	------------
Giddings	147.2200	+	O 114.8	NE5DX	------------
Goldthwaite	147.1000	+	O 100	K5AB	------------
Goliad	146.7400	–	O 103.5	WB5MCT	VICTORIA ARC
Graham	147.0000	+	O	N5SMX	Young County ARC
Graham	147.3400	+	Ol	WB5BJW	LCARC
Granbury	147.0800	+	O 110.9 (CA)	WD5GIC	NTARA
Granbury	147.2400	+	O 162.2er	KE5WEA	------------
Grapevine	145.4000	–	O 136.5	N5EOC	NE TARRANT ARC
Greenville	147.1600	+	Oa	WD5GSL	MFRC
Halletsville	147.0800	+	O 173.8	KD5RCH	------------
Hamilton	146.9200	–	O 100	K5AB	------------
Hamilton	147.2000	+	O 88.5	AB5BX	HARC
Harlingen	145.3900	–	O 114.8elr	K5VCG	------------
Harlingen	146.7000	–	O 114.8els WX	W5RGV	STARS
Harlingen	146.8000	–	O 114.8l	W5RGV	STARS
Harlingen	146.9600	–	Or	K5DG	EARTH ARC
Harlingen	147.1000	+	O 114.8ls WX	W5RGV	STARS
Harlingen	147.1400	+	O 114.8els WX	W5RGV	STARS
Harlingen	147.2000	+	O 114.8ael r	AG5B	VBMC-HRL
Harlingen	147.3900	+	O 114.8ls WX	W5RGV	STARS
Haskell	146.7400	–	O	WA5YSZ	------------
Hawkins	147.1000	+	O	W5CKO	ETARS
Helotes	145.1100	–	O 141.3	KB5ZPZ	------------
Hemphill	146.9000	–	O 141.3rs	KA5BQM	------------
Henderson	146.7800	–	O 131.8 WX	KB5NXW	------------
Henly	146.9200	–	O	W5IZN	------------
Henrietta	146.6800	–	O 192.8 (CA)	K5REL	------------
Henrietta	146.8000	–	O 192.8	KA5WLR	------------
Henrietta	147.3200	+	O 192.8	K5REJ	CCOARC
Hewitt	146.9800	–	Or	W5ZDN	HOTARC
Hillsboro	146.7800	–	OaeWX	WB5YFX	------------
Hollywood Park	146.6200	–	O 162.2	K5AWK	------------
Hondo	145.2700	–	O 162.2 (CA)	WA5PPI	------------
Hondo	145.2900	–	O 162.2e	KD5DX	MCARC
Houston	145.1700	–	O 103.5	KA5QDG	------------
Houston	145.1700	–	O 123	KA5QDG	------------
Houston	145.1900	–	O 123	W5BSA	------------
Houston	145.3700	–	O 123	N5TRS	Harris County Transta
Houston	145.3900	–	O 123	KA5QDG	------------

Location	*Output*	*Input*	*Notes*	*Call*	*Sponsor*
Houston	145.4500	–	O(CA)e	KD5HKQ	TARMA
Houston	145.4700	–	O 123	W5RPT	MERA
Houston	146.6200	–	O 123 (CA)	KB5NNP	LHOURA
Houston	146.6400	–	O	W5RRR	JSCARC
Houston	146.6600	–	O 141.3	KA5AKG	NARS
Houston	146.7000	–	O 103.5	WA5TWT	HTTY
Houston	146.7400	–	O 103.5	KA5QDG	HAMS
Houston	146.7600	–	O 103.5 (CA)el	K5WH	COMPAQ AMAT
Houston	146.8200	–	O 103.5	K5GZR	GCRC
Houston	146.8400	–	O 103.5	KF5GDR	CHEM
Houston	146.8800	–	O 103.5x	WR5AAA	HRRC
Houston	146.9200	–	O 103.5l WX	WB5UGT	SALTGRASS
Houston	146.9400	–	O 167.9e	WA5CYI	PRRL
Houston	146.9600	–	O 103.5	W5JUC	SFA
Houston	147.0000	+	O 103.5	KR5K	CYPRESS REPE
Houston	147.0800	+	O 103.5ae	W5ATP	ECHO
Houston	147.1000	+	O 114.8	K1BDX	------------
Houston	147.2400	+	O 167.9ae	KD5HKQ	TARMA
Houston	147.3000	+	O 151.4	KDØRW	------------
Houston	147.3200	+	O 100ae	WA5QXE	ECHO
Houston	147.3600	+	O 100	K5DX	TDXS
Humble	146.8000	–	O 103.5	KD5KHV	------------
Humble	147.2800	+	O 100el	W5SI	TEAC
Huntsville	145.2700	–	O 103.5	W5RJV	------------
Huntsville	146.6400	–	O 131.8e	AE5EP	------------
Huntsville	146.8600	–	O 131.8	W5HVL	WCARG
Hurst	147.1000	+	●	W5HRC	HURST ARC
Irving	145.4500	–	●	N2DFW	DFW REPEATE
Irving	146.7200	–	O 110.9 (CA)	WA5CKF	IRVARC
Ivanhoe	145.1300	–	O 100	K5FRC	Fannin County R
Jacksonville	145.4300	–	O 136.5	KR5Q	------------
Jacksonville	146.8000	–	O 136.5	K5JVL	CCARC
Jasper	147.0000	–	O 118.8l	W5JAS	LAREAARC
Jewett	145.2300	–	O 146.2	KC5SWI	JEWETT PWR
Johnson City	145.2700	–	O 146.213	KR4K	6.25 kHz RAN 13
Katy	147.2000	+	O 141.3e	KT5TX	KARS
Kaufman	146.8400	–	O 136.5s	KE5IGO	KAUFMAN ARE
Kaufman	146.9800	–	●	N5RSE	------------
Keller	147.2000	+	●	KA5HND	ERG
Kenedy	146.9200	–	O 179.9	W5DK	------------
Kerrville	145.1500	–	O 162.2ael	W5RP	HOTROCS
Kerrville	146.9800	–	O 162.2a	N5HR	HCARC
Kilgore	145.4500	–	O 136.5 (CA)	W5CKO	EAST TX ARC
Killeen	147.0400	+	O 173.8	KK5AN	------------
Kingsville	146.6200	–	O 107.2	KD5QWJ	WILD HORSE D

TEXAS

Location	*Output*	*Input*	*Notes*	*Call*	*Sponsor*
Kingsville	146.6800	–	O 107.2	K5WHD	WHDH
Kingwood	145.4300	–	Oe	W5SI	TEAC
Kountze	145.2300	–	O 103.5e	N5BTC	BTARC
La Coste	146.6800	–	O 162.2	K5YDE	------------
La Grange	145.2700	–	O 114.8	WB5HVH	------------
La Grange	146.8000	–	O 100	KG5YH	FCRC
Lakeway	145.4100	–	O 103.5l	WB5PCV	------------
Lakeway	147.3000	+	O 131.8	K5GJ	T441/LKY EOC
Lamarque	146.9000	–	O 103.5e	KE5AIL	GCARC
Lamesa	145.1500	–	O 100	N5BNX	------------
Lamesa	146.8600	–	O 100	N5BNX	NONE
Lampasas	147.2200	+	O 88.5eWX	KB5SXV	------------
Laredo	145.1500	–	●	W5EVH	------------
Laredo	146.8400	–	O	N5LNU	RRGRC
Laredo	146.8800	–	O 100elr WX	W5EVH	------------
Laredo	146.9400	–	O 100elr WX	W5EVH	------------
Laredo	147.1200	+	O 100elWX	W5EVH	------------
League City	145.4100	–	O 131.8e WX	WR5GC	GCECG
Leonard	145.4100	–	O	KW5DX	DX CONTEST CLUB
Levelland	146.6800	–	O 103.5e	W5CP	EDXS
Levelland	146.7800	–	O 179.9l	WB5BRY	CRRC
Levelland	146.8800	–	O 103.5	WB5EMR	HCARC
Levelland	147.1200	+	O 162.2al	N5SOU	------------
Lindale	147.1200	+	Ors	W5ETX	ETX Emergency Com
Littlefield	146.6400	–	O 179.9l	WB5BRY	CRRC
Livingston	147.0400	+	O 136.5	WB5HZM	ULLWA
Longfellow	147.3400	+	O 88.5e	N5BPJ	------------
Longview	145.3500	–	O 136.5e	KD5UVB	------------
Longview	147.3400	+	Oa	KI5UA	LETARC
Los Fresnos	145.2900	–	●	K5RGV	K5RGV
Lubbock	146.9400	–	O 179.9	WB5BRY	CRRC
Lubbock	147.0000	–	O 179.9l	WB5BRY	CRRC
Lubbock	147.2000	+	O 162.2	WA5OEO	------------
Lubbock	147.3000	+	O 88.5e	N5ZTL	------------
Lufkin	145.3700	–	O 100	KD5TD	------------
Lufkin	146.9400	–	O 141.3ers	W5IRP	DETARC
Lufkin	147.2600	+	O 141.3	K5RKJ	------------
Lufkin	147.3600	+	O 107.2el	KB5LS	LSARC
Luling	145.2300	–	O 123elx	W5CTX	------------
Madisonville	146.7800	–	O 103.5r WX	WA5GED	MCARC
Magnolia	146.9800	–	O 156.7	W5JSC	------------
Marathon	147.0200	+	Oelr	AD5BB	BIGBENDARC
Marathon	147.3200	+	O 88.5l	N5SOR	WTXC
Marble Falls	145.3900	–	O 103.5	K5WGR	------------
Marshall	146.8600	–	O	KB5MAR	MARC

Location	*Output*	*Input*	*Notes*	*Call*	*Sponsor*
Mathis	145.1500	–	O 233.6	KC5QPP	------------
Mayflower	147.1200	+	O 203.5l	W5JAS	LAARC
Mcallen	145.2300	–	O 114.8	N5SIM	EARTH
Mckinney	145.3500	–	O 100x	N5GI	NTRA
Mckinney	146.7400	–	O 110.9e	W5MRC	MARC
Mesquite	145.2500	–	O 110.9	AK5DX	------------
Mesquite	145.3100	–	O 110.9er WX	WJ5J	HAM
Mesquite	147.0400	+	O 136.5	KD6FWD	------------
Mexia	145.3900	–	O 146.2es WX	W5NFL	NARC
Miami	145.1100	–	O 88.5lWX	KA5KQH	CRII
Midland	145.1300	–	O 88.5l	W5LNX	SWLS
Midland	146.7600	–	O 88.5	W5QGG	MARC
Midland	146.9000	–	O 88.5l	N5XXO	WTC
Midland	147.2200	+	O 29325e	K5MSO	MIDLAND SO
Midland	147.2800	+	O 88.5l	KB5MBK	------------
Midland	147.3000	+	O	W5QGG	MARC
Midland	147.3800	+	O	W5CAF	MARC
Minden	145.2500	–	O 123	WB5WIA	------------
Mineral Wells	146.6400	–	O	W5ABF	MWARC
Mission	146.6600	–	O 114.8	KC5ZVC	------------
Moody	145.1500	–	O 123 WX	W5ZDN	HOTARC
Mount Pleasant	146.9400	–	O 151.4	WA5YVL	MT PLEASANT
Mount Vernon	147.3200	+	O 151.4	W5XK	------------
Nacogdoches	146.8400	–	O 141.3e	W5NAC	NARC
Nacogdoches	147.3200	+	O 141.3e	W5NAC	NARC
Nassau Bay	145.1500	–	Oae	NB5F	BAARC
New Braunfels	147.0000	–	O 103.5 (CA)	WB5LVI	GVARC
New Waverly	147.1800	+	O 136.5	W5SAM	WCARES
New Waverly	147.3400	+	●	NA5SA	------------
Nocona	147.3600	+	O 110.9ers WX	N5VAV	------------
North Richland Hills	145.3700	–	O 110.9	K5NRH	N. Richland Hills
Notrees	147.0200	+	O 88.5l	N5XXO	SWLS
Oak Hill	147.3200	+	O 114.8 (CA)	W5MOT	CMARC
Odessa	145.3900	–	O 88.5	WT5ARC	WTXARC
Odessa	145.4100	–	O 88.5	W5CDM	------------
Olmito	147.1800	+	O 114.8	KC5WBG	------------
Orange	147.0600	+	O 103.5e	AA5P	DUPONTARC
Orange	147.1800	+	O 103.5e WX	W5ND	OrangeARC
Palestine	145.4900	–	O 136.5	KR5Q	------------
Palestine	146.7400	–	O	KR5Q	------------
Palestine	147.0800	+	O 103.5e WX	W5DLC	------------

Location	*Output*	*Input*	*Notes*	*Call*	*Sponsor*
Palestine	147.1400	+	O 103.5e	W5DLC	------------
Pampa	146.9000	–	Ox	W5TSV	------------
Paradise	146.6200	–	O 131.8	KJ5HO	------------
Paris	146.7600	–	O 203.5er WX	WB5RDD	RRVARC
Paris	147.0400	+	O 100	KC5OOS	------------
Paris	147.3400	+	O 110.9	KA5RLK	------------
Pasadena	145.2500	–	O 167.9	KD5HKQ	TARMA
Pasadena	145.2700	–	O 123 WX	W5PAS	PECG
Pasadena	145.2900	–	O 103.5er WX	W5PAS	PECG
Pasadena	147.0600	+	O 123	KA5QDG	------------
Pasadena	147.1200	+	O 167.9 (CA)	WB5WOV	ARMS
Payne Springs	146.9000	–	O 136.5e	K5CCL	Cedar Creek ARC
Pearland	147.2200	+	O 167.9e	K5PLD	PARC
Perryton	146.6400	–	O 88.5s	K5IS	------------
Perryton	146.8200	–	O 88.5	K5IS	CAPROCK INTER
Pipe Creek	147.2800	+	O 156.7 (CA)	WD5FWP	BARK
Pittsburg	147.2600	+	O 151.4	WW5DC	------------
Plainview	146.7200	–	O 88.5 (CA)	W5WV	PARC
Plano	145.2500	–	O 123	WD5ERD	------------
Plantersville	145.2500	–	O 203.5	KB5JJE	Cochran
Pleasanton	145.4300	–	O 100 (CA) er	KD5ZR	ACARC
Pleasanton	147.3400	+	O 123	W5ROS	ROOST
Point	146.8000	–	O 141.3	WR5L	------------
Port Aransas	145.2900	–	O 110.9elx	KG5BZ	------------
Port Aransas	147.0400	+	O 107.2alx	KG5BZ	------------
Port Arthur	146.8600	–	O 103.5	WD5GJP	PARG
Port Arthur	147.2000	+	O 118.8e	KC5YSM	------------
Port Lavaca	147.0200	+	O 103.5a	W5KTC	PLARC
Post	147.0600	+	O 179.9l	WB5BRY	CRC
Quanah	146.6400	–	O	KY7D	------------
Quitman	147.3600	+	O 136.5	W5CKO	ETARS
Ranger	147.0600	+	O 131.8	N5RMA	------------
Ranger	147.3800	+	O 88.5	K6DBR	------------
Refugio	147.1800	+	O 136.5e	AD5TD	------------
Rice	145.4700	–	O 110.9	W5TSM	------------
Richardson	147.1200	+	O(CA)r	K5RWK	RWC
Richmond	145.4900	–	O 123erWX	KD5HAL	EMROG
Robert Lee	147.3400	+	O 88.5eWX x	KC5EZZ	------------
Rockdale	147.2800	+	O 162.2	AF5C	TEMPLE ARC
Rockport	147.2600	+	O 103.5	KM5WW	ROCARC
Rosanky	145.4300	–	●	WB6ARE	------------
Rose Hill	146.7200	–	O 123	K5IHK	TMBLRPTCRP
Rosharon	147.1600	+	O 123eWX	N5QJE	------------

Location	*Output*	*Input*	*Notes*	*Call*	*Sponsor*
Rosston	145.4900	–	○ 85.4e	WD5U	------------
Round Rock	146.7000	–	○ 110.9e	N5MNW	------------
Rusk	147.0400	+	○ 110.9a	KA5AEP	------------
Sacse	145.2500	–	○ 141.3	N5LOC	------------
San Angelo	145.2700	–	○ 88.5x	W5QX	SAARC
San Angelo	146.8800	–	○ 88.5	K5CMW	------------
San Angelo	146.9400	–	○ 103.5	KC5EZZ	SAARC
			WX		
San Angelo	147.0600	+	○ 103.5	N5DE	------------
San Angelo	147.3000	+	○ 88.5	N5SVK	------------
San Antonio	145.1700	–	○ 141.3el	WD5IEH	------------
San Antonio	145.3300	–	○ 146.2	KC5RXY	------------
San Antonio	145.3700	–	○ 114.8als	KE5HBB	------------
San Antonio	145.3900	–	○ 100	W5SC	SARC
San Antonio	145.4500	–	○ 141.3	N5UAP	------------
San Antonio	145.4700	–	○ 110.9	KD5GSS	------------
			(CA)		
San Antonio	146.6600	–	○ 110.9e	W5STA	STARS
San Antonio	146.7000	–	○ 173.8	KA5IID	------------
San Antonio	146.8200	–	○ 179.9	WA5FSR	SARO
			(CA)		
San Antonio	146.8800	–	○	WB5LJZ	------------
San Antonio	146.9000	–	○(CA)	KD5GAT	SAHARA
San Antonio	146.9400	–	○ 179.9e	WB5FWI	SARO
			WX		
San Antonio	147.0200	+	○	W5RRA	SWRCARC
San Antonio	147.0400	+	○ 123e	KK5LA	------------
San Antonio	147.0600	+	○ 141.3	K5DSF	------------
San Antonio	147.0800	+	○ 162.2	N5CSC	EXPLO700
San Antonio	147.1800	+	○ 103.5	K5EOC	SAEM
San Antonio	147.2400	+	●	K5GE	------------
San Antonio	147.2600	+	○ 103.5	K5SOJ	------------
San Antonio	147.2800	+	○ 162.2	WD5FWP	------------
			(CA)		
San Antonio	147.3000	+	○ 107.2e	W5XW	BEARS
San Antonio	147.3600	+	○ 179.9	K5SUZ	SARO
			(CA)		
San Antonio	147.3800	+	○ 162.2	AA5RO	AARO
			(CA)		
Santa Anna	147.1200	+	○ 94.8	KE5NYB	------------
Santa Anna	147.1400	+	○ 94.8	N5RMO	COLEMAN ARC
Sattler	147.1400	+	○ 179.9	K5PWX	SARO
Schertz	147.2200	+	○ 172	W5TXR	------------
Seabrook	147.2600	+	○ 162.2	WB5KCA	LYCRC
Seguin	145.4900	–	○ 123alx	W5CTX	------------
Seguin	146.7600	–	○ 141.3	WA5GC	C.A.R.C.
Seminole	145.4500	–	○ 88.5	N5SOR	------------
Seminole	146.7800	–	○ 88.5l	N5SOR	WTC
Seymour	147.1000	+	○ 192.8	N5ENS	------------

Location	Output	Input	Notes	Call	Sponsor
Shepp	145.2300	–	O 88.5	NZ5V	BCARN
Sherman	147.0000	+	O 100	W5RVT	GCVHFSOC
Sherman	147.2800	+	O 107.2	W5COP	------------
Shiner	147.1200	+	O 141.3	W5CTX	------------
Sinton	147.0800	+	O 107.2	W5CRP	W5CRP
Smithville	145.3500	–	O 114.8	KE5FKS	BCARC
Smithville	147.2000	+	O 103.5el	N5ZUA	------------
Snyder	146.9200	–	O 67aer	K5SNY	SARA
South Padre Island	147.1200	+	O 114.8ls WX	W5RGV	STARS
South Padre Island	147.2400	+	O 114.8	KE5KLY	------------
Spearman	147.0400	+	O 88.5el WX	N5DFQ	DUST BOWL LINK S
Spring	145.3400	–	O	KF5KHM	------------
Stafford	145.2300	–	O 88.5	W5TI	HTEXIARC
Stephenville	147.3600	+	O 110.9e WX	K5IIY	CTARC
Sterling City	146.6400	–	O 88.5l	N5FTL	WTXC
Stinnett	147.3800	+	O 88.5el WX	N5DFQ	DUST BOWL LINK S
Streetman	146.7600	–	O 136.5	KE5DFY	Navarro ARC
Sulphur Springs	146.6800	–	O 151.4er	K5SST	HCARC
Sulphur Springs	147.0600	+	O	K5SST	DStar of SS
Sweetwater	145.2500	–	O 162.2l WX	KC5NOX	NCARA
Sweetwater	146.6800	–	O 186.2	KJ5CQ	------------
Taft	147.0000	–	O 107.2x	W5CRP	W5CRP
Taylor	145.4500	–	O 162.2s	WC5EOC	WC-ARES
Temple	146.8200	–	O 123	W5LM	TARC
Temple	147.3400	+	O	W5ARO	------------
Texas City	147.1400	+	O 167.9ae	WR5TC	GCRA
The Colony	147.3800	+	O 110.9	K5LRK	LAARK
Timpson	145.1500	–	O 107.2e	KK5XM	------------
Tomball	147.3800	+	●	WB5ZMV	------------
Trinity	145.3300	–	O 103.5	N5ESP	------------
Tulia	147.3600	+	O 88.5	WU5Y	------------
Tyler	145.2100	–	O 88.5e	W5ETX	ETMC TYLER TEXA
Tyler	145.3700	–	O 88.5el WX	N1EW	------------
Tyler	146.9600	–	Oa	W5CKO	ETARS
Tyler	147.0000	–	O 110.9er WX	K5TYR	TYARC
Tyler	147.2400	+	O 88.5 (CA) e	W5ETX	E TX Emergency Co
Tyler	147.3800	+	O	K5PDQ	------------
Utopia	147.1000	+	O 127.3	W5FN	------------
Uvalde	146.9000	–	O 100a	N5RUI	------------
Uvalde	147.2600	+	O 100	W5LBD	------------

Location	*Output*	*Input*	*Notes*	*Call*	*Sponsor*
Van	146.6200	–	OaesWX	WD5JLE	------------
Venus	145.3900	–	O 136.5er WX	WA5FWC	------------
Vernon	147.0200	+	O	NC5Z	------------
Victoria	145.1300	–	O 103.5e	W5DSC	VARC
Victoria	145.1900	–	O 103.5ex	W5DSC	VCARC
Victoria	147.1600	+	O 141.3el	WD5IEH	------------
Waco	146.6600	–	O 123a	AA5RT	------------
Waco	147.1600	+	O	WA5BU	BAYLOR ARC
Waco	147.3200	+	O 123e	W5TSG	Texas State Gua
Waco	147.3600	+	O 123	AA5RT	------------
Weatherford	145.2500	–	O 103.5	WØBOD	------------
Weatherford	146.9000	–	O 110.9	KG5CW	------------
Weatherford	147.0400	+	O 110.9	W5URH	------------
Weesatche	147.3200	+	O 162.2el	WD5IEH	------------
Weslaco	146.7200	–	O 114.8	KC5WBG	------------
Wharton	145.3300	–	O 167.9	W5DUQ	Golden Crescent
Whitewright	145.2500	–	O 114.8	KE5HWQ	------------
Whitney	146.6200	–	O 123eWX	NZ5T	LWARS
Wichita Falls	146.6200	–	O 156.7	KD5INN	------------
Wichita Falls	146.6600	–	O 192.8 (CA)	K5WFT	------------
Wichita Falls	146.9400	–	O 192.8ar	W5US	WF VHF CLUB
Wichita Falls	147.0600	+	O 156.7ar	W5GPO	Wichita Falls RC
Wichita Falls	147.1200	+	O 192.8lx	N5LEZ	------------
Wichita Falls	147.1400	+	O 192.8 (CA)	N5WF	Morton
Wills Point	145.2700	–	O 136.5	WB5HGI	TVARC
Wills Point	147.2800	+	O 136.5er WX	KK5AU	ESARA
Wimberley	147.0600	+	O 103.5	W5FUA	------------
Wimberley	147.1000	+	O 141.3alx	W5CTX	WARS
Winnsboro	147.1400	+	O 118.8e	KG5E	------------
Yoakum	147.0400	+	O	WA5VIO	LCRC
Yorktown	146.6400	–	O 103.5	KD5BXV	CCARC
Zapata	147.0200	+	O 114.8	KJ5HW	------------
UTAH					
FREQUENCY USAGE					
Salt Lake	147.6000	147.6000		SIMPLEX	
Statewide	145.4100	–	Ot	SHARED	
Statewide	145.7100	145.7100		SIMPLEX	
CENTRAL					
East of Holden	147.1000	+	O 100a (CA)x	N7GGN	------------
Ephriam	146.6600	–	O 100a L(146.86)xz	W7DHH	------------
Manti	145.2900	–	O 131.8a L(146.66)xz	WB7REL	------------

Location	Output	Input	Notes	Call	Sponsor
Manti	146.7200	–	O 131.8a L(146.66)z	WB7REL	------------
Marysvale	147.2000	+	Ox	K1ENT	------------
Monroe	146.6400	–	O 100a L(146.72)xz	W7JVN	------------
Richfield	146.8600	–	O 100a L(146.66)z	KD7YE	WB7REL
Salina	146.8600	–	O 100a L(146.66)z	KD7YE	WB7REL
NORTH					
Bear Lake	147.0200	+	O 100e L(147.18)x	K7OGM	K7JL
Bear Lake	147.1200	+	O 100	K7OGM	K7JL
Clarkston	147.2000	+	O 103.5e L(146.72)	AC7O	BARC
Fielding-Riverside	147.2200	+	O 123.0x	AB7TS	GSARC
Logan	145.1500	–	O	AC7O	BARC
Logan	145.4100	–	O 103.5	AC7O	BARC
Logan	146.6400	–	OA(*/#)	WA7MXZ	BARC
Logan	146.7200	–	O 103.5a (CA) L(147.26/145.31/449.625)xz	AC7O	BARC/VHFS
Logan	147.2400	+	O 79.7 L(449.325)	N7RRZ	------------
Logan	147.3200	+	O 88.5	KA7FAP	------------
Malad	146.4300	146.4300	Oe L(146.85/147.180)x	WA7FDR	------------
Montpelier	147.1200	+	O 123	AG7BL	K7OGM
Montpelier	147.3800	+	O 100.0 E-SUN RBx	AC7TJ	------------
Red Spur	145.3100	–	O 103.5a (CA) L(146.72/147.26/449.625)x	WA7KMF	BARC
Tremonton	145.4300	–	O 123ae L(145.29/448.300)	KK7DO	GSARC
NORTH EAST					
Altamont	146.7000	–	Oa	WB7CBS	------------
Altamont	146.7400	–	O 100a	WB7CBS	------------
Coalville	147.2400	+	O 136.5a L(147.140/147.160)x	K7HEN	------------
Duchesne	147.2600	+	O	N7PQD	BARC
Myton	145.4900	–	O 136.5a L(147.32)	W7BAR	W7BYU
Roosevelt	146.9200	–	O 136.5e	W7BYU	------------
Vernal	147.0400	+	O 136.5e L(147.32)x	W7BAR	BARC
Vernal	147.1000	+	O 136.5ae x	W7BAR	BARC
Vernal	147.3400	+	O 136.5x	KK7EX	------------
PRICE					
Carbon County	145.4100	–	Oe	KA7LEG	------------

Location	*Output*	*Input*	*Notes*	*Call*	*Sponsor*
Castledale	147.0600	+	O 88.5a	K7SDC	SDARC
			(CA) L(147.32) RBx		
Castledale	147.1400	+	O 88.5a	K7SDC	SDARC
			(CA) L(147.32) RBx		
Price	145.4300	–	O 88.5a	KA7LEG	------------
Price	145.4700	–	O 88.5a	AA7AM	------------
Price	147.2200	+	O 88.5	W7CEU	------------
Scofield	145.3100	–	O 88.5a	K7SDC	SDARC
			(CA) L(147.32) RBx		
Scofield	147.0800	+	O 88.5a	K7SDC	SDARC
			(CA) L(147.32) RBx		
Sunnyside	147.3200	+	O 88.5a	K7SDC	SDARC
			(CA)lRBx		
SOUTH					
Bryce Canyon	145.3500	–	O 123.0	W6DGL	------------
			E-SUNx		
Kanab	146.7200	–	O 100a	W7NRC	------------
			L(146.94)		
Kanab	146.8800	–	O	W7NRC	------------
Kanab	147.3600	+	O	WI7M	------------
			L(E216167)		
Kanab / Jacob Lake	147.3000	+	O 100.0e	N7YSE	------------
			L(146.800)x		
Page AZ	146.9600	–	O 100	W7WAC	------------
			L(146.8)x		
SOUTH EAST					
Boulder	146.9200	–	O	KE7ZDV	------------
Hanksville	147.0800	+	O 136.5a	K7SDC	SDARC
			(CA) L(147.32) RBx		
Mexican Hat	145.4100	–	O 100.0	KD7HLL	------------
			E-SUN		
Moab	146.7600	–	O 88.5a	K7QEQ	------------
			(CA) L(147.32) RBx		
Moab	146.9000	–	O 88.5a	K7QEQ	------------
			(CA) L(146.76) RB		
Monticello	146.6100	–	O 88.5a	K7SDC	SDARC
			(CA) L(147.32) RBx		
SOUTH WEST					
Beaver	146.8400	–	O	K1ENT	------------
Cedar City	145.1500	–	O	WA7GTU	------------
Cedar City	145.4700	–	O	WV7H	------------
Cedar City	146.7600	–	Oa(CA)x	K7JH	------------
Cedar City	146.8000	–	OL(146.94)	WV7H	------------
			x		
Cedar City	146.9800	–	O	N7KM	------------
Cedar City	147.0600	+	Oa(CA)	N7DZP	------------
Delta	147.3800	+	O	KB7WQD	------------
Hinckley	147.2600	+	O	N7WPF	------------
Milford	146.9400	–	O 100	WR7AAA	WA7GTU
			L(147.18)x		

Location	Output	Input	Notes	Call	Sponsor
Panguitch	147.1600	+	O 100x	N7NKK	ERC
St George	145.3700	–	Ox	N7ARR	------------
St George	145.4900	–	O 100 L(145.450/146.640) WX(*127 *128)x	W7DRC	DARC
St George	146.6400	–	O 100a	W7DRC	------------
St George	146.7000	–	O 100a (CA)	KA7STK	------------
St George	146.7400	–	O 100x	NR7K	------------
St George	146.8200	–	O 100 L(146.94)x	NR7K	DARC
St George	146.9100	–	O 100ex	NR7K	------------
St George	147.2600	+	OE-SUNx	K7SG	------------
Toquerville	145.1500	–	Oes	KF7YIX	Washington County A
Toquerville	145.4500	–	O 100e L(146.49/146.640)x	KD7HUS	------------
WASATCH FRONT					
Antelope Is	147.0400	+	O 123a (CA)exz	K7DAV	DCARC/VHFS
Bacchus	145.3500	–	O 100 L(HF)	NM7P	UVHFS
Bountiful	147.3000	+	O 123	W7CWK	------------
Brigham City	145.2900	–	O 123e L(145.43/448.300)	N7WFM	UBET
Brighton	145.2700	–	O 100e L(147.180)x	K7JL	------------
Brighton	146.6200	–	O L(146.62(FARNSWORTH))x	W7SP	UARC
BYU Campus	145.3300	–	O 100a (CA)	N7BYU	KI7TD
Coalville	147.3600	+	O 100x	WA7GIE	------------
Coalville	147.3800	+	Ox	WB7TSQ	------------
Huntsville	145.2100	–	O	W7DBA	------------
Huntsville	146.6800	–	O 123a L(145.49)x	N7JSQ	ARI
Layton	146.9600	–	O 100x	K7MLA	ERC
Levan Peak	145.2700	–	O 103.5e L(147.120)x	K7JL	------------
Magna	145.3700	–	Ox	K7MLA	ERC
Mapleton	146.8000	–	O 100.0 E-SUN L(448.250)	N6EZO	------------
Midway	147.2000	+	O 88.5 L(449.525)	N7ZOI	------------
Mirror Lake	147.3800	+	O 100x	WA7GIE	------------
Morgan	147.0600	+	O	KB7ZCL	------------
Ogden	145.1125	–	Osz	KE7EGG	------------
Ogden	145.2500	–	Oa	KE7FO	------------
Ogden	145.4100	–	O 123	WB7TSQ	SNP
Ogden	145.4900	–	O 123a L(146.68)x	K7HEN	ARI

Location	*Output*	*Input*	*Notes*	*Call*	*Sponsor*
Ogden	146.8200	–	O 123x	W7SU	OARC/VHFS
Ogden	146.9000	–	O 123a	W7SU	OARC/VHFS
Ogden	146.9200	–	O 123	N7TOP	------------
			L(449.775)		
Ogden	147.3800	+	Ox	WB7TSQ	------------
Orem	145.4700	–	O 100a	N7BSA	ExPst1973
Orem	146.7800	–	Oax	N7PKI	------------
Park City	145.2300	–	O 100e	NZ6Z	------------
			L(447.5)		
Payson	147.0200	+	Oax	K7MLA	ERC
Payson	147.3400	+	O 100ex	K7UCS	UTCOARES
Powder Mtn	145.4700	–	O 123x	KC7SUM	------------
Promentory	145.4100	–	O 123	N7TOP	SNP
			E-SUN L(146.92)z		
Promentory	147.2600	+	O 103.5a	AC7O	BARC
			(CA) L(146.72/147.26/449.625)x		
Provo	145.2300	–	O 131.8es	K7UCS	UTCOARES
Provo	145.6300	145.6300	O	NV7V	------------
			L(SHUTTLE AUDIO)		
Provo	146.7600	–	Oa(CA)ex	W7SP	UARC
Provo	147.2800	+	O 141.3e	K7UCS	UTCOARES
			L(449.675 8.325)x		
Provo Edgemont	147.2200	+	Oa	WA7YZR	KR7D
			L(145.25)		
Salt Lake	145.1250	–	Ol	KF6RAL	------------
Salt Lake	145.1900	–	O 123	W7IHC	------------
Salt Lake	145.2100	–	Oae	AA7JR	UVHFS
Salt Lake	145.4500	–	O 100ex	WA7UAH	ERC
Salt Lake	146.6200	–	Oe	W7SP	UARC
			L(146.62 (SCOTTS))x		
Salt Lake	146.7000	–	O 100e	KDØJ	SLCOARES
Salt Lake	146.7400	–	O 114.8	KD7NX	MARA
Salt Lake	146.8400	–	Os	N7PCE	SLCOARES
Salt Lake	146.8800	–	O 88.5s	KDØJ	UVHFS
Salt Lake	146.9400	–	O 88.5ex	K7JL	UVHFS
Salt Lake	147.0600	+	O	K7CEM	UVHFS
Salt Lake	147.0800	+	O 77	WX7Y	SDARC
			L(147.32)x		
Salt Lake	147.1200	+	O 100e	K7JL	------------
			L(147.18)x		
Salt Lake	147.1400	+	O 127.3e	K7MLA	------------
			L(147.160/147.240)x		
Salt Lake	147.1600	+	O 127.3a	K7MLA	------------
			L(147.140/147.240)		
Sandy	145.4100	–	O 162.2	KE7GHK	SNP
Snowbird	147.1800	+	O 100e	K7JL	------------
			L(147.12)x		
Statewide	145.4100	–	O 100e	W7DES	SNP
Sundance	145.2500	–	OL(147.22)	KR7D	------------

Location	Output	Input	Notes	Call	Sponsor
WEST					
Delle	145.3500	–	O	K7HK	------------
Tooele	146.9800	–	Oa L(145.39)	W7EO	TCARES
Tooele	147.3000	+	O 100	W7EO	------------
Vernon	145.3900	–	O 100.0a L(146.98)	W7EO	TCARES
Wendover	147.2000	+	O 100 L(146.98)x	W7EO	TCARES
VERMONT					
BURLINGTON					
Bolton	145.1500	–	O 100.0elx	WB1GQR	RANV
Burlington	146.6100	–	O 100.0e	W1KOO	BrlngtnARC
Essex Jct	146.7900	–	O 103.5	W1HIO	W1HIO
Essex Jct	146.8500	–	O 100.0	W1CTE	Essex HS
Mt Mansfield	146.9400	–	O 100.0	W1CTE	BrlngtnARC
CENTRAL					
Fayston	145.4100	–	O 100.0	K1VIT	VT Intercnt
Killington	146.8800	–	O 110.9ex	W1ABI	NFMRA
EAST CENTRAL					
Barre	147.3900	+	O 100.0	N1IOE	N1IOE
Cabot	146.8200	–	O 100.0	W1BD	CentVtARC
Corinth	147.2100	+	O 100.0l	KB1FDA	KB1FDA
Norwich	145.1300	–	O 100.0	N1CIV	N1CIV
Tunbridge	146.9700	–	O	K1MOQ	K1MOQ
Williamstown	146.6250	–	O 100.0e	W1BD	CentVtARC
NORTHEAST					
Glover	147.3750	+	O	KB1BRN	BARF
Jay Peak	146.7450	–	O 100.0	K1JAY	StAlbansRC
NORTHWEST					
St Albans	145.2300	–	O 100.0	N1STA	StAlbansRC
SOUTHEAST					
Marlboro	147.0150	+	O 100.0e	N1HWI	N1HWI
Mt Ascutney	146.7600	–	O 110.9e	W1UWS	CtVlyFMA
Newfane	147.0900	+	O 110.9l	WA1KFX	NFMRA
SOUTHWEST					
Mt Equinox	145.3900	–	O 100.0ex	WA1ZMS	WA1ZMS
Shaftsbury	146.8350	–	O	K1SV	SOVARC
WEST CENTRAL					
Middlebury	147.3600	+	O 100.0	WA1NRA	Add Co ARA
Rutland	147.0450	–	O 100.0e	W1GMW	GreenMtWS
VIRGIN ISLANDS					
USVI					
St Croix	147.1100	+	O 100	WP2E	St. Croix ARC (NP2VI
St Croix	147.2500	+	Oae	WP2E	St Croix ARC (NP2VI)
St John	146.6300	–	O 100	KP2SJ	St. John ARC
St John	146.9100	–	Oe	NP2OW	St John ARC (KP2SJ)

Location	Output	Input	Notes	Call	Sponsor
St Thomas	146.8100	–	Oa(CA)el	KP2O	------------
St Thomas	146.9700	–	O	KP2T	------------

VIRGINIA

Location	Output	Input	Notes	Call	Sponsor
Abingdon	147.3450	+	O	NM4L	MEARS (MOUNT
Accomac	147.2550	+	O	K4BW	ESHARC
Alexandria	144.9700	430.7500	O	WA9GVK	METROVISN
Alexandria	145.1500	–	O	WB4MJF	------------
Alexandria	146.6550	–	O	WD4PDP	------------
Alexandria	147.3150	+	O	W4HFH	------------
Altavista	146.6550	–	O	WA4ISI	WA4ISI
Amelia	145.1900	–	O	WB3R	------------
Amelia Courthous	145.2500	–	O	KB4YKV	KB4YKV
Amherst	145.4900	–	O	K4CQ	K4CQ
Arlington	145.4700	–	O	N4EFJ	------------
Axton	146.6250	–	O	K4TFC	K4TFC
Bald Knob	146.9100	–	O	KD4BNQ	KD4BNQ
Bassett	145.1700	–	O	KF4RMT	KF4RMT
Beaverdam	145.2500	–	O	N4CZJ	N4CZJ
Bedford	145.2300	–	O	N4CH	N4CH
Bedford	147.1050	+	Oes	WB4JBJ	WB4JBJ
Bedfrd/apl Orch	146.6850	–	O	WA1ZMS	MTN TOP ASSO
Big a Mtn	146.8050	+	O	KD4TC	TCARC
Big Stone Gap	146.7000	–	O	KR4KB	KR4KB
Blacksburg	146.7150	–	O	W9KIC	K4KDJ
Blackstone	146.8200	–	O	N4RAG	SHEN. VAL. LIN
Bland	145.3500	–	O	N4AZJ	T.E. MALLORY J
Bluefield	145.2500	–	O	KD8XK	ARA-SOUTH
Bluefield	145.4900	–	O	W8MOP	W8MOP
Bluefield	146.9550	–	O	WZ8E	ARA-SOUTH
Bluemont	147.3000	+	O	WA4TSC	------------
Boydton	147.2400	+	O	KD4ZTK	KD4JMH
Bristol	146.8800	–	O	WD4CYZ	WD4CYZ
Bristol	147.0750	–	O	KK4MW	KK4MW
Buckingham	146.7900	–	O	WW4GW	WW4GW
Charlottesville	145.4500	–	O	K4DND	K4DND
Charlottesville	146.7600	–	O	WA4TFZ	AARC
Charlottesville	146.8950	–	O	WA4TFZ	WA4TFZ/ALBEM
Charlottesville	146.9250	–	O	WA4TFZ	ALBEMARLE AR
Chesapeake	145.1500	–	O	W4FOS	K4AMG
Chesapeake	145.2900	–	O	K4NDH	NAVAL SEC.GR
Chesapeake	146.6100	–	O	W4CAR	WA4YSE/CARS
Chesapeake	146.7900	–	O	N4SD	HAMPTON RDS
Chesapeake	146.8200	–	O	W4CAR	W4CAR
Chesterfield	145.3100	–	O	KD4KWP	KD4KWP
Chesterfield	147.3600	+	O	KA4CBB	KA4CBB
Claypool Hill	146.8050	+	O	KU4RK	KU4RK
Clinchco	147.1500	+	O	KB4RFN	KB4AKS

Location	*Output*	*Input*	*Notes*	*Call*	*Sponsor*
Clinchco	147.2550	+	O	WD4CYZ	WD4CYZ
Coeburn	145.4300	–	O	AD4OV	AD4OV
Collinsville	147.1200	+	O	KN4DE	KN4DE
Colonial Heights	145.3900	–	O	KE4EUE	------------
Covington	146.8050	–	O	WA4HTI	VHF COMM ASSOC
Culpeper	147.1200	+	O	AA4VI	------------
Danville	146.7000	–	O	K4AU	K4AU
Dublin	146.6700	–	O	W4CBM	W4CBM
Dublin	147.1800	+	O	N4NRV	NEW RIVER VALLEY
Eastville	147.3450	+	O	KN4GE	ESHARC
Elk Crk/iron Mt	147.2400	+	O	N4MGQ	N4MGQ
Fairfax	146.7900	–	O	W4LBL	------------
Falls Church	145.3500	–	O	W4AQD	------------
Fancy Gap	145.1100	–	O	WA4CQK	WA4CQK
Fancy Gap	146.9700	–	O	NC4BL	N4JNE
Fancy Gap	147.0450	+	O 103.5/103.5	K4EZ	W4VSP
Farmville	145.3300	–	O	KE4ZBH	SARA
Farmville	146.9100	–	O	KE4ZBH	SARA
Farmville	146.9550	–	O	N4CFA	N4CFA
Fincastle	146.6400	–	O	W4WIC	T.E. CHAMBLIN
Floyd	147.2100	+	O	W4FCV	------------
Forest	147.1650	+	O	W8CXD	W8CXD
Franklin	147.2700	+	O	WT4FP	FRANKLIN PD
Franklin	147.3000	+	O	W4LG	FRANKLIN REP.CLU
Fredricksburg	147.0150	+	O	WB4LNT	RAPPAHANNOCK V
Galax	147.0900	+	O	W4BRC	W4BRC
Gate City	146.8200	–	O	N4WWB	SCOTT CO ARA
Gloucester	145.3700	–	O	W4HZL	W4HZL
Goochland	147.0900	+	O	N4TZE	------------
Greenbay	145.1500	–	O	K4ARO	K4ARO
Grundy	147.3150	+	O	K4NRR	K4NRR
Grundy/big A Mt	146.8350	–	O	KK4EH	KK4EH
Gum Spring	147.2700	+	O	WB4IKL	WB4IKL
Hampton	145.1700	–	O	WA4ZUA	WA4ZUA
Hampton	145.4900	–	O	KE4UP	KE4UP
Hampton	146.6700	–	O	KG4NJA	NASA LANGLEY AR
Hampton	146.7300	–	O	W4QR	SPARK
Hampton	146.9250	–	O	K4TM	LI4JNI
Hampton	147.2250	+	O	KA4VXR	KA4VXR
Hansonville	145.3700	–	O	WR4RC	WR4RC
Harrisonburg	145.1300	–	O	N4YET	------------
Harrisonburg	147.2250	+	O	N4RAG	N4RAG
Harrisonburg	147.3150	+	O	N4YET	MASSANUTTEN AR
Heathsville	147.3300	+	Oe	W4NNK	W4NNK
Herndon	145.3100	–	O	N4FXP	------------
High Knob Mt	145.2100	–	O	K4QZJ	K4QZJ
Hillsville	145.2700	–	O 103.5/103.5r	W4GHS	------------

Location	*Output*	*Input*	*Notes*	*Call*	*Sponsor*
Jarratt I-95	146.6250	–	O	N4LLE	K4SVA
Kilmarnock	145.2100	–	O	W2MS	W2MS
Kilmarnock	146.8350	–	O	W4GFS	KI4ORV
Lexington	147.3000	+	O	KI4ZR	ROCKBRIDGE A
Lexington	147.3300	+	O	KI4ZR	ROCKBRIDGE A
Lorton	145.1700	–	O	N4JOQ	------------
Lorton	145.1700	–	O	KE4ZN	FBI ARA
Lynchburg	145.2900	–	O	N4TZE	------------
Lynchburg	145.3700	–	O	KC4RBA	KC4RBA
Lynchburg	146.6100	–	O 136.5/136.5ls	NN4RB	NN4RB
Lynchburg	147.0150	–	O	AB4FU	AB4M
Lynchburg	147.1650	+	O	KE4VNN	------------
Lynchburg	147.1950	+	Os	WA4RTS	LYNCHBURG A
Lynchburg	147.3750	+	O	KB4ILD	------------
Madison	147.3900	+	O	N4AJO	------------
Manassas	146.9700	–	O	WA4FPM	OVHARC
Marion	146.6400	–	O 103.5/103.5	KM4X	KM4X
Martinsville	147.1200	+	O	WG8S	KC4SUE
Martinsville	147.2850	+	O	K4MVA	PATRICK HENR
Mclean	147.2100	+	O	WD4IWG	AMRAD
Mechanicsville	146.8050	–	O	W4TTL	W4TTL
Mechanicsville	147.0600	+	O	KJ4IT	------------
Mecklenburg	147.0000	+	O	KB2AHZ	KB2AHZ
Mineral	146.7300	–	O	K4SU	K4SU
Monterey	147.1800	+	O	WD4ITN	WD4ITN
Montpelier	145.2500	–	O	KQ4RH	KQ4RH
Mountain Lake	146.8650	+	O	WZ8E	ARA-SOUTH
New Kent/norge	145.4100	–	O	NK4AR	K2QIJ
New Market	146.6250	–	O	K4AVW	BIGMTNRA
Newport News	145.2300	–	O	W4MT	PARC
Newport News	147.0750	+	O	AD4ZK	AD4ZK
Newport News	147.1650	+	O	W4CM	NEWPORT NEW
Norfolk	145.3300	–	O	W4VB	K4DA
Norfolk	146.7000	–	O	KF8PT	KF8PT
Norfolk	147.3750	+	O	W4VB	W4VB
Norton	146.8650	–	O 103.5/103.5	KG4VFO	KG4VFO
Norton	147.0150	–	O	WD4GSM	K4AXO
Pageco	146.6700	–	O	KD4DDI	KE4LZJ
Palmyra	145.1700	–	O	W4FCO	W3DRY
Pearisburg	147.1350	+	O	N4AZJ	DISMAL PEAK A
Pearisburg	147.3750	+	O	W4NRV	W4NRV
Pennington Gap	146.7000	–	O	AF4FB	LEE CO ARC IN
Petersburg	146.9850	–	O	KE4SCS	KE4SCS
Petersburg	147.3900	+	O	K4SRM	WC4VAA
Pgap Airport	145.4900	–	O	KG4OXG	KE4PVL
Portsmouth	145.4400	–	O	KI4KWR	KI4KWR

Location	*Output*	*Input*	*Notes*	*Call*	*Sponsor*
Portsmouth	146.7000	–	O	AA4AT	K4SM
Portsmouth	146.8500	–	O	W4POX	PORTSMOUTH ARC(
Pound	145.2100	–	O	KC4UBU	AD4NZ
Powhatan	147.2100	+	O	KC4NSE	------------
Pungoteague	145.1100	–	O	N4TIK	N4TIK
Radford/riner	145.1500	–	O	N3ZE	KA4IXK
Richlands	147.1500	+	O	KM4FY	KM4FY
Richmond	145.1100	–	O	WA4MAS	CENT. VIRGINIA A
Richmond	145.4300	–	O	W4SQT	METROPOLITAN RE
Richmond	146.6400	–	O	WB4QEY	------------
Richmond	146.8800	–	O	W4RAT	W4RAT
Richmond	146.9400	–	O	N4VEM	VDEM/ARCA
Richmond	147.0300	–	O	WA4JST	COMMONWEALTH A
Richmond	147.1350	+	O	KC4VDZ	WB4YMA/KC4ZSH
Richmond	147.1800	+	O	W4VCU	WC4VAA
Richmond	147.2550	+	O	W4FJ	K4YEF
Roanoke	145.2100	–	O	N2EDE	N2EDE
			107.2/107.2e		
Roanoke	145.4500	–	O	KA4THY	KA4THY
Roanoke	146.7450	–	O	K4ROA	SW VA.WIRELESS A
Roanoke	146.9400	–	O	N4AP	N4AP
Roanoke	146.9850	–	O	W4CA	ROANOKE VALLEY
Roanoke/poor Mt	145.3900	–	O	K4ARO	K4ARO
Roanoke/poor Mt	147.2700	+	O	KB4QWO	ARA-SOUTH
Rustburg	145.2900	–	O	N4UTN	N4UTN
Rustburg/long Mt	146.8350	–	O	N4UTN	N4UTN
Salem	146.8800	–	O	KF4RGH	W4KZK
Saluda	145.4500	–	O	AA4HQ	AA4HQ KB4JIR KB4
Shenandoah	147.2550	+	O	K4SAD	------------
Smithfield	147.1950	+	O 100/100a	WT4RA	WT4RA
			(CA)ersWX		
South Boston	145.3500	–	O	W4HCH	W4HCH
South Boston	147.0600	–	O	KF4AGO	PIEDMONT ARC
South Hill	145.4700	–	O	N4ZCM	N4ZCM
South Hill	147.2400	+	O	W4CMH	WC4VAA
Spotsylvania	146.7750	–	O	K4SPT	SPOTSYLVANIA AR
Stafford	145.2700	–	O	NM7J	S.A.R.A.
Staunton	145.4500	–	O	KD4KAU	KD4KAU
Staunton	146.7000	–	O	KD4WWF	TEL PIO OF AMERI
Staunton	146.8500	–	O	WA4ZBP	TELE.PIONEERS OF
Staunton	146.9700	–	O	W4WRN	------------
Staunton	147.0450	+	O	KE4CKJ	EKRA
Sterling	146.7150	–	O	WA4TXE	WA4TXE
Stuarts Draft	147.3600	+	O	KB4OLM	KB4OLM
Suffolk	147.0000	–	O	W4LG	W4LG
Tysons Corner	146.9100	–	O	W4XG	------------
Vesta	145.1100	–	O 100/100l	N4FU	NJ1K
Vienna	146.6850	–	O	K4HTA	VWS
Virginia Beach	145.3500	–	O	W4BBR	W4RVN

Location	*Output*	*Input*	*Notes*	*Call*	*Sponsor*
Virginia Beach	146.8950	–	O	W4KXV	VBEARS
Virginia Beach	146.9700	–	O	W4KXV	VBEARS
Virginia Beach	147.0450	+	O	WA4TCJ	WA4TCJ
Virginia Beach	147.3750	+	O	W4NV	TIDEWATER AR
Walkerton	146.7150	–	O	W4TTL	W4TTL & HANO
Warrenton	147.1650	+	O	NZ4N	------------
Warsaw	147.2850	+	O	KA4ZIP	K3RZR
Waynesboro	147.0750	+	O	W4PNT	WAYNSBRO RE
Williamsburg	146.6700	–	O	K4RC	WAARC
Williamsburg	146.7600	–	O	KB4ZIN	KC4CMR
Williamsburg	147.1050	+	O	KB4ZIN	KC4CMR
Winchester	145.2100	–	O	N4RAG	LAUREL HILL R
Wise	145.2100	–	O	KF4VDF	KF4VDF
Wise	147.3900	+	O	KC4MAI	KC4MAI
Woodbridge	147.2400	+	O	WB4FQR	------------
Wytheville	146.7750	–	O 103.5/103.5	K4EZ	W4VSP
Wytheville	146.8950	–	O 103.5/103.5	K4EZ	W4VSP
ALL OF TMARC AREA					
SNP	145.1700	–	O		------------
CULPEPER					
Culpeper	147.1200	+	O 146.2	W4CUL	ClpprARA
DAHLGREN					
King George	146.7450	–	O 107.2er	W4KGC	NNARC
FREDERICKSBURG					
Fredericksburg	147.0150	+	Oe	K4TS	RVARC
Quantico	147.3450	+	O 167.9	K3FBI	FBI ARA
Stafford	147.3750	+	O 79.7aer	WW4VA	SARA
Stafford County	145.2700	–	O 79.7 (CA) eWX	WW4VA	SARA
FRONT ROYAL					
Front Royal	145.2100	–	O 141.3 A(*911)	K4QJZ	K4QJZ
HARRISONBURG					
Harrisonburg	145.1300	–	O 131.8es WX	K4MRA	MARA
Penn Laird	147.2250	+	O 131.8	K4KLH	K4KLH
LURAY					
Luray	147.0300	+	O 131.8	KE4JSV	KE4JSV
Mt Jackson	146.7150	–	O 146.2e	KB6VAA	ShenCo ARES
New Market	146.6250	–	O 131.8e WX	KQ4D	Big Mtn RA
SPOTSYLVANIA					
Spotsylvania	146.7750	–	O 79.7 (CA) el	K4MQF	K4MQF
WARRENTON					
Warrenton	147.1650	+	O 167.9	W4VA	Fauquier ARA

Location	Output	Input	Notes	Call	Sponsor
WASHINGTON AREA					
Alexandria	146.6550	–	O 141.3 (CA)eZ(911)	K4US	MVARC
Alexandria	147.3150	+	O 107.2l	W4HFH	Alex RC
Alexandria	147.3150	449.6000	O 107.2l	W4HFH	Alex RC
Arlington	145.1500	–	O	WB4MJF	WB4MJF
Arlington	145.4700	–	O 107.2	W4WVP	Arlington ARC
Arlington	146.6250	–	O 107.2er	W4AVA	ARPSC
Dulles	147.3300	+	O 203.5e	K4IAD	E-STAR
Dulles Airport	145.3100	–	O 77.0 (CA) e	W4DLS	DARG
Fairfax	146.7900	–	Oae	NV4FM	NVFMA
Fairfax	146.7900	222.5000	O(CA)elz	NV4FM	NVFMA
Haymarket	145.1300	–	O 107.2	N3KL	N3KL
Loudoun	146.7000	–	O 77.0ae WX	WA4TXE	WA4TXE
Manassas	146.9700	–	O 100.0e	W4OVH	OVHARC
Tysons Corner	146.9100	–	Oa(CA)el LITZz	NV4FM	NVFMA
Vienna	146.6850	–	Oe	K4HTA	VWS
Vienna	147.2100	+	Oae	W4CIA	AMRAD
Woodbridge	147.2400	+	O 107.2 (CA)e	W4IY	WWI
WEST					
Page Co	146.6700	–	O 114.8 (CA)	N4PJI	KE4ZLH
WESTMORELAND					
Montross	146.8950	–	O 146.2es	W4GMF	W4GMF
WINCHESTER					
Berryville	145.3900	–	O 146.2	K4USS	K4USS
Bluemont	147.3000	+	O 146.2ar	WA4TSC	WA4TSC
Winchester	146.8200	–	O 146.2 (CA)	W4RKC	SVARC

WASHINGTON

FREQUENCY USAGE--IACC AREAS		
Snp	145.1300	
Snp	145.2900	
W WA - FREQUENCY USAGE		
Crossband	146.6000	146.6000
Experimental	145.5000	145.8000
Rptr Inputs	144.5100	144.8900
Rptr Inputs	146.0200	146.4000
Rptr Inputs	147.6200	147.9800
Rptr Outputs	145.1000	145.4900
Rptr Outputs	146.6200	147.3800
Satellite	145.8000	146.0000
Shared	145.1300	145.1300
Shared	145.2900	145.2900

Location	*Output*	*Input*	*Notes*	*Call*	*Sponsor*
Simplex	146.4200	146.5800			
Simplex	146.5200	146.5200			
Simplex	147.4000	147.5800			
UNB #2 Repeater Input	147.3950	147.3950			
UNB#1 Repeater Input	146.6050	146.6050			
UNB#1 Repeater Output	146.0050	146.0050			
UNB#2 Repeater Output	147.9950	147.9950			
VNB Repeater Inputs	147.40625	147.50625			
VNB Repeater Output	146.40625	146.50625			
E WA - ALMIRA					
Almira	147.0000	+	100.0l	WC7LC	LCRG
E WA - CENTRAL					
Saddle Mtn	145.3500	–	100.0a	N7MHE	N7MHE
E WA - CHELAN					
Manson	146.8200	–	103.5/103.5	K7YR	LCRC
McNeal Canyon	147.1000	+	O	K7SMX	LCRC
E WA - CLARKSTON					
Clarkston	145.3500	–	O 114.8e	N7SAU	N7SAU
Potter Hill	145.3900	–	O(CA)r	KA7FAJ	KA7FAJ
E WA - CLE ELUM					
Cle Elum	147.1600	+	O 131.8ae z	WR7UKC	UKCARC
Sky Meadows	147.3600	+	O 131.8el	WR7KCR	KCRA
E WA - COLFAX					
Kamiak Butte	146.7400	–	Oelx	W7HFI	W7OE
E WA - COLVILLE					
Monumental Mtn	146.6200	–	O 77.0elrx	K7JAR	PARC
E WA - COULEE DAM					
Coulee Dam	146.8600	–	O 100.0	KE7NRA	CDRC
E WA - DAVENPORT					
Teel Hill	147.0400	+	Ol	WC7LC	LCRP
E WA - ELLENSBURG					
Ellensburg	145.2100	–	151.4e	W7HMT	W7HMT
Ellensburg	146.7200	–	O 131.8z	WR7KCR	KCRA
E WA - EPHRATA					
Beezly Hill	145.3100	–	O 100.0 (CA)z	W7TT	W7TT
E WA - GOLDENDALE					
Emer Only	145.3300	–	● 173.8p	KC7SR	KC7SR
Juniper Point	146.8200	–	82.5el	KF7LN	KF7LN
Simcoe Mtn	146.9200	–	88.5a	KC7UTD	KC7UTD
E WA - GRANGER					
Cherry Hill	147.0400	+	O 123.0	KA7IJU	KA7IJU

Location	Output	Input	Notes	Call	Sponsor
E WA - MEDICAL LAKE					
Booth Hill	145.3700	–	O 141.3	KA7ENA	KA7ENA
E WA - MOLSON					
Ne Wa	145.4100	–	100.0	KK7EC	OCEM
E WA - MOSES LAKE					
Wheeler Rd	146.7000	–	100.0	N7MHE	N7MHE
E WA - NEWPORT					
Cooks Mtn	147.1200	+	O 100.0	WB7TBM	Pend ARC
E WA - NORTHEAST					
Chewelah Pk	145.4300	–	O 100.0e	WR7VHF	IEVHF
Stranger	145.2500	–	O	N7BFS	N7BFS
Stranger Mtn	147.3600	+	O(CA)lx	KF7QLH	W7OE
E WA - OKANOGAN					
Pitcher Mtn	146.7200	–	Oz	KK7EC	OCEC
E WA - OMAK					
Omak	147.2000	+	O 127.0lx	AK2O	SpoRptGr
E WA - OROVILLE					
Buckhorn Mtn	147.1400	+	O 103.5e	KD7ITP	KD7ITP
E WA - PLYMOUTH					
Sillusi Butte	145.4900	–	67.0	KC7RWC	UMESRO
Sillusi Butte	147.0200	+	O 103.5	AI7HO	HARC
E WA - PROSSER					
Prosser	147.1800	+	123.0	KA7SSB	KA7SSB
E WA - PULLMAN					
Pullman	145.4700	–	O	WA7WNJ	WA7WNJ
E WA - REPUBLIC					
Republic	145.1900	–	O(CA)lrz	N7XAY	FCARES
E WA - RICHLAND					
Rattlesnake	146.7600	–	100.0e	W7VPA	TCARC
E WA - RITZVILLE					
Ritzville	146.7200	–	Oa	WD7C	WD7C
E WA - RIVERSIDE					
Tunk Mtn	145.4500	–	O 100.0ex	W7GSN	OMRA
E WA - SPOKANE					
Browns Mtn	147.3000	+	O 100.0erx	W7GBU	SPO CO DES
Farm Bank	147.3400	+	123.0e	WR7VHF	IEVHF
Krell	145.3900	–	O 127.3el	W7UPS	W7UPS
Krell	146.8800	–	O 123.0ae	WR7VHF	IEVHF
Lookout Point	147.0600	+	77.0l	N7BFS	N7BFS
Mica Peak	145.1100	–	O 118.8l	WA7UOJ	WA7UOJ
Mica Peak	145.1500	–	118.8l	WA7RVV	WA7RVV
Mica Peak	147.2400	+	Oelx	WA7HWD	NW Tri. St.
Mica Peak	147.3800	+	O 131.8el	W7OE	W7OE
Spokane	145.1700	–	114.8	K7MMA	K7MMA
Spokane	145.2100	–	100.0 (CA)e	W7TRF	SpoHRC
Spokane	146.6600	–	100.0	N7FM	N7FM
Spokane	147.1600	+	● 136.5	K7EKM	K7EKM
Spokane	147.3200	+	O	AK2O	SpoRptGr
Spokane Vly	145.3300	–	100.0	N7FM	WA6HSL

Location	*Output*	*Input*	*Notes*	*Call*	*Sponsor*
Spokane Vly	147.1400	+	○ 127.3e	AD7DD	AD7DD
Spokane [1]	147.2000	+	○ 141.3el	AK2O	SpoRptGr
Spokane [2]	147.2000	+	● 141.3	AK2O	SpoRptGr
E WA - SPRAGUE					
Sprague	145.1900	–	100.0	WC7LC	LCRG
E WA - TONASKET					
Aeneas Vly	145.3300	–	○ 100.0	KK7EC	OCEM
E WA - TRI-CITIES					
Horse Heaven Hills	145.3900	–	103.5l	W7UPS	W7UPS
Joe Butte	145.4100	–	○ 100.0	N7LZM	N7LZM
Johnson Butte	146.6400	–	○ 100.0e	W7AZ	TCARC
Jump Off Joe	147.0800	+	● 94.8e	KC7WFD	KC7WFD
Kennewick Water Tank	147.2200	+	○ae	N7LZM	N7LZM
E WA - TROUT LAKE					
King Mtn	147.0800	+	○ 123.0	WA7SAR	YCS&R
E WA - TWISP					
McClure Mtn	147.2200	+	100.0l	KB7SVP	KB7SVP
E WA - WALLA WALLA					
Dixie	146.9600	–	○ 74.4er	AL1Q	AL1Q
Pikes Peak	147.2800	+	○elx	KD7DDQ	KD7DDQ
Walla Walla	147.1400	+	94.8e	KH6IHB	KH6IHB
E WA - WENATCHEE					
Birch Mtn	146.6800	–	156.7 (CA)r z	W7TD	ACARC
E Wenatchee	146.7800	–	156.7	N7RHT	N7RHT
Mission Ridge	146.9000	–	○ 173.8ex	WR7ADX	MRRA
Naneum	147.2600	+	○ 156.7elx	KB7TYR	KB7TYR
Wenatchee	147.2000	+	●tl	AK2O	SpoRptGr
E WA - WHITE SWAN					
Fort Simcoe	146.7200	–	123.0e	KA7IJU	KA7IJU
E WA - YAKIMA					
Ahtanum Ridge	146.9400	–	173.8	W7CCY	W7CCY
Bethel Ridge	145.1700	–	123.0	WA7SAR	YakSO
Bethel Ridge	147.3000	+	○ 123.0erx	W7AQ	YakARC
Darland Mtn	146.8600	–	123.0e	WA7SAR	YCS&R
Eagle Pk	145.4700	–	103.5	WA7AAX	WA7AAX
Moxee	146.8400	–	123.0 (CA)lr z	W7AQ	YakARC
Moxee	147.1200	+	94.8	KC7WFD	KC7WFD
Moxee	147.2000	+	○ 141.3	AK2O	SpoRptGr
Quartz Mtn	145.2700	–	123.0 E-SUN	WA7SAR	YakSO
Selah	147.2400	+	192.8	KC7VQR	KC7VQR
Yakima	147.0600	+	○ 123.0	KB7HDX	BCARES
Yakima Ridge	146.6600	–	123.0 (CA)e rz	W7AQ	YakARC

Location	Output	Input	Notes	Call	Sponsor
NW OREGON & SW WASHINGTON					
Vancouver	145.3700	–	O 123el	AB7F	AB7F
SW WASHINGTON					
Vancouver	147.2400	+	Oe	W7AIA	W7AIA
W WA - NORTH					
Bellingham	146.7000	–		WC7SO	W7CDC
Camano Is	147.3600	+	O 123el	W7PIG	CAMANO IS
Coupeville	146.8600	–	O 127.3l	W7AVM	ICARC
Friday Harbor	145.2500	–	O 131.8	N7JN	San Juan Cnty ARS
Granite Falls	146.9200	–	O 123	WA7VYA	SNOHOMISH DEM
Green Mtn	146.9200	–	O 103.5e	KD7VMK	KD7VMK
King Mtn	147.1600	+	O 103.5	K7SKW	MT. BAKER
Lookout Mtn	146.7400	–	O 127.3 (CA)elz	K7SKW	MT BAKER ARCRG
Lyman Hill	145.1900	–	O 127.3esx	N7GDE	R.A.S.C.
Lyman Hill	147.2000	+	O 118.8el	K7MMI	PSMRG
Mt Constitution	146.7400	–	O 103.5e	K7SKW	MT BAKER A
Orcas Island	145.2500	–	O 131.8	N7JN	San Juan Cnty ARS
Orcas Island	146.9000	–	O 131.8e	N7JN	SAN JUAN C
Sumas Mtn	145.2300	–	O 103.5el	W7BPD	Blaine P.D
W WA - NORTH COAST					
Forks	145.3700	–	O 114.8ael	K7MMI	PSMRG
Mt Octopus	147.2800	+	O 123.0 (CA)el	K7PP	K7PP
Port Angeles	145.1300	–	O 100aez	WF7W	------------
Port Townsend	145.1500	–	O 114.8ae	W7JCR	Jefferson Cnty
Striped Peak	146.7600	–	O 100ael	W7FEL	Clallam Cn
W WA - SEATTLE-TACOMA					
Auburn	147.2400	+	O 123	K7SYE	Auburn Val
Baldi Mtn	146.9800	–	O 107.2e	K7MMI	COUGAR MT
Belfair	145.1700	–	O 103.5 (CA)e	NM7E	------------
Bellevue	147.0000	–	O 103.5	W7DX	W.W. DX CL
Enumclaw	147.3000	+	O 88.0e	WB7DOB	------------
Everett	145.3900	–	O 123	W2ZT	SCARES
Everett	147.1800	+	O 103.5 (CA)e	WA7LAW	SNOHOMISH
Federal Way	146.7600	–	O 103.5ae	WA7FW	FEDERAL WA
Federal Way	147.0400	+	O 103.5e	WA7FW	FWARC
Gold Mtn	146.6200	–	O 103.5 (CA)ez	WW7RA	W W RPTR A
Grass Mtn	145.3700	–	O 136.5e	W7AAO	Pierce Cnt
Green Mtn	146.8800	–	O 88.5e	WR7V	WR7V
Issaquah	147.0800	+	O 103.5e	W7GLB	SEATAC RPT
Kirkland	145.4900	–	O 103.5	K7LWH	Lake Wa. Ham Club
Lakewood	145.4100	–	O 118.8ael z	K7EK	KC7J
Langley	147.2200	+	O 127.3ae z	W7AVM	ISLAND COU

Location	*Output*	*Input*	*Notes*	*Call*	*Sponsor*
Lynnwood	145.1300	–	O 136.5 TT e	W7UFI	SCARES
Lynnwood	146.7800	–	O 103.5	NU7Z	NU7Z
Lynnwood	146.8000	–	O 136.5 TT e	W7UFI	SCARES
Mercer Island	147.1600	+	O 146.2e	W7MIR	Mercer Is. ARES
Olalla	145.3500	–	O 103.5e	W7ZLJ	W7ZLJ
Rattlesnake Mtn	145.1100	–	O 103.5el	KC7SAR	KC SAR Ass
Redmond	145.3100	–	O 103.5e	KC7IYE	KC7IYE
Seatac	146.6600	–	O 103.5	WA7ST	WA7ST
Seattle	146.9000	–	O 103.5el	W7SRZ	WWMST
Seattle	146.9600	–	O 103.5	W7VHY	PSRG
Shelton	146.7200	–	O 103.5e	N7SK	MASON COUN
Silverdale	145.4300	–	O 179.9 (CA)ez	KD7WDG	KITSAP CNT
Skykomish	145.1100	–	O 123el	KC7SAR	KC SAR Ass
Tacoma	145.2100	–	O 141.3	W7DK	Radio Club
Tacoma	146.6400	–	O 103.5 (CA)elz	KB7CNN	KB7CNN
Tacoma	146.9400	–	O 103.5ez	K7HW	K7HW
Tacoma	147.0200	+	O 103.5 (CA)lz	W7TED	STARS-ARS
Tacoma	147.2800	+	O 103.5e	W7DK	R.C. of Ta
Tiger Mtn East	145.2300	–	O 127.3	W7FHZ	CH 1 Rptr
Tiger Mtn East	146.8200	–	O 103.5e	K7LED	MIKE & KEY
Tiger Mtn East	147.1000	+	O 123.0	KC7RAS	KC7RAS
Tiger Mtn West	145.3300	–	O 179.9el	K7NWS	Boeing/ be
Woodinville	147.3400	+	O 100 (CA) e	K6RFK	Alan Chand
W WA - SOUTH					
Alder	145.4500	–	O 110.9ael	KB7CNN	KB7CNN
Ashford	145.2500	–	O	K7DNR	DNR ARC
Baw Faw Pk	147.0600	+	O 110.9e	N7PRJ	BAW FAW RP
Capitol Peak	145.4700	–	O 100ael	K7CPR	Capitol Pk
Chehalis	145.4300	–	O 110.9	WA7UHD	Chehalis V
Chehalis	146.7400	–	O 110.9	K7KFM	K7KFM
Crawford Mtn	147.3800	+	O 103.5	W7DK	R.C. of Ta
Eatonville	146.7000	–	103.5e	W7EAT	------------
Graham	147.1400	+	O 103.5l	K7EK	K7EK
Kelso	147.2000	+	O 91.5al	K7MMI	PSMRG
Lacey	146.8000	–	O 97.4ae	WC7I	WC7I
Longview	147.2600	+	O 114.8e	W7DG	Lower Colu
Mineral	146.6800	–	O 103.5e	K7HW	K7HW
Olympia	145.1500	–	O 103.5e	W7PSE	PSE ARG
Olympia	147.3600	+	O 103.5ael z	NT7H	OLYMPIA AR
South Mtn	145.2700	–	O 103.5	W7UVH	W7UVH
Tumwater	147.1200	+	O 173.8e	N7EHP	N7EHP
Woodland	147.3000	+	O 114.8e	W7DG	Lwr Clmbia

Location	Output	Input	Notes	Call	Sponsor
W WA - SOUTH COAST					
Aberdeen	147.1600	+	O 88.5a	W7ZA	GRAYS HARB
Cathlamet	147.0200	+	O 118.8el	NM7R	BEACHNET
Cosmopolis	145.3900	–	O 118.8e	W7EOC	ARES Dist.
Grayland	145.3100	–	O 118.8	NM7R	Beachnet
Ilwaco	146.8600	–	O 114.8	W7RDR	------------
KO Peak	147.2000	+	O 127.3ael	K7MMI	PSMRG
Meglar Mtn	145.4500	–	O 118.8 (CA)elz	W7BU	Sunset Empire ARC
Megler	147.1800	+	O 82.5	NM7R	PACIFIC CO
Neilton	146.9600	–	O 203.5l	WA7ARC	NDCRT
Raymond	147.2400	+	O 103.5 (CA)	KA7DNK	KA7DNK
Saddle Mtn	146.9000	–	O 88.5el	W7ZA	GRAYS HARB
South Bend	147.3400	+	O 82.5	NM7R	NM7R

WEST VIRGINIA

Location	Output	Input	Notes	Call	Sponsor
Amber Ridge	147.2100	+	O	KB8NJH	KB8NJH
Ansted	146.7900	–	O	KC8ZQZ	PLATEAU ARA
Beckley	145.1700	–	O	WV8B	ARA NORTH
Beckley	145.2300	–	O	N8FWL	N8FWL 222 RAD NT
Beckley	145.3100	–	O	WV8B	ARA NORTH
Beckley	145.3700	–	O	WV8BD	BLACK DIAMOND A
Beckley	146.8500	–	O	KC8AFH	KC8AFH
Beckley	147.0750	–	O	KC8AFH	PLATEAU ARA INC
Beckley	147.3600	+	O	N8FWL	N8FWL 222 RAD NT
Berkeley Springs	146.7450	–	O	KK3L	------------
Birch River	145.2700	–	O	N8FMD	N8FMD
Bluefield	147.0600	–	O	W8MOP	W8MOP
Bridgeport	147.1200	+	O	W8SLH	W8SLH
Buckhannon	145.4100	–	O	W8LD	------------
Buckhannon	146.8500	–	O	K8VE	K8VE
Buckhannon	146.9250	–	O	AA8CC	AA8CC
Charles Town	146.9850	–	O	N8EIV	WD8RWG
Charleston	145.3500	–	O	W8GK	KANAWHA ARC
Charleston	145.4300	–	O	WB8YST	WB8YST
Charleston	146.8200	–	O	WB8CQV	WB8CQV
Charleston	147.0000	–	O	W8XF	W8XF
Charleston	147.0450	–	O	KB8LFJ	KB8LFJ
Clarksburg	146.6850	–	O	N8FMD	N8FMD
Clarksburg	147.1650	+	O	WV8HC	CENTRAL WV WIRE
Clarksburg	147.2100	+	O	N8FMD	N8FMD
Clay	145.1500	–	O	KA8SVN	------------
Cowen	146.8350	–	O	KC8ECX	NICHOLAS ARC
Crawford	147.0600	+	O 103.5/103.5els	W8DDW	W8DDW
Danville	146.6850	–	O	WB8NAM	BOONE ARC
Davis	147.1350	+	O 103.5/103.5l	KC8AJH	KC8AJH

Location	*Output*	*Input*	*Notes*	*Call*	*Sponsor*
MOOREFIELD					
Moorefield	145.1900	–	O 118.8	N8VAA	+N8VAA
Moorefield	146.9850	–	O 123.0e	KD8IFP	PHARC

WISCONSIN

Location	*Output*	*Input*	*Notes*	*Call*	*Sponsor*
WAR					
Algoma	146.8050	–	O 100.0aers	K9KEW	K9KEW
Antigo	145.3100	–	O 114.8aelr	KC9JZY	LCARA
Antigo	147.2550	+	O 114.8aelr	KC9JZY	LCARA
Antigo	147.3150	+	O 114.8aelr	N9TEV	N9TEV
Appleton	145.3300	–	O 100.0aers	W9ZL	FCARC
Appleton	146.6550	–	O 100.0aers	KB9BYP	ECR LTD
Appleton	146.7600	–	O 100.0aers	W9ZL	FCARC
Appleton	147.1650	+	O 100.0aers	AB9PJ	AB9PJ
Baldwin	145.2500	–	O 110.9ers	WE9COM	WeComm,Ltd
Balsam Lake	147.1950	+	O 110.9ers	N9XH	PCARA
Baraboo	146.8800	–	O 123.0aelrs	WR9ABE	C.W.R.A.
Baraboo	147.3150	+	O 123.0aelrs	WB9FDZ	YTARC
Beetown	146.8950	–	O 131.8es	NØWLU	HVARC
Beldenville	146.9550	–	O 110.9ers	NØNIC	B.A.T.S.
Beldenville	147.2250	+	O 110.9ers	NØNIC	B.A.T.S.
Beloit	147.1200	+	O 123.0aelrs	WA9JTX	K9GJN
Big Flats	146.6250	–	O 123.0aelrs	N9WYQ	N9WYQ
Black River Falls	145.3900	–	O 131.8es	KC9GEA	N9PPB
Bluff Siding	146.8350	–	O 131.8es	WØNE	Winona ARC
Cambria	147.0150	+	O 123.0aelrs	KC9CZH	KC9CZH
Cambridge	147.3600	+	O 123.0aelrs	WE9COM	WeComm,Ltd
Cedarburg	146.9700	–	O 127.3aes	W9CQO	O.R.C.
Chaffey	147.1050	+	O 110.9ers	KC9EMI	AB9AC
Chippewa Falls	145.2300	–	O 110.9ers	N9MMU	N.V.W.A.
Chippewa Falls	147.2400	+	O 110.9ers	W9EAU	E C ARC
Chippewa Falls	147.3750	+	O 110.9ers	WD9HFT	WD9HFT
Clam Lake	145.2100	–	O 110.9ers	K9JWM	K9JWM
Clinton	146.7150	–	O 123.0aelrs	WB9SHS	RCRA

Location	Output	Input	Notes	Call	Sponsor
Coloma	146.7000	–	O 123.0aelrs	W9LTA	W9LTA
Delafield	146.8200	–	O 127.3aes	K9ABC	SEWFARS
Durand	145.3500	–	O 131.8es	WB9NTO	WB9NTO
Earl	145.1100	–	O 110.9ers	N9MMU	N.V.W.A.
Eau Claire	146.9100	–	O 110.9ers	W9EAU	E C ARC
Eau Galle	145.2100	–	O 110.9ers	KB9LUK	KB9LUK
Egg Harbor	146.7300	–	O 100.0aers	W9AIQ	DCARC
Elkhorn	146.8650	–	O 123.0aelrs	W9ELK	LAARC
Fond Du Lac	145.4300	–	O 100.0aers	K9FDL	F.A.R.A
Fond Du Lac	147.0900	+	O 100.0aers	K9DJB	FDL RPT
Fond Du Lac	147.3750	+	O 100.0aers	KB9YET	FOX1
Galesville	147.0000	+	O 131.8es	N9TUU	W.I.N.
Gilmanton	145.4300	–	O 131.8es	WE9COM	WeComm,Ltd
Granton	146.7750	–	O 114.8aelr	N9RRF	N9RRF
Green Bay	146.6850	–	O 100.0aers	KB9GKC	KB9GKC
Green Bay	147.0750	+	O 100.0aers	N9DKH	ATC
Green Bay	147.1200	+	O 100.0aers	K9GB	G B M&K
Green Bay	147.2700	+	O 100.0aers	KB9ALN	PASS
Green Bay	147.3600	+	O 100.0aers	K9EAM	G B M&K
Hayward	147.2550	+	O 110.9ers	N9MMU	NVWA
High Bridge	147.2100	+	O 110.9ers	KC9GSK	KC9GSK
Holcombe	145.4700	–	O 110.9ers	N9LIE	N9LIE
Holcombe	147.3450	+	O 110.9ers	N9MMU	N.V.W.A.
Hollandale	146.6550	–	O 123.0aelrs	N9QIP	WIN
Hudson	145.1300	–	O 110.9ers	K9ZMA	SCC RACES
Hurley	147.1650	+	O 110.9ers	KCØIPA	LSAC
Irma	146.6400	–	O 114.8aelr	KB9QJN	M.A.R.G.
Irma	146.9700	–	O 114.8aelr	KC9NW	KC9NW
Janesville	145.4500	–	O 123.0aelrs	WB9SHS	RCRA
Janesville	147.0750	+	O 123.0aelrs	K9FRY	K9FRY
Jefferson	145.4900	–	O 123.0aelrs	W9MQB	TCARC

Location	Output	Input	Notes	Call	Sponsor
Juneau	146.6400	–	O 123.0aelrs	W9TCH	ROCK R RC
Kewaskum	146.7900	–	O 127.3aes	N9NLU	KMCG
Kewaunee	146.8050	–	O 100.0aers	K9KEW	K9KEW
La Crosse	146.9700	–	O 131.8es	WR9ARC	RVRLND ARC
Lac Du Flambeau	146.6700	–	O 114.8aelr	N9AFN	N9AFN
Lac Du Flambeau	146.7000	–	O 114.8aelr	W9BTN	W9BTN
Lampson	146.6550	–	O 110.9ers	N9PHS	NorWesCo
Lohrville	145.2700	–	O 123.0aelrs	KB9JJB	KB9JJB
Madison	145.3700	–	O 123.0aelrs	KC9FNM	Empire
Madison	146.6850	–	O 123.0aelrs	W9YT	UW BARS
Madison	146.7600	–	O 123.0aelrs	W9HSY	M A R A
Madison	146.9400	–	O 123.0aelrs	WR9ABE	C W R A
Madison	147.1500	+	O 123.0aelrs	W9HSY	M A R A
Madison	147.1800	+	O 123.0aelrs	WD8DAS	NERT
Manitowish Waters	145.3900	–	O 114.8aelr	KB9WCK	KB9WCK
Manitowoc	145.1100	–	O 100.0aers	K9MTW	ManCoRad
Manitowoc	146.6100	–	O 100.0aers	W9MTW	ManCoRad
Marinette	147.0000	+	O 114.8aelr	W8PIF	W8PIF
Markesan	146.9550	–	O 123.0aelrs	WB9RBC	G FOX ARC
Marshfield	147.1800	+	O 114.8aelr	AA9US	MAARS
Mauston	146.8500	–	O 123.0aelrs	KB9WQF	JCARC
Mauston	147.1050	+	O 123.0aelrs	K9UJH	K9UJH
Medford	145.4900	–	O 114.8aelr	N9LIE	N9LIE
Medford	147.1500	+	O 114.8aelr	KB9OBX	BRARA
Melrose	145.4500	–	O 131.8es	W9LLB	W9LLB
Menomonie	146.6100	–	O 110.9ers	K9KGB	R CDR RA
Menomonie	146.6850	–	O 110.9ers	N9QKK	N9QKK

Location	*Output*	*Input*	*Notes*	*Call*	*Sponsor*
Meteor	147.0750	+	O 110.9ers	WE9COM	WeComm
Milwaukee	145.1300	–	O 127.3aes	N9LKH	MAARS
Milwaukee	145.2500	–	O 127.3aes	KA9WXN	KA9WXN
Milwaukee	145.2700	–	O 127.3aes	W9HHX	MSOE ARC
Milwaukee	145.3900	–	O 127.3aes	W9RH	MRAC
Milwaukee	146.6250	–	O 127.3aes	N9BMH	N9BMH
Milwaukee	146.9100	–	O 127.3aes	WI9MRC	MKE RPTR
Milwaukee	146.9400	–	O 127.3aes	N9PAY	GFD/EOC
Milwaukee	147.0000	+	O 127.3aes	W9PY	PHANTOM
Milwaukee	147.0450	+	O 127.3aes	WBØAFB	MATC RC
Milwaukee	147.1050	+	O 127.3aes	K9IFF	K9IFF
Milwaukee	147.1650	+	O 127.3aes	W9WK	AREC, INC.
Monroe	145.1100	–	O 123.0aelrs	KO9LR	GCARA
Montello	146.7450	–	O 123.0aelrs	KC9ASQ	Marq EM
Mount Sterling	147.3600	+	O 131.8es	W9DMH	W9DMH
Necedah	147.2100	+	O 123.0aelrs	KC9IPY	JCARC
New Holstein	147.3000	+	O 100.0aers	KA9OJN	C.A.R.E.S
New Richmond	145.2700	–	O 110.9ers	N9LIE	N9LIE
Oconto Falls	146.8350	–	O 114.8aelr	KB9DSV	KB9DSV
Ogdensburg	146.9250	–	O 114.8aelr	W9GAP	W9GAP
Oshkosh	147.3450	+	O 100.0aers	N9GDY	N9GDY
Osseo	145.3300	–	O 131.8es	N9LIE	N9LIE
Park Falls	147.0000	+	O 110.9ers	W9PFP	PCRA
Plymouth	147.0600	+	O 100.0aers	WE9R	SHEB ARC
Port Washington	147.3300	+	O 127.3aes	WB9RQR	OZARES
Prairie Du Chien	147.1200	+	O 131.8es	WØSFK	W.I.N.
Racine	147.2700	+	O 127.3aes	KR9RK	LRA Racine
Rhinelander	145.1500	–	O 114.8aelr	NS9Q	NS9Q

Location	*Output*	*Input*	*Notes*	*Call*	*Sponsor*
Rhinelander	146.9400	–	O 114.8aelr	KC9HBX	KC9HBX
Rice Lake	146.7150	–	O 110.9ers	W9GDH	Barron EM
Richland Center	146.9100	–	O 131.8es	W9PVR	PVRARC
Roberts	147.3300	+	O 110.9ers	N9KMY	SCVRA
Rubicon	145.3500	–	O 123.0aelrs	WB9KPG	WB9KPG
Sayner	145.1300	–	O 114.8aelr	WE9COM	WeComm
Shawano	145.3500	–	O 114.8aelr	KA9NWY	KA9NWY
Shawano	147.2250	+	O 114.8aelr	N9FZH	N9FZH
Shell Lake	147.0450	+	O 110.9ers	N9PHS	NORWESCO
Siren	146.6250	–	O 110.9ers	N9PHS	NORWESCO
Sister Bay	147.1800	+	O 100.0aers	W9AIQ	DC ARC
Slinger	147.2100	+	O 127.3aes	KC9PVD	KC9PVD
Solon Springs	145.4900	–	O 110.9ers	N9QWH	DC RACES
Spooner/Hertel	145.1900	–	O 110.9ers	KB9OHN	BARS
Spooner/Hertel	147.3000	+	O 110.9ers	KB9OHN	BARS
Stevens Point	146.6700	–	O 114.8aelr	WB9QFW	CWRA LTD
Stevens Point	146.9850	–	O 114.8aelr	WB9QFW	CWRA LTD
Sturgeon Bay	147.2100	+	O 100.0aers	W9AIQ	DC ARC
Superior	146.7600	–	O 110.9ers	K9UWS	UWS-ARC
Superior	146.8200	–	O 110.9ers	WA9VDW	T P T G
Suring	145.2900	–	O 114.8aelr	WE9COM	WeComm,Ltd
Suring	145.4700	–	O 114.8aelr	AB9PJ	AB9PJ
Sussex	147.3900	+	O 127.3aes	W9CQ	WARC, Inc
Three Lakes	147.1950	+	O 114.8aelr	N9GHE	N9GHE
Tomah	146.8050	–	O 131.8es	N9BOE	N9BOE
Tomahawk	145.4300	–	O 114.8aelr	N9CLE	TOM RP A
Tripoli	147.1200	+	O 114.8aelr	KC9HBX	KC9HBX
Two Rivers	147.0300	+	O 100.0aers	N9XFD	N9GHE
Union Grove	146.7450	–	O 127.3aes	N9OIG	N9OIG
Unity	145.4100	–	O 114.8aelr	W9BCC	RMRA

Location	Output	Input	Notes	Call	Sponsor
Viroqua	145.1700	–	O 131.8es	N9TUU	N9TUU
Wabeno	145.1100	–	O 114.8aelr	K9ARF	PASS
Watertown	145.1900	–	O 123.0aelrs	K9LUK	W.I.N.
Wausau	145.2450	–	O 114.8aelr	W9BCC	RMRA
Wausau	146.8200	–	O 114.8aelr	W9BCC	RMRA
Wausau	146.8650	–	O 114.8aelr	W9SM	WVRA
Wausau	147.0600	+	O 114.8aelr	KC9NW	Rich Maier
Wausau	147.1350	+	O 114.8aelr	W9SM	W.V.R.A.
Wausaukee	146.8800	–	O 114.8aelr	WA8WG	WA8WG
West Milwaukee	147.1350	+	O 127.3aes	N9FSE	Viking Com
Willard	147.2700	+	O 114.8aelr	N9UWX	N9UWX
Wisconsin Rapids	146.7900	–	O 114.8aelr	W9MRA	MSRA
Wisconsin Rapids	147.3300	+	O 114.8aelr	W9MRA	MSRA

WYOMING

CENTRAL

Location	Output	Input	Notes	Call	Sponsor
Atlantic City - Limestone Mtn	147.0300	+	O 100.0	KD7BN	KD7BN
Casper	145.1450	–	Oaersxz	N7OSW	N7OSW
Casper	145.2350	–	O 100.0rs	W7VNJ	CARC
Casper	147.2800	+	O 107.2aWX	W7VNJ	CARC
Casper	147.3450	+	Oaex	K7KMT	K7KMT
Casper - Grand View	145.3250	–	O(CA)e	NG7T	NG7T
Casper Mountain	146.6400	–	O 173.8 L(449.575)x	KD7AGA	CDK Net
Casper Mountain	146.9400	–	O 123.0arsx	W7VNJ	CARC
Lander	145.4450	–	110.9	KC7CJN	KC7CJN
Lander	146.7900	–	O L(448.200)	WB7AHL	WB7AHL
Lander	147.0600	+	Ol	N7HYF	WYAME
Riverton	145.1150	–	O 100.0esWX	KØFOP	WYAME
Riverton	145.2800	–	O 100.0aez	KC7BNC	KC7BNC

Location	*Output*	*Input*	*Notes*	*Call*	*Sponsor*
Shoshoni	147.3000	+	O(CA)	KB7PLA	KB7PLA
Shoshoni - Copper Mtn	146.8050	–	O 100.0 L(HERC)x	KD7BN	KD7BN
Wheatland - Laramie Peak	145.4150	–	O 100.0 E-SUN L(147.300)x	KD7QDM	NWARA
EAST CENTRAL					
Douglas	145.2650	–	Ot L(449.575)	KD7AGA	CDK Net
Douglas	146.9100	–	146.9l	WB7AEM	GPARA
Douglas	147.1500	+	Oe	KK7BA	CCARC
Esterbrook	147.0300	+	100.0a	KT7V	KT7V
Glenrock	145.2650	–	O	KB7FGN	KB7FGN
Lusk	147.3300	+	Oe	KK7LI	W7IFW
HERC - STATEWIDE					
Casper Mountain	147.4600	147.4600	O 100.0# L(HERC)x	KD7BN	HERC
Cheyenne - Laramie Summit	146.8200	–	O 114.8 L(HERC)x	KC7SNO	ShyWy ARC
Douglas	147.5300	147.5300	O 100.0# L(HERC)	KD7BN	HERC
Dubois	146.8200	–	O 100.0 L(HERC)x	KD7BN	HERC
Gillette	147.5800	147.5800	O 100.0# L(HERC)	KD7BN	HERC
Lander	147.4300	147.4300	O 100.0# L(HERC)	KD7BN	HERC
Medicine Bow	147.5000	147.5000	O 100.0# L(HERC)	KD7BN	HERC
Rawlins - Nine Mile Hill	147.3900	147.3900	O 100.0#el x	N7RON	N7RON
Rock Springs - Aspen Mtn	146.9400	–	O 100.0 L(HERC)x	KC7LOR	SWARC
Shell Mountain	146.6700	–	O 100.0 L(HERC)x		HERC
Shoshoni - Copper Mtn	146.8050	–	O 100.0 L(HERC)x	KD7BN	HERC
NORTH CENTRAL					
Basin	147.1350	+	O	WB7S	WB7S
Powell	147.2550	+	O	WA7QNS	WA7QNS
Shell	146.6100	–	O 103.5lrx	KI7W	BHBARC
Shell	146.6700	–	O	WA7NZI	CMARC
Sheridan	146.7300	–	Oa	N7KEO	N7KEO
Sheridan	146.8200	–	O 100.0	W7GUX	SRAL
Thermopolis	147.1650	+	OE-SUN	WA7JRF	WA7JRF
Worland	147.2250	+	O	KB7PLA	KB7PLA
NORTH EAST					
Evanston	146.8600	–	O 100 L(147.18)x	K7JL	UVHFS
Gillette - Antelope Butte	147.3600	+	O 123.0 L(147.300 AND 146.790)x	NE7WY	NWARA

WYOMING

Location	Output	Input	Notes	Call	Sponsor
Newcastle - Little Thunder	147.0900	+	O 100.0 L(147.300) WXxz	NE7WY	NWARA
Newcastle - Mt Pisgah	147.3000	+	O 162.2 L(147.360 AND 146.790)rx	NE7WY	NWARA
Rocky Point - Dinosaur	147.2700	+	O 123.0 E-WIND L(147.300)x	K7WIZ	NWARA
Sundance - Warren Peak	146.7900	–	O 100.0e L(147.360 AND 147.300)x	NE7WY	NE7WY
Wright	146.9850	–	Ot L(449.575)	KD7AGA	CDK Net
Wright - Little Thunder	147.0600	+	O 100.0 L(147.300) WXxz	NE7WY	NWARA
NORTH WEST					
Cody - Cedar Mountain	146.8500	–	O 103.5els	KI7W	CMARC
SOUTH CENTRAL					
Baggs	147.0600	+	O	WB7CBQ	CCARS
Rawlins	147.0450	+	O	WD4MYL	HAMS
Rawlins	147.1800	+		KI7QG	CCARS
Rawlins - Choke Cherry	146.7600	–	Oer	KC7CZU	CCARS
Rawlins - EOC	147.2400	+	O	N7GCR	CCARS
Rawlins - Nine Mile Hill	147.3900	+	O 100.0elx	N7RON	N7RON
Rawlins - R Hill	146.7000	–	O 162.2	N7RON	CCARS
SOUTH EAST					
Albin	147.1650	+	O 114.8e L(146.775)rWXx	KC7SNO	ShyWy ARC
Cheyenne	145.2350	–	O 131.8x	KB7SWR	KB7SWR
Cheyenne	146.7750	–	O 114.8 TT eL(147.165)rWXxz	KC7SNO	ShyWy ARC
Cheyenne	147.1050	+	O 114.8er	KC7SNO	ShyWy ARC
Cheyenne - CJHS	147.0150	+	Ox	KC7OEK	Carey ARC
Cheyenne - Cowboy Estates	147.0300	+	O 131.8el	WB4UIC	WB4UIC
Laramie	145.4450	–	O 123.0 L(COLO CONN)	KBØVJJ	KBØVJJ
Laramie	146.6100	–	Oz	N7UW	UARC
Laramie - Sherman Hill	146.8200	–	O 114.8 L(HERC)x	KC7SNO	ShyWy ARC
Torrington	146.7300	–	O	KF7BR	KF7BR
Torrington	146.8050	–	O	N7CFR	N7CFR
Wheatland	146.8800	–	L(446.975)	WA7SNU	GPARA
SOUTH WEST					
Cokeville	147.3000	+	O	N7BRQ	N7BRQ
Evanston	145.3300	–	O	WA7MEK	UCRACES
Evanston	146.8600	–	100.0l	K7JL	K7JL
Evanston - Medicine Butte	147.0200	+	Ol	K7OGM	------------

Location	Output	Input	Notes	Call	Sponsor
Kemmerer	147.0900	+	Oarx	W7PIF	LCRACES
Kemmerer	147.3900	+	O	W7PIF	W7PIF
Rock Springs - Aspen Mtn	146.6100	–	O 100.0arx z	N7ERH	SWRACES
Rock Springs - Aspen Mtn	146.6700	–	O 100.0# TTelx	N7ABC	N7ABC
Rock Springs - Aspen Mtn	146.9400	–	O 100.0x	KC7LOR	SWARC
WEST CENTRAL					
Afton - The Narrows	146.9700	–	100.0ers	KD7LVE	SVARC
Big Piney - Hogback Mtn	146.8800	–	O 100.0erx	KC7BJY	SCARC
Dubois	146.8200	–	O 100.0e L(HERC)x	KD7BN	KD7BN
Dubois	147.3150	+	Oelx	KG7ST	KG7ST
Jackson - Rendezvous Mtn	146.7300	–	O 123.0rx	W7TAR	TARRA
Jackson - Snow King East	146.9100	–	O 123.0erx	W7TAR	TCEM
Marbleton	145.1450	–	O 100.0 (CA)er	KC7BJY	KC7BJY
Pinedale - Mt Airy	146.7750	–	O 100.0e L(448.100)rx	KC7BJY	SCARC
Smoot - Salt River Pass	145.2500	–	Oers	W7UY	SVARC

ALBERTA

Location	Output	Input	Notes	Call	Sponsor
BANFF					
Banff	146.6700	–	O	VE6MPR	WRN
Canmore	147.3600	+	O 110.9/110.9el	VE6RMT	CARA
Lake Louise	146.8800	–	Ol	VE6BNP	WRN
Lake Louise	147.3300	+	OE-SUNsx	VE6HWY	CARA
CALGARY					
Airdrie	145.3100	–	Os	VE6AA	ARES
Calgary	145.2900	–	Olx	VA6CTV	VA6DD
Calgary	146.6100	–	Oe	VE6OIL	SARA
Calgary	146.6400	–	110.9/110.9 ep	VE6NQ	CARA
Calgary	146.7300	–	Oa	VE6MX	VE6MX
Calgary	146.7600	–	O 110.9/110.9a	VE6NOV	CARA
Calgary	146.8500	–	O 110.9/110.9el	VE6RYC	CARA
Calgary	146.9400	–	O 131.8/131.8l	VE6RPT	WRN
Calgary	147.0600	–	O 110.9/110.9e	VE6AUY	CARA

ALBERTA

Location	*Output*	*Input*	*Notes*	*Call*	*Sponsor*
Calgary	147.1800	+	O	VE6REC	CARA
Calgary	147.2100	+	O	VE6RPC	CARA
Calgary	147.2400	+	Oes	VE6QCW	VE6NLF
Calgary	147.2700	+	O 110.9/110.9	VE6RY	CARA
Calgary	147.3900	+	Oael	VE6WRT	VE6CPT
Crossfield	147.1350	+	Ol	VE6TPA	FARS/CCC
CENTRAL					
Clive	145.4300	–	O	VE6GAS	VE6ONE
CENTRAL EAST					
Alix/Bashaw	147.2100	+	Oael	VE6PAT	VE6ZH
Stettler	146.7000	–	Oa	VE6STR	------------
Three Hills	147.3150	–	O	VE6TRO	WRN
Youngston	145.4700	–	O	VE6YSR	VE6NBR
CENTRAL NORTH					
Camrose	146.7600	–	O	VE6WW	RCARC
Pigeon Lake	146.8800	–	Oex	VE6SS	------------
Wetaskiwin	145.3700	–	O	VE6WCR	VE6KP
CENTRAL SOUTH					
Carbon	146.7150	–	Oe	VE6RCB	CARA
Kathryn	145.3900	–	Ol	VE6OTR	WRN
Olds	145.4900	–	Oal	VE6OLS	VE6KN
Wimborne	146.9700	–	Oelx	VE6BT	THARC
CENTRAL WEST					
Limestone Mountain	145.2700	–	Ol	VE6MTR	SARA
Nordegg	145.2100	–	Ol	VE6PZ	CARL
Rocky Mtn House	146.9100	–	Oaelx	VE6VHF	CARL
Sundre	147.0750	+	O 100.0e E-SUNlx	VE6GAB	VE6GAB
DRUMHELLER					
Hanna	146.8200	–	Ol	VE6HB	THARC
EDMONTON					
Beaumont	147.1800	+	Oa	VE6BUZ	LEMIRE
Devon	146.6850	–	O	VE6LOS	VE6FQ
Edmonton	145.4100	–	Ol	VE6NHB	SARA
Edmonton	146.6400	–	O	VE6QCR	QCARC
Edmonton	146.8500	–	Oae	VE6ETR	VE6BJP
Edmonton	146.9400	–	O	VE6MR	VE6MR
Edmonton	147.0600	–	Oa	VE6HM	NARC
Edmonton	147.1200	+	OaeWX	VE6RES	RAES
Edmonton	147.2400	+	Ol	VE6JN	NARC
Edmonton	147.2850	+	O	VE6OSM	VE6JDD
Ft Saskatchewan	147.2700	+	O	VE6CWW	------------
Ft Saskatchewan	147.2700	+	O	VE6FSR	VE6TCK
Ft Saskatchewan	147.3600	+		VE6GNS	VE6TCK
North Morinville	146.9400	–	O	VE6LAW	VE6ZA
Sherwood Park	145.2900	–	O	VE6SRV	------------

Location	Output	Input	Notes	Call	Sponsor
FT MCMURRAY					
Ft McMurray	146.9400	–		VE6TAC	------------
Ft McMurray	147.0000	+	Oae	VE6TRC	TARC
GRANDE PRAIRIE					
Grande Prairie	146.3600	146.3600	Oa	VE6LGL	PCARC
Grande Prairie	146.8500	–	O	VE6BL	PCARC
Grande Prairie	147.0600	–	Ox	VE6OL	PCARC
Grande Prairie	147.1500	+	O	VE6XN	PCARC
Rycroft	146.9700	–	O	VE6MAR	VE6BHH
Valleyview	147.2400	+	O	VE6YK	------------
LETHBRIDGE					
Lethbridge	146.8800	–	Oe	VE6CAM	VE6CAM
Lethbridge	147.1500	+	Oa	VE6UP	CCRG
Raymond	145.3700	–	O	VE6EEK	VE6FIE
MEDICINE HAT					
Brooks	147.1200	+	Oel	VE6EID	BARC
Brooks	147.2700	+	Oa	VE6NEW	BARC
Medicine Hat	145.4100	–	Ol	VE6CDR	VE6GLF
Medicine Hat	146.7000	–	O	VE6HHO	MHARC
Medicine Hat	147.0600	–	Oalx	VE6HAT	MHARC
Medicine Hat	147.1800	+	O	VE6MHT	MHARC
NORTH					
Athabaska	146.7300	–	Oe	VE6BOX	VE6BOY
NORTH EAST					
Andrew	146.7000	–	Oa	VE6JET	VE6BIK
Ashmont	147.1800	+	EXP	VE6TTL	VE6ARJ
Cold Lake	147.0900	+	Oae	VE6ADI	CLARC
Elk Island	146.6100	–	O	VE6REI	VE6BEX
Glendon	145.4500	–		VE6HOG	VE6XLR
La Corey	147.3750	+	O	VE6MBJ	CLARC
Lloydminster	145.2900	–	Ol	VE6YLL	------------
May Lakes	147.1500	+	Ol	VE6TBC	VE6RMB
Poe	145.4900	–	O	VE6POE	VE6TCK
Slave Lake	147.0300	+	O	VE6SLR	VE6AMY
St Paul	146.6700	–	Oa	VE6SB	VE6SB
Willingdon	146.7900	–	Oelx	VE6RJK	VE6BIK
NORTH WEST					
Grande Cache	147.3900	+	Ol	VE6YGR	------------
Whitecourt	146.8200	–	Ox	VE6PP	QCARC
PEACE RIVER					
Fairview	147.3750	+	O	VE6AZZ	VE6NN
Peace River	146.7900	–	O	VE6PRC	PRARC
Peace River	146.8200	–	Oa	VE6PRR	------------
Peace River	146.9400	–	Oa	VE6AAF	------------
RED DEER					
Red Deer	147.1500	+	Oaelx	VE6QE	CARL
Red Deer/Penhold	145.3300	–	Olx	VE6REP	SARA

Location	*Output*	*Input*	*Notes*	*Call*	*Sponsor*
SOUTH					
Claresholm	146.7900	–	Oe	VE6ROT	PHARTS
High River	145.1900	–	O	VE6HWC	FARS
High River	147.0000	+	Oae	VE6CQM	VE6BGL
Milk River	146.7600	–	Oal	VE6BRC	VE6BRX
Nanton	145.1700	–	Oelsx	VE6HRB	FARS
Warner	146.6700	–	O	VE6BBR	VE6BD
SOUTH WEST					
Black Diamond	145.3700	–	Olsx	VE6HRD	FARS
Burmis	145.3900	–	O	VE6HRP	FARS
/Crowsnest Pass			A(*ON/#OFF)lsx		
Chain Lakes	147.0300	+	Ol	VE6WRO	WRN
Claresholm	145.2100	–	O	VE6AAH	VE6ARS
Coleman	145.4900	–	O	VE6CNP	FARS
Millarville	145.1900	–	Ol	VE6HRC	FARS
Pincher Creek	145.4500	–	O	VE6PAS	VE6COM
Turner Valley	147.3000	+	●	VE6CBI	VE6CBI
SUNDRE					
Barrier Mountain	147.0300	–	O 131.8#lx	VE6AMP	Wild Rose Network
YELLOWHEAD					
Hinton	146.7600	–	Oaex	VE6YAR	VE6YAC
Jasper	146.9400	–	O	VE6YPR	YARC
Jasper	147.4800	–	O	VE6KMC	------------

BRITISH COLUMBIA

Location	*Output*	*Input*	*Notes*	*Call*	*Sponsor*
FRASER VALLEY					
Abbotsford	145.0300	+	O	VE7PKV	FVARESS
Abbotsford	146.6100	–	O 110.9	VE7RVA	FVARESS
Abbotsford	147.2800	+	110.9	VE7RST	AARESS
Aldergrove	147.3800	+	203.5e	VE7RLY	Langley AR
Chilliwack	145.1100	–	O	VA7RSH	Cheam Rptr
Chilliwack	146.9600	–	110.9	VA7CRC	VE7BHG
Chilliwack	147.0000	+	88.5	VE7VCR	VE7HD
Chilliwack	147.1000	+	110.9e	VE7RCK	VE7BHG
Hope	146.7000	–	77	VE7UVR	VE7HZR
Hope	147.0800	+	O 110.9	VE7RVB	FVARESS
Langley City	147.3800	+	77.0e	VE7RLY	Langley AR
Langley South	147.3800	+	110.9e	VE7RLY	Langley AR
Maple Ridge	146.8000	–	156.7	VE7RMR	Maple Ridg
GREATER VANCOUVER					
Burnaby	145.1700	–	O	VE7TEL	TPARC
Burnaby	145.3500	–	127.3	VE7RBY	BARC
Burnaby	147.0600	+	O	VE7FVR	IPARN
Coquitlam	145.3100	–	O	VE7MFS	Coq. Fire
Delta	147.3400	+	107.2	VE7SUN	VE7DID
New Westminster	145.3900	–	O 100el	VE7NWR	NWARC
Pemberton	146.9800	–	O	VE7PVR	Squamish A
Port Coquitlam	145.4900	–	94.8e	VA7RPC	Poco Fire
Richmond	147.1400	+	79.7	VE7RMD	Richmond A

Location	*Output*	*Input*	*Notes*	*Call*	*Sponsor*
Sea-to-Sky	146.9600	–	151.4	VA7SQU	VE7IDQ
Squamish	147.0000	+		VE7SQR	Squamish A
Surrey	147.3600	+	110.9e	VE7RSC	Surrey ARC
Vancouver	145.1500	–	○ 123.0l	VE7ROX	VE7ROX
Vancouver	145.2100	–	○	VE7RTY	VE7BBL
Vancouver	145.2700	–	100	VE7RHS	UBC ARS
Vancouver	145.2900	–	100	VA7IP	VE7LTD
Vancouver	145.4500	–	●	VE7TOK	VE7MBG
Vancouver	146.7200	–		VE7RBC	CBC ARC
Vancouver	146.7200	–		VE7RBI	CBC ARC
Vancouver	146.9400	–	●el	VE7RPT	BCFMCA
Vancouver	147.0400	+	○	VE7RCH	Cheam Rptr
Vancouver	147.1200	+	156.7l	VE7VAN	VE7DBK
Vancouver	147.2600	+		VE7RHB	VE7QH
Vancouver	147.2600	+		VE7RNS	VE7QH
Vancouver	147.3000	+	●	VE7RDX	BCDX Club
Whistler	147.0600	+		VE7WHR	VE7WHR
White Rock	146.9000	–	91.5	VE7RWR	WRARC
NORTH COAST					
Hazelton	146.9400	–	○	VE7RHD	BVARC
Kitimat	146.8200	–	○	VE7SNO	Kitimat AR
Kitimat	147.0600	–	○	VE7RAF	VE7ACF
Prince Rupert	146.8800	–	○	VE7RPR	PRARC
Prince Rupert	146.9400	–	○	VE7RKI	VE7EDZ
Prince Rupert	147.2800	+	○	VE7RMM	Prince Rup
Queen Charlotte	146.6800	–	○	VE7RQI	QCI ARC
Terrace	146.0000	+	○	VE7RTK	Terrace AR
Terrace	146.8000	–		VE7FFU	VE7IJJ
Terrace	146.9400	–	○	VE7RDD	Doug Davie
NORTH INTERIOR					
Burns Lake	146.9400	–	100	VE7LRB	LDARC/VE7L
Fishpot - Nazko	147.1500	+	l	VE7MBM	QRES
Fort St James	147.2400	+	100	VE7RFF	VE7XJC
Fort St James	147.3300	+	100	VE7DPG	VA7RC
Fraser Lake	146.8400	–	100l	VE7RES	PGARC
Houston	147.0600	+	100l	VE7RHN	BV ARC
Hudson's Hope	146.8800	–	100	VA7RHH	Hudson's H
Loos	146.8800	–	100.el	VE7RES	PGARC
Mackenzie	146.8200	–	100l	VE7MKR	VE7MKR
Mackenzie	147.3300	–	●e	VE7ZBK	Mackenzie
McBride	146.7600	–	100	VE7RMB	PGARC
Pine Pass	146.6400	–	100	VE7RES	PGARC
Prince George	145.4300	–	100el	VE7RES	Prince Geo
Prince George	146.7000	–	100l	VE7FFF	Prince Geo
Prince George	146.9100	–	100l	VE7RWT	Prince Geo
Prince George	146.9400	–	100el	VE7RPM	Prince Geo
Prince George	147.0000	+	l	VE7RUN	VE7EAA
Prince George	147.3000	+	100el	VE7RES	PGARC
Quesnel	146.9700	–	100	VE7GPC	VE7JIU

BRITISH COLUMBIA

Location	Output	Input	Notes	Call	Sponsor
Quesnel	147.0600	–	O	VE7RQL	Quesnel AR
Quesnel	147.2100	+	100el	VE7RES	PGARC
Smithers	146.8800	–	l	VE7RBH	BV ARC
Tumbler Ridge	147.2700	+	O	VE7RTR	VA7XX
Valemont	147.0000	+	100el	VE7RES	PGARC
Vanderhoof	146.8000	–	100l	VE7RSM	Nechako Cl
Vanderhoof	146.8800	–	O	VE7RON	VE7UP
Verdun	146.7600	–	100	VE7LRB	LDARC
Wells/Barkerville	147.3800	+	100	VE7RLS	QARC
Williams Lake	146.6200	–	100	VE7RTI	QARC/VE7EQ
Williams Lake	147.1200	+		VE7RWL	W'S LK ARC
Williams Lake	147.1800	+		VE7WLP	WLARC/VE7B
Williams Lake	147.3000	+	100	VE7KDL	VE7PW
PEACE RIVER					
Chetwynd	146.9100	–		VE7ATY	VA7XX
Dawson Creek	146.7600	–	O	VE7RMS	VA7CC
Dawson Creek	146.9400	–	O	VE7RDC	VE7DSD
Fort Nelson	146.9400	–	Ol	VE7VFN	FNARC
Fort St John	146.6400	–		VE7RSJ	VA7XX
Fort St John	147.2100	+		VE7RUC	VA7XX
Pouce Coupe	146.2500	+		VE7AGJ	VE7AGJ
SOUTH CENTRAL					
100 Mile House	146.7400	–	a	VE7SCQ	VE7GTH
Apex Mtn	146.9200	–	Ol	VE7OKN	Penticton
Barriere	147.2400	+		VE7RTN	IPARN
Barriere	147.3000	+	e	VE7RTN	VE7PW
Barriere	147.3600	+	O	VE7LMR	VE7KDL
Barriere	147.3800	+	O	VA7RTN	VE7MOB
Blackpool	146.9000	–	O 100	VE7RBP	Wells Gray
Christina Lake	146.7600	–	O	VE7RCL	Grand Fork
Clearwater	146.9200	–	O	VE7RWG	Wells Gray
Clinton	146.6800	–	O	VE7RKL	IPARN
Clinton	147.3600	+	O	VE7LMR	VE7PW
Coquihalla	146.9800	–	123.0	VE7TYN	Kamloops A
Coquihalla	147.1000	+	O	VE7LGN	VE7FFK
Ellison	147.2600	+	88.5	VA7UN	VA7UN
Ellison	147.2600	444.7000	88.5	VA7UN	VA7UN
Granite Peak	146.7600	–	a	VE7RNH	Shuswap AR
Kamloops	146.8000	–	100	VE7TRU	VE7PW
Kamloops	146.9400	–	O	VE7DUF	Kamloops A
Kamloops	146.9600	–	e	VE7RKA	Kamloops A
Kamloops	147.1800	+	Oe	VE7KEG	VE7EFL
Kamloops	147.2400	+	O	VE7KIG	VE7LGF
Kamloops	147.3200	+	el	VE7RLO	Kamloops A
Kelowna	145.4900	–	88.5	VE7HWY	OCARC
Kelowna	146.6200	–	Oa	VE7ROK	OCARC
Kelowna	146.6800	–		VE7OGO	OCARC
Kelowna	146.7000	–	e	VA7NBC	VA7UN
Kelowna	146.7200	–	O	VE7EJP	VA7UN

Location	*Output*	*Input*	*Notes*	*Call*	*Sponsor*
Kelowna	146.7200	–	l	VE7OGO	OCARC
Kelowna	146.7800	–	O	VE7SFX	VE7EQN
Kelowna	146.8200	–		VE7ROC	OCARC
Kelowna	146.8400	–	88.5	VA7CNN	VA7UN
Kelowna	146.8600	–	88.5l	VE7RBG	OCARC
Kelowna	147.0000	+	l	VE7ROW	OCARC
Kelowna	147.1400	+	O	VE7VTC	VE7VTC
Kelowna	147.2400	+	O	VE7RIM	VE7KHQ/IPA
Kelowna	147.3000	+	e	VE7KTV	VA7UN
Kelowna	147.3600	+		VA7JPL	VA7UN
Lillooett	147.3800	+	O	VE7TJS	Tyler Schw
Lone Butte	147.2200	+	88.5	VE7AZQ	VE7LX
Lytton	147.0600	+	O	VE7HGR	IPARN
Manning Park	147.0600	+	O	VE7MPR	IPARN
Merritt	146.6600	–	O	VE7IRN	IPARN
Merritt	147.0800	+	110.9	VE7RIZ	VE7RIZ
Monashee Pass	146.7400	–	123	VE7SMT	NORAC
Mt Avola	145.3500	–	O	VE7RBP	Wells Gray
Okanagan Shuswap	147.0600	+	O	VE7RNR	NORAC
Oliver	147.1600	+	100	VE7RBD	Oliver ARC
Oliver	147.3800	+	O	VE7ROR	OARC
Osoyoos	145.2700	–	107.2	VE7OSY	KARTS
Osoyoos	145.2900	–	107.2	VE7EHF	KARTS
Osoyoos	146.6600	–	O 156.7l	VE7OSY	KARTS
Osoyoos	146.9400	–		VE7STA	VE7STA
Osoyoos	147.1800	+	88.5	VE7OJP	VA7UN
Penticton	146.6400	–	● 131.8elp	VE7RCP	Penticton
Penticton	147.1200	+	O	VE7RPC	Penticton
Revelstoke	147.2000	+	l	VE7RJP	VE7UN
Salmon Arm	146.1600	+	a	VE7CAL	Shuswap AR
Salmon Arm	147.0200	+		VE7RSA	Salmon Arm
Shuswap	147.0800	+	O	VE7LIM	VE7DTN
Sicamous	145.4700	–	O	VE7QMR	VE7HMN
Silver Star	146.9000	–	123	VE7RHW	VE7HW/VE7O
Sorrento	146.6400	–		VE7RXX	VE7EHL
Sorrento	147.1400	+	O	VA7AHR	R.Hickman
Tappen	146.6400	–		VE7RAM	VE7LOG
Tatlayoko Valley	147.2800	+	162.2	VA7TKR	VA7XK
Thompson Shuswap	147.0000	–	a	VE7RLD	Kamloops A
Valemont	146.6000	–		VE7YCR	Wells Gray
Vernon	146.8000	–	O	VE7EGO	NORAC
Vernon	146.8800	–		VE7RSS	NORAC
Vernon	147.0400	+	a	VE7RIP	NORAC
Vernon	147.2200	+	O	VA7VMR	VE7OHM
SOUTH EAST					
Cranbrook	146.9400	–		VE7CAP	EKARC
Creston	146.8000	–	O	VE7RCA	CVARC

Location	*Output*	*Input*	*Notes*	*Call*	*Sponsor*
FairmontHotSpring	146.8500	–		VE7RIN	EKARC
Golden	147.1600	+	l	VE7DMO	East Koote
Grand Forks	146.9400	–	100el	VE7RGF	Grand Fork
Grand Forks	147.2800	+		VE7RGF	Grand Fork
Kimberley	145.1900	28.6000		VE7REK	EKARC
Kimberley	146.9400	–	O	VE7CAP	Ken MacDon
Kootenay Lake	147.0600	–		VE7BTU	WKARC
Nakusp	146.9400	–	e	VE7RDM	VE7EDA
Nelson	146.6400	–		VE7RCT	WKARC
Rossland	147.1400	+	O	VE7OGM	Ben Peach
Sparwood	147.3000	+	100	VE7RSQ	Karl Ehrle
Trail	146.8400	–		VE7CAQ	BVARC
VANC ISLAND CENTRAL					
Alberni Valley	145.2900	–	141.3	VE7RTE	VE7TFM
Chemainus	146.6800	–	141.3	VE7RNA	Cowichan V
Comox	147.1600	+		VE7KIG	VE7LGF
Lund	147.0000	+	100.0	VA7LND	Powell Riv
Nanaimo	145.4300	–	141.3l	VA7DJA	NARA
Nanaimo	146.6400	–	l	VE7ISC	NARA
Nanaimo	146.9800	–	141.3	VE7TUB	NARA
Nanaimo	147.1800	+	O	VE7RBB	VE7PI
Parksville	145.3700	–	Oa	VE7RPQ	Mid Island
Parksville	147.0800	+	141.3p	VA7RFR	VA7DMN
Parksville	147.2800	+	O 141.3ael	VE7PQA	ORCA
Parksville	147.3400	+	141.3	VE7MIR	MIRA
Port Alberni	147.1500	+	151.4	VE7RPA	Arrowsmith
Port Alberni	147.2400	+		VE7KU	VA7JY
Powell River	147.2000	+	141.3	VE7PRR	Powell Riv
Sunshine Coast	147.2200	+	100.0l	VE7RXZ	VE7ALT
Tofino	146.8800	–	141.3	VE7TOF	Comox Vall
Tofino	147.0000	–	100.0l	VE7RWC	Arrowsmith
VANC ISLAND NORTH					
Campbell River	146.7600	–	O	VE7XJR	VE7BMR
Campbell River	146.8200	–		VE7RVR	VE7DAY
Campbell River	146.9600	–		VE7CRC	VE7BMR
Comox Valley	146.7800	–	141.3e	VE7RCV	Comox Vall
Courtenay	146.6200	–	141.3	VE7NIR	North Isla
Courtenay	146.9100	–	141.3	VE7RAP	Comox Vall
Port McNeil	146.9200	–	e	VA7RNI	North Isla
Port McNeil	146.9400	–	O	VE7RNI	North Isla
Sayward	146.7000	–	O	VE7RNC	North Isla
Woss Lake	146.8800	–	O	VE7RWV	NIARS
VANC ISLAND SOUTH					
Duncan	145.4700	–	127.3e	VE7RVC	CVARS
East Sooke	145.4300	–	100	VE7RAH	Base ARC
Malahat	146.9800	–	O 123.0	VE7XMR	CERT-BC
Oak Bay	146.8400	–	107.2	VE7XIC	WARA
Saanich	145.2900	–	167.9e	VE7SER	Saanich EP

Location	*Output*	*Input*	*Notes*	*Call*	*Sponsor*
Saltspring Is	146.6600	–	100	VE7RMT	WARA
Saltspring Is	147.3200	+	O	VE7RSI	Saltspring
Sidney	146.6600	–	123.0	VE7MXT	WARA
Sooke	146.8400	–	123.0	VE7XSK	WARA
Sooke	146.9800	–	103.5	VE7RWS	VE7ED
Sooke	147.2200	+		VE7RSK	Paul Johns
Triangle Mtn	146.8400	–	131.8	VE7RMT	WARA
Victoria	145.1300	–	114.8e	VE7US	CRERCC
Victoria	145.4100	–	103.5	VE7RSR	Victoria N
Victoria	146.8400	–	100	VE7VIC	WARA
Victoria	147.1200	+	100l	VE7RBA	VE7IA
Victoria	147.2400	+	el	VE7RFR	VE7DAT
MANITOBA					
INTERLAKE					
Ashern	146.7000	–	O	VE4SHR	VE4KE
East Selkirk	146.7300	–	O	VE4SLK	SelkirkARC
Gimli	146.8500	–	Otae	VE4GIM	MANRS
Lundar	146.9700	–	Ol	VE4LDR	VE4GM
Teulon	145.4100	–	O	VE4TEU	ILARC
Woodlands	145.4300	–	Ol	VE4SIX	------------
NORTH					
Thompson	146.9400	–	#	VE4TPN	THOMPSON AR
NORTHWEST					
Dauphin	146.6400	–	Oa	VE4DPN	DARC
Dauphin	147.0300	–	Ox	VE4BMR	MANRS
Flin Flon	146.9400	–	Ox	VE4FFR	FliFlonRC
Swan River	146.9400	–	Ol	VE4SRR	SWANRARC
The Pas	145.3500	–	O	VE4PAS	------------
SOUTH CENTRAL					
Austin	146.9100	–	O	VE4MTR	VE4RE
Basswood	145.1500	–	O 127.3	VE4BAS	VE4TOM
Bruxelles	146.8800	–	Olx	VE4HS	SWARC
Elie	147.2400	+	O 127.3	VE4RAG	VE4TOM
Morris	145.2700	–	Oae	VE4CDN	MANRS
Neepawa	147.2100	+	Oae	VE4NEP	MANRS
Portage	147.1650	+	O	VE4PTG	VE4KE
Winkler	145.1900	+	O	VE4VRG	WinklerARC
SOUTHEAST					
Falcon Lake	146.6400	–	Ol	VE4FAL	VE4AS
Hadashville	147.3600	+	Oers	VE4EMB	MANRS
Lac Du Bonnet	145.3700	–	Ox	VE4PIN	PARC
SOUTHWEST					
Brandon	146.7300	–	Oa	VE4TED	BrandonRC
Brandon	146.9400	–	Ox	VE4BDN	BrandonRC
Killarney	146.8500	–	Ox	VE4KIL	VE4RO
WEST CENTRAL					
Foxwarren	147.0600	+	Ol	VE4PCL	PCLRS
Russell	147.2400	+	Ol	VE4BVR	RARC

Location	Output	Input	Notes	Call	Sponsor
WINNIPEG					
Bird's Hill	146.8200	–	O	VE4INT	------------
Milner Ridge	145.2100	–	Oae	VE4MIL	------------
Starbuck	146.6100	–	Olrs	VE4MAN	MANRS
Winnipeg	145.2300	–	O 127.3	VE4ARC	------------
Winnipeg	145.3500	–	Oa	VE4WNR	VE4VE
Winnipeg	146.7600	–	O	VE4CNR	PMCStaff
Winnipeg	147.1200	+	Ol	VE4AGA	VE4AGA
Winnipeg	147.2700	+	O	VE4UMR	UMARS
Winnipeg	147.3000	+	Ol	VE4EDU	MANRS
Winnipeg	147.3300	+	O	VE4RRC	RedRvrCC
Winnipeg	147.3900	+	Olrsx	VE4WPG	MANRS
Winnipeg	147.7800	–	●	VE4WDX	WnpgDXClb

NEW BRUNSWICK

Location	Output	Input	Notes	Call	Sponsor
ACADIEVILLE					
Acadieville	145.4300	–	Oel	VE9ACD	IRG
BATHURST					
Allardville	147.3150	+	Oel	VE1BRD	IRG
BELLEDUNE					
Elmtree	145.4100	–	Oel	VE9ELM	IRG
CAMPBELLTON					
7 Mile Ridge	147.3900	+	Oel	VE9VDR	IRG
Campbellton	146.6550	–	O	VE9CTN	VE2FXM
Campbellton	146.9550	–	O	VE9SMR	VE2FXM
DALHOUSIE					
Dalhousie	145.3900	–	O	VE9LED	------------
Dalhousie	145.4900	–	O	VE9DNB	VE9YN
Dalhousie	146.9700	–	O	VE9MDM	------------
DOAKTOWN					
Doaktown	146.9100	–	Oel	VE1XI	IRG
EDMUNDSTON					
Edmundston	147.3000	+	Ol	VE9TMR	CRAM
Riceville	145.1300	–	Oel	VE9RCV	IRG
FREDERICTON					
Crabbe Mtn	146.7600	–	Oel	VE1PD	IRG
Fredericton	146.6550	–	O/123.0 L(446.650)p	VE9CWM	VE9HAM
Fredericton	147.1200	+	Oael	VE1BM	IRG
Fredericton	147.1650	+	O 123.0	VE9FTN	VE1KO
Fredericton	147.2550	+	O 123.0	VE9HAM	VE9HAM
Fredericton	147.3000	+	OL(IRLP)	VE9FNB	FARC
Fredericton	147.3600	+	O	VE9DGP	VE9AI
Oromocto	145.3100	–	Oe	VE9OPH	Hospital
FUNDY					
Fundy Park	145.1700	–	Ol	VE9TCF	------------
GRAND MANAN IS					
Grand Manan Is	146.9550	–	Ol	VE9GMI	IRG

Location	*Output*	*Input*	*Notes*	*Call*	*Sponsor*
MINTO					
Minto/Chipman	145.1900	–	O	VE9GLA	------------
MIRAMICHI					
Chapin Is Rd	147.1500	+	Oel	VE9MIR	IRG
Newcastle	146.7300	–	O	VE1NCW	VE1DAB
MONCTON					
Moncton	146.8800	–	O	VE1RPT	VE1NU
Moncton	147.0900	+	Oel	VE1MTN	IRG
Moncton	147.3450	+	OL(IRLP)	VE9TCR	TCARC
PERTH					
Kintore Mtn	147.0600	–	Oel	VE9KMT	IRG
SACKVILLE					
Fairfield	145.2300	–	Oel	VE9SKV	IRG
SAINT JOHN					
Grove Hill	145.3300	–	Oel	VE9STM	IRG
Hampton	145.1300	–	O	VE9HPN	LCARC
Otter Lake	147.3900	+	O	VE9PSA	VE1BAC
Saint John	145.1100	–	O	VE9SNB	VE9SNB
Saint John	146.8200	–	O	VE9STJ	IRG
Saint John	147.2700	+	O/100.0e L(IRLP)	VE9SJN	LCARC
Spruce Lake	146.8950	–	O	VE9SJW	LCARC
SHEDIAC					
Shediac	147.2250	+	Ol	VE9SBR	SBRG
Shediac	147.3750	+	O	VE9DRB	------------
ST GEORGE					
St George	147.2250	+	Ol	VE9STG	IRG
ST LEONARD					
St Leonard	145.3500	–	OlBI WX	VE9STL	IRG
ST QUENTIN					
St Quentin	145.2300	–	Oel	VE9SQN	IRG
St Quentin	145.4500	–	O	VE9MIK	VE1MIK
ST STEPHEN					
Pleasant Ridge	146.7000	–	Oel	VE1BI	IRG
STANLEY					
Stanley	147.0300	+	Oe	VE9NRV	IRG
SUSSEX					
Scotch Mtn	146.6100	–	Ol	VE9SMT	IRG
TRACADIE					
Pokemouche	147.0300	+	O	VE1AZU	VE1BKU
St Isidore	146.7000	–	Oel	VE9SID	IRG
Tracadie	145.4700	–	O	VE9CR	------------
WOODSTOCK					
Skiff Lake	145.3700	–	Oe	VE9IRG	IRG
Woodstock	146.9700	–	Oa	VE9CCR	CCARC
Woodstock	147.1800	+	O	VE9TOW	CARC

Location	*Output*	*Input*	*Notes*	*Call*	*Sponsor*
NEWFOUNDLAND AND LABRADOR					
AVALON EAST					
Cape Pine	147.1200	+	O	VO1CPR	ILARC
Ferryland	147.2800	+	O	VO1CQD	ILARC
Holyrood	146.7600	–	Oal	VO1BT	SONRA
Mount Pearl	146.8800	–	OL(EIRLP)	VO1CGR	VO1VCP
Portugal Cove South	147.0300	+	O	VO1ILR	ILARC
St John's	146.7900	–	OL(IRLP)	VO1AAA	SONRA
St John's	146.9400	–	tTTel	VO1GT	SONRA
St John's	147.3450	+	O	VO1RCR	AVRAC
Transportable	146.6100	–	ep	VO1RNC	VO1RWT
Transportable	147.0000	–	ep	VO1NET	VO1EMO
AVALON WEST					
Heart's Content	146.9700	–	O	VO1TCR	BARK
Heart's Content	147.3000	+	O	VO1TBR	UTARC
New Harbour	147.0900	+	L(IRLP)	VO1PCR	VO1BIL
Placentia	146.8200	–	OL(IRLP)	VO1ARG	PARA
Placentia	147.0100	+	OL(ECHO)	VO1PAR	PARA
Placentia	147.3850	–	O	VO1AWS	VO1ANJ
Sunnyside	147.2200	+	O	VO1PBR	VO1IRA
Transportable	147.0000	–	ep	VO1NET	VO1EMO
BURIN PEN					
Marystown	146.8500	–	L(EIRLP)	VO1MST	VO1EE
Transportable	147.0000	–	ep	VO1NET	VO1EMO
CENTRAL NF					
Botwood	147.2850	+	O	VO1BOT	VO1AJ
Eastport	147.3850	+	OL(E)	VO1ISR	VO1ISR
Gander	146.8800	–	Oa	VO1ADE	ARCON
Gander	147.1800	+	Ol	VO1GLR	ARCON
Grand Falls	146.6000	–	Oe	VO1HHR	EVARC
Grand Falls	146.7600	–	Oe	VO1JY	EVARC
Lewisporte Junction	147.3200	+	Ol	VO1LJR	ARCON
Shoal Hr	146.6600	–	Ol	VO1SHR	ARCON
Transportable	147.0000	–	ep	VO1NET	VO1EMO
LABRADOR					
Goose Bay	146.3400	+	O	VO2GB	GARS
Labrador City	146.9400	–	O	VO2KG	HOWL
Labrador City	147.7600	–	Oa	VO2LMC	HOWL
Transportable	147.0000	–	ep	VO1NET	VO1EMO
WESTERN AVALON					
Carbonear	147.9850	–	O#	VO1FRR	Dean Penny
WESTERN NF					
Baie Verte	146.9700	–	O	VO1BVR	BVARC
Corner Brook	147.3600	+	Ol	VO1MO	HUMBARS
Ramea	147.2800	+	O	VO1RIR	VO1UG
St Anthony	147.9600	–	O	VO1GNP	SAARA
Transportable	147.0000	–	ep	VO1NET	VO1EMO

Location	Output	Input	Notes	Call	Sponsor
WESTERN REGION					
Birchy Lake	146.6400	–	Ol	VO1BLR	HUMBARS
NORTHWEST TERRITORIES					
FT RAE					
Ft Rae	145.1500	–	O	VE8RAE	Yellowknife ARS
YELLOWKNIFE					
Yellowknife	146.9400	–	O L(224.940/224.340)	VE8YK	Yellowknife ARS
NOVA SCOTIA					
AMHERST					
Amherst	147.2850	+	OL(IRLP)	VE1WRC	WCARC
ANTIGONISH					
Antigonish	146.8200	–	Oel	VE1RTI	AARC
BARRINGTON					
Barrington Passage	146.8800	–	O	VE1JNR	VE1MM
French Lake	147.2550	+	Oel	VE1OPK	SCARC
BRIDGETOWN					
Bridgetown	147.0600	–	Oel	VE1BO	NSARA
BRIDGEWATER					
Bridgewater	147.1200	+	OL(IRLP)	VE1KIN	LCARC
Italy Cross	147.0900	+	Oel	VE1VL	LCARC
CHESTER					
Sherwood	147.3300	+	Oel	VE1LUN	LCARC
DARTMOUTH					
Dartmouth	147.1500	+	Oae	VE1DAR	DARC
DIGBY					
Digby	147.0150	+	Oel	VE1AAR	FARC
EAST KEMPTVILLE					
East Kemptville	147.1050	+	Oel	VE1EKV	YARC
GREENWOOD					
Greenwood	145.2100	–	Ol	VE1VAL	VE1II
Greenwood	147.2400	+	OL(IRLP)	VE1WN	GARC
GUYSBOROUGH					
Lundy	146.7000	–	Oel	VE1GYS	AARC
HALIFAX					
BeaverBank	147.0450	+	Oe	VE1MTT	TPARC
Halifax	146.9400	–	O/82.5e L(IRLP)	VE1HNS	HARC
Halifax	147.2700	+	Oel	VE1PSR	HARC
Hammonds Plains	146.6850	–	Oel	VE1PKT	VE1YZ
HFX Airport	146.9700	–	Oel	VE1CDN	VE1YZ
HALIFAX-ALL NS					
Halifax Portable	145.2500	–	Oep	VE1ECT	HARC
Halifax Portable	145.4100	–	Oep	VE1HRM	VE1AJP

NOVA SCOTIA

Location	Output	Input	Notes	Call	Sponsor
INVERNESS					
Kiltarllty Mtn	146.7300	–	Oel	VE1KIL	SARC
KEJIMKUJIK					
Kejimkujik Nat Park	147.1950	+	OE-SUNI	VE1KEJ	QCARC
KENTVILLE					
Glenmount	147.1800	+	Oael	VE1AEH	KCARC
LIVERPOOL					
Granite Village	147.3600	+	Oe	VE1BBY	QCARC
Liverpool	147.0600	+	O	VE1QW	QCARC
Liverpool	147.3000	+	Oael	VE1VO	QCARC
Middlefield	147.3900	+	O	VE1AVA	QCARC
LOCKEPORT					
Lockeport	147.2250	+	O	VE1LFD	------------
MUSQUODOBOIT					
Musquodoboit Hrbr	147.0300	+	Oel	VE1MHR	ESARC
NEW GERMANY					
Church Lake	145.2900	–	O	VE1DSR	DSTAR
NEW GLASGOW					
Pictou	146.7600	–	Oel	VE1HR	PCARC
PARRSBORO					
Parrsboro	145.4700	–	OE-SUNI	VE1PAR	VE1BXK
Parrsboro	146.7450	–	Ol	VE1NET	VE1BXK
SHEET HARBOUR					
Sheet Harbour	145.4500	–	Oel	VE1ESR	ESARC
SHELBURNE					
Middle Ohio	146.6100	–	Oael	VE1SCR	SCARC
SHERBROOKE					
Sherbrooke	145.3900	–	Oel	VE1SAB	ESARC
SPRINGFIELD					
Springfield	146.8350	–	Oel	VE1LCA	LCARC
SPRINGHILL					
Lynn Mtn	147.0000	–	Oel	VE1SPR	VE1ZX
Springhill	146.8050	–	Oel	VE1SPH	WARC
Sugarloaf	145.3500	–	OeL(IRLP) WX	VE1BHS	VE1ZX
ST PETERS					
Oban	147.1050	+	Oel	VE1OBN	NSARA
SYDNEY					
Cape Smokey	147.2400	+	Oael	VE1CBI	SARC
Glace Bay	147.3900	+	O	VE1QSL	VE1APE
Rear Boisdale	146.8800	–	Oel	VE1HAM	SARC
Sydney	146.6100	–	Oel	VE1CR	SARC
Sydney	146.9400	–	Oa	VE1HK	SARC
Sydney	146.9700	–	O	VE1QRZ	VE1APE
TRURO					
Harmony	147.1350	+	OL(IRLP)	VE1HAR	VE1III
Nuttby Mtn	146.7900	–	Oel	VE1XK	TARC

Location	*Output*	*Input*	*Notes*	*Call*	*Sponsor*
Nuttby Mtn	147.2100	+	Oe	VE1TRO	TARC
WINDSOR					
Gore	146.6400	–	Oe	VE1OM	TPARC
Windsor	146.9100	–	O	VE1HCA	HCARC
YARMOUTH					
Yarmouth	146.7300	–	OeL(IRLP)	VE1YAR	YARC
Yarmouth	146.8650	–	Oes	VE1LN	EMO
ONTARIO					
CENTRAL					
Barrie	147.0000	+	O 156.7e	VE3RAG	BARC
Barrie	147.1500	+	O 127.3as	VE3KES	VE3OKS
Berkeley	145.2900	–	O 156.7e	VA3CAX	RARC
Dwight	145.2700	–	O 156.7e	VE3MUS	VE3MUS
			L(IRLP ECHOLINK COARC)		
Dwight	146.7750	–	O 156.7e	VE3MUS	VE3MUS
			L(IRLP ECHOLINK)		
Dwight	146.8200	–	O 156.7e	VE3MUS	VE3MUS
			L(IRLP ECHOLINK COARC)		
Edgar	146.8500	–	O 156.7e	VE3LSR	LSRA
Edgar	147.3150	+	O 156.7e	VE3LSR	LSRA
			L(IRLP)		
Edger	147.2850	+	O 156.7e	VA3IMB	------------
			L(ANALOG & P25)		
Keswick	147.2250	+	O 118.8e	VE3YRC	YRARC
			L(IRLP)		
Lions Head	146.7150	–	O 156.7e	VE3CAX	RARC
Midland	146.7600	–	O	VE3SGB	SGBARC
Midland	146.7900	–	O 156.7e	VE3BMR	BMARC
Midland	146.9100	–	OL(ULR)	VE3UGB	SGBARC
Orillia	146.6550	–	O 156.7	VA3OPS	------------
			L(ECHOLINK)		
Orillia	147.2100	+	O 156.7	VE3ORR	OARC
Parry Sound	145.4900	–	OaL(IRLP)	VE3RPL	PARRA
			WX		
Port Sydney	146.8650	–	O 156.7	VA3MRR	MRG
Sarnia	146.9550	–	O(CA)e	VE3WHO	------------
			L(IRLP)		
Shelburne	146.6850	–	O 88.5 (CA)	VE3ZAP	------------
			eL(VE3ULR) WX		
CENTRAL EAST					
Bridgenorth	147.3000	+	O 162.2e	VA3OME	OCR
			L(IRLP)		
Colborne	147.1650	+	O 162.2	VE3RTY	------------
			L(TFMCS)		
Dysart Township	147.1050	+	Oe	VA3LTX	------------
Essonville	147.2400	+	Oae	VE3TBF	TBFRA
			L(IRLP ECHOLINK TFMCS)		
Haliburton	145.2100	–	O 162.2	VA3MIN	VHARA

ONTARIO

Location	*Output*	*Input*	*Notes*	*Call*	*Sponsor*
Lindsay	147.1950	+	Oe L(IRLP ECHOLINK)	VE3LNZ	VHARA
Minden	147.0750	+	O 162.2 (CA) L(443.55)	VE3VHH	------------
Omemee	147.0900	+	O 162.2 L(IRLP)	VA3OME	------------
Oshawa	147.1200	+	O 156.7	VE3OSH	NSARC
Peterborough	146.6250	–	O(CA)el	VE3PBO	PARC
CENTRAL WEST					
Kincardine	146.6100	–	Oe	VE3TIV	BRUCE ARC
Meaford	146.8950	–	O 156.7e L(VE3OSR)	VE3GBT	GBARC
Owen Sound	146.6400	–	O 156.7	VA3YOS	------------
Owen Sound	146.9400	–	Oae L(146.895)	VE3OSR	GBARC
Paisley	146.7300	–	O 97.4 L(IRLP)	VE3XTX	------------
FRONTENAC/LENNOX-ADDINGTON					
Clarendon Station	147.0900	+	O 151.4/151.4#es	VE3KAR	KARC
Kingston	146.7750	–	O	VE3KNR	Kingston ARES
Kingston	146.8050	–	O 151.4/151.4	VE3FRG	Frontenac ARES
Kingston	146.9400	–	L(I 2750)sx	VE3KBR	KARC
GLENGARRY					
Lancaster	147.5250	145.6700	O 131.8/131.8l	VE2REH	ARAI
HASTINGS					
Eldorado	145.4100	–	O 118.8/118.8 (CA)e	VA3SDR	Tri-County ARC
HASTINGS/PRINCE EDWARD					
Bancroft	147.2850	+	O/118.8ae WX	VA3FOY	VE3ATP
Belleville	146.9850	–	/118.8 L(I 2090)s	VE3QAR	QARC
Mcarthur Mills	147.1800	+	OE-SUN L(442.700 +)	VA3PLA	Planica ARC
Picton	146.7300	–	O/118.8	VE3TJU	PERC
Stockdale	147.0150	+	O 91.5/91.5	VE3TRR	VA3CAF
Tweed	145.3700	–	(CA)e L(KJG/ I 2947)sx	VE3RNU	VE3LCA
LANARK/LEEDS-GRENVILLE					
Almonte/Union Hall	147.2400	+	O 100.0/100.0	VA3ARE	Almonte ARC
Brockville	146.8200	–	O 100.0/100.0 L(444.000 E.)x	VE3IWJ	VA3TN
Christie Lake	145.2300	–	151.4/151.4 L(KJG/I 2947)	VA3TEL	VE3LCA
Kemptville	146.8500	–	151.4/151.4	VE3KPT	VA3WHS

Location	*Output*	*Input*	*Notes*	*Call*	*Sponsor*
Lansdowne	146.6250	–	100.0/100.0 s	VA3LGA	LGARES
Lavant	146.6400	–	A(*74 / #)e L(RNU/I 2947)sx	VE3KJG	VE3LCA
Mount Pakenham	145.3300	–	110.9/110.9 (CA)eL(I2018)	VE2REH	ARAI
Perth	146.9550	–	L(KJG)ps	VE3GWS	Lanark North Lee
Smiths Falls	147.2100	+	/100.0a	VE3RLR	RLARC
Toledo	146.8650	–	a	VE3HTN	HTMLUG
METRO TORONTO					
Ajax	147.3750	+	O 103.5e L(IRLP)	VE3SPC	SPARC
Ballantrae	145.4700	–	O 103.5e L(CANWARN)	VE3ULR	VE3ULR RA
Ballantrae	147.3300	+	O 103.5 (CA) L(IRLP COARC)x	VA3BAL	COARC
Baltimore	145.1500	–	O 186.2 L(CANWARN)	VE3RTR	VE3ULR RA
Brampton	146.8800	–	Oe L(443.550) WX	VE3PRC	PARC
Dufferin	145.4500	–	O 85.4	VE3YPL	------------
Grand Valley	146.8350	–	O 103.5	VE3POR	------------
Inglewood	146.7000	–	O 103.5	VE3RDP	PARC
King City	145.3100	–	O 103.5 L(IRLP ECHOLINK)	VE3GSR	VE3GSR
King City	145.3500	–	O 103.5e	VE3YRA	YRARC
King City	146.6100	–	O 103.5e WX	VE3WAS	------------
Mississauga	145.4300	–	O 103.5 (CA)e	VE3MIS	MARC
Scarborough	146.7450	–	O 131.8	VA3RTC	------------
Scarborough	146.9400	–	O 103.5	VE3TOR	ETRG
Toronto	145.1100	–	O 82.5	VE3WOO	------------
Toronto	145.1300	–	O 103.5e L(GTU)	VA3GTU	------------
Toronto	145.2300	–	O 103.5l	VE3OBN	SSPBD
Toronto	145.3700	–	O 103.5e L(CANWARN)	VE3CTV	CTV ARC
Toronto	145.4100	–	O 103.5e L(TFM IRLP)	VE3TWR	TFMCS
Toronto	146.9850	–	OL(IRLP)	VE3SKY	SARC
Toronto	147.1800	+	O 103.5e L(VE3YRC)	VE3YRK	------------
Toronto	147.2700	+	O	VE3TNC	------------
Uxbridge	146.6700	–	O 67.0	VE3PIC	PRA
Uxbridge	147.0600	+	O 103.5e L(IRLP TFM)z	VE3RPT	TFMCS
Whitby	146.9700	–	O 156.7e	VA3SUP	------------
Whitby	147.1500	+	O 103.5e	VE3WOM	WARC

Location	Output	Input	Notes	Call	Sponsor
NATIONAL CAPITOL REGION					
Cumberland	145.2100	–	O 77.0/77.0 es	VA3EMV	EMRG
Ottawa	145.1900	–	al	VA3OTW	SARC
Ottawa	145.4500	–	/151.4 A(*#) eL(I2596)	VE3RIX	MARG
Ottawa	146.6700	–	136.5sx	VA3EMV	EMRG
Ottawa	146.7000	–	136.5/136.5 L(I 2210)x	VE3TST	VE3HXP
Ottawa	146.7900	–	/156.7a	VA3LCC	Cite Collegiale
Ottawa	146.8800	–	/136.5ps	VA3EMV	EMRG
Ottawa	147.0300	–	/100.0	VE3TEL	PARC
Ottawa	147.1500	+	O 100.0/100.0aeL(444.400 +)	VE3MPC	RCMP EOG
Ottawa	147.3000	+	/100 A(*123/#) L(444.2/53.03)	VE3TWO	OVMRC
Ottawa (E/W)	146.9850	–	123.0/123.0 s	VA3EMV	EMRG
Ottawa area	145.1100	–	/136.5ps	VA3EMV	EMRG
NIAGARA					
Dunnville	147.0750	+	O 107.2e	VE3HNR	DARC
Fonthill	147.3000	+	O 107.2e L(IRLP)	VE3WCR	NPARC
Ridgeway	147.1650	+	O 107.2e L(TFM) RB	VE3RAC	------------
Thorold	145.1900	–	O 107.2 L(VE3RAF)	VE3RAF	RAFMARC
Thorold	147.2400	+	O 107.2 (CA)e	VE3NRS	NPARC
NIPPISSING					
Madawaska	147.2550	+		VA3RRR	------------
NORTHEASTERN ONTARIO					
Cobalt	146.9700	–		VE3TAR	------------
Driftwood	147.3600	+	L(VE3AA)	VE3XAA	------------
Elliot lake	147.0000	+	a	VE3TOP	Elliot Lake ARC
Gogama	146.6100	–	L(VE3AA)	VE3OPO	------------
Hearst	146.7000	–	a(CA) Z(911)	VA3YHF	------------
Hearst	146.9400	–	a	VA3GJY	------------
Heyden	145.5700	–	O 100.0/100.0 E-WINDl	VE3SNS	SN Cluster
Kagawong	146.6700	–	Oex	VE3LTR	MARC
Kapuskasing	146.6400	–	a	VE3KKC	------------
Kapuskasing	146.9400	–		VE3NWA	------------
Kirkland lake	146.8800	–		VE3KLR	------------
Little Current	145.3100	–	O 156.7/156.7elx	VE3RXR	VE3AJB
Little current	146.6700	–		VE3LTR	------------
Little Current	147.2700	+	OaesWXx	VE3RMI	MARC

Location	*Output*	*Input*	*Notes*	*Call*	*Sponsor*
Little Current	147.2700	+	a	VE3RMI	------------
Mattawa	145.4100	–		VE3EOR	------------
Mattawa	147.1500	+		VE3NBR	------------
Montreal r hbr	145.2100	–	L(442.650)	VA3SNR	------------
Powassan / north bay	145.1100	–	a(CA)l	VE3NFM	------------
Ramore	147.2100	+	L(VE3AA)	VE3TIR	------------
Richards landing	146.8800	–	L(442.650)	VE3SJI	------------
Sault Ste Marie	146.9400	–	az	VE3SSM	------------
Sault Ste Marie	147.0600	–		VE3SAP	------------
Sault Ste Marie	147.1500	–	a	VE3YAK	------------
Sudbury	146.7000	–	a	VE3JPF	------------
Sudbury	147.0600	–		VE3SRG	------------
Sudbury	147.0900	+		VA3SRG	------------
Sudbury	147.3900	+		VE3RKN	------------
Temagami	146.9100	–	**O**	VE3TEM	------------
Timmins	147.0600	+	l	VE3AA	------------
Valley east	147.1200	+		VE3VLY	------------
Wawa	146.9400	–	a	VE3WAW	------------
NORTHWESTERN ONTARIO					
Atikokan	147.1200	+		VE3RIB	------------
Blackhawk	147.0600	+	l	VE3RBK	------------
Dryden	147.2400	+	**O**	VE3DRY	DARRC
Dryden	147.2550	+	aez	VE3DRY	------------
Ear falls/red lake	147.0000	+		VE3RLD	------------
Fort Frances	146.8200	–	al	VE3RLC	------------
Fort Frances	147.0600	–		VE3FHS	------------
Geraldton	147.9000	–	a	VE3GLD	------------
Ignace	146.5200	146.5200	**O**	VE3XAK	WARG
Kenora	146.9100	–	a	VE3YQK	------------
Kenora	147.0300	–	al	VE3LWR	------------
Longlac	147.0600	–		VE3LLT	------------
Sioux lookout	146.8500	–		VE3YXL	------------
Sioux narrows	146.9400	–	al	VE3RSN	------------
Thunder bay	146.8200	–	az	VE3TBR	------------
Thunder bay	146.9400	–		VE3WNJ	------------
Thunder bay	147.0600	–	a L(VE3TBB)	VE3YQT	------------
Thunder Bay	147.2700	+	●	VE3RUM	------------
Thunderbay	145.4500	–	**O**	VE3BGA	VE3OJ
Upsala	145.4700	–	aL(147.060)	VE3TBB	------------
PRESCOTT-RUSSELL					
Alfred	145.4700	–	**O** 110.9/110.9aeL(I 2115)sx	VA3PRA	PR ARES
Embrun	147.1950	+	**O** 110.9/110.9e	VE3EYV	VE3GF
Hammond	147.3300	+	**O** 110.9/110.9ls	VE3PRV	PR ARES

Location	*Output*	*Input*	*Notes*	*Call*	*Sponsor*
RENFREW					
Bissett Creek	147.1200	+	A(#22/#) L(146.760)sx	VE3ZBC	RCARC
Foymount	145.4300	–	L(147.000)	VE3UCR	RCARC
Mt St Patrick	147.0600	–	114.8x	VE3STP	CRRA
Pembroke	146.7600	–	/100.0 A(*22/#) L(ZBC/ I 2520)sx	VE3NRR	RCARC
Pt Alexander	146.7900	–	sx	VA3RBW	RCARC
Renfrew	146.9100	–	114.8/114.8 L(E 131218)x	VE3ZRR	ZRRRG
SOUTH					
Acton	147.0300	+	Os	VE3RSS	------------
Brantford	145.2700	–	O(CA)e	VE3MBX	BLPG
Brantford	147.1500	+	Oe	VE3TCR	BARC
Burlington	147.2100	+	O 131.8e	VE3RSB	BARC
Cambridge	146.7900	–	O 131.8e	VE3SWR	SWARC
Carlisle	146.7150	–	O 131.8 L(ERA)	VEWIK	------------
Fonthill	147.0450	+	O 107.2 L(ERA)	VE3WIK	------------
Georgetown	147.1350	+	O 131.8ae L(IRLP)	VE3OD	HARC
Goring	147.1050	+	O 156.7e L(ERA)	VE3MBR	ERA
Greens Corner	147.2250	+	O 131.8e	VE3BIC	------------
Guelph	145.2100	–	Oesz	VE3ZMG	G.A.R.C.
Kitchener	146.8650	–	O 131.8ez	VE3RCK	KWARC
Kitchener	146.9700	–	O 131.8	VE3KSR	KWARC
New Dundee	145.3300	–	O 131.8e	VE3WIK	ERA System
Oakville	147.0150	+	O(CA)e	VE3OAK	OARC
Simcoe	146.9250	–	O 131.8e L(IRLP)	VE3SME	NARC
Stoney Creek	147.3450	+	O 131.8e	VE3OBP	------------
Waterloo	147.0900	+	O 131.8 (CA) L(IRLP)	VE3WFM	------------
Woodstock	146.6550	–	131.8	VA3OHR	OCARC
SOUTHWEST					
Chatham	147.1200	+	O 100.0ael WXz	VE3KCR	CKARC
Dorchester	147.2400	+	O	VE3NDT	------------
Dutton	147.3600	+	O 114.8	VE3ISR	------------
Goderich	146.9100	–	O 123.0	VE3OBC	SRAR
Goderich	147.0300	+	O 123.0	VE3GOD	BWRC
Goderich	147.1950	+	O 123.0e	VE3DFJ	SRARC
Grand Bend	146.7600	–	Oe	VE3RGB	GBRA
Ingersoll	145.1700	–	O 114.8e	VA3PLL	PCARC
Ingersoll	147.2700	+	O 114.8	VE3OHR	OCARC
Ipperwash	146.9400	–	O 114.8 (CA) L(VE3SUE)	VE3TCB	SORT

Location	*Output*	*Input*	*Notes*	*Call*	*Sponsor*
Leamington	147.3000	+	O	VE3TOM	SPARC
Leamington	147.3300	+	O 118.8	VA3PPL	PARC
London	145.3900	–	O 114.8	VA3MGI	LARC
London	145.4500	–	O 114.8 L(CANWARN) WX	VE3OME	------------
London	147.0600	+	O 114.8e	VA3LON	LARC
London	147.1800	+	O 114.8e L(VE3SUE ECHOLINK)	VE3TTT	SORT
Lucan	147.0000	+	O 114.8	VE3MCR	MCRA
McGregor	145.4100	–	O 118.8 WX	VE3EOW	ARES
Mitchell	147.2850	+	O 114.8e L(VE3RFC) WX	VE3XMM	FCARC
Paris	145.4900	–	O 131.8e	VE3DIB	------------
Richmond	145.2300	–	O 131.8 L(IRLP)	VE3XXL	------------
Sarnia	145.3700	–	O 123.0e	VE3SAR	LCRC
Sarnia	146.9550	–	O 118.8 (CA)eL(442.350 IRLP)	VE3WHO	------------
St Marys	147.3750	+	O 114.8	VE3SDF	SMARC
St Thomas	147.3300	+	O 114.8e	VE3STR	EARS
Stratford	145.1500	–	O 114.8el WX	VE3RFC	FCARC
Windsor	145.3900	–	O(CA)	VE3SXC	WART
Windsor	145.4700	–	O 118.8e L(444.5)	VE3RRR	WARC
Windsor	147.0600	+	O 118.8ae L(IRLP)	VE3III	SPRARC
STORMONT-DUNDAS-GLENGARRY					
Cornwall	145.1700	–	a(CA)	VE3YGM	VE3IGM
Cornwall	147.1800	+	110.9/110.9 aL(443.650)	VE3SVC	------------
Iroquois	145.2900	–	123.0/123.0 a	VE3IRO	IARG
Moose creek	145.3700	–		VE3OJE	EOVHFRG
Winchester	146.9700	–	O 100.0/100.0	VA3NDC	Iroquois ARC

PRINCE EDWARD ISLAND

Location	*Output*	*Input*	*Notes*	*Call*	*Sponsor*
CAVENDISH					
Cavendish	145.1500	–	Ol	VY2PEI	VY2RU
CENTRAL					
Glen Valley	146.7150	–	Ol	VE1UHF	VE1AIC
CHARLOTTETOWN					
Charlottetown	146.6700	–	Oae L(IRLP)	VE1CRA	VE1AIC
Charlottetown	147.3900	+	O	VY2CRS	CARC
Stratford	147.2550	+	Oel	VY2VB	VY2ROB

Location	Output	Input	Notes	Call	Sponsor
MONTAGUE					
Montague	147.1650	+	Oel	VY2EKR	VY2ROB
OLEARY					
OLeary	147.1200	+	Oel	VY2CFB	SPARC
SUMMERSIDE					
Summerside	146.8500	–	Oae L(IRLP) WX	VE1CFR	SPARC

QUEBEC

Location	Output	Input	Notes	Call	Sponsor
Albanel	147.3700	+	Oe	VA2TFL	VE2EFQ
Alma	146.6700	–	O	VE2RCA	VE2CRS
Alma	147.0000	–	O	VE2CVT	VE2CVT
Alma	147.0400	+	O	VA2RIT	VE2TMR
Alma	147.2700	+	O	VE2RVX	VE2DIA
Alma	147.2800	+	O	VE2RPJ	VE2JMP
Alma	147.3600	+	O	VE2LPO	VE2XCP
Amos	147.1500	+	O	VE2RAZ	VE2MLS
Anse St-Jean	146.7700	–	85.4x	VA2RUA	VA2BCA
Arthabaska	147.1400	+	O	VE2RBF	VE2FQG
Arvida	145.3700	–	O 127.3	VE2RAL	VE2FIX
Baie-Comeau	145.2300	–	Oe	VA2RRB	VE2FAZ
Baie-Comeau	146.8200	–	Oex	VA2RSP	VE2FAZ
Baie-Comeau	146.9700	–	Oex	VE2RMH	VE2FAZ
Baie-Comeau	147.0400	+	Oe	VA2LMH	VE2FAZ
Baie-Comeau	147.3000	+	Oex	VE2RBC	VE2FAJ
Baie-Comeau	147.3900	+	Oex	VE2RDE	VE2FAZ
Baie-Johan-Beetz	146.9400	–	O	VE2RJI	VE2AGT
Baie-Trinité	145.4700	–	Oe	VA2RBT	VE2FAZ
Beloeil	147.1600	+	Oe	VE2RGB	VE2GAB
Black Lake	145.1300	–	O 100e	VE2RVA	VE2LES
Blainville	145.4500	–	O 103.5ae	VE2RMR	VE2DJE
Blainville	146.8200	–	136.5p	VE2THE	VE2THE
Blainville Nord	146.8200	–	O 103.5	VE2RNO	VE2THE
Boucherville	145.2500	–	O 103.5	VE2MRQ	VE2MRI
Buckingham	145.4900	–	O 110.9ex	VE2REG	VE2ZVL
Cantley	147.1900	+	O 110.9	VE2MDC	VE2GUY
Cap-à-L'aigle	145.2900	–	O	VA2RKT	VE2CSQ
Cap-de-la Madeleine	145.7400	145.7400	O 136.5	VE2RBN	VE2MTE
Carleton	147.0600	147.7600	x	VE2RXT	VE2FWZ
Causapscal	145.1300	144.6300	O	VE2RTF	VA2DD
Chambord	146.6400	–	O	VE2RVP	VE2SV
Chandler	146.8500	–	Oex	VE2CGR	VA2CEY
Charlesbourg	147.1800	+	O 100e	VA2UX	VE2YSU
Chibougamau Chapais	147.3900	+	O	VA2RRC	VE2PR
Chicoutimi	144.3900	144.3900	O	VE2CCD	VE2CCD
Chicoutimi	145.0900	145.0900	O	VE2SAY	VE2JHG

Location	*Output*	*Input*	*Notes*	*Call*	*Sponsor*
Chicoutimi	145.2300	–	O	VE2RHS	VA2CRR
Chicoutimi	145.4300	–	O	VE2RMI	VE2MDH
Chicoutimi	147.0700	+	127.3x	VE2RCI	VE2BLM
Chicoutimi	147.1200	+	O	VE2RCC	VE2CRS
Chicoutimi	147.3000	+	Oe	VE2RPA	VE2SV
Chicoutimi - Portatif	147.1800	+	Op	VE2RCF	VE2CRS
Chute des passes	147.2700	+	Oe	VE2RFN	VE2FNN
Coaticook	147.3600	+	O 118.8	VE2RDM	VE2DPD
Contrecoeur	145.3500	–	O 141.3	VE2CKC	VE2AN
Coupe du ciel	147.0300	+	127.3 E-SUN	VE2RKJ	VA2CRR
Covey Hill	144.0000	144.0000	O 100e	VA2REX	VE2JT
Covey Hill	147.2100	+	O	VE2RBV	VE2BCM
Dolbeau	146.7000	–	O	VE2RCD	VE2CRS
Donnacona	145.3300	–	O 100e	VE2RBJ	VE2SBR
Drummondville	146.6200	–	O 110.9	VE2RDL	VE2CRD
Drummondville	146.8300	–	O 110.9	VA2RCQ	VE2ZDB
Drummondville	147.0900	+	O 110.9	VE2RDV	VE2CRD
Fermont	146.8200	–	Oex	VE2RGA	VE2ACP
Fire Lake	147.0600	+	Ox	VE2RGF	VE2ACP
Fleurimont	146.8900	–	O	VA2LGX	VE2LGX
Forestville	146.7000	–	O 151.4 (CA)e	VE2RLI	VE2VD
Forestville	146.9100	–	O 151.4 (CA)e	VE2RFG	VE2VD
Forestville	147.2500	+	Oe	VE2REE	VE2JVJ
Forestville	147.2800	+	Oe	VE2REJ	VE2JEA
Gagnon	146.6900	–	OE-SUNx	VE2RGH	VE2ACP
Gaspé	146.8900	–	Oex	VE2RLE	VE2EPY
Gaspé	146.8900	–	ex	VE2RLE	VE2FXG
Gatineau	147.1000	+	O 110.9e	VE2REH	VE2ZVL
Granby	146.7900	–	O(CA)	VE2RVM	VE2TVM
Granby	147.1800	+	O 118.8e	VE2RTA	VE2EKY
Grand-Mère	146.9200	–	Oex	VE2RGM	VE2GM
Grand-Mère	147.0300	+	O 100	VE2REY	------------
Grand-Mère	147.1600	+	O 100	VE2REY	VE2VXT
Grande Ance	147.0000	–	O(CA)e	VE2RLT	VE2DNB
Grande-Rivière	145.1700	–	Ox	VE2RDI	VE2AIY
Grande-Rivière	146.7300	–	Oe	VE2RBM	VE2FXG
Grenville	146.8000	–	Oex	VE2RWC	VE2CWB
Ham Sud	145.1900	–	O 123	VE2RFX	VE2OPA
Havelock	146.6800	–	Oex	VE2REX	VE2CYH
Havre-St-Pierre	145.4900	–	O	VE2TIO	------------
Havre-St-Pierre	146.9700	–	Oe	VE2RFD	VE2AGT
Hebertville	146.7900	–	x	VE2RCV	VE2CRS
Hull	146.7400	–	O 123ae	VE2RAO	VE2CRO
Hull	146.9400	–	O 100	VE2CRA	VE2CRA
Hull	147.3600	+	Oe	VE2KPG	VE2KPG

Location	*Output*	*Input*	*Notes*	*Call*	*Sponsor*
Joliette	147.0300	+	O 103.5e	VE2RHO	VE2BFK
Joliette	147.3000	+	Oe	VE2RLJ	VE2EML
Jonquière	145.0900	145.0900	O	VE2RNU	VE2JHG
Jonquière	145.1700	–	O	VE2RHJ	VE2QY
Jonquière	146.8200	–	Oe	VE2VP	VE2SV
Jonquière	146.8500	–	O	VA2NA	VA2NA
Jonquière	147.0600	+	O	VE2DHC	VE2DHC
Jonquière	147.2400	+	O	VE2RVG	VE2SMP
Jonquière	147.3900	+	O	VE2RLG	VE2JCM
L'Anse-St-Jean	145.1500	–	Oex	VE2RME	VE2XIT
L'Ascension	145.1300	–	x	VE2RMX	VE2DIA
L'Ascension	147.5100	147.5100	O	VA2RGP	VE2APJ
L'Ascension	147.5100	147.5100	O	VA2RGP	VE2APJ
La Baie	146.6100	–	O 85.4e	VE2RCX	VA2BCA
La Baie	146.7300	–	O 127.3a	VE2RCE	VA2BCA
La Pocatière	146.6200	–	O 151.4	VE2RDJ	VE2DBU
La Pocatière	147.3600	+	O 100	VE2RDJ	VE2DBU
La Sarre	146.7000	–	Oe	VE2RSL	CRANOQ
La Tuque	146.7900	–	Oe	VE2RTL	VE2DGS
La Tuque	146.9400	–	Oe	VE2RLF	VE2BGX
Labrieville	147.1000	+	Oe	VE2ROA	VE2AOO
Lac Aux Sables	147.2100	+	OE-SUN	VE2RSA	VE2CSP
Lac Brassard	145.2100	–	E-SUN	VE2RIT	VE2LSO
Lac Castor	145.3900	–	x	VA2RLC	VE2CSQ
Lac Daran	145.2900	–	x	VE2RLD	VE2CSQ
Lac Des Commissaires	146.9700	–	O	VE2RHC	VE2DHC
Lac Édouard	147.2200	+	Oe	VE2RCL	VE2YJA
Lac Etchemin	147.2400	+	O 100x	VE2RKM	VE2KCB
Lac Ha! Ha!	147.3300	+	x	VE2RCK	VE2CRS
Lac Ouachishmana	147.0900	+	OE-SUN	VA2RLL	VE2KIK
Lac Paul (Zone 2)	147.6900	–	O 127.3	VA2RHS	VA2CRR
Lac-à-L'Épaule	145.4900	–	O	VE2RPL	VE2CSQ
Lac-a-la-Tortue	146.8900	–	O	VE2RBR	VE2GM
Lac-Canot	145.4500	–	OE-SUNx	VE2RGU	VE2AFR
Lac-des Commissaires	146.7300	–	O	VE2RHC	VE2DHC
Laterrière	146.7600	–	O	VE2RGT	VA2BCA
Laval	147.1000	+	O 107.2e	VA2OZ	VE2JKA
Le Bic	145.4500	–	O	VE2RXY	VE2BQI
Les Escoumins	146.6700	–	O	VE2REB	VE2PYB
Les Méchins	147.2700	+	Ox	VE2RNM	VE2ENM
Levis-Lauzon	145.1100	–	O 100	VE2RYC	VE2YCQ
Levis-Lauzon	147.1500	+	O 100	VE2RCT	VE2YGB
Longueuil	145.3900	–	Oe	VE2RSM	VE2AZX
Longueuil	146.7300	–	O 100	VE2RVC	VE2SVM
Maria	146.9100	–	O	VE2RXL	VE2KF
Mascouche	147.3400	+	O 103.5e	VE2RHL	VE2AIE

Location	*Output*	*Input*	*Notes*	*Call*	*Sponsor*
Maskinongé	147.0900	+	O	VA2MLP	VE2MLP
Matagami	146.9100	–	OE-SUN	VE2RBO	VE2SGS
Matane	146.8800	–	Oe	VA2RAM	VE2MWA
Matane	147.1200	+	Oe	VE2RAS	CRAM
Metabetchouan	147.1500	+	O	VE2RPE	VA2NA
Mont Bélair	146.6500	–	O 100	VE2UCD	------------
Mont Bélair	146.7900	–	O 100e	VE2RAX	VE2EZZ
Mont Fournier	147.2700	+	O	VE2RMQ	------------
Mont Jacob (Jonquiere)	145.0100	145.0100	O	VE2RJD	VE2SDJ
Mont Laurier	146.9700	–	O	VE2RMC	VE2RMC
Mont Mégantic	147.1000	+	O 118.8x	VE2RJC	VE2TIC
Mont Rougemont	146.7000	–	Oex	VE2RXW	VE2AIK
Mont St-Adrien	145.1300	–	O 100e	VE2RVA	VE2LES
Mont St-Marguerite	146.6800	–	Ox	VE2LRE	VE2LRE
Mont Ste-Marguerite	147.2500	+	x	VE2RCB	VE2CRS
Mont Ste-Marie	146.6100	–	O 110.9ex	VA2REH	VE2ZVL
Mont Triquet	145.4500	–	O	VE2RAG	VE2LVD
Mont Victor-Tremblay	147.3400	+	OE-SUNx	VE2RTV	VE2SV
Mont Yamaska	146.7750	–	O 123 (CA) eL(147.225) BIx	VE2RAU	VE2MKJ
Mont-Adstock	146.7300	–	O	VE2CTM	VE2TMA
Mont-Apica	145.3500	–	O	VE2RHX	VE2CSQ
Mont-Apica	146.9100	–	O	VE2RCP	VE2CRS
Mont-Bélair	146.9400	–	O	VE2OM	VE2AP
Mont-Bélair	147.0700	+	O 100	VA2TEL	VE2OSQ
Mont-Bromont	146.8800	–	O 94.8x	VE2RMK	VE2KYP
Mont-Carmel	145.4300	–	O	VE2RLB	VE2MEL
Mont-Carmel	146.6700	–	Oex	VE2RTR	VE2MO
Mont-Gladys	147.0900	+	Oe	VE2RMG	VE2CQ
Mont-Laurier	147.1000	+	O 131.8ex	VE2REH	VE2ZVL
Mont-Noir	147.0000	–	Oex	VE2CTT	VE2CCR
Mont-Oneil	147.3900	+	Oex	VE2RMF	CRAQ
Mont-Orford	145.2700	–	O 103.5ex	VE2RTO	VE2EKL
Mont-Orford	147.3300	+	O 123ex	VE2TA	VA2RAE
Mont-St-Grégoire	145.5100	145.5100	O	VE2RKL	VE2EKL
Mont-Ste-Anne	146.8200	–	O 100ex	VE2RAA	VE2CQ
Mont-Tremblant	146.7200	–	O	VE2RMT	VE2GCK
Mont-Valin	146.8800	–	x	VE2RES	VE2CRS
Mont-Valin	147.2100	+	x	VE2RJZ	VE2CRS
Mont-Wright	145.1300	–	O 77ex	VE2RGW	VE2ACP
Montmagny	146.9700	–	O	VE2RAB	VE2PIA
Montréal	144.3900	144.3900	O	VE2PSL	VE2AH
Montréal	146.6700	–	O	VE2PSL	VE2AH
Montréal	146.9100	–	O 141.3ex	VE2RWI	VE2CWI
Montreal	147.0400	+	Oex	VE2RCU	VE2CUA

Location	*Output*	*Input*	*Notes*	*Call*	*Sponsor*
Montréal	147.0700	+	Oe	VE2RVL	VE2JGA
Montréal	147.1200	+	O 103.5e	VE2MRC	VE2ESU
Montreal	147.2700	+	O 103.5	VE2RED	VE2ARC
Montréal	147.3900	+	O 103.5e	VE2RIO	RAQI
New Richmond	147.1800	+	Ox	VE2RPG	VE2DSJ
Parc Chibougamau	147.0300	–	O	VE2RTG	VE2CRS
Parc de Chibougamau	145.1100	–	O	VA2RRH	VE2PR
Parc de la Vérendrye	145.4900	–	O	VE2RPV	VE2DY
Parent	145.1900	–	O(CA)e	VE2RPC	VE2NZ
Passes Dangereuses	145.2500	–	O	VA2ADW	VE2EFL
Percé	146.7900	–	Oex	VE2RLC	CRAG
Petite-Rivière Saint-François	147.3900	+	O	VA2RAT	VE2CBA
Pic-Champlain	146.6100	–	Oex	VE2RWM	VE2FWZ
Pierrefonds	145.4900	–	O	VE2RKE	VE2KRA
Pointe-Claire	147.0600	+	Oe	VE2BG	VE2ARC
Pontbriand	147.3700	+	Oex	VE2RSQ	VE2CSQ
Province-de Québec	147.0100	+	O	VE2RUK	VE2DOG
Province-de Québec	147.0100	+	O	VE2RUR	VE2DOG
Québec	144.3900	144.3900	O	VE2ROW	VE2TSO
Québec	145.0300	145.0300	O 100	VE2TPE	VE2TPE
Québec	145.1700	–	O 100	VE2RHT	VE2YSU
Québec	145.3500	–	O 85.4x	VE2RRS	VE2DSU
Québec	146.4900	146.4900	O	VE2DBR	VE2AB
Québec	146.6800	–	O 156.7el	VE2REA	VE2SG
Québec	146.8800	–	O 100e	VE2RIG	VE2SIG
Québec	147.2500	+	O 100	VE2RQE	VE2MEW
Québec	147.3000	+	O 100e	VE2RCQ	CRAQ
Rapide Blanc	146.6100	–	Ox	VE2RRB	VA2HQ
Relai 22 milles (La Tuque)	146.8300	–	Oex	VA2RVD	VE2YJA
Richmond	147.2500	+	O 123	VE2RHP	VE2LBN
Rigaud	147.0000	–	Oe	VE2RM	VE2RM
Rimouski	145.3100	–	O	VE2RKI	VE2FWZ
Rimouski	146.9400	–	Oe	VE2CSL	VE2FWZ
Rimouski	147.2400	+	O	VE2RXA	VE2BQA
Rimouski	147.3600	+	O	VE2ROE	VE2FWZ
Ripon	145.4100	–	O 123e	VE2RBH	VE2CRO
Rivière-à-Pierre	146.8000	–	O 100e	VA2SBR	VE2SBR
Riviere-au Tonnerre	147.0300	+	O	VE2RET	VE2AGT
Rivière-du-Loup	146.9500	–	O	VE2RML	------------
Rivière-du-Loup	147.1500	+	O	VE2RAY	VE2EOT

Location	*Output*	*Input*	*Notes*	*Call*	*Sponsor*
Roberval	144.3900	144.3900	O	VA2RBM	VA2JGC
Roberval	145.4900	–	O	VA2RRE	VE2PR
Roberval	146.7400	–	O	VE2RRE	VE2PR
Roberval	147.0100	+	O	VE2RSF	VE2PR
Rosemere	145.2100	–	Oe	VE2RXZ	VE2GXZ
Rougemont	145.3100	–	O 103.5e	VE2RAW	VE2AW
Rouyn-Noranda	146.6400	–	Oex	VE2RNR	VE2CFR
Rouyn-Noranda	146.8200	–	Oex	VE2RON	VE2NOQ
Rouyn-Noranda	147.0900	+	O	VE2RYN	VE2PIO
Saguenay (La Baie)	146.9700	–	O	VE2RDC	VE2PLC
saint jean de cherbourg	147.0900	+	Oe	VA2RSJ	CRAM
Saint-Adolphe d'Howard	146.8900	–	O 141.3ex	VE2RUN	VE2WCC
Saint-Lin Laurentides	147.0900	+	O 103.5e	VE2RFO	VE2BFK
Saint-Lin Laurentides	147.3600	+	O 103.5e	VE2RFO	VE2BFK
Senneterre	145.1100	–	O	VE2RSZ	VE2MLS
Sept-Iles	145.1900	–	O 88.5	VE2RDO	VE2NN
Sept-Iles	146.6400	–	O 88.5	VE2RNN	VE2NN
Sept-Iles	146.7000	–	O 88.5	VE2RNN	VE2NN
Sept-Iles	146.7900	–	O 88.5ex	VE2RRU	VE2NN
Sept-Iles	146.9400	–	O	VE2RSI	VE2NN
Sept-Iles	147.0000	+	Oe	VA2RNY	VE2YDQ
Sept-Iles	147.2100	+	O	VA2RSM	VACANT
Sherbrooke	145.2300	–	O	VE2RGX	VE2LGX
Sherbrooke	145.3300	–	O 118.8	VE2RZA	VE2ZAC
Sherbrooke	145.6100	145.6100	O	VE2PAK	VE2SBK
Sherbrooke	146.9700	–	O 118.8e	VE2RSH	VA2HF
Sorel	145.3700	–	O 103.5e	VE2RBS	VE2GFF
Sorel	146.6100	–	O 103.5	VE2FCT	VE2GFF
St-Adolphe d'Howard	146.6500	–	O	VE2RYV	VE2AIK
St-Adrien d'Irlande	145.1300	–	O 100x	VE2RVA	VE2LES
St-Agathe	145.3100	–	O 100	VE2RLO	VE2LLA
St-Aimé-des-Lacs	147.1300	+	OE-SUNx	VE2RJO	VE2JOQ
St-Calixte	145.1900	–	O 141.3ex	VA2 RLD	VA2 DU
St-Calixte	145.3300	–	O 141.3e	VA2RLD	VA2DU
St-Calixte	145.4300	–	O 103.5e	VA2RLD	VA2DLU
St-Calixte	146.7300	–	O 103.5ex	VE2PCQ	VE2PCQ
St-Calixte	146.8600	–	141.3e	VE2RVK	VE2VK
St-Calixte	147.0100	+	O	VE2REM	VE2AAS
St-Charles-de Bourget	146.9400	–	x	VE2RCR	VE2CRS
St-Damien-De Brandon	145.2900	–	O 103.5x	VE2RGC	VE2EML

Location	*Output*	*Input*	*Notes*	*Call*	*Sponsor*
St-Donat	144.3900	144.3900	O 103.5 E-SUN	VA2RIA	VE2MCM
St-Donat	147.0000	+	O 103.5 E-SUN	VA2RIA	VE2MCM
St-Donat	147.0900	+	O 103.5 E-SUN	VE2RRA	VE2BFK
St-Donat de Rimouski	146.7300	–	O 123e	VE2RAC	VE2DLE
St-Donat-de Montcalm	147.3700	+	O 141.3	VA2RSD	VA2HMC
St-Elzéar	146.7600	–	O 100x	VE2RVD	VE2CQ
St-Etienne-des Gres	147.1900	+	Oe	VE2RZX	VE2FJZ
St-Félix D'Otis	145.3100	–	O 85.4	VE2RUS	VA2BCA
St-François-de Sales	145.4700	–	O	VE2RRR	VE2CJQ
St-Georges	147.2800	+	Oe	VE2RSG	VE2BPD
St-Honoré	147.1800	+	Oe	VE2RKT	VE2VJA
St-Honoré	147.2200	+	Oe	VA2RMV	VE2DOG
St-Honoré de Chicoutimi	144.3900	144.3900	O	VA2RCR	VE2SO
St-Honoré de Chicoutimi	144.3900	144.3900	O	VA2RCH	VE2CSQ
St-Honoré de Chicoutimi	145.3300	–	x	VA2RCH	VE2CSQ
St-Honoré de Chicoutimi	147.4800	147.4800	O	VA2RCH	VE2CSQ
St-Hubert	147.3000	+	O	VA2CSA	VA2CSA
St-Hyacinthe	146.9500	–	O	VE2RBE	VE2GGM
St-Jean de Matha	145.4100	–	O 103.5x	VE2RMM	VE2GMV
St-Jean-Port-Joli	147.3100	+	O 100e	VA2RWW	VE2JJN
St-Jean-sur Richelieu	147.2400	+	Oe	VE2RVR	VE2MRW
St-Jérome	145.2900	–	O 141.3e	VE2RFR	VE2BFK
St-Jérome	146.8200	146.0200	O 103.5e	VE2RFR	VE2BFK
St-Jérome	146.8500	–	Oe	VE2RVS	VE2APL
St-Jogues	146.8200	–	Ox	VE2RIN	VE2FXN
St-Joseph-de Beauce	146.9800	–	O 100	VE2RSJ	VE2BDP
St-Joseph-du-Lac	145.1300	–	Oe	VE2RST	VE2GSB
St-Joseph-du-Lac	147.3100	+	Oe	VE2REL	VE2GDR
St-Michel des Saints	145.4700	–	O 141.3ex	VA2HMC	VE2EIL
St-Michel-des Saints	145.3300	–	O 103.5e	VE2RLP	VE2SMS
St-Nazaire	145.1900	–	x	VA2RAU	VE2NA
St-Onésime-de Kamouraska	147.2100	+	Oe	VE2RAF	VE2BVC
St-Pacome	146.7000	–	Oe	VE2RAK	VE2GEU

Location	*Output*	*Input*	*Notes*	*Call*	*Sponsor*
St-Pascal	147.0600	+	Oe	VE2RGP	VE2CCS
St-Pascal-de Kamouraska	145.1900	–	O 107.2e	VE2RQA	VE2PAC
St-Philémon	145.3700	–	O 100	VA2RMS	VA2CCS
St-Raymond	147.2800	+	O 100	VE2RCJ	VE2SBR
St-Simon-les Mines	146.6400	–	O	VE2RSG	VE2BPD
St-Tite-des-Caps	144.3900	144.3900	O	VA2RSL	VE2CSQ
St-Tite-des-Caps	145.4700	–	Oe	VE2RTI	VE2CSQ
St-Tite-des-Caps	147.0400	+	Oe	VE2RJA	VE2MDA
St-Tite-des-Caps	147.3400	+	Oe	VE2RHM	VE2MRJ
St-Ubalde	145.3900	–	O 100e	VE2RBT	VE2SBR
St-Ubalde	146.8500	–	O 100ex	VE2RPW	VE2CSP
St-Urbain	146.9100	–	O	VE2RAT	VE2CCR
St-Zénon	147.3600	+	O 103.5	VA2KIK	VE2KIK
Ste-Anne-des Monts	146.7400	–	O	VE2GIT	VE2GIT
Ste-Anne-du-Lac	146.7600	–	Ox	VE2RMP	VE2BOA
Ste-Aurélie	146.8600	–	Oe	VE2RFB	VE2RIK
ste-catherine de la J C	144.9100	144.9100	O	VE2PKT	VE2PKT
Ste-Foy	146.6100	–	Oe	VE2RQR	VE2CQ
Ste-Foy	147.1200	+	O	VE2SRC	VE2FTD
Ste-Marcelline	147.0300	–	Oe	VE2RMA	VE2BFK
Ste-Sophie D'Halifax	146.7300	–	OE-SUNx	VE2CTM	VE2NBE
Sutton	146.6400	–	Oex	VE2RTC	VE2DIW
Thetford Mines	147.1600	+	Ox	VE2RDT	VE2JMO
Trois-Rivières	146.9800	–	O 110.9e	VE2ROX	VE2EX
Trois-Rivières	147.0600	–	O	VE2CTR	VE2CTR
Val-Brillant	147.0000	+	O	VE2ROL	VE2FZR
Val-D'Irene	146.7600	–	Oex	VE2RKH	VE2FWZ
Val-D'Irene	147.3700	+	Oe	VE2RDD	VA2DD
Val-D'Or	146.7600	–	O 114.8x	VE2RYL	VE2DY
Varennes	145.1700	–	Oe	VE2REQ	VE2ESM
Ville de La Baie	145.2700	–	O	VE2RCZ	VE2CRS
Ville de Saguenay (Jonquière) Holiday Inn	145.4100	–	O 100ex	VE2RKA	VE2EFL
Ville Marie	146.7300	–	Oe	VE2RTE	VE2EUA
Weedon	144.3900	144.3900	O	VE2RDX	VE2BOG
ZEC Gros Brochet	147.3900	+	O 103.5	VA2ZGB	VE2VXT
ARGENTEUIL					
Grenville	146.7150	–	O 123.0/123.0	VE2RCS	VE2HMA
GATINEAU					
Aylmer	146.6650	146.0550	O 123.0/123.0	VE2AAR	VE2AAR

Location	Output	Input	Notes	Call	Sponsor
LAURENTIDES					
Lachute	146.8050	–		VE2RWC	Brownsburg Amateur
Rigaud	147.0000	–		VE2RM	------------
NATIONAL CAPITOL REGION					
Chelsea	146.9400	–	O 100.0/100.0eL(I 2040)x	VE2CRA	OARC
Chelsea	147.3600	+	203.5/203.5 #ex	VE2KPG	VE2CV
OUTAOUAIS					
Cantley	147.1050	+	110.9/110.9 (CA) L(I 2018)	VE2REH	ARAI
Gatineau	145.3500	–	● 162.2/162.2 (CA)e	VA2XAD	VA2XAD
Gatineau	145.4900	–	110.9/110.9 (CA) L(I 2018)	VE2REH	ARAI
Gatineau	146.7450	–	123.0/123.0 A(*/#) L(RBH)	VE2RAO	CRAO
Lac Ste-Marie	146.6100	–	110.9/110.9 (CA) L(I 2018)x	VE2REH	ARAI
PAPINEAU					
Ripon	145.4100	–	123.0/123.0 A(*78/#) L(RAO)x	VE2RBH	CRAO
PONTIAC					
Campbell's Bay	147.3900	+	O 114.8/114.8	VE2REH	ARAI
Mansfield	147.5100	147.5100	O 100.0/100.0	VE2REH	ARAI
Ripon	147.3900	+	O 146.2/146.2l	VE2REH	ARAI

SASKATCHEWAN

Location	Output	Input	Notes	Call	Sponsor
CENTRAL					
Bruno	147.2100	+	OL(IRLP)	VE5DNA	VE5RY
Davidson	145.1900	–		VE5RPD	VE5NED
Kenaston	147.2700	+	O	VE5DPR	VE5NED
Last Mtn	146.8500	–	OE-SUN	VE5AT	VE5UJ
Leroy	146.9100	–	Ol	VE5HVR	VE5HV
Watrous	146.7000	–	Oal	VE5IM	VE5IM
EAST CENTRAL					
Canora	147.3000	+	L(IRLP)	VE5RJM	PARC
Endeavour	147.0800	+	#L(IRLP)	VA5INV	VE5RJM
Norquay	147.3900	+	L(IRLP)	VE5PWO	VE5SS
Preeceville	146.6100	–	L(IRLP)	VE5SS	VE5SS
St Gregor	146.7600	–	Ol	VE5NJR	VE5RY
Theodore	147.3300	+	Ol	VE5CNR	------------
Yorkton	145.4900	–	L(IRLP)	VA5PAR	VE5RJM
LLOYDMINSTER					
Lloydminster	146.9400	–	O	VE5RI	S-A R

Location	Output	Input	Notes	Call	Sponsor
MELFORT					
Little Bear Lk	146.8500	–	O	VE5NLR	VE5KRB
Melfort	146.8800	–	Oae L(IRLP)	VE5MFT	MARC
Nipawin	146.7900	–	OaL(IRLP)	VE5NIP	MARC
Tisdale	146.7000	–	OL(IRLP)	VE5FXR	VE5FX
MOOSE JAW					
Moose Jaw	146.9400	–	O	VE5CI	Pioneer
NORTH BATTLEFORD					
Lizard Lake	145.3900	–	O	VA5LLR	VE5WDB
Meadow Lake	147.3300	+	OL(IRLP)	VE5MLR	VE5RAE
N Battleford	146.8800	–	aL(IRLP)	VE5BRC	BARC
Unity	147.0000	–	O	VE5URC	VE5BBH
PRINCE ALBERT					
Birch Hills	145.4300	–		VE5VY	VE5VY
Christopher Lk	146.6100	–	OaL(IRLP)	VE5LAK	VE5QU
Elk Point	145.3500	–	l	VE5QU	VE5QU
La Ronge	146.9700	–	O	VE5LAR	------------
Minitinas	147.1500	+	Oel	VE5RPA	NSARC
Prince Albert	146.8200	–	O 100a L(IRLP)	VE5IOU	VE5QU
Prince Albert	147.0600	–	a	VE5PA	N SK ARC
Snowden	147.0900	+	OL(IRLP)	VE5NDR	VE5ND
Waskesiu	146.7600	–	el	VE5BBI	NSARC
Yellow Creek	147.1800	+	OEXP	VE5AG	VE5AG
REGINA					
Regina	147.1200	+	aL(IRLP)	VE5YQR	RARA
Regina	147.2100	+	Os	VE5RTV	ARES
SASKATOON					
Saskatoon	145.2900	147.9900	O 107.2 RB EXP	VE5UFO	MARS
Saskatoon	145.3300	–	l	VA5SV	VE5WDB
Saskatoon	145.4100	–	O	VE5SD	VE5SD
Saskatoon	146.6400	–		VE5SK	VE5AA
Saskatoon	146.7900	–	O	VE5NER	------------
Saskatoon	146.9400	–	O(CA) TT L(IRLP)s	VE5SKN	MARS
Saskatoon	146.9700	–	OL(IRLP)	VE5CC	VE5HG
Saskatoon	147.0900	+	O	VE5EMO	ARES
Saskatoon	147.2700	145.2700	O	VE5ZH	VE5HZ
SOUTH CENTRAL					
Avonlea	147.0600	–	O	VE5ARG	ARG
SOUTHEAST					
Arcola	146.8200	–	EXP	VE5MMR	MooseMtRC
Balgonie	146.6400	–	O	VE5REC	RARA
Estevan	147.0300	+	O	VA5EST	VE5AJ
Estevan	147.1800	+	lEXP	VE5EST	VE5HD
Melville	147.0000	+	OL(IRLP)	VE5MDM	VE5MDM
Moosomin	146.7900	–		VE5MRC	MARC

Location	Output	Input	Notes	Call	Sponsor
Weyburn	146.7000	–	L(IRLP)	VE5WEY	VE5HD
Wolseley	146.6700	–	a	VE5WRG	VE5DC
SOUTHWEST					
Eyebrow	147.3600	+	O	VE5YMJ	VE5BBB
Lucky Lake	146.7300	–	O	VE5XW	VE5TT
Stranraer	147.0300	–	Ol	VE5UB	VE5HG
Tompkins	146.6700	–		VE5TOM	SWARC
SWIFT CURRENT					
Swift Current	146.7900	–	OL(IRLP)	VE5SCR	SW ARC
Swift Current	146.8800	–	O	VE5SCC	SW ARC

YUKON TERRITORY

Location	Output	Input	Notes	Call	Sponsor
YUKON					
Atlin	147.3400	+		VA7ATN	YARA
Atlin Mountain	146.3400	+	Ol	VA7ATN	YARA
Bennett Lake	146.9400	–	Ol	VE7RFT	YARA
Bennett Lake	147.2400	+		VE7RFT	YARA
Carcross	146.8200	–	Ol	VY1RMM	YARA
Carmacks	146.8200	–	Ol	VY1RMB	YARA
Dawson City	146.8200	–	Ol	VY1RMD	YARA
Faro	147.0600	+	Ol	VY1RRH	YARA
Fraser Mountain	146.9400	–	Ol	VE7RFT	YARA
Haines Junction	146.8200	–	Ol	VY1RHJ	YARA
Haines Junction	146.8800	–		VY1RPM	YARA
Hayes Peak	147.0600	+	Ol	VY1RHP	YARA
Keno	146.9400	–	Ol	VY1RBT	YARA
Stewart Crosng	147.0600	+	Ol	VY1RFH	YARA
Watson Lake	146.8200	–	O	VY1RTM	YARA
Whitehorse	146.8800	–	100	VY1IRL	YARA
Whitehorse	146.9400	–	Ol	VY1RPT	YARA
Whitehorse	147.1800	+	Ol	VY1RM	YARA
Whitehorse	147.2800	+		VY1ECH	YARA

222-225 MHz

Location	Output	Input	Notes	Call	Sponsor
ALABAMA					
Albertville	224.6600	–	O 100.0	N4TZV	KF4EYT
Auburn	224.8400	–	O 88.5/88.5	W4KEN	W4KEN
Birmingham/ Pilots Knob	224.2200	–	OaTTe L(146/222/440)rRB	K4TQR	H&H RA
Dadeville	224.2400	–	O 146.2	KB4MDD	KB4MDD
Hueytown	224.4000	–	O	KD4EM	KD4EM
Huntsville	224.9400	–	O 100.0/100.0e	N4HSV	NARA
Loxley	224.8600	–	O 118.8/118.8	WB4GMQ	WB4GMQ
Mentone	224.7200	–	O 114.8el	W4OZK	W4OZK
Ranburne/ Turkey Heaven Mtn	224.4800	–		N4THM	Turkey HRA
Roanoke	224.9200	–	Oae	KA4KBX	KA4KBX
Russellville	224.3400	–	OeEXP	NV4B	NV4B/PCRS
Santuck	224.8800	–	O	W4KEN	W4KEN
Shelby Co	224.5000	–	O 100.0/100.0eWX	N4PHP	N4PHP
Warrior	224.1200	–	O	W4GQF	W4GQF
ALASKA					
INTERIOR					
Fairbanks	224.8800	–	O 103.5el	AL7FG	+KL7XO
SOUTH CENTRAL					
Anchorage	224.9400	–	Oe	KL7AA	AARC
SOUTHEAST					
Lena Point	224.0400	–	Oel	KL7PF	JARC
ARIZONA					
CENTRAL					
Towers	224.0400	–	●telRBx	KA6CAT	CMRA
Union Hills	224.5600	–	O 67 (CA)e x	N6IME	J.D.Ward
EAST CENTRAL					
Clay Springs	224.9400	–	O	N7KQ	MCRG
NORTH CENTRAL					
Mingus Mt	224.8200	–	O 156.7ex	KI6FH	Rod Rosenbarge
Mt Elden	223.8400	–	● 107.2lx	K6DLP	Don Petrone
Prescott	224.7800	–	Oe	KJ7DX	Matt Strandberg
NORTHWEST					
Dolan Springs	224.1400	–	O	WA7ICI	Allen Tobin

Location	Output	Input	Notes	Call	Sponsor
PHOENIX					
Goodyear	224.9600	–	○	KF6LCC	KF6LCC
Mesa	224.6800	–	○ 156.7a	W7ARA	ARA
Phoenix	223.9400	–	○ 156.7	WK7B	Gary Duffield
Phoenix	224.6400	–	○ 88.5e	NØFPE	Dan Nicholson
Phoenix	224.8000	–	○ 94.8 (CA)	KA7ATV	KA7IOG c/o Lavern H
Phoenix	224.9400	–	○ 156.7	K7ZWI	MCRG
Shaw Butte	224.9000	–	○ 156.7ae x	W7ARA	ARA
Tempe	224.2000	–	○	WA2DFI	Scott Cowling
Tempe	224.4000	–	○	WA2DFI	Scott Cowling
Usery Pass	224.0200	–	●lx	N7TWW	FHART
White Tanks	223.9800	–	○ 156.7x	N6IME	J.D. Ward
White Tanks	224.6000	–	○ 156.7elx	KD7TKT	Condor Connection
SOUTH CENTRAL					
Maricopa	223.8600	–	○ 156.7	KE7JVX	Monty Dana
Pima	224.4400	–	○	WB7ONJ	David Wells
Pinal Peak	224.1000	–	○ 156.7x	N7MK	Chris Radicke
Sacaton Peak	224.9200	–	○ 156.7x	KE7JVX	Monty Dana
SOUTHEAST					
Sierra Vista	224.9600	–	○ 100ael	NØNBH	Paul Herman
SOUTHWEST					
Yuma	224.0800	–	○ 88.5ar	W7DIN	Desert Intertie Networ
TUCSON					
Mt Lemmon	224.0600	–	○ 156.7lRB x	KA7LFX	Paul Van Beverhoudt
Mt Lemmon	224.5000	–	○ 156.7ex	N7EOJ	U.S.E.R.S.
Oro Valley	224.7600	–	○ 156.7ael	WØHF	Oro Valley ARC
Tucson	223.9400	–	○	N7EOJ	U.S.E.R.S
Tucson	224.1800	–	○	N7EOJ	Budd Turner
Tucson	224.3000	–	○x	K7IOU	BART
Tucson	224.4800	–	○	K6VE	Mountain Repeater A
Tucson	224.7000	–	○ 179.9e	W7SA	Catalina Radio Club
Tucson	224.7400	–	○ 136.5	K7IOU	BART
Tucson	224.9800	–	○ 156.7al RB	N7EOJ	U.S.E.R.S.
WEST CENTRAL					
Black Peak	224.0000	–	●t(CA)elx	K7ZEU	CARRA
Bullhead City	224.9600	–	○ 123.0e	KD7MIA	William Smith
Guadalupe Peak	224.8800	–	○ 156.7elx	KJ6KW	Condor
Lake Havasu	224.2400	–	○ 156.7 (CA)	KF7X	James Gould
Lake Havasu	224.8600	–	●l	WC6MRA	CMRA
ARKANSAS					
EAST CENTRAL					
Forrest City	224.8400	–	○ 107.2ers	NØHNQ	NØHNQ
NORTH					
Harrison	224.4000	–	○l	WA9SSO	GathMtARC

Location	*Output*	*Input*	*Notes*	*Call*	*Sponsor*
Harrison	224.5600	–	Oe	KFØPB	KFØPB
NORTHEAST					
Batesville	224.5000	–	● 107.2	N5TSC	N5TSC
NORTHWEST					
Prairie Grove	224.6000	–	Oae L(444.7(+))	WA5VTW	WA5VTW
SOUTHWEST					
Centerpoint	224.9000	–	Ox	KB5RYP	KB5RYP
WEST CENTRAL					
Russellville	224.7000	–	Oe	KE5EIY	KE5EIY

CALIFORNIA

FREQUENCY USAGE - SOUTHERN CALIFORNIA ----> SEE 220SMA ORG

	222.0000	222.1000		WEAK SIG, CW, SSB	
	222.0001	222.0250		EME	
	222.0500	222.0600		PROPAGATION BEACONS	
	222.1000			CW&SSB CALLING FREQ	
	222.1200			FM SIMP~NO AUTO BASE	
	222.1400			FM SIMP~NO AUTO BASE	
	223.4000			FM SIMPLEX (T~HUNTS)	
	223.4200			FM SIMPLEX	
	223.4400			FM SIMPLEX	
	223.4600			FM SIMPLEX	
	223.4800			FM SIMPLEX (ARES)	
	223.5000			FM NATIONAL CALL FREQ	
	223.5200			FM SIMPLEX	
	223.5400			DIG INTER~AREA LINKING	
	223.5600			DIG SIMPLEX LAN	
	223.5800			DIG INTER~AREA LINKING	
	223.6000			DIG GENERAL USE	
	223.6200	223.6650		AUTOMATED SIMP(<5W)	
	223.6800	223.7400		COORD LNKS&CNTL15KH	
NORCAL-CENTRAL COAST					
Bonny Doon	224.0600	–	O 110.9el	N6NAC	N6NAC
Monterey	224.2400	–	O 123aelrs x	N6SPD	N6SPD RG
Salinas	224.3200	–	O 146.2el	N6LEX	CCARN
SanLuisObispo	224.5800	–	O 151.4#el x	WB6NYS	WB6NYS
SanLuisObispo	224.6800	–	O 94.8#	WB6JWB	WB6JWB
SanLuisObispo	224.8600	–	●ex	WC6MRA	CMRA
SanLuisObispo	224.9200	–	●#elx	N6HYM	TCARS
Shandon	224.7400	–	O 131.8#	WB6NYS	ShandonRG
Watsonville	224.3800	–	●#	KB6MET	KB6MET
Watsonville	224.8400	–	O 156.7#	KB6MET	KB6MET
NORCAL-EAST BAY					
Berkeley	223.7800	–	O 131.8x	K6GOD	K6GOD
Berkeley	224.9000	–	O 131.8ers	N6BRK	NALCO
Concord	224.7800	–	O 77aelrsx	W6CX	MDARC

CALIFORNIA

Location	*Output*	*Input*	*Notes*	*Call*	*Sponsor*
Dublin	224.4000	–	●l	W6WCN	KQ6RC
Fremont	223.9000	–	○	WA6PWW	TRICO ARC
Fremont	224.1800	–	○ 94.8elx	KU6V	KU6V
Hayward	223.7600	–	○ 123#el	K6GOD	K6GOD
Hayward	223.9400	–	●lrx	KQ6RC	KQ6RC
Hayward	224.4400	–	○ 107.2#e x	KC6ZIS	Echo Club
Livermore	224.7400	–	○ 100aelrs	KO6PW	SANDIA RAC
Livermore	224.8800	–	○ 94.8	K6LRG	L.A.R.G.E.
Moraga	223.9800	–	○ 100elx	W6AV	NRA
Oakland	224.0000	–	○ 123x	W6JMX	NCHR
Oakland	224.1600	–	○ 156.7#l	N6WTY	KQ6RC
Oakland	224.7600	–	○ 85.4lrx	W6YOP	WA6YOP
San Jose	224.8400	–	○ 127.3#	NC6EO	N. CA Assn
San Lorenzo	224.7000	–	○ 156.7	KQ6YG	BAARC
San Pablo	224.3000	–	○ 82.5ers	WA6KQB	CCCC
NORCAL-NORTH BAY					
Healdsburg	224.3600	–	○ 88.5rx	NN6J	Sonomarin
Petaluma	224.9600	–	○ 103.5ex	AC6ET	SMRS
Rohnert Park	223.9000	–	○ 156.7#a	WD6FTB	NORCAL ARG
Santa Rosa	223.7600	–	○ 85.4elrx	KE6N	KE6N
Santa Rosa	223.8000	–	○ 156.7l	AC6VJ	CONDOR
Santa Rosa	224.8200	–	○ 103.5aer x	K6ACS	ACS
Sebastopol	224.4800	–	○ 88.5ers	W6SON	SCRA
Vacaville	223.9200	–	●	K6INC	SCAN INT'L
NORCAL-NORTH COAST					
Crescent City	224.6200	–	○ 91.5ael	KA7PRR	KA7PRR
Crescent City	224.7200	–	○ 103.5ael x	KA7PRR	KA7PRR
Willits	224.1600	–	○ 156.7lx	AC6VJ	CONDOR
NORCAL-NORTH EAST					
Redding	224.8600	–	○ 107.2e	KR7CR	W6QWN
NORCAL-SACRAMENTO VALLEY					
Arbuckle	224.5400	–	○ 118.8e	N6NHI	N6NHI
Auburn	223.8600	–	○ 100e	W6EK	SFARC
Auburn	223.9000	–	○ 100	N6NMZ	N6NMZ
Auburn	224.0200	–	○ 100elx	W7FAT	W7FAT
Auburn	224.5800	–	○ 100#e	W4WIL	W4WIL
Carmichael	224.8800	–	○ 162.2#	KJ6JD	CE ARC
Chico	223.9600	–	●a	WA6UHF	WA6UHF
Chico	224.2800	–	○ 110.9x	WA6UHF	WA6UHF
Citrus Heights	224.8000	–	○ 131.8es	AB6OP	Jim
Cohassett	224.3600	–	○ 110.9ex	N6YCK	N6YCK
Concord	224.9200	–	○ 85.4elrx	W6YOP	WA6YOP
Fairfield	224.3800	–	○ 77#rx	W6ER	Solano/ACS
Folsom	223.8200	–	○ 136.5elx	N6NMZ	N6NMZ
Folsom	224.7200	–	○ 136.5elx	KS6HRP	SHARP
Foresthill	223.7600	–	○ 100e	W6SAR	PCSAR

Location	*Output*	*Input*	*Notes*	*Call*	*Sponsor*
Georgetown	224.8400	–	O 100x	W6HIR	RAMS
Grass Valley	224.3200	–	O 151.4elsx	AB6LI	AB6LI
Grass Valley	224.4800	–	O 131.8lx	KF6GLZ	N6UG
Grass Valley	224.9000	–	O 151.4aelrsx	KD6GVO	KD6GVO
Lincoln	224.0400	–	O 123lx	KU6V	KU6V
Oroville	224.5000	–	O 110.9ex	WA6UHF	WA6UHF
Paradise	224.4400	–	O 100l	K6JSI	The WIN Sy
Plymouth	224.9800	–	●lx	AB6MJ	AB6MJ
Rancho Cordova	224.1000	–	O 100r	W6AK	SARC
Red Bluff	224.8000	–	O 110.9ex	N6YCK	N6YCK
Rescue	224.0600	–	O 127.3x	K6ZWZ	K6ZWZK6KRD
Sacramento	223.8800	–	O 100#	K6TTD	K6TTD
Sacramento	224.2200	–	O 123ae	KC6MHT	KC6MHT
Sacramento	224.4000	–	O 162.2el	K6IS	NHRC
Sacramento	224.5600	–	O 94.8#esx	WA6ZZK	WA6ZZK
Sacramento	224.7000	–	O 107.2el	AA6IP	AA6IP
Sacramento	224.8200	–	O 67e	KJ6JD	KJ6JD
Vacaville	223.8400	–	O 141.3lx	AC6VJ	CONDOR
Vacaville	223.9000	–	O 136.5	N6NMZ	N6NMZ
Vacaville	224.1200	–	O 141.3ex	KJ6MB	KJ6MB
Vacaville	224.2000	–	O 127.3aelrsx	WV6F	Western Va
Vacaville	224.2400	–	O 136.5elx	KG6TXA	salac
Vacaville	224.4200	–	O 100	N6NMZ	N6NMZ
Vacaville	224.7600	–	O 100lrx	W6YOP	YOP HLLS
Williams	224.2600	–	O 100elx	N6NMZ	Colusa SO
Yuba City	224.9600	–	O 100#x	W6GNO	W6GNO
NORCAL-SAN JOAQUIN VALLEY					
Bakersfield	224.0600	–	O 100elx	W6LIE	KCCVARC
Bakersfield	224.4200	–	O 156.7#l	W6PVG	W6PVG
Bakersfield	224.5200	–	O 100el	KG6KKV	KG6KKV
Bakersfield	224.7800	–	O 100el	K6RET	K6RET
Clovis	224.3800	–	O 141.3aelx	N6JXL	CARP
Coalinga	224.4400	–	O 100elrsx	KD6OM	KARC
Coalinga	224.8200	–	O 100elrsx	N6DL	Kings ARC
Copperopolis	224.3400	–	O 141.3ex	KG6TXA	SALAC
Fiddletown	224.8600	–	O 141.3ex	KG6TXA	SALAC
Fresno	223.7800	–	O 141.3#ex	K6JSI	CCAC
Fresno	223.9400	–	O 141.3lx	W6TO	Fresno Ama
Fresno	224.7600	–	●elrx	W6SCE	EARN
Fresno	224.9400	–	O 141.3ex	W7POR	FARA
Glennville	224.3200	–	●elrx	W6SCE	EARN
Ione	224.0000	–	O 107.2#	K6KBE	K6KBE
Lake Isabella	224.6400	–	O 156.7#elx	WB6RHQ	CONDOR

Location	Output	Input	Notes	Call	Sponsor
Maricopa	224.9800	–	●elx	KC6WRD	FCC
Mariposa	224.1600	–	○ 74.4ex	KF6CLR	Delhi ARC
Mariposa	224.3000	–	○ 74.4ex	KF6CLR	Delhi ARC
Mariposa	224.5000	–	○ 123#elsx	W6BRB	W6DNC
Mariposa	224.9600	–	○ 156.7ersx	W6BXN	W6BXN
Modesto	224.1400	–	○ 136.5esx	WD6EJF	SARA
Oakhurst	224.9000	–	○ 156.7elx	WB6BRU	CONDOR
Patterson	224.0800	–	●elsx	NV6RN	VARN
Shaver Lake	223.8200	–	○ 114.8ex	K6HJ	SRG
Shaver Lake	224.7000	–	○ 156.7x	KE6JZ	SRG
Stockton	223.9400	–	●elx	KD6ITH	KH7I
Stockton	224.6200	–	○ 192.8#ex	WA6TCG	VHF-FM
Tehachapi	224.7000	–	○ 100ex	W6SCE	EARN
Visalia	223.8800	–	○ 103.5elx	N6VYT	TCARC
Visalia	224.1800	–	○ 88.5	KM6OU	KM6OU
Walnut Grove	224.6800	–	○#	N6MDJ	N6MDJ
WoffordHeights	224.5400	–	○ 74.4#aex	KB6DJT	KB6DJT

NORCAL-SOUTH BAY

Location	Output	Input	Notes	Call	Sponsor
Fremont	223.7800	–	○ 110.9elx	K6GOD	K6GOD
Los Gatos	223.8200	–	○ 156.7el	KB6LCS	KB6LCS
Los Gatos	223.8800	–	○ 100ersx	K6FB	LCARC
Los Gatos	224.4800	–	●ex	K6INC	AD1U
Los Gatos	224.5800	–	○ 107.2#el	K6RPT	K6RPT
Los Gatos	224.8000	–	○ 118.8aex	NU6P	NU6P
Los Gatos	224.8800	–	○ 88.5e	N6DVC	K6UB
Milpitas	224.7200	–	○ 100ers	W6MLP	MARES
Morgan Hill	223.8000	–	○ 107.2#el	WA6YBD	WA6YBD
Mountain View	224.1400	–	○ 100aelrs	W6ASH	SPECS RA
Palo Alto	223.8600	–	○ 107.2ex	K6GOD	K6GOD
San Jose	223.9600	–	○ 156.7aels	W6PIY	WVARA
San Jose	224.0200	–	○ 88.5elx	K6UB	K6UB
San Jose	224.0400	–	○ 100elx	KU6V	KU6V
San Jose	224.0800	–	○ 107.2#l	K6RPT	K6RPT
San Jose	224.1000	–	○ 156.7#ae	WA2IBM	IBM ARC
San Jose	224.2600	–	○ 123alx	WB6OQS	SCVRS
San Jose	224.2800	–	○ 100ex	WA6GFY	LMERA ARC
San Jose	224.3400	–	○ 88.5el	NV6RN	VARN
San Jose	224.3600	–	○ 156.7#	NV6RN	BKRN
San Jose	224.5400	–	●elx	KC6WRD	Friends Co
San Jose	224.6000	–	○ 156.7elx	KB6ABM	CONDOR
San Jose	224.6200	–	○ 110.9elrsx	KA2FND	KA2FND

Location	*Output*	*Input*	*Notes*	*Call*	*Sponsor*
San Jose	224.6400	–	O 110.9elx	N6NAC	N6NAC
San Jose	224.6600	–	●elsx	NV6RN	VARN
San Jose	224.6800	–	O 107.2	WB6KHP	CFMA
San Jose	224.8600	–	O 100#	KB6HDA	KB6HDA
San Jose	224.9400	–	Oex	WA6YCZ	BAYCOM
San Jose	224.9800	–	O 110.9l	NT6S	NT6S
San Martin	223.9200	–	O 100el	KU6V	KU6V
Santa Clara	223.9400	–	●elx	KQ6RC	KQ6RC
Saratoga	224.4600	–	●aelrx	K6BEN	W2NYC
NORCAL-TAHOE					
So Lake Tahoe	224.0200	–	Oex	NR7A	TARA
So Lake Tahoe	224.6400	–	O 203.5ael	W6SUV	W6SUV
Tahoe City	224.7600	–	O 123#elx	W6AV	W6AV
Truckee	223.8200	–	O 100lx	W6SAR	PCSAR
NORCAL-WEST BAY					
San Francisco	224.2200	–	O 100elrx	NC6EO	NCAERO
San Francisco	224.4200	–	O 136.5alx	KB6LCS	KB6LCS
San Francisco	224.5000	–	O 114.8#	W6TP	GSPLRC
San Francisco	224.5200	–	O 136.5#el	KA6TGI	KA6TGI
San Francisco	224.8400	–	O 141.3#e	KF6QCH	KF6QCH
Woodside	224.5600	–	O 100l	KB6LED	KB6LED
SIERRA/TAHOE					
Truckee	223.8200	–	O 100	N6NMZ	W6SAR
SOCAL-IMPERIAL COUNTY					
Quartz Pk	224.9600	–	●(CA)e	WB6YFG	COUVRA
SOCAL-KERN COUNTY					
Inyokern	224.9800	–	●(CA)x	W5WH	------------
Rosamond	224.6600	–	O 110.9 (CA)e	KK6KU	------------
Shirley Peak	224.6400	–	O 156.7lx	WB6RHQ	Condor
Tehachapi	224.4400	–	O 94.8x	WB6FYR	------------
Tehachapi	224.7000	–	●lx	W6SCE	EARN
SOCAL-LOS ANGELES COUNTY					
Blueridge	224.0200	–	O 110.9x	KC6JAR	------------
Blueridge	224.4800	–	O 100.0	W6CPA	IRC
Catalina	224.4200	–	O 110.9	AA6DP	CARA
Contractor Pt	224.2400	–	O 162.2x	W6WAX	------------
Contractor Pt	224.2600	–	●(CA)x	KF6HKM	------------
Contractor Pt	224.4800	–	O 110.9 (CA)eL(MRA/IRL)xZ(811)	K6VE	MRA
Contractor Pt	224.5200	–	O 103.5/103.5 (CA) RB BIx	KC6PXL	------------
Covina	223.8400	–	O 151.4/151.4 (CA)eRB	WA6NJJ	------------
Flint Pk	224.9200	–	●	WB6FYR	ASTRO
Hollywood Hls	224.6800	–	O 114.8 (CA)eE-SUN L(WCRN)sRBx	WA6MDJ	BHARC
Hollywood Hls	224.9600	–	●	W6EEA	AARC
Inglewood	224.4600	–	O 131.8 (CA)	WS6C	------------

Location	Output	Input	Notes	Call	Sponsor
Johnstone Pk	223.9800	–	O 103.5e	W6NRY	EARS
La Canada	224.0800	–	O 156.7/156.7x	WR6JPL	JPL ARC
Lancaster	223.9200	–	O 100.0	WA6YVL	------------
Long Beach	224.5000	–	O 156.7	K6SYU	AARA
Loop Cyn-FS	224.8600	–	●x	WC6MRA	CMRA
Los Angeles	224.7000	–	O 114.8	WR6JPL	JPL ARC
Mt Lukens	223.8600	–	●(CA)ex	WS6RG	WestsidARC
Mt Lukens	224.0400	–	●BI	KF6JBN	KARA
Mt Lukens	224.7800	–	●	KF6JWT	------------
Mt Wilson	224.9400	–	O 94.8	WA6DVG	------------
MtDisappntment	224.3000	–	O 100.0rx	K6CPT	LACoDCS
Newhall	223.9800	–	O 110.9 (CA)elRB	WB6DZO	VRA
Oat Mtn	224.3600	–	O 107.2/107.2 (CA) TT(361)esRBx	K6VER	VERA
Oat Mtn	224.4000	–	●lx	WD6FZA	PAPA
Oat Mtn	224.6200	–	O 82.5x	K6LRB	------------
Oat Mtn	224.7400	–	●lx	W6SCE	EARN
Palos Verdes	223.7800	–	O 100.0e L(IRLP)rRBx	WA6LA	WALA
Palos Verdes	224.3800	–	O 192.8 (CA)e	W6SBA	SBayARC
Palos Verdes	224.6000	–	O 82.5	K6ZMI	------------
Rowland Heights	224.4400	–	O 100.0/100.0 (CA) BI	N6XPG	------------
Saddle Pk	224.3400	–	●	KD6ODU	------------
Santa Anita Rg	224.2800	–	O 107.2	WA6CGR	SCEARA
Signal Hill	223.8000	–	O 156.7s	K6CHE	LB CD&DR
Sunset Ridge	224.0000	–	O 146.2	K6TSG	Sunset Gp
Sunset Ridge	224.0600	–	●	KB6MQQ	------------
Sunset Ridge	224.1600	–	O 71.9 L(WINS)	K6JSI	WIN System
Sunset Ridge	224.8400	–	O 151.4	WA6NJJ	------------
Table Mtn	223.9600	–	O 156.7	WR6AZN	JPL ARC
Verdugo Pk	224.2000	–	O 123.0 (CA)	N6MQS	------------
West Hollywood	224.5600	–	O 77.0	K6CBS	------------
Whittier Hills	223.9400	–	O 100.0/100.0elrsx	W6GNS	RHARC
Whittier Hills	224.1200	–	O 151.4 (CA)e	N6DHZ	SERG
SOCAL-ORANGE COUNTY					
Costa Mesa	224.3200	–	O 151.4	AD6HK	CARA
Fullerton Hills	224.1800	–	O 103.5/103.5 L(145.40)rs	N6ME	WARA
Huntington Bch	223.7600	–	O 94.8ers	KD6KQ	------------
La Habra	224.5000	–	O 162.2	K6SYU	AARA
Mission Viejo	223.9600	–	●	N6QLB	SOC ARES

Location	*Output*	*Input*	*Notes*	*Call*	*Sponsor*
Pleasants Pk	224.8000	–	●	W7BF	SPARK
Santiago Pk	223.8200	–	●x	KD6ZLZ	------------
Santiago Pk	224.2200	–	● 151.4x	WR6AAC	Vulture
Santiago Pk	224.5400	–	●x	W6YQY	------------
Santiago Pk	224.6200	–	O 74.8x	K6LRB	------------
Santiago Pk	224.6400	–	●x	K6SOA	------------
Santiago Pk	224.7600	–	●e L(EARN)x	W6SCE	EARN
Santiago Pk	224.8000	–	●x	W7BF	SPARK
Santiago Pk	224.8200	–	O 156.7x	K6AEQ	Condor
Santiago Pk	224.8800	–	O 107.2x	KB6TRD	HRAN
Temple Hill	224.1000	–	O 110.9	K6SOA	SOARA
SOCAL-RIVERSIDE COUNTY					
Blythe	224.3200	–	●lx	W6SCE	EARN
Box Springs	224.4600	–	O 110.9r	W6CDF	RivRACES
Chuckwalla Mtn	224.0400	–	●x	WC6MRA	CMRA
Chuckwalla Mtn	224.7000	–	●x	W6YQY	------------
Chuckwalla Mtn	224.7600	–	●lx	W6SCE	EARN
Hemet	224.1200	–	O 97.4pr	W6COH	HemetRACES
Indio	224.3200	–	●lx	W6SCE	EARN
Palm Desert	224.9200	–	O 156.7e	W6DRA	Desert RC
Riverside	224.9800	–	●	KA6RVK	------------
Santa Rosa Mtn	223.8800	–	O 110.9rsx	WA6HYQ	------------
Sierra Pk	223.7600	–	O 110.9ers	W6KRW	OC RACES
Sierra Pk	224.9000	–	●	WA6TQQ	------------
Toro Pk	224.1000	–	●x	W6YQY	------------
Toro Pk	224.1800	–	O 156.7	WB6RHQ	Condor
SOCAL-SAN BERNARDINO COUNTY					
Barstow	224.0400	–	O 156.7	WR6AZN	JPL ARC
Crestline	224.2000	–	●	N6QCU	GTE EARC
Crestline	224.8600	–	O 77.0	W6JBT	CBARC
Keller Pk	224.3400	–	●L(CMRA) sx	KD6ODU	CMRA
Mt Rodman	224.0800	–	O 131.8x	KC6KUY	------------
Ord Mtn	224.3200	–	●lx	W6SCE	EARN
Rim Forest	224.2600	–	O 110.9rsx	W6CDF	------------
Twin Peaks	224.5600	–	O 100.0	WA6TJQ	------------
Upland	224.5800	–	O 88.5 (CA)	K6PQN	------------
Wrightwood	224.4000	–	O 91.5	KW6WW	WCG
SOCAL-SAN DIEGO COUNTY					
Chula Vista	224.9400	–	O 107.2	KK6KD	CV ARC
El Cajon	224.0800	–	O 107.2	WA6BGS	------------
La Mesa	223.8800	–	O 107.2rs	WA6HYQ	------------
Lyons Pk	223.8000	–	●	K6JCC	SDC RACES
Lyons Pk	223.9400	–	O 141.3x	W2IRI	Condor
Mission Hills	223.8000	–	●	WD6APP	SDC RACES
Mt Laguna	224.0600	–	O 107.2	WB6WLV	SANDRA
Mt Otay	223.8600	–	O 107.2	KN6KM	SoBay RG
Mt Otay	224.1600	–	O 107.2lrx	WA6HYQ	------------

Location	*Output*	*Input*	*Notes*	*Call*	*Sponsor*
Mt Otay	224.2000	–	O 107.2	N6ICC	SANDRA
Mt Otay	224.2600	–	O 107.2	N6VVZ	FILAMARS
Mt Otay	224.6800	–	O 107.2	W6CRC	------------
Mt Palomar	223.9800	–	O 107.2	WA6RKK	------------
Mt Palomar	224.9000	–	O 107.2e	WD6HFR	220 of SD
San Diego	223.9600	–	O 107.2	WD6APP	------------
San Diego	224.7400	–	O 107.2	WD6APP	------------
San Diego	224.9200	–	O 107.2 (CA)	KD6GNB	ECRA
San Marcos	224.1400	–	O 156.7/156.7	AE6GM	------------
Woodson	223.8000	–	●	K6JCC	SDC RACES
SOCAL-SAN LUIS OBISPO COUNTY					
San LuisObispo	224.5800	–	O 151.4elx	WB6NYS	------------
SOCAL-SANTA BARBARA COUNTY					
Brush Peak	224.0000	–	O 156.7	N6HYM	Condor
Gibraltar Pk	224.0400	–	●l	WC6MRA	CRMA
Goleta	224.1600	–	O 131.8ers	K6TZ	SBARC
Goleta	224.6600	–	O 131.8	K6RCL	CMRA
La Cumbre Pk	224.0800	–	O 131.8/131.8ersRBx	K6TZ	SBARC
Santa Barbara	224.3200	–	O 131.8	N6HYM	------------
Santa Barbara	224.8600	–	O 131.8	WB9KMO	------------
Santa Barbara	224.9000	–	O 131.8	WB6OBB	SBCoRA
Santa Cruz Is	223.9200	–	O 131.8/131.8 E-SUNrsRBx	K6TZ	SBARC
Santa Ynez Pk	224.1200	–	O 131.8/131.8ersRBx	K6TZ	SBARC
Santa Ynez Pk	224.8000	–	●	K6RCL	CMRA
SOCAL-VENTURA COUNTY					
Frazier Mtn	224.7200	–	O 156.7lx	WB6RHQ	Condor
La Conchita	224.7600	–	●lx	W6SCE	EARN
Rasnow Pk	223.9600	–	O 141.3	N6CFC	------------
Red Mtn	224.0200	–	O 127.3/127.3ersx	K6ERN	SMRA
South Mtn	224.1000	–	O 127.3ers WXx	WA6ZSN	SMRA
Thousand Oaks	224.7000	–	O 156.7 (CA)e	K6HB	------------

COLORADO

FREQUENCY USAGE		
STATEWIDE	224.0400	–
STATEWIDE	224.2800	–
STATEWIDE	224.4400	–
STATEWIDE	224.5000	–
STATEWIDE	224.5400	–
STATEWIDE	224.6600	–
STATEWIDE	224.9200	–

Location	Output	Input	Notes	Call	Sponsor
BOULDER COUNTY					
Boulder	224.0200	–	OI	WØIA	RMVHFS
Rolliinsville	224.6000	–	O 100	WØRM	WØRM
COLORADO SPRINGS					
Colo Sprs	224.7200	–	O 103.5/103.5 RB	WØMOG	WØMOG
Colorado Springs	224.0600	–	●elx	KBØSRJ	PPFMA
Colorado Springs	224.9000	–	107.2/107.2 L(IRLP 3621)	WDØC	WDØC
DENVER METRO					
Aurora	223.9800	–	O 100 (CA)	KEØJM	KEØJM
Denver	224.0000	–	O 103.5 (CA)	NØMHU	RMRL
Denver	224.1000	–	O 107.2/107.2l	WRØAEN	CARN
Denver	224.3800	–	O 100/100e l	WØTX	DRC
Denver	224.9800	–	O 107.2/107.2 (CA)ex	WØCRA	CRA
Golden	224.7400	–	O 88.5a	NØPOH	ARA
GRAND JUNCTION					
Grand Junction	224.2600	–	● 107.2 (CA)ersWX	WA4HND	GMRA
NORTH FRONT RANGE					
Fort Collins	224.5200	–	O 100el	WØUPS	NCARC
Fort Collins	224.8400	–	Ox	WØUPS	NCARC
Fort Lupton	224.9600	–	O	ACØKC	ACØKC
Loveland	224.3200	–	O 100/100 (CA)e	KN6VV	KN6VV
PUEBLO					
Canon City	223.9600	–	O 103.5es RB	WDØEKR	RGARC
Pueblo	224.2600	–	O 88.5ex	NDØQ	PuebloHC
SOUTH CENTRAL					
Cripple Creek	224.9400	–	O 67/67el	WBØWDF	WBØWDF
Walsenburg	224.3200	–	O 88.5e	NDØQ	PuebloHC
WEST CENTRAL					
Glenwood Springs	224.0200	–	●	KIØG	SCARC
Vail	224.8000	–	Ot	NØAFO	ECHO

CONNECTICUT

Location	Output	Input	Notes	Call	Sponsor
FREQUENCY USAGE					
SNP Pair	224.1400	–			
SNP Pair	224.4400	–	O		
FAIRFIELD & SOUTHWEST					
Bridgeport	224.9600	–	77.0/136.5	N1LXV	W1BHZ
Danbury	223.9600	–	O 100.0/100.0 (CA)e	W1QI	CARA

Location	Output	Input	Notes	Call	Sponsor
Fairfield	224.1000	–	O	N3AQJ	FUARA
HARTFORD & N CENTRAL					
Avon	224.9400	–	Oe	W1JNR	------------
Bristol	224.1600	–	O 77.0/77.0 l	KB1AEV	KB1AEV
Bristol	224.2200	–	O 118.8ae	W1IXU	W1JJA
Hebron	224.7000	–	156.7	N1CBD	------------
Newington	224.8400	–	Oe	W1AW	NARL
Vernon	224.1200	–	O 82.5/82.5 el	W1HDN	PVRA
Vernon	224.3600	–	O 77.0/77.0 el	KB1AEV	KB1AEV
Vernon	224.6000	–	O 123.0/123.0	K1WMS	K1WMS
W Hartford	224.2800	–	O 114.8	N1XLU	N1XLU
Wethersfield	224.6800	–	O	K1WMS	K1WMS
LITCHFIELD & NORTHWEST					
Torrington	223.7800	–	O 82.5/82.5 el	W1HDN	PVRA
Warren	224.3200	–	O 77.0/77.0 els	NA1RA	NARA
NEW HAVEN & S CENTRAL					
Ansonia	224.4200	–	Oe	KA1LSD	AnsoniaCD
Meriden	224.8000	–	O 77.0l	K1HSN	Southingtn
Milford	223.8800	–	O	N1JKA	------------
New Haven	224.1800	–	O	WA1UFC	------------
New Haven	224.5000	–	O 77.0/77.0 (CA)e	K1SOX	SPARC
NEW LONDON & SOUTHEAST					
Groton	223.9600	–	O 156.7 (CA)e	W1NLC	SCRAMS
Ledyard	224.3800	–	O 103.5l	W1DX	AWASEC
New London	224.2600	–	Oe	W1NLC	SCRAMS
Salem	224.1400	–	O 103.5el	W1DX	AWASEC

DELAWARE

Location	Output	Input	Notes	Call	Sponsor
ALL					
SNP	223.8000	–	O		------------
SOUTH					
Delmar	224.0200	–	O	N3FJM	DARC
Greenwood	224.4400	–	O	W3WMD	CSARC
Millsboro	224.8400	–	OaeZ(911)	K3JL	Sussex ARA
WILMINGTON					
Newark	224.0000	–	O 67.0e	KB3MEC	KB3MEC
Newark	224.7200	–	Oa	N3JCR	+N3JFS
Wilmington	224.5200	–	O 131.8l	W3DRA	DRA

Location	*Output*	*Input*	*Notes*	*Call*	*Sponsor*
DISTRICT OF COLUMBIA					
ALL					
SNP	223.8000	–	O		------------
FLORIDA					
CENTRAL - ORLANDO					
Clermont	223.9400	–	Ot	KAØOXH	KAØOXH
Umatilla	224.1400	–	Oe	KA4OPN	SHRA
EAST CENTRAL					
Cocoa	224.5000	–	O	N4LEM	N4LEM
NORTH CENTRAL					
Anthony	224.1000	–	O	N4TSV	SCARS
			103.5/103.5ex		
Gainesville	224.1600	–	Ors	K4GNV	GARS
NORTH EAST					
Bunnell	224.0200	–	OL(145.45)	KB4JDE	KB4JDE
Holly Hill	223.8500	–	O 100/100e	KI4RF	KI4RF
			L(146 655 53.05 444.175 EC-50666)		
NORTH EAST - JACKSONVILLE					
Middleburg	224.0000	–	O	N4RVD	N4RVD
SOUTH CENTRAL					
Okeechobee	224.1000	–	O	KF4EA	KF4EA
SOUTH EAST - MIAMI/FT LAUD					
Coral Springs	224.6800	–	O	N2DUI	WA4EMJ
			131.8/131.8 L(444.575)rsRB LITZx		
Ft Lauderdale	224.4000	–	O	KF4LZA	KF4LZA
			110.9/110.9 L(927.7)		
Ft Lauderdale	224.7600	–	O	W4AB	BARC
			110.9/110.9		
Hialeah	223.9400	–	O	WB4IVM	WB4IVM
			110.9/110.9a(CA)ersBIx		
Hialeah	224.0600	–	O	WB4IVM	WB4IVM
			110.9/110.9a(CA)ersBIx		
Hialeah	224.5800	–	O	WB4IVM	WB4IVM
			110.9/110.9a(CA)ersBIx		
Miami	224.1000	–	O	KC4MND	KC4MND
Miami	224.1400	–	●t	AE4WE	AE4WE
Miami	224.1600	–	O	WB4TWQ	WB4TWQ
			118.8/118.8e		
Miami	224.8200	–	O	WB4DD	WB4DD
			103.5/103.5		
Miami	224.9200	–	OBI	KB4AIL	KB4AIL
Pembroke Pines	224.8800	–	O 88.5/88.5	KP4BM	KP4BM
SOUTH WEST					
Naples	224.3800	–	●	KD4OZW	KD4OZW
			131.8/131.8 L(444.450 443.900 444.075 44		
SOUTH WEST - FT MYERS					
Ft Myers	224.5200	–	O	WA4PIL	FMARC
			103.5/103.5e		

Location	*Output*	*Input*	*Notes*	*Call*	*Sponsor*
WEST CENTRAL					
New Port Richey	224.5400	–	O	WA4GDN	GCARC
			103.5/103.5		
WEST CENTRAL - TAMPA/ST PETE					
Clearwater	224.9400	–	Oe	K4JMH	CARS
			L(146.970 444.150 444.450 444.575)		
Riverview	224.2800	–	●te	NI4CE	WCFG
			L(145.290 145.430 146.760 442.550 442.825 4		
Tampa	224.7400	–	eL(444.250	W4RNT	RANT
			443.675 442.725 IR-4880 EC-7960)rsx		

GEORGIA

Location	*Output*	*Input*	*Notes*	*Call*	*Sponsor*
Acworth	224.3200	–	O	N4MTA	DELTA 4 RG
Acworth	224.5000	–	O	N4MTA	DELTA 4 RG
Alpharetta	224.5800	–	O	K9RFA	RF ACRES
Alpharetta	224.6200	–	O	W4PME	W4ZF
Atlanta	224.1200	–	O	N4NFP	BSRG
Atlanta	224.2200	–	O	N4NEQ	BSRG
Atlanta	224.3400	–	O	W4DOC	W4DOC
Atlanta	224.4400	–	O	N4NEQ	BSRG
Atlanta	224.6200	–	O	W4PME	MATPARC
Atlanta	224.9600	–	O	K4RFL	GIRA
Augusta	224.9400	–	O	WB4KXO	WB4KXO
Baconton	224.3000	–	O	N1QJ	N1QJ
Biskey Mtn	224.1600	–	O	KC4JNN	KC4JNN
Cedartown	224.7800	–	O	KC4KLW	KC4KLW
Chatsworth	224.2400	–	O	N4YYD	N4YYD
Chatsworth	224.8600	–	O	KC4AQS	KC4AQS
Concord	224.4600	–	O	WB4GWA	WB4GWA
			110.9/110.9 WX		
Conley	224.2800	–	O	N4MNA	N4MNA
Cumming	224.8200	–	O	W4FRT	W4PX
Dahlonega	224.4800	–	O	N4KHQ	N4KHQ
Dallas	224.1800	–	O	N4YDX	N4YDX
Dallas	224.5400	–	O	N4YEA	N4YEA
Dallas	224.7000	–	O	W4TIY	K4RJJ
Dalton	224.4600	–	O	N4BZJ	N4BZJ
Dalton	224.6800	–	O	N4BZJ	7.135 RPTR GRP
Dalton	224.7400	–	O	N4KVC	7.135 RPTR GRP
Decatur	224.7600	–	O	W4BOC	W4BOC
Eastanollee	224.6400	–	O	W4BNG	W4BNG
Fayetteville	224.5600	–	O	AG4ZR	AG4ZR
			131.8/131.8elsWX		
Hawkinsville	224.8200	–	O	WR4MG	KB8CUH
Jasper	224.4000	–	O	KC4AQS	KC4AQS
Jasper	224.6000	–	O	KC4AQS	NP2Y
Lagrange	224.7200	–	O	WB4BXO	WB4BXO
Lookout Mt	224.5600	–	O	W4RRG	KS4QA

Location	*Output*	*Input*	*Notes*	*Call*	*Sponsor*
Macon	224.6400	–	O	WA4DDI	WA4DDI
Marietta	224.2600	–	O	KE4QFG	KE4QFG
Marietta	224.9000	–	O	W4LMA	LARC-LOCKHEE
Pickens	224.2000	–	O	N4GHT	N4GHT
Pine Log Mtn	224.5200	–	O	K4AIS	K4AIS
Pine Mtn	224.6600	–	O	WB4ULJ	W4OM
Pine Mtn Valley	224.3600	–	O	WB4ULJ	WA4ULK
Ray City	224.2200	–	O	WR4SG	KBØY
Rome	224.6400	–	O	WB4LRA	WB4LRA
Snellville	224.9200	–	O	W4CSX	MARCEL
Thomasville	224.3200	–	O	WR4SG	SGRA
Union	224.8800	–	OelWX	WD4LUQ	WD4LUQ
Valdosta	224.4600	–	O	WR4SG	SGRA
Villa Rica	224.3000	–	O	KB4TIW	VILLA RICA RAD
Waleska	224.1400	–	O	KD4ALC	KD4ALC
Waleska	224.9400	–	O	N4GIS	N4GIS
Warner Robins	224.8400	–	O	WR4MG	MID GA RADIO
Watkinsville	224.4200	–	O	KD4AOZ	KD4AOZ
Young Harris	224.6600	–	O	NP2Y	WP2ADK
HAWAII					
KAUAI					
Hanamaulu	223.9800	–	O	KH6BFU	Ohana ARC
OAHU					
Honolulu	223.9400	–	O	KH6OJ	Ohana ARC
Honolulu	224.7400	–	O	NH7ZD	Ohana ARC
Honolulu	224.9400	–	O	KH7NM	Ohana ARC
Leeward	224.9200	–	O#	NH7QH	NH7QH
IDAHO					
FREQUENCY USAGE - IACC AREAS					
# Snp	224.7200	–			
# Snp	224.8400	–			
N ID - WALLACE					
Goose Hump	224.7600	–	O 131.8	WB7BTU	SCHRA
SOUTH CENT					
Burley	223.2300	224.9200	O	K6ZVA	K6ZVA
SOUTHEAST IDAHO					
Shelley	224.7600	–	O	W7QJR	w7qjr
SW-ID					
Boise	223.9400	–	O	KB7ZD	KB7ZD
Boise	224.5000	–	Oel	KA7EWN	KA7EWN
Emmett	224.8800	–	O 100	K7WIR	WIARA
ILLINOIS					
CENTRAL					
Forest City	223.9800	–		WI9MP	WI9MP
CHICAGO					
Chicago	223.8800	–	110.9	KC9EBB	KC9EBB

Location	Output	Input	Notes	Call	Sponsor
Chicago	224.0200	–	103.5	W9TMC	TMCARC
Chicago	224.0600	–	110.9	WD9GEH	WD9GEH
Chicago	224.1000	–	(CA)	WA9ORC	CFMC
Chicago	224.3400	–	103.5	W9RA	DONFAR
DECATUR					
Lovington	223.8600	–	103.5e	KR9X	LRA
EAST CENTRAL					
Danville	224.8400	–	100.0 (CA)e	KC9USH	KC9USH
NORTH CENTRAL					
Freeport	224.9200	–	100.0 (CA)e	W9FN	W9FN
Joliet	223.8200	–	Oael	W9OFR	WCARL
NORTHEAST					
Batavia	224.4000	–	110.9el	W9XA	W9XA
Bloomingdale	224.2200	–	110.9	K9NB	BARK
Bolingbrook	224.5400	–	110.9e	K9BAR	BARS
Bridgeview	224.4800	–	110.9	KB9EPL	KB9EPL
Brookfield	224.1600	–	110.9aelz	K9SAD	SADFAR
Buffalo Grove	224.5800	–	110.9 (CA)l	WB9TAL	ARCOMLEAGU
Crystal Lake	224.7000	–	100.0el	K9VI	K9QI
Deerfield	224.2400	–	110.9e	KA9REN	CHINET
Downers Grove	224.6800	–	110.9 (CA)e l	W9DUP	DARC
Glen Ellyn	224.1400	–	110.9aelz	W9CCU	WCRA
Glenview	224.6000	–	110.9	W9AP	NORA
Gurnee	224.0800	–	127.3 (CA)e	W9MAB	GURNEE RG
Hampshire	223.9200	–	● 114.8	W9ZS	W9ZS
Itasca	224.5000	–	192.8	WA9ZZU	WA9ZZU
Lake Zurich	223.8400	–	110.9	K9SA	K9SA
Lake Zurich	224.8600	–	110.9s	W9SRO	SRO/CFAR
Lisle	224.3600	–	110.9	WB9QXJ	FUBAR
Lisle	224.6200	–	110.9 (CA)e LITZ	WA9AEK	WA9AEK
Lockport	224.9400	–	114.8	N2BJ	ANDREW RC
Lombard	224.2600	–	110.9	WA9VGI	FISHFAR
Naperville	224.2000	–	110.9	W9NPD	NPDARC
New Lenox	224.4200	–	114.8	N2BJ	N2BJ
North Riverside	224.8200	–	110.9	K9ONA	SMCC
Oswego	224.9200	–	110.9	NK9M	NK9M ATVN
Park Forest	223.9600	–	110.9 (CA)	WB9UAR	WB9UAR
Park Ridge	224.7800	–	110.9e	WA9ZMY	FAROUT
Rolling Meadow	224.3800	–	110.9al	WB9WNK	MATS
Schaumburg	223.9400	–	110.9l	N9EP	N9EP
Schaumburg	224.5600	–	110.9l	K9EL	EGDXA
Schaumburg	224.6600	–		WB9YBM	WB9YBM
Schaumburg	224.7600	–	110.9 (CA)e lz	N9CXQ	NAPS
Schaumburg	224.8800	–	110.9	KB2MAU	RAYJACK
Schiller Park	224.9800	–	110.9 (CA)	WB9AET	WAFAR
Techny	224.3200	–	110.9e	NS9RC	NSRC

Location	*Output*	*Input*	*Notes*	*Call*	*Sponsor*
West Chicago	224.6400	–	110.9	N9XP	N9XP
West Chicago	224.7200	–	103.5l	W9DMW	MOOSEFAR
Westmont	223.8600	–	110.9	N9TO	N9TO
Worth	224.1800	–		WA9ORC	CFMC
NORTHWEST					
Lanark	224.8600	–		WB9NLQ	SRG
Rock Island	224.1000	–	110.9e	N9TPQ	N9TPQ
PEORIA					
Dunlap	224.0800	–	156.7 (CA)e l	N9BBO	N9BBO
ROCKFORD					
Mt Morris	224.1200	–	118.8elx	K9AMJ	K9AMJ
Mt Morris	224.8400	–	118.8elrs WX	K9AMJ	K9AMJ
Rockford	223.8800	–	118.8	W9AXD	RARA
Rockford	224.0400	–	118.8 (CA)e l	K9AMJ	K9AMJ
Rockford	224.2800	–	114.8a	N9CWQ	ARECOMM
Rockford	224.4400	–	118.8 (CA)e l	K9AMJ	K9AMJ
SOUTH					
Eagleton	224.8500	–		W9IMP	OTHG
Tunnel Hill	224.8600	–	88.5ers	WB9F	L. CLORE
SOUTH CENTRAL					
Greenville	224.4400	–	103.5e	W9KXQ	OVARC
Mulberry Grove	224.1400	–	103.5	W9KXQ	W9KXQ
SPRINGFIELD					
Tallula	224.4800	–	94.8	K9KGO	K9KGO
ST LOUIS					
Belleville	224.1200	–	127.3az	K9GXU	ST CLAIR
Collinsville	224.0600	–	127.3ers WX	W9AIU	EGYPTN RC
Godfrey	224.3000	–	123.0el	N9GGF	N9OWS+
Maryville	224.7000	–	151.4e	KG9OV	KG9OV
Mascoutah	224.2000	–	l	AA9ME	AA9ME
WEST CENTRAL					
Dallas City	224.0200	–	100.0ex	KC9JIC	KC9JIC
Versailles	224.9200	–	103.5	KB9JVU	------------
INDIANA					
EAST CENTRAL					
Hartford City	224.5600	–	**O**ersWX	WB9HLA	WB9HLA
Marion	224.5200	–	**O**	KA9IYJ	KA9IYJ
Muncie	223.9200	–	**O**ls	WB9HXG	MuncieARC
Muncie	224.7000	–	**O**ae	WD9HQH	Evans/Rust
New Castle	224.1800	–	**O**rs	N9EYG	N9EYG
Parker City	224.0400	–	**O**eWX	K9EKP	K9EKP
Richmond	224.7400	–	**O** 127.3ers WX	W1IDX	W1IDX

INDIANA

Location	Output	Input	Notes	Call	Sponsor
INDIANAPOLIS					
Franklin	223.9600	–	O 151.4e	KC9LGZ	KC9LGZ
Indianapolis	224.5000	–	O	KC9COP	KC9COP
Indianapolis	224.5400	–	O	KB9RBF	KB9RBF
Indianapolis	224.5800	–	O 127.3 (CA)el	N9ILS	N9ILS
Indianapolis	224.8000	–	O 88.5r	K9XV	K9XV
Indianapolis	224.9800	–	O 77.0e	W9ICE	ICE
Martinsville	224.6600	–	OesWX	K9PYI	MorganRA
Mccordsville	224.9200	–	O 88.5	WA4QQR	WA4QQR
Shelbyville	224.4400	–	OesWX	W9JUQ	BRV ARS
NORTH CENTRAL					
Elkhart	223.9400	–	O 131.8e WX	N8AES	N8AES
Elkhart	224.0800	–	O 131.8el WX	KC9GMH	KC9GMH
Elkhart	224.9000	–	O 131.8 (CA)ex	W9LZX	ElkhartCRA
Plymouth	224.5000	–	O 131.8	K9ZLQ	MrshlARC
South Bend	223.9800	–	O 131.8ael	WB9YPA	WB9YPA
NORTHEAST					
Angola	224.9400	–	O 131.8e	WB9DGD	WB9DGD
Columbia City	223.9000	–	O 141.3ers WX	K9KOP	K9KOP
Columbia City	224.8600	–	Oer	N9FGN	N9FGN
Roanoke	224.4000	–	O 131.8	WB9VLE	WB9VLE
Warren	224.4600	–	● 171.3e	N9QVI	N9QVI
NORTHWEST					
Gary	224.4600	–	O 131.8e	W9CTO	W9CTO
Hammond	224.7400	–	O 131.8ae WX	KA9QJG	KA9QJG
Munster	224.0000	–	O 131.8el WX	W9FXT	IARA
Valparaiso	224.1200	–	O 131.8lx	KB9KRI	Duneland
SOUTH CENTRAL					
Bloomington	224.6400	–	O 107.2l WX	K9SOU	BlmHS-ARC
Floyds Knob	224.8200	–	Oe	W9BGW	W9BGW
Frenchtown	224.7000	–	O 103.5e	WB9GNA	WB9GNA
Seymour	224.8600	–	O 203.5	KC9JOY	KC9JOY
Springville	223.8000	–	O 107.2	N9HXU	N9HXU
SOUTHEAST					
Brookville	224.2800	–	Oe	N9HHM	N9HHM
Brookville	224.3200	–	O	N9HHM	N9HHM
Greensburg	224.7800	–	OrsWX	N9LQP	DecaturARC
Versailes	224.4600	–	OerWX	KC9MBX	KC9MBX
SOUTHWEST					
Vincennes	224.6000	–	Oe	W9DP	W9DP

Location	Output	Input	Notes	Call	Sponsor
WEST CENTRAL					
Terre Haute	224.8800	–	O 123.0	W9TLC	W9TLC
West Lafayette	224.9600	–	O 88.5e	W9YB	PurdueARC
IOWA					
CEDAR RAPIDS					
Cedar Rapids	224.9400	–	O(CA)l	WØHUP	CRRA+SEIT
DES MOINES					
Des Moines	224.9800	–	● 114.8a (CA)elrsWXx	WDØFIA	------------
Grimes	224.5400	–	114.8elWX x	NØINX	WsideComm
EAST CENTRAL					
Clinton	224.1800	–	O	KNØBS	BSARC
SIOUX CITY					
Sioux City	224.1200	–	O	KØTFT	SARA
SOUTHWEST					
Bridgewater	224.8200	–	● 136.5a (CA)ersWXx	WDØFIA	WDØFIA
WATERLOO					
Waterloo	224.9000	–	136.5e	NKØT	NKØT
KANSAS					
CENTRAL					
Hays	224.2800	–	O 131.8/131.8eL(ECHOLINK#3917)	N7JYS	N7JYS
McPherson	223.9400	–	O	WBØUUB	WBØUUB
KANSAS CITY METRO					
Basehor	224.5400	–	O 88.5/88.5 rs	KØHAM	NEKSUN
Basehor	224.5400	–	O 88.5/88.5 ers	KØHAM	NEKSUN
Gardner	224.7800	–	Oa(CA)er	KØNK	KØNK
Kansas City	224.1000	–	Oaer	WBØKIA	KC220ARA
Kansas City	224.1000	–	Oaer	WBØKIA	KC220ARA
Kansas City	224.2000	–	Or	WBØKIA	KC220-BYRG
Kansas City	224.2000	–	Oar	WBØKIA	KC220ARA
Kansas City	224.3000	–	Oar	WBØKIA	KC220ARA
Kansas City	224.3000	–	Oar	WBØKIA	KC220ARA
Olathe	224.9400	–	Oa(CA)e	WØQQ	SFTARC
Olathe	224.9400	–	Oers	WØQQ	SFTARC
Shawnee	223.9400	–	Oe	WAØCBW	WAØCBW
Shawnee Msn	223.9400	–	Oe	WAØCBW	WAØCBW
WICHITA					
El Dorado	224.5800	–	O	KØFCQ	------------
Wichita	224.0600	–	Oe	KFØM	KFØM
KENTUCKY					
Artemus	224.6000	–	O 100/100e l	KF4FWF	KF4FWF

Location	*Output*	*Input*	*Notes*	*Call*	*Sponsor*
Ashland	223.9400	–	O	KC4QK	ASHLAND 24 REP G
Buckhorn Lake	224.4600	–	O	K4XYZ	K4XYZ
Corbin	224.8200	224.2200	O 100/100e I	WR4AMS	WR4AMS
Dorton	224.5200	–	O	WR4AMS	WR4AMS
Garrett	224.2600	–	O	K4NLT	KF4ZTB
Hazard	224.7200	–	O 203.5/203.5elsWX	WR4AMS	------------
Hopkinsville	224.7800	–	O	WD9HIK	WD9HIK
Irvine	224.9400	–	O	AD4RT	KY4LD
Lexington	224.8000	–	O	KR4BD	KR4BD/KA8MJQ
Louisville	224.3000	–	O	KA4MKT	KA4MKT
Louisville	224.8200	–	O	W4MOP	------------
Louisville Area	224.7000	–	O	N4RBL	------------
Lynch	224.3200	–	O	KK4WH	KK4WH
Madisonville	224.2600	–	O 103.5/103.5	KC4FIE	KC4FIE
Manchester	224.9800	–	ODCSel	WR4AMS	WR4AMS
Mayfield	224.8200	–	O 179.9/179.9	WA6LDV	KF4GCD
Middlesboro	224.1200	–	O	WM4MD	KF4GXQ
Nancy	224.1000	–	O 100/100e	AC4DM	AC4DM
Pikeville	224.5800	–	O	WB4F	KEYSER HEIGHTS R
Pikeville	224.6200	–	O	KD4DAR	------------
Somerset	224.3000	–	O	N4AI	N4AI
Somerset	224.8800	–	O	N4AI	N4AI
Stanville	224.6800	–	O	KJ4VF	------------
Versailles	224.2200	–	O	KY4WC	KY4WC
Whitesburg	224.9600	–	O 203.5/203.5els	KK4WH	KK4WH
LOUISIANA					
REG 1 NEW ORLEANS					
New Orleans	224.0000	–	O 114.8	W5MCC	SELCOM
New Orleans	224.9000	–	114.8	WDØGIV	WDØGIV
REG 8 MONROE					
West Monroe	224.9000	–	O 127.3e	K5RUS	K5RUS
REG 9 HAMMOND					
LaCombe	224.6600	–	● 114.8	AA5UY	AA5UY-RA
Madisonville	224.1400	–	O 114.8e	W5NJJ	NLAKE ARC+
STATEWIDE					
Shared	224.6000	–	#	SNP	------------
MAINE					
ALL AREAS					
Statewide	224.1400	–	O	SNP	NESMC
Statewide	224.1400	–	O	SNP	NESMC
AUGUSTA					
Augusta	224.7200	–	O/103.5 L(224.24)	KQ1L	KQ1L

Location	Output	Input	Notes	Call	Sponsor
CENTRAL/BANGOR					
Corinna	224.8400	–	O E-SUN E-WIND	KB1UAS	RPS
Exeter	224.2400	–	O 103.5	AA1PN	AA1PN
MID-COAST					
Hope	224.0000	–	O	WA1ZDA	WA1ZDA
Washington	224.2800	–	O 91.5 (CA) ex	KC1CG	KC1CG
NORTHWEST					
Hebron	224.6200	–	O 103.5	W1IF	W1IF
Woodstock	223.9400	–	O 103.5e L(53.09 449.025)	W1IMD	FrtnlARTS
PORTLAND/SOUTH COAST					
Nobleboro	224.3200	–	O 103.5 L(LINKED TO 224.72 AUGUSTA ME)	W1AUX	W1AUX
Standish	224.7800	–	O 107.2	N1PS	N1PS

MARYLAND

Location	Output	Input	Notes	Call	Sponsor
ALL					
SNP	223.8000	–	O		------------
ANNAPOLIS					
Davidsonville	223.8800	–	O 107.2ae Z(911)	W3VPR	AARC
BALTIMORE					
Baltimore	224.9600	–	O(CA)elWX	WB3DZO	BRATS
Columbia	224.8600	–	O	W3CAM	W3CAM
Ellicott City	224.3200	–	O	N3EZD	N3EZD
Jessup	224.7600	146.1600	O 107.2l	WA3DZD	MFMA
Jessup	224.7600	–	O 107.2l	WA3DZD	MFMA
Jessup	224.7600	449.0000	O 107.2l	WA3DZD	MFMA
Millersville	224.5600	–	O 107.2	W3VPR	AARC
NW Baltimore	224.8000	–	O	WB3DZO	BRATS
Perry Hall	223.8400	–	O	W3JEH	W3JEH
S Baltimore	224.6800	–	O	KS3L	SummitAR
Towson	224.2400	–	O 107.2ael r	W3FT	BARC
W Baltimore	224.6400	–	O	WA3Z	SummitAR
CENTRAL MD					
Damascus	224.5800	–	O	K3LNZ	PAVHFS
Odenton	224.6000	–	O	N3MIR	N3MIR
FREDERICK					
Frederick	224.2000	–	O 123.0 (CA)e	K3MAD	MADXRA
NORTH CENTRAL					
Manchester	224.1200	–	Oa	N3KZS	N3KZS
NORTH EASTERN SHORE					
Galena	224.0000	–	O 131.8e	KB3MEC	KB3MEC
NORTHEAST MD					
Bel Air	223.9600	–	O(CA)	N3EKQ	N3EKQ

Location	Output	Input	Notes	Call	Sponsor
Shawsville	224.9200	–	O	N3UR	N3UR
SOUTH EASTERN SHORE					
Salisbury	224.0200	–	O	N3FJM	DARC
SOUTHERN MD					
Lexington Park	223.9000	–	O	WA3UMY	WA3UMY
WASHINGTON AREA					
Ashton	224.5400	–	O 156.7a	K3WX	K3WX
Jessup	224.7600	146.1600	O 107.2l	WA3DZD	MFMA
Jessup	224.7600	–	O 107.2l	WA3DZD	MFMA
Jessup	224.7600	449.0000	O 107.2l	WA3DZD	MFMA
Rockville	224.9400	–	O(CA)er	K3ATV	MACS

MASSACHUSETTS

Location	Output	Input	Notes	Call	Sponsor
ALL AREAS					
Statewide	224.1400	–	O	SNP	NESMC
Statewide	224.1400	–	O	SNP	NESMC
BLACKSTONE VALLEY					
Medway	224.6600	–	OL(147.06)	W1KG	W1KG
BOSTON METRO					
Belmont	223.8600	–	O 100/131 L(I4314)	KB1FX	+KB1GXW
Milton	224.3600	–	Oe	N1MV	MVARG
Quincy	224.4000	–	O 103.5 (CA) L(MMRA)	N1KUG	MMRA
Wakefield	223.8000	–	OeEXP	WA1RHN	N1CSI
Wakefield	224.2600	–	O 67ae	WA1WYA	Wake EMA
Wakefield	224.7200	–	Oae	WA1WYA	+WB1HKY
Waltham	224.9400	–	Oe	W1MHL	WARA
BOSTON SOUTH					
Taunton	224.4800	–	O/123x	KC1TAC	TACG
Walpole	224.3200	–	O 118.8er WX	W1ZSA	WalpoleEMA
Wrentham	224.7800	–	O/146.2	N1UEC	EMARG
CAPE AND ISLANDS					
Bourne	224.1400	–	O 110.9e	N1YHS	N1YHS
Harwich	224.3400	–	O 100e L(E468451)	K1KEK	K1KEK
CENTRAL					
Fitchburg	224.3400	–	O 103.5e L(147.315)	WB1EWS	WB1EWS
Leominster	224.7600	–	O 85.4 L(224.44 WINCHENDON MA)x	AA1JD	MEGASYSTEM
Paxton	224.3800	–	O 136.5e	WR1O	WR1O
Spencer	224.5400	–	O	N1VOR	PC Wood
Winchendon	224.4400	–	O(CA)e L(224.76 LEOMINSTER MA)rsx	AA1JD	MEGASYSGRP
MERRIMACK VALLEY					
Andover	224.6800	–	O#ar	WA1WLU	COORDEXP
Haverhill	224.1200	–	O 103.5#e L(224.42 STONEHAM MA)	N1IRS	COORDEXP

Location	*Output*	*Input*	*Notes*	*Call*	*Sponsor*
Lawrence	224.3000	–	O	N1EXC	N1EXC
Methuen	223.9200	–	O 141.3#	WB1CXB	COORDEXP
Methuen	224.9600	–	O 103.5e	N1WPN	NE MUDDUCK
North Andover	224.5200	–	O#ar	WA1WLU	COORDEXP
Pepperell	224.6400	–	OL(919.10 1270.40)	WA1VVH	WA1VVH
Wilmington	224.1600	–	O 67/71.9# e	K1KZP	COORDEXP
METROWEST					
Framingham	224.2400	–	O 103.5x	WB1CTO	222 Club
Hopkinton	223.9400	–	O 103.5 L(MMRA)	K1KWP	MMRA
Lincoln	223.8400	–	Oer	K9YB	Lincoln CD
Marlborough	224.8800	–	O 103.5 L(MMRA)	W1MRA	MMRA
Weston	224.7000	–	O 103.5 (CA) L(MMRA)	N1NOM	MMRA
NORTH SHORE					
Danvers	223.8800	–	Oex	NS1RA	NSRA
Gloucester	224.9000	–	Oe	W1GLO	CAARA
SOUTH COAST					
Dartmouth	224.8000	–	O 67 L(E4049 I8249)	W1AEC	SEMARA
Fall River	224.1800	–	O 67	K1ZZN	RJL ARC
SOUTH SHORE					
Brockton	223.7800	–	O 88.5r	N1PYN	N1PYN
Norwell	224.0600	–	O 103.5e L(53.33)	N1ZZN	N1ZZN
SPRINGFIELD/PIONEER VALLEY					
Pelham	224.7400	–	O 88.5	WA1VEI	MSRA
THE BERKSHIRES					
Adams	224.1000	–	O 100	K1FFK	NoBARC
MICHIGAN					
LOWER PEN NORTHEAST					
Lewiston	224.4200	–	Ol	N8SCY	N8SCY
Saginaw	224.2800	–	Ors	K8DAC	SVARA
West Branch	224.2200	–	●tl	W8YUC	RARG
LOWER PEN NORTHWEST					
Manistee	224.1200	–	O 100	KB8BIT	KB8BIT
Stutsmanville	224.5600	–	O 100x	WB8DEL	WB8DEL
LOWER PEN SOUTHEAST					
Ann Arbor	224.3400	–	Oe	W8UHW	W8UHW
Canton	224.7400	–	O 100 (CA)	W8PMN	W8KFN
Chelsea	224.1600	–	Oe	WD8IEL	CARC
Clio	224.0600	–	O 100	N8NJN	FAIR
Dearborn	224.5200	–	O 100	K8UTT	Ford ARL
Detroit	224.3600	–	O 103.5ex	KC8LTS	KC8LTS
Durand	224.8600	–	O 100lrs WX	N8IES	N8IES

Location	Output	Input	Notes	Call	Sponsor
Flint	224.1800	–	O 88.5elrs WX	KF8UI	KF8UI
Flint	224.4800	–	O 100 (CA) elrsWXz	KC8KGZ	N8IES/MSCG
Glennwood	224.8400	–	O 94.8lrs WXx	W8GDS	W8GDS
Holly	224.6200	223.0600	O 100 (CA) x	W8FSM	W8FSM
Inkster	224.5800	–	O 100lrs WX	K8DNS	K8DNS
Monroe	224.7800	–	O 100lrs WX	K8RPT	River Raisin repeater
Pontiac	224.5600	–	O	WD8INW	WD8INW
Rankin	224.9600	–	●tlWX	W8YUC	RARG
Roseville	224.4600	–	Ol	N8EDV	N8EDV
Waterford	224.4200	–	●t(CA)e WX	W8JIM	W8JIM
Wayne	224.0000	–	O 107.2ael	W8RIF	W8RIF
Westland	224.6800	–	●tl	W2PUT	W2PUT
LOWER PEN SOUTHWEST					
Battle Creek	224.2400	–	Oaez	W8DF	SMARS
Berrien Springs	224.3000	–	O(CA)x	W8YKS	DOCRG
Buchanan	224.2000	–	O(CA)x	N8NIT	DOCRG
Cedar Springs	224.1400	–	O 94.8	NW8J	NW8J
Grand Rapids	224.4400	–	O 91.5	KB8YNC	KB8YNC
Grand Rapids	224.6400	–	O 94.8al	W8DC	GRARA
Grand Rapids	224.7600	–	Oae	K8SN	K8SN
Lansing	224.9800	–	O 100aers	WB8CQM	LCDRA
Moline	223.9200	–	O 94.8 (CA) eWXx	N8JPR	N8JPR
Muskegon	224.7000	–	●tal	N8KQQ	N8KQQ
MINNESOTA					
DULUTH					
Duluth	223.9400	–	O	NØBZZ	NØBZZ
METRO					
Arden Hills	223.9400	–	O 100.0l	KAØPQW	HANDIHAMS
Burnsville	224.5400	–	O 100.0a	WØBU	TCRC
Columbia Hts	224.5000	–	O 114.8l	NØFKM	NØFKM
Columbia Hts	224.6600	–	O 114.8l	NØFKM	NØFKM
Gem Lake	224.1000	–	O	KØLAV	KØLAV
Maplewood	224.8800	–	O	NØFKM	NØFKM
Mounds View	224.9400	–	O 100.0e	WØYFZ	ANOKACRC
SOUTH CENTRAL					
St Peter	224.5200	–	O	NØKP	SCAN
SOUTH EAST					
Ellendale	224.6400	–	O 110.9	KAØPQW	HANDIHAM

Location	Output	Input	Notes	Call	Sponsor
MISSISSIPPI					
Ackerman	224.7800	–	O	NM5D	------------
Ackerman	224.8200	–	O	NM5D	------------
Bay St Louis	224.8800	–	O	KØVNO	------------
Biloxi	224.5000	–	O	K5TYP	------------
Byhalia	224.5000	–	O	N4DRL	N4DRL
Corinth	224.5200	–	O	KA5RPB	KA5RPB
Ellisville	224.4000	–	O	N5EKR	------------
Hattiesburg	224.1400	–	O	K5PN	K5PN
Hattiesburg	224.7400	–	O	W5CJR	------------
Pontotoc	224.9000	–	O	KE5ST	------------
Taylorsville	224.4800	–	O	W5NRU	AA5SG
Vicksburg	224.7800	–	O	WB5OWY	------------
Warsaw	224.8800	–	O	N4DRL	N4DRL
Waynesboro	224.1400	–	O	W5SAR	W5SAR
MISSOURI					
CENTRAL					
Belle	224.6000	–	O	NØVHN	------------
Eldon	224.5800	–	Ox	NØGYE	------------
EAST CENTRAL					
Union	224.9400	–	O(CA)	WAØFYA	Zero Beaters AR
NORTHEAST					
Troy	224.5400	–	Oel	KAØEJQ	PkeLincCo
SOUTHWEST					
Nixa	224.2800	–	O 162.2/162.2ex	KØNXA	Nixa ARC
ST LOUIS METRO					
Clayton	224.3400	–	O	WBØRPN	------------
Imperial	224.0400	–	O	WAØPEZ	------------
Olivette	224.5200	–	O 141.3/141.3ers	WØSRC	SLSRC
St Louis	224.9800	–	O/141.3a (CA)ex	KØGOB	UHF ARA
St Paul	224.6600	–	Or	NØEEA	NØEEA
WEST CENTRAL					
Warrensburg	224.8800	–	O	WØAU	WAARCI
MONTANA					
SOUTH CENTRAL					
Bozeman	224.7200	–	O 100.0l	W7ED	GHRC
NEBRASKA					
FREMONT					
Fremont	224.6600	–	Oe	WNØL	------------
LINCOLN					
Lincoln	224.3000	–	O	NØGMR	N0GMR

Location	Output	Input	Notes	Call	Sponsor
OMAHA					
Omaha	223.9400	–	Oael	WBØCMC	------------
Omaha/KPTM	224.8200	–	Olx	WBØCMC	------------
Omaha/KPTM	224.9400	–	Ox	KØUSA	AKSARBEN A
NEVADA					
CENTRAL					
Warm Springs	222.1000	+	O	WB7WTS	WB7WTS
E SIERRA/TAHOE					
Lake Tahoe	224.0200	–	Oe	NR7A	WA6EWV
South Lake Tahoe	224.6400	–	O 123	W6SUV	W6SUV
LAS VEGAS VALLEY					
Angels Peak	224.5000	–	O 131.8/131.8	K7EET	------------
Las Vegas	223.5800	223.5800	O L(145.050)	W7EB	------------
Lo Potosi Mtn	224.4800	–	O 110.9/110.9	W7EB	------------
NORTH CENTRAL					
Elko	224.1400	–	O 100	KE7LKO	WV3LMA
NORTH EAST CLARK COUNTY					
Moapa/Coyote Springs	223.9200	–	O	N7MLF	------------
NYE COUNTY					
Pahrump	223.8400	–	O	N7HYV	------------
SOUTHERN CLARK COUNTY					
Christmas Tree Pass	223.8400	–	O 107.2/107.2	K6DLP	------------
Christmas Tree Pass	224.9800	–	O 100/100	N7LD	NARC
WEST CENTRAL					
Reno	224.1000	–	O	W7UIZ	W7UIZ
Reno	224.1800	–	O 156.7l	KB6TDJ	KB6TDJ
Reno	224.3000	–	O 156.7	W7DED	W7DED
Reno	224.5400	–	O 123	N7KP	N7KP
Reno	224.5800	–	O 123e	AE7I	AE7I
Reno	224.7000	–	Oe	KA7ZAU	KA7ZAU
Reno/Sparks	224.5000	–	O 103.5e	N7KP	N7KP
Reno/Sparks	224.8000	–	O 114.8	N7OVC	N7OVC
Sparks	223.9200	–	O 103.5	KK7RON	KK7RON
Sparks	224.7000	–	O	KA7ZAU	KA7ZAU
NEW HAMPSHIRE					
ALL AREAS					
Statewide	224.1400	–	O	SNP	NESMC
Statewide	224.1400	–	O	SNP	NESMC
DARTMOUTH/LAKE SUNAPEE					
Claremont	224.0600	–	O 97.4eWX	WX1NH	GMARS

Location	*Output*	*Input*	*Notes*	*Call*	*Sponsor*
LAKES REGION					
Pittsfield	224.5400	–	O 103.5	N1AKE	N1AKE
Rochester	224.7800	–	O 131.8	WM1P	MLP
MERRIMACK VALLEY					
Amherst	224.0200	–	O 136.5e	K1ZQ	K1ZQ
Candia	224.8200	–	O 88.5s	W1YVM	W1YVM
Chester	224.2000	–	O 103.5	K1OX	K1OX
Derry	224.4600	–	O 85.4 (CA) ers	K1CA	IntrStRS
Goffstown	223.9000	–	O 103.5esx	W1AKS	NHRADIO
Mont Vernon	224.1800	–	O	WB1CMG	WB1CMG
Nashua	224.5000	–	O 88.5e L(N1IMO-N1IMN)s	N1IMO	N1IMO
Northwood	223.9600	–	O 114.8e L(E267136)	N1QVS	FBG
Pembroke	224.8000	–	O 103.5e	KA1OKQ	KA1OKQ
MONADNOCK REGION					
Milford	224.8600	–	O 136.5 L(2/440 CROSSBAND LINK)	W1DIO	W1DIO
Rindge	224.6000	–	O 88.5	WA1HOG	WA1HOG
Spofford	223.9800	–	O 100eEXP	KK1CW	SLR
SEACOAST					
Exeter	224.2200	–	O 67 L(E54908)	K1KN	K1KN
WHITE MOUNTAINS					
Cannon Mtn	224.0800	–	O 114.8	K1EME	LARK
NEW JERSEY					
ATLANTIC					
Absecon	224.1400	–	●(CA)	N2LXK	------------
BERGEN CO					
Glen Rock	224.3400	–	OtelrsBI	N2SMI	------------
Saddle Brook	224.4200	–	O 88.5	WB2IZC	------------
Saddle Brook	224.5200	–	O	WA2UXC	------------
Wanaque	224.8400	–	O 141.3 (CA)ersWX	W2PQG	10-70 RA
BURLINGTON					
Browns Mills	224.8600	–	O 131.8eBI	K2JZO	------------
Willingboro	223.8800	–	O 131.8 (CA)e	WB2YGO	WARG Inc.
CAMDEN					
Washington Twp	224.6600	–	O 131.8rs	W2MMD	GCARC
Waterford Wks	224.6200	–	OTTer	W2MX	MSARC
CAPE MAY					
Ocean City	223.9800	–	O 156.7 (CA)elrRB LITZ WX	W3PS	METRO-COMM
CUMBERLAND					
Bridgeton	224.8200	–	O 127.3el	KB3LRA	K3PHL

Location	Output	Input	Notes	Call	Sponsor
ESSEX CO					
Newark	224.2200	–	O 74.4 TTl RB BI	KE2TT	------------
Newark	224.2800	–	O 123.0er	W2KB	------------
Verona	224.4800	–	Oe	K2DEE	ESSEX OEM
HUDSON CO					
Union City	224.2000	–	O 131.8 BI	KD2VN	------------
HUNTERDON					
Mt Kipp	224.1200	–	O 203.5 (CA)el	K2PM	W2CRA
MIDDLESEX CO					
Old Bridge	224.5000	–	O 131.8/131.8 (CA)elrsz	W2CJA	CJRA
Sayreville	224.7800	–	O 123.0	NE2E	------------
MONMOUTH CO					
Ellisdale	224.1800	–	O 131.8a TT	K2NI	HRG
Hazlet	224.9600	–	O(CA)ers EXP WX	KB2SEY	HazltTpOEM
Ocean Twp	224.3800	–	O 156.7el WX	W2UG	AERIALS
MORRIS CO					
Boonton	224.8600	–	O	WA2PTD	------------
Butler	224.7000	–	O 141.3/141.3eE-SUNlrsRB EXP	WB2FTX	Butler RACES
Lk Hopatcong	224.6200	–	OL(INT)	NJ2MC	NNJDSA
Morris Twp	224.9400	–	O 107.2/107.2er	WS2Q	------------
OCEAN					
Barnegat	224.2800	–	OersWX	N2NF	------------
Dover Twp	224.7200	–	O 82.5e LITZ	N4TCT	------------
Forked River	224.7000	–	O 146.2	KE2HC	------------
Jackson	224.3000	–	O 127.3r	N2RDM	CrmRdgRG
Lakewood	223.8200	–	O 162.2el	N2AYM	------------
Toms River	223.9200	–	O 151.4 BI	NJ2AR	JSARS
PASSAIC CO					
Clifton	224.3600	–	O(CA)e	KB2N	CliftonOEM
SALEM					
Salem	224.4600	–	O 77ersWX	N2KEJ	SCOEM
SOMERSET CO					
Martinsville	224.6400	–	O 151.4	N2ZAV	------------
Martinsville	224.8800	–	O 103.5 (CA) TTeLITZ WX	WX3K	SOMERSET
Warrenville	224.0000	–	O 151.4 TT eRB LITZ	K2PM	------------
Watchung	223.9600	–	Oers	K2ETS	ETS
SUSSEX					
Newton	224.5000	–	O 151.4elr sRB	W2LV	SCARC

Location	Output	Input	Notes	Call	Sponsor
UNION CO					
Newark	224.0200	–	O 123.0	NE2E	------------
Springfield	224.1400	–	O 123.0	W2FCC	------------
WARREN					
Washington	223.7800	–	● 110.9ers	WC2EM	WC EMCOMM
NEW MEXICO					
ALBUQUERQUE					
Albuquerque	223.8200	–	Oe	WA5VJY	NM 220 S
Albuquerque	224.0000	–	O 100.0/127.3x	K5CQH	JRANM
Albuquerque	224.5800	–	O 100ae L(146.58)	KH6JTM	KH6JTM
Rio Rancho	224.4800	–	O	K6LIE	------------
Sandia Park	224.9400	–	O L(444.1500) RB	W5AOX	W5AOX
NORTH CENTRAL					
Los Alamos	223.9400	–	Oesx	KB5RX	JMRA
Los Alamos	224.0400	–	O 100.0e L(442.000)	KA5BIW	KA5BIW
SOUTH CENTRAL					
Almogordo	224.6000	–	O	WA5IPS	WA5IPS
Dona Ana	224.3400	–	Os	KC5SJQ	KC5SJQ
Las Cruces	223.9400	–	O	N5IAC	N5IAC
SOUTH EAST					
Carlsbad	222.4600	–	O 127.3/127.3#ae	N5MJ	------------
STATEWIDE					
Statewide	224.1600	–	Otprs		ARES/SAR
NEW YORK					
ADIRONDACKS/EAST					
Blue Mtn Lake	224.0400	–	O 123lx	N2JKG	RACES
Plattsburgh	223.9600	–	O 123.0r	WA2LRE	Clin RACES
ALBANY/CAPITAL REGION					
Albany	224.1400	–	O 100 (CA) elx	K2AD	MT Assoc
Gloversville	224.7000	–	OrWX	K2JJI	TRYON AMATE
Schenectady	224.0600	–	Oae	K2AE	SCHENECTADY
Troy	224.4200	–	O(CA)l	W2SZ	RPI AMATEUR
Troy	224.6400	–	Oe	KB2HPW	ARDVARC
BINGHAMTON					
Vestal	224.4800	–	O 88.5 (CA) l	AA2EQ	AA2EQ
CANANDAIGUA					
Bristol	224.6800	–	O 110.9	W2IMT	W2IMT
South Bristol	224.4600	–	O 110.9 E-WIND	NR2M	QHRA

Location	Output	Input	Notes	Call	Sponsor
CATSKILLS NORTH					
Schenevus	223.9600	–	O 100e	KC2AWM	CTRC
Sprngfld Ctr	224.9800	–	O	NC2C	OTSEGO COUNTY A
ELMIRA/CORNING					
Elmira	223.9800	–	Oal	NR2P	RATS
Elmira	224.2200	–	O	WB2VPY	CHEMUNG CO AMA
LONG ISLAND - NASSAU CO					
East Rockaway	224.5400	–	O 131.8/131.8 (CA) TT(131.8)e	WA2YUD	------------
LONG ISLAND - SUFFOLK CO					
Bayshore	224.1200	–	O 131.8 (CA)lrs	KB2UR	SSARC
Dix Hills	224.5600	–	O 136.5e L(443.525)	W2RGM	------------
East Hampton	224.6000	–	O(CA)e	W2HLI	------------
Smithtown	224.6200	–	● 136.5elr	W2LRC	LARKFIELD ARC
West Islip	223.8600	–	O 110.9/110.9aeL(HRDWIRE)rsRB WX	W2GSB	GSBARC
Yaphank	224.6800	–	O 103.5e	W2DQ	SCARC
LOWER HUDSON - WESTCHESTER					
Armonk	224.3000	–	O 114.8	W2TWY	YARCKidz
Valhalla	224.4000	–	O 114.8 (CA)elRB WX	WB2ZII	WECA
White Plains	224.2600	–	O 074.4/074.4sRB	NY4Z	Alive Network
Yonkers	224.0800	–	O 114.8	N2PAL	------------
Yonkers	224.9400	–	O 088.5 (CA)ersBlz	W2YRC	Yonkers ARC
MID HUDSON					
Cragsmoor	224.6000	–	O	W2NYX	W2NYX
Harriman	223.8000	–	O 107.2elx	W2AEE	COLUMBIA UNIVER
Hudson	224.2800	–	Oes	K2RVW	Rip Van Winkle Amat
Mahopac	224.0000	–	O 74.4al	K2HR	ALIVE NETWORK A
Mahopac	224.7000	–	O 141.3al	K2HR	ALIVE NETWORK A
Middletown	224.5400	–	O 156.7lsx	WR2MSN	METRO 70 CM NET
Mount Beacon	223.9200	–	O 100 (CA) e	W2GIO	MOUNT BEACON A
New Windsor	224.7600	–	O 88.5/88.5 e	W2TRR	W2TRR
Nyack	224.3800	–	O 114.8 (CA)el	WA2MLG	ROCKLAND REPEA
Nyack	224.9000	–	O 114.8x	WR2I	WR2I
Patterson	224.8800	–	O 88.5	KC2CQS	KC2CQS
Pomona	223.8200	–	O 114.8l	N2ACF	ROCKLAND REPEA
NEW YORK CITY - KINGS					
Brooklyn	223.9400	–	O 107.2er	WA2ZLB	MAARC
Brooklyn	223.9800	–	141.3	KB2PRV	LARA
Brooklyn	224.1000	–	O 136.5rs	W2CXN	AVARA

Location	Output	Input	Notes	Call	Sponsor
Brooklyn	224.6000	–	O 100.0	W2SN	------------
NEW YORK CITY - MANHATTAN					
Manhattan	223.7600	–	● 151.7 TT DCS(23) L(430.175)rs	WR2MSN	METRO 70cm
Manhattan	223.9000	–	OeBI	KD2TM	------------
Manhattan	224.0600	–	O	WA2HDE	------------
Manhattan	224.4400	–	O 74.4	NY4Z	K2VZG
Manhattan	224.4600	–	Oelz	N2XBA	LEARC
Manhattan	224.6600	–	O	WA2HDE	66 Rptr Club
NEW YORK CITY - QUEENS					
Glen Oaks	224.8200	–	O 136.5 (CA)eLITZ	WB2NHO	LIMARC
NEW YORK CITY - STATEN ISLAND					
Staten Island	223.8400	222.4000	O 141.3/141.3el	W2RJR	------------
NIAGARA					
Buffalo	224.7600	–	O 107.2	WB2ECR	------------
Buffalo	224.8200	–	O(CA)e L(BARRA)rs	W2EUP	BARRA
Lackawanna	224.5600	–	O 88.5e	W2RFL	------------
Lancaster	224.6400	–	O 107.2e L(LARC IRLP) WX	W2SO	LARC
Lockport	224.3600	–	O 107.2	K2MJ	------------
Newfane	223.9400	–	O 88.5 (CA) L(224.94)	N2CVQ	NCARA
Newfane	224.9400	–	O 88.5 (CA) eL(223.94) RB	K2AER	NCARA
Niagara Falls	224.4200	–	O 107.2e L(443.925 ECHOLINK)	N3AU	------------
ROCHESTER					
Rochester	224.2600	–	Oaelxz	KE2MK	Xerox ARC
Rochester	224.5800	–	O 110.9ael rz	N2HJD	ROCHESTER R
Rochester	224.9000	–	O	WS2F	GRIDD
SOUTHERN TIER					
Delevan	224.2000	–	O	K2XZ	------------
Ripley	224.9200	–	O 127.3	N2LXD	------------
ST LAWRENCE					
Canton	224.7400	–	r	KA2JXI	SLVRA
SYRACUSE					
Syracuse	224.1200	–	Oe	KD2SL	LARC
UTICA/ROME					
Utica	224.6600	–	Oa	WA2CAV	WA2CAV
Verona	224.2600	–	O	KA2NIL	KA2NIL
WAYNE/NEWARK					
Ontario	224.0200	–	O	KA2CKR	DrmInsARC
WEST					
Orangeville	224.7000	–	O	K2XZ	------------

Location	*Output*	*Input*	*Notes*	*Call*	*Sponsor*
NORTH CAROLINA					
Asheville	224.5200	–	O	W4MOE	W4MOE
Asheville	224.6000	–	O	KI4DNY	KI4DNY
Barium Springs	224.3000	–	O	WA4WRS	------------
Burnsville	224.7400	–	O	KD4WAR	KD4WAR
Cary	224.8800	–	O	W4JYV	KD4WJD
Charlotte	224.4000	–	O	W4BFB	W4BFB
Charlotte	224.8600	–	O	KA4YMZ	JI
Cherry Mtn	224.6400	–	O	KG4JIA	KG4JIA
Clemmons	224.7000	–	O 100/100s	WB9SZL	W4NC
Clemmons	224.7000	–	O	WB9SZL	FORSYTH ARC
Cleveland	224.7600	–	O	KU4PT	BARBER JCT RA
Clinton	224.2800	–	O	W4TLP	W4TLP
Coats	224.7000	–	O	K4JDR	CAROLINA 440
Delco	224.5000	–	O	AD4DN	AD4DN
Gastonia	224.6200	–	O	KC4IRA	KC4IRA
Greensboro	224.4400	–	O	WB4GUG	------------
Greensboro	224.9600	–	O	KD4TPJ	KD4TPJ
Grifton	224.8400	–	O	WA4DAN	ENC 220 RPT GRP
Hendersonville	224.2400	–	O	WA4KNI	WA4KNI
Hendersonville	224.9600	–	O	N4UQS	CAP/SUGARLOAF
Hillsborough	224.2600	–	O	WR4AGC	DURHAM FM ASSN
Jacksonville	224.3200	–	O	KA4SQN	KA4SQN/RACES/AR
Jefferson	224.2200	–	O	W4JWO	W4JWO
Kernersville	224.2400	–	O 107.2/107.2	KF4OVA	KF4OVA
Lenoir	224.1600	–	O	KN4K	HIBRITEN RTP ASS
Locust	224.4800	–	O	W4DEX	W4DEX & N4DBM
Louisburg	224.2200	–	O	KD4CPV	KD4CPV
Lumberton	224.9200	–	O	K4TH	K4TH
Mars Hill	224.6600	–	O	N2GE	N2GE
Mars Hill	224.7800	–	O 100/100e l	KG4LGY	------------
Marshall	224.3600	–	O	KF4ZDS	KF4ZDS
Moravian Falls	224.1200	–	O	KA2NAX	KA2NAX
Mt Mitchell	224.5400	–	O	N2GE	N2GE
Mt Pisgah	224.2600	–	O	N2GE	N2GE
Raleigh	224.1600	–	O	K4ITL	PCRN
Rocky Mount	224.5800	–	O	KR4AA	N4TUF
Shelby	224.0600	–	O	W4NYR	SHELBY ARC
Sophis	224.1400	–	O	WR4BEG	BROADCAST PKT+R
Spruce Pine	224.6800	–	O	N2EMD	N2EMD
Thomasville	224.4200	–	O	W4TNC	EFARG
Trenton	224.7200	–	O	WA4DAN	ENC 220 RPTR GRP
West Jefferson	224.8400	–	O	W4TRP	W4TRP
Wilmington	224.2000	–	O	WA4US	WA4US
Wilmington	224.6800	–	O	N4ILM	WILMINGTON VHF A
Zebulon	224.8000	–	O	WB4IUY	WB4IUY

Location	Output	Input	Notes	Call	Sponsor
NORTH DAKOTA					
FREQUENCY USAGE					
Statewide	224.2400	–		SNP	
OHIO					
ALLEN					
Lima	224.9000	–	O 118.8	WB8PJZ	LimaUHFRA
ASHLAND					
Widowville	224.5800	–	O 110.9lp	KD8BIW	W8LY
ASHTABULA					
Austinburg	224.6200	–	Ota	K8PEX	Ash.CoARC
Geneva	223.9600	–	O 146.2	N8WPZ	N8WPZ
ATHENS					
Athens	224.1400	–		K8WJW	K8WJW
AUGLAIZE					
Uniopolis	223.8800	–	O 107.2a	KC8KVO	ACARES
BROWN					
Mt Orab	224.1800	–	Oa	W8UJM	WA8CFX
BUTLER					
Fairfield	224.1200	–	OaeRB	KA8YRN	FARA
Oxford	224.3400	–	O 77.0	N8ECH	Oxford RS
Oxford	224.6400	–	Oe	N8FTS	#NAME?
CHAMPAIGN					
Cable	224.8600	–	O 100.0s	WB8UCD	WB8UCD
St Paris	224.6000	–	O 100.0s	WB8UCD	WB8UCD
Urbana	224.9800	–	O 100.0	KB7TSE	KB8PVX
CLERMONT					
Batavia	224.0000	–	O 123.0rs	K8YOJ	ARPSC
CLINTON					
Blanchester	224.5200	–	t	KB8CWC	KB8CWC
Wilmington	224.0800	–	O 123.0	K8IO	K8IO
CUYAHOGA					
Cleveland	224.9000	–	O 141.3e	WB8CQR	LEARA
Cleveland	224.9400	–	O	WX8CLE	ND8B
N Royalton	224.7600	–	O	K8SCI	N Cst ARC
Parma	224.3000	–	O 141.3el	N8SO	N8SO
Parma	224.4800	–	O 131.8l	KB8WLW	KB8RST
Shaker Hts	223.9200	–	O	K8ZFR	C.A.R.S.
Walton Hills	224.1000	–	O 141.3l	KA8WDX	KA8WDX
DARKE					
Greenville	224.3800	–	O	N8NR	N8NR
FRANKLIN					
Columbus	224.0600	–	O	K8DDG	C OH ARES
Columbus	224.4600	–	Ol	AA8EY	C OH ARES
Columbus	224.6600	–	Oal	W8RUT	C OhioARG
Columbus	224.7800	–	O	WG8I	KG8I
Columbus	224.8400	–	O 179.9aelz	K8DRE	CCRA

Location	Output	Input	Notes	Call	Sponsor
GEAUGA					
Thompson	224.9600	–	O 141.3 (CA)eWX	KB8FKM	KB8FKM
GREENE					
Xenia	224.8200	–	O	W8RTL	KB8III
HAMILTON					
Cincinnati	224.0600	–	O	K8YOJ	HmltARPSC
Cincinnati	224.2400	–	O 114.8el	KD8TE	AWARE
Cincinnati	224.6200	–	O 110.9er	W8ESS	E.S.S.
JACKSON					
Ray	223.8800	–	O	WB8LDB	WB8LDB
LAKE					
Fairport Hrbr	224.0800	–	O 141.3e	N8JCV	N8JCV
Painesville	224.5000	–	O 141.3	N8BC	LCARA
LICKING					
Newark	223.9400	–	Ol	KA8PCP	KA8PCP
LOGAN					
Bellefontaine	224.5000	–	O(CA)elz	KA8GRP	TopOfOhio
LUCAS					
Oregon	224.4400	–	O 103.5e	WJ8E	WJ8E
Toledo	224.1400	–	O 103.5123 aTTez	W8HHF	TMRA
Toledo	224.5400	–	103.5aTTe z	WB8OET	WB8OET
MEDINA					
Brunswick	224.8600	–	Oe	W8UQZ	W8UQZ
Valley City	224.6800	–	●	K8WW	K8WW
MIAMI					
Ludlow Falls	224.1000	–	Oa	WD8JPP	WD8JPP
Tipp City	224.4200	–	O(CA)el	WB8WIQ	WB8WIQ
Troy	223.9800	–	O	N8OWV	N8OWV
Troy	224.9400	–	O(CA)l	WB8PMG	WB8PMG
MONTGOMERY					
Dayton	223.9400	–	Oa	W8BI	DARA
Dayton	224.0200	–	O(CA)elz	WB8SMC	FaroutARC
Dayton	224.1600	–	O(CA)el	WC8OH	WCOARA
Dayton	224.6800	–	Oe	KB8CSL	KB8GDE
Dayton	224.7200	–	Oe	KB8CSL	KC8YEX
Dayton	224.8000	–	OeRB	KC8NDF	KC8NDF
Fairborn	224.2600	–	●(CA)	KI6SZ	KI6SZ
Huber Heights	224.3000	–	O 442.95l	NO8I	HHARC
Miamisburg	223.9000	–	Oel	WC8OH	WCOARA
Trotwood	224.2000	–	Oa	W8KEL	W8KEL
Vandalia	224.7600	–	O	KB8CSL	KC8YEX
MORROW					
Mt Gilead	224.9400	–	O 71.9e	WY8G	MCRG
MUSKINGUM					
Zanesville	224.9400	–	Oae	KJ8N	Y-City WC
Zansville	224.1000	–	74.4	W8ACE	W8ACE

Location	*Output*	*Input*	*Notes*	*Call*	*Sponsor*
PORTAGE					
Atwater	224.1400	–	O	WA8LCA	WA8LCA
Kent	224.0200	–	O 141.3e	N8BHU	N8BHU
PREBLE					
Eaton	224.4800	–	el	K8YR	PrebleARA
ROSS					
Bainbridge	224.9200	–	O	KD8EAD	KD8EAD
STARK					
Canton	224.6000	–	OaEXP	W8TUY	W8TUY
Canton	224.7800	–	Oae	KB8LWP	KB8LWP
SUMMIT					
Akron	223.9400	–	Oal	WB8CXO	AKCOM
Hudson	224.6400	–	O	N8FNF	WRARG
Norton	224.0600	–		WB8UTW	WB8UTW
TRUMBULL					
Warren	224.1600	–	131.8	N8DOD	N8DOD
VAN WERT					
Van Wert	224.0600	–	O 156.7	N8IHP	N8IHP
WARREN					
Franklin	224.9600	–	O 118.8	KD8EYB	BCAREC
Springboro	223.8200	–	Oel	W8CYE	DrakeARC
Springboro	224.2200	–	O 100.0	N8RXL	N8RXL
WASHINGTON					
Marietta	224.2600	–	●alp	W8JL	W8JL
OKLAHOMA					
NORTHEAST					
Bartlesville	224.2600	–	O 88.5/88.5 E-SUN	W5RAB	W5RAB
Muskogee	224.3400	–	OtE-SUN	KK5I	MUSKOGARC
OKLAHOMA CITY METRO					
Bethany	224.9600	–	O 103.5/103.5 E-SUN	N5USR	N5USR
Norman	224.4400	–	Ot	K9KK	K9KK
Oklahoma City	224.1000	–	OtE-SUN	W5PAA	MMACARC
Oklahoma City	224.3000	–	O 123/123	NZ5W	NZ5W
Oklahoma City	224.4000	–	O 141.3/141.3 E-SUN	KK5FM	KK5FM
Oklahoma City	224.8800	–	Ot	WN5J	WN5J
SOUTHEAST					
Nashoba	224.5600	–	O 114.8/114.8 E-WIND	KM5VK	KM5VK
Poteau	224.8800	–	O 88.5/88.5 E-SUNSX	W5ANR	WC5I
SOUTHWEST					
Granite	224.9200	–	O 151.4/151.4 E-SUN WX	KE5HRS	------------
Tuttle	224.6800	–	Ot	WA7WNM	KS5B

Location	Output	Input	Notes	Call	Sponsor
OREGON					
CENTRAL WILLAMETTE VALLEY					
Monmouth	224.5000	–	O 162.2e	KE7AAJ	KE7AAJ
Salem	224.1600	–	O 100e	KE7DLA	KE7DLA
Salem	224.2400	–	Oe	WB7RKR	N/A
Salem	224.6000	–	O 100e	KE7DLA	KE7DLA
COAST-SOUTH					
North Bend	224.9200	–	O 103.5	K6TC	W6JRN
NORTH WILLAMETTE VALLEY					
Sheridan	224.5600	–	O 100e	AC7ZQ	AC7ZQ
NORTHEAST					
Pendleton	224.5600	–	O	N7NKT	N7NKT
NW OREGON & SW WASHINGTON					
Colton	223.9400	–	Oe	W7OTV	W7OTV
Government Camp	224.0000	–	Ote	KB7APU	KB7APU
Longview	224.6600	–	O 114.8rs	NU7D	NU7D
PORTLAND METRO					
Estacada	224.4600	–	O 107.2l	KD7DEG	KD7DEG
Newberg	224.0600	–	O 107.2el	KR7IS	WORC
Portland	224.9400	–	O 100e	K7RPT	ARRG
SOUTH WEST OREGON					
Roseburg	224.1000	–	O 114.8e	WB7RKR	WB7RKR
STATEWIDE					
Statewide	224.6800	–	Oters	TEST	ORRC
Statewide	224.8000	–	Oters	TEST	ORRC
PENNSYLVANIA					
FREQUENCY USAGE - ALL WPA SECTION					
WPA SNP	223.8000	–		SNP	
BEAVER 131.8					
Beaver	224.8800	–	Oer	N3TN	TAARA
Beaver Falls	223.8800	–		W3UJT	W3UJT
Freedom	224.4600	–	O	N3TN	N3TN
New Brighton	224.7200	–	Oael	N3ALL	N3ALL
BERKS					
Pottstown	224.0200	–	O 131.8e	K3ZMC	P.A.R.T.
Reading	224.6400	–	O 114.8	K3TI	DDXA
BUCKS					
Chalfont	223.9000	–	O 107.2e	W3DBZ	------------
Feasterville	223.8000	–	O 131.8	N3SP	------------
Feasterville	224.9800	–	O	WB3BLG	PARA Group
Hilltown	224.5800	–	Ote	W3CCX	Packrats
Morrisville	224.5400	–	O 141.3el	WBØYLE	------------
Warminster	223.7600	–	O 186.2ael	K3NAL	NAWC ARC
CARBON					
Palmerton	224.2600	–	O 94.8 (CA) ersRB	N3DVF	EPA-VHF

Location	Output	Input	Notes	Call	Sponsor
CHESTER					
Thorndale	224.3600	–	O	AA3VI	------------
Valley Forge	224.9000	–	O 77el	WN3A	------------
Valley Forge	224.9400	–	O	W3PHL	PARA Group
DELAWARE					
Booth's Corner	224.2200	–	O 91.5elrs WX	KA3TWG	Penn-Del
Darby	224.5000	–	O 131.8 (CA)elsRB	W3UER	DCARA
Glenolden	224.1000	–	O 77 (CA)e s	N3FCX	------------
ERIE 186.2					
Albion	223.9400	–	O	WA3USH	WA3USH
JOHNSTOWN 123.0					
Johnstown	224.2600	–	O	W3IW	W3IW
Johnstown	224.6800	–	aerRB	KC3DES	CCDES
LANCASTER					
Cornwall	224.8200	–	O 114.8el	N3TPL	LRTS
Cornwall	224.8400	–	O 131.8	KA3CNT	R.H.R.A.
Lititz	224.4400	–	O 131.8al RB	KA3CNT	R.H.R.A.
Rawlinsville	224.3200	–	O 131.8el	WA3WPA	------------
LUZERNE					
Wilkes-Barre	224.6000	–	O 94.8e	N3JDV	------------
LYCOMING					
Williamsport	224.2800	–	O 85.4elBI	N3XXH	EMRG
MONROE					
Long Pond	224.3400	–	O 131.8 (CA)e	KB3WW	------------
Long Pond	224.9200	–	O 127.3el RB	K4MTP	STORM Group
Tannersville	224.6600	–	O 71.9	KB3DCM	------------
MONTGOMERY					
Bryn Mawr	224.4200	–	O(CA)ers	WB3JOE	MidAtlARC
Fairview Village	224.2000	–	O 88.5e	N3CVJ	------------
Norristown	223.8600	–	O	N3CDP	PARA Group
Wyncote	224.3800	–	O 107.2 (CA)e	N3FSC	------------
NORTHAMPTON					
Easton	224.7400	–	O 100e	KB3AJF	------------
NORTHWEST 186.2					
Corry	224.0600	–	O 186.2	KE3PD	KE3PD
Franklin	224.7400	–	Oer	N3QCR	N3MBR
Titusville	224.8200	–		WB3KFO	WB3KFO
PHILADELPHIA					
Philadelphia	224.0000	–	O 69.3e	KB3MEC	------------
Philadelphia	224.0600	–	O 131.8eBI	WB3EHB	------------
Philadelphia	224.8000	–	O 131.8 (CA)elRB	K3TU	TUARC

Location	*Output*	*Input*	*Notes*	*Call*	*Sponsor*
PITTSBURGH 131.8					
Apollo	224.3000	–	O 131.8aer z	N1RS	SARA
New Kensington	224.6400	–	O 131.8	K3MJW	Skyview
Pittsburgh/Carrick	223.9800	–	l	W3PGH	GPVHFS
Pittsburgh Homestead	223.9400	–	O	WA3PBD	GtwyFM
Pittsburgh Homestead	224.1400	–	O	KA3IDK	KA3IDK
Pittsburgh/N Hills	224.1000	–	O 88.5er	W3EXW	NHARC-RPT
SOMERSET 123.0					
Meyersdale	224.5200	–	Ol	KK3L	AHRA
SOUTH CENTRAL 123.0					
Bedford	224.4800	–	O	K3NQT	BCARS
Boswell	224.9600	–	Oael	N3XCC	N3XCC
SOUTHWEST 131.8					
Bentleyville	224.5800	–	O	WA3QYV	M.A.R.C.
E Monongahela	223.9000	–	O(CA)el	N3OVP	N3OVP
Rochester Mills	224.9000	–	O	KB3CNS	------------
Washington	224.4000	–	O	W3CYO	W3CYO
WEST CENTRAL 131.8/186.2					
Cowansville	224.1800	–	Oar	KA3HUK	WPA-220
Evans City	224.9800	–	Oar	KA3HUK	WPA-220
Mars	224.9400	–	Oel	WB3FAD	WB3FAD
New Castle	224.0400	–	O	KA3UEX	KA3UEX
New Castle	224.8000	–	O	NO3I	NO3I
Prospect	224.2400	–	O(CA)er	N3HWW	MRG
Slippery Rock	224.8400	–	Oalr	KA3HUK	M.R.G.

PUERTO RICO

E					
Rio Grande	224.2200	–	O	WP4N	------------
N					
Corozal	224.4600	–	OE-SUN	KP4DH	CACIQUE
S					
Barranquitas	224.0800	–	O	KP4LP	------------
Cayey	223.9800	–	O	KP3AB	------------
Cayey	224.0200	–	O	KP3AB	------------
W					
Aguada	224.9200	–	O	KP3AB	------------

RHODE ISLAND

ALL AREAS					
Statewide	224.1400	–	O	SNP	NESMC
Statewide	224.1400	–	O	SNP	NESMC
EAST BAY					
Newport	223.8200	–	O 88.5e	N1JBC	N1JBC
NORTHERN					
Coventry	223.9000	–	Oex	KA1ABI	KA1ABI

Location	*Output*	*Input*	*Notes*	*Call*	*Sponsor*
Coventry	224.1000	–	O 67eWX	N1JBC	N1JBC
Coventry	224.8600	–	O 67ers	N1JL	N1JL
Cranston	224.4400	–	O	KA1BRJ	KA1BRJ
East Providence	224.6200	–	O 88.5e	N1LEO	N1LEO
Johnston	223.9600	–	O 127.3 (CA)eL(KA1RCI)rsx	KA1RCI	KA1RCI
Johnston	223.9800	–	O	W1OP	ProvRA
Lincoln	224.0400	–	O 67 (CA)e L(KA1RCI)	KA1RCI	KA1RCI
Lincoln	224.2000	–	O 100 (CA) er	W1MPC	W1MPC
North Providence	224.9200	–	O 88.5e L(QUAHOG REPEATER NET (QRN))	N1JBC	N1JBC
North Scituate	223.7600	–	OesWXx	AA1PL	RIAFMRS
Warwick	223.9200	–	Oe L(E111074)	KA1LMX	KA1LMX
West Warwick	224.3000	–	O 100e	K1WYC	K1WYC
West Warwick	224.7600	–	Oe	KA1RCI	KA1RCI
SOUTH COUNTY					
Exeter	224.5600	–	O 100e L(KA1RCI REPEATER NETWORK)	KA1RCI	KA1RCI
Westerly	224.9800	–	Oe L(446.575/449.675/448.425/147.27) WX	N1LMA	N1LMA

SOUTH CAROLINA

Columbia	224.9000	–	O	N4EOY	AL HARNEY
Fort Mill	224.8000	–	O	KD4TRL	SUGAR CREEK
Gaffney	224.5000	–	O	KG4JIA	KG4JIA
Greenville	224.2000	–	O	W4ILY	EXPERIMENTAL
Leesville	224.5600	–	O	N5CWH	N5CWH
Myrtle Beach	224.1400	–	O	NE4SC	K4SHP
Pickens	224.1400	–	O	WR4XM	PICKENS CO C
Pickens	224.3200	–	O	W4IT	W4IT
Rock Hill	224.8400	–	O	KB4GA	KB4GA
Six Mile	224.1000	–	O	KK4SM	WA4SSJ
Spartanburg	224.4400	–	Oe	K4II	K4II
Sumter	224.1200	–	O	W4GL	SARA

SOUTH DAKOTA

SOUTH EAST					
Sioux Falls	223.8600	–	146.2	WØFSD	SEARES

TENNESSEE

Arlington	224.1200	–	O	N4GMT	N4GMT
Blountville	224.2000	–	O	W4CBX	W4FXO
Brownsville	224.2000	–	O	KB4YTU	LARRY FORSYT
Caryville	224.2800	–	O	KA4OAK	KA4OAK

TENNESSEE

Location	*Output*	*Input*	*Notes*	*Call*	*Sponsor*
Chattanooga	224.4200	–	Oe	K4VCM	KA4EMA
Chattanooga	224.7800	–	O	K4VCM	W4AM
Cleveland	224.1000	–	O	KA4ELN	KA4ELN
Cleveland	224.3200	–	O	KK4US	KK4US
Culleoka	224.8600	–	O	WR3S	W4RRG
Erwin	224.1800	–	O	KB8FPK	KB8FPK
Gallatin	223.9800	–	O	W4CAT	CATS
Gallatin	224.7000	–	O	KD4VUW	KD4VUW
Gatlinburg	224.6200	–	O	WR3S	REBEL REPEATER
Greenbriar	224.8000	–	O	WQ4E	WQ4E
Greenbrier	224.7600	–	O	WQ4E	WQ4E
Greeneville	224.3000	–	O	WD2E	WD2E
Greeneville	224.7200	–	O	K4MFD	K4MFD
Greeneville	224.9000	–	O	W4WC	W4WC
Greeneville	224.9400	–	O	KB4PSI	KB4PSI
Jackson	224.2400	–	O	KA4BNI	KA4BNI
Knoxville	224.2200	–	O	KB4FZK	N4OQJ
Knoxville	224.3400	–	O	WB4GBI	WB4GBI
Knoxville	224.3800	–	O	N4OQJ	KB4FZK
Knoxville	224.4600	–	O	N4KFI	------------
Knoxville	224.5000	–	O	W4BBB	RACK
Knoxville	224.5800	–	O	N4KFI	N4KFI
Knoxville	224.7600	–	O	K4PCK	K4PCK
Knoxville	224.9800	0	O	AC4JF	AC4JF
Memphis	224.4200	–	O	W4BS	DELTA ARC (DARC)
Memphis	224.7800	–	O	WB4KOG	WA4KOG
Morristown	224.4000	–	O	N4RBB	N4RBB
Morristown	224.6400	–	O	KC4RGQ	KC4RGQ
Mountain City	224.2800	–	O	K4DHT	------------
Murfreesboro	224.6000	–	O	KD4TZZ	KD4TZZ
Nashville	224.1600	–	O	WR3S	TMS
Nashville	224.4600	–	O	WR3S	WR3S
Nashville	224.6600	–	O	WR3S	WR3S
Nashville	224.8400	–	O	KC4PRD	------------
Nashville	224.9600	–	O	WR3S	WR3S
Newbern	224.6000	–	O	K4DYR	DYER CO ARA
Newport	224.5600	–	O	AC4JF	AC4JF
Oneida	224.1400	–	O 77/77l	KB4PNG	------------
Rockwood	224.8400	–	O	AC4DR	AC4DR
Rogersville	224.4800	–	O	KD4HZN	KD4HZN
S Pittsburg	224.7600	–	O	WR3S	W4LOC
Sevierville	224.4400	–	O	N2FUV	N2FUV
Sevierville	224.7000	–	O	K4IBW	K4IBW
Sevierville	224.8000	–	O	K4IBW	K4IBW
Seymour	224.0600	–	O	K4ARO	K4ARO
Short Mtn	224.2000	–	O 127.3/127.3elWX	KF4TNP	KF4TNP
Springfield	224.2200	–	O	KO4BN	KO4BN
Sweetwater	224.9000	–	O	WD9JGI	WD9JGI

Location	*Output*	*Input*	*Notes*	*Call*	*Sponsor*
TEXAS					
Alto	223.7800	–	Or	KB2EF	------------
Argyle	223.8600	–	O	WB5NDJ	------------
Arlington	224.8000	–	O 110.9	K5SLD	AARC
Austin	223.9400	–	O	W5HS	------------
Austin	224.8000	–	O	W5KA	AARC
Austin	224.9400	–	Ol	WB5PCV	------------
Blanket	224.7200	–	O	N5AG	------------
Burleson	224.7400	–	O 110.9a	W8KPJ	KONTAK FAMIL
Cedar Hill	224.1000	–	●	AI5TX	------------
Cedar Hill	224.5000	–	●	W5MAY	SBE 220
Cleveland	224.7800	–	O	N5AK	SHARK
Corpus Christi	224.3400	–	O 107.2e	W5FOF	------------
Cut And Shoot	223.9800	–	O 103.5e	W5WP	------------
Dallas	224.1800	–	O	W5RDW	TI ARC
Dallas	224.4800	–	O 110.9	K5JOI	------------
Dallas	224.6000	–	●	N5MIJ	------------
Dallas	224.7000	–	●	N5MIJ	------------
Dallas	224.8800	–	O	W5FC	DARC
Devers	224.9200	–	O 123	KA5QDG	------------
El Paso	224.8200	–	O	KC5EJ	------------
Euless	224.5600	–	O 110.9	WB4QHM	------------
Everman	224.8600	–	O	AB5XD	------------
Forest Hill	224.1400	–	O	KA5GFH	------------
Fort Worth	224.3200	–	O(CA)e	WØBOD	------------
Fort Worth	224.4200	–	O 110.9	W5SJZ	LRARC
Fort Worth	224.6800	–	Oae	WØBOD	------------
Fort Worth	224.7800	–	O 110.9	N5UN	FW220
Fort Worth	224.9400	–	O 110.9r	K5FTW	FWCTVHFFM
Granbury	224.3400	–	O 88.5 (CA)	WD5GIC	NTXARA
Houston	223.8000	–	O 123	KA5QDG	------------
Houston	223.9600	–	O 123	KA5QDG	HAMS
Houston	224.1000	–	O 103.5	KR5K	CYPRESS
Houston	224.1400	–	●	KA5QDG	HAMS
Houston	224.1600	–	O 103.5e	KB5IAM	HCTA
Houston	224.2000	–	O	WA5TWT	HTTY
Houston	224.2600	–	O	W5WP	HOUSTON ECH
Houston	224.3000	–	O 103.5el	KD5HKQ	TARMA
Houston	224.3200	–	O 123	KA5QDG	HAMS
Houston	224.8000	–	O 103.5	NA5CW	------------
Houston	224.9600	–	O 123	K5ILS	------------
Hurst	224.3000	–	O	WB5TCD	------------
Idalou	223.9000	–	O 123	KC5MVZ	------------
Irving	224.4000	–	O 110.9	WA5CKF	IARC
Jasper	224.8600	–	O	K5PFE	------------
Karnes City	224.4600	–	Oe	WA5S	------------
Lubbock	224.8200	–	O(CA)elx	WB5R	------------
Lucas	224.6600	–	O 110.9	K5XG	------------
Lufkin	224.0400	–	O 103.5	KD5TD	------------

Location	*Output*	*Input*	*Notes*	*Call*	*Sponsor*
Marshall	223.9400	–	O	K5HR	------------
Midland	223.9400	–	O(CA)elx	WB5RCD	WTX220ASN
Midland	224.9400	–	O(CA)elx	WB5RCD	WTX220ASN
Murphy	223.8200	–	O 110.9	W5RDW	------------
North Richland Hills	223.9400	–	O	W5URH	------------
Odessa	223.9400	–	O(CA)elx	WB5RCD	#NAME?
Parker	224.9600	–	O	K5RA	ESIARC
Pasadena	224.4000	–	O 103.5	KD5HKQ	TARMA
Pflugerville	224.4800	–	O 110.9	KG5BZ	------------
Port Aransas	224.4800	–	O 107.2lx	KG5BZ	------------
Prosper	224.4400	–	Oe	N5TPS	------------
Rose Hill	223.8400	–	O	K5SOH	------------
San Antonio	223.9400	–	O	WR5Q	------------
San Antonio	224.3800	–	O 179.9e	K5SUZ	SARO
San Antonio	224.6600	–	O	KA5OHJ	------------
Spring Branch	224.5800	–	O 131.8	W5DK	------------
Sulphur Springs	224.5800	–	O 151.4	N5REL	------------
The Colony	224.9800	–	●	KB5HOV	LAARK
Trinity	224.6000	–	O 103.5	N5ESP	------------
Vernon	224.4200	–	O 192.8	WB5AFY	------------
Weatherford	223.9000	–	O	KA5HND	RREPGRP
Weatherford	224.2600	–	O	W5URH	------------
Weslaco	224.6200	–	Oel	WA5S	------------
Wichita Falls	224.4000	–	O(CA)	K5HRO	------------
Willis	224.2400	–	O 103.5	WD5CFJ	------------
UTAH					
FREQUENCY USAGE					
Statewide	224.8600	–	O	SHARED	
CENTRAL					
Ephriam	223.9200	–	O 88.5 RBx	WX7Y	------------
NORTH					
Thiokol	224.4000	–	Oa	KE7FO	MTARC
NORTHEAST					
Vernal	223.9000	–	O	WX7Y	------------
PRICE					
Price	224.5000	–	O 88.5	W7CEU	CEU
Scofield	224.9800	–	OeRBx	WX7Y	IREAN/SD
SOUTH					
Hanksville	224.4800	–	O 88.5 RBx	WX7Y	------------
SOUTHEAST					
Moab	224.5800	–	Ol	WX7Y	------------
Monticello	223.9400	–	●x	K7QEQ	GMRA
Monticello	223.9600	–	Olx	WX7Y	------------
WASATCH FRONT					
American Fork	224.4200	–	O 156.7	W7WJC	UCRC
Clearfield	223.8600	–	O 123x	NJ7J	------------
Lehi	224.5600	–	O 100	KB7M	------------
			L(448.200 HF)sx		

Location	*Output*	*Input*	*Notes*	*Call*	*Sponsor*
Ogden	224.5000	–	O 167.9 A(*/#)	WB6CDN	IREAN
Payson	224.4800	–	O 88.5 RBx	WX7Y	------------
Payson	224.6000	–	O	WD7N	------------
Pleasant Grove	223.8800	–	O 167.9e	KB7YOT	------------
Point of the Mountain	224.8800	–	156.7	N7IMF	UHDARC
Powder Mtn	224.0000	–	O 167.9lRB x	N7TOP	IREAN
Provo	224.6400	–	O 156.7e	N7IMF	------------
Provo	224.7000	–	O 107.2x	KE7AU	------------
Riverton	224.5400	–	O	K7HEN	------------
Salt Lake	223.8400	223.8400	OaelRBxz	WB6CDN	IREAN
Salt Lake	223.9400	–	O 100s	KDØJ	SLCOARES
Salt Lake	224.7800	–	O 100e	KDØJ	------------
Salt Lake	224.8200	–	OaelRBxz	WB6CDN	IREAN
Sandy	224.6200	–	O 167.9	W7ROY	------------
Sandy	224.7200	–	O 167.9	W7ROY	------------
Syracuse	224.9600	–	O	NJ7J	------------

VERMONT

SOUTHWEST

Wells	224.9600	–	O	N1VT	NFMRA

VIRGINIA

Abingdon	224.1000	–	O	K4YW	K4YW
Alexandria	224.8200	–	O	WA4CCF	------------
Arlington	224.0600	52.0500	O	KI4MB	------------
Arlington	224.0600	–	O	KI4MB	------------
Bedford	222.6600	+	O	N4CH	N4CH
Bedford	224.8400	–	O	N4PLV	BEDFORD ARC
Bedfrd/apl Orch	224.1800	–	O	WA1ZMS	MTN TOP ASSO
Bell Knob	224.4400	222.8200	O	WD4KHP	NOVA6MGP
Bland/pearisburg	224.8600	–	O	KQ4Q	DPARS
Bluefield	224.4400	–	O	N8FWL	N8FWL 222 RAD
Bluefield	224.9200	–	O	WA8O	N8LGA
Bluemtn	224.1600	–	O	KF4VED	WA4JR
Buck's Elbow	224.3200	–	O	N4RAG	N4RAG
Buckingham	224.4000	–	O	KF4UCI	KF4UCI
Bucks Elbow	224.2200	–	O	KC4MZN	KC4MZN
Charlottesville	224.1400	–	O	N4HRV	N4HRV
Charlottesville	224.7600	–	O	WA4TFZ	WA4TFZ
Chesapeake	224.7400	–	O	WF4R	CITY OF CHESA
Chesapeake	224.9600	–	O	W4LG	W4LG
Deltaville	224.9000	–	O	AA4HQ	AA4HQKB4JIRK
Fairfax	224.1000	–	O	WB4YHD	------------
Fairfax	224.1000	–	O	WB4YHD	NVFMA
Falls Church	224.9800	–	O	N4CHP	------------

VIRGINIA

Location	Output	Input	Notes	Call	Sponsor
Fancy Gap	224.8800	–	O	K4DQ	BEAR CREEK ARC
Gloucester	224.6200	–	O	W4GSF	W4GSF
Hampden-sydney	224.2000	–	O	W4JAS	HAMPDEN-SYDNEY
Hampton	224.5400	–	O	WB4PVT	TIDEWATER 220AR
Hampton	224.8600	–	O	WB4PVT	TIDEWATER 220 AR
Hillsville	224.3200	–	O	K4YW	K4YW
Jonesville	224.5200	–	O	WM4MD	WM4MD
Lake Gaston	224.6000	–	O	W4LG	W4LG
Leesburg	224.0200	–	O	WA4TXE	------------
Lovettsville	224.4600	–	O	WB4FUJ	------------
Luray	224.3600	–	O	KE4JSV	KE4JSV
Lynchburg	224.2800	–	O	AB4M	AB4M
Manassas	224.3400	–	O	KB4CVL	------------
Manassas	224.6600	–	O	WA4FPM	------------
Marshall Manor	224.6000	–	O	KG4HOT	K4RKA
Martinsville	224.5000	–	O	K4RCA	K4RCA
Norfolk	224.4000	–	O	W4VB	W4VB
Norton/high Knb	224.4200	–	O	WD4GSM	WD4GSM
Patrick Springs	224.4200	–	O	WG8S	WB8POC
Petersburg	224.7000	–	O	K4ARO	K4ARO
Poor Mountain	224.7800	–	O	K5JCT	K5JCT
Prince George	224.5200	–	O	WA4FC	WA4FC
Richmond	224.4200	–	O	W4MEV	W4MEV
Richmond	224.5200	–	O	WA4ONG	------------
Roanoke	224.1000	–	O	N4CH	N4CH
Roanoke	224.4600	–	O	K4IJ	K4IJ
Roanoke	224.8000	–	O	K4ARO	------------
Roanoke	224.9400	–	O	AB4EM	------------
Roanoke	224.9400	–	O 107.2/107.2e	N2EDE	N2EDE
Roanoke/tinker	224.9000	–	O	K4YDG	K4YDG
Rocky Mountain	224.5800	–	O	KG4HOT	K4RKA
Singers Glen	224.8200	–	O	K4SAD	------------
Spotsylvania	224.9000	–	O	K4SPT	SPOTSYLVANIA AR
Staunton	224.7400	–	O	N4RAG	N4RAG
Staunton/el Knob	224.3000	–	O	KE4CKJ	WD4FOZ
Sterling	223.7200	–	O	WD4KHP	STERLING PARK AR
Tysons Corner	224.3400	–	O	KM4OI	NVFMA
Tysons Corner	224.4200	–	O	WD4KHP	NOVA6MGP
Tysons Corner	224.7200	–	O	WD4KHP	N. VA 6-METER GR
Vienna	223.9400	–	O	K4HTA	------------
Waynesboro	224.6800	–	O	KA4RCL	KA4RCL
Winchester	224.2200	–	O	N3HXT	N3HXT
Woodbridge	224.7800	–	O	W4IY	WWI
Woodbridge	224.7800	–	O	WB4GJZ	------------
Wytheville	224.5600	–	O	K4YW	K4YW
Wytheville	224.6800	–	O	N8FWL	N8FWL
ALL OF TMARC AREA					
SNP	223.8000	–	O		------------

Location	Output	Input	Notes	Call	Sponsor
CULPEPER					
Clark Mtn	224.1800	–	O	K3VB	K9SP
FRONT ROYAL					
Blue Mt	224.1600	–	O(CA)e	KR4DO	KR4DO
LEESBURG					
Leesburg	224.0200	–	●a	NØNW	NØNW
Lovettsville	224.4600	–	●	W4LAM	W4LAM
LURAY					
Luray	224.3600	–	O	KE4JSV	KE4JSV
SPOTSYLVANIA					
Spotsylvania	224.2600	–	OaWX	KD4QNA	KD4QNA
Spotsylvania	224.9000	–	O 100.0el	K4MQF	K4MQF
WASHINGTON AREA					
Alexandria	224.8200	–	O 107.2	W4HFH	Alex RC
Arlington	224.0600	52.0500	Ol	WB4MJF	+KI4MB
Arlington	224.0600	–	Ol	WB4MJF	+KI4MB
Arlington	224.6200	–	O	WB4MWF	WB4MWF
Bluemont	224.3400	–	O 77.0el	K8GP	DVMS
Fairfax	224.1000	146.1900	O(CA)elr LITZz	W4YHD	NVFMA
Fairfax	224.1000	–	Oel	W4YHD	NVFMA
Haymarket	224.4000	–	O 77.0el	W4BRM	BRM ARA
Manassas	224.6600	–	O 100.0e	W4OVH	OVHARC
Woodbridge	224.7800	–	O(CA)e	W4IY	WWI
WINCHESTER					
Winchester	224.2200	–	O(CA)	N3HXT	N3HXT

WASHINGTON

Location	Output	Input	Notes	Call	Sponsor
FREQUENCY USAGE - IACC AREAS					
Snp	224.7200	–	t		
Snp	224.8400	–	t		
W WA - FREQUENCY USAGE					
Control	223.5200	223.5400			
Crossband	224.0000	224.0000			
Hi Speed Data	223.5600	223.6000			
Hi Speed Data	223.6600	223.7600			
Rptr Inputs	222.1800	222.3800			
Rptr Inputs	222.4200	223.3000			
Rptr Inputs	223.2600	223.3800			
Rptr Outputs	223.7800	223.9800			
Rptr Outputs	224.0200	224.8200			
Rptr Outputs	224.8600	224.9800			
Shared	224.7200	224.7200			
Shared	224.8400	224.8400			
Simplex	223.4000	223.4800			
Simplex	223.5000	223.5000			
COLUMBIA RIVER GORGE					
Carson	224.0200	–	O 136.5	KB7APU	KB7APU

Location	Output	Input	Notes	Call	Sponsor
E WA - CHEWELAH					
Chewelah	223.8800	–	O	AK2O	SpoRG
E WA - NORTHEAST					
Springdale	223.9000	–	Olx	AK2O	SpoRG
E WA - SPOKANE					
Lookout	224.9800	–	77.4	N7BFS	N7BFS
Spokane	223.9400	–	O	AK2O	SpoRG
Spokane	223.9800	–	O	AK2O	SpoRG
Spokane	224.9200	–	●l	AK2O	SRG
Spokane	224.9400	–	Ol	AK2O	SpoRG
Spokane Vly	224.4000	–	O 114.8l	K7MMA	WA6HSL
Spokane Vly	224.6800	–	O	K7HRT	K7HRT
E WA - WENATCHEE					
Mission Ridge	224.7400	–	O	WR7ADX	W7CCY
E WA - YAKIMA					
Elephant Pk	224.9000	–	Oaelrz	W7AQ	YakARC
NW OREGON & SW WASHINGTON					
Yacolt	224.4200	224.8400	ters	K7CLL	K7CLL
PORTLAND METRO					
Vancouve	224.6400	–	O 123l	AB7F	AB7F
Vancouver	224.7200	–	O 100e	KB7APU	KB7APU
SOUTHWEST WASHINGTON					
Yacolt	224.8800	–	O 77e	W7RY	W7RY
SW WASHINGTON					
Battle Ground	223.7000	223.7000	O	K7YFJ	K7CLL
Vancouver	224.3600	–	O 94.8s	W7AIA	CCARC
W WA - NORTH					
Bellingham	224.8600	–	O 103.5	N7FYU	------------
Blyn Mtn	224.2400	–	O 103.5e	N7NFY	------------
Buck Mtn	224.5800	–	O 100	K5IN	------------
Camano Island	223.8800	–	O 103.5	W7MBY	5 Cnty Grp
East Sound	224.9800	–	O 103.5e	WA6MPG	------------
Lyman Hill	223.8600	–	O 103.5e	WA7ZWG	5 Cnty Grp
Lyman Hill	224.7800	–	O 103.5e	N7IPB	------------
Marysville	224.3800	–	O 103.5e	WA7DEM	SNO CNTY D
Mt Constitution	224.4800	–	O 103.5	N7JN	San Juan C
Mt Constitution	224.5400	–	O 67	WA6PMG	------------
W WA - NORTH COAST					
Pt Angeles	224.0600	–	O 107.2a (CA)e	W6MPD	W6MPD
W WA - SEATAC					
Brier	224.2200	–	O 77	WA7FUS	------------
Lake Forest Park	224.2200	–	O 103.5	WA7FUS	------------
Monroe	224.1000	–	O 123e	K7MJ	------------
Tiger Mtn East	224.1200	–	O 103.5e	K7LED	MIKE AND K
Tiger Mtn West	224.3400	–	O 110.9 (CA)e	K7NWS	BEARS
W WA - SEATTLE-TACOMA					
Baldi Mtn	224.7600	–	O 103.5 (CA)	WB7DOB	GERMAN SHEPARD

Location	*Output*	*Input*	*Notes*	*Call*	*Sponsor*
Carnation	223.9000	–	O 103.5ael	KA7AEF	------------
Enumclaw	223.9200	–	O 103.5l	WB7DOB	German Shep S
Gold Mtn	224.6600	–	O 103.5e	W7UFI	------------
Haystack Mtn	223.9400	–	O 123e	W2ZT	------------
Kirkland	224.3600	–	O 103.5e	NU7Z	5 Cnty Grp
Seattle	224.6800	–	O 103.5e	W7SRZ	WWMST
Tacoma	224.5200	–	O 103.5	K7HW	------------
Tiger Mtn	223.9800	–	O 100.0	N7NW	------------
W WA - SOUTH					
Crawford Mtn	224.4600	–	O 103.5ael z	NT7H	OLYMPIA AR
Eatonville	224.1800	–	O 103.5e	W7EAT	------------
Longview	224.1400	–	114.8e	W7DG	Lower Columbia
Olympia	224.0800	–	O 103.5l	K5IN	K5IN
South Mtn	224.9200	–	O 103.5	W7FHZ	CH 1 RPTR
W WA - SOUTH COAST					
Raymond	224.0400	–	O 118.8e	N7AXC	Beach Net
Raymond	224.8600	–	O 103.5e	KA7DNK	------------
South Bend	224.8200	–	O 82.5e	NM7R	NM7R

WEST VIRGINIA

Location	*Output*	*Input*	*Notes*	*Call*	*Sponsor*
Ansted	224.8400	–	O	N8FWL	N8FWL 22 RAD
Beckley	224.2400	–	O	N8FWL	N8FWL-222 RAD
Beckley	224.3400	–	O	N8FWL	N8FWL-222 RAD
Beckley	224.5400	–	O	N8FWL	N8FWL 222 RAD
Beckley	224.7400	–	O	N8FWL	N8FWL 222 RAD
Charleston	224.3600	–	O	WB8YST	WB8YST
Charleston	224.7000	–	O	WS8L	HUNT KNOB RP
Craigsville	224.4800	–	O	KC8LRN	KC8LRN
Flat Top	224.1200	–	O	WV8B	ARA NORTH
Green Bank	224.5200	–	O	KC8CSE	KC8CSE
Hillsboro	224.2200	–	O	KC8LRN	KC8LRN
Hinton	224.6400	–	O	N8FWL	N8FWL 222 RAD
Leon	223.7800	–	O	WD8OHX	WD8OHX
Lewisburg	224.1400	–	O	N8FWL	N8FWL-222 RAD
Lewisburg	224.8000	–	O	KC8LRN	KC8LRN
Lobelia	224.6000	–	O	KC8CSE	KC8CSE
Richwood	223.8600	–	O	WB8YST	WB8YST
Slanesville	222.1600	52.6700	O	KD4JBY	KD4JBY
Slaty Fork	224.7200	–	O	KC8LRN	KC8LRN
Sutton	224.4000	–	O	W8COX	W8COX
Webster Springs	224.6600	–	O	KC8CSE	KC8CSE
Williamson	224.1400	–	O	WR8M	SAWS
ALL OF TMARC AREA					
SNP	223.8000	–	O		------------
BERKELEY SPRINGS					
Berkeley Springs	224.7000	–	Oel	W3VLG	222-West

Location	Output	Input	Notes	Call	Sponsor
MARTINSBURG					
Martinsburg	224.2800	–	O	K8EP	EPARC
WISCONSIN					
WAR					
Appleton	224.5000	–	O 100.0aers	WJ9K	W9RIC
Baraboo	224.6600	–	O 123.0aelrs	KC9FNM	Empire
Beldenville	224.8400	–	O 110.9ers	NØNIC	B.A.T.S.
Cedarburg	224.1800	–	O 127.3aes	W9CQO	O.R.C.
Green Bay	223.9400	–	O 100.0aers	K9JQE	K9JQE
Madison	224.1600	–	O 123.0aelrs	WB9RSQ	WB9RSQ
New Berlin	224.9600	–	O 127.3aes	WD9EUF	WD9EUF
Niagara	223.8200	–	O 114.8aelr	W9MB	W9MB
Oshkosh	223.9000	–	O 100.0aers	W9OSH	W9OSH
Racine	223.8000	–	O 127.3aes	N9WWR	N9WWR
Racine	224.8000	–	O 127.3aes	KC9QKJ	ARLOW
Sheboygan Falls	224.9400	–	O 100.0aers	KB5ZJU	KB5ZJU
Spooner/Hertel	224.5000	–	O 110.9ers	KB9OHN	BARS
Three Lakes	224.5400	–	O 114.8aelr	N9GHE	N9GHE
Tomahawk	223.7600	–	O 114.8aelr	N9CLE	TOM RP A
Wausau	224.6400	–	O 114.8aelr	W9SM	W.V.R.A.
West Allis	224.5200	–	O 127.3aes	KA9JCP	KA9JCP
Wisconsin Dells	223.8600	–	O 123.0aelrs	N9ROY	N9ROY
WYOMING					
CENTRAL SOUTH					
Rawlins	223.8600	–	O	KD7SU	KS7SU
SOUTH EAST					
Wheatland	224.6800	–	O	AE7AF	AE7AF
ALBERTA					
CALGARY					
Calgary	224.8500	–	O 110.9/110.9	VE6RYC	CARA

Location	*Output*	*Input*	*Notes*	*Call*	*Sponsor*
Calgary	224.9400	–	●	VE6AMC	VE6AMC
EDMONTON					
Edmonton	224.7600	–	O	VE6TTC	VE6TTC
NORTH EAST					
St Paul	223.5000	–	Ox	VE6SB	------------
RED DEER					
Red Deer	224.8000	–	Oa	VE6KLM	VE6MB
BRITISH COLUMBIA					
FRASER VALLEY					
Abbotsford	224.2600	–	110.9	VE7RVA	FVARESS
Maple Ridge	224.8800	–	O	VE7RMR	Maple Ridg
GREATER VANCOUVER					
Burnaby	224.8000	–	127.3e	VE7RBY	VE7BYY
Burnaby	224.9600	–		VE7VYL	VE7EWS
Coquitlam	223.9200	–		VE7VFB	VA7LNX
Coquitlam	224.9200	–		VE7MFS	VE7NZ
Vancouver	224.3000	–	●e	VE7RPT	BCFMCA
Vancouver	224.6000	–	127.3	VE7NYE	PJ Van Bag
Vancouver	224.6400	–	e	VE7VCT	VECTOR
Vancouver	224.7000	224.1000	1011lpr	VE7RHS	UBC ARS
Vancouver	224.8400	–	O	VE7TOK	Murray Gje
SOUTH CENTRAL					
Kelowna/Vernon	224.9400	–	Ol	VA7OKN	VE7OHM
Osoyoos	222.6000	+	156.7	VE7OSY	KARTS
VANC ISLAND CENTRAL					
Chemainus	224.9400	–	141.3e	VE7RNA	Cowichan A
Ladysmith	224.0400	–	131.8e	VA7DXH	VA7DN
VANC ISLAND NORTH					
Sayward	224.6200	–	O	VE7RNC	NIARS
VANC ISLAND SOUTH					
Sidney	222.5400	146.0600	100	VE7XMT	WARA
Victoria	224.1400	–	100.0	VE7VIC	WARA
Victoria	224.5000	–	O	VE7RGP	Rogers Cab
MANITOBA					
WINNIPEG					
Winnipeg	224.9400	–	Ox	VE4RPT	VE4ABA
ONTARIO					
CENTRAL EAST					
Essonville	224.8400	–	Oae	VE3TBF	TBFRA
			L(TFMCS)		
LANARK/LEEDS-GRENVILLE					
Lavant	224.7800	–	#	VE3KNA	VA3WK
METRO TORONTO					
Mississauga	224.6200	–	O 103.5ae	VE3RSD	------------
			L(444.250 IRLP) WX		
Oakville	224.2400	–	O 131.8e	VE3RSD	------------
			L(PMO / TNK ASTERISK)		

Location	Output	Input	Notes	Call	Sponsor
Toronto	224.4000	–	O 103.5	VE3KRC	KAO
Uxbridge	224.8600	–	O 103.5e L(TFM IRLP)	VE3BEG	TFMCS
York	224.8400	–	O 105.3e	VE3EBX	------------
NATIONAL CAPITOL REGION					
Ottawa	223.5400	223.5400	EXP	VE3YMK	VE3BYT
Ottawa	224.7200	–		VE3ORF	OVMRC
Ottawa	224.8000	–	#	VE3OTT	OVMRC
NIAGARA					
Fonthill	224.5800	–	O 107.2	VE3NRS	NPARC
Fonthill	224.8000	–	O 107.2 RB	VE3PLF	COBRA
Niagara Falls	224.1800	–	O 107.2e L(ERA IRLP)	VE3WAJ	------------
SOUTH					
Acton	224.7200	–	O 103.5e L(442.125)	VE3PAQ	PRO-ARA
Burlington	224.7400	–	O 131.8e	VE3RSB	BARC
Carlisle	224.9600	–	O 131.8 L(ERA)	VE3WIK	ERA
Hamilton	224.4800	–	O 131.8 L(ECHOLINK)	VA3ODX	ODXA
Hamilton	224.5200	–	O 131.8 L(ERA)	VE3WIK	ERA
Kitchener	224.3400	–	O 131.8e	VE3IXY	KWARC
Woodstock	224.4400	–	O 131.8	VA3OHR	OCARC
SOUTHWEST					
St Thomas	224.7800	–	O 114.8	VE3STR	EARS
Windsor	224.6600	–	O	VE3OOO	------------
Windsor	224.7000	–	O 118.8e	VE3RRR	WARC

QUEBEC

Location	Output	Input	Notes	Call	Sponsor
Beaconsfield	224.6000	–	Oe	VE2RNC	VE2HOT
Blainville Nord	224.4000	–	O	VE2RNO	VE2THE
Chicoutimi	224.5000	–	O	VA2RDI	VE2MDH
Drummondville	223.9000	–	O 110.9	VE2ROK	VE2YLA
Farnham	224.8400	–	O 103.5	VA2RDH	VE2WDH
Havelock	224.7000	–	Oe	VE2RPT	VE2FMK
Havelock	224.8000	–	O	VE2HOT	VE2HOT
Joliette	224.6200	–	O	VE2RHO	VE2BFK
L'ange Gardien	224.5000	–	O 110.9e	VE2REH	VE2ZVL
Mont-Yamaska	224.3000	–	Oe	VE2RMV	VE2ULU
Montreal	224.9000	–	Oe	VE2RHH	MTL220
Rigaud	224.9800	–	Oe	VE2RM	MTL220
Saint-Lin Laurentides	224.9200	–	O 103.5e	VE2RFO	VE2BFK
St Calixte	224.4000	–	Ox	VA2RLD	VA2DLU
St-Adolphe d'Howard	224.7600	–	141.3ex	VE2RUN	VE2WCC

Location	*Output*	*Input*	*Notes*	*Call*	*Sponsor*
St-Adolphe D'howard	224.2200	–	O 141.3	VE2RVK	VE2VK
St-Bruno	224.7600	–	O 141.3	VE2RVK	VE2VK
St-Calixte	222.0500	2310.0000	O	VE2RVK	VE2VK
St-Calixte	224.7400	–	O 141.3	VE2LED	VE2VK
Ste-Foy	224.2200	–	O 100e	VA2MD	VE2CMD
Ste-Marcelline	224.5600	–	Oe	VE2RJR	VE2BLV
Trois-Rivieres Ouest	224.1000	–	O	VE2RTZ	VE2TRZ
OUTAOUAIS					
Buckingham	224.5000	–	110.9/110.9 (CA) L(I 2018)	VE2REH	ARAI
Hull	224.7600	–	O 110.9/110.9 (CA)eL(I 2018)	VE2REH	ARAI

SASKATCHEWAN

Location	*Output*	*Input*	*Notes*	*Call*	*Sponsor*
SASKATOON					
Saskatoon	222.7000	+	O	VE5UFO	VE5SD
SOUTHEAST					
Estevan	224.7000	223.7000	O	VA5EST	VE5AJ

420-450 MHz

Location	Output	Input	Notes	Call	Sponsor
ALABAMA					
Alabaster/Shelby County	444.5500	+	O 100.0e WX	N4PHP	N4PHP
Albertvfille	442.9500	+	OtelrRB WXx	KI4RYX	MCEARS
Anniston	444.0500	+	O 203.5 (CA)eWX	KF4RGR	------------
Anniston / Oak Mtn	443.3500	+	Oe	KJ4JGK	EMA / DHS
Anniston/Cheaha Mt	444.7500	+	O 131.8e	WB4GNA	Calhoun ARC
Arab	443.2250	+	O 77.0/77.0 eL(EL/640610)z	KE4Y	BMARC
Argo/ Trussville	442.1250	+	O	K4YNZ	KE4ADV
Ashcroft Corner Pickens Co	444.4000	+	O 110.9e RB	W4GLE	W4GLE
Athens	442.8500	+	O	KD4NTK	WD4LPG
Auburn	444.1250	+	O/ARESae rWXz	W4LEE	East AL: ARC
Auburn	444.8000	+	O 156.7ae	K4RY	AUARC
Battleground / Cullman	444.9500	+	O 107.2/107.2	WR4JW	WR4JW
Bay Minette	444.1750	+	O 203.5/203.5	K4JIE	North Baldwin A
Bessemer	443.7000	+	O 131.8/131.8e	KK4BSK	HC ARC
Bessemer	444.6250	+	O 100.0	KA4KUN	ALABEARS
Birmingham	443.1250	+	O 146.2l	N4VSU	Alabama Po
Birmingham	443.4500	+	O 131.8/131.8e	KK4BSK	HC ARC
Birmingham	443.9000	+	O	W4CUE	BARC
Birmingham	444.4250	+	● 131.8e L(52.525) RBx	KE4ADV	KE4ADV
Birmingham Red Mt	443.1750	+	O 131.8/131.8	KK4BSK	HC ARC
Birmingham/ Forestdale	444.7250	+	Oa	W4YMW	W4YMW
Birmingham/ Red Mtn	444.6500	+	O 131.8	KA5GET	KA5GET
Birmingham/ Ruffner Mtn	444.1000	+	O 162.2e L(ECHOLINK 146760)	K4TQR	H&H Repeat
Birmingham/ RuffnerMtn	444.8250	+	O 131.8/131.8ae	AG4ZV	AG4ZV

Location	*Output*	*Input*	*Notes*	*Call*	*Sponsor*
Birmingham/ ShadesMtn	444.9750	+	● 156.7/156.7	KB4TUE	KB4TUE
Blountsville	442.7500	+	Oal	W4BLT	Blount ARC
Bluff / Fayette	443.0750	+	O 203.5el	N7OEY	N7OEY
Boaz	443.0500	+	O 123.0el RB	KCØONR	KC0ONR
Boaz	443.0500	+	O 100.0/100.0	KCØONR	KCØONR
Brewton	444.6500	+	Oe L(ECHOLINK)	KI4GGH	KI4GGH
Brewton	444.7250	+	O	WB4ARU	Brewton ARU
Chalkville/Pinson	442.6500	+	O 131.8	KA5GET	KA5GET
Cherokee County	444.4000	+	O 100.0ez	KC4OR	KC4OR
Clanton EMA	443.5000	+	O/RACESr	KF4LQK	Montgomery
Columbiana	444.6000	+	O 156.7/156.7	KC4EUA	WA4CYA
Cordova	442.3000	+	Oe	W4WCA	Walker Co. ARES
Cullman	444.9000	+	O	N4UAI	N4UAI
Dadeville	444.5250	+	O 146.2ae RB WXz	KB4MDD	KB4MDD
Decatur	442.3500	+	Oe	W9KOP	W9KOP
Decatur	442.6750	+	Oe	W9KOP	W9KOP
Decatur/ Brindley Mtn	443.8500	+	Oe	W4ATD	DARC
Dothan	444.0250	+	107.2/107.12	KD1Z	KD1Z
Dothan	444.0250	+	107.2/107.12	KD1Z	KD1Z
Dothan	444.0250	+	O 107.2/107.2	KD1Z	KD1Z
Dothan	444.6750	+	O 156.7/RACESer	KI4ZP	KI4ZP
Dothan	444.7750	+	O	WB4ZPI	WARC
Dothan	444.8500	+	O 186.200/186.200e	KE4GWW	------------
Dothan	444.9000	+	O	WA4MZL	WA4MZL
Douglas	442.4500	+	O 100.0/100.0e	KCØONR	KCØONR
Douglas	442.6250	+	203.5elRB WXx	KI4RYX	MCEARS
Eufaula	442.0750	+	O 203.5el	N4TKT	N4TKT
Eufaula	444.9250	+	O 151.4e	WB4MIO	WB4MIO
Falkville	444.3250	+	O 107.2/107.2 RB	WR4JW	WR4JW
Fayette	444.8500	+	O	N4GRX	N4GRX
Flagg Mountain	442.5000	+	O 88.5 TT	W4YH	W4YH
Flint Ridge	444.2000	+	O 179.0/179.0#(CA) DCSe	W4TH	Bankhead ARC
Florence	444.1250	+	O 123.0/123.0e	K4NDL	NFRA

Location	*Output*	*Input*	*Notes*	*Call*	*Sponsor*
Florence	444.2000	+	O 123.0/123.0	KI4SP	KI4SP
Florence	444.7750	+	O 100.00/ARESe	KF4GZI	EMA/ARES
Florence	444.7750	+	O 100.0/100.0 E-SUNs	KF4GZI	EMA ARES
Florence, North	444.6500	+	O 123.0/123.0el	KQ4RA	KQ4RA
Foley	444.7500	+	O 186.2/186.2	KG4LWP	KG4LWP
Fort Payne	442.6000	+	O 100.0/100.0elWX	KF4FWZ	KF4FWZ
Fort Payne	444.6250	+	O 141.3e	W4OZK	ALBDR
Fort Payne	444.8000	+	O 100.0/100.0 RB	KF4FWX	KF4FWX
Friendship	444.5750	+	O 100.0e	KE4LTT	KE4LTT
Gadsden	444.7750	+	O 100.0 (CA)ex	K4BWR	K4BWR
Gadsden	444.8500	+	O 100.0	N4NAK	N4NAK
Gadsden/ Hensley Mtn	444.6750	+	O 100.0/100.0	K4VMV	K4VMV
Georgiana	444.9000	+	103.5/103.5 e	K4TNS	Jim Bell Wireless
Guntersville	444.2500	+	O 100.00/100.00	KCØONR	KCØONR
Gurley/ Keel Mt	442.9750	+	O 100.0/100.0 (CA) RB	K4DED	K4DED
Helicon	442.7250	+	O	W4FSH	W4FSH
Holtville	444.9500	+	O 88.5	K4IZN	K4IZN
Hoover / Shades Mt	444.9750	+	● 156.7/156.7a	KB4TUE	KB4TUE
Horton	443.7250	448.7350	● 203.5 (CA)el	AG4LU	AG4LU
Huntsville	442.0000	+	O 203.5	KE4BLC	KE4BLC
Huntsville	442.3750	+	● 156.7/156.7	KC4HRX	KI4QWP
Huntsville	443.0000	+	OTTe	W4DNR	W4DNR
Huntsville	443.1250	+	O 107.2e	WA1TDH	WA1TDH
Huntsville	443.1500	+	● 103.5	W4DYN	Dynatics ARC
Huntsville	443.2500	+	O 103.5lRB	KE4LRX	W4VM
Huntsville	443.3000	+	O 156.70	KE4GNN	R.F. HSV
Huntsville	443.4750	+	O 103.5a RB	W4VM	W4VM
Huntsville	443.7500	+	O 186.2/186.2	W4LDX	W4LDX
Huntsville	443.8000	+	O 110.9	W4PS	NARA
Huntsville	444.2250	+	O 100.0/100.0	N4DTC	AI4PJ
Huntsville	444.3750	+	O 100.0 L(ECHOLINK)	W4XE	W4XE

Location	*Output*	*Input*	*Notes*	*Call*	*Sponsor*
Huntsville	444.5000	+	●	WB4LTT	WB4LTT
Huntsville	444.5750	+	○ 100.0e RB	KB4CRG	KB4CRG
Huntsville	444.9750	+	○ 103.5/103.5	W4FMX	W4FMX
Huntsville/ Brindley Mt	444.5250	+	○DCS(143)	W4WLD	W4WLD
Huntsville/ Drake Mtn	442.7750	+	○ 203.5l	KB4CRG	KB4CRG
Huntsville/ Green Mtn	444.3000	+	103.5ae	W4XE	W4XE
Huntsville/ Monte Sano	443.6250	+	○ 127.3/127.3 (CA) L(RB) RB	W4XE	W4XE
Huntsville/ MonteSano	443.5000	+	○ 110.9a RB	W4HSV	NARA
Huntsville/ MonteSano	444.1750	+	○ 151.4 (CA)el	KD4TFV	KD4TFV
Jasper	441.8000	+	○ 123.0e	W4JMT	WA4JUJ
Jasper	443.2750	+	○ 123.0/123.0eWX	WR4Y	Walker Co. ARC
Jasper	443.9250	+	○ 123.0/123.0elWXx	N4MYI	N4MYI
Jemison	444.4750	+	○ 100.00/100.00	WB4UQT	------------
Killen	444.4250	+	○ 203.5/203.5 (CA)eE-SUN E-WIND WX	KS4QF	WX4LC/ELFS
Killen/Central	444.7000	+	○ 123.0/123.0	KC4YLB	KC4YLB
Lanett	442.0500	+	○ 141.3	K4DXZ	Chattahoochee Valley
Leesburg	443.1750	+	○ 100.0	N4GIS	N4GIS
Leesburg	444.0250	+	○ 100.0ae WXz	KB4AEA	Cherokee EMA
Lineville	444.0000	–	○	WB4VBA	WB4VBA
Loxley	443.2000	+	○ 118.8/118.8	WB4GMQ	WB4GMQ
Loxley	443.6500	+	○ 118.8/118.8	WB4GMQ	WB4GMQ
Madison	443.0250	+	○ 110.9/110.9 L(IRLP)	W4WWM	W4WWM
Magnolia Springs	444.5500	+	○ 82.5	WA4VSH	WA4VSH
Mentone	443.4000	+	○ 103.5el WX	W4OZK	W4OZK
Minor	444.9250	+	○ 203.5/203.5el	N7OEY	------------
Minor / B,ham	444.9250	+	○ 203.5el	N7OEY	N7OEY
Mobile	442.5000	+	○ 100.0/100.0	KI4ADV	KI4ADV
Mobile	444.5000	+	123.0/ARES eL(ECHOLINK/IRLP) WX	WB4QEV	Mobile EMA

Location	*Output*	*Input*	*Notes*	*Call*	*Sponsor*
Mobile County	444.5250	+	O 123.0/123.0eWX	WX4MOB	WX4MOB
Monroeville	444.7750	+	O 123.0/123.0ae	K8IDX	K8IDX
Montgomery	444.4500	+	O 100.0aelz	WD4JRB	WD4JRB
Montgomery	444.5000	+	O 100.0/100.0 (CA)el	W4AP	MARC
Montgomery	444.6250	+	● 141.3/141.3e	W4OZK	ALBDR
Moulton	442.4250	+	OeRB WX	N4IDX	Bankhead ARC
Moulton	444.7750	+	Oe	N4IDX	Bankhead ARC
Nectar/Skyball Mt	443.7750	+	O	W4BLT	Blount Co. ARC
Odenville/ Bald_Rock	443.7750	+	O	K4JDH	K4YNZ
Opelika	442.1750	+	O 203.5e	N4TKT	N4TKT
Opelika	442.9000	+	O	W4LEE	EAARC/EAMC
Opelika	444.4250	+	OeWX	WX4LEE	EMA ARC
Pelham	446.4000	29.5600	Ol	KR4UD	KR4UD
Pell City	442.5750	+	O 131.8/131.8 TTe	K4CVH	CVHRA
Phenix City	444.2000	+	O 123.0 (CA)elz	WA4QHN	WA4QHN
Phenix City	444.7250	+	O 203.5e	N4TKT	N4TKT
Piedmont	443.6250	+	O 131.8/131.8	KJ4MTX	KJ4MTX
Quinton/Flint Ridge	444.2000	+	O 179.9/179.9 (CA)e	W4TH	Bankhead DX Cl
Rainsville	442.5500	+	● 100.00	KF4BCR	KF4BCR
Ranburne/Turkey Heaven	444.1750	+	●x	N4THM	Turkey Heaven R
Roanoke	444.2750	+	O 141.3/141.3aelsWX	KA4KBX	KA4KBX
Roanoke	444.9000	+	O	KJ4JNX	D-STAR
Robertsdale	444.6250	+	O 141.3/141.3e	W4OZK	ALBDR
Rogersville	442.0250	+	O 100.0/100.0elrWX	KF4GZI	EMA/ARES
Rogersville	442.5000	+	Ol	KJ4LEL	ELRA/KJ4LEL
Rogersville	442.9250	+	O 203.5/203.5a(CA)elr	AE4HF	AE4HF
Rogersville	444.4750	+	88.5l	KF4CSZ	KF4CSZ
Ruffner Mt	439.5250	146.1600	O 88.5/88.5e	KK4BSK	HC ARC
Russellville	444.6750	+	O	KI4OKJ	PCRS/K4NXB
Russellville	444.8000	+	O 210.7/210.7el	KD9Q	KD9Q
Salem	444.1000	+	Oe	WA4QHN	WA4QHN
Santuck	444.2250	+	O/PKTe	K4GR	K4GR

Location	*Output*	*Input*	*Notes*	*Call*	*Sponsor*
Selma	442.0250	+	O 100.00e	N4KTX	N4KTX
Shelby / Lay Lake	444.3500	+	O	WB4CCQ	WB4CCQ
Shelby Co	442.0000	+	100.0elp	N4PHP	N4PHP
Shelby Co Signal Mt	444.7000	+	O 156.7/156.7e	WA4CYA	WA4CYA
Smith	444.8500	+	O 123.0/123.0eL(ECHOLINK)	KF4AEJ	KF4AEJ
South Community	444.8250	+	O 100.0	KI4ONH	KI4ONH
Spanish Fort	444.6000	+	O	KC4JPD	KC4JPD
Springville	443.7500	+	O 103.5/103.5	KJ4SQP	KJ4SQP
Springville/ SimonsMtn	443.6500	+	O 131.8	KA5GET	KA5GET
Straight Mt /Oneonta	443.8750	+	● 77.0/77.0 ex	KK4CWX	KK4CWX
Theodore	444.1000	+	O	N4LMZ	N4LMZ
Troy	443.0000	+	100.0l	W4NQ	Troy Radio
Trussville	442.1000	+	O 103.5e RB	KC4ANB	KC4ANB
Turkey Haven Mt	444.1750	+	●x	N4THM	THRA
Tuscaloosa	442.1500	+	OeRB	W4MD	W4MD
Tuscaloosa	442.3750	+	Oa	N4BWP	N4BWP
Tuscaloosa	442.5500	+	173.8	KX4I	KX4I
Tuscaloosa	442.9500	+	●	W4MD	Tri Net
Tuscaloosa	443.8250	+	O 118.8ae WXz	W4XI	TARC
Tuscaloosa	444.1250	+	O 210.7/210.7	W4UAL	Unjiversity of AL ARC
Tuscaloosa	444.1250	+	O	W4UAL	Unjiversity of AL ARC
Tuscaloosa	444.1750	+	210.7/210.7 #	W4UAL	University Of AL ARC
Tuscaloosa	444.5750	+	O 210.7/210.7	KD9Q	KD9Q
Tuscaloosa	444.9000	+	O 210.7el	KD9Q	KD9Q
Tuscaloosa/ Birmingham	443.5750	+	●lx	KX4I	AICN Hub
Union Hill	442.8000	+	● 162.2	W5MEI	W5MEI
University of North AL	442.3250	+	O 77.0/77.0	KK4NGG	UNA ARC
Vernon	444.2500	+	● 110.9/110.9	KI4QAH	KI4QAH
Vinemont	444.2750	+	110.9l	W4CFI	W4CFI
Waterloo	442.1250	+	O 100.0el	KF4GZI	Lauderdale EMA/ARE
Wetumpka	443.7250	+	O 100.0e	KG4RCK	KG4RCK
Wood Mtn	443.8250	+	O	W4CCA	CCARC

ALASKA

INTERIOR

Canyon Creek	444.9000	+	103.5lx	KL7KC	ARCTIC ARC

Location	Output	Input	Notes	Call	Sponsor
Delta Junction	449.6000	–	103.5	KL2AV	KL2AV
Fairbanks	444.1000	+	O x	KL7NO	KL7NO
Fairbanks	444.8000	+	O 103.5ael x	KL7KC	ARCTIC ARC
Nenana	449.6500	–	O 103.5	WL7BDO	WL7BDO
SOUTH CENTRAL					
Anchorage	444.7000	+	O 103.5ae z	KL7AA	AARC
Bethel	444.1000	+	O 100e	AL7YK	BARK
Eagle River	444.1000	+	O 100.0 (CA) TTe	KL7GG	KL7GG
Ft Richardson	444.5000	+	O 100.0 (CA) TTeRB	KL7GG	GG/ADES
Kodiak	444.5500	+	O 136.5lRB	WL7AML	WL7AML
Palmer	443.9000	+	O 103.5els	WL7CVF	AARC/ARES
Wasilla	444.6000	+	O	KL7SG	MARA
SOUTHCENTRAL					
Anchorage	443.3000	+	O 103.5els	WL7CVG	AARC/ARES
Anchorage	444.8500	+	O 103.5l		CARA
State Wide (aeronautical)	444.9750	+	O 203.5p	KL8DW	KL8DW
SOUTHEAST					
Juneau	444.5000	+	O ael	KL7PF	JARC
Juneau	444.7000	+	O ael	WA6AXO	WA6AXO

ARIZONA

Location	Output	Input	Notes	Call	Sponsor
FREQUENCY USAGE					
Arizona	440.5000	+		TEST PAIR	
Arizona	441.0250	441.0250			
Arizona	445.5500	–		TEST PAIR	
Arizona	446.0000	446.0000			
Arizona	446.0250	446.0250			
Arizona	446.0500	446.0500			
Arizona	446.5000	446.5000			
CENTRAL					
Anthem	442.5250	+	O 114.8e	W6PAT	Griffin A.R.C.
Bill Williams Mtn	448.0200	–	● tx	NR7G	K7FY
Bill Williams Mtn	448.2750	–	● tlx	K6DLP	Don Petrone
Bill Williams Mtn	449.7500	–	O 91.5x	K7NAZ	Bill Williams Mt.
Chino Valley	449.2500	–	O 192.8	K7POF	Bob Sitterley
Clarkdale	441.7750	+	O 156.7	K9FUN	K9FUN
Crown King	447.3000	–	O 88.5x	W7WHP	W7WHP
Glassford Hill	442.3500	+	O 100	N7KPU	N7KPU
Mingus Mtn	442.1500	+	O 100elx	WA7UID	M.M.R.G.
Mingus Mtn	449.4250	–	● tel	WA6LSE	WA6LSE
Mingus Mtn	449.7000	–	● tlRBx	N7CI	S.A.R.B.A.
Mingus Mtn	449.7250	–	● telx	K6DLP	Donald Petrone
Mt Ord	444.5000	+	O 100elx	W7MDY	A.R.A.
Mt Ord	444.9000	+	● tx	WB7TUJ	S.A.R.B.A.

Location	Output	Input	Notes	Call	Sponsor
Mt Tritle	442.1000	+	●tx	W1OQ	NORTHLINK
Prescott	441.8500	+	● 151.4 (CA)	K7CBK	Lee T. Cunningham
Prescott	449.6750	–	●t(CA)lRB	WB7BYV	Steve Crumley
Prescott Valley	443.0500	+	○ 136.5	WB6ALS	WB6ALS
Squaw Peak	447.4000	–	○ 100x	KB7EDI	KB7EDI
Squaw Peak	447.5000	–	●tel	WA6LSE	WA6LSE
Squaw Peak	447.7000	–	●tlx	K6DLP	Don Petrone
Squaw Peak	448.2000	–	●tx	WB7EVI	NORTHLINK
Tonopah	440.4750	+	○ 123	WT9S	Jay Freeman
Towers Mtn	448.5750	–	○ 100ex	WB7EVI	W1OQ
Towers Mtn	448.6000	–	●t DCS(411)elx	KA7MIZ	KA7MIZ
Towers Mtn	449.0000	–	●tlRBx	K7STA	S.A.R.B.A.
Towers Mtn	449.1750	–	○ 100elx	WB7EVI	NORTHLINK
Wild Flower	447.2250	–	●tx	K7YXD	K7YXD
Wild Flower	449.2250	–	○ 123ex	WW7B	D.A.W.N.
EAST CENTRAL					
Clay Springs	442.8000	+	○ 100	N7KQ	H.T.A.W.A.
Greens Peak	448.3750	–	○ 100lx	W7ARA	A.R.A.
Greens Peak	448.8500	–	○ 110.9x	W7IXA	S.A.R.B.A.
Greens Peak	449.3500	–	○ 162.2elx	W7OTA	W7OTA
Greens Peak	449.8500	–	●tx	K7KI	S.A.R.B.A.
Porter Mtn	449.0500	–	○ 100eRB	W7OTA	W7OTA
Red Sky Ranch	449.6250	–	○ 136.5e	NR7G	NR7G
Show Low	449.1500	–	○ 110.9 RB x	W7EH	K.A.R.C.
Signal Peak	449.6500	–	○ 100ex	WR7GC	Gila County Emergen
FLAGSTAFF					
Flagstaff	440.4000	+	○ 100	W7LUX	W7LUX
Mormon Mtn	449.6000	–	○ 162.2ex	KD7IC	Jonathan P. Koger
Mt Elden	448.1000	–	●tlx	K6DLP	Donald Petrone
Mt Elden	448.4750	–	○ 100ex	W7ARA	A.R.A.
Mt Elden	448.6250	–	●tlx	N7MK	S.A.R.B.A.
Mt Elden	448.8750	–	○ 100ex	W7ARA	A.R.A.
Mt Elden	449.3250	–	○ 103.5ae x	NO7AZ	John Lindsey
NORTH CENTRAL					
Grand Canyon	442.0750	+	○ 100elx	N7FHQ	NORTHLINK
Navajo Mtn	448.7500	–	●telRBx	NA7DB	NA7DB
NORTH WEST					
Bullhead City	449.3750	–	○ 123elx	K7REW	K7REW
Golden Valley	448.0500	–	● 100lx	WB7BTS	WB7BTS
Kingman	446.2250	–	○ 151.4	K7RLW	K7RLW
Kingman	448.5000	–	● 114.8lx	K7MCH	K7MCH
Kingman	448.6500	–	○ 151.4el	K7MPR	KD7MIA
Kingman	449.4750	–	● 94.8lRBx	K7RLW	K7RLW
Kingman	449.5500	–	○ 151.4el	KD7MIA	KD7MIA
Kingman	449.8000	–	● 151.4	K7RLW	K7RLW

Location	Output	Input	Notes	Call	Sponsor
Kingman	449.9000	–	●	K7RLW	K7RLW
Meadview	449.9000	–	●	K7RLW	K7RLW
NORTHEASTERN					
Overgaard	446.6000	–	O 100e	N7QVU	Jerry Wyatt
South Mtn - Alpine	448.7250	–	●telx	WB5QHS	J.P.A.R.A.
NORTHWEST					
Golden Valley	449.8750	–	O 127.3e	W8MIA	August Hoecker
Hualapai Mtn	446.4000	–	●t(CA)elx	N7DPS	N7DPS
Hualapai Mtn	447.1250	–	O 156.7x	KA6NLS	S.A.R.S
Hualapai Mtn	448.5500	–	O 123ex	K7MPR	M.A.R.C.
Kingman	443.1750	+	O 156.7 (CA)x	WA7I	Jack Gunnoe
Kingman	449.5500	–	O 151.4l	W6EZU	Michael Kazmier
Kingman	449.7500	–	O 79.7e	KC8UQP	KC8UQP
White Hills	447.6000	–	O 107.2e	K7OK	K7AC
PHOENIX					
Bell Butte	447.7500	–	O 100ael	AI7R	City of Tempe
Chandler	442.9750	+	O 100	W7MOT	M.A.R.C.A.
Chandler	444.2750	+	O 100	KE7JVX	Monte Dana
Chandler	447.5000	–	O 100ae	WB5DYG	Sgt. Scott Picque
Chandler	448.4500	–	O 136.5e	NØFPE	NØFPE
Chandler	448.9250	–	O 123	N7SCE	N7SCE
Chandler	448.9500	–	O 100el	WW7CPU	I.E.A.R.S
Far North Mountain	448.8500	–	O 136.5lx	K7PNX	City of Phoenix,
Fountain Hills	447.7750	–	●tx	N7MK	F.H.A.R.T.
Gilbert	449.8250	–	O 100e	AJ7T	Ron McKee
Glendale	445.6000	–	●t	KB7NAS	Steve Mendelsoh
Glendale	447.4000	–	O 100e	KD7HJN	Glendale Radio
Glendale	447.5750	–	O 151.4a RB	KC7GHT	KC7GHT
Glendale	448.3250	–	O 100eRB	KB7FQO	KB7FQO
Glendale	449.5750	–	O 100eRB	KB7OBJ	N6IME
Goodyear	446.5500	–	O 100	KD7YAT	Monty Dana
Mesa	440.4250	+	●tDCS(54) e	KF7EUO	Tim Owen
Mesa	449.3750	–	O 100lx	K7DAD	M.A.R.A.
Mesa	449.6000	–	O 100el	WB7TJD	SUP-ARC
Mesa	449.6250	–	O 100a	W7ARA	A.R.A.
Mesa	449.8500	–	●tRB	W5WVI	W5WVI
Mesa	449.9500	–	●te	WB7TUJ	Doug Pelley
North Mountain	449.0250	–	O 136.5lx	K7PNX	City of Phoenix,
Peoria	441.1750	+	●t	KA7ATV	KA7ATV
Peoria	444.7500	+	●t	KA7PTW	KA7PTW
Phoenix	441.2000	+	O 77	KB7CGA	Gary L. Duddy
Phoenix	441.8000	+	●t	WA7UID	WB7CWW
Phoenix	442.0500	+	O 100	W7MOT	M.A.R.C.A.
Phoenix	442.6000	+	O 100l	N1KQ	M.C.R.G.

Location	*Output*	*Input*	*Notes*	*Call*	*Sponsor*
Phoenix	442.6750	+	O 123e	WW7B	Morgan E. Hoaglin
Phoenix	442.7000	+	●t	WW7B	Morgan E. Hoaglin
Phoenix	444.3000	+	O 100ae	W7ARA	A.R.A.
Phoenix	446.1500	–	O 100el	W7TBC	T.A.R.C.
Phoenix	446.2250	–	O 114.8	WA7MKS	WA7MKS
Phoenix	447.3250	–	O 131.8lRB	KB7OBJ	Chris Barford
Phoenix	447.9500	–	O 100 (CA) e	N7TWB	N7TWB
Phoenix	449.2000	–	O 100el	KC5CAY	KC5CAY
San Tan Valley	449.3250	–	O 100.0	N7DJZ	Doug Pelley
Scottsdale	440.0000	+	O 100	WA7APE	S.A.R.C.
Scottsdale	440.4500	+	O 100	W7JSW	W7JSW
Scottsdale	441.1000	+	O 103.5	WØNWA	Jeff Daugherty
Scottsdale	441.6250	+	O 100el	W7ARA	A.R.A.
Scottsdale	442.0250	+	O 100el	W7MOT	M.A.R.C.A.
Scottsdale	443.1500	+	O 100	W7MOT	M.A.R.C.A.
Scottsdale	444.0750	+	●tx	WB7NNP	L.R.G.
Scottsdale	444.1250	+	●t	WB7NNP	L.R.G.
Scottsdale	448.6750	–	●tl	W7IXA	S.A.R.B.A.
Scottsdale	448.9000	–	●tlRB	WA7VEI	WA7VEI
Scottsdale	449.0500	–	●t(CA)lRBx	WA7VEI	P.M.C. Inc
Scottsdale	449.4250	–	O 100x	KØNL	Gregory Banks
Shaw Butte	442.8500	+	O 100ex	WB7EVI	A.R.A.
Shaw Butte	447.6250	–	●tRBx	WA7ZZT	S.M.U.G.
Shaw Butte	449.3500	–	●el	N7ULY	WB7TUJ
Shaw Butte	449.5250	–	O 100aex	W7ARA	A.R.A.
South Mtn	442.0000	+	●tlRBx	WA7ZZT	S.M.U.G.
South Mtn	442.1250	+	O 100elx	N7AUW	NORTHLINK
South Mtn	442.2000	+	O 136.5lx	K7PNX	City of Phoenix, EOC
South Mtn	442.5500	+	O 100x	WA7ZZT	W.S.R.G.
South Mtn	442.8000	+	O 100x	KX7KW	M.C.R.G.
South Mtn	442.9000	+	O 100x	W7ZAA	Zachary Altman
South Mtn	443.0500	+	O 100x	W7MOT	M.A.R.C.A.
Sun City	449.8000	–	O 100ae	W7JHQ	W.V.A.R.C.
Sun City West	442.4500	+	O 146.2	KA7G	Gerald R. McManus
Tempe	443.1250	+	O 100	WD8MHM	WD8MHM
Tempe Butte	442.3750	+	O 100aex	K7JGB	Andrew Moccaldi
Thompson Peak	448.8250	–	O 100ex	W7IFH	W7IFH
Tolleson	448.0750	–	O 100 RB	AJ9Y	AJ9Y
Usery Mtn	447.2500	–	●teRBx	WB7TUJ	Harold Pierson
Usery Mtn	447.4250	–	O 107.2x	KC7WYD	Roger Chico M. Lope
Usery Mtn	447.6500	–	O 186.2 (CA)lx	W7SGK	Doug Pelley
Usery Mtn	448.8000	–	O 100elx	W7BSA	Explorer Post 599
Usery Mtn	449.1000	–	O 100lx	W7ARA	A.R.A.
White Tanks E Peak	446.4000	–	O 100ex	W7GDY	Tri City ARA
White Tanks E Peak	446.6750	–	O 146.2x	KC7WVE	Felix H. Pinto

Location	Output	Input	Notes	Call	Sponsor
White Tanks E Peak	448.2250	–	●tex	N7ULY	WB7TUJ
White Tanks E Peak	448.4000	–	●ex	W7ATN	ATN-AZ
White Tanks E Peak	448.8750	–	●tlx	K6DLP	Don Petrone
White Tanks E Peak	449.1500	–	●tlRB	WA7GBL	S.A.R.B.A.
White Tanks Mid Peak	441.7250	+	O 100elx	W7EX	A.R.A.
White Tanks Mid Peak	442.2750	+	O 100elx	W1OQ	NORTHLINK
White Tanks Mid Peak	442.9250	+	O 114.8x	AE7JG	Zachary A. Altma
White Tanks W Peak	448.7500	–	●telx	KD7GC	W.T.M.R.G., Inc.
SOUTH CENTRAL					
Casa Grande	446.8250	–	O 88.5a	KJ7YM	KJ7YM
Childs Mtn	448.1000	–	O 100ex	KL7DSI	A.A.R.C.
Coolidge	446.6000	–	O 151.4	KC7KMM	Tony Starns
Elephant Head Peak	449.3750	–	O 107.2ex	WE7GV	G.V.A.R.C.
Elephant Head Peak	449.8500	–	●telx	WA7BGX	C.A.R.B.A.
Elgin	448.5000	–	O 91.5	K6RCK	K6RCK
Green Valley	449.2250	–	O 100	AA7RP	AA7RP
Keystone Mtn	444.8750	+	O 100x	KCØLL	KCØLL
Mt Lemmon	444.9750	+	O 100ex	KCØLL	KCØLL
Mt Lemmon	445.2250	–	O 103.5x	W7ATN	ATN-AZ
Mt Lemmon	448.3500	–	O 107.2x	N1DHS	N1DHS
Mt Lemmon	448.6250	–	●tlx	AK7Z	C.A.R.B.A.
Mt Lemmon	449.7750	–	●tx	KB7GNX	Marvin G. Staffor
Sacaton Peak	447.7250	–	O 100ex	N7ULY	WB7TUJ
Vail	446.5500	–	O 100e	KE7ULC	Ronald P. Barton
Vail	449.5500	–	O 107.2el	K7LHR	Don Stiver
SOUTHEAST					
Benson	445.3000	–	O 131.8x	K7SPV	S.P.V. ARC
Benson	448.8250	–	O 107.2e	WA7PIQ	WA7PIQ
Dragoon	449.7000	–	●telx	WA7PIQ	C.A.R.B.A.
Guthrie Peak	448.9750	–	●tlRBx	N7GP	J.P.A.R.A.
Guthrie Peak	449.3750	–	●t	K7EAR	E.A.A.R.S. Inc.
Heliograph Peak	440.6500	+	O 141.3x	K7EAR	E.A.A.R.S. Inc.
Heliograph Peak	440.7000	+	O 141.3ex	K7EAR	E.A.A.R.S. Inc.
Heliograph Peak	447.8250	–	O 100eRBx	K7EAR	E.A.A.R.S. Inc.
Heliograph Peak	448.6750	–	●telx	K7JEM	C.A.R.B.A.
Heliograph Peak	449.4000	–	●tex	K7EAR	E.A.A.R.S. Inc.
Juniper Flats	449.5250	–	O 100ex	K7RDG	C.A.R.A.
Mule Mtn	448.7500	–	●tRBx	KC7IM	C.A.R.B.A.
Oracle	448.7000	–	●tRB	WA7ELN	WA7ELN

Location	Output	Input	Notes	Call	Sponsor
Pinal Peak	448.1750	–	●tx	WB5QHS	J.P.A.R.A.
Pinal Peak	448.4250	–	O 103.5elx	KD7DR	S.A.R.B.A.
Pinal Peak	448.4750	–	O 100lx	W7ARA	A.R.A.
Pinal Peak	448.6500	–	●telRBx	WA7KUM	S.A.R.B.A.
Red Mountain	449.9500	–	●tel	W7JPI	C.A.R.B.A
Sierra Vista	444.1250	+	●t	W6SEL	Dx-Pony
Sierra Vista	447.9500	–	O 100el	K7RDG	C.A.R.A
Sierra Vista	449.8250	–	O 100ael	NØNBH	NØNBH
SOUTHWEST					
Oatman Mtn	448.3000	–	●tlx	KD7DR	S.A.R.B.A.
Telegraph Pass	448.6250	–	●tlRBx	W7SRC	Y.A.R.B.A.
Telegraph Pass	449.0750	–	O 88.5elx	W7DIN	D.I.N.
Yuma	445.6800	–	O 123 (CA)	KE7LVR	Peter Efroymson
Yuma	446.6000	–	O 162.2 (CA)	KD7GXW	Mark Buono
Yuma	449.9250	–	O 88.5el	W7DIN	D.I.N.
Yuma	449.9750	–	●t(CA)el RB	W7DIN	D.I.N.
TUCSON					
Catalina	440.4000	+	O 156.7e	WØHF	O.V.A.R.C
Marana	448.0000	–	O 100e	KC7CPB	Michael Ellis
Mt Lemmon	444.9250	+	O 156.7lx	K7RST	R.S. of T.
Mt Lemmon	448.5500	–	O 110.9ex	N7OEM	Pima County
Oro Valley	447.4250	–	● 107.2	WB7NUY	S.A.R.A.
Tucson	441.7500	+	O 107.2e	K7PCC	P.C.C.A.R.C.
Tucson	442.1500	+	●t(CA)e	AB7AA	AB7AA
Tucson	444.1000	+	O 156.7al	WØHF	O.V.A.R.C
Tucson	446.9000	–	O 100e	K7ICU	N7ZQT
Tucson	447.5000	–	O 136.5 (CA) RBx	N7XJQ	N7XJQ
Tucson	447.6250	–	●te	W7HSG	C.A.R.B.A.
Tucson	447.8750	–	●te	KB7RFI	KB7RFI
Tucson	448.3000	–	●tl	W7RAP	C.A.R.B.A.
Tucson	448.3250	–	O 156.7	K7RST	R.S. of T.
Tucson	448.7750	–	O 179.9l	W7SA	C.R.C.
Tucson	448.9000	–	●t(CA)el RB	KG7KV	S.P.A.R.C.
Tucson	448.9750	–	●t(CA)lRBx	N7CK	C.A.R.B.A.
Tucson	449.3000	–	O 156.7	K7RST	R.S. of T.
Tucson	449.4750	–	O 107.2 (CA)e	N7DQP	N7DQP
Tucson	449.6750	–	O 77	NR7J	N7OXL
Tucson	449.8000	–	Ot DCS(503)e	N1DHS	N1DHS
Vail	449.6250	–	O 123el	N7ZQT	K7ICU
WEST CENTRAL					
Black Peak	448.2750	–	●tlx	K6DLP	Don Petrone
Black Peak	448.6500	–	●telx	WB6VTM	Cactus Radio Club
Bullhead City	448.9500	–	O 123 (CA)	K7PFK	Paul Krick

Location	*Output*	*Input*	*Notes*	*Call*	*Sponsor*
Bullhead City	449.3750	–	O 123	K7REW	Darryl Whiteside
Bullhead City	449.9750	–	O 123	K7REW	Darryl Whiteside
Crossman Peak	447.5400	–	●tlx	WB6T	KB6CRE
Fort Mohave	449.9500	–	O 100x	K9TLT	Thomas L. Tatro
Golden Valley	448.4000	–	O 123 (CA) e	N7FK	N7FK
Golden Valley	448.5000	–	O 123 (CA)	K7MCH	K7MCH
Guadalupe Peak	448.9000	–	●tlx	WD6FM	Sw.R.R.C.
Guadalupe Peak	448.9750	–	●tlRBx	WB7FIK	Cactus Radio Clu
Hualapai Mtn	446.3000	–	O 123x	K3MK	Matt Krick
Hualapai Mtn	448.2500	–	O 131.8x	N7SKO	WECOM, INC
Kingman	446.1500	–	O 100e	W7KDS	N.A.D.R.S.
Lake Havasu City	448.7250	–	●tRB	W7DXJ	W7DXJ
Lake Havasu City	449.9500	–	O 141.3e	W7DXJ	W7DXJ
Oatman Mtn	448.6200	–	●telx	KF6BXP	Cactus Radio Clu
Parker	447.7250	–	●t	KE6PCV	KE6PCV
Potato Patch	448.1000	–	●tx	K6DLP	K6DLP
Potato Patch	448.6800	–	●telx	W6PNM	Cactus Radio Clu
Ram Peak	448.0200	–	●tx	WR7RAM	K7FY
Smith Peak	443.7750	+	O 100elx	W7ARA	A.R.A.
Topock	449.3500	–	O 67x	K6PNG	Ray Retzlaff

ARKANSAS

CENTRAL

Location	*Output*	*Input*	*Notes*	*Call*	*Sponsor*
Alexander	444.3000	+	O 131.8/131.8e	N5TKG	N5TKG
Bauxite	443.8250	+	O 141.3	KJ5ZT	KJ5ZT
Cabot	442.4750	+	O 85.4e	WA5JK	WA5JK
Cabot	442.5500	+	O 210.7ep	W5STR	STARS
Cabot	443.6500	+	O 82.5lrs WX	W5RHL	W5RHL
Center Ridge	444.1000	+	O 114.8e	N5XF	N5XF
Conway	443.5250	+	O 114.8	W5AUU	FaulkCoARC
Conway	443.8000	+	O 114.8	W5AUU	FalkCoARC
Conway	443.9750	+	O 114.8	W5AUU	W5AUU
Damascus	442.1000	+	O	KD5GMX	KD5GMX
Greers Ferry	443.6500	+	O 88.5lrs WX	W5RHL	W5RHL
Hot Springs	444.0000	+	O	WB5PIB	WB5PIB
Hot Springs	444.6000	+	O 114.8ers WXx	W5LVB	W5LVB
Hot Springs Village	444.7250	+	O 114.8	W5HSV	HSV ARC
Jacksonville	442.6000	+	O	N5KRN	N5KRN
Little Rock	443.0000	+	O 100.0elr sWX	N5CG	CAUHF
Little Rock	443.1250	+	O 114.8el	AC5XV	AC5XV
Little Rock	443.2000	+	O 114.8elr sWX	N5CG	CAUHF

Location	Output	Input	Notes	Call	Sponsor
Little Rock	444.0750	+	● 114.8	WA5OOY	WA5OOY
Little Rock	444.2000	+	○ 114.8el	W5DI	CAREN
Little Rock	444.4000	+	○ 114.8l	WA5OOY	WA5OOY
Little Rock	444.4500	+	○ 100.0	W5FD	CAREN
Little Rock	444.8000	+	● 146.2e WX	K5XT	K5XT
Little Rock	444.8500	+	○ 114.8lrs WX	N5CG	CAUHF
Malvern	442.2250	+	○ 114.8el	N5CG	CAUHF
Malvern	443.5000	+	○ 136.5ael WXx	W5BXJ	W5BXJ
Malvern	443.6000	+	○ 114.8 (CA)elrsWX	N5CG	CAUHF
Malvern	444.1500	+	○ 88.5elx	K5TAC	K5TAC
Maumelle	442.7000	+	○ 114.8ae	K6MFM	K6MFM
North Little Rock	442.3250	+	○ 85.4/85.4	NT5LA	ElksARC
North Little Rock	443.9000	+	○ 114.8	N5QLC	N5QLC
North Little Rock	444.6500	+	○ 114.8	W5RXU	W5RXU
North Little Rock	444.7000	+	○ 114.8elr sWX	N5CG	CAUHF
Prattsville	442.8750	+	○ 85.4/85.4	KD5RTO	PVARC
White Hall	442.1750	+	○ 85.4ers	KJ5PE	PinBlufARC
White Hall	443.7000	+	○esWX	AF5AR	WhtHallCC
Wrightsville	444.4250	+	○ 85.4el	N5CG	CAUHF
EAST					
Forrest City	443.4500	+	○ 100.0/100.0	KD5DF	KD5DF
Helena	444.8750	+	○ 91.5x	N5JLJ	N5JLJ
EAST CENTRAL					
Searcy	444.5000	+	○ 192.8e	N5QS	NCAARS
Stuttgart	443.2500	+	○	KB5LN	KB5LN
Vilonia	444.8250	+	○ 84.5e	W5AMI	W5AMI
NORTH					
Green Forest	442.4500	+	○WX	KE5LXK	NWAUHF
Harrison	442.9000	+	○	N5NBJ	N5NBJ
Harrison	443.5000	+	○elx	KCØUJZ	KC0UJZ
Harrison	444.8500	+	○ 100.0l	WA9SSO	GathMtARC
Mountain Home	442.3000	+	○ 103.5/103.5e	K5OZK	OZARC
Mountain Home	442.5500	+	s	K5BAX	K5BAX
Mountain Home	443.1250	+	○	K5FOY	K5FOY
Mountain Home	444.0000	+	○ 100.0	WB5NFC	WB5NFC
Mountain Home	444.9750	+	○ 100.0lRB	WB5NFC	NAR VoIP
Mtn View	442.8500	+	○ 97.4/97.4 ex	KF5BZP	WRMC ARC
Yellville	444.0250	+	○e	W5YS	Marion Cty
NORTH CENTRAL					
Clinton	443.3000	+	○ 114.8el	W5DI	CAREN
Quitman	444.0500	+	○ 127.3e	KC5PLA	KC5PLA

Location	Output	Input	Notes	Call	Sponsor
NORTHEAST					
Batesville	444.2500	+	O 94.8rs WX	KD5HPK	KD5HPK
Batesville	444.7500	+	O 94.8 WX	KD5AYE	KD5AYE
Batesville	444.9000	+	O 94.8rs	KD5HPK	KD5HPK
Black Rock	442.4000	+	O	W5WEC	W5WEC
Dell	444.6500	+	O 131.8e L(146.670)rsWX	W5ENL	MissCoARA
Harrisburg	444.5250	+	O	N5OHO	PARC
Jonesboro	443.1500	+	O 107.2e	K5NEA	NEARC
Jonesboro	443.5750	+	O 100.0er WX	KE5HKW	CC RACES
Jonesboro	443.8750	+	O	W5FGD	W5FGD
Jonesboro	444.4750	+	Ol	K5CRS	K5CRS
Jonesboro	444.6000	+	O 107.2el	NI5A	AISTC
Lake City	444.3250	+	OersWX	KC5TEL	RESPOND
Trumann	443.5000	+	O 107.2l	NI5A	AISTC
NORTHWEST					
Bentonville	442.9500	+	O 97.4	KE5LXK	NWAUHF
Berryville	443.8000	+	O 100.0/100.0	N6WI	------------
Brentwood	442.0750	+	O 97.3	KE5LXK	NWAUHF
Cedarville	444.9000	+	O 141.3/141.3e	W5BUB	W5BUB
Decatur	442.8500	+	O 123.0/123.0l	N5UXE	N5UXE
Decatur	443.9250	+	O 114.8/114.8lx	N5UXE	N5UXE
Elkins	444.1750	+	O	K5HOG	K5HOG
Eureka Springs	444.4750	+	O 110.9ers WX	WC5AR	WashCoEM
Farmington	442.5250	+	O 103.5	KC5PET	KC5PET
Fayetteville	442.5000	+	O	AB5UB	AmRedCross
Fayetteville	443.1000	+	O(CA)el	KA9UBD	KA9UBD
Fayetteville	443.1500	+	O	KA5TGN	KA5TGN
Fayetteville	444.0750	+	O 141.3/141.3	W4GYV	W4GYV
Fayetteville	444.9250	+	O	N5SRA	N5SRA
Ozone	442.6250	+	Oe	KC5LVW	KC5LVW
Prairie Grove	444.7000	+	Oe L(224.6(-))	WA5VTW	WA5VTW
Rogers - Mercy	443.1750	+	O 97.4e	N5KWL	N5KWL
Rudy	443.7250	+	● 123.0ers WX	KD5ZMO	CCARC
Siloam Spgs	444.3250	+	O 114.8e	N5YEI	N5YEI
Springdale	442.0500	+	O 110.9ael	WC5AR	WC5AR
Springdale	443.6500	+	O	WA5NUO	WA5NUO
SOUTH					
Crossett	444.9750	+	O 127.3e	N5SEA	SEAARC

Location	*Output*	*Input*	*Notes*	*Call*	*Sponsor*
SOUTH CENTRAL					
Sheridan	444.9000	+	O 114.8	KB5ZES	Grant ARC
SOUTHEAST					
Monticello	444.8250	+	O 127.3/127.3lx	W5GIF	W5GIF
SOUTHWEST					
Arkadelphia	444.8750	+	O 114.8e	KB5ILY	KB5ILY
Athens	444.9750	+	O 88.5/88.5 esx	KD5NUP	HowCoSAR
Dequeen	444.8000	+	O 85.4	WA5LTA	SWARC
Manning	444.6750	+	O 114.8/114.8elWX	W5RHS	W5RHS
Nashville	444.3500	+	O 88.5/88.5 esWX	N5BAB	N5BAB
Nashville	444.9750	+	O 88.5/88.5 es	KD5NUP	HowCoSAR
Willisville	444.9250	+	O 100.0l	KB5ROZ	ARKLA
WEST					
Fort Smith	444.3000	+	O 88.5l	W5ANR	FSAARC
Hartford	442.4250	+	O 136.5e	WD5MHZ	WD5MHZ
Mena	443.3500	+	O 100.0#er sWXx	W5HUM	Oua ARA
Mt Magazine	442.8250	+	Oex	WD5MHZ	WD5MHZ
Van Buren	444.7750	+	Ot	KC5YQB	KC5YQB
WEST CENTRAL					
Mount Ida	444.4750	+	O 114.8ex	KA5WPC	KA5WPC
Mt Magazine	443.2500	+	O 123.0/123.0 WX	N5XMZ	N5XMZ
Ola	444.5500	+	Oa	WA5YHN	WA5YHN
Russellville	442.7500	+	O 114.8e	K5RLB	K5RLB
Russellville	443.4000	+	O	K5PXP	ARVARF
Russellville	443.5750	+	O 114.8	K5PXP	ARVARF
Russellville	444.5750	+	O 114.8e	W5MAN	W5MAN
WESTCENTRAL					
Lake Dardanelle	443.8750	+	O 79.9/79.9 RB	WD5B	WD5B

CALIFORNIA

FREQUENCY USAGE - SOUTHERN CALIFORNIA

So Cal	431.0000		O	PACKET	
So Cal	439.0000		O	PACKET	
So Cal	440.0000		O	SIMPLEX	
So Cal	441.5000		O	PACKET	
So Cal	441.5200		O	CONTROL	
So Cal	444.4600		O	SIMPLEX	
So Cal	445.0000		O	SIMPLEX	
So Cal	446.0000		O	SIMPLEX	
So Cal	446.5000		O	SIMPLEX	
So Cal	446.5200		O	SIMPLEX	

Location	*Output*	*Input*	*Notes*	*Call*	*Sponsor*
So Cal	446.8600	–	○	TESTPAIR	
So Cal	446.8800	–	○	TESTPAIR	
So Cal	449.4600		○	SIMPLEX	
So Cal ATV	439.5000		○	SIMPLEX	
E SIERRA/TAHOE					
Tahoe City	440.9250	+	● 94.8l	KH8AF	KH8AF
Tahoe City	442.1750	+	○ 167.9l	KH6AF	KH8AF
Truckee	440.7000	+	○ 131.8el	W6SAR	W6SAR
EASTERN SIERRAS					
Bishop	444.2000	+	● 94.8	K6BDI	K6BDI
Bishop	444.7250	+	● 131.8e	W6KGB	W6KGB
Bishop	444.8000	+	○ 88.5	WA6ZFT	WA6ZFT
Laws	444.6500	+	○ 94.8	WA6TLW	WA6TLW
NORCAL-CENTRAL COAST					
Aptos	441.9250	+	○ 100	WA6HHQ	WA6HHQ
Arroyo Grande	443.9750	+	○ 127.3elrs	W6SLO	SLOECC
Bonny Doon	441.3000	+	○ 156.7#a	WB6ECE	WB6ECE RG
Bonny Doon	441.3000	+	○ 100#elx	WB6ECE	WB6ECE RG
Carmel	443.8000	+	○ 110.9el	KG6UYZ	KG6UYZ
Coalinga	441.8250	+	●x	K6INC	SCAN INT'L
Greenfield	442.0750	+	○ 114.8el	K6LNK	CARLA
Grover Beach	442.0250	+	○ 100	N6ADU	A UNTALAN
King City	441.6500	+	○ 94.8elrsx	N6SPD	N6SPD RG
King City	443.9750	+	●lx	WB6FRM	NCCRA
King City	444.0750	+	●#elsx	WB6ORK	WB6ORK
King City	444.5500	+	●ex	W6FM	W6FM
Lompoc	443.2750	+	●el	K7AZ	K7AZ
Lompoc	444.8000	+	●ls	WA6VPL	WA6VPL
Los Osos	444.9750	+	○ 127.3ers	WB6MIA	SLOECC
Monterey	440.4500	+	○ 110.9#ael	KG6NRI	KG6NRI
Monterey	441.3000	+	○ 136.5#ex	WB6ECE	WB6ECE RG
Monterey	441.3250	+	●elrs	WE6R	WE6R
Monterey	441.6500	+	○ 123aelrsx	N6SPD	N6SPD RG
Monterey	444.2750	+	○ 100aelrsx	N6SPD	N6SPD RG
Monterey	444.5250	+	○ 123ersx	W6JSO	W6JSO
Monterey	444.7000	+	○ 123ers	K6LY	NPSARC
Nipomo	443.7000	+	○ 100#	KA7DXP	KA7DXP
Nipomo	444.2750	+	●	WA6VPL	WA6VPL
Nipomo	444.7000	+	○ 100#e	KB6Q	KB6Q
Panoche	442.6500	+	○ 141.3e	WR6E	AC6E
Paso Robles	442.6750	+	○ 110.9ae	W6HD	RadioRanch
Pismo Beach	444.6000	+	○ 131.8e	KB6BF	KB6BF
Prunedale	441.1250	+	○ 123#	KC6UDC	KC6UDC

Location	*Output*	*Input*	*Notes*	*Call*	*Sponsor*
Prunedale	442.7750	+	O 110.9l	KG6NRI	KG6NRI
Prunedale	443.9000	+	O 123ers	N6SPD	N6SPD RG
Salinas	440.7000	+	O 100l	W6RTF	w6rtf
Salinas	441.4500	+	O 123ersx	K6JE	FPRA
Salinas	442.0250	+	O 146.2#el	N6LEX	CCARN
Salinas	442.6000	+	O 110.9el	KG6UYZ	KG6UYZ
Salinas	443.6000	+	O 110.9ex	W6MOW	W6MOW
San Simeon	444.1000	+	O 127.3elrsx	KD6EKH	SLOECC
SanLuis Obispo	443.5000	+	O 100elx	K6LNK	CARLA
SanLuisObispo	441.0750	+	O 94.8#	WB6JWB	WB6JWB
SanLuisObispo	442.3000	+	O 127.3elrs	W6BHZ	CPARC
SanLuisObispo	442.7000	+	O 127.3#ersx	WB6FMC	WB6FMC
SanLuisObispo	442.8750	+	●#elrsx	WB6FMC	WB6FMC
SanLuisObispo	443.5750	+	●ex	W6FM	W6FM
SanLuisObispo	443.8000	+	●#el	N6HYM	N6HYM
SanLuisObispo	444.0500	+	O 127.3elrsx	KF6QYJ	SLOECC
SanLuisObispo	444.4750	+	●elx	W6FM	W6FM
SanLuisObispo	444.5250	+	O 127.3ex	W6FM	W6FM
SanLuisObispo	444.9000	+	●e	KC6WRD	FCC
Santa Cruz	440.5500	+	O 94.8#els	AB6VS	LPARC
Santa Cruz	440.8500	+	O 94.8aersx	W6JWS	W6JWS
Santa Cruz	440.9250	+	O 123ers	K6BJ	SCCARC
Santa Cruz	441.6750	+	Oers	K6BJ	SCCARC
Santa Cruz	443.4750	+	O 127.3#elrs	WB6PHE	WB6PHE
Santa Cruz	443.6750	+	O 136.5aes	WA6NMF	WA6NMF
SantaMargarita	444.1500	+	O 127.3elrsx	W6SLO	SLOECC
Scotts Valley	444.0000	+	O 94.8l	W6WLS	W6WLS
Soledad	440.5250	+	O 146.2#el	N6LEX	CCARN
Soledad	444.3750	+	O 100er	WA6RQX	WEST COAST
Watsonville	443.0500	+	O 94.8ers	K6RMW	K6RMWK6GDI
Watsonville	443.3500	+	O 123#	KB6MET	KB6MET
NORCAL-EAST BAY					
Alameda	444.5750	+	O 88.5#es	K6QLF	A.R.C.A
Alamo CA	444.8750	+	●e	KK6XK	KK6XK
Antioch	440.6500	+	O 127.3ers	K6RGK	O.T.H.E.R.
Antioch	444.7250	+	O 114.8l	KD6QDW	NORCALRUG
Bakersfield	442.7500	+	O 141.3elrx	WA6RQX	WCRN
Berkeley	440.1750	+	O 156.7x	K6GOD	K6GOD
Berkeley	440.8250	+	O 114.8lx	WI6H	WI6H
Berkeley	440.9000	+	O 131.8ers	N6BRK	NALCO

Location	*Output*	*Input*	*Notes*	*Call*	*Sponsor*
Berkeley	440.9250	+	●DCSelx	KH8AF	KH8AF
Berkeley	442.2750	+	O 100#	WA6ZTY	WA6ZTY
Berkeley	442.6750	+	●elsx	WB6UZX	WB6UZX
Berkeley	442.7250	+	●elx	K6DJR	CALNET
Berkeley	443.1750	+	O 179.9x	K6ATF	K6ATF and
Concord	440.3000	+	●aelx	N6AMG	ERG
Concord	440.3250	+	●#lx	WB6FRM	NCCRA
Concord	440.8750	+	O 79.7aelrsx	WA6HAM	CCRA
Concord	441.2000	+	●aelx	N6GVI	CATS
Concord	441.3250	+	O 100aelrsx	W6CX	MDARC
Concord	441.7500	+	●elrx	W6YOP	YOP HLLS
Concord	442.4500	+	●ersx	KI6O	KI6O
Concord	443.5750	+	●#elx	K6IRC	ARN
Concord	443.8000	+	O 100ex	K6POU	MDRA
Danville	440.6500	+	Ol	N6TRB	W6FQ
Dublin	442.1500	+	O 123ael	WD6INC	W1LLE
El Cerrito	444.7000	+	●ael	N6GVI	CATS
Fremont	440.0000	+	O 110.9l	WA6FSP	WA6FSP
Fremont	440.1750	+	O 131.8ersx	K6GOD	SPV FIRE
Fremont	441.1250	+	O 100#e	KC6WXO	ACWDRC
Fremont	441.1250	+	O 100es	N3MMQ	ACWD
Fremont	442.6000	+	O 107.2	WA6PWW	TRICO ARC
Fremont	443.4000	+	●ex	WA6KPX	YAARC
Fremont	443.7000	+	O 136.5elx	K6JJC	RMRG
Fremont	443.7250	+	O 127.3elrsx	N6HWI	WB6PHE
Fremont	444.8000	+	●erx	WA6GEL	Red Carpet
Hayward	440.0500	+	O 156.7	KQ6YG	KQ6YG
Hayward	440.1750	+	O 131.8e	K6GOD	GOD
Hayward	440.4750	+	O 71.9aels	KK6AN	NorCal RUG
Hayward	440.9500	+	O 100	KB6LED	KB6LED
Hayward	441.8000	+	●l	KQ6RC	KQ6RC
Hayward	442.1000	+	O 141.3lx	W6JMX	W6JMX
Hayward	442.3500	+	O 107.2	K6GOD	GOD
Hayward	442.8750	+	O 100	K6DDR	K6DDR
Hayward	443.3250	+	O 114.8el	K6LNK	CARLA
Hayward	444.5500	+	O 77	K6EMV	K6EMV
Hayward	444.8250	+	O 127.3#ers	K6EAG	Hayward RC
Livermore	444.1250	+	O 100e	K7FED	K7FED
Martinez	444.4500	+	O 107.2ers	KF6HTE	MtzARC
Monterey	442.2250	+	●e	WH6KA	WH6KA
Moraga	442.4500	+	●ersx	KI6O	KI6O
Newark	444.1500	+	O 103.5e	N3EL	DX2N CLUB
Oakland	440.3500	+	O 123elrs	KM6EF	GSARC
Oakland	440.4000	+	●elx	WB6WTM	WB6WTM

Location	*Output*	*Input*	*Notes*	*Call*	*Sponsor*
Oakland	440.5750	+	O 118.8ersx	W6EBW	EBMUD
Oakland	441.2250	+	O 100#lx	W6RCA	W6RCA
Oakland	441.4250	+	O 114.8	WT6L	WT6L
Oakland	441.4750	+	O 127.3lrx	W6YOP	YOP HLLS
Oakland	442.2000	+	●elx	KH8AF	KH8AF
Oakland	442.2500	+	O 103.5lx	KD6QDW	KD6QDW
Oakland	442.4000	+	O 77aersx	WB6NDJ	ORCA
Oakland	443.2000	+	●aelx	N6GVI	CATS
Oakland	443.3500	+	O 186.2rsx	AC6OT	OARC
Oakland	443.3750	+	O 114.8#ex	WB6SHU	W6BUR
Oakland	443.4750	+	O 100	N6QOP	CARLA
Oakland	443.8750	+	●l	W6MTF	W6MTF
Oakland	443.9750	+	O 100elx	WW6BAY	Bay Net
Oakland	444.2500	+	O 100ex	WB6TCS	WB6TCS
Oakland	444.6500	+	●#lx	W6PUE	NORCAL
Oakland	444.6750	+	●#elx	W6RCA	W6CBS
Oakland	444.7250	+	O 114.8	KK6RQ	KK6RQ
Oakland	444.8000	+	●#	KD6GLT	KD6GLT
Orinda	440.6250	+	O 79.7aelrsx	WA6HAM	CCRA
Orinda	441.9750	+	●#elx	W6CBS	W6CBS
Orinda	443.0500	+	O 114.8el	N6QOP	CARLA
Orinda	443.5000	+	Oel	K6LNK	CARLA
Orinda	443.8250	+	O 136.5elx	K6JJC	RMRG
Orinda	444.7750	+	O 127.3lrx	W6YOP	YOP HLLS
Pittsburg	440.1250	+	Oaelrsx	K6PIT	K6BIV
Pittsburg	442.6500	+	●l	KF6ZOO	KF6ZOO
Pleasanton	442.0750	+	O 103.5el	K6LNK	CARLA
Pleasanton	442.6250	+	O 94.8elrsx	W6SRR	Sunol Ridg
Pleasanton	442.9250	+	●rx	W6RGG	W6RGG
Pleasanton	443.6500	+	●DCSx	K6TEA	K6TEA
Pleasanton	444.2750	+	Oel	N6LDJ	HORK
Richmond	440.9750	+	●#e	K6LOU	K6LOU
Richmond	442.1500	+	O 100ae	WA6DUR	WA6DUR
Richmond Heigh	441.6500	+	O 100l	K6JSI	WIN System
San Francisco	441.5750	+	O 146.2l	KC6IAU	KC6IAU
San Leandro	442.7750	+	●#el	KB6NCL	KG6KCL
San Leandro	444.2000	+	O 107.2er	W6RGG	AC RACES
San Pablo	444.2750	+	O 82.5ers	WA6KQB	CCCC
San Ramon	440.4250	+	O 79.7aelrsx	WA6HAM	CCRA
San Ramon	442.5500	+	●#	N6APB	N6APB
South San Fran	440.6000	+	●l	KR6WP	KR6WP
Union City	441.9250	+	O 88.5al	AA6QP	THROPA MPL
Walnut Creek	442.5250	+	O 88.5e	K6MFM	K6MFM
Walnut Creek	443.4750	+	O 114.8el	K6LNK	CARLA

Location	Output	Input	Notes	Call	Sponsor
NORCAL-NORTH BAY					
American Canyo	443.9000	+	O 173.8el	W6FMG	MARRN
Benicia	441.2500	+	O 100er	KR6BEN	BeniciaARC
Benicia	442.7500	+	O 100aer	KR6BEN	BeniciaARC
Calistoga	441.6750	+	O 123elrx	WA7G	WIN System
Calistoga	441.9000	+	O 151.4ers x	W6CO	SARS
Calistoga	444.1500	+	●elrsx	N6PMF	YOP HLLS
Calistoga	444.1750	+	O 151.4el	N6TKW	NARC
Calistoga	444.4750	+	●#elx	K6IRC	ARN
Clear Lake	442.8250	+	●elx	WR6COP	K6COP
Cobb	442.8750	+	O#e	KE6QDW	KE6QDW
Geyserville	442.0500	+	O 100#e	WA6OYK	WA6OYK
Geyserville	443.4750	+	O 110.9el	K6LNK	CARLA
Kelseyville	441.3500	+	O 100#ex	KG6UFR	CRS
Kelseyville	441.4250	+	O 100#ex	N6GJM	CDF/VIP
Laytonville	440.8250	+	O 114.8el	WI6H	WI6H
Mill Valley	440.9250	+	●DCSel	KH8AF	KH8AF
Mill Valley	442.2000	+	ODCSelx	KH8AF	KH8AF
Mill Valley	443.2500	+	O 179.9erx	K6GWE	ACS
Mill Valley	444.6750	+	●#elx	KJ6RA	Patio RS
Napa	440.0500	+	Oers	W6CO	SARS
Napa	440.8500	+	O 173.8#a e	N6NAR	NARS
Napa	441.6750	+	O 107.2erx	WA7G	WA7G
Napa	441.8000	+	O 151.4aer	W6CO	SARS
Napa	442.2500	+	O 151.4elr	N6TKW	HAMSEXY
Napa	443.4500	+	O 127.3er	WU7Q	WU7Q
Napa	444.5250	+	OaDCSel	K6ZRX	K6ZRX
Novato	440.2500	+	●aelx	N6GVI	CATS
Novato	440.9250	+	●DCSelx	KH8AF	KH8AF
Novato	442.2000	+	●elx	KH8AF	KH8AF
Novato	443.6000	+	●elsx	KI6B	SMRS
Petaluma	444.2250	+	●elr	NI6B	SMRS
Pt Reyes Stn	444.5250	+	●el	WB6TMS	SMRS
San Anselmo	440.5500	+	O 100#	W6RV	WY8T
San Rafael	440.9250	+	●DCSel	KH8AF	KH8AF
San Rafael	442.1750	+	●DCSel	KH8AF	KH8AF
San Rafael	443.5250	+	O 82.5er	K6GWE	ACS
Santa Rosa	440.2000	+	O 88.5elrs	KD6CJQ	KD6CJQ
Santa Rosa	440.4500	+	O 88.5	K6EAR	EARA
Santa Rosa	441.3000	+	O 88.5lrs	KV6A	SKM
Santa Rosa	441.3750	+	O 114.8es	W6SON	SCRA
Santa Rosa	444.3750	+	●lrx	WB6RUT	WB6RUT
Santa Rosa	444.9000	+	O 88.5#es	KF6SZA	KF6SZA
Sausalito	442.5250	+	O 114.8e	K6ER	K6ER
Sebastopol	441.1000	+	O 192.8ers	WA6FUL	WA6FUL
Sebastopol	441.3750	+	O 88.5ers	W6SON	SCRA
Sebastopol	442.3250	+	●el	N6AMG	ERG

Location	Output	Input	Notes	Call	Sponsor
Sebastopol	443.4250	+	O 114.8elrs	WA6FUL	Seb C ERT
Sebastopol	444.8250	+	O 131.8	WA6TIP	WA6TIP
Vallejo	442.8500	+	●l	K6INC	SCAN INT'L
Willits	444.1500	+	●elr	WB6TMS	SMRS
Yountville	444.7250	+	O 151.4es	N6TKW	NARC
NORCAL-NORTH COAST					
Crescent City	442.5250	+	O 127.3ael	KA7PRR	KA7PRR
Crescent City	443.0500	+	O 100#	KD6GDZ	KD6GDZ
Eureka	442.0000	+	O 100#	AE6R	AE6R
Eureka	442.2250	+	●elrx	WA6RQX	WA6RQX
Hopland	444.7500	+	O 100elrx	WA6RQX	WA6RQX
Hopland	444.8750	+	O 141.3#elr	WA6RQX	SMRA
Laytonville	443.0000	+	O 100l	K6JSI	WIN System
Laytonville	444.8000	+	●elrx	WA6RQX	WA6RQX
McKinleyville	440.1000	+	O 100e	KJ6BDK	ESARA
Pt Arena	443.0750	+	O 100el	N6MVT	CARLA
Scotia	443.2500	+	O 103.5#l	K6FWR	FWRA
Smith River	443.1000	+	O 100#l	K6SLS	WIN System
Ukiah	440.0250	+	O 141.3elrx	WA6RQX	SMRA
Ukiah	440.8500	+	O 141.3elr	WA6RQX	WA6RQX
Ukiah	444.0750	+	O 141.3elr	WA6RQX	WCRN
Ukiah	444.7750	+	O 141.3elr	WA6RQX	WCRN
Willits	440.0750	+	●elrx	WA6RQX	WA6RQX
Willits	443.1750	+	O 123elx	K7WWA	K7WWA
Willits	444.5000	+	O 103.5ex	WD6FGX	LLVRG
Willits	444.9250	+	O 100elrsx	K7WWA	K7WWA
NORCAL-NORTH EAST					
Alturas	441.2250	+	O 100#el	K6PRN	KJ6RA
Alturas	442.3500	+	O 85.4#ex	WB6HMD	WB6HMD
Bella Vista	444.6250	+	O 107.2	W6DY	W6DY
Burney	440.2500	+	O 103.5#	KI6WG	KI6WG
Burney	440.7500	+	O 123el	K6LNK	CARLA
Canby	444.6750	+	O 156.7#el	K6PRN	KJ6RA
Chester	444.5000	+	O 103.5e	KF6CCP	KF6CCP
Cohasset	444.1250	+	●DCSlx	KH8AF	KH8AF
Lakehead	442.1750	+	●ex	KH8AF	KH8AF
McCloud	443.4750	+	O 100l	K6JKL	CARLA
Mineral	440.9750	+	O 100#elx	N6TZG	N6TZG
Mount Shasta	444.8750	+	O 167.9aelx	KH8AF	KH8AF
Mt Shasta City	444.3500	+	●#elx	K6PRN	Patio RS
Mt Shasta City	444.4750	+	O 100#aelsx	K7TVL	Ore Conn
Mt Shasta City	444.8250	+	O 100e	AB6MF	AB6MF
Quincy	440.7250	+	O 100el	K6LNK	CARLA
Quincy	441.6250	+	O 100#x	W6RCA	W6CBS

Location	Output	Input	Notes	Call	Sponsor
Quincy	444.7000	+	○ 123#ers	KR6G	KR6G
Red Bluff	444.1500	+	●lx	KH8AF	KH8AF
Redding	440.0500	+	●#elx	NAØSA	N.A.S.A.
Redding	442.8500	+	●el	WR6TV	W6QWN
Redding	443.0500	+	○ 110.9#el	WR6TV	W6QWN
Redding	444.3250	+	○ 100elx	K6LNK	CARLA
Redding	444.5500	+	○ 100#elrsx	NC6SV	SCARS
Redding	444.6500	+	○ 131.8	KD6LOM	KD6LOM
Shasta Lake	442.0750	+	○ 114.8el	K6JKL	CARLA
Susanville	443.9000	+	○ 91.5elsx	K6LRC	K6LRC
Susanville	444.9750	+	○ 91.5elrsx	K6LRC	K6LRC
Westwood	442.2000	+	●DCSelx	KH8AF	KH8AF
Yreka	443.7500	+	○ 100aelrx	K6SIS	SCARA
Yreka	444.4250	+	●#elx	K6PRN	Patio RS
Yreka	444.9000	+	○ 100e	AB6MF	AB6MF
NORCAL-SACRAMENTO VALLEY					
Alleghany	444.9250	+	○ 88.5x	WR6ASF	WA6HWT
Auburn	440.5750	+	○ 94.8e	W6EK	SFARC
Auburn	443.6000	+	○ 141.3#elx	N6LYE	N6LYE
Auburn	444.4750	+	○ 162.2	KO6KD	KO6KD
Auburn	444.5000	+	○ 94.8#ex	WA6IOK	GBAY
Auburn	444.6000	+	○ 192.8e	N6NMZ	N6NMZ
Auburn	444.9000	+	○ 94.8#	W6CUL	W6CUL
Auburn	444.9250	+	○ 151.4#	AB6LI	AB6LI
Cameron Park	440.1250	+	●aelx	N6RDE	N6RDE
Camino	441.2250	+	○ 82.5#aelx	N6YBH	N6YBH
Chico	440.0000	+	○ 100ers	KI6PNB	KI6PNB
Chico	440.5000	+	●a	WA6UHF	WA6UHF
Chico	440.5500	+	●el	WB6RHC	WB6RHC
Chico	440.6500	+	○ 110.9aesx	W6RHC	GEARS
Chico	440.6750	+	●#elrsx	N6EJX	N6EJX
Chico	440.9000	+	○ 110.9er	W6SCR	Butte SCR
Chico	441.2250	+	○ 114.8#	W6CBS	W6CBS
Chico	441.4000	+	○ 110.9#elx	WB6RHC	WB6RHC
Chico	442.3750	+	○ 100ex	W6ECE	CARA
Chico	444.4000	+	○ 136.5#	KE6ADC	BARE
Citrus Heights	441.1750	+	○ 123e	KG6ZTE	PARA
Citrus Heights	444.7250	+	●ae	KA6FTY	KA6FTY
Colfax	440.9500	+	○ 192.8l	N6NMZ	N6NMZ
Cool	440.9750	+	●	N6TZG	N6TZG
Diamond Spring	444.0750	+	●lx	W6AW	ADC Assc.
Dixon	444.5250	+	●l	K6JWN	K6JWN
El Dorado	444.8000	+	●	N2THD	The Group

Location	*Output*	*Input*	*Notes*	*Call*	*Sponsor*
El Dorado Hill	441.1000	+	O 123el	N6QDY	N6QDY
ElDoradoHills	444.4500	+	O 85.4#aelx	WT6G	WT6G
Elk Creek	444.2000	+	O 100#ersx	N6YCK	N6YCK
Esparto	441.1250	+	O 127.3#lrx	K6SCA	RMRG
Fair Oaks	440.7250	+	O 162.2ex	WB6HEV	PARE
Fairfield	440.9250	+	●DCSelx	KH8AF	KH8AF
Fairfield	441.1500	+	O 77elr	K6SOL	SCARS
Fairfield	442.2250	+	●elx	KH8AF	KH8AF
Fairfield	442.7750	+	O 77e	KC6UJM	KC6UJM
Fairfield	443.4000	+	●	WL3DZ	DX-PINOY
Fiddletown	443.8750	+	O 156.7elrx	K6SZQ	RMRG
Folsom	440.3500	+	O 156.7elx	AB6LI	AB6LI
Folsom	442.3500	+	O 136.5e	KS6HRP	SHARP
Folsom	442.5250	+	O 77ae	K6MFM	K6MFM
Folsom	443.1250	+	O 100e	W6YDD	YDD 1.2
Foresthill	442.7000	+	O 114.8#ae	KA6ZRJ	KA6ZRJ
Foresthill	442.8750	+	O 131.8ae	N6NMZ	PCSAR
Georgetown	441.5750	+	●#lx	K6IRC	ARN
Georgetown	443.5500	+	●lx	K6SRA	NCCRA
Georgetown	443.8500	+	●#x	WA6APX	WA6APX
Grass Valley	440.1000	+	O 151.4lsx	KO6CW	KO6CW
Grass Valley	440.5250	+	O 192.8aelx	KB6LCS	KB6LCS
Grass Valley	441.0250	+	O 100#elx	W6RCA	W6CBS
Grass Valley	442.1500	+	O 151.4	AB6LI	AB6LI
Grass Valley	442.4250	+	●elx	KF6GLZ	N6ZN
Grass Valley	442.6250	+	O 151.4#	W6AI	W6AI
Grass Valley	442.9500	+	O 107.2#el	N6VYQ	INTERCITY
Grass Valley	443.0250	+	O 114.8aelrsx	WA6WER	CPRA
Grass Valley	443.6500	+	O 118.8es	KG6BAJ	CPRA
Grass Valley	444.0500	+	O 136.5ex	K6NP	GBTPRC
Grass Valley	444.7500	+	O 167.9e	K6RTL	NCAA
Jackson	443.6750	+	O 156.7elx	W6LP	RMRG
Kelsey	444.8250	+	●#	W6TIQ	W6TIQ
Lincoln	443.2250	+	O 167.9el	W6LHR	LHARG
Lotus	441.7250	+	O 82.5ls	AG6AU	EDCARC
Marysville	440.4250	+	O 123#	KG6PND	KG6PND
Marysville	443.3250	+	O 136.5elx	K6JJC	RMRG
Maxwell	442.2750	+	O 100el	N6NMZ	Patio RS
Mt Shasta	440.2750	+	O 118.8elrx	N6QGZ	WA6YOP
Nevada City	444.9500	+	O 100e	W6JP	W6JP
Oroville	441.4750	+	O 114.8elrx	W6YOP	YOP HLLS

Location	*Output*	*Input*	*Notes*	*Call*	*Sponsor*
Oroville	442.3500	+	○ 110.9ex	WA6UHF	WA6UHF
Placerville	440.7000	+	○ 123elx	WA6BTH	P&F
Placerville	441.0500	+	○ 127.3#	N6UUI	TEL PNRS
Placerville	441.6250	+	●#e	W6RCA	W6CBS
Placerville	442.4750	+	○ 110.9lx	WA6BTH	P&F
Placerville	443.9250	+	○ 179.9aes	N6QDY	CARUN
Plymouth	442.0500	+	○ 156.7lx	K6SCA	RMRG
Pollock Pines	442.4750	+	○ 123#aelx	WA6KQV	P&F
Quincy	441.9250	+	○ 127.3lx	W6PBX	WA6YOP
Red Bluff	442.4000	+	○ 110.9#e	W6QWN	W6QWN
Red Bluff	442.9500	+	○ 67elx	KI6FEO	KI6FEO
Red Bluff	443.1000	+	○ 100#	N6YCK	N6YCK
Redding	444.1000	+	○ 131.8#	KD6LOM	KD6LOM
Rescue	441.2500	+	●es	W7KEZ	W7KEZ
Rocklin	442.9500	+	○ 67el	KI6FEO	KI6FEO
Roseville	442.1250	+	○ 179.9#	N6UG	N6UG
Roseville	442.5750	+	○ 162.2e	KD6PDD	HPARCS
Roseville	444.3500	+	○ 114.8e	K6GBM	GBM School
Sacramento	440.2000	+	○ 131.8	KU6P	SCCESA
Sacramento	441.4500	+	○ 100#alr	KJ6KO	KJ6KO
Sacramento	441.7750	+	●er	N6ICW	N6ICW
Sacramento	441.8500	+	○ 77#e	NA6DF	SHARK
Sacramento	441.9500	+	○ 151.4#el	K6YC	K6YC
Sacramento	442.3250	+	●#elx	KF6BIK	W6GU
Sacramento	442.4000	+	●#elx	WB6GWZ	WB6GWZ
Sacramento	442.5000	+	○ 151.4#esx	WA6ZZK	WA6ZZK
Sacramento	442.6000	+	○ 100	N6NA	RCARCS
Sacramento	442.8000	+	○ 100#alr	W6AK	SARC
Sacramento	442.9000	+	○ 136.5e	K6NP	GBTPRC
Sacramento	443.1500	+	●l	K6INC	SCAN INT'L
Sacramento	443.2750	+	●e	KJ6JD	WU7Q
Sacramento	443.4500	+	●e	NØRM	WB6RVR
Sacramento	443.9000	+	○ 136.5aelrs	W6YDD	YDD 1.2
Sacramento	444.3000	+	●ers	N6ICW	N6ICW
Sacramento	444.4250	+	●#elx	K6PRN	Patio RS
Sacramento	444.6250	+	○ 123#ael	KC6MHT	KC6MHT
Shingle Spring	441.3000	+	●e	N2THD	The Group
Stonyford	443.0750	+	○ 114.8elx	K6LNK	CARLA
Vacaville	440.0250	+	○ 127.3aelrsx	WV6F	Western Va
Vacaville	440.5250	+	○ 136.5	KB6LCS	KB6LCS
Vacaville	440.7500	+	○ 100elx	K6LNK	CARLA
Vacaville	441.6000	+	●#alx	W6RCA	W6CBS
Vacaville	441.7750	+	●#elrx	N6ICW	N6ICW
Vacaville	441.9750	+	●#alx	W6RCA	W6CBS

Location	Output	Input	Notes	Call	Sponsor
Vacaville	442.0000	+	O 179.9	N6UG	N6UG
Vacaville	442.0250	+	O 179.9lx	W6KCS	W6KCS
Vacaville	442.3000	+	●elx	W6NQJ	N6ZN
Vacaville	442.5500	+	●#ex	N6APB	N6APB
Vacaville	443.3000	+	O 131.8	KB5JR	WV6F
Vacaville	443.7500	+	●#elr	K6NOX	CALNET
Vacaville	443.9500	+	O 136.5x	K6MVR	MVRC
Vacaville	444.1250	+	●e	W6SEL	DX-PINOY
Vacaville	444.5250	+	●lsx	AA6GV	SMRS
Vacaville	444.7500	+	O 107.2#e x	WA6RTL	NCAA
Vacaville	444.8500	+	●#lx	W6PUE	NORCAL
Volcano	440.4500	+	O 127.3x	W6KAP	W6KAP
Walnut Grove	443.7000	+	●#ex	WA6JIV	WA6JIV
Woodland	440.4750	+	O 192.8ers	KC6UDS	YoloARS
Woodland	444.1000	+	O 71.9esx	KE6YUV	BARK
Zamora	440.1500	+	●x	W6OF	HQPPARC
Zamora	441.8500	+	O 156.7#x	K6KCP	K6KCP
NORCAL-SAN JOAQUIN VALLEY					
Ahwahnee	444.5000	+	O 131.8ae x	WB6NIL	WB6NIL
Angels Camp	441.1250	+	O 156.7lrx	K6SCA	RMRG
Auberry	444.2750	+	O 127.3lrsx	KG6IBA	KG6IBA
Bakersfield	440.8500	+	O 141.3el	KK6AC	KERN
Bakersfield	441.2000	+	O 123el	K6ARN	KPARN
Bakersfield	441.9250	+	●elx	AB6MJ	AB6MJ
Bakersfield	443.0000	+	O 141.3lsx	KK6AC	KERN
Bakersfield	443.2750	+	O 141.3#x	N6RDN	N6RDN
Bakersfield	443.5500	+	●el	WA6KLB	CII
Bakersfield	443.9000	+	O 100e	W6LIE	KCCVARC
Bakersfield	444.6750	+	O 107.2#el	KG6FOS	KG6FOS
Bakersfield	444.7500	+	O 141.3#	N6SMU	N6SMU
Bakersfield	444.9250	+	O 103.5el	K6RET	K6RET
Bakersfield	447.6400	–	O 100#elx	K6JSI	WIN System
Bakersfield	447.7200	–	●#elx	KB6OOC	CALNET
Clovis	440.1000	+	●#ars	W6NBK	Nigel Keep
Clovis	440.3500	+	O 141.3ael	NI6M	CARP
Clovis	443.8000	+	O 114.8e	KE6JZ	KE6JZ
Clovis	444.7250	+	O 141.3ael x	K6ARP	CARP
Coalinga	440.5250	+	O 146.2el	N6LEX	CCARN
Coalinga	440.6750	+	O 146.2#a elrsx	W6EMS	CNARN
Coalinga	440.7500	+	O 114.8elx	K6JKL	CARLA
Coalinga	441.6750	+	O 100#elx	K6JSI	WIN System
Coalinga	441.9000	+	O 100elrsx	N6OA	Kings ARC
Coalinga	442.0250	+	O 146.2#el x	N6LEX	PBI
Coalinga	442.4250	+	●lx	KF6FM	SwRRC

Location	*Output*	*Input*	*Notes*	*Call*	*Sponsor*
Coalinga	443.3250	+	O 94.8elx	K6JJC	RMRG
Coalinga	443.3250	+	O 141.3#elx	W6WYT	W6WYT
Coalinga	443.7250	+	O 107.2lx	K6NOX	N6LYE
Coalinga	444.7750	+	O 141.3el	WA6RQX	WA6RQX
Coarsegold	442.9000	+	O 127.3e	W6HMH	W6HMH
Coarsegold	444.3750	+	O 123al	WY6L	WY6L
Columbia	440.7750	+	O 107.2#aex	K6NOX	K6NOX
Columbia	440.8500	+	O 146.2	K6DEL	DELCOM
Columbia	440.9750	+	O 103.5aers	N6EUO	TCARES
Columbia	442.2750	+	O 103.5#e	K6LPG	MCRA
Concord	440.7750	+	●elrx	K6NOX	CALNET
Copperopolis	440.0000	+	O 141.3lx	KG6TXA	SALAC
Copperopolis	441.6500	+	O 156.7	KD6FVA	KD6FVA
Copperopolis	442.3750	+	●elrsx	N6MAC	N6MAC
Dunlap	443.8250	+	●aelx	N6IB	CVRC
Fiddletown	442.2500	+	O 107.2lrx	W6SF	KD6FVA
Fresno	440.3750	+	●elx	N6AMG	ERG
Fresno	441.4000	+	●elx	K6TVI	Calnet
Fresno	441.8000	+	O 141.3elx	N6LYE	N6LYE
Fresno	442.1000	+	O 103.5elx	AB6BP	CC-ARLS
Fresno	442.8000	+	O 94.8	KJ6NKZ	KJ6NKZ
Fresno	442.9500	+	O 141.3elsx	KK6AC	KERN
Fresno	443.1250	+	O#e	N6PNZ	N6PNZ
Fresno	443.2500	+	O 107.2sx	WQ6CWA	QCWA
Fresno	443.3000	+	O 107.2x	K6NOX	N6LYE
Fresno	443.3750	+	●lx	KE6JZ	SRG
Fresno	443.4000	+	●lx	WB6FRM	NCCRA
Fresno	443.4250	+	O 141.3ex	W6WYT	W6WYT
Fresno	443.4500	+	O 141.3#elx	W6FSC	N6MTS
Fresno	443.6000	+	O 141.3#elx	W6FSC	N6MTS
Fresno	443.6000	+	O 114.8ex	N6LYE	N6LYE
Fresno	443.6500	+	O 141.3#	KE6SHK	KE6SHK
Fresno	443.8750	+	O 107.2#ael	N6LDG	N6LDG
Fresno	443.9500	+	O 141.3#aelx	N6VRC	CVRC
Fresno	443.9750	+	●lx	K6SRA	NCCRA
Fresno	444.1000	+	O 100e	W6NIF	Jim Erbe
Fresno	444.2000	+	O 141.3x	W6TO	Fresno ARC
Fresno	444.2500	+	O 100#elx	K6JSI	CCAC
Fresno	444.6000	+	OaDCSelx	N6IB	CVRC
Fresno	444.9750	+	●aDCSel	K6WGJ	CVRC
Hanford	444.9500	+	O 100#aelrs	N6CVC	Kings ARC

Location	*Output*	*Input*	*Notes*	*Call*	*Sponsor*
Lemoore	442.1500	+	○ 123	KG6OOD	KG6OOD
Lodi	444.2500	+	○ 114.8elrx	WB6ASU	WB6ASU
Los Banos	443.1500	+	○ 123	AA6LB	LB-ARC
Los Banos	444.0000	+	○ 123e	K6TJS	AA6LB
Madera	443.6000	+	○ 186.2e	N6LYE	N6LYE
Maricopa	443.0750	+	●es	KC6WRD	FCC
Mariposa	441.3500	+	○ 107.2#ex	K6SIX	K6SIX
Mariposa	441.4250	+	○ 74.4ex	KF6CLR	Delhi ARC
Mariposa	442.3500	+	○ 141.3elx	N6IB	CVRC
Mariposa	442.7000	+	○ 88.5#l	AB6BP	AB6BP
Mariposa	442.7000	+	○ 88.5ex	NV6RN	VARN
Mariposa	443.0750	+	○ 107.2aelsx	K6IXA	K6IXA
Mariposa	444.7000	+	○ 94.8elsx	W6BXN	TurlockARC
Meadow Lakes	442.5250	+	●aelx	N6IB	CVRC
Merced	440.8000	+	○ 114.8ex	N6LYE	N6LYE
Merced	442.2000	+	○ 141.3#lx	KM6OR	KM6OR
Merced	442.4000	+	●elx	KF6FM	SwRRC
Merced	442.6750	+	○ 107.2#elx	KG6KKV	ARRG
Modesto	440.2250	+	○ 136.5esx	WD6EJF	SARA
Modesto	440.8000	+	○ 107.2elx	N6LYE	N6LYE
Modesto	442.0750	+	○ 123elx	K6LNK	CARLA
Modesto	442.5500	+	●x	N6APB	K6PBX
Modesto	443.1750	+	○ 107.2ex	K6JJC	RMRG
Modesto	443.5250	+	○ 107.2lx	K6JSI	WIN System
Modesto	444.2250	+	○ 107.2#x	N6OGN	KI6AG
Mount Bullion	441.5500	+	○ 77elx	K6RDJ	WB6PBN
Mountain Ranch	440.9000	+	●aelx	N6GVI	CATS
Oakhurst	441.1750	+	○ 146.2erx	W6WGZ	MCARC
Oakhurst	444.0500	+	○ 107.2ae	WB6NIL	WB6NIL
Parkfield	443.7000	+	○ 141.3elx	N6GSM	N6GSM
Pine Grove	441.5250	+	○ 100aesx	K6ARC	ACARC
Pinehurst	441.4750	+	●lx	WC6HP	W6JCA
Pinehurst	442.0500	+	●rsx	AB6MJ	AB6MJ
Pinehurst	443.5750	+	●#ex	N6VQL	N6VQL
Pioneer	443.6250	+	●#lx	K6MSR	MSR
Porterville	440.2500	+	●elrsx	WC6HP	AB6MJ
Porterville	440.8250	+	●elx	W6KGB	GRONK
Porterville	441.5250	+	○ 67aelrs	WC6HP	KR6DK
Porterville	443.0500	+	○ 100ex	KE6YF	KE6YF
Porterville	443.9250	+	○ 141.3#ex	AE6WR	AE6WR
San Andreas	441.7000	+	●#ex	W6ALL	W6ALL
San Andreas	443.3500	+	○ 156.7lrx	K6SCA	RMRG
San Benito	440.6000	+	○ 67#elx	KI6FEO	KI6FEO
Sonora	440.4000	+	●lx	WB6WTM	WB6WTM

Location	Output	Input	Notes	Call	Sponsor
Sonora	442.4750	+	O 136.5ael	KJ6NRO	KJ6NRO
Sonora	443.4750	+	O 103.5ael	K6LNK	CARLA
Sonora	444.6500	+	●elx	K6KVA	K6KVA
Springville	441.9750	+	O 100elrsx	KE6DWX	KE6DWX
Stockton	440.0750	+	O 131.8#x	KE6DXF	KE6DXF
Stockton	440.7750	+	O 100#aex	K6NOX	K6NOX
Stockton	440.8250	+	O 107.2#a ex	K6NOX	Knox LaRue
Stockton	442.7250	+	O 77elx	KI6FEO	KI6FEO
Stockton	442.8250	+	●l	K6INC	SCAN INT'L
Stockton	443.1000	+	●ael	N6GVI	CATS
Stockton	444.0000	+	O 107.2	AB6IS	AB6IS
Stockton	444.3250	+	O 94.8e	K6KJQ	K6KJQ
Stockton	444.5750	+	O 107.2#e	W6SF	W6SF
Stockton	444.6750	+	O 123#e	KC6TTZ	kc6ttz
Tehachapi	440.6250	+	O 88.5elx	W6SLZ	BVSET
Tehachapi	442.9250	+	O 131.8ex	KI6HHU	KI6HHU
Tehachapi	444.4250	+	O 100el	KG6KKV	KG6KKV
Three Rivers	440.5500	+	O 156.7es	WA7HRG	WA7HRG
Tracy	443.0000	+	●el	KH7I	KH7I
Turlock	442.1750	+	O 110.9	WB6PBN	K6RDJ
Twain Heart	441.9250	+	O 123lrx	W6YOP	YOP HLLS
Valley Springs	441.0750	+	O 118.8ers	W6EBW	EBMUD
Visalia	440.4000	+	O 103.5elr sx	WA6BAI	TCARC
Visalia	440.4500	+	O 141.3#e x	N6BYH	N6BYH
Visalia	443.0250	+	O 88.5#ae	WA6BLB	WA6BLB
Visalia	443.2000	+	●#elx	KM6OR	KM6OR
Visalia	443.3500	+	O 141.3ex	WA6YLB	WA6YLB
Visalia	444.4500	+	O 127.3#	WA6MSN	WA6MSN
Visalia	444.8250	+	O 141.3ers x	W6BLP	N6SGW
Visalia	444.8750	+	O 192.8lrx	WA6RQX	WCRN
Weldon	444.0500	+	O 131.8	KA6IYS	KA6IYS
Westley	440.5000	+	●elx	N6AMG	ERG
Westley	440.7250	+	O 123#e	WB6JKV	WB6JKV
Westley	441.2750	+	O 77elx	K6RDJ	KF6EQR
Westley	443.6250	+	●aelx	K6MSR	MSR
Westley	443.8250	+	O 107.2erx	N5FDL	N5FDL
Westley	444.1750	+	O 141.3elr x	WA6RQX	WA6RQX
NORCAL-SOUTH BAY					
Boulder Creek	441.3000	+	O 100#elx	WB6ECE	WB6ECE RG
Campbell	441.0250	+	O 156.7ers	K9GVF	K9GVF
Campbell	442.1750	+	O 100el	K9GVF	CalNet
Cupertino	440.1250	+	O 114.8#l	W6AMT	AMT ARC
Cupertino	440.1500	+	O 100ers	W6TDM	Cupertino
Cupertino	441.5500	+	●aels	W6VB	W6VB

Location	*Output*	*Input*	*Notes*	*Call*	*Sponsor*
Cupertino	442.1250	+	●aesx	WR6BAT	K6LLK
Cupertino	442.3500	+	●e	K6GOD	GOD
Cupertino	443.1500	+	○ 100lrs	K6SA	SARA
Daly City	442.6500	+	●el	KQ6RC	KQ6RC
Fremont	443.4250	+	○ 100lrx	NC6EO	N. CA Assn
Gilroy	444.2000	+	○ 123e	KJ6WZS	GilroyRPTR
Hollister	441.9000	+	○ 110.9el	W6MOW	W6MOW
Los Altos	440.8750	+	○ 100rs	KH6N	KH6N
Los Altos	441.2500	+	●el	WB6WTM	WB6WTM
Los Altos	443.6750	+	●#ael	K6MSR	MSR
Los Gatos	440.6500	+	○ 94.8#ex	WA6JZN	WA6JZN
Los Gatos	441.0500	+	○ 100ex	K6NN	T&BC
Los Gatos	441.0500	+	○ 123#ex	N6UUI	TEL PNRS
Los Gatos	441.6250	+	○ 100#	W6RCA	W6CBS
Los Gatos	441.7000	+	○ 127.3el	K6UB	K6UB
Los Gatos	442.3000	+	○ 114.8elx	K6INC	SCAN INT'L
Los Gatos	443.0250	+	●aex	WA6ABB	WA6ABB
Los Gatos	443.7500	+	○ 100elrx	K9GVF	K9GVF
Los Gatos	443.9500	+	●	K6INC	SCAN INT'L
Los Gatos	444.9250	+	○ 156.7elx	KB6LCS	WA6HWT
Los Gatos	444.9750	+	○ 127.3ex	WB6KHP	CFMA
LosAltosHills	443.8500	+	●el	W6BUG	Bay Users
LosAltosHills	444.2250	+	○ 131.8#a ex	KE6JTK	KE6JTK
Milpitas	441.3000	+	○ 100#ex	WB6ECE	WB6ECE RG
Milpitas	442.3500	+	○ 100e	K6GOD	GOD
Milpitas	443.0250	+	●ers	K6EXE	K6EXE
Milpitas	444.3750	+	●l	N6INC	KQ6RC
Morgan Hill	440.5750	+	○ 114.8#	KA6ZRJ	KA6ZRJ
Morgan Hill	442.9750	+	○ 100elx	K7DAA	MHARS
Mountain View	440.8000	+	○ 100aelrs	W6ASH	SPECS RA
Palo Alto	440.2000	+	○ 123ers	N6BDE	N6BDE
Palo Alto	441.1000	+	○ 114.8elr sx	K6GOD	K6GOD
Palo Alto	441.5750	+	●#elx	K6IRC	ARN
Palo Alto	441.8500	+	○ 114.8#x	K6OTR	SCAR
Palo Alto	442.0000	+	○ 151.4ex	WW6HP	HPSVRC
Palo Alto	442.5750	+	○ 100elrsx	K6FB	LCARC
Palo Alto	442.8000	+	○ 114.8	K6OTR	SCAR
Palo Alto	443.0000	+	●aex	W6OOL	W6OOL
Palo Alto	443.2250	+	○ 100elx	WW6BAY	Bay Net
Palo Alto	444.3500	+	●elx	KJ6VU	NCCRA
Palo Alto	444.4250	+	○ 127.3ers x	KJ6VU	Bay-Net
Palo Alto	444.9500	+	○ 162.2ex	KB6LED	KB6LED
San Jose	440.1000	+	○ 127.3elr sx	W6SMQ	W6SMQ
San Jose	440.2250	+	○ 123e	K6LLC	LAPU-LAPU
San Jose	440.2750	+	○ 127.3elr x	W6YOP	YOP HLLS

Location	*Output*	*Input*	*Notes*	*Call*	*Sponsor*
San Jose	440.3750	+	●elx	N6TNR	ERG
San Jose	441.1500	+	O 100e	KC6BJO	KAISER HP
San Jose	441.1750	+	O 103.5aer	KF6FWO	MARA
San Jose	441.2750	+	●elrx	K6BEN	W2NYC
San Jose	441.3000	+	O 100#elx	WB6ECE	WB6ECE RG
San Jose	441.3500	+	O 88.5aels	W6PIY	WVARA
San Jose	441.7250	+	●elx	WA6QDP	WA6QDP
San Jose	441.7750	+	O 100#	W6NSA	CCARC
San Jose	441.8250	+	●l	AD1U	AD1U
San Jose	441.9500	+	O 100el	N6MPX	MSARC
San Jose	442.1750	+	●#elx	N1UFD	CALNET
San Jose	442.3500	+	O 123	K6GOD	K6GOD
San Jose	442.3750	+	O 114.8	K6JDE	K6JDE
San Jose	442.4250	+	O 107.2er	W6UU	SCCARA
San Jose	442.5000	+	O 100ersx	WB6ZVW	CPRA
San Jose	442.7000	+	O 100e	N6MNV	Rolm ARC
San Jose	442.7750	+	O 131.8e	KU6V	KU6V
San Jose	442.8250	+	●elx	WR6COP	K6COP
San Jose	442.8750	+	O 100#	WA6YLV	WA6YLV
San Jose	442.9000	+	O 162.2elx	WR6ABD	LPRC
San Jose	442.9500	+	O 85.4#ex	K6YZS	K6YZS
San Jose	443.0750	+	O 123e	K6LNK	CARLA
San Jose	443.2750	+	O 107.2ers x	K6SNY	SARES-RG
San Jose	443.3000	+	O 136.5#el x	KB5JR	KB5JR
San Jose	443.4500	+	●el	K6MF	K6MF
San Jose	443.4750	+	O 123elx	K6LNK	CARLA
San Jose	443.5500	+	●elx	WB6FRM	NCCRA
San Jose	443.5750	+	O 110.9al	KE6STH	KE6STH
San Jose	443.6250	+	●#aelx	K6MSR	MSR
San Jose	443.7750	+	O 100ex	WA6GFY	LMERA ARC
San Jose	443.9000	+	O 100#	K6RDC	CCARC
San Jose	444.0000	+	●	WA6INC	AD1U
San Jose	444.0250	+	O 136.5elx	K6JJC	RMRG
San Jose	444.0500	+	●als	KB6FEC	KB6FEC
San Jose	444.1000	+	●#er	N6TLQ	N6TLQ
San Jose	444.1750	+	O 192.8elr x	WA6RQX	WA6RQX
San Jose	444.3000	+	O 173.8ers x	W7AFG	AREA-Amate
San Jose	444.3000	+	O 162.2aer s	W7AFG	AREA-Amate
San Jose	444.3250	+	O 127.3#	KD6AOG	KD6AOG
San Jose	444.4000	+	●elx	WA6YCZ	BAYCOM
San Jose	444.4500	+	O 100e	WB6JSO	WB6JSO
San Jose	444.6000	+	O 141.3alx	WB6OQS	SCVRS
San Jose	444.6250	+	O 110.9ael sx	N6NAC	N6NAC

Location	*Output*	*Input*	*Notes*	*Call*	*Sponsor*
San Jose	444.7000	+	O 127.3	WB6KHP	CFMA
San Jose	444.7500	+	O 100e	N9JIM	K6LHE
San Jose	444.8000	+	●e	WA6GEL	Red Carpet
San Jose	444.9000	+	O 110.9elx	KU6V	KU6V
Santa Clara	442.0250	+	O 100rs	K6SNC	SCARS
Santa Clara	444.8750	+	●elx	KQ6RC	KQ6RC
Saratoga	443.1250	+	●aelr	K6BEN	W2NYC
Soledad	441.6000	+	●el	N6HU	KQ6RC
NORCAL-TAHOE					
Alpine	441.5500	+	●#	N6LZR	SARC
Cisco Grove	443.4750	+	O 100el	K6LNK	CARLA
Incline	441.5500	+	O 127.3elx	K6LNK	CARLA
InclineVillage	440.8500	+	O 100#e	NU7Y	NU7Y
Loyalton	440.1000	+	●	N5TEN	N5TEN
Meyers	442.0750	+	O 127.3el	K6LNK	CARLA
Rubicon Spring	444.9875	+	O 156.7elrs	KA6GWY	KA6GWY
So Lake Tahoe	442.4750	+	O 114.8el	WA6EWV	TARA
So Lake Tahoe	442.8250	+	O 88.5#ael	W6SUV	W6SUV
So Tahoe Ca	444.1750	+	O 85.4el	W6SUV	W6SUV
Tahoe City	440.2750	+	O 114.8elrx	K1BMW	YOP HLLS
Tahoe City	440.9250	+	●DCSelx	KH8AF	KH8AF
Tahoe City	441.1750	+	O 107.2elx	N7VXB	N7VXB
Tahoe City	442.1750	+	●elx	KH8AF	KH8AF
Tahoe City	442.9500	+	O 131.8#	WA6FJS	Tahoe ARC
Tahoe City	443.9750	+	●lx	K6SRA	NCCRA
Tahoe City	444.9500	+	●lx	W6PUE	NORCAL
Truckee	440.7000	+	O 131.8elx	W6SAR	PCSAR
Truckee	441.7500	+	●elr	W6XN	YOP HLLS
NORCAL-WEST BAY					
Belmont	440.0750	+	O 114.8e	KR6WP	KR6WP
Belmont	444.6750	+	O 114.8	K6JDE	K6JDE
Brisbane	440.7000	+	●elx	K6CV	K6CV
Daly City	440.5000	+	●elx	N6AMG	ERG
Daly City	440.5250	+	O 225.7	N3TC	N3TC
Daly City	440.6750	+	●DCSlx	K6TEA	K6TEA
Daly City	441.3750	+	O 146.2l	KC6IAU	KC6IAU
Daly City	442.3250	+	●#	KC6YDH	KC6YDH
Daly City	442.3750	+	O 114.8	K6JDE	K6JDE
Daly City	442.4750	+	O 114.8ae	KF6REK	BAARC
Daly City	442.7500	+	●#x	W6BUR	W6BUR
Daly City	444.8000	+	●elx	WA6GEL	Red Carpet
Kensington	441.8875	+	O#lx	AH6KD	Trbo-6
La Honda	440.1000	+	O 114.8#es	WA6DQP	WA6DQP
Los Altos Hill	441.5250	+	O 123es	K6AIR	K6AIR
Pacifica	440.0250	+	O 114.8#e	W1RAB	ross burto
Pacifica	440.7250	+	O 114.8#ersx	WB6JKV	WB6JKV

Location	Output	Input	Notes	Call	Sponsor
Pacifica	441.0750	+	O 114.8ersx	WA6TOW	CARC
Pacifica	441.7250	+	●DCSl	KR6WP	KR6WP
Pescadero	442.3250	+	●l	KB6NAN	KB6NAN
Redwood City	440.4000	+	O 127.3l	WB6WTM	WB6WTM RG
Redwood City	441.4000	+	O 114.8#e	WD6GGW	WD6GGW
Redwood City	444.5000	+	O 100es	K6MPN	SCARES
San Bruno	442.8500	+	O 114.8	K6JDE	K6JDE
San Carlos	444.1250	+	●alx	W6CBS	W6CBS
San Francisco	441.4500	+	O 85.4#e	W6EE	W6EE
San Francisco	442.0500	+	O 127.3elr	WA6GG	Northern C
San Francisco	442.0750	+	O 100ael	N6MVT	CARLA
San Francisco	443.1000	+	O 114.8elx	W6TP	GSPLRC
San Francisco	443.6750	+	●#lx	K6MSR	MSR
San Francisco	444.8500	+	O 114.8el	K6KYA	K6KYA
San Francisco	444.9250	+	O 136.5	KB6LCS	N6NMZ
SoSanFrancisco	441.2500	+	O 141.3es	K6DNA	GNEARC
SoSanFrancisco	442.7000	+	O 173.8ae	N6MNV	N6MNV
SoSanFrancisco	443.9250	+	O 136.5	KG6TN	KG6TN
Woodside	440.4500	+	O 107.2es	N6ZX	KMARC
Woodside	440.9500	+	O 162.2x	KB6LED	KB6LED
Woodside	441.3000	+	O 123#e	WB6ECE	WB6ECE RG
NORTH EAST					
Susanville	443.0250	+	O 91.5e	K6LRC	K6ME
Susanville	443.9000	+	O 91.5e	K6LRC	K6ME
Susanville	444.9750	+	O 91.5	K6LRC	K6ME
SIERRA/TAHOE					
Meyers	442.0750	+	O 127.3l	K6LNK	CARLA
Truckee	440.2750	+	● 114.8l	KJ6GM	KJ6GM
SOCAL -LA,OR,RIV,SBAR,SBER,SD,VE					
Covers Area	449.4400	–	●	K6XI	------------
SOCAL RIV,SBER					
Covers Area	448.6400	–	●RBx	KF6BYA	CACTUS
SOCAL-#29 PALMS					
Yucca Valley	447.0000	–	O 136.5	N6GIW	------------
SOCAL-#BIG BEAR					
Big Bear	446.4000	–	O 162.2	WA6ITC	------------
SOCAL-#FALLBROOK					
Red Mtn	445.6000	–	O 103.5	N6FQ	FARC
SOCAL-#KERN					
Ridgecrest	447.0200	–	O 123.0	W5HMV	------------
SOCAL-#LA CENTRAL					
Altadena	445.6400	–	O 156.7	W6TOI	Downey ARC
Cerro Negro	445.2000	–	O 103.5	WR6JPL	JPLARC
Covers Area	445.9000	–	O 123.0	KB6MRC	------------
Culver City	445.6000	–	O 131.8	K6CCR	CCARES
Hollywood Hills	445.6600	–	O 156.7 OR MOTOTRBO CC11 & ALL CALL	N6DVA	DV ARA
Mt Lukens	445.9200	–	O 186.2 Blx	KD6AFA	------------

Location	Output	Input	Notes	Call	Sponsor
Mt Lukens	449.2000	–	O 88.5x	KO6TD	------------
Mt Thom	445.6800	–	O 136.5x	N6JLY	CVRC
Mt Wilson	449.7000	–	O 131.8x	W6NVY	LAUSDARC
SOCAL-#LA EAST					
Bellflower	448.3400	–	O 192.8 BI	KB6MRC	------------
Johnstone Peak	446.4000	–	O 103.5x	WA6FZH	------------
Sunset Ridge	449.5000	–	O 146.2x	WA6ITC	------------
Whittier Hills	445.5600	–	O 100.0	W6GNS	RHARC
SOCAL-#LA NORTH					
Cyn Country	445.9000	–	O 107.2	KC6TKA	------------
Oat Mtn	447.2000	–	O 67.0	WB5EKU	------------
Santa Clarita	448.3400	–	O 67.0	N6NMC	------------
Simi Valley	445.5800	–	O 141.3	N6KYD	------------
SOCAL-#LA SOUTH					
Bellflower	448.3400	–	O 151.4 BI	KA6GXY	------------
Palos Verdes	447.0000	–	O 203.5	W6TRW	TRW ARC
SOCAL-#LA WEST					
El Segundo	445.6200	–	O 127.3	W6HA	HARC
Pac Palisades	445.5200	–	O 123.0	K6BDE	BDE ARC
W Los Angeles	447.3200	–	O 103.5	WA6QAG	VA Hospital
SOCAL-#ONTARIO					
Alta Loma	447.2000	–	O 114.8	K6ONT	ONT RACES
Chino Hills	445.5600	–	O 136.5	K6OPJ	CHINO RACES
Ontario	445.5800	–	O 131.8	K6ONT	ONT RACES
SOCAL-#ORANGE					
Fountain Valley	447.3200	–	O 94.8er	WA6FV	FVACT
Huntington Bch	445.5800	–	O 94.8	W6VLD	BOEING
Knotts Berry Farm	445.5200	–	O 85.4	K6KBF	KNOTTS ARC
SOCAL-#ORANGE SOUTH					
Aliso Viejo	445.1000	–	O 110.9	KI6DB	LNACS
Laguna Hills	445.6600	–	O 110.9	K6SOA	SOARA
Seal Beach	449.3000	–	O 141.3	KI6RBW	------------
SOCAL-#PALM SPRINGS					
Goat Mtn	447.5800	–	O 136.5	WB6QFE	------------
Indio	445.6400	–	O 131.8	K6IFR	------------
Indio	447.5800	–	O 100.0	W6KSN	------------
Palm Springs Tram	449.7000	–	O 107.2	KF6BM	Desert Repeater Ass
Thousand Palms	447.2000	–	O 107.2	KA6GBJ	------------
SOCAL-#PALMDALE					
Hauser Peak	446.4000	–	O 100.0	KD6PXZ	------------
Juniper Hills	449.5000	–	O 192.8	WA6GDF	------------
Ten-Hi	445.2000	–	O 123.0	N6GLT	------------
Ten-Hi	445.6000	–	O 100.0	KJ6W	------------
SOCAL-#SAN BERNARDINO					
Alta Loma	445.9000	–	O 146.2	N6RPG	------------
Fontana	447.3200	–	O 136.5	KA6GRF	RACES
Loma Linda	445.6000	–	O 118.8	K6LLU	LLHARC

Location	*Output*	*Input*	*Notes*	*Call*	*Sponsor*
Loma Linda	447.0000	–	O 156.7	KE6CPF	LLRACES
SOCAL-#SAN DIEGO					
El Cajon	445.9000	–	O 107.2	WA6BGS	ARC EL CAJON
Laguna Pk	449.5000	–	O 107.2	WB6WLV	SANDRA
Mission Valley	447.3200	–	O 107.2	W6UUS	CONVAIR
Mt Otay	449.2000	–	O 107.2	WB6WLV	SANDRA
Mt San Miguel	447.5800	–	O 123.0	KF6HPG	CORA
Palomar Mtn	446.4000	–	O 67.0	KE6YRU	Motorola User Gr
Palomar Mtn	447.0000	–	O 107.2	W6NWG	PARC
Palomar Mtn	449.3000	–	O 100.0	KA6UAI	------------
San Diego	445.2000	–	O 123.0 BI	W2NOR	------------
San Diego	445.5800	–	O	K6KHO	------------
San Diego	445.6800	–	O 123.0	N6DCR	------------
SOCAL-#SANTA BARBARA					
Broadcast Pk	449.3000	–	O 131.8	WB6OBB	------------
Painted Cave	447.2000	–	O 131.8	N6HYM	------------
Santa Barbara	446.4000	–	O 131.8	K6TZ	SBARC
SOCAL-#SD NORTH					
Vista	445.5600	–	O 146.2	KJ6ZD	------------
SOCAL-#VENTURA					
Newbury Park	445.9000	–	O 123.0	W4EG	------------
Sulphur Mtn	447.3200	–	O 100.0	WA6ZSN	SMRA
Ventura	445.6000	–	O 114.8	KB6LJQ	------------
Ventura	447.0000	–	O 103.5	K6ERN	SMRA
SOCAL-#VICTORVILLE					
Adelanto	445.6800	–	O 100.0	KR1IS	------------
Hesperia	447.0000	–	O 136.5	KC6OPU	------------
Table Mtn	447.2000	–	O 94.8	WR6AZN	JPLARC
SOCAL-IMP					
Covers Area	448.6200	–	●x	W7SRC	CACTUS
SOCAL-IMP,LA,OR,RIV,SBER,SD					
Covers Area	446.0400	–	●	KF6FM	SWRRC
Covers Area	446.2600	–	●	N6CIZ	------------
Covers Area	446.6000	–	●	K6SBC	SBER CNTY
Covers Area	446.6800	–	●	WA6LWW	BFI
Covers Area	448.0200	–	●	WR6TWE	TWEMARS
Covers Area	448.2000	–	●	WR6RED	SCRN
Covers Area	448.2200	–	●RBx	WB6VTM	CACTUS
Covers Area	448.6000	–	●RBx	WA6COT	RRN
Covers Area	448.6600	–	●RBx	WB6TZC	CACTUS
Covers Area	448.8400	–	●	K6OW	LARA
Covers Area	448.9400	–	●	KE6VK	DRONK
Covers Area	449.3400	–	●	KB6CRE	BARN
Covers Area	449.4400	–	●	WR6OP	------------
Covers Area	449.5200	–	●	WB6SLC	------------
Covers Area	449.7200	–	●	WB6TZL	GRONK
Covers Area	449.8600	–	●	KD6DRS	------------
Covers Area	449.9200	–	●	K6DLP	------------

Location	Output	Input	Notes	Call	Sponsor
SOCAL-IMP,RIV,SBER					
Covers Area	448.6400	–	●RBx	K6TMD	CACTUS
Covers Area	448.6800	–	●RBx	WA6VAW	CACTUS
SOCAL-IMP,RIV,SBER,SD					
Covers Area	447.1400	–	●	WB6SLR	GRONK
Covers Area	447.7200	–	●	WB6DIJ	CALNET
Covers Area	447.8000	–	●	WA6SYN	ECRA
Covers Area	448.7400	–	●RBx	KF6BYA	CACTUS
Covers Area	448.7800	–	●	K6JB	------------
Covers Area	448.8000	–	●	K6JSI	WINSYSTEM
Covers Area	449.0000	–	●RBx	WB6TZF	CACTUS
Covers Area	449.1800	–	●	N6LVR	ECRA
Covers Area	449.5800	–	●	N6CKS	------------
SOCAL-IN,KE,LA,MO,SBER					
Covers Area	442.2400	+	●	W6TD	GRONK
Covers Area	442.3400	+	●	W6TD	GRONK
Covers Area	444.3000	+	●	W6TD	GRONK
Covers Area	444.4000	+	●	W6TD	GRONK
Covers Area	444.5000	+	●	W6IY	------------
Covers Area	444.5800	+	●	WA6VVC	------------
Covers Area	447.1600	–	●	K6RFO	GRONK
Covers Area	447.4800	–	●	N6SRC	SWRRC
Covers Area	447.7200	–	●	KB6OOC	CALNET
COVERS AREA	448.8000	–	●	WI6RE	WINSYSTEM
SOCAL-KE,LA,OR,RIV,SBAR,SBER,SD,VE					
Covers Area	448.9800	–	●RBx	WA6KXK	CACTUS
SOCAL-KE,LA,OR,RIV,SBAR,SBER,VE					
Covers Area	447.0400	–	●	WA6GML	------------
Covers Area	447.0800	–	●	WA6LWW	BFI
Covers Area	447.1000	–	●	WB6ORK	SARS
Covers Area	447.1600	–	●	K6KMN	GRONK
Covers Area	447.2800	–	●	N6ME	WARN
Covers Area	447.4400	–	●	KD6OFD	CALNET
Covers Area	447.5400	–	●	KB6CRE	BARN
Covers Area	447.6400	–	●	K6JSI	WINSYSTEM
Covers Area	448.3800	–	●	WD6AWP	------------
Covers Area	448.4600	–	●	N6RTR	------------
Covers Area	448.5200	–	●	N6ENL	SCRN
Covers Area	448.6800	–	●RBx	WB6TZH	CACTUS
Covers Area	448.7600	–	●RBx	WA6COT	RRN
Covers Area	448.8600	–	●	W6HWW	LARA
Covers Area	449.0200	–	●	WR6WHT	SCRN
Covers Area	449.1200	–	●	N6KHZ	AARC
Covers Area	449.3800	–	●	WD6FZA	------------
So Cal	447.8600	–	●	KK6AC	------------
SOCAL-KE,LA,SBER					
Covers Area	445.0800	–	●	AD6VR	------------
Covers Area	445.2400	–	●	KW6WW	------------
Covers Area	445.3400	–	●	KA6YTT	------------

Location	Output	Input	Notes	Call	Sponsor
Covers Area	445.4800	–	●	KA6YTT	------------
Covers Area	446.0400	–	●	WD6FM	SWRRC
Covers Area	446.0600	–	●	K6SRC	SWRRC
Covers Area	446.1000	–	●	K7GIL	HDRN
Covers Area	446.3000	–	●	K7GIL	HDRN
Covers Area	446.3800	–	●	K7GIL	HDRN
Covers Area	446.5400	–	●	N6LXX	PIN
Covers Area	446.6000	–	●	K6SBC	SBER CNTY
Covers Area	446.8200	–	●	WB6FIU	------------
Covers Area	446.9000	–	●	WD6DIH	ALERT
Covers Area	446.9400	–	●	WB6BVY	------------
Covers Area	447.2800	–	●	WR6TM	TWEMARS
Covers Area	447.5600	–	●	KB6CRE	BARN
Covers Area	447.8200	–	●	W6IY	------------
Covers Area	447.9000	–	●	WD6AML	SARS
Covers Area	448.0800	–	●	KC6WRD	------------
Covers Area	448.3600	–	●	W7BF	------------
Covers Area	448.4200	–	●	WB6IOJ	------------
Covers Area	448.4600	–	●	N6RTR	------------
Covers Area	448.6400	–	●	K6BDI	------------
Covers Area	448.9400	–	●	K6SBC	SBER CNTY
Covers Area	449.3800	–	●	K6SBC	SBER CNTY
Covers Area	449.4000	–	●	WA6SBH	------------
Covers Area	449.6800	–	●	K7GIL	HDRN
Covers Area	449.7800	–	●	K7GIL	HDRN
Covers Area	449.8000	–	●	WB6BWU	------------
So Cal	446.9000	–	●	WA6WDB	------------
So Cal	447.2200	–	●	W6IER	IEARC
SOCAL-KE-LA-OR-RIV-SBER-VE					
Covera Area	448.6600	–	RBx	KF6BXW	CACTUS
SOCAL-LA					
Covers Area	447.6200	–	●RB	N6GKR	CACTUS
SOCAL-LA,OR					
Covers Area	445.0800	–	●	WB6BBZ	------------
Covers Area	445.1200	–	●	KK6HS	------------
Covers Area	445.2200	–	●	W6BAB	Pasadena City C
Covers Area	445.3600	–	●	KA6P	BARC
Covers Area	445.3600	–	●	KA6P	BARC
Covers Area	445.4000	–	●	K6BBB	------------
Covers Area	445.4600	–	●	K6LAM	------------
Covers Area	445.7200	–	●	WA6TWF	SS
Covers Area	446.1000	–	●	WB6NLU	------------
Covers Area	446.3000	–	●	N6SIM	------------
Covers Area	446.3200	–	●	WA6TWF	SS
Covers Area	446.3600	–	●	WA6TWF	SS
Covers Area	446.4400	–	●	KB6VWN	------------
Covers Area	446.4400	–	●	K6QEH	Raytheon
Covers Area	446.4400	–	●	WA6FZH	------------
Covers Area	446.5400	–	●	N6MIK	------------

CALIFORNIA

Location	*Output*	*Input*	*Notes*	*Call*	*Sponsor*
Covers Area	446.6000	–	●	W6KGB	GRONK
Covers Area	446.8600	–	●	W6AGO	ELSEG ARC
Covers Area	446.9200	–	●	W6SCE	EARN
Covers Area	447.0600	–	●	WA6DYX	------------
Covers Area	447.1000	–	●	WD6AML	SARS
Covers Area	447.1400	–	●	KE6SWJ	SPEAR
Covers Area	447.6600	–	●	KE6QH	SCRN
Covers Area	447.9400	–	●	N6XZE	------------
Covers Area	447.9800	–	●	NW6B	SWAN
Covers Area	448.0200	–	●	WR6PV	TWEMARS
Covers Area	448.5400	–	●	W6YRA	UCLA RC
Covers Area	448.8000	–	●	KØVAC	PALMTREE
Covers Area	449.0400	–	●	N6MH	------------
Covers Area	449.0800	–	●	WB6HTS	------------
Covers Area	449.1200	–	●	N6KHZ	AARC
Covers Area	449.3200	–	●	WD6CZH	ZARC
Covers Area	449.3600	–	●	N6WZK	MCARC
Covers Area	449.6200	–	●	WA6TFD	BHARC
Covers Area	449.8400	–	●	NG6Q	------------
Covers Area	449.8400	–	●	NG6Q	------------
Covers Area	449.9800	–	●	K6IUM	RTD ARC
SOCAL-LA,OR,RIV,SBAR,SBER,SD,VE					
Covers Area	445.0200	–	●	W6CDF	------------
Covers Area	445.1600	–	●	KE6FQA	------------
Covers Area	445.1800	–	●	WB9RNW	------------
Covers Area	445.3000	–	●	K6RH	------------
Covers Area	445.3200	–	●	N6EW	BHARC
Covers Area	445.4200	–	●	WD6FZA	PAPA
Covers Area	445.5400	–	●	WB6AJE	ABC RC
Covers Area	445.7000	–	●	K7SA	------------
Covers Area	445.7200	–	●	WA6TWF	SS
Covers Area	445.7400	–	●	K6JHX	------------
Covers Area	445.7600	–	●	KD6DDM	------------
Covers Area	445.7800	–	●	N6OYF	------------
Covers Area	445.7800	–	●	N6VYA	------------
Covers Area	445.8000	–	●	WA6IBL	------------
Covers Area	445.8200	–	●	KA6CBE	HAMS
Covers Area	445.8600	–	●	K6IFR	------------
Covers Area	445.8800	–	●	W6OC	------------
Covers Area	445.9400	–	●BI	K6JP	SCJHC
Covers Area	445.9800	–	●	WZ6A	SWAN
Covers Area	446.0200	–	●	K6BFS	WEEVIL
Covers Area	446.0800	–	●	N6AOL	SRARC
Covers Area	446.1000	–	●	WB6NLU	------------
Covers Area	446.1200	–	●	WB6MIE	------------
Covers Area	446.2400	–	●	K6VGP	DARN
Covers Area	446.3200	–	●	WA6TWF	SS
Covers Area	446.3400	–	●	WA6TWF	SS
Covers Area	446.3400	–	●	WA6TWF	SS

Location	*Output*	*Input*	*Notes*	*Call*	*Sponsor*
Covers Area	446.3600	–	●	WA6TWF	SS
Covers Area	446.3800	–	●	KD6KQ	BRAVO
Covers Area	446.4200	–	●	W6YJ	------------
Covers Area	446.4200	–	●	W6YJ	------------
Covers Area	446.4600	–	●	WA6APQ	------------
Covers Area	446.4800	–	●	WA6LSE	FASTNET
Covers Area	446.5800	–	●	WD6FZA	PAPA
Covers Area	446.7000	–	●	WA6TWF	SS
Covers Area	446.7200	–	●	KB6CRE	BARN
Covers Area	446.7400	–	●	K6VGP	DARN
Covers Area	446.7800	–	●	WA6LWW	BFI
Covers Area	446.8200	–	●	WA6LIF	------------
Covers Area	446.8400	–	●	W6OCS	------------
Covers Area	446.9000	–	●	WD6DIH	ALERT
Covers Area	446.9400	–	●	K6PVC	------------
Covers Area	446.9600	–	●BI	KG6ALU	------------
Covers Area	447.0800	–	●	K6ZXZ	BFI
Covers Area	447.0800	–	●	K6ZXZ	BFI
Covers Area	447.1200	–	●	K6PV	PV ARC
Covers Area	447.1400	–	●	WB6TZL	GRONK
Covers Area	447.1600	–	●	WB6TZL	GRONK
Covers Area	447.1800	–	●	KG6GI	HROC
Covers Area	447.2400	–	●	AA4CD	------------
Covers Area	447.2400	–	●	WA6UZS	CDMARC
Covers Area	447.2600	–	●	AA4CD	------------
Covers Area	447.2600	–	●	WA6UZS	CDMARC
Covers Area	447.3600	–	●	W6TWE	TWEMARS
Covers Area	447.3800	–	●	W6YJ	------------
Covers Area	447.4200	–	●BI	W6EMS	------------
Covers Area	447.4600	–	●	WA6VLD	------------
Covers Area	447.5400	–	●	KB6CRE	BARN
Covers Area	447.6400	–	●	W6PL	WIN
Covers Area	447.6800	–	●	WR6ORG	SCRN
Covers Area	447.7000	–	●	W6YQY	------------
Covers Area	447.7600	–	●	KB6OOC	CALNET
Covers Area	447.7800	–	●	WA6EQU	CROSSBAR
Covers Area	447.8400	–	●	WA6JQB	LPARG
Covers Area	447.8600	–	●	WR6SP	TWEMARS
Covers Area	447.8800	–	●	K6DLP	------------
Covers Area	447.9600	–	●	NW6B	SWAN
Covers Area	448.0200	–	●	W6TWE	TWEMARS
Covers Area	448.0400	–	●	WD6AWP	------------
Covers Area	448.0600	–	●	K6JSI	WINSYSTEM
Covers Area	448.1000	–	●	K6JTH	------------
Covers Area	448.1200	–	●	KA6JRG	CALNET
Covers Area	448.1400	–	●	WB6SRC	SWRRC
Covers Area	448.2000	–	●	WB6DYM	SCRN
Covers Area	448.2400	–	●RBx	WA6ZPS	SPARC
Covers Area	448.2600	–	●BI	K6IRF	------------

Location	Output	Input	Notes	Call	Sponsor
Covers Area	448.3000	–	●	WA6ZJT	------------
Covers Area	448.3200	–	●	W6KRW	CPRA
Covers Area	448.4000	–	●	KE6PCV	CALNET
Covers Area	448.4200	–	●	WJ6A	------------
Covers Area	448.4400	–	●	WA6ZJT	------------
Covers Area	448.4800	–	●	KB6C	FRN
Covers Area	448.5000	–	●	WA6VLD	------------
Covers Area	448.5000	–	●	WA6VLD	------------
Covers Area	448.5200	–	●	N6ENL	SCRN
Covers Area	448.5600	–	●	WA6ZRB	SWAT
Covers Area	448.6000	–	●RBx	K6TVE	RRN
Covers Area	448.7000	–	●	WR6BRN	SCRN
Covers Area	448.7200	–	●RBx	WA6COT	RRN
Covers Area	448.7400	–	●RBx	WA6COT	RRN
Covers Area	448.7600	–	●RBx	WA6COT	RRN
Covers Area	448.8200	–	●	W6ZOJ	LARA
Covers Area	448.8800	–	●	W6ZOI	LARA
Covers Area	448.9000	–	●	WA6ZSG	WIN
Covers Area	448.9200	–	●	N6SLD	CRA
Covers Area	448.9600	–	●	K6MOT	MARC
Covers Area	448.9600	–	●	K6MOT	MARC
Covers Area	449.0200	–	●	N6JAM	DRONK
Covers Area	449.0200	–	●	WB6DTR	------------
Covers Area	449.0400	–	●	WB6ZQX	------------
Covers Area	449.0600	–	●	W6NVY	------------
Covers Area	449.1000	–	●	W6KRW	OC RACES
Covers Area	449.1800	–	●	W6KRW	OC RACES
Covers Area	449.2200	–	●	WB6CYT	GFRN
Covers Area	449.2200	–	●	WB6YMH	GFRN
Covers Area	449.2400	–	●	WA6TXY	OMARS
Covers Area	449.2600	–	●	W6NVY	------------
Covers Area	449.3400	–	●	WB6UKD	------------
Covers Area	449.3800	–	●BI	WD6FZA	------------
Covers Area	449.4000	–	●	WA6SBH	------------
Covers Area	449.4000	–	●	WA6SBH	------------
Covers Area	449.4400	–	●	WB6SSO	------------
Covers Area	449.5200	–	●	WB6SLC	------------
Covers Area	449.5400	–	●	W6AP	------------
Covers Area	449.5600	–	●	W6AP	------------
Covers Area	449.6000	–	●	WV6H	CARE
Covers Area	449.6000	–	●	N6UL	------------
Covers Area	449.6200	–	●	WB6DTR	DRONK
Covers Area	449.6400	–	●	WA6VLF	------------
Covers Area	449.6600	–	●	W6YJ	------------
Covers Area	449.6800	–	●	KC6N	------------
Covers Area	449.7400	–	●	W6KGB	GRONK
Covers Area	449.7600	–	●	WB6YMI	GFRN
Covers Area	449.7800	–		K6CHE	LBARC
Covers Area	449.7800	–	●	WB6DTR	DRONK

Location	*Output*	*Input*	*Notes*	*Call*	*Sponsor*
Covers Area	449.8000	–	●	WB6BWU	------------
Covers Area	449.8000	–	●	WB6BWU	------------
Covers Area	449.8200	–	●	KE6LE	------------
Covers Area	449.9000	–	●	WB6IOS	------------
Covers Area	449.9200	–	●	K6DLP	------------
Covers Area	449.9600	–	●	W6AP	------------
So Cal	447.0200	–	●	KC6IJM	Ventura OES/AC
So Cal	449.4400	–	●	W6AMG	------------
SOCAL-LA,OR,RIV,SBER					
Covers Area	445.1200	–	●	W6GAE	LAPRG
Covers Area	445.1200	–	●	W6GAE	LPARG
Covers Area	445.1400	–	●	K6IFR	AARC
Covers Area	445.2400	–	●	WB6VMV	ELSEG ARC
Covers Area	445.3400	–	●	W6LAR	------------
Covers Area	445.3600	–	●	KA6P	BARC
Covers Area	445.3800	–	●	WA6LSE	FASTNET
Covers Area	445.3800	–	●	K6CCC	FASTNET
Covers Area	445.4000	–	●	K6BBB	------------
Covers Area	445.4000	–	●	WD6DIH	ALERT
Covers Area	445.4400	–	●	W6UE	CALTEC ARC
Covers Area	445.5000	–	●	WB6ZSU	SCEARA
Covers Area	445.8400	–	●	W6AJP	------------
Covers Area	446.0200	–	●	W6FNO	SJARC
Covers Area	446.1000	–	●	WB6EVM	------------
Covers Area	446.2200	–	●	KI6QK	------------
Covers Area	446.2200	–	●	KI6QK	------------
Covers Area	446.2800	–	●	KF6JEE	------------
Covers Area	446.5600	–	●	WD6FZA	PAPA
Covers Area	446.6600	–	●	W6KGB	GRONK
Covers Area	447.1400	–	●	WB6TZL	GRONK
Covers Area	447.1600	–	●	WB6IZC	GRONK
Covers Area	447.1600	–	●	WB6TZL	GRONK
Covers Area	447.8200	–	●	KJ6TQ	MARS
Covers Area	447.9200	–	●	KD6LVP	------------
Covers Area	448.0000	–	●	N6RDK	------------
Covers Area	448.0800	–	●	KD6ZLZ	------------
Covers Area	448.2800	–	●	K6MIC	------------
Covers Area	448.3600	–	●	W7BF	------------
Covers Area	448.7600	–	●RBx	WA6COT	RRN
Covers Area	448.7800	–	●	WH6NZ	------------
Covers Area	448.9400	–	●BI	AC6PT	------------
Covers Area	449.0400	–	●	N6MH	------------
Covers Area	449.0800	–	●	K6JR	------------
Covers Area	449.1600	–	●	AB6Z	------------
Covers Area	449.2800	–	●	WB6VSJ	------------
Covers Area	449.3000	–	●	N6BOX	Moreno Valley A
Covers Area	449.3400	–	●	N3RP	------------
Covers Area	449.4800	–	●	N6YN	LAX RB
Covers Area	449.6400	–	●	W6NVY	------------

Location	Output	Input	Notes	Call	Sponsor
Covers Area	449.6800	–	●	W6KRW	OC RACES
Covers Area	449.7400	–	●	W6KGB	GRONK
Covers Area	449.8000	–	●	WB6VPQ	------------
Covers Area	449.8000	–	●	WB6BWU	------------
Covers Area	449.8400	–	●	N7QT	------------
Covers Area	449.8400	–	●	N6JXI	------------
Covers Area	449.8800	–	●	K6TEM	HAMWATCH
Covers Area	449.9000	–	●	WB6IOS	------------
SOCAL-LA,OR,RIV,SBER,SD					
Covers Area	445.0200	–	●	W6CDF	------------
Covers Area	445.0400	–	●	K6HOG	------------
Covers Area	445.1000	–	●	WA6KRC	------------
Covers Area	445.2600	–	●	K6VGP	HAMS
Covers Area	445.2800	–	●	K6AHM	DARN
Covers Area	445.4600	–	●	NO6B	LARG
Covers Area	445.4800	–	●	K6TEM	HAMWATCH/FIRES
Covers Area	445.5000	–	●	N6EX	SCEARA
Covers Area	445.8400	–	●	WB6ALD	------------
Covers Area	445.9400	–	●BI	K6JP	SCJHC
Covers Area	445.9600	–	●	KE6QH	AARC
Covers Area	445.9600	–	●	AA6FV	------------
Covers Area	446.0400	–	●	WA6FM	SWRRC
Covers Area	446.0600	–	●	KF6FM	SWRRC
Covers Area	446.1000	–	●	WB6EVM	------------
Covers Area	446.1600	–	●	KA6KVX	------------
Covers Area	446.2000	–	●	WD6AZN	OERBA
Covers Area	446.5400	–	●	KA6ANH	PIN
Covers Area	446.5400	–	●	KA6ANH	PIN
Covers Area	446.5600	–	●	WD6FZA	PAPA
Covers Area	446.5800	–	●	WD6FZA	PAPA
Covers Area	446.6200	–	●	WB6TZL	------------
Covers Area	446.6400	–	●	N6RTR	------------
Covers Area	446.6800	–	●	WA6LWW	BFI
Covers Area	446.7600	–	●	WD6FZA	PAPA
Covers Area	446.8000	–	●	N6LXX	------------
Covers Area	446.8200	–	●	WA6LIF	------------
Covers Area	446.8200	–	●	WA6LIF	------------
Covers Area	446.9000	–	●	WD6DIH	ALERT
Covers Area	446.9200	–	●	W6SCE	EARN
Covers Area	446.9800	–	●	WA6WLZ	------------
Covers Area	447.0600	–	O 114.8	AA1Z	------------
Covers Area	447.0600	–	●	WA6DYX	------------
Covers Area	447.1400	–	●	KK6KK	------------
Covers Area	447.3000	–	●	W6NRY	EARS
Covers Area	447.3400	–	●	KM6JY	------------
Covers Area	447.3600	–	●	WR6HP	TWEMARS
Covers Area	447.4000	–	●RBx	W6LKO	LKO ARC
Covers Area	447.4600	–	●	KM6NP	SCARA
Covers Area	447.4800	–	●	NA6S	------------

Location	Output	Input	Notes	Call	Sponsor
Covers Area	447.4800	–	●	KK6KK	------------
Covers Area	447.5000	–	●	KØJPK	------------
Covers Area	447.5200	–	●	K6CF	------------
Covers Area	447.5200	–	●	K6CF	------------
Covers Area	447.5600	–	●	WB6LST	BARN
Covers Area	447.6000	–	●	W6GAE	LAPRG
Covers Area	447.6200	–	●RBx	N6DD	RAVEN
Covers Area	447.6600	–	●	KE6QH	SCRN
Covers Area	447.7200	–	●	N6DKA	CALNET
Covers Area	447.7400	–	●	KE6PCV	CALNET
Covers Area	447.7600	–	●	WB6DIJ	CALNET
Covers Area	447.8000	–	●	WB6EGR	------------
Covers Area	447.8800	–	●	K6DLP	------------
Covers Area	447.9000	–	●	WD6AML	------------
Covers Area	447.9400	–	●	W6BRP	------------
Covers Area	447.9800	–	●	KV6D	SWAN
Covers Area	447.9800	–	●	N6ACV	SWAN
Covers Area	448.1000	–	●	AF6J	SCRN
Covers Area	448.1600	–	●	KF6FM	SWRRC
Covers Area	448.1600	–	●	W7DOD	SWRRC
Covers Area	448.1800	–	●RBx	WB6TZU	SKYLINE
Covers Area	448.3600	–	●	W7BF	------------
Covers Area	448.3600	–	●	W7BF	------------
Covers Area	448.4000	–	●	N6AJB	CALNET
Covers Area	448.4200	–	●	K6IOJ	------------
Covers Area	448.4200	–	●	K6IOJ	------------
Covers Area	448.4800	–	●	KB6C	FRN
Covers Area	448.5000	–	●	WA6VLD	------------
Covers Area	448.5200	–	●	N6ENL	SCRN
Covers Area	448.5400	–	●	N6MQS	A-TECH
Covers Area	448.5800	–	●	KF6JBN	KARA
Covers Area	448.6200	–	●RBx	K6DLV	CACTUS
Covers Area	448.6800	–	●RBx	WA6JAF	CACTUS
Covers Area	448.7000	–	●	K6JTH	SCRN
Covers Area	448.7200	–	●RBx	WA6TZF	CACTUS
Covers Area	448.8200	–	●	W6JYP	LARA
Covers Area	448.8400	–	●	K6MVH	LARA
Covers Area	448.9400	–	●BI	KF6ITC	------------
Covers Area	448.9600	–	●	K6MOT	MARC
Covers Area	449.0400	–	●	N6MH	------------
Covers Area	449.1200	–	●	N6KHZ	AARC
Covers Area	449.2800	–	●	KK6KK	------------
Covers Area	449.3200	–	●	WD6CZH	------------
Covers Area	449.4000	–	●	WA6SBH	------------
Covers Area	449.4200	–	●	KE6TZF	SRRG
Covers Area	449.5200	–	●	WA6HJW	------------
Covers Area	449.5800	–	●	N6IPD	IREC/ALERT
Covers Area	449.6600	–	●	W6YJ	------------
Covers Area	449.7200	–	●	WB6IZC	GRONK

Location	Output	Input	Notes	Call	Sponsor
Covers Area	449.8000	–	●	WA6DPB	------------
Covers Area	449.9000	–	●	WB6IOS	------------
Covers Area	449.9400	–	●	W6JBO	------------
Covers Area	449.9400	–	●	WB6NVD	------------
Covers Area	449.9800	–	●	KA6MEP	RTD ARC
Covers Area	449.9800	–	●	K6IUM	RTD ARC
So Cal	445.2600	–	●	N6AJB	------------
So Cal	445.7400	–	●	AF6HP	------------
So Cal	447.0200	–	●	N6AJB	------------
So Cal	449.1400	–	●	WD6AZN	OERBA
So Cal	449.6000	–	●	AF6HP	------------
SOCAL-LA,OR,RIV,SBER,SD,VE					
Covers Area	448.2200	–	●RBx	WA6EQU	CROSSBAR
Covers Area	448.6400	–	●RBx	WB6TZD	CACTUS
SOCAL-LA,RIV,SBER					
Covers Area	447.6200	–	●RBx	WA6JBD	------------
SOCAL-LA,SBAR,SD,VE					
Covers Area	447.2200	–	●	WB6TZE	RRN
Covers Area	447.7400	–	●	W6AMS	CALNET
Covers Area	447.9200	–	●	N6HYM	------------
Covers Area	449.0000	–	●RBx	WB6TZE	RRN
Covers Area	449.0200	–	●	WB6DYM	SCRN
Covers Area	449.3600	–	●BI	N6VVY	------------
SOCAL-LA,SBAR,VE					
Covers Area	440.1200	+	●	WB6DAO	LPARG
Covers Area	445.3400	–	●	KC6JAR	------------
Covers Area	446.2000	–	●	WB6TZL	------------
Covers Area	446.2800	–	●	KC6YIO	SPEAR
Covers Area	446.6000	–	●	W6KGB	GRONK
Covers Area	446.7600	–	●	WD6FZA	PAPA
Covers Area	446.7800	–	●	WA6LWW	BFI
Covers Area	446.9000	–	●	WD6DIH	ALERT
Covers Area	447.3400	–	●	W6TWE	TWEMARS
Covers Area	447.3400	–	●	W6FRT	OFARTS
Covers Area	447.4800	–	●	W8AKF	------------
Covers Area	447.5000	–	●	KE6HGO	------------
Covers Area	447.5400	–	●	KB6CRE	BARN
Covers Area	447.6000	–	●	KE6DTF	LPARG
Covers Area	447.8200	–	●	KJ6TQ	MARS
Covers Area	448.1400	–	●	W7DOD	SWRRC
Covers Area	448.1800	–	●RBx	K6ERN	SMRA
Covers Area	448.3600	–	●	W7BF	------------
Covers Area	448.3800	–	●	WD6AWP	------------
Covers Area	448.4000	–	●	N6NHJ	CALNET
Covers Area	448.4800	–	●	KB6C	FRN
Covers Area	448.7400	–	●RBx	WA6COT	RRN
Covers Area	448.8000	–	●	WD5B	------------
Covers Area	449.1400	–	●	W6NM	GRONK
Covers Area	449.1400	–	●	WA6VPL	------------

Location	Output	Input	Notes	Call	Sponsor
Covers Area	449.3600	–	●	N6WZK	MCARC
SOCAL-OR					
Covers Area	445.3600	–	●	KA6P	BARC
Covers Area	445.3600	–	●	KA6P	BARC
Covers Area	446.1400	–	●	W6OPD	------------
Covers Area	446.7000	–	●	WA6TWF	SS
Covers Area	446.7200	–	●	N6KXK	IDEC
Covers Area	448.1200	–	●	WB6KOD	------------
Covers Area	449.4800	–	●	WB6NLU	------------
Covers Area	449.9800	–	●	K6IUM	RTD ARC
SOCAL-OR,RIV,SBER,SD					
Covers Area	448.9800	–	●RBx	KF6BYB	CACTUS
SOCAL-OR,RIV,SD					
Covers Area	449.0000	–	●RB	KF6ALG	CACTUS
SOCAL-OR,SD					
Covers Area	448.7600	–	●x	WD6APP	------------
SOCAL-RIV,SBER					
Covers Area	445.3000	–	●	W6CDF	------------
Covers Area	447.2800	–	●	K6JB	HDRN
Covers Area	447.9200	–	●	WB6AMY	------------
Covers Area	448.0400	–	●	K6SBC	SBER CNTY
Covers Area	448.4400	–	●	K6SBC	SBER CNTY
Covers Area	448.5000	–	●	K7SRC	SWRRC
Covers Area	448.6200	–	●RBx	WD6ASB	CACTUS
Covers Area	448.6500	–	●	W7DXJ	CACTUS
Covers Area	448.6800	–	●RBx	W6PNM	CACTUS
Covers Area	448.9200	–	●	K7SRC	SWRRC
Covers Area	448.9800	–	●RBx	WB7FIK	CACTUS
Covers Area	449.0000	–	●RBx	N6DD	CACTUS
Covers Area	449.2400	–	●	K6JR	SWRRC
SOCAL-SBAR					
Covers Area	444.8000	+	●	WA6VPL	------------
Covers Area	445.4800	–	●	N6VMN	------------
SOCAL-SBER					
Covers Area	446.8600	–	●I	KN3ICK	------------
Covers Area	448.2400	–	●RB	WB6LVZ	CACTUS
SOCAL-SD					
Covers Area	445.2200	–	●	KF6ATL	CALNET
Covers Area	445.3000	–	●	KM6VH	------------
Covers Area	445.7400	–	●	K6ODB	------------
Covers Area	445.8800	–	●	KM6NP	SCARA
Covers Area	446.0400	–	●	W6SRC	SWRRC
Covers Area	446.1400	–	●	WB6FMT	------------
Covers Area	446.1800	–	●	N6JOJ	------------
Covers Area	446.4200	–	●	W6CRC	------------
Covers Area	446.6600	–	●	KM6NP	SCARA
Covers Area	446.8000	–	●	KG6HSQ	------------
Covers Area	447.0400	–	●	KK6KD	------------
Covers Area	447.3600	–	●	AA4CD	------------

Location	*Output*	*Input*	*Notes*	*Call*	*Sponsor*
Covers Area	447.6000	–	●	AA4CD	------------
Covers Area	447.6200	–	●RBx	KB6BOB	CACTUS
Covers Area	447.9400	–	●	N6CRF	------------
Covers Area	448.2800	–	●	WB6NIL	------------
Covers Area	448.7800	–	●	K6JCC	RACES
Covers Area	449.0800	–	●	K6JSI	WINSYSTEM
Covers Area	449.1200	–	●	K6XI	------------
Covers Area	449.1400	–	●	N6VCM	ECRA
Covers Area	449.1600	–	●	WA6SYN	ECRA
Covers Area	449.2400	–	●	N6WB	Escondido ARC
Covers Area	449.3200	–	●	W6YJ	------------
Covers Area	449.6000	–	●	WV6H	CARE
Covers Area	449.8200	–	●BI	W6LKK	------------
Covers Area	449.8400	–	●	N6OEI	------------
Covers Area	449.9000	–	●	K6RYA	------------
Covers Area	449.9800	–	●	WA6SYN	ECRA
SOCAL-VE					
Covers Area	446.6600	–	●	W6KGB	GRONK
Covers Area	447.1400	–	●	WB6TZL	GRONK
Covers Area	447.1800	–	●	W6KGB	GRONK
Covers Area	448.3400	–	●	W6NE	------------
SOCAL-VE,LA,OR,RIV,SBER,SD					
Covers Area	448.6200	–	●RBx	WB6LVZ	CACTUS
Covers Area	449.0000	–	●RBx	WB6TZA	CACTUS
SOUTH CENTRAL					
Independence	442.3000	+	● 131.8l	W6TD	W6TD

COLORADO

FREQUENCY USAGE					
STATEWIDE	447.0500	–			
STATEWIDE	447.3000	–			
STATEWIDE	448.0500	–			
STATEWIDE	448.3250	–			
STATEWIDE	448.8250	–			
STATEWIDE	449.0750	–			
STATEWIDE	449.1000	–			
STATEWIDE	449.2750	–			
STATEWIDE	449.4250	–	O		
BOULDER COUNTY					
Boulder	447.7500	–	O 141.3/141.3 L(IRLP 3450)	NØSZ	RMHR
Boulder	447.9750	–	O 107.2/107.2 (CA)x	WØCRA	CRA
Boulder	448.9000	–	O 100 (CA)	WØDK	BARC
Boulder	449.4000	–	O 91.5	KØDK	KØDK
Boulder	449.5500	–	O 100l	WØIA	RMVHFS
Longmont	448.5250	–	O 151.4 L(ECHOLINK 223853)	NØEPA	NØEPA
Longmont	448.8000	–	O 88.5es	WØENO	LARC

Location	Output	Input	Notes	Call	Sponsor
Longmont	449.3750	–	●	N7ONI	N7ONI
CENTRAL					
Aspen	447.0500	–	O 136.5/136.5lx	KØVQ	RFARC
El Jebel	447.1500	–	O 136.5/136.5l	KØVQ	RFARC
Lake George	449.7000	–	O 107.2elx	KCØCVU	CMRG
Salida	449.9250	–	O 103.5/103.5x	WZØN	WZØN
COLORADO SPRINGS					
Colorado Springs	446.9500	–	ODCSelx	K7PFJ	RMHR
Colorado Springs	447.0250	–	O 123 (CA) elRB	KFØWF	CSARA
Colorado Springs	447.1000	–	O 107.2/107.2 L(IRLP 3621)	WDØC	WDØC
Colorado Springs	447.3500	–	O 151.4/151.4e	KØIRP	GGARC
Colorado Springs	447.4750	–	O 107.2 (CA)el	NXØG	MARC
Colorado Springs	447.5500	–	O 123e	WA6IFI	WA6IFI
Colorado Springs	448.0000	–	O 107.2/107.2 (CA)	NØCAM	CMRG
Colorado Springs	448.1000	–	O 192.2 (CA)elx	KCØCVU	CMRG
Colorado Springs	448.2500	–	O 123	NØKG	NØKG
Colorado Springs	448.3000	–	O 100/100e	AAØL	AAØL
Colorado Springs	448.4500	–	OtelrsWXx	KBØSRJ	PPFMA
Colorado Springs	448.6000	–	O 114.8l	WØMOG	WØMOG
Colorado Springs	448.7250	–	O 123	KAØTTF	KAØTTF
Colorado Springs	448.8000	–	O 100 (CA) el	KBØSRJ	PPFMA
Colorado Springs	449.4750	–	O 110.9/110.9e	KØHYT	KØHYT
Colorado Springs	449.5750	–	●	W9USN	RMHARC
Monument	447.7250	–	O 100/100 (CA) RB	KØNR	KØNR
Palmer Divide	449.7250	–	O 100	NØPWZ	NØPWZ
Woodland Park	447.6750	–	O 179.9/179.9 (CA) DCS(205)els	KAØWUC	MARC
Woodland Park	448.6500	–	O 107.2el	NXØG	MARC
Woodland Park	449.0250	–	O 141.3ls	KAØWUC	MARC
DENVER METRO					
Arvada	448.6250	–	O 100/100e l	WØTX	DRC
Aurora	448.2750	–	O 156.7/156.7 (CA)e	WØBG	WØBG
Aurora	448.4000	–	O 94.8/94.8	NØZUQ	NØZUQ
Aurora	448.7000	–	O 146.2/146.2	WQ8M	WQ8M

COLORADO

Location	Output	Input	Notes	Call	Sponsor
Aurora	449.1500	–	O 136.5/136.5el	WRØAEN	CARN
Boulder	446.9875	–	ODCSelx	K7PFJ	RMHR
Brighton	449.9250	–	O	KDØBJT	KDØBJT
Broomfield	448.9250	–	O 131.8 RB	WØLMA	WØLMA
Broomfield	449.8250	–	O 103.5el WXx	WØWYX	RMRL
Castle Pines North	449.9500	–	● 77	W9SL	W9SL
Como	448.1750	–	O 100/100els	ABØPC	ParkCntyRC
Conifer	447.5000	–	O 88.5ex	NØOWY	ARA
Deckers	446.9250	–	ODCSelr	NØESQ	EmCommCO
Denver	446.8000	–	Oelx	NØSZ	RMHR
Denver	446.9375	–	ODCSelx	NØSZ	RMHR
Denver	447.0750	–	O 156.7/156.7	WAØMJX	WAØMJX
Denver	447.1500	–	O 107.2/107.2 (CA)ex	WØCRA	CRA
Denver	447.2250	–	O 141.3elx	WØKVA	RMHR
Denver	447.5250	–	O 203.5/146.2ersWX	NØESQ	EmCommCO
Denver	447.5750	–	O 107.2/107.2esx	WØCRA	CRA
Denver	447.8250	–	O 100/100es	WØTX	DRC
Denver	447.9000	–	●	WBØTPT	WBØTPT
Denver	447.9250	–	O 100 (CA)	KØFEZ	RADOPS EJ
Denver	448.0750	–	O 123	WØIG	WØIG
Denver	448.5000	–	O 100e	KBØUDD	CRRG
Denver	448.5500	–	O 82.5e	WØKIZ	HPRA
Denver	448.6750	–	O 100x	KAØHTT	KAØHTT
Denver	448.7500	–	Ote	NØELY	NØELY
Denver	448.7750	–		KAØHJB	J & V
Denver	449.0000	–	O 136.5/136.5elx	WRØAEN	CARN
Denver	449.0500	–	O 107.2/107.2ex	WGØN	WGØN
Denver	449.2250	–	O 141.3/141.3 (CA)esx	NØSZ	RMHR
Denver	449.3500	–	O 100/100ex	WØTX	DRC
Denver	449.4500	–	O 103.5e WXx	WB5YOE	RMRL
Denver	449.6000	–	O 100e	WBØTUB	DRL
Denver	449.6500	–	O 136.5/136.5lWX	WRØAEN	CARN
Denver	449.6750	–	O 136.5/136.5el	WRØAEN	CARN

Location	*Output*	*Input*	*Notes*	*Call*	*Sponsor*
Denver	449.7500	–	●	WNØEHE	RMRL
Denver	449.8750	–	O 103.5exz	NØMHU	RMRL
Devils Head	447.5250	–	O 146.2/146.2ersWX	NØESQ	EmCommCO
Evergreen	448.2250	–	O 141.3/141.3eL(IRLP 7132)	NØSZ	RMHR
Fairplay	447.1250	–	O 103.5/103.5e	WZØN	WZØN
Firestone	447.6500	–	O 141.3/141.3	K2AD	RMHR
Golden	446.8375	–	ODCSe	WA2YZT	WA2YZT
Golden	447.1750	–	O 186.2es WX	WA2YZT	WA2YZT
Golden	448.1250	–	O 107.2	NØPYY	DenPDEEB
Golden	448.3750	–	●	WØOX	WØOX
Golden	448.8500	–	O 88.5ae	KØIBM	ARA
Golden	448.9750	–	O 123x	WØGV	FRG
Golden	449.5250	–	O 100elr	KEØSJ	KEØSJ
Golden	449.6250	–	O 141.3/141.3eL(IRLP 3750)	WØKU	RMHR
Lakewood	446.7875	–	Oe	WØTX	DRC
Lakewood	449.7750	–	● 100/100 (CA)	WAØYOJ	WAØYOJ
Lakewood	449.9750	–	●	WNØEHE	WNØEHE
Parker	448.4250	–	●	KØVKM	CRA
Red Feather Lakes	447.3250	–	O 100/100	KTØL	KTØL
Sedalia	449.1250	–	O 103.5x	WØWYX	RMRL
Westminster	449.3000	–	O 100/100 L(IRLP 3699)	N1UPS	N1UPS
EAST CENTRAL					
Limon	449.2500	–	O 123/123	KØUPS	N1UPS
Punkin Ctr	449.9000	–	O 107.2/107.2	N1FSX	N1FSX
GRAND JUNCTION					
Collbran	449.5000	–	O 107.2/107.2 E-SUN E-WINDlrsWX	KBØSW	GMRA
Grand Junction	447.5000	–	O 114.8/114.8	KCØARV	KCØARV
Grand Junction	448.1500	–	O 107.2	KEØTY	KEØTY
Grand Junction	449.0000	–	●te	KBØSW	KBØSW
Grand Junction	449.2000	–	O 107.2/107.2 (CA)elrsRB WX	NØNHP	GMRA
Grand Junction	449.3000	–	O 107.2/107.2 (CA)elrsWXx	WA4HND	GMRA
Grand Junction	449.5750	–	O 131.8/131.8elrsRB WXx	WA4HND	GMRA
GrandJct	448.9500	–	O 127.3/127.3	KDØNDG	KDØNDG

Location	Output	Input	Notes	Call	Sponsor
Loma	447.0000	–	O 107.2/107.2elrsx	KBØSW	GMRA
NORTH CENTRAL					
Winter Park	447.4500	–	O 103.5/103.5	WA4CCC	WØIG
NORTH FRONT RANGE					
Estes Park	449.8000	–	O 123/123e l	NØFH	EVARC
Fort Collins	447.2750	–	O 100 (CA) ersWXx	WØUPS	NCARC
Fort Collins	447.4500	–	O 123/123l x	KCØRBT	WØIG
Fort Collins	447.7000	–	O 100/100e lWX	WØUPS	NCARC
Fort Collins	449.8500	–	O 100 (CA)	WØQEY	CSUARC
Ft Collins	446.7500	–	ODCSx	NØSZ	RMHR
Ft Collins	447.7250	–	O 100 E-SUN	W7RF	W7RF
FtCollins	446.7375	–	ODCS	NØAOL	KDØCJS
Greeley	448.4750	–	O 100/100	KCØKWD	WARS
Greeley	449.3250	–	O 136.5/136.5el	WRØAEN	CARN
Greeley	449.7250	–	O 127.3ars WX	KØOJ	KØOJ
Loveland	448.0250	–	O 100/100s WX	WØUPS	NCARC
Loveland	449.5750	–	O 100 (CA) es	WØLRA	LRA
Severance	447.2000	–	O 82.5/82.5	N6RFI	N6RFI
NORTHEAST					
Greeley	447.3500	–	91.5/91.5e	KCØFNE	KCØFNE
NORTHWEST					
Steamboat Springs	449.6250	–	Otex	NØPRG	NØPRG
PUEBLO					
Canon City	447.7500	–	O 103.5es	WDØEKR	RGARC
Canon City	447.9750	–	O 100/100l s	KØJSC	KØJSC
Pueblo	446.8750	–	O(CA) DCS	KFØKR	KFØKR
Pueblo	447.1750	–	O 88.5ex	NDØQ	PuebloHC
Pueblo	447.9500	–	O 88.5ex	NDØQ	PuebloHC
Pueblo	448.9750	–	O 100/100l s	KØJSC	KØJSC
Pueblo	449.6250	–	O 186.6el	KCØCVU	CMRG
Pueblo	449.8000	–	O 118.8/118.8elrsWXx	KCØYWX	KCØYWX
Pueblo	449.8500	–	O	WAØVTO	STARS
Pueblo	449.9750	–	O 103.5/103.5lRB	KØJSC	KØJSC

Location	Output	Input	Notes	Call	Sponsor
Westcliffe	448.1500	–	O 103.5e	KBØTUC	RGARC
SOUTH CENTRAL					
Canon City	446.7375	–	ODCSel	KØJSC	KØJSC
Canon City	449.0000	–	O 67 E-SUNl	WBØWDF	WBØWDF
Cripple Creek	447.4000	–	O 67 E-SUNl	WBØWDF	WBØWDF
Salida	449.6500	–	Oelx	KCØCVU	CMRG
SOUTHEAST					
La Junta	449.6500	–	O 100/100e	KØIKN	CCRC
Lamar	449.5000	–	O 123l	KCØHH	LAMAR ARC
Springfield	449.2000	–	O 118.8/118.8elrsWX	KZØDEM	BCDEARC
Trinidad	449.6000	–	O 107.2elx	KCØCVU	CMRG
SOUTHWEST					
Cortez	449.1750	–	O 127.3	KD5LWU	KD5LWU
Durango	449.8500	–	O	KØEP	DARC
Mancos	447.3750	–	O 100/100e	KB5ITS	KB5ITS
Pagosa Springs	448.7250	–	● 82.5	N7EX	N7TX
Silverton	447.5250	–	OE-SUNx	KB5ITS	KB5ITS
WEST CENTRAL					
Breckenridge	447.8500	–	O 100/100e x	NØSZ	RMHR
Carbondale	449.7250	–	O 179.9x	KØELK	RFARC
Cedaredge	447.3500	–	O 107.2/107.2elrsWX	KDØEH	GMRA
Cedaredge	449.8250	–	O 100/100	WØALC	WØALC
Delta	449.4000	–	O 131.8/131.8 E-SUNlrsWX	NØMOR	GMRA
Glenwood Springs	447.1000	–	O 107.2	KIØG	SCARC
Glenwood Springs	447.6000	–	●	KIØG	SCARC
Glenwood Springs	449.6000	–	O 107.2/107.2elrsWX	NØXLI	GMRA
Grand Junction	449.6500	–	O 151.4/151.4e	KBØYNA	KBØYNA
Gunnison	449.9500	–	O	K5GF	K5GF
Montrose	447.2000	–	O 107.2/107.2elrsWX	WA4HND	GMRA
Parachute	449.8000	–	O 107.2/107.2 (CA)elrsWX	N2XYY	GMRA
Rio Blanco	449.7000	–	O 107.2/107.2 (CA)elrsWX	N2XYY	GMRA
Vail	449.9000	–	O 107.2/107.2	NØAFO	ECHO

Location	Output	Input	Notes	Call	Sponsor
CONNECTICUT					
FREQUENCY USAGE					
SNP Pair	442.0000	+	○		
FAIRFIELD & SOUTHWEST					
Ansonia	442.9000	+	○ 77.0e	WK1M	------------
Bridgeport	441.5000	+	77.0ae	N1LXV	------------
Bridgeport	443.5500	+	77.0	WA1YQE	------------
Bridgeport	449.4000	–	○ 114.8	KA1HCX	CAFI
Danbury	443.6500	+	○ 114.8/114.8el	W1HDN	PVRA
Danbury	447.7750	–	○ 100.0	W1QI	CARA
Fairfield	446.8250	–	○ 100.0	N3AQJ	FUARA
Greenwich	443.4000	+		N1LNA	------------
New Canaan	447.2750	–	○ 123.0/123.0a	W1FSM	W1FSM
Norwalk	448.0750	–	○ 114.8/114.8 (CA)	W1NLK	GNARC
Stamford	447.1250	–	○ 114.8/114.8e	W1EE	SARA
Westport	442.2500	+	○	KG1M	------------
HARTFORD & N CENTRAL					
Avon	444.9500	+	●	K1IIG	AVON RPT
Bristol	442.8500	+	○ 77.0/77.0 l	N1JGR	ICRC
Bristol	444.6500	+	○ 77.0/77.0 el	KB1AEV	KB1AEV
Bristol	448.8750	–	○ 110.9e	W1IXU	W1JJA
Coventry	449.8750	–	○ 162.2	K1JCL	------------
E Hartford	443.2500	+	○ 141.3/141.3e	W1EHC	EH CERT
E Hartland	448.0000	–	○ 162.2e	W1XOJ	YANKEE NET
Farmington	442.7000	+	○ 173.8e	N1GCN	N1GCN
Glastonbury	449.6250	–	○ 110.9/110.9e	W1EDH	CT ARE SVC
Hartford	443.1000	+	○ 114.8e	W1HDN	PVRA
Manchester	449.2250	–	○ 77.0/77.0	WA1YQB	------------
Newington	443.0500	+	○ 100.0/100.0	W1OKY	NARL
Newington	444.3500	+	○	KA1BQO	------------
Newington	449.5750	–	○ 79.7 (CA) el	WA1UTQ	------------
Plainville	447.0750	–	○ 110.9/110.9e	AA1WU	N1GLA
Vernon	442.6000	+	○ 77.0/77.0 el	KB1AEV	KB1AEV
Vernon	443.3000	+	○ 114.8/114.8	W1HDN	PVRA
Vernon	443.7500	+	○ 77.0/77.0 e	W1BRS	BEARS MAN

Location	Output	Input	Notes	Call	Sponsor
LITCHFIELD & NORTHWEST					
Torrington	443.6000	+	O 82.5/82.5 (CA)el	W1HDN	PVRA
Torrington	447.2250	+	O 77.0/77.0 aelz	KB1AEV	KB1AEV
Torrington	449.7750	–	O 141.3/141.3e	K1KGQ	------------
Washington	441.8500	+	O 77.0/77.0 els	NA1RA	NARA
Watertown	441.6500	+	O 77.0/77.0 el	KB1AEV	KB1AEV
NEW HAVEN & S CENTRAL					
Bethany	441.1000	+	Olr	W1EDH	MARA
Branford	449.3250	–	O 103.5/103.5eWX	N1HUI	BFD-OEM
Durham	446.9250	–	O 77.0/77.0 el	KB1MMR	------------
East Haven	449.8250	–	O 110.9/110.9e	KA1MJ	SCARA
EastHaddam	440.8000	+	O 110.9	K1IKE	Ares/Races
Guilford	449.4750	–	O 110.9ael r	NI1U	KM1R
Guilford	449.9000	444.4000	● 110.9	KM1R	KM1R
Hamden	444.4500	+	O 100.0/100.0e	WA1MIK	------------
Meriden	448.0000	–	192.8	W1XOJ	NYNES
Middletown	446.8750	–	O 156.7elr	K1IKE	------------
Milford	441.7000	+	O 77.0 (CA) el	N1KGN	------------
Woodbridge	442.5000	+	O#(CA) DCS(073)e	W1WPD	SPARC
NEW LONDON & SOUTHEAST					
Groton	448.9750	–	O 156.7	W1NLC	SCRAMS
Mystic	446.5750	+	O 127.3/127.3	KB1CJP	KB1CJP
Norwich	441.9500	+	O 67.0/67.0	W1HLO	------------
Norwich	449.7250	–	O 156.7/156.7	N1NW	RASON
WINDHAM & NORTHEAST					
Killingly	444.1000	+	O 77.0/77.0 el	N7PRD	KB1AEV

DELAWARE

Location	Output	Input	Notes	Call	Sponsor
ALL					
SNP	442.9000	+	O		------------
SNP	447.8750	–	O		------------
DOVER					
Dover	444.5000	+	O 114.8	N3IOC	N3IOC
Dover	449.7250	–	O 131.8 (CA)lWX	W3BXW	BEARS

Location	*Output*	*Input*	*Notes*	*Call*	*Sponsor*
Wyoming	449.7750	–	O 114.8	N3IOC	N3IOC
SOUTH					
Bethany Beach	448.7250	–	O 131.8 (CA)lWX	W3BXW	BEARS
Delmar	444.0500	+	O 156.7	K3RIC	K3RIC
Harrington	442.4500	+	O 131.8	N3HTT	N3HTT
Lewes	443.5500	+	O 156.7ers	W4ALT	STAR-NET
Millsboro	449.8250	–	O 156.7e	K3JL	Sussex ARA
WILMINGTON					
Delaware City	448.8250	–	O 127.3	N3HTT	DelMarVa
Newark	444.9500	+	O 100.0	W3CER	ChristianaHosp
Newark	449.0250	–	O 131.8	W3DRA	DRA
Wilmington	444.4000	+	O 100.0	W3CER	ChristianaHosp
Wilmington	448.3750	–	O 131.8	W3DRA	DRA

DISTRICT OF COLUMBIA

ALL					
SNP	442.9000	+	O		------------
SNP	447.8750	–	O		------------
WASHINGTON AREA					
Washington	448.5750	–	O	K3VOA	VOA ARC
Washington	448.8750	–	O	KC3VO	RACES/AR
Washington	449.9750	–	O 107.2al	WA3KOK	NERA

FLORIDA

CENTRAL					
Bartow	444.9500	+	O 127.3/127.3eL(146.985 444.625)rsWXx	WC4PEM	PCEM
Clermont	442.4750	+	O 103.5/103.5 E-SUN	K4VJ	K4VJ
Davenport	442.1500	+	O 103.5/103.5es	WA1VHF	WA1VHF
Davenport	444.6250	+	O 127.3/127.3eL(146.985 444.950)rsWX	WC4PEM	PCEM
Lake Wales	442.4250	+	O 127.3/127.3es	K4LKW	LWRA
Lakeland	442.6750	+	O 114.8/114.8 BI	N4AMC	N4AMC
Lakeland	442.9750	+	O 100/100	W4CLL	W4CLL
Lakeland	444.3000	+	O 127.3/127.3eL(145.13) BI	WP3BC	WP3BC
Pebbledale	442.8250	+	O 100/100e L(145.290 145.430 442.550 442.950 443.450 I	NI4CE	WCFG
The Villages	444.5750	+	O 91.5/91.5 e	WA1UTQ	WA1UTQ
Winter Haven	441.8000	+	O 127.3/127.3	KE4WDP	KE4WDP
Winter Haven	444.8000	+	O 127.3/127.3	KE4WDP	KE4WDP

Location	*Output*	*Input*	*Notes*	*Call*	*Sponsor*
CENTRAL - ORLANDO					
Altamonte Springs	442.9750	+	O 103.5/103.5e	N4EH	LMARS
Bushnell	443.1250	+	Otae	W1LBV	W1LBV
Clermont	442.4500	+	O 103.5/103.5	KG4RPH	KG4RPH
Clermont	444.9750	+	Ot	KAØOXH	KAØOXH
Deland	442.2000	+	O 88.5/88.5 DCS(411) L(IR-4672 EC)	K4KWQ	K4KWQ
Deland	444.1500	+	O 88.5/88.5 E-SUN L(IR-4563)	K4HEK	K4HEK
Deland	444.8000	+	O 88.5/88.5 E-SUN	K4HEK	K4HEK
Eustis	443.5500	+	O 103.5/103.5e	K4VJ	KD4MBN
Eustis	444.8750	+	O 103.5/103.5	N4ZSN	N4ZSN
Kissimmee	442.1000	+	O 103.5/103.5 DCS(411) L(147.210 444.450 4	N4OTC	OTARC
Kissimmee	444.4500	+	O 103.5/103.5a(CA) L(147.210 927.7000 IR-4	K4SLB	K4SLB
Lake Buena Vista	442.0500	+	O 123/123	KD4JYD	KD4JYD
Lake Buena Vista	442.0500	+	O 123/123	KD4JYD	KD4JYD
Lake Buena Vista	444.0000	+	O 103.5/103.5e	WD4WDW	DEARS
Longwood	443.7000	+	O 103.5/103.5eL(927.65)	KD4JYD	KD4JYD
Orange City	442.8750	+	ODCS(411) e	W4ORL	W4ORL
Orlando	442.0750	+	O 103.5/103.5x	W4LOV	KD4JYD
Orlando	442.1750	+	O 103.5/103.5a(CA)e	W4MFC	LMARA
Orlando	442.2500	+	O 103.5/103.5e	KD4Z	KD4Z
Orlando	442.3750	+	● 100/100 DCS(411)el	NN4TT	NN4TT
Orlando	442.7000	+	O 103.5/103.5ers	W4MCO	OCCA
Orlando	443.1000	+	O 103.5/103.5 L(IR-4949 EC-44310)	K4ZPZ	K4ZPZ
Orlando	443.3250	+	O 103.5/103.5a(CA)eRB	WD4IXD	WD4IXD
Orlando	443.3500	+	Ot	KAØOXH	KAØOXH
Orlando	443.3750	+	O 103.5/103.5eL(IR-4775 EC-225634)	K4UCF	ARCUCF
Orlando	443.5250	+	O 103.5/103.5ers	W4MCO	OCCA
Orlando	443.8500	+	O 103.5/103.5a(CA)ex	N4ATS	N4ATS

Location	*Output*	*Input*	*Notes*	*Call*	*Sponsor*
Orlando	443.9500	+	O tel	KAØOXH	KAØOXH
Orlando	443.9750	+	O 103.5/103.5	KA4QXP	KA4QXP
Orlando	444.1250	+	O 103.5/103.5eL(EC-38990)	W4AES	AESOARC
Oviedo	442.9500	+	O 103.5/103.5a(CA)e	WD4DSV	WD4DSV
St Cloud	444.1000	+	O 123/123e L(145.350 EC-458245)rsx	KG4EOC	EOCARDS
Winter Park	442.5250	+	O 103.5/103.5ers	W4MCO	OCCA
DEEP SOUTH					
Big Pine Key	442.3750	+	● 110.9/110.9 A(220-111-110) TT(*05ON/#05OFF)e	NQ2Z	N2GKG
Key West	443.1000	+	O 156.7/156.7	WA4JFJ	FKARC
Key West	443.3750	+	● 110.9/110.9rsBlx	W4HN	W4HN
Marathon	444.0250	+	O 94.8/94.8 elWX	KA4EPS	ATTATA
EAST CENTRAL					
Cocoa	444.4000	+	O 103.5/103.5e	W4JAZ	ARJS
Cocoa	444.7500	+	● 107.2/107.2r	N4LEM	N4LEM
Cocoa Beach	444.6500	+	O 107.2/107.2esx	W4NLX	IRARC
Ft Pierce	443.4750	+	O 107.2/107.2ers	W4SLC	SLC EAR
Ft Pierce	444.6000	+	O 107.2/107.2er	W4SLC	SLC EAR
Ft Pierce	444.8000	+	O 107.2/107.2a(CA)eL(147.345 IR-4545 EC-2004)r	W4AKH	FPARC
Melbourne	443.0000	+	●a(CA)l	WB2GGP	WB2GGP
Melbourne	443.8000	+	O 103.5/103.5	WB4OEZ	WB4OEZ
Melbourne	444.4250	+	O 100.0/100.0a(CA)e	W4MLB	PCARS
Melbourne	444.5750	+	O 103.5/103.5	WB4OEZ	WB4OEZ
Melbourne	444.8250	+	● 167.9/167.9e	KI4SWB	KI4SWB
Merritt Island	444.7750	+	O 107.2/107.2a(CA) E-SUN L(IR-4227 EC-302025)	KC2UFO	SKYANDCOM
Palm Bay	444.4750	+	O 107.2/107.2aTT(# * IN # OUT)eL(IR-4954 EC-255	KI4HZP	KI4HZP
Palm Bay	444.5750	+	O 151.4/151.4aTT(# *)	KI4HZP	KI4HZP
Port St John	444.3500	+	O 103.5/103.5e	W4PLT	W4PLT

Location	Output	Input	Notes	Call	Sponsor
Port St Lucie	443.6500	+	O 107.2/107.2es	K4PSL	PSLARA
Port St Lucie	444.0000	+	O 107.2/107.2eL(927.6625 IR)rsWXxz	K4NRG	NRG
Rockledge	444.5250	+	O 103.5/103.5er	K4EOC	BEARS
Titusville	442.8500	+	O 107.2/107.2es	N3EH	N3EH
Valkaria	444.7000	+	● 77/77e	K4HV	K4HV
Vero Beach	444.7250	+	O 107.2/107.2aeL(EC)	K4CPJ	TCRA
Vero Beach	444.8500	+	O 107.2/107.2elWX	KA4EPS	ATTATA
NORTH CENTRAL					
Gainesville	444.9250	+	OE-WINDrs	K4GNV	GARS
Lake City	444.9000	+	O 110.9/110.9eL(442.100 442.900)rsx	NF4CQ	CARS
Live Oak	442.9250	+	O 127.3/127.3e	KC4GOL	KC4GOL
Live Oak	443.6000	+	O 127.3/127.3a(CA)eL(EC-198563) BI	KC4GOL	KC4GOL
Macclenny	444.0750	+	O 100/100	AB4GE	AB4GE
Ocala	444.3250	+	Oe L(145.43)x	KA2MBE	KA2MBE
Summerfield	443.2500	+	O 141.3/141.3a(CA)eL(147.360 EC-317403)	KI4LOB	KI4LOB
NORTH EAST					
Bunnell	444.0000	+	O 123/123 L(145.450 224.020 145.190 EC-158400)	KB4JDE	KB4JDE
Daytona Beach	444.8500	+	O 127.3/127.3	W4TAM	W4TAM
Deltona	444.2500	+	O 103.5/103.5e	NP4ND	NP4ND
Hollister	443.9000	+	O 94.8/94.8 e	W4OBB	PARCI
Holly Hill	444.1750	+	O 156.7/156.7eL(146 655 53.05 EC-50666)	KI4RF	KI4RF
Orange City	442.9250	+	O 103.5/103.5eL(EC-369183)X	KW4LCB	KW4LCB
Ormond Beach	443.8250	+	O 118.8/118.8a(CA)	KE4NZG	KE4NZG
Palm Coast	443.1500	+	O 107.2/107.2es	AF2C	FECA
San Mateo	444.9500	+	O 156.7/156.7e	W4OBB	W4OBB
Vero Beach	444.8750	+	O 107.2/107.2	W4VRB	RATS

Location	*Output*	*Input*	*Notes*	*Call*	*Sponsor*
NORTH EAST - JACKSONVILLE					
Jacksonville	444.2000	+	O 127.3/127.3eL(EC-444200 442.100 444.900 442	K4QHR	K4QHR
Jacksonville	444.4000	+	O 127.3/127.3aeL(146.700 145.370)rsxz	W4IZ	NOFARS
Jacksonville	444.8250	+	O 156.7/156.7er	W4IJJ	W4IJJ
Jacksonville Beach	444.8750	+	O	KB4ARS	BARS
St Augustine	443.5000	+	Oe	KF4MX	KF4MX
NORTH WEST					
Chattahoochee	444.9750	+	O 94.8/94.8 e	K4GFD	K4GFD
Chipley	443.2000	+	O 103.5/103.5	KJ4BDU	KJ4BDU
Freeport	443.1000	+	O 100/100 E-SUNrsWX	WF4X	WCARC
Lee	442.0000	+	O 123/123e sRB	W4FAO	W4FAO
Madison	444.3000	+	O 94.8/94.8 L(444.1)	K4III	K4III
Marianna	444.9500	+	O	W4BKD	Chipola AR
Perry	444.1000	+	O 94.8/94.8 eL(444.3)x	K4III	K4III
Tallahassee	444.1750	+	O 94.8/94.8 e	K4GFD	K4GFD
NORTH WEST - PENSACOLA					
Crestview	444.9500	+	O 100/100e sz	N4NID	N4NID
Eglin AFB	444.8000	+	O 100/100a	W4NN	Eglin ARS
Milton	444.4000	+	O 100/100 E-SUN L(EC-629157)sx	W4VIY	Milton ARC
Navarre	444.2000	+	O 131.8/131.8	KC4ERT	NCERT
Pensacola	443.7000	+	O 100/100e	WB4OQF	WB4OQF
Pensacola	443.8500	+	O 100/100e	WA4ECY	CSARC
NORTH WEST - TALLAHASSEE					
Crawfordville	444.4500	+	O 94.8/94.8 E-SUNrs	K4WAK	SPARC
Tallahassee	442.1000	+	O 94.8/94.8 esx	K4TLH	TARS
Tallahassee	442.8500	+	O 94.8/94.8 esx	K4TLH	TARS
Tallahassee	443.9500	+	O 94.8/94.8 aerx	AE4S	AE4S
Tallahassee	444.0000	+	O 94.8/94.8 eL(EC-1922)	KD4MOJ	KD4MOJ
Tallahassee	444.4000	+	O 131.8/131.8	N4NKV	N4NKV

Location	*Output*	*Input*	*Notes*	*Call*	*Sponsor*
Tallahassee	444.8000	+	O 94.8/94.8 ersx	K4TLH	TARS
SOUTH CENTRAL					
Arcadia	444.2000	+	O 100/100e L(147.075)	W4MIN	DARC
Avon Park	444.1250	+	ODCS(51)e L(444.825 444.925 145.330 147.270 145.2	W4HEM	HCEM
Avon Park	444.8250	+	O 100/100e s	W4HEM	HCEM
Brighton	444.9250	+	O 100/100e s	W4HEM	HCEM
Clewiston	443.5250	+	O 82.5/82.5 L(145.150 442.800 443.525 224.160 EC)	KJ4GNM	WB4TWQ
Clewiston	444.4000	+	O 82.5/82.5 E-SUN L(145.350 443.525 444.500 442.80	WB4TWQ	KJ4GVO
Lake Placid	442.3500	+	O 100/100e	KE4WU	HCARC
Lake Placid	443.9500	+	O 100/100e L(442.95)	KK4LI	KK4LI
Lake Placid	444.1750	+	ODCS(51)e L(444.825 444.925 145.330 147.270 145.2	W4HEM	HCEM
Lake Placid	444.5250	+	O 206.5/206.5rs	WW4EOC	WW4EOC
Okeechobee	444.0500	+	O 100/100	K4OKE	OARC
Sebring	444.1500	+	ODCS(51)e L(444.825 444.925 145.330 147.270 145.2	W4HEM	HCEM
Wauchula	442.3250	+	O 127.3/127.3eL(146.625)rs	N4EMH	HARG
SOUTH EAST					
Boca Raton	442.0000	+	O 110.9/110.9er	KS4VT	KS4VT
Boca Raton	442.2250	442.2250	●e L(IR-8641 EC-86410) WXx	W2WDW	W2WDW
Boca Raton	442.6000	+	O 107.2/107.2 L(IR-4548)	KG4GOQ	KG4GOQ
Boca Raton	442.8750	+	O 110.9/110.9ers	WB4QNX	BRARA
Boca Raton	443.1500	+	O 110.9/110.9	K4LFK	K4LFK
Boca Raton	443.5000	+	O 131.8/131.8e	WF3I	WEBARK
Boca Raton	444.7000	+	O 123/123a (CA)e	KC4GH	BRFD
Boynton Beach	443.1000	+	O 110.9/110.9e	KG4DWP	BBFR
Boynton Beach	444.6500	+	O 127.3/127.3a(CA)elz	NR4P	NR4P
Indiantown	444.4500	+	O 110.9/110.9ersxz	AG4BV	AG4BV
Juno Beach	444.2000	+	● 110.9/110.9eL(IR-8641 EC-86410) WX	W2WDW	W2WDW

Location	*Output*	*Input*	*Notes*	*Call*	*Sponsor*
Jupiter	443.8250	+	O 103.5/103.5eWX	KA4EPS	ATTATA
Jupiter Farms	444.4000	+	O 110.9/110.9ex	AG4BV	AG4BV
Lake Worth	444.8500	+	O 103.5/103.5elWX	KA4EPS	ATTATA
Mangolia Park	444.3250	+	O 179.9/179.9 BI	KD4JM	KD4JM
Palm Beach Gardens	444.2250	+	O 110.9/110.9a(CA)ers	W4JUP	JTRG
Royal Palm Beach	443.9750	+	O 110.9/110.9es	K4EEX	PWARC
Stuart	444.9000	+	O 107.2/107.2eL(EC-315546)rs	WX4MC	MCARES
Wellington	442.0500	+	O 103.5/103.5eL(IR-4394 EC)rx	K4WRC	WRC
West Palm Beach	443.8750	+	O 110.9/110.9eL(IR-4111 EC-41119)	W2WDW	KF4LZA
West Palm Beach	444.1250	+	O 107.2/107.2 L(IR-4548)	KG4GOQ	KG4GOQ
West Palm Beach	444.2750	+	O 110.9/110.9er	W4PBC	PBCRACES

SOUTH EAST - MIAMI/FT LAUD

Location	*Output*	*Input*	*Notes*	*Call*	*Sponsor*
Aventura	442.2500	+	O 114.8/114.8 L(46.850 147.375 443.825 IR-4022)	K4PAL	PARC
Aventura	443.8250	+	O 114.8/114.8eL(IR-4022)	K4PAL	PARC
Belle Glade	443.9000	+	O 131.8/131.8eL(443.925 927.525) WX	KF4ACN	KF4ACN
Coral Springs	443.8500	+	O 110.9/110.9eL(145.110 EC-46246) WX	WR4AYC	WR4AYC RG
Coral Springs	444.5750	+	O 131.8/131.8eL(224.68)rsRB LITZx	N2DUI	WA4EMJ
Deerfield Beach	442.7500	+	O 110.9/110.9aeL(444.125 444.850 IR-4983 EC)	KA4EPS	KA4EPS
Deerfield Beach	444.4250	+	O 110.9/110.9	N4ZUW	N4ZUW
Ft Lauderdale	442.5000	+	O 110.9/110.9el	W4BUG	GCARA
Ft Lauderdale	443.0000	+	O 88.5/88.5 esx	N4MOT	MARC
Ft Lauderdale	443.0500	+	O 131.8/131.8a(CA)eBI	K4BRY	K4BRY
Ft Lauderdale	443.4000	+	● teWX	K4MAP	K4MAP
Ft Lauderdale	443.6250	+	O 110.9/110.9 L(IR-4864 EC-48646 147.0750)	W2GGI	KF4LZA
Ft Lauderdale	443.7500	+	O 110.9/110.9a(CA)eL(927.700 IR-4787 EC-47873)	KF4LZA	CCRC
Ft Lauderdale	443.8000	+	O 131.8/131.8e	KD4CPG	KD4CPG

Location	Output	Input	Notes	Call	Sponsor
Ft Lauderdale	444.0500	+	●DCS(25)e WX	KB2TZ	KB2TZ
Ft Lauderdale	444.8250	+	O 110.9/110.9a(CA)e	W4AB	BARC
Hiaheah	442.3750	+	O 103.5/103.5a(CA) TT(*05ON/#05OFF) E-SU	N2GKG	N2GKG
Hialeah	441.8500	+	ODCS(205) BI	W4PHR	W4PHR
Hialeah	442.9250	+	O 110.9/110.9lBI	WD4DPS	WD4DPS
Hialeah	443.9500	+	O 110.9/110.9a(CA)ersBIx	WB4IVM	WB4IVM
Hialeah	444.2250	+	● 67/67a (CA)e	KE4YUW	KE4YUW
Hialeah	444.3500	+	O 94.8/94.8 e	KA4EPS	ATTATA
Hialeah	444.7500	+	O 110.9/110.9a(CA)ersBIx	WB4IVM	WB4IVM
Hialeah	444.8000	+	O 110.9/110.9a(CA)ersBIx	WB4IVM	WB4IVM
Hollywood	442.7750	+	O 110.9/110.9 L(EC-329701) BI WX(99*)	K4ABB	K4ABB
Hollywood	443.2500	+	Oa(CA)	N2VNG	KZ4TI
Hollywood	444.1500	+	O 88.5/88.5 a(CA)	WF2C	HMRH
Hollywood	444.1750	+	O 107.2/107.2a(CA)eL(53.030 145.210) LITZ x	AC4XQ	AC4XQ
Lake Worth	444.2500	+	●DCS(205) ex	W4YVM	W4YVM
Margate	444.0250	+	O 107.2/107.2eWX	KA4EPS	ATTATA
Miami	442.0750	+	● 88.5/88.5 el	KI4GQO	KI4GQO
Miami	442.1000	+	O 88.5/88.5 eL(EC-4410)	W4CSO	W4CSO
Miami	442.1500	+	● 94.8/94.8 rsBIx	K4AG	K4AG
Miami	442.1750	+	O 94.8/94.8 ex	W4ILQ	W4ILQ
Miami	442.2750	+	Ot	AE4WE	AE4WE
Miami	442.5250	+	O 88.5/88.5 ex	KR4DQ	KR4DQ
Miami	442.6250	+	O 103.5/103.5eBI	KC4SJL	KC4SJL
Miami	442.6500	+	O 94.8/94.8 eL(IR-4489 EC-44891)rsBIx	KB4ELI	KB4ELI
Miami	442.7250	+	O	KC4MND	KC4MND
Miami	442.8000	+	O 118.8/118.8e	WB4TWQ	WB4TWQ

Location	*Output*	*Input*	*Notes*	*Call*	*Sponsor*
Miami	442.9750	+	Oa(CA) BI	WD4RXD	RC de Cuba
Miami	443.0750	+	O 107.2/107.2ex	KZ4TI	KZ4TI
Miami	443.1750	+	● 107.2/107.2exz	AC4XQ	AC4XQ
Miami	443.4250	+	O 94.8/94.8 L(IR-8369 EC-83690)	KF4LZA	KF4LZA
Miami	443.4500	+	O 110.9/110.9rsRB BIx	AE4EQ	AE4EQ
Miami	443.4750	+	Ot	KB4AIL	KB4AIL
Miami	443.5250	+	O 110.9/110.9	WB4TWQ	KE4WZD
Miami	443.5500	+	O 110.9/110.9 L(145.41)rsx	W4HN	W4HN
Miami	443.6000	+	O 103.5/103.5a(CA) L(EC-210790) WX	N4LJQ	N4LJQ
Miami	443.7750	+	OBI	KS4WF	KS4WF
Miami	444.1250	+	O 94.8/94.8 e	KA4EPS	ATTATA
Miami	444.2000	+	O 94.8/94.8 eL(442.075 442.350 146.835 146.925 147.000)r	KA4HLO	DRC
Miami	444.2500	+	Ot	AE4WE	AE4WE
Miami	444.2750	+	O 94.8/94.8	K4PCS	K4PCS
Miami	444.3000	+	O 103.5/103.5	WB4DD	WB4DD
Miami	444.3750	+	O 94.8/94.8 L(145.470 224.600 147.045 145.170 442.950 2	KC4MNE	KC4MNE
Miami	444.4500	+	● 110.9/110.9 BI	WA4PHG	Teletrol
Miami	444.5000	+	O 127.3/127.3 L(145.230 146.700) RB BIxz	KC2CWC	KI4RAL
Miami	444.5250	+	O 114.8/114.8e	KD4IMM	KD4IMM
Miami	444.6000	+	O 94.8/94.8	K4AG	K4AG
Miami	444.6750	+	O 110.9/110.9 L(29.620 145.150 442.800 443.525	WB4TWQ	WB4TWQ
Miami	444.8750	+	● 88.5/131.8 L(147.000 146.835 442.350 444.200	KI4GQO	KI4GQO
Miramar	444.1000	+	O 103.5/103.5a(CA) TT(*789 #987) DCS(23)eL(147.	N2YAG	N2YAG
North Dade	443.1250	+	● 107.2/107.2ersWXx	AC4XQ	AC4XQ
Pembroke Pines	441.9000	+	O 110.9/110.9 L(EC-468418)	K2HXC	K2HXC
Pembroke Pines	444.5500	+	● 146.2/146.2 E-SUN E-WIND BI	KC4MNI	KC4MNI
Pembroke Pines	444.7750	+	O 88.5/88.5 BI	KP4BM	KP4BM
Plantation	441.4250	+	O 110.9/110.9 L(IR-8091)	K4GET	K4GET

Location	*Output*	*Input*	*Notes*	*Call*	*Sponsor*
Plantation	442.8500	+	O 110.9/110.9	WA4YOG	WA4YOG
Port Saint Lucie	442.5750	+	O 110.9/110.9l	W4RCC	W4RCC
Princeton	442.3500	+	O 94.8/94.8 eL(442.075 444.200 146.835 146.925 147.	KF4ACN	KF4ACN
Riviera Beach	443.9250	+	O 131.8/131.8eL(443.900 927.525)s	KF4ACN	KF4ACN
Southwest Ranches	442.5750	+	O 103.5/103.5l	W4RCC	W4RCC
SOUTH WEST					
Ave Marie	444.0750	447.0750	O 103.5/103.5 RB	N4DJJ	KC1AR
Ft Myers	444.4500	+	O 77/77 L(443.900 444.075 442.125 224.380)	WB4FOW	WB4FOW
Marco Island	443.6500	+	O 141.3/141.3	K5MI	MIRC
Murdock	444.6000	+	O 82.5/82.5 eL(442.600 444.875 EC-209942)	N9OJ	N9OJ
Naples	442.7500	+	O 67/67 RB	KC1AR	KC1AR
Naples	443.9000	+	● 67/67 L(444.450 442 125 444.075 224.380)	N5ICT	N5ICT
SOUTH WEST - FT MYERS					
Cape Coral	442.4750	+	O 136.5/136.5	W4LAZ	W4LAZ
Cape Coral	444.7250	+	O 136.5/136.5eL(IR-4171 EC-41712)sRB WX(	KN2R	KN2R
Estero	442.1250	+	● 131.8/131.8 L(444.450 449.900 444.075 22	N5ICT	GAS
Ft Myers	442.2250	+	O 103.5/103.5eL(444.450 443.900) RB	WB4FOW	WB4FOW
Ft Myers	442.4500	+	O 136.5/136.5e	WB2FAU	FMARC
Ft Myers	443.0500	+	O 141.3/141.3eL(EC-326006)	NG2F	NG2F
Ft Myers	444.7750	+	O 136.5/136.5	WX4L	WX4L
Lehigh Acres	442.8000	+	O 82.5/82.5 eL(145.150 442.800 443.525 224.160 29.6	WB4TWQ	WB4TWQ
Naples	444.9000	+	O 67/67e	WA1QDP	WA1QDP
Port Charlotte	442.9250	+	O 136.5/136.5e	W4DUX	PRRA
Punta Gorda	444.8500	+	● 136.5/136.5eL(52.525)rs	KØRTU	KØRTU
Punta Gorda	444.9750	+	O 136.5/136.5 L(146.745)rs	WX4E	CARS
WEST CENTRAL					
Brooksville	442.1250	+	Or	K4BKV	HCARA
Dade City	443.6000	+	O 146.2/146.2 E-SUN	KD4QLF	KD4QLF

Location	Output	Input	Notes	Call	Sponsor
Port Richey	442.6500	+	O 146.2/146.2eWX(*)	KG4YZY	KG4YZY
Port Richey	444.6500	+	O 103.5/103.5	WA4GDN	GCARC
Spring Hill	442.0500	+	O 103.5/103.5e	K4SH	K4SH
Spring Hill	443.8250	+	O 103.5/103.5e	N4TIA	N4TIA
WEST CENTRAL - SARASOTA					
Bradenton	442.1250	+	O 100/100 Z(*911)	KF4MBN	MC ARES/RACES
Bradenton	443.2250	+	O 103.5/103.5	KF4MBN	MC ARES/RACES
Bradenton	444.2750	+	● 103.5/103.5	K4MPX	K4MPX
Bradenton	444.7000	+	O 100/100e L(145.13)s	N4SER	SERC
Bradenton	444.8750	+	O 151.4/151.4eL(442.300 444.600 EC-209942)	N9OJ	N9OJ
Englewood	444.6250	+	O 77/77	KØDGF	KØDGF
Sarasota	442.3000	+	O 82.5/82.5 eL(444.600 444.875 EC-209942)	N9OJ	N9OJ
Sarasota	443.5500	+	O 100/100e rsx	WC4EM	SCEM
Sarasota	443.8750	+	O 100/100 RB	WA2HCV	SSMART
Sarasota	444.5500	+	O 141.3/141.3e	KD4MZM	KD4MZM
Sarasota	444.8250	+	O 100/100 RB	WA2HCV	SSMART
Sarasota	444.9250	+	Oae L(146.91)	W4IE	SARA
Venice	443.7500	+	O 100/100r s	WC4EM	SCEM
Venice	444.1000	+	O 100/100e	W4AC	TARC
Verna	442.9500	+	O 100/100e lrWX	NI4CE	WCFG
WEST CENTRAL - TAMPA/ST PETE					
Brandon	443.5000	+	O 127.3/127.3	K4TN	BARS
Brandon	443.7250	+	O 77/77ers BI	WA8ZZC	WA8ZZC
Dunedin	444.0750	+	●l	KA9RIX	Homey HC
Dunedin	444.1500	+	O 146.2/146.2eL(146.970 224.940 444.450 444.57	K4JMH	CARS
Dunedin	444.9750	+	O 100/100 E-SUN L(146.7)x	KE4EMC	KE4EMC
Holiday	443.4500	+	O 100/100e L(145.290 145.430 224.280 442.550 442.875 4	NI4CE	WCFG

Location	Output	Input	Notes	Call	Sponsor
Largo	442.1500	+	O 103.5/103.5e	N4PK	N4PK
Largo	442.9250	+	O 146.2/146.2es	KJ4RUS	KJ4RUS
Largo	443.4000	+	O 156.7/156.7eL(145.17)rs	WE4COM	PCACS
Largo	444.5000	+	●I	KA9RIX	Homey HC
Lutz	443.6750	+	O 146.2/146.2eL(224.740 442.725 444.250 I	W4RNT	RANT
Lutz	444.2500	+	O 146.2/146.2 L(443.675 442.725 224.74 IR-4	W4RNT	RANT
New Port Richey	444.2000	+	O 146.2/146.2	KJ4ZWW	UPARC
Palm Harbor	442.5000	+	O 146.2/146.2	KJ4ZWW	UPARC
Riverview	442.5500	+	O 100/100e IrWX	NI4CE	WCFG
Seffner	444.0000	+	O 103.5/103.5aeL(444.675 443.425 1291.500	W4AQR	W4AQR
Seminole	443.4250	+	O 88.5/88.5 E-SUN L(444.0000 147.0000 444.2250) BI	K3AAF	FDWS
St Petersburg	442.9000	+	O 103.5/103.5eL(145.31)	N4AAC	N4AAC
St Petersburg	443.6250	+	O 151.4/156.7e	NØRW	NØRW
St Petersburg	444.0625	+	ODCS(546) L(145.110 444.725)	KA9RIX	KA9RIX
St Petersburg	444.1750	+	O 88.5/88.5 aeL(444.000 444.725 145.390) RBz	KA9RIX	BEARS
St Petersburg	444.7250	+	OtaTT(*) E-SUN L(145.390 444.175 444.275 444.07	KA9RIX	Homey HC
Sun City Center	442.4500	+	O 162.2/162.2a(CA)e	W4KPR	KPARC
Tampa	442.7250	+	O 146.2/146.2eL(224.740 443.675 444.250 I	W4RNT	RANT
Tampa	443.0000	+	O 146.2/146.2 L(EC)	NI4M	MOSI ARC
Tampa	443.0250	+	O 146.2/146.2a(CA)z	N4TP	TARCI
Tampa	443.3500	+	O 127.3/127.3eRB BI	KP4PC	KG4GYO
Tampa	443.7750	+	O 103.5/103.5x	WA4SWC	WA4SWC
Tampa	443.9875	+	O 88.5/88.5 E-SUN L(444.0000 443.4250 1291.500 14	KJ4ARB	FDWS
Tampa	444.0000	+	O 88.5/88.5 a(CA) E-SUN L(444.675 443.425 1291.500	W4AQR	W4AQR
Tampa	444.6000	+	O 88.5/88.5	W4EFK	W4EFK
Tampa	444.7500	+	O 146.2/146.2ers	N4TP	TARCI

Location	*Output*	*Input*	*Notes*	*Call*	*Sponsor*
Tampa	444.9000	+	O	W4HSO	STARC
			141.3/141.3a(CA)ers		
Tarpon Springs	444.4500	+	O	K4JMH	CARS
			146.2/146.2eL(146.970 224.940 444.150 444.57		
Valrico	443.1500	+	O	W7RRS	W7RRS

GEORGIA

Location	*Output*	*Input*	*Notes*	*Call*	*Sponsor*
Acworth	441.8000	+	O	KC4YNF	KC4YNF
Adairsville	443.7250	+	O	WB4AEG	WB4AEG
			167.9/167.9s		
Albany	444.5000	+	OesWX	W4MM	W4MM
Athens	442.9500	+	O	N4ZRA	KD4AOZ
Athens	444.3000	+	O	K4GZX	K4GZX
Atl	442.8000	+	O	N4NFP	BSRG
Atlanta	421.2500	434.0000	O	W4ZTL	MATPARC
Atlanta	427.2500	1253.0000	O	N4NEQ	BSRG
Atlanta	442.0250	+	O	W4CML	------------
Atlanta	442.2250	+	O	WB5EGI	WB5EGI
Atlanta	442.5250	+	O	N4XQM	N4XQM
Atlanta	442.6250	+	O	WD4EIW	WD4EIW
Atlanta	442.6750	+	O	KE4PVE	KE4PVE
Atlanta	442.8750	+	O	K4RFL	GIRA
Atlanta	442.9750	+	O	W4OO	WA4YNZ
Atlanta	443.3125	+	O	W4AQL	ALEXANDER CARVE
Atlanta	443.6000	+	O	KA5WZY	GPEARC
Atlanta	443.6500	+	O	W4CML	W4CML
Atlanta	443.8000	+	O	N4NFP	BSRG
Atlanta	444.0500	+	O	N4NEQ	N4NEQ
			151.4/151.4ls		
Atlanta	444.1500	+	O	W4PME	MATPARC
Atlanta	444.4500	+	O	W4DOC	W4DOC
Atlanta	444.5000	+	O	KD4GPI	TURNER ARA
Atlanta	444.7750	+	O	N4NEQ	BSRG
Atlanta	444.8250	+	OsWX	W4DOC	W4DOC
Atlanta	444.9750	+	O	W4OO	WA4YNZ
Austell	442.8250	+	O 100/100	WA4YUR	WA4YUR
Bainbridge	443.0000	+	O 100/100e	W4DXX	W4DXX
Baldwin	442.3500	+	O	WD4NHW	SPARC
Ball Ground	443.9500	+	O	KB3KHP	KB3KHP
Barnesville	443.6750	+	O	N4GWO	N4GWO/N4GWN
Biskey Mtn	443.5000	+	O	KC4JNN	KC4JNN
Blairsville	442.2000	+	O	KF4SKT	KF4SKT
Blueridge	442.1250	+	O	KD4GRU	KD4GRU
Bogart	443.3000	+	O	WW4GA	WW4GA
Bogart	443.4750	+	O	W4EEE	OCONEE CTY ARS
Braselton	441.8250	+	O 88.5/88.5	WX4TC	------------
			sWX		
Brunswick	443.4250	+	O	KD4CPO	KD4CPO

Location	*Output*	*Input*	*Notes*	*Call*	*Sponsor*
Brunswick	443.8000	48.8000	O	KJ4SLT	KJ4PHZ
Brunswick	444.9750	+	O	K4TVE	K4TVE
Buchanan	444.2750	+	O	N4CHC	N4CHC
Buford	442.6500	+	O	KD4YOR	KD4YOR
Calhoun	443.6750	+	O	K4WOC	K4WOC
Canton	443.0750	+	O 107.2/107.2elrsWX	WA4EOC	WB4NWS
Cartersville	443.1750	+	O	N4GIS	N4GIS
Cedartown	443.5750	+	O	KD4NTF	KD4NTF/KD4EK
Cedartown	444.9500	+	O	KE4VCV	KE4VCV
Chatsworth	443.0000	+	O 141.3/141.3	W4DRC	KI4IG
Chatsworth	444.8500	+	ODCSes	K4SSP	K4SSP
Clayton	444.5000	+	Oe	KK4BSA	WB2OGY
Cleveland	442.6250	+	O	K4VJM	K4VJM
Cleveland	443.3250	+	O	WC4DK	WC4DK
Cleveland	443.5500	+	O 123/123e	K4GAR	K4RBM
Cleveland	443.5500	+	O	K4GAR	GATEWAY ARC
Cobb County	443.4500	+	O	WC4RAV	WC4RAV
Cochran	442.8750	+	O	W4MAZ	W3LAP
Cochran	444.7750	+	O	N4MXC	MGRA
Cochran	444.9750	+	O	W4MAZ	W3LAP
College Park	442.3500	+	O	KG4PTO	KG4PTO
Columbus	441.9750	+	O	WB4ULK	WB4ULK
Commerce	441.9750	+	O	NE4GA	NORTHEAST G
Commerce	442.2625	+	O	NE4GA	NORTEAST GA
Concord	443.4000	+	O 110.9/110.9 WX	WB4GWA	WB4GWA
Conyers	442.5500	+	O	WB4JEH	------------
Conyers	444.5500	+	O	WB4JEH	------------
Conyers	444.7500	+	O	KC4ELV	KC4ELV
Cornelia	444.2750	+	O	WB4VAK	WB4VAK
Covington	443.5750	+	O	KA4IJL	KA4IJL
Covington	444.1750	+	O	KE4PVE	KE4PVE
Covington	444.8000	+	O	WA4ASI	GEORGE HAWK
Cumming	441.9000	+	O	WB4GQX	WB4GQX
Cumming	442.5750	+	O	W4BPY	W4BPY
Cumming	443.4000	+	O	N1IB	N1IB
Cumming	443.8750	+	O	W4PX	W4PX
Cumming	444.6250	+	OesWX	W4CBA	W4CBA
Dahlonega	443.1000	+	O	N4KHQ	N4KHQ
Dahlonega	444.9000	+	O	N4BBQ	N4KHQ
Dallas	441.9250	+	O	W4CSX	W4CSX
Dallas	442.9500	+	O	KJ4KKB	KJ4KKB
Dallas	443.2500	+	O 77/77e	K4RJJ	K4RJJ
Dallas	443.4750	+	O 77/77ers WX	WB4QOJ	WB4QOJ
Dallas	443.7000	+	O	W4TIY	K4RJJ
Dallas	444.7000	+	OTTelWX	WD4LUQ	WD4LUQ

Location	*Output*	*Input*	*Notes*	*Call*	*Sponsor*
Dallas	444.7250	+	O	AG4PR	AG4PR
Dalton	441.8500	+	O	KC4YVV	KC4YVV
Dalton	442.1750	+	O	N4BZJ	N4BZJ
Dalton	444.5000	+	O	N4BZJ	N4BZJ
Decatur	442.2000	+	O	N3APR	N3APR
Decatur	444.2500	+	O	W4BOC	W4BOC
Douglas	443.0000	+	O	KE4ZRT	KE4ZRT
Douglasville	444.5750	+	O	W4SCR	SKINT CHESNUT AR
Dry Branch	444.6500	+	O	KC4TVY	KF4CXL
Duluth	442.4000	+	O	W2SJB	W2SJB
Eastanollee	442.5000	+	O	W4BNG	W4BNG
Eatonton	443.1750	+	O 179.2/179.2 E-SUNs	K4PAR	PARES
Eatonton	444.4250	+	Oels	K4EGA	K4EGA
Elberton	444.7000	+	O 118.8/118.8	KI4CCZ	KI4CCZ
Ellijay	442.7000	+	O	KC4ZGN	KC4ZGN
Emerson	443.4250	+	O	AE4JO	ETOWAH VALLEY A
Evans	444.9000	+	O	K4KNS	KR4XN
Fayetteville	444.6000	+	O 77/77ls WX	W4PSZ	W4PSZ
Flintstone	443.0250	+	O	KK4MH	KK4MH
Flowery Branch	443.9000	+	O	W4TL	W4TL
Gainesville	444.0750	+	O	AA4BA	AA4BA
Gainesville	444.9250	+	O	W4GM	W4GM
Gainesville	444.9500	+	O 131.8/131.8esWX	W4ABP	W4ABP
Glennville	443.6000	+	O	N4SFU	N4SFU
Gray	444.2750	+	O	W4OCL	W4OCL
Gray	444.4875	+	O	WR4DH	WM4F
Graysville	444.5250	+	O	N4YAV	N4YAV
Greensboro	444.8500	+	O	N4YXL	------------
Griffin	441.8500	+	O	KF4QLF	KF4QLF
Griffin	443.5500	+	O	NQ4AE	NQ4AE
Hapeville	442.8250	+	O	KC4ENL	KC4ENL
Hiawassee	444.6750	+	O	KC4CBQ	KC4CBQ
High Pt	443.4500	+	O	KB4VAK	G.R.O.U.P.
Hogansville	444.3000	+	O	KC4YNY	KC4YNY
Irwinton	443.2750	+	O	WB4NFG	WB4NFG
Irwinton	444.9250	+	O	WB4NFG	WB4NFG
Jackson	443.3250	+	Oes	W4DNS	W4DNS
Jasper	442.7500	+	O 141.3/141.3	N3DAB	N3DAB
Jasper	443.2500	+	O 100/100	N4GHT	N4GHT
Jasper	443.3750	+	O	KC4AQS	KC4AQS
Jasper	443.4250	+	O	KB4MDE	KB4MDE
Jasper	443.5625	+	O	KC4AQS	KC4AQS
Jasper	443.6250	+	O	KF4OYP	KF4LMW
Jasper	444.3750	+	O	KB4IZF	KB4IZF

Location	Output	Input	Notes	Call	Sponsor
Jasper	444.4250	+	O	KD4YDD	KD4YDD
Jasper	444.4250	+	O	W4MAA	M&M 10-10 CHA
Jesup	441.6750	+	O	N4ZON	N4ZON
Jesup	444.9250	+	O	N4PJR	N4PJR & N4RR
Jonesboro	443.2250	+	O	WA4DIW	WA4DIW
Kingston	444.1250	+	O	AF4PX	KG4EYJ
Knoxville	443.5250	+	O	N4PQR	------------
Lafayette	442.3000	+	O	KJ4ILK	KJ4ILK
Lafayette	444.5500	+	O	KS4QA	KS4QA
Lagrange	440.5125	+	O	WB4BXO	WB4BXO
Lakemont	444.7500	+	O	N4ZRF	------------
Lavonia	442.4750	+	O 203.5/203.5	K4NVG	K4NVG
Lavonia	443.2000	+	O 151.4/151.4	N4VNI	N4VNI
Lawrenceville	442.8500	+	O	WB4HJG	WB4HJG
Lawrenceville	442.9000	+	O 123/123	N5JMD	N5JMD
Lawrenceville	442.9000	+	O	KF4RLZ	KF4RLZ
Lawrenceville	444.0000	+	OesWX	WB4QDX	WB4QDX
Lawrenceville	444.0250	+	O	W4CML	------------
Lawrenceville	444.2000	+	O 100/100	KF4HQV	KF4HQV
Lindale	443.3000	+	O	KA4ZTY	KA4ZTY
Lithia Springs	442.9250	+	O	WB4RL	WB4RL
Lookout Mt	442.6500	+	O	W4RRG	W4RRG
Lula	444.4000	+	O	WB4HJG	WB4HJG
Mableton	442.3250	+	O	W4JLG	------------
Macon	442.2000	+	O	WA9DDK	WA9DDK
Macon	442.2750	+	O	WA4DDI	WM4F
Macon	442.7000	+	O	W4MAZ	W4MAZ
Macon	443.0750	+	O	WX4EMA	KJ4PEO
Macon	444.7000	+	O	WA4DDI	WA4DDI
Madison	443.7500	+	O 118.8/118.8s	WR4MC	WR4MC
Madras	442.2500	+	O 141.3/141.3e	K4HAC	K4HAC
Marietta	442.0000	+	O	N1KDO	N1KDO
Marietta	442.3500	+	O	KG4PTO	KG4PTO
Marietta	442.3750	+	O	KE4QFG	KE4QFG
Marietta	442.4250	+	O 107/107es	WK4E	WK4E
Marietta	442.6000	+	O	WA4OKJ	WA4OKJ
Marietta	442.7250	+	O	KE4QFG	KE4QFG
Marietta	443.5000	+	O	WB4BQX	DELTA 4 RG
Marlow	442.4750	+	O	W1MED	W1MED
Martinez	441.9000	+	O	WE4GW	WE4GW
Martinez	446.8000	–	O	WE4GW	------------
Mc Donough	444.8750	+	O 100/100ers	KE4UAS	KE4UAS
Monroe	442.0500	+	O 88.5/88.5 esWX	WE4RC	WE4RC

GEORGIA

Location	*Output*	*Input*	*Notes*	*Call*	*Sponsor*
Monroe	443.9250	+	O	KQ4XL	KD4WOU
Morrow	442.1750	+	O	K4USD	W2XAB
Moultrie	443.3250	+	O 114.8/114.8e	N4JMD	N4JMD
Moultrie	444.6250	+	O	W1BPP	FBC-MOULTRIE
Newnan	441.8750	+	O	WX4ACS	WX4ACS
Norcross	442.1000	+	OesWX	W4GR	W4GR
Omaha	443.7250	+	O	KI4VDP	KI4VDP
Peachtree City	442.5000	+	O 77/77ls WX	W4PSZ	W4PSZ
Perry	444.6250	+	O	KN4DS	KN4DS
Perry	444.9500	+	O	WR4MG	MID GA RADIO ASS
Pine Mountain	444.4000	+	O	WB4ULJ	WA4ULK
Quitman	444.6000	+	O	WA4NKL	------------
Rex	443.9750	+	O	KB4NPO	------------
Ringgold	443.9250	+	O	W4BAB	W4BAB
Rockmart	443.2750	+	O	NU4T	NU4T
Rome	441.8250	+	O	KA4MLK	N4GIS
Rome	443.5250	+	O	NU4T	NU4T
Rossville	442.4750	+	O	W4RRG	KS4QA
Roswell	442.0750	447.0250	O	W8BLA	W8BLA
Roswell	443.1500	+	O	W4PME	MATPARC
Saint Marys	443.0250	+	O	N3EAY	N3EAY
Sandy Springs	441.9500	+	O	KE4OKD	ETOWAH VALLEY A
Savannah	427.2500	439.2500	O	WA4VHP	SAVANNAH ATV SO
Savannah	442.7000	+	Os	W4LHS	W4LHS
Smyrna	444.6500	+	O	N4IBW	------------
Snellville	443.0500	+	O	W7QO	N1IP
Snellville	444.5250	+	OesWX	W4GR	W4GR
Social Circle	443.8250	+	O	W4VZB	W4VZB
Split Silk	444.1000	+	O	KD4HLV	KD4HLV
Statham	442.3000	+	O	WW4T	WW4T
Stockbridge	443.1250	+	O	KG4PUW	KG4PUW
Sugar Hill	442.1500	+	O	KD4GPI	KD4GPI
Sugar Hill	443.7750	+	O	N4YF	NY4F
Sumner	444.9000	+	O	W4CCS	W4CCS
Sweat Mt	444.4750	+	O	NF4GA	NF4GA
Sycamore	444.9250	+	O	KF4BI	KF4BI
Sylvania	441.8000	+	O	AF4MI	AF4MI
Tifton	444.8750	+	O	KE4RJI	KE4RJI
Toccoa	441.9250	+	O	KI4AEM	KI4AEM
Twin City	444.2500	+	O	N4SFU	N4SFU
Tyrone	444.6750	+	OesWX	KN4YZ	KD4YDC
Valdosta	444.3500	+	O	WR4SG	WR4SG
Valdosta	444.7000	+	O	KF4BJM	VARC
Vidalia	442.5000	+	O	KE4PMP	KE4PMP
Villa Rica	442.7750	+	O	KB4TIW	VILLA RICA RADIO
Waleska	441.3500	+	O	KD4DXR	KD4DXR
Waleska	441.6250	+	O	N4GIS	N4GIS

Location	Output	Input	Notes	Call	Sponsor
Waleska	443.8500	+	O	K4PLM	PINE LOG MTN
Warm Springs	442.4000	+	O	N4UER	KN4FE
Warner Robins	442.9000	+	O	WR4MG	MGRA
Warner Robins	443.1500	+	O 82.5/82.5 elsWX	WM4B	WM4B
Watkinsville	444.7250	+	O	KD4AOZ	KD4AOZ
Waycross	444.0250	+	O	AE4PO	AE4PO
Winder	443.0000	+	OWX	AK4GA	AK4GA
Woodstock	442.2750	+	O	KF4RMB	KF4RMB
Woodstock	444.2250	+	O	KE4SJO	KE4SJO
Wrightsville	443.0250	+	O	WA4RVB	WA4RVB
HAWAII					
HAWAII					
Glenwood	442.0250	+	O 156.7al	AH6GG	AH6GG
Hilo	442.9250	+	O 107.2e	NH6XO	NH6XO
Hilo	444.9250	+	Oel	KH6KL	KH6KL
Kahua	442.2750	+	O 136.5	AH6GR	MCDA
Kau	443.4000	+	O 77.0els	KH7MS	KH7MS
Kau	444.1500	+	Oalr	KH6EJ	KH7MS
Kau	444.6000	+	Oael	KH6EJ	BIARC
Kohala	444.4500	+	O	KH7EJ	BIARC
Kona	443.4000	+	O 100.0e	KH7MS	KH7MS
Kona	443.6500	+	O 100.0	WB6EGR	WB6EGR
Kona	444.9000	+	O	AH6RF	AH6RF
Mauna Loa	444.7500	+	O 103.5elr x	KH6HPZ	HCDA
Mountain View	444.3500	+	Oel	KH6QAJ	KH6QAJ
Pahoa	442.2500	+	O 114.8el	NH6P	W6YM
Waikoloa	444.9750	+	Oes	KH6CQ	KH6CQ
KAUAI					
Kapaa	444.3000	+	O#	WH6TF	WH6TF
Lihue	442.9250	+	O 107.2	NH6XO	NH6XO
Lihue	444.6750	+	● 100	KH6CVJ	KH6CVJ
LANAI					
Lanai City	442.2250	+	O 110.9	KH6RS	MCDA
Puu Kilea	442.0750	+	O 110.9	KH6RS	MCDA
MAUI					
Crater	442.8500	+	O 110.9	AH6GR	AH6GR
Haleakala	442.1000	+	O 136.5e RB	AH6GR	AH6GR
Haleakala	443.1500	+	O(CA)eRB z	KH6DT	KH6DT
Haleakala	443.9250	+	O 123.0	NH6XO	NH6XO
Haleakala	444.2250	+	O 110.9	AH6GR	MCDA
Hana	442.3000	+	O 110.9	AH6GR	MCDA
Kaanapali	442.3500	+	O 136.5 RB	KH6RS	MCDA
Kapalua	442.0000	+	O 110.9	KH6RS	MCDA
Portable	443.8000	+	O 100.0	AH6GR	AH6GR

HAWAII

Location	Output	Input	Notes	Call	Sponsor
Puu Mohoe	442.0500	+	O 136.5	KH6RS	MCDA
Wailuku	442.7500	+	O 136.5el	AH6GR	AH6GR
Wailuku	444.9500	+	O(CA)pr	KH6DT	KH6DT
Wailulu	442.7500	+	O 136.5el	AH6GR	AH6GR
Wailulu	443.2250	+	O 110.9	AH6GR	MCDA
MOLOKAI					
Puu Hoku	442.1250	+	O 110.9	AH6GR	MCDA
Puu Nana	442.3000	+	O 136.5	AH6GR	MCDA
OAHU					
Diamond Head	444.5000	+	Oel	WH6CZB	EARC
Honolulu	442.3000	+	O 103.5	WH6DIG	HIPRN
Honolulu	442.8000	+	Oel	KH6AZ	KH6AZ
Honolulu	443.3000	+	Ol	WH6F	WH6F
Honolulu	443.4500	+	O 103.5l	KH6OJ	Ohana ARC
Honolulu	443.6750	+	O	WH6UG	WH6UG
Honolulu	443.7750	+	O 123.0	NH6XO	NH6XO
Honolulu	443.9500	+	O 118.8	KH7TK	AH7GK
Honolulu	444.0000	+	O	NH6WP	SFHARC
Honolulu	444.0500	+	Opr	KH6OCD	DEM
Honolulu	444.2000	+	Oer	KH6OCD	DEM
Honolulu	444.3250	+	O 103.5er	AH6RH	RACES
Honolulu	444.3500	+	O 103.5elr	AH6CP	RACES
Honolulu	444.4750	+	●	WH7MN	UFN
Honolulu	444.7250	+	O 123.0l	WH6FM	WH6FM
Honolulu	444.8250	+	O	AH6HI	AH6HI
Honolulu	444.8750	+	O	KH6MP	KH6MP
Honolulu	444.9000	+	O 103.5el	AH6CP	AH6CP
Kaala	444.7750	+	O	NH6XO	KH6MP
Kailua	443.9750	+	O 88.5#	KH7HO	KH7HO
Kailua	444.1500	+	Ol	WH6CZB	EARC
Kailua	444.4250	+	O	AH6HI	AH6HI
Kaimuki	443.1000	+	Oel	NH6WP	OARC
Kaimuki	444.6500	+	O 114.8e	KH6FV	KH6FV
Kaimuki	444.8500	+	O 114.8e	KH6FV	KH6FV
Kaneohe	443.2750	+	O 118.8	NH6XO	KH6MP
Kokohead	442.7750	+	O 123.0el	NH6XO	KH6MP
Leeward	442.1750	+	O 103.5	KH6MEI	KH6MEI
Leeward	442.6000	+	O	KH6NYC	KH6NYC
Leeward	444.8000	+	O 171.3	NH7QH	NH7QH
Manawahua	443.5500	+	O 114.8e	KH6HFD	HFD
Maunakapu	442.4500	+	O 167.9ex	KH7O	KH7O
Maunakapu	442.4750	+	elx	WR6AVM	WR6AVM
Maunakapu	444.1000	+	Ol	WH6CZB	EARC
Mokuleia	443.4000	+	O 114.8e	KH6HFD	HFD
Mokuleia	444.5500	+	O 114.8e	KH6FV	KH6FV
Portable	444.0750	+	Opr	KH6OCD	DEM
Portable	444.1750	+	Opr	KH6OCD	DEM
Portable	444.2750	+	Opr	KH6OCD	DEM
Portable	444.8750	+	O	KH6MP	KH6MP

Location	Output	Input	Notes	Call	Sponsor
Round Top	443.4250	+	O 114.8el	KH6HFD	HFD
Round Top	443.7750	+	O 123.0el	NH6XO	NH6XO
Round Top	443.8250	+	O 100.0e	KH6HFD	HFD
Round Top	444.7000	+	O 100.0	KH6MEI	KH6MEI
Waimanalo	442.5000	+	●	KH7Q	KH7Q
Waimanalo	444.0250	+	O	KH6CB	KH6CB
Waimanalo	444.3750	+	O 114.8el	KH6HFD	HFD
STATE					
STATE	443.3750	+	O	SNP	SNP
IDAHO					
FREQUENCY USAGE - IACC AREAS					
Snp	443.0000	+	t		
FREQUENCY USAGE - N ID LINK					
Mullan	439.0500				
Mullan	439.2000				
CENT ID					
McCall	442.5000	+	O 100	KC7MCC	CI ARC
N ID - BONNERS FERRY					
Bonners Ferry	443.0250	+	100.0	KE7MDQ	KE7MDQ
Moyie Springs	444.2750	+	O	KF7MJA	NSDAssn
N ID - COTTONWOOD					
Cottonwood Butte	444.9500	+	O 100.0lx	K7EI	K7EI
N ID - KELLOGG					
Wardner Pk	444.0000	+	O 127.3	N7SZY	N7SZY
N ID - LEWISTON					
Craig Mtn	442.1000	+	● 103.5	K7EI	K7EI
Craig Mtn	444.9250	+	O 100.0lx	K7EI	K7EI
Lewiston Hill	444.9000	+	O 100.0lx	K7EI	K7EI
N ID - MOSCOW					
Moscow Mtn	444.9750	+	O 100.0lx	K7EI	K7EI
Moscow Mtn/West	442.8000	+	103.5e	W7NGI	W7NGI
N ID - OROFINO					
Wells Bench	444.8750	+	100.0l	K7EI	K7EI
N ID - RATHDRUM					
Rathdrum	442.8500	+	● 110.9	KC7TIG	KC7TIG
Rathdrum	444.2500	+	110.9	KC7TIG	KC7TIG
N ID - SANDPOINT					
Cocolalla	444.7750	+	● 127.3	N7LNA	K7LNA
Sagle	444.0250	+	100.0	KD6PGS	KD6PGS
Sandpoint	443.6250	+	136.5l	K7LNA	K7LNA
Schweitzer	444.0750	+	100.0l	K7MEE	BCEM
N ID - SPIRIT LAKE					
Spirit Lake	442.0000	+	110.9e	K7ZOX	K7ZOX
NORTH					
Burley ID	449.2000	–	Ox	WA7UHW	------------
Lava Hot Spr	449.3750	–	O 88.5 A(80*/#)lx	AE7TA	BARC

Location	Output	Input	Notes	Call	Sponsor
S CENT					
Burley	449.2000	–	O	KC7SNN	ISRA MHCH
Twin Falls	442.6000	+	O	W7CTH	W7CTH
S WEST ID					
Ontario, OR	444.1500	+	100	K7OJI	TVRA
S-CENT					
Cascade	441.9250	+	O 100 RB	W7CIA	W7CIA
McCall	444.1250	448.1250	O 100 RB	N7IBC	N7IBC
SOUTH WEST					
Boise	444.5000	+	O 100	WR7ID	W7OHM
SOUTHEAST IDAHO					
Idaho Falls	443.0000	+	O 100.0	WA4VRV	WA4VRV
Idaho Falls	448.1750	–	O 100.0	K6LOV	K6LOV
Pocatello	447.7500	–	O 100.0	W7RSR	------------
Pocatello	449.6750	–	O	KØIP	------------
SW ID					
Boise	443.2000	+	O 100 RB	KB7SYE	KB7SYE
Boise	443.8000	+	O	N7DJX	N7DJX
Boise	444.6750	+	O 156.7/156.7alx	N7KNL	N7KNL
Marsing	443.5500	+	O 100/100e lx	K7ZZL	DP ARC
SW ID / E OR					
Nyssa, OR	442.3500	+	O 100	W7PAG	W7PAG
SW ID, E OR					
Ontario, OR	443.0500	+	O	NB7C	NB7C
SW IDAHO					
Boise	443.0000	+	O 100	W7NCG	W7NCG
Idaho City	443.3500	+	O 100	KD7LXW	KD7LXW
SW-ID					
Boise	443.2500	+	O 110.9/110.9elRB	K7ZZL	DP ARC
Boise	443.6000	+	OE-SUNlrs WXx	W7VOI	VOI ARC
Boise	443.8500	+	O 100 E-SUNrsWX	KD7QAS	VOI ARC
Boise	444.0250	+	O	N7FYZ	N7FYZ
Boise	444.2750	+	O 123/123e	W7VWR	Vy Wide React
Boise	444.3000	+	O(CA)	W7VOI	VOI ARC
Boise	444.3250	448.3250	O 100	KE7NKF	KE7NKF
Boise	444.4500	+	O 100.0 (CA)elx	KB7LVC	KB7LVC
Boise	444.6500	+	O 110.9ex	KA7EWN	KA7EWN
Boise	444.9000	+	O 100	W7VOI	VOIARC
Cascade	443.3000	+	O 110.9/110.9elRB	K7ZZL	W7ZRQ+DPARC
Centerville	443.6750	+	O 100p	KA7ERV	ID Rly Grp
Centerville	443.9750	+	Op	KA7ERV	ID Rly Grp
Centerville	444.0750	+	p	KA7ERV	KA7ERV

Location	*Output*	*Input*	*Notes*	*Call*	*Sponsor*
Fruitland	443.6500	+	O	KC7BSA	KC7BSA

ILLINOIS

BLOOMINGTON					
Athens	444.9750	+	210.7els WX	KD9Q	KD9Q
Bloomington	444.9500	+	97.4	W9NUP	W9NUP
El Paso	444.3500	+	107.2	KE9HB	KE9HB
Normal	442.7000	+	107.2eWX	WB9UUS	WB9UUS
CENTRAL					
Litchfield	444.4500	+	103.5	AC9P	AC9P
Nokomis	442.1500	+	88.5	N9TZ	W9COS
Odell	444.1250	+	127.3ex	WA9SGJ	WA9SGJ
CHAMPAIGN					
Champaign	443.48125	+		W9YR	Synton ARC
Champaign	444.1000	+	162.2e	K9SI	K9SI
Champaign	444.5250	+	162.2e	K9BF	Ben Fisher
Champaign	444.6500	+	103.5	W9YH	SYNTON ARC
CHICAGO					
Chicago	440.3000	+	114.8	W9BMK	DUCFAR
Chicago	441.2750	+	114.8	KA2DRQ	KA2DRQ
Chicago	441.90625	+		WA9ORC	CFMC
Chicago	442.09375	+	e	NS9RC	NSRC
Chicago	442.1250	+	203.5	WD9GEH	WD9GEH
Chicago	442.1750	+	107.2	AA9RA	AA9RA
Chicago	442.4000	+	114.8e	K9NBC	PARC
Chicago	442.4500	+	●	K9QKB	MRCA
Chicago	442.5750	+	131.8	N9OZG	SATURN
Chicago	442.7250	+	114.8e	NS9RC	NSRC
Chicago	442.9750	+	114.8 (CA)l WXx	WA9VGI	FISHFAR
Chicago	443.3750	+	114.8	K9QKW	WB9RFQ
Chicago	443.6750	+	114.8 (CA) WX	KC9DFK	CHI-TOWN
Chicago	443.7500	+	114.8 (CA)	WA9ORC	CFMC
Chicago	443.8000	+	114.8a	K9SAD	SADFAR
Chicago	443.8750	+	114.8ae	WA9TQS	WSNSTVARC
Chicago	443.9250	+	114.8	K9VO	CHIFAR
Chicago	443.9750	+	114.8	KB9PTI	AIRA
Chicago	444.3750	+	114.8 (CA)z	K9GFY	SARA
Chicago	444.6250	+	110.9	N9SHB	N9SHB
Chicago	444.7250	+	114.8l	W9TMC	TMC ARC
Homewood	442.3750	+	114.8lWX	WA9WLN	WALDOFAR
Schiller Park	443.6000	+	114.8 (CA)	WB9AET	WAFAR
Tinley Park	441.8000	+	107.2 (CA)	W9IC	W9IC
DECATUR					
Bement	443.5750	+	103.5 (CA)e	KB9WEW	PCESDA
Cadwell	440.64375	+	e	W9BIL	MARK
Decatur	442.2500	+	103.5e	WA9RTI	MACONCOARC

Location	Output	Input	Notes	Call	Sponsor
Decatur	443.8000	+	123	K9HGX	CENOIS ARC
Decatur	444.1750	+	100.0elWX	K9MCA	KC9CWL
Lovington	444.2750	+	103.5e	WC9V	KR9X
Monticello	442.7250	+	103.5esWX	KB9ZAM	UBIQUITOUS
Mt Zion	444.8000	+	103.5 (CA)e	KO9I	#NAME?
EAST CENTRAL					
Arcola	444.3750	+	192.8	WA9WOB	ARC NET
Clinton	442.3750	+	91.5es	KA9KEI	DARC
Danville	443.7250	+	100	NE9RD	NERD
Hoopeston	444.8250	+	67	KB9YZI	KB9YZI
Kansas	443.6250	+	162.2	W9COD	W9COD
Loda	442.4250	+	179.9 (CA)	K9UXC	K9UXC
Watseka	444.6250	+	103.5 WX	AD9L	ICARC
NORTH CENTRAL					
Channahon	444.6000	+	114.8e	W9PXZ	W9PXZ
Dixon	443.8250	+	136.5	KA9PMM	KA9PMM
Dixon	444.8000	+	114.8	W9DXN	RRARC
Freeport	442.0000	+	146.2ers WX	W9SBA	NWIL ARES
Freeport	443.2750	+	114.8	KB9RNT	KB9RNT
Joliet	440.1500	+	114.8 (CA)	KB9LWY	KB9LWY
Joliet	442.3000	+	114.8e	W9OFR	WCARL
Joliet	442.9250	+	114.8 (CA)l WXx	WA9VGI	FISHFAR
Malta	442.9500	+	131.8 (CA)l WXx	WA9VGI	FISHFAR
Marseilles	442.6000	+	23elWX	KA9FER	KA9FER
Oregon	443.9500	+	141.3e	KB9DBG	KB9DBG
Princeton	444.1500	+	103.5 (CA)	N9ECQ	N9ECQ
Roscoe	440.8750	+	88.5	N9EIM	N9EIM
Roscoe	442.7500	+	131.8ers WX	WX9WAS	WX9WAS
Sterling	444.0250	+	82.5el	N9JWI	N9JWI
Winnebago	442.3500	+	88.5 (CA)e	W9TMW	W9TMW
NORTHEAST					
Algonquin	444.0250	+	103.5	N9IVM	N9IVM WEST
Arlington Heig	444.0250	+	100.0e	N9IVM	N9IVM EAST
Aurora	443.4250	+	114.8e	W9LSL	W9LSL
Barrington Hil	442.1500	+		WD9IAE	WD9IAE
Batavia	442.10625	+		W9CEQ	FRRL
Batavia	443.6500	+	114.8 (CA)l	W9XA	W9XA
Batavia	444.1000	+	100.0ex	KA9LFU	ELFAR
Batavia	444.2250	+	114.8	WB9IKJ	FERMI RC
Batavia	444.3000	+	114.8	W9CEQ	FRRL, INC.
Bellwood	444.5750	+	114.8	KC9ZI	KC9ZI
Berwyn	444.1500	+	146.2	WA9HIR	WA9HIR
Blue Island	442.6750	+	131.8	W9SRC	STARS
Bolingbrook	443.5250	+	114.8e	K9BAR	BARS
Bolingbrook	443.7000	+	114.8 (CA)e lWXz	W9BBK	V BOLNGBRK

Location	*Output*	*Input*	*Notes*	*Call*	*Sponsor*
Calumet City	443.9500	+	131.8	KA9OOI	CHUMPS
Calumet City	444.4250	+	114.8e	KA9QPN	CC ESDA
Cary	443.0750	+	114.8 (CA)l	WB9PHK	STROKE
Cherry Valley	442.6250	+	100	W9FT	PIGFAR
Chicago	443.8250	+	114.8	K9OB	K9OB
Crystal Lake	443.2000	+	131.8l	N9EAO	FROGFAR #2
Crystal Lake	443.4750	+	114.8e	N9HEP	N9HEP
Crystal Lake	444.1750	+	114.8	KA9ATL	KA9ATL
Crystal Lake	444.8000	+	203.5	KB2MAU	RAYFAR
Deer Park	444.0000	+	114.8	KP4EOP	KP4EOP
Dekalb	444.4500	+	114.8px	KB9FMU	KB9FMU
Downers Grove	442.5500	+	114.8 (CA)	W9DUP	DARC
Downers Grove	442.8750	+	114.8	W9YRC	York RC
Downers Grove	443.2000	+	100	N9EAO	FROGFAR #3
Downers Grove	443.9000	+	114.8	N9ATO	SERCOMM
Downers Grove	444.4750	+	114.8	W9CCU	WCRA
East Dundee	443.0250	+	114.8	W9DWP	W9DWP
Elgin	444.9500	+	114.8	WR9ABQ	VARA
Elmhurst	440.8500	+	114.8	KB9UUU	KB9UUU
Elwood	441.9750	+	114.8eWX	WØCOP	WØCOP
Frankfort	443.3250	+	114.8	WD9HSY	WD9HSY
Frankfort	444.5500	+	114.8ers WX	WW9AE	PRL WCEMA
Geneva	444.5250	+	er	N9NLE	N9NLE
Glendale Heigh	440.10625	+		KC9PWC	SPRAG-SWC
Glendale Heigh	444.8750	+	114.8epx	K9XD	K9XD
Grant Park	441.3000	+	114.8lWX	WA9WLN	WALDOFAR
Grayslake	444.6000	+	114.8	W9GWP	W9GWP
Gurnee	443.1500	+	114.8e	N9OZB	ARG
Gurnee	443.5000	+	127.3 (CA)e	W9MAB	GURNEE RG
Hampshire	444.6750	+	114.8 (CA)e lz	W8ZS	SKYHAWK
Hampshire	444.7000	+	114.8l	W8ZS	SKYHAWK
Hinsdale	444.2000	+	114.8e	KB9OYP	KB9OYP
Ingleside	444.5500	+	107.2	N9IFG	WeLCARS
Kankakee	444.8000	+	100.0ael	W9AZ	KARS
La Grange Park	443.3000	+	114.8	K9ONA	SMCC
Lake In The Hi	440.5750	+	114.8	N9SRW	N9SRW
Lake Villa	444.4000	+	114.8aelz	WB9RKD	WB9RKD
Lake Zurich	440.74375	+		KC9OKW	SUHFARS
Lake Zurich	443.2500	+	114.8	K9SA	SUHFARS
Lake Zurich	443.3500	+	114.8el	K9SA	K9SA
Lake Zurich	443.8500	+	114.8ers WX	KD9GY	LC RACES
Libertyville	442.5250	+	114.8ers WX	K9IQP	LKCNTRACES
Lisle	442.2250	+	114.8l	WA9WSL	IHARC
Lisle	442.7000	+	203.5 (CA)e LITZ	WA9AEK	WA9AEK

ILLINOIS

Location	*Output*	*Input*	*Notes*	*Call*	*Sponsor*
Lockport	442.0250	+	100	NC9T	P.A.D.X.A.
Lockport	443.2250	+	141.3	KB9KV	ANDREW RC
Lombard	444.2500	+	114.8 (CA)e lWX	N9ECQ	LOMBRD OEM
Manteno	441.8750	+	131.8	W9LEO	W9LEO
Marengo	442.3750	+	151.4l	W9DMW	MOOSEFAR
Mchenry	444.0750	+	● 88.5	KB9I	KB9I
Melrose Park	442.6250	+	114.8	W9FT	PIGFAR
Morris	442.0000	+	94.8	KC9KKO	JP WATTERS
Morris	442.3250	+	114.8eWX	KB9SZK	GCARC
Naperville	443.0500	+	114.8erWX	NE9MA	NEMA
New Lenox	444.4000	+	141.3l	N2BJ	N2BJ
North Chicago	442.3250	+	107.2e	N9FJS	LBRG
Oak Brook	443.1250	+	114.8	N9XKY	SRA
Oak Forest	443.2750	+	114.8	N9ZD	N9ZD
Oak Lawn	444.6500	+	110.9	KB9WGA	BCRC
Oak Lawn	444.9000	+	114.8 (CA)e lz	W9OAR	W9OAR
Orland Park	444.7750	+	114.8 (CA)	WA9PAC	PIONEER
Orland Park	444.8500	+	71.9	WD9HGO	WD9HGO
Palatine	443.0000	+	114.8r	KA9ORD	KA9ORD
Plainfield	440.0750	+	162.2ep	KC9QHH	PARC
Plainfield	442.8500	+	114.8	W9CJC	ARP
Plato Center	444.9750	+	● 114.8	W9ZS	VARA
Rolling Meadow	442.8000	+		KC9RBB	SPRAG-N9EP
Rolling Meadow	442.8000	+	114.8l	N9EP	SPRAG-N9EP
Round Lake Bea	443.7750	+	127.3	N9JSF	KC9PDU
Sandwich	444.4250	+	131.8ers WX	KA9QPN	SEMA
Schaumburg	440.8000	+	114.8 (CA)e	KC9GFU	ANTFACTORY
Schaumburg	442.2750	+	114.8	K9IIK	SARC
Schaumburg	442.9000	+	114.8 (CA)l WXx	WA9VGI	FISHFAR
Schaumburg	443.1000	+	114.8 (CA)l	WB9PHK	STROKE
Schaumburg	443.4000	+	114.8	KB2MAU	RAYFAR
Schaumburg	443.5750	+	114.8e	N9KNS	MARC MOTO1
Schaumburg	443.6250	+	114.8 (CA)e lz	N9CXQ	NAPS
Schaumburg	443.7250	+	114.8el	N9KNS	MARC MOTO2
Schaumburg	444.5000	+	114.8	K9PW	CARP
Schaumburg	444.8000	+	203.5	KB2MAU	RAYFAR
Schiller Park	441.3250	+	114.8	K9TOW	TOWFAR
Sugar Grove	442.4750	+	a	KA9HPL	KA9HPL
Wasco	444.9250	+	411e	N9MEP	GFAR
Wauconda	442.5000	+	114.8	K9SGR	K9SGR
Waukegan	441.3750	+	88.5	N9IJ	N9IJ
Wayne	440.26875	+	esWX	W9DPA	DCERA
West Chicago	441.8500	+	114.8e	KC9JBW	WC ESDA
Wheaton	444.0500	+	114.8e	WA9E	Tower ARC

Location	Output	Input	Notes	Call	Sponsor
Wheaton	444.2750	+	114.8 (CA)e l	KA9KDC	KA9KDC
Wheeling	444.3250	+	114.8	WB9OUF	WB9OUF
Yorkville	443.5500	+	114.8	WA9JON	WA9JON
Zion	444.8250	+	74.4	KA9VMV	KA9VMV
NORTHWEST					
Rock Island	444.9000	+	100.0e	W9WRL	QCRG
Stockton	443.9750	+	127.3	N9NIX	N9NIX
PEORIA					
Canton	444.7250	+	103.5e	K9ILS	FCARC
Dunlap	443.1250	+	156.7	N9BBO	N9BBO
East Peoria	443.0000	+	103.5aez	KA9GCI	PEKIN RPTG
Kickapoo	444.2000	+	103.5e	W9HOI	HIFC
Metamora	444.7500	+	103.5 (CA)e p	KC9GQR	KC9GQR
Pekin	444.0000	+	103.5az	KA9GCI	PEKIN RPTG
Peoria	442.1250	+	103.5e	W9GAO	HIFC
Peoria	443.46875	+		W9PIA	PAARC
Peoria	444.0500	+	103.5e	WX9PIA	PALS
Peoria	444.3750	+	156.7 (CA)e	N9BBO	N9BBO
Peoria	444.4750	+	103.5	W9JWC	BUARC
Tremont	444.5500	+	e	W9TAZ	TCARS
ROCKFORD					
Belvidere	442.8250	+	114.8e	N9KUX	N9KUX
Mt Morris	442.6750	+	114.8elrs WX	K9AMJ	K9AMJ
Rockford	442.0750	+	114.8a	N9CWQ	ARECOMM
Rockford	442.1750	+	118.8elx	K9AMJ	K9AMJ
Rockford	442.6500	+	192.8eWX	K9RFD	RTG
Rockford	442.7750	+	118.8	WW9P	P.A.R.S.
Rockford	443.3250	+	123.0ae	KE4CLD	RVCITHAMS
Rockford	443.4500	+	114.8e	WB9TFX	WB9TFX
Rockford	443.9250	+	118.8elx	K9AMJ	K9AMJ
Rockford	444.3500	+	114.8 (CA)e l	K9AMJ	K9AMJ
Rockford	444.7250	+	107.2esWX x	WX9MCS	NIRA
Rockford	444.8500	+	114.8 (CA)e l	K9AMJ	K9AMJ
SOUTH					
Carbondale	442.0250	+	88.5	W9UIH	SIU ARC
Carbondale	442.65625	+		W9UIH	SIU ARC
Carbondale	443.5250	+	88.5e	KA9YGR	KA9YGR
Eagleton	443.4000	+		W9IMP	OTHG
Metropolis	444.9750	+	123.0 (CA)e z	N9IBS	MAMA ARC
SOUTH CENTRAL					
Effingham	444.1250	+	110.9e	K9UXZ	NTARC
Farina	443.0500	+	103.5	W9FIU	ROGER RIES

Location	Output	Input	Notes	Call	Sponsor
Geff	444.4000	+	123.0esWX	KC9GMX	WC ARES
Greenville	442.9250	+	103.5e	KB9EGI	OVARC
Johnsonville	442.6250	+	123.0ers WX	KC9NPJ	KC9NPJ
Mattoon	444.9250	+	103.5e	W9MBD	MARK
Salem	442.2000	+	103.5ez	W9CWA	CWA
SOUTHEAST					
Herod	444.8000	+	88.5	K9OWU	SCAN
Mt Carmel	442.3250	+	114.8sWX	AI9H	W9GH
Mt Carmel	444.7750	+	114.8esWX	AI9H	K9BJE
Olney	444.9750	+	114.8 (CA)e sWX	N9QZA	RADIO
Robinson	442.8000	+	107.2esWX	WA9ISV	CCARC/IEMA
SPRINGFIELD					
Jacksonville	444.6750	+	103.5 (CA)e z	K9JX	JARS
Pawnee	442.6000	+	94.8	N9MAF	N9MAF
Springfield	443.3750	+	94.8	WA9KRL	WA9KRL
Springfield	443.78125	+	e	W9DUA	SVRC
Springfield	444.1000	+	(CA)	K9PLR	PIONEER AR
Springfield	444.4000	+	103.5	K9CZ	K9CZ
Springfield	444.5000	+	103.5ae	WX9DX	WX9DX
Springfield	444.6000	+	103.5 (CA)e lxz	WS9V	MR DX
Tallula	442.6750	+	151.4	K9KGO	K9KGO
Tallula	444.9000	+	151.4	K9KGO	K9KGO
Taylorville	442.0500	+	79.7	N9HW	CCARC
ST LOUIS					
Albers	444.7750	+	151.4 (CA)	WD9IQN	WD9IQN
Alton	442.7750	+	123.0e	K9HAM	LCRC
Alton	442.9000	+	123.0aelz	K9HAM	LCRC
Belleville	442.2750	+	127.3lrs	K9GXU	ST CLAIR
Belleville	444.6250	+	127.3	K9GXU	ST CLAIR
Carlinville	443.2750	+	100.0e	N9OWS	N9OWS
Carlinville	443.7500	+	107.2e	N9OWS	N9OWS
Carlyle	443.1750	+	103.5	K9XWX	K9XWX
Collinsville	442.1750	+	103.5 (CA)	KD6TVP	KD6QKX
Collinsville	443.1250	+	103.5	KA9YMH	KA9YMH
Edwardsville	442.4000	+	127.3ers WX	W9AIU	EGYPTN RC
Gillespie	444.2500	+	103.5 (CA)e sWXxz	WS9V	MR DX
Godfrey	442.2250	+	123.0aelz	K9HAM	LCRC
Godfrey	442.3500	+	123.0e	KB9GPF	KB9GPF
Godfrey	443.2750	+	123	N9GGF	N9GGF
Godfrey	443.4000	+	123	N9GGF	N9OWS
Granite City	442.5500	+	127.3	KZ9D	KZ9D
Maryville	443.2000	+	103.5e	KB9KLD	KB9KLD
Mascoutah	443.9000	+	l	AA9ME	AA9ME

Location	Output	Input	Notes	Call	Sponsor
Mascoutah	443.9750	+	l	AA9ME	AA9ME
Mascoutah	444.2250	+	l	AA9ME	AA9ME
Mascoutah	444.8750	+	110.9l	KB9QKR	KB9QKR
O'fallon	443.1000	+	127.3	K9AIR	SPARC
Shiloh	444.3000	+	127.3e	AA9RT	KB9VTP
Troy	442.0750	+	al	AA9MZ	AA9MZ
Troy	444.5750	+	al	AA9MZ	AA9MZ
Waterloo	444.7000	+	127.3aez	N9OMD	N9OMD
WEST CENTRAL					
Aledo	443.8750	+	100.0esWX x	KC9HDD	KC9HDD
Beardstown	443.9500	+		W9ACU	IVARC
Dallas City	444.9250	+	123.0eWXx	KA9JNG	KA9JNG
Galesburg	444.4500	+	103.5l	W9GFD	KNOXCARC
Galva	443.3000	+	103.5	WA9BA	AARO
Galva	443.3500	+	225.7ep	W9YPS	AARO
Geneseo	444.5000	+	136.5ex	W7COK	SIMS MEM
Geneseo	444.8750	+	136.5e	W9MVG	SHAFER MEM
Griggsville	442.5250	+	100.0elrs WXx	WS9V	MR DX
Kewanee	442.1750	+	225.7	N9ZK	AARO
Macomb	444.3000	+	103.5	WB9TEA	LEARC
Monmouth	444.3250	+	173.8	KD9J	KD9J
Quincy	442.9000	+	114.8l	WA9VGI	FISHNET
Quincy	443.6750	+	186.2ex	KC9JBD	H.R.G.
Quincy	443.9000	+	103.5e	W9AWE	WIARC
Versailles	443.9250	+	88.5	KB9JVU	KB9JVU

INDIANA

EAST CENTRAL

Location	Output	Input	Notes	Call	Sponsor
Connersville	442.0500	+	OsWX	N9TU	N9TU
Dalton	441.9500	+	O 127.3ers	KG9ND	KG9ND
Eaton	444.1000	+	O	K9NZF	K9NZF
Hartford City	443.5750	+	OersWX	WB9HLA	WB9HLA
Liberty	444.8000	+	O 186.2e WX	KB9YSN	KB9YSN
Marion	442.7500	+	O 131.8er	KB9CRA	KB9CRA
Marion	444.2250	+	Oaer	KB9CRA	KB9CRA
Marion	444.7500	+	O 131.8l	WB9VLE	WB9VLE
Modock	443.3250	+	OeWX	K9NZF	K9NZF
Muncie	441.8250	+	O 110.9e WXx	N9CZV	N9CZV
Muncie	443.4500	+	O 127.3ae	WD9HQH	Evans/Rust
Muncie	444.3750	+	OalrsWX	WB9HXG	MuncieARC
New Castle	444.2750	+	Ors	N9EYG	N9EYG
Portland	442.2000	+	O 131.8er	WA9JAY	WA9JAY
Portland	443.4750	+	O 100.0 WX	W9JKL	W9JKL
Richmond	441.6500	+	O 131.8	KD8AKE	KD8AKE

INDIANA

Location	Output	Input	Notes	Call	Sponsor
Rushville	442.6000	+	O 127.3ers	K9PQP	E Ctrl Rpt
Winchester	441.8000	+	O 110.9	N9CZV	N9CZV
Yorktown	441.7000	+	O 127.3es WX	W9YFD	EmCommECI
INDIANAPOLIS					
Anderson	443.3500	+	Oer	WA9CWE	MadisonEMA
Anderson	444.6750	+	O 131.8els WX	WA9EOC	ChfAndARC
Brownsburg	444.2000	+	Oe	KC9CTQ	KC9CTQ
Danville	442.9000	+	Oelr	WB9CIF	WB9CIF
Danville	444.5750	+	O 88.5aelr sx	WX9HC	HendrixARC
Danville	444.7000	+	O 88.5ers	KB9DJA	KB9DJA
Edinburgh	444.7750	+	O 88.5e	KC9AWX	KC9AWX
Franklin	443.5250	+	O 118.8	AA9YP	AA9YP
Franklin	444.6250	+	O 151.4e	KC9LGZ	KC9LGZ
Greenfield	444.4500	+	Oers	W9ATG	HancockARC
Greenfield	444.7250	+	Or	W9ATG	HancockARC
Indianapolis	441.2000	+	O	W9AMT	W9AMT
Indianapolis	441.9250	+	O 100.0e	K9RAG	K9RAG
Indianapolis	442.0000	+	O	KA9GIX	KA9GIX
Indianapolis	442.3750	+	O	K9DC	K9DC
Indianapolis	442.5000	+	O 100.0	WA9MVP	CentralIN
Indianapolis	442.6500	+	O 77.0eWX	W9ICE	ICE
Indianapolis	442.7250	+	Oer	W9SEM	InHomeSec
Indianapolis	442.8500	+	O(CA)	NF9K	NF9K
Indianapolis	442.9500	+	O	KB9RBF	KB9RBF
Indianapolis	443.0000	+	O 100.0e	WB9PGW	WB9PGW
Indianapolis	443.1000	+	O 100.0e	KC9GMJ	WISH Tech
Indianapolis	443.2000	+	O 127.3 (CA)el	N9ILS	N9ILS
Indianapolis	443.2500	+	O 100.0el WX	KM9E	HarrisnARA
Indianapolis	443.4250	+	O 94.8l	K9IP	DREGs
Indianapolis	443.6000	+	O 156.7ers WX	W9VCS	W9VCS
Indianapolis	443.7500	+	O 100.0r WX	K9LPW	Cent IN RA
Indianapolis	443.8000	+	O	KC9COP	KC9COP
Indianapolis	443.8500	+	OsWX	W9IRA	Indy RA
Indianapolis	443.9500	+	O(CA)e	WB9OLI	WB9OLI
Indianapolis	444.0000	+	O 100.0	NE9T	IndyMidARC
Indianapolis	444.3250	+	O 136.5els WXx	KB9SGN	KB9SGN
Indianapolis	444.8750	+	O	KA9GIX	KA9GIX
Martinsville	444.9500	+	O 100.0e WX	K9PYI	MorganRA
New Whiteland	444.0750	+	O 100.0	KM9S	KM9S
Nineveh	442.1500	+	Oe	KA9SWI	KA9SWI

Location	*Output*	*Input*	*Notes*	*Call*	*Sponsor*
Noblesville	443.5500	+	O 77.0elrs WX	N9EOC	HamCoARES
Noblesville	443.9000	+	O 118.8l	W9ICE	ICE
Plainfield	442.2750	+	O 123.0 (CA)	AB9D	AB9D
Shelbyville	444.9750	+	O	W9JUQ	BRV ARS
NORTH CENTRAL					
Culver	444.9250	+	O 131.8es WXz	N9GPY	N9GPY
Delong	443.9250	+	O 131.8e WXz	N9GPY	N9GPY
Elkhart	442.3750	+	O 131.8e WX	KC9GMH	KC9GMH
Elkhart	442.6000	+	O 131.8rs	N8AES	N8AES
Elkhart	443.1500	+	O 131.8 WX	KC9OHC	KC9OHC
Elkhart	443.2250	+	Oe	KC9VRV	KC9VRV
Elkhart	443.3250	+	O 131.8	KC9GMH	KC9GMH
Elkhart	443.4750	+	O 131.8ers x	AA9JC	AA9JC
Frankfort	442.0750	+	O 131.8	W9FAM	W9FAM
Frankfort	442.5750	+	O	N9SFA	N9SFA
Fulton	442.7000	+	OesWX	WD8IEJ	WD8IEJ
Goshen	443.8500	+	O 131.8e	KB9ORC	KB9ORC
Kokomo	442.3000	+	Oe	W9KRC	KRC
Kokomo	442.4000	+	O 131.8	KA9GFS	KA9GFS
Kokomo	443.3000	+	O	KA9GFS	KA9GFS
Kokomo	444.0250	+	O 131.8l	N9LLO	N9LLO
Logansport	443.6500	+	Oes	W9VMW	Cass ARC
Middlebury	442.4750	+	O 131.8ers x	AA9JC	AA9JC
Mishawaka	442.0500	+	O 131.8ae	W9AMR	W9AMR
Mishawaka	444.1000	+	O 131.8	N9GVU	N9GVU
Nappanee	443.0250	+	O 97.4e	WD9ATU	WD9ATU
Notre Dame	443.3500	+	O 131.8	ND1U	ND ARC
Rossville	443.5000	+	O 88.5es WX	WI9RES	WIRES
Russiaville	442.5250	+	Oe	N9KYB	N9KYB
Sharpsville	443.7000	+	O 88.5elrs WX	K9TRC	TiptonARC
South Bend	440.4750	+	O 192.8els WX	N9UPW	N9UPW
South Bend	442.1000	+	O 100.0ael rWX	WB9AGX	StJoe EMA
South Bend	442.5000	+	O	N9OCB	N9OCB
South Bend	442.6500	+	O 131.8	KC9MEC	KC9MEC
South Bend	444.1750	+	O 131.8e	KA9MXW	KA9MXW
South Bend	444.7000	+	O 131.8 (CA)e	W9TEW	W9TEW

Location	Output	Input	Notes	Call	Sponsor
South Bend	444.9750	+	O 107.2e	K9SIQ	K9SIQ
Syracuse	444.2750	+	O 131.8elr sWX	AA9JC	AA9JC
Tipton	443.1250	+	Oe	K9TRC	TiptonARC
Wabash	442.3250	+	O 131.8er	KB9LDZ	WabashARC
Warsaw	443.0500	+	O 131.8s WXx	KA9OHV	KA9OHV
NORTHEAST					
Andrews	442.9250	+	O	KC9DZ	Huntinton
Angola	442.8750	+	O 131.8e	KC9QDO	KC9QDO
Angola	444.3500	+	O 131.8 (CA)e	WB9DGD	WB9DGD
Angola	444.9000	+	O 131.8el WXx	W9LKI	W9LKI
Auburn	442.4500	+	O 131.8e	KA9LCF	TCXO
Bluffton	443.8750	+	O 141.3elr sWX	K9SLQ	EMA
Columbia City	442.5500	+	OersWX	N9WNH	N9WNH
Columbia City	442.9000	+	O 141.3ers WX	K9KOP	K9KOP
Columbia City	444.5500	+	O 131.8ers WX	WC9AR	WhitleyARC
Decatur	443.7250	+	O	KB9KYM	AdamsARC
Decatur	444.3250	+	O	K9OMW	K9OMW
Fort Wayne	443.1000	+	O 131.8	WB9VLE	WB9VLE
Fort Wayne	443.2750	+	O 131.8e	KC9AUQ	KC9AUQ
Fort Wayne	443.8000	+	Oers	W9INX	ACARTS
Fort Wayne	444.2500	+	O 131.8e	WD9AVW	WD9AVW
Fort Wayne	444.3000	+	O 131.8	W9VD	W9VD
Fort Wayne	444.6000	+	Oe	WA7NXI	WA9NXI
Fort Wayne	444.8000	+	Ol	W9FEZ	MizpahARC
Fort Wayne	444.8750	+	O	W9TE	FWRC
Gary	442.7500	+	O 131.8e WX	W9CTO	W9CTO
Huntington	443.9750	+	O 131.8ls	KC9GX	KC9GX
Kendallville	443.5250	+	Oe	KC9LUT	KC9LUT
Lagrange	443.6750	+	O 131.8rs	WS9S	WS9S
Larwill	444.4250	+	O 131.8	N9STR	N9STR
Roanoke	444.1500	+	O	WB9VLE	WB9VLE
Wolflake	442.8000	+	O	N9MTF	N9MTF
NORTHWEST					
Burns Harbor	444.6750	+	O 97.4	N9FI	BethSteel
Crown Point	443.4500	+	O 131.8r WX	W9EMA	Lake EMA
Hammond	442.2000	+	O 173.8 (CA)eWX	W9FXT	W9FXT
Hammond	444.7500	+	O 131.8ae WX	KA9QJG	KA9QJG
Hebron	442.3500	+	O 131.8ep	N9TAX	N9TAX

Location	Output	Input	Notes	Call	Sponsor
Knox	442.9500	+	Oe	W9QN	W9QN
Laporte	444.9500	+	O 131.8	W9SAL	W9SAL
Merrillville	442.0750	+	O 131.8elr sWXx	W9LJ	LakeCoARC
Michigan City	441.9500	+	O 131.8	W9LY	MCARC
New Carlisle	442.4250	+	O 131.8	AB9OZ	AB9OZ
New Carlisle	444.5250	+	O	AB9OZ	AB9OZ
Valparaiso	442.2500	+	O 131.8ers	K9PC	PorterARC
Valparaiso	444.3500	+	O 131.8x	KB9KRI	Duneland
Valparaiso	444.4500	+	O 131.8rs WX	KI9EMA	Porter Emg
SOUTH CENTRAL					
Bedford	442.2500	+	O 136.5alr sWXx	N9UMJ	N9UMJ
Bedford	442.6750	+	O(CA)e	N9WEV	N9WEV
Bedford	444.0500	+	O 107.2er WX	W9QYQ	HoosrHills
Bloomington	442.8250	+	O 136.5es	K9IU	K9IU
Bloomington	442.9250	+	O 107.2l WX	K9SOU	BlmHS-ARC
Bloomington	443.7750	+	O 136.5elr sWXx	KB9SGN	KB9SGN
Columbus	443.0750	+	O 136.5ers WX	WB9AEP	CARC
Floyds Knob	442.3000	+	O 146.2e	WB9GNA	WB9GNA
Floyds Knob	444.2000	+	O 67.0 (CA) e	N9CVA	N9CVA
Kirksville	443.0500	+	O 136.5e	WB9TLH	WB9TLH
Marengo	443.3000	+	OrsWX	KC9OLF	SolnARC
Nashville	443.2750	+	O 136.5elr sWX	KA9SWI	KA9SWI
Paoli	444.0250	+	O 103.5e	KB9OHY	OrangeARC
Salem	444.9250	+	O 136.5els WXx	KB9SGN	KB9SGN
Seymour	441.5500	+	OWX	KC9JOY	KC9JOY
Seymour	443.7250	+	O 103.5ers	N9KPA	N9KPA
Springville	442.8750	+	O 107.2	N9HXU	N9HXU
SOUTHEAST					
Brookville	442.2500	+	OeWX	KB9YSN	KB9YSN
Greensburg	444.5250	+	OersWX	N9LQL	N9LQL
Lawrenceburg	443.8750	+	O 146.2rs	K9GPS	LV ARC
North Vernon	442.9750	+	O 103.5s WX	KC9TME	JCARC
Osgood	441.7750	+	OsWXx	WY9L	RCARC
SOUTHWEST					
Alfordsville	441.9000	+	OelrsWX	KC9QAG	KC9QAG
Boonville	442.4000	+	O 107.2ers	WB9QVR	WB9QVR
Chrisney	443.6000	+	O	W9DRB	W9DRB
Evansville	443.2500	+	O 146.2elr sWXx	W9KXP	W9KXP

Location	Output	Input	Notes	Call	Sponsor
Evansville	443.3250	+	O 123.0	N9JCA	N9JCA
Evansville	443.5500	+	O 107.2	K9RVB	K9RVB
Evansville	444.1500	+	O 88.5 (CA) ersWX	WB9KQF	WB9KQF
Evansville	444.5000	+	O	W9MAR	MidwestARS
Francisco	442.0500	+	O 210.7	KC9MEW	KC9MEW
Jasper	444.6750	+	O 107.2er WX	N9MZF	N9MZF
Linton	444.4250	+	O 100.0el	KA9JOK	KA9JOK
Lynnville	443.8500	+	O 136.5elr sWXx	W9KXP	W9KXP
Monroe City	442.7500	+	O 156.7el WXx	W9KXP	W9KXP
Petersburg	443.1250	+	O 136.5e	K9MNS	K9MNS
Petersburg	444.0000	+	O	KB9EDT	KB9EDT
Vicksburg	442.4250	+	O 118.8els WXx	KB9SIP	KB9TUN
Vincennes	443.6750	+	OesWX	W9EOC	Old Post
Vincennes	443.9250	+	O 107.2al WXxz	W9EAR	EARS
Washington	442.7000	+	O 107.2	KB9LOW	KB9LOW
WEST CENTRAL					
Battleground	444.1750	+	O 88.5eps	WB9CZC	WB9CZC
Clinton	442.1750	+	O 151.4ers WX	W9COD	W9COD
Clinton	442.4750	+	O 192.8	NS9M	NS9M
Cloverdale	444.4750	+	O 136.5els WXx	KB9SGN	KB9SGN
Coatesville	444.4000	+	O 151.4e	KC9HKT	KC9HKT
Crawfordsville	444.8000	+	O 77.0	KB9GPB	KB9GPB
Foster	443.4500	+	O	N9UWE	N9UWE
Greencastle	442.2250	+	Ors	WB9EOC	PutRACES
Otterbein	444.0750	+	O 88.5e	KC9BPE	KC9BPE
Terre Haute	442.5500	+	Oe	NC9U	NC9U
Terre Haute	443.0250	+	O	NS9M	NS9M
Terre Haute	444.3500	+	OelrsWXx	W9SKI	Skywarn
Terre Haute	444.6000	+	O 77.0els WX	WØTHI	WØTHI
Terre Haute	444.7500	+	O 151.4	W9EQD	TerreHaute
Terre Haute	444.8500	+	O 151.4	K9EDP	K9EDP
West Lafayette	444.5000	+	O 88.5e	W9YB	PurdueARC
Williamsport	443.6750	+	O 156.7elr WX	WB9ARC	BARC
Wolcott	442.1500	+	O 131.8e	WA9RAY	WA9RAY

IOWA

BURLINGTON

Location	Output	Input	Notes	Call	Sponsor
Burlington	444.7000	+	100.0e	WA6GUF	WA6GUF
Winfield	444.3500	+	O	WBØVHB	WBØVHB

Location	*Output*	*Input*	*Notes*	*Call*	*Sponsor*
CEDAR RAPIDS					
Cedar Rapids	443.0000	+	192.8e	WØVCK	Venture2K
Cedar Rapids	443.8000	+	192.8	NØMA	rf.org
Cedar Rapids	444.0750	+	**O**e	N3AVA	N3AVA
Coralville	444.7500	+	**O**ex	KØGH	CvilleRPT
Homestead	442.4250	+	151.4	WCØC	------------
Iowa City	442.1500	+	● 192.8ae prs	KDØMJV	J Co EIC
Iowa City	443.1500	+	192.8aeprs WX	KDØMJV	J Co EIC
Marion	444.3750	+	192.8	KX9Y	rf.org
Morse	443.2000	+	151.4l	WCØC	------------
Van Horne	444.4000	+	136.5p	WØRTM	WØRTM
CENTRAL					
Afton	442.4000	+	151.4el	KØCSQ	SWIARA
Ames	443.3750	+	114.8ael WXz	WØISU	CARC
Boone	443.9000	+	**O**aers	KBØTLM	BARK
Chelsea	442.1250	+	151.4l	WDØGAT	------------
Grundy Center	444.3250	+	110.9aelrs WX	NØMXK	NØMXK
Herndon	444.2750	+	151.4e	N2DRP	N2DRP
Laurel	444.8000	+	151.4elWX	WCØC	WCØC
Madrid	443.8500	+	151.4	KCØMTE	KCØMTE
Marshalltown	443.3250	+	110.9aelrs	NØMXK	NØMXK
Perry	444.3750	+	● 151.4aer s	KDØNEB	HARC
Sheldahl	442.2000	+	**O**	NØQFK	NØQFK
COUNCIL BLUFFS					
Council Bluffs	442.5250	+	51503aepr s	WBØGXD	WBØGXD
Honey Creek	444.8000	+	97.4e	ABØVX	ABØVX
DAVENPORT					
Davenport	444.4250	+	**O**	WBØVQP	WBØVQP
Muscatine	444.2750	+	192.8e	WAØVUS	WAØVUS
DES MOINES					
Alleman	444.6750	+	114.8el	WØTWR	WØTWR
Des Moines	442.1000	+	127.3	KØCSS	KØCSS
Des Moines	443.5000	+	151.4e	WØKWM	CITS
Des Moines	444.1000	+	151.4aers	KØDSM	PlkCoARES
Des Moines	444.5250	+	151.4e	KAØOMM	KAØOMM
Des Moines	444.5750	+	4110ex	WØKWM	CITS
Des Moines	444.6250	+	151.4	WAØQBP	WAØQBP
Gilman	444.1500	+	3162elWX	NFØT	NFØT
Grimes	443.4000	+	151.4elWX x	NØINX	WsideComm
Indianola	444.1250	+	114.8aeprs	NØFAM	NØPBO
Johnston	442.5750	+	151.4aeprs	NØVPR	NØVPR
Johnston	442.7250	+	151.4ep	KCØZMT	KCØZMT

Location	*Output*	*Input*	*Notes*	*Call*	*Sponsor*
Johnston/Camp	442.8000	+	151.4elWX	KCØMTI	KCØMTI
Kelly	444.4250	+	151.4elWXx	KCØMTI	KCØMTI
Madrid	442.6000	+	151.4e	NØSFF	NØSFF
DUBUQUE					
Dubuque	444.2250	+	114.8ex	WØDBQ	GRARC
EAST CENTRAL					
Clinton	444.6500	+	elp	KNØBS	BSARC
Grand Mound	444.8250	+	100.0e	W1HAM	W1HAM
Maquoketa	442.2250	+	O	KBØCAQ	MaqARG
MASON CITY					
Mason City	443.2000	+	O	KØUXA	KØUXA
NORTH CENTRAL					
Humboldt	442.4000	+	3245el	KØHU	KØHU
West Bend	443.3000	+	110.9e	WØIOA	WØIOA
Williams	444.5000	+	151.4lWXx	KBØJBF	WCRA
NORTHEAST					
Frankville	444.1000	+	103.5	KØRTF	KØRTF
NORTHWEST					
Gillette Grove	444.7000	+	224540ex	KGØCK	KGØCK
Scranton	444.3000	+	● 151.4aelrsWXx	NØVPR	WCRA
SIOUX CITY					
LeMars	444.6750	+	56352e	KIØEO	KIØEO
Sioux City	444.4750	+	110.9	KCØDXD	KCØDXD
Sioux City	444.7250	+	110.9l	KØNH	KØNH
SOUTHEAST					
Moravia	444.4750	+	146.2lWXx	WØALO	WØALO
SOUTHWEST					
Atlantic	444.2000	+	151.4	WAØC	WAØC
Avoca	443.9500	+	151.4l	NØDYB	------------
Bedford	443.7000	+	136.5aelrs	KAØRDE	TlrCoARA
Bridgewater	443.8000	+	O	WDØFIA	WDØFIA
Corning	444.4500	+	127.3l	NØDTS	NØDTS
Elk Horn	444.9000	+	151.4l	WAØC	WAØC
Glenwood	444.3250	+	OaelrsWXxz	NØWKF	NØWKF
Greenfield	444.7000	+	114.8aelrsWX	NØBKB	NØBKB
Menlo	444.5500	+	151.4aelrsWX	NØBKB	NØBKB
Minden	442.0750	+	736067elx	NØZHX	NØZHX
Mineola	442.0250	+	OaelrsWXx	NØWKF	NØWKF
Mo Valley	444.0750	+	736067elx	NØZHX	NØZHX
Pacific Jct	443.0250	+	O	NØWKF	NØWKF
Thurman/Tabor	444.5000	+	136.5aersWX	WBØYLA	WBØYLA

Location	Output	Input	Notes	Call	Sponsor
WATERLOO					
Independence	444.7000	+	103.5e	KCØRMS	BCoARC
Oelwein	443.9500	+	O	KFØHA	KFØHA
Readlyn	442.3250	+	136.5e	KØCLR	C-L REACT
Waterloo	444.9000	+	136.5 WXx	WØALO	WØALO
Waterloo	444.9250	+	136.5ex	WØALO	WØALO
Waterloo	444.9750	+	136.5e	WØMG	NE IA RAA
WEST CENTRAL					
Denison	444.0000	+	Oe	KCØLGI	------------
Mondamin	444.9250	+	3328aers	KØBVC	BVARC
Woodbine	444.3500	+	136.5aelrs	KØBVC	BVARC
KANSAS					
CENTRAL					
Belpre	444.6000	+	O 88.5/88.5	KCØEVO	KCØEVO
Ellsworth	444.7750	+	O 162.2/162.2elrs	KØHAM	WØDOB
Hays	442.4500	+	O 131.8/131.8eL(#3917)	N7JYS	N7JYS
Hays	443.6000	+	O 107.2/107.2e	KCØPID	EllisCo
Hays	444.0000	+	O	NØECQ	FHSUARC
Hays	444.8250	+	O 100/100a elr	NØECQ	FHSU ARC
Hillsboro	442.5000	+	O 110.9/110.9	NØSGK	K-Link
Hillsboro	442.7750	+	O	KCØRVV	MCARC
Hoisington	443.6500	+	●a(CA)el	WA6LIF	T2 RADIONE
McPherson	442.3750	+	O 88.5/88.5 lrs	KØHAM	MCRC
McPherson	443.8500	+	O 110.9/110.9	N5NIQ	N5NIQ
McPherson	444.6000	+	O 162.2/162.2el	NØSGK	N5NIQ
Pawnee Rock	444.3250	+	O 88.5/88.5 elrs	KØHAM	WØDOB
Russell	442.8500	+	O 141.3/141.3eL(ECHOLINK#3917)	KCØHFA	KCØHFA
Russell	444.9500	+	O 162.2/162.2el	ABØUO	RUSSELL CO
Salina	442.2000	+	Or	NØKSC	NØKSC
Salina	443.9000	+	O	WØCY	CKARC
St Marys	443.5750	+	O 88.5/88.5 ers	KØHAM	NEKSUN
Sterling	444.4500	+	O 162.2/162.2aer	WBØLUN	WBØLUN
EAST CENTRAL					
Burlingame	443.8750	+	O 88.5/88.5	NØOFG	------------
Emporia	443.0000	+	O 103.5/103.5eL(ECHOLINK#350451)	WXØU	------------

Location	Output	Input	Notes	Call	Sponsor
Eskridge	444.9750	+	O 88.5/88.5 eL(IRLP)	WL7LZ	------------
Mound City	444.4250	+	Oer	WØPT	MnCrkARC
New Strawn	444.9250	+	O	NØMSA	------------
Paola	442.4750	+	O 151.4	NØSWP	WSWA KØHAM
Paola	444.7000	+	O	WSØWA	WhtStWrls
Towanda	443.0000	+	O	NØRDZ	------------
KANSAS CITY METRO					
Basehor	443.5500	+	Oel	NØGRQ	NØGRQ
Basehor	443.5500	+	Oel	NØGRQ	NØGRQ
Basehor	443.6500	+	●t(CA)elrs	KØSUN	NEKSUN
Basehor	443.6500	+	●TTelrs	KØSUN	NEKSUN
Belton	442.8000	+	O 151/151	KAØOXO	BARC
Blue Springs	444.9500	+	O 107eRBx	KBØVBN	BluSprRPTR
Edgerton	442.4750	+	Oe	WBØOUE	WBØOUE
Edgerton	442.4750	+	Oe	WBØOUE	WBØOUE
Excelsior Spgs	443.3250	+	● 141/141a (CA)elx	KØAMJ	KØBSJ
Excelsior Spgs	444.6500	+	O 156	KØESM	RayClay RC
Holden	444.3750	+	O 107/107x	NØNDP	NØNDP
Hoover	442.0750	+	O 151	KAØFKL	------------
Independence	444.5750	+	O 186l	NØOEV	------------
Kansas City	442.5500	+	O 186.2./186.2eL(ECHOLINK#375305)	WBØYRG	BYRG
Kansas City	442.8500	+	O 186.2/186.2a(CA)	WDØGQA	BYRG
Kansas City	442.8500	+	O 186.2/186.2a(CA)	WDØGQA	BYRG
Kansas City	442.9750	+	O 151/151x	KØORB	SJMC ARC
Kansas City	443.1000	+	O	NGØN	BYRG
Kansas City	443.1750	+	●x	WØWJB	------------
Kansas City	443.2500	+	O 131/131e sx	WØOEM	WØOEM
Kansas City	443.3500	+	Oa(CA)	WVØT	SEIDKR
Kansas City	443.4500	+	Olx	WØWJB	WØWJB
Kansas City	443.7750	+	O 110/110	WAØNQA	ArtShrnRC
Kansas City	443.8500	+	O 107.2/107.2a(CA)	WDØGQA	BYRG
Kansas City	443.8500	+	O 107.2/107.2a(CA)	WDØGQA	BYRG
Kansas City	444.0000	+	Oe	NØHYG	NØHYG
Kansas City	444.0000	+	Oe	NØHYG	NØHYG
Kansas City	444.0250	+	O 186/186a e	WBØYRG	BYRG
Kansas City	444.1250	+	O 123/123	NØNKX	NØNKX
Kansas City	444.2500	+	O 151.4/151.4	KØHAM	NEKSUN
Kansas City	444.2500	+	O 151.4/151.4	KØHAM	NEKSUN

Location	Output	Input	Notes	Call	Sponsor
Kansas City	444.3500	+	O	NØAAP	NØAAP
Kansas City	444.8500	+	O 151.4/151.4elr	WBØNSQ	WBØNSQ
Kansas City	444.8500	+	O 151.4/151.4elr	WBØNSQ	WBØNSQ
Kearney	443.9000	+	O 127e	KBØEQV	KBØEQV
Kearney	444.2000	+	Oa(CA)e	KØKMO	MJARS
Leavenworth	442.3500	+	O 100/100e	NØMIJ	------------
Leavenworth	442.3500	+	O 107.2/107.2e	NØMIJ	------------
Lee's Summit	444.3000	+	O 131	KØMRR	------------
Lee's Summit	444.4500	+	O 151/151e L(PAOLA KS REPEA)x	NØNDP	NØNDP
Lenexa	442.0500	+	O 151.4/151.4 L(IRLP#5870)	KCØEFC	KCØEFC
Lenexa	442.0500	+	O 151.4/151.4l	KCØEFC	KCØEFC
Lenexa	442.6000	+	O 186.2/186.2a(CA)el	WBØYRG	BYRG
Lenexa	442.6000	+	O 186.2/186.2a(CA)eL(433.8)	WBØYRG	BYRG
Mission	442.1000	+	O 167.9/167.9r	NØWIZ	WB6DWW
Mission	442.1000	+	O 167.9/167.9r	NØWIZ	WB6DWW
Oak Grove	444.2750	+	O 123/123	KBØTHQ	PHRRL
Olathe	442.2000	+	O 151.4/151.4a(CA)eL(IRLP#3534)	KE5BR	SFTARC
Olathe	442.2000	+	O 151.4/151.4a(CA)el	KE5BR	SFTARC
Overland	442.1500	+	● 82.5/82.5	WØLHK	WØLHK
Overland Park	442.1500	+	● 82.5/82.5	WØLHK	WØLHK
Overland Park	443.7250	+	O 151.4/151.4a(CA)er	WØERH	JCRAC
Peculiar	442.0250	+	●a(CA)el	WØMCJ	BYRG
Platte City	444.1500	+	O 88/88e	WØUSI	WØUSI
Platte Woods	444.0500	+	O 151/151e lsLITZx	KDØEAV	PlatteCoAR
Platte Woods	444.5500	+	O 151/151l LITZx	KDØEAV	KDØEAV
Roeland Park	443.7250	+	O 151.4/151.4a(CA)er	WØERH	JCRAC
Shawnee Msn	442.2500	+	●/141.3a (CA)e	KØGXL	SMMC
Shawnee Msn	442.2500	+	●/141.3a (CA)e	KØGXL	SMMC
Shawnee Msn	443.5250	+	● 118.8/118.8e	KØGXL	SMMC
Shawnee Msn	443.5250	+	● 118.8/118.8e	KØGXL	SMMC

Location	Output	Input	Notes	Call	Sponsor
Shawnee Msn	444.7500	+	●a(CA)elr	WBØRJQ	WBØRJQ
Smithville	443.6250	+	O 114	NØVER	NØVER
NORTH CENTRAL					
Beloit	442.8000	+	Oae L(ECHOLINK)	WAØCCW	SVRC
Clay Center	442.7500	+	O 162.2/162.2al	NØXRM	NØXRM
Miltonvale	442.1000	+	Oel	WBØSRP	WBØSRP
Minneapolis	442.5000	+	O 110.9/110.9 E-SUNl	KCØNPM	NØUJQ
Minneapolis	444.8500	+	O 162.2/162.2aeL(ECHOLINK#382015)rsLITZ	KSØLNK	K-LINK
Phillipsburg	442.7250	+	O	KDØARW	KDØARW
NORTHEAST					
Alma	444.5250	+	O 162.2/162.2elrs	WØKHP	K-Link
Basehor	442.0000	+	Oe	KUØK	NEKSUN
Carbondale	443.1250	+	Oe	WBØPTD	------------
Home City	444.3500	+	O 88.5/88.5 aer	NØNB	NØNB
Lawrence	443.8000	+	Ol	KØUSY	DMR-BFARC
Lawrence	444.7500	+	Ol	KØUSY	BFARC
Lawrence	444.9000	+	O 88.5/88.5 eL(ECHOLINK#444900)rs	KØHAM	NEKSUN
Leavenworth	444.8000	+	O 151.4/151.4aer	WØROO	PKARC
Lecompton	444.8250	+	O 88.5/88.5 eL(ECHOLINK#399595)	KØUSY	BFARC
Manhattan	444.1750	+	O 88.5/88.5	WØQQQ	KSU ARC
Ottawa	444.1000	+	O 88.5/88.5 e	KXØN	------------
Stilwell	444.0750	+	Otel	KØHQ	WBØJQM-SMC
Topeka	443.0500	+	O	KØUSY	DMR-BFARC
NORTHWEST					
Colby	444.4000	+	O 141.3/141.3el	KØECT	SKECT
Colby	444.7500	+	O 162.2/162.2l	KSØLNK	K-Link
Edson	444.5500	+	O 88.5/88.5	KCØGLA	------------
Grainfield	442.6250	+	O 162.2/162.2l	KSØLNK	K-Link
SOUTH CENTRAL					
Anthony	442.4000	+	O 103.5/103.5l	W5ALZ	GSPARC
Haviland	442.0250	+	O 103.5/103.5	KBØOKR	KBØOKR
Haviland	444.1250	+	O 156.7/156.7a(CA)	KBØVFV	NØFEK
Kingman	442.1250	+	O 103.5/103.5e	KDØSLE	KDØSDS

Location	Output	Input	Notes	Call	Sponsor
Kiowa	442.1500	+	Oael	KB5MDH	KDE-TV36
Newton	443.1000	+	O 103.5/103.5elr	KSØLNK	K-Link
Newton	443.1000	+	Oa(CA)lrx	KBØSOF	NEWTON ARC
Pratt	444.8000	+	O 100/100e rs	WGØQ	WGØQ
Wellington	444.2500	+	O	WAØZFE	WAØZFE
Winfield	442.1000	+	O 97.4/97.4 L(ECHOLINK#48439)	N5API	------------
Winfield	444.0250	+	O 97.4/97.4	KDØHNA	------------
Winfield	444.3000	+	O 97.4/97.4 e	KDØHNA	------------
SOUTHEAST					
Chanute	442.6500	+	O	WA5FLV	------------
Coffeyville	442.8750	+	O 91.5/91.5 r	WRØMG	CARC/MGARC
Coffeyville	444.5500	+	O 91.5/91.5 e	NØTAP	COFYVLARC
Elk Falls	442.8250	+	Oer	WXØEK	EKRS
Fort Scott	444.1750	+	O	KBØSWH	FT. SCOTT
Gas	442.4500	+	O 179.9	WIØLA	IARC
Humboldt	442.9000	+	● 156.7/156.7	KZØV	KZØV
Independence	443.5250	+	O 91.5/91.5 e	NØVDS	------------
Independence	443.7000	+	OE-SUN	NØVDS	NØVDS
Parsons	442.2000	+	O L(ECHOLINK#453003)	AAØPK	PAARC
Parsons	443.4750	+	O L(ECHOLINK#305758)	WØPIE	WØPIE
Pittsburg	444.8000	+	O 91.5/91.5 a(CA)e	KØPRO	PRO
Pittsburg	444.9000	+	O 91.5/91.5	KØPRO	PRO
SOUTHWEST					
Dodge City	442.3750	+	O 123/123a e	KUØL	KUØL
Dodge City	444.5500	+	O 141.3/141.3el	KØECT	SKECT
Ensign	444.3750	+	Or	KUØL	KUØL
Garden City	442.5000	+	O 141.3/141.3el	KØECT	SKECT
Garden City	443.2250	+	O 100/100	WØMI	SANDHILLS
Hugoton	444.5250	+	O 141.3/141.3el	KØECT	SKECT
Hugoton	444.9000	+	O 88.5/88.5 el	WØQS	SPARK
Jetmore	444.5000	+	O 141.3/141.3e	KØECT	SKECT
Liberal	443.1000	+	O 141.3/141.3ar	KØECT	SPARK

Location	Output	Input	Notes	Call	Sponsor
Liberal	444.1000	+	Oel	WØKKS	SPARK
Montezuma	444.2500	+	O 141.3/141.3a(CA)ls	KØECT	SKECT
Russell Spring	444.3000	+	O 141.3/141.3el	KØECT	SKECT
Syracuse	444.0000	+	O 141.3/141.3el	KØECT	SKECT
TOPEKA					
Hoyt	444.7250	+	O 88.5/88.5 a(CA)elrs	KØHAM	NEKSUN
Topeka	442.2250	+	O 88.5/88.5 eL(ECHOLINK#157353)r	WØCET	KVARC
Topeka	444.4000	+	O 88.5/88.5 er	NØCBG	GldnCyRA
WEST CENTRAL					
Horace	442.1750	+	O	KDØEZS	------------
Ransom	443.5750	+	O 88.5/88.5 elrs	KØHAM	NEKSUN
Syracuse	443.1250	+	O 100/100	KAØTAO	KAØTAO
WICHITA					
College Hill	444.5750	+	O 100/100e L(ECHOLINK)	NØEQS	CHARS
Colwich	444.2000	+	O 94.8/94.8	WØKA	------------
Derby	443.2750	+	O 156.7/156.7 L(ECHOLINK#44447)	KCØSOK	ALRERC
El Dorado	444.1500	+	O	KØCKN	FlntHlsRC
Haysville	442.6000	+	Oa(CA)er	KAØRT	KAØRT
Mulvane	443.5500	+	O	NØKTA	MLVANEARC
Rose Hill	442.7000	+	O 103.5/103.5	KFØAO	KFØAO
Wichita	442.0000	+	O(CA)	NØITL	NCRARC
Wichita	443.3250	+	Oe	WØVFW	------------
Wichita	444.0000	+	Oa(CA)er	WAØRJE	TECNICHAT
Wichita	444.0750	+	O 82.5/82.5 (CA)r	NØHM	I.C.U.C

KENTUCKY

Location	Output	Input	Notes	Call	Sponsor
Agnes	442.6000	+	O	W4RRA	W4XXA
Allen	444.7750	+	O	N4IWZ	N4IWZ
Artemus	443.9250	+	O 100/100e l	KF4FWF	KF4FWF
Ashland	444.9750	+	O	KC4QK	ASHLAND 24 RPTR
Black Mtn	443.4000	+	O	K4XYZ	K4XYZ
Bowling Green	444.1000	+	O	W4WSM	W4WSM
Brooks	443.7000	+	O 79.7/79.7 esWX	KY4KY	KY4KY
Brushy Fork	444.6000	+	O	KD4DZE	KF4WMM
Burlington	443.5250	+	O	N8OXA	WA4ZKO

Location	*Output*	*Input*	*Notes*	*Call*	*Sponsor*
Cerulean	444.6500	+	Oe	KY4KEN	KY4KEN
Clearfield	441.8750	+	O	KD4DZE	KD4DZE
Corbin	444.9000	+	O	WB4IVB	WB4IVB
Cox's Creek	443.4500	+	O	AE4NU	KT4GB
Dixon	443.1500	+	O	AJ4SI	------------
Dorton	442.1500	+	O	KD4RTR	KD4RTR
Dry Ridge	444.4250	+	O	WA4ZKO	NKDXE-NKRA
Earlington	443.9500	+	O	KG4WCQ	KG4WCQ
Edgewood	444.3500	+	O	K4CO	K4CO
Elizabethtown	444.8000	+	O	W4BEJ	LINCOLN TRAIL
Fairdealing	443.5000	+	O 118.8/118.8	KI4HUS	KI4HUS
Fort Wright	441.8500	+	O	KY4JD	KY4JD
Fort Wright	442.5250	+	O	KY4JD	NKRA
Foster	443.1250	+	O	KU4ML	KU4ML
Frankfort	443.3250	+	O	WA4CMO	DIV. OF EMERG
Garrett	442.4000	+	O	KF4JJD	KF4ZTB
Georgetown	443.6250	+	O	KF4NTQ	SCOTT CO. AR
Glasgow	444.2500	+	O	KF4DC	DEWAYNE CON
Glasgow	444.9250	+	O	KY4X	KY4X
Graefenburg	443.5500	+	O	N4HZX	------------
Grayson	441.9750	+	O	KD4DZE	KD4DZE
Grethel	444.5250	+	O	KJ4VF	KJ4VF
Harlan	442.6250	+	O	W4YMT	------------
Hartford	442.6750	+	O	KD4BOH	KD4BOH
Hazard	443.9750	+	O 103.5/103.5e	K4TDO	------------
Henderson	444.7250	+	O 82.5/82.5 e	KY4K	------------
Highland Heights	444.9000	+	O	W4YWH	W4YWH
Hindman	444.4000	444.9000	O 162.2/162.2e	K4TDO	------------
Irvine	442.9000	+	O	W4CMR	CHESTNUT MT
Irvine	444.0000	+	O 100/100	AD4RT	KY4LD
Jenkins	444.3000	+	O	KK4WH	KK4WH
Latonia	442.4000	+	O	AA4XV	AA4XV
Lawrenceburg	444.3750	+	O	KY4LAW	K4TG
Lexington	442.6000	+	O	KD4ADJ	KC4ZY
Lexington	444.1250	+	O	KB8QLC	KA4MKG
Lexington	444.5500	+	O	KC4DUU	KC4DUU
Lexington	444.7250	+	O	AD4YJ	AD4YJ
London	442.1250	+	O	KJ4JCP	KJ4JCP
London	442.9000	+	O	KI4FRJ	KI4FRJ
London	443.3000	+	O	N8OCX	N8OCX
Louisville	442.0000	+	O	N4ORL	N4ORL
Louisville	442.1000	+	O	N4RBL	N4RBL
Louisville	442.4500	+	O 151.4/151.4er	KD4CLR	KD4CLR
Louisville	443.5000	+	O	WD9EQC	------------

Location	*Output*	*Input*	*Notes*	*Call*	*Sponsor*
Louisville	443.9750	+	O	N4KWT	------------
Louisville	444.1000	+	O	N4UL	N4UL
Louisville	444.3000	+	O	KY4NDN	KY4NDN
Louisville	444.5000	+	O	W4MOP	------------
Louisville	444.6000	+	O	N4NMC	N4MRM
Madisonville	442.7750	+	O	KC4FIE	KC4FIE
Madisonville	444.6000	+	O 103.5/103.5	KC4FIE	KC4FIE
Magnolia	443.6750	+	O	WA4FOB	------------
Manchester	444.2750	+	O	KF4IFC	KF4IFC
Mayfield	441.8750	+	O 179.9/179.9	WA6LDV	KF4GCD
Maysville	441.9500	+	O	KE4YEY	------------
Maysville	443.5000	+	O	KF4BRO	GREATER MASON C
Middlesboro	442.3250	+	O	WM4MD	KF4GXQ
Middlesboro	443.9500	+	O 100/100	W4HKL	WM4MD
Middlesboro	444.1500	+	O	WB4IVB	WB4IVB
Millard	443.4250	+	O	KD4RTR	------------
Monticello	444.7500	+	O	WB9SHH	WB9SHH
Morehead	442.5000	+	O	K4GFY	K4GFY
Morehead	443.2500	+	O	KJ4VF	------------
Mt Sterling	442.0500	+	O	KD4ADJ	NX4B
Munfordville	444.8500	+	O	KY4X	KD4SS
Murray	443.8000	+	O 91.5/91.5 e	K4MSU	K4MSU
Nancy	443.6000	+	O 100/100e	AC4DM	AC4DM
Nicholasville	444.9750	+	O	WB4CWF	JAWS
Olive Hill	444.9250	+	O	KO4LI	KO4LI
Owensboro	443.1000	+	O 110.9/110.9	N4WJS	N4WJS
Owensboro	443.6500	+	O	N4WJS	N4WJS
Owensboro	444.5500	+	O	KI4JXN	KI4JXN
Owingsville	442.0000	+	OsWX	W4WOO	------------
Paducah	443.0000	+	O 179.9/179.9e	KD4DVI	KD4DVI
Paintsville	441.5250	+	O 127.3/127.3elsWX	N4KJU	N4KJU
Paintsville	443.8250	+	O	KR4MT	KR4MT
Paris	444.5250	+	O	WD4GPO	------------
Phelps	444.5750	+	O	N4MVY	N4MVY
Pikeville	444.2000	+	O	KD4RTR	KD4RTR
Pikeville	444.3750	+	O	KD4DAR	KD4DAR
Pleasure Ridge Park	444.6000	+	O	N4MRM	------------
Richmond	444.6250	+	O	KE4ISW	KE4ISW
Rineyville	444.2250	+	O	KF4RBD	KF4RBD
Robinson Creek	444.6750	+	O	KC4VYX	KC4VYX
Rockport	444.0750	+	O	KD4BOH	KD4BOH
Russell Springs	444.4000	+	O	KV4D	KV4D

Location	Output	Input	Notes	Call	Sponsor
Salyersville	444.0500	+	O	KE4NLL	KE4NLL
Shelbyville	442.3750	+	O	KE4YRE	KF4ALP
Shepherdsville	444.4000	+	O	AC4VV	------------
Somerset	443.4000	+	O	KE4LVT	KE4LVT
Springfield	444.6000	+	O	W4SJH	J. MURRAY WA
Stanton	442.0750	+	O	N4VOS	N4VOS
Union	441.8000	+	O	AD4CC	AD4CC
Versailles	443.7750	+	O	KY4WC	KY4WC
Versailles	444.2500	+	O	AD4CR	AD4CR
Waddy	443.2250	+	O	KS4TO	KE4ZIJ
Watergap	444.3250	+	O	KR4MT	KR4MT
Waynesburg	442.9750	+	O	AG4TY	------------
Whitesburg	444.2500	+	O	KK4WH	KK4WH
Williamsburg	444.0500	+	O	KB4PTJ	KB4PTJ
Winchester	441.9000	+	O	KF4CBT	KF4CBT
LOUISIANA					
REG 1 NEW ORLEANS					
Belle Chasse	444.1750	+	O 114.8elrs	KA5EZQ	PPOEP
Gretna	444.2000	+	O 114.8l	W5UK	GNOARC
Metairie	444.0000	+	O 114.8e L(147.240)	W5GAD	JARC
Metairie	444.5750	+	114.8	N5OZG	N5OZG
Metairie	444.7750	+	114.8	N5OZG	N5OZG
New Orleans	444.1500	+	Oae	KB5AVY	KB5AVY
New Orleans	444.3250	+	●elrs	WB5LHS	GOHSEP
New Orleans	444.3750	+	●ers	N5NWM	N5NWM
New Orleans	444.5500	+	O(CA)el	N5GWF	FUN F ARC
New Orleans	444.6500	+	Oae	KE5WWX	------------
New Orleans	444.7000	+	O 114.8ae	WB5HVV	WB5HVV
New Orleans	444.8000	+	Oe L(146.61)	W5MCC	SELCOM
New Orleans	444.8250	+	O 114.8el	W5MCC	SELCOM
New Orleans	444.9750	+	O 110.9ael	KB5AVY	KB5AVY
Port Sulphur	444.0750	+	O 114.8e L(146.655)rs	KA5EZQ	PPOEP
REG 2 BATON ROUGE					
Baton Rouge	442.4000	+	●elrs	WB5LHS	GOHSEP
Baton Rouge	442.9250	+	O 107.5er	KD5CQB	EBRP OEP
Baton Rouge	443.1000	+	107.2 L(IRLP)	KD5QZD	KD5QZD
Baton Rouge	443.5500	–	O 107.5er	KD5CQB	EBRP OEP
Baton Rouge	443.9250	–	O 107.5er	KD5CQB	EBRP OEP
Baton Rouge	444.3000	+	O	N5UHT	N5UHT
Baton Rouge	444.3500	+	O	N5NXL	BRRG
Baton Rouge	444.4000	+	O 107.2e	W5GIX	BR ARC
Baton Rouge	444.4500	+	O 107.2/107.2 (CA)ersBI WXz	W5GSU	OMIK-BR

Location	Output	Input	Notes	Call	Sponsor
Baton Rouge	444.6000	+	O 136.5/136.5 (CA)e	W5GQ	WAFB-TV-E
Baton Rouge	444.6750	+	●elrs	WB5LHS	GOHSEP
Baton Rouge	444.8500	+	O 107.2elr	KC5BMA	RASC
Baton Rouge	444.9500	+	O 107.2el	KE5QJQ	CARCC
Gonzales	444.7250	+	Oae L(147.225) Z(*911)	K5ARC	ASCN ARC
Ravenswood	443.2000	+	●elrs	WB5LHS	GOHSEP
Walker	444.5250	+	O 107.2e	W5LRS	LARS
REG 3 THIBODAUX					
Des Allemands	443.4000	+	O 100 (CA) z	KC5OYJ	KC5PBN
LaPlace	443.8250	+	O 114.8 (CA)	KD5CQA	Plantation
Schriever	444.5000	+	Oe	W5YL	THBDX ARC
REG 4 LAFAYETTE					
Carencro	443.8000	+	Oel	W5NB	DRCC
Eunice	444.8250	+	O(CA)e	KE5CTU	KE5CTU
Krotz Springs	443.2500	+	O 103.5/103.5 TTel	W5SJL	LaCrossConn
Lafayette	443.1500	+	103.5/103.5	NG5T	TV-10 RG
Morgan City	444.6250	+	O 100 (CA) ez	KB5GON	N5DVI
Opelousas	444.8750	+	O 103.5 (CA)eBI	N5TBU	N5TBU
REG 5 LAKE CHARLES					
Kinder	444.9250	+	O 131.8ex	W5ELM	W5ELM
Lake Charles	444.2250	+	O 103.5	KI5EE	KI5EE
Lake Charles	444.3000	+	O 88.5	W5BII	SWLARC
REG 6 ALEXANDRIA					
Alexandria	443.3000	+	O 173.8ael rZ(911)	KC5ZJY	CLARC
Leesville	444.7000	+	O 118.8e	W5LSV	WCLARC
Many	444.2000	+	O 173.8rz	K5MNY	ARCS
Moreaville	444.7000	+	O 173.8	KA5KON	KA5KON
REG 7 SHREVEPORT					
Bossier City	444.3000	+	●ters	N5FJ	N5FJ
Linville	443.9000	+	O 107.5es	KB5VJY	KB5VJY
Shreveport	444.5000	+	O 186.2e	KC5OKA	ARK-LA-TEX
Shreveport	444.9000	+	O 186.2	N5FJ	SARA
REG 8 MONROE					
Bastrop	443.9250	+	O 127.3e	NE5WX	NE5WX
Bernice	444.0750	+	O	W5JC	W5JC
Calhoun	444.0000	+	OarsRB LITZ WXz	W5KGT	W5KGT
Calhoun	444.1000	+	OE-SUN L(145.17)prsRB	W5KGT	NELA-ARES
Calhoun	444.7000	+	OarsRB LITZ WXz	W5KGT	W5KGT

Location	*Output*	*Input*	*Notes*	*Call*	*Sponsor*
Columbia	444.5250	+	O	K5NOE	K5NOE
Jonesboro	444.8000	+	O	WB5NIN	JAARO
Rayville	444.9500	+	O	WA5KNV	WA5KNV
Ruston	444.3500	+	O 94.8 (CA) e	W5MCH	PHARA
Ruston	444.8750	+	O	AD5AQ	AD5AQ
West Monroe	443.7000	+	Oe	KB5VJY	KB5VJY
West Monroe	443.8000	+	Oe	KB5VJY	KB5VJY
West Monroe	444.2500	+	OsWX	KB5TLB	KB5TLB
West Monroe	444.3000	+	O	KB5TLB	KB5TLB
REG 9 HAMMOND					
Franklinton	442.4250	+	●elrs	WB5LHS	GOHSEP
Hammond	442.3250	+	●elrs	WB5LHS	GOHSEP
Hammond	444.2500	+	O 107.2e	WB5NET	SELARC
Kentwood	442.0500	+	O 107.2el	WB5ERM	WB5ERM
LaCombe	443.2000	+	O 114.8lx	W5UK	N5UK
LaCombe	443.9500	+	O 114.8els	W5MCC	SELCOM
LaCombe	444.1000	+	Oe	K5OZ	K5OZ
Loranger	443.8750	+	O 107.2el	KC5WDH	KC5WDH
Madisonville	444.0500	+	Oe	W5NJJ	NLAKE ARC+
Slidell	444.4250	+	O 114.8e	W5SLA	OzoneARC
STATEWIDE					
Shared	440.5500	+	#p		------------
Shared	442.9000	+	#		------------
MAINE					
ALL AREAS					
Statewide	441.4500	+	OpEXP	SNP	NESMC
AUGUSTA					
Belgrade Lakes	449.2750	–	O 88.5e L(W1PIG)sx	W1PIG	KARS
Fayette	443.2000	+	O 88.5ae L(E15061 W1PIG)rsWXx	W1PIG	KARS
CENTRAL/BANGOR					
Holden	444.4000	+	O	KD1OM	PSARC
Millinocket	449.2750	–	O	KA1EKS	KA1EKS
MID-COAST					
Hope	449.5250	–	O	WA1ZDA	WA1ZDA
Knox	443.5000	+	O 103.5erx	KD1KE	KD1KE
Knox	444.3000	+	OL(D*V)rs	W1EMA	WCARA
Washington	444.9000	+	O 91.5ae L(147.135)x	WZ1J	WZ1J
NORTHWEST					
Farmington	449.9250	–	O 123.0	W1BHR	BHRG
Rangeley	449.5750	–	O 173.8a E-SUN L(E387155 CL-100)	KD5FUN	KD5FUN
Saint Albans	449.7250	–	O 103.5	N1GNN	N1GNN
Skowhegan	446.3250	–	O 203.5	W1LO	W1LO
Woodstock	449.0250	–	O 82.5/136.5 L(223.94 & 53.09)x	W1IMD	W1IMD

Location	Output	Input	Notes	Call	Sponsor
PORTLAND/SOUTH COAST					
Acton	441.5000	+	O 156.7ae L(D*V DMR CCS NETWORK) EXPx	N1KMA	CLEOSYS
Alfred	448.7250	–	O 103.5aer	WJ1L	RACES
Auburn	442.0000	+	OaeWX	W1HOW	W1HOW
Brunswick	444.4000	+	O 88.5 E-WINDsx	KS1R	MARA
Brunswick	447.5750	–	OE-WIND L(D*V)sx	KS1R	MARA
Cornish	441.5000	+	O 146.2e L(D*V DMR CCS NETWORK) EXPx	N1KMA	CLEOSYS
Cornish	444.0000	+	O 167.9e L(CCS NETWORK)x	N1VAR	DESME
Sanford	441.5000	+	O 156.7e L(D*V DMR CCS NETWORK)x	N1KMA	CLEOSYS
Sanford	441.6000	+	O 203.5e	W1LO	W1LO
Waterboro	444.6000	+	O 82.5e L(E44600) WXx	W1CKD	PRG
West Newfield	441.7000	+	O 127.3e L(D*V DMR CCS NETWORK)sEXPx	N1KMA	CLEOSYS
Windham	444.9500	+	O 146.2e L(29.68)	N1FCU	N1FCU
WASHINGTON COUNTY					
Cooper	444.3000	+	O 100.0esx	W1LH	W1LH

MARYLAND

Location	Output	Input	Notes	Call	Sponsor
ALL					
SNP	442.9000	+	O		------------
SNP	447.8750	–	O		------------
ANNAPOLIS					
Annapolis	442.3000	+	O 107.2ael rsz	KB3CMA	AARC/MMARC
Davidsonville	444.4000	+	O 156.7	W3VPR	AARC
Millersville	449.1250	–	O 107.2aer z	W3CU	MMARC
BALTIMORE					
Baltimore	443.8500	+	Oe L(MOTOTRBO CC6 TS 1/ID-1 TS2/ID-2)	K3OCM	K3OCM
Baltimore	447.5250	–	O	N3MCQ	N3MCQ
Baltimore	448.3250	–	Oaelz	WB3DZO	BRATS
Baltimore	449.6750	–	O 167.9els	N3ST	N3ST
Baltimore City	448.2750	–	O 156.7	K3CUJ	Col.ARA
Cockeysville	448.5250	–	O	KB3BHO	Boumi AR
Dayton	443.9500	+	te	W3YVV	W3YVV
E Baltimore	449.5750	–	Ol	W3PGA	Aero ARC
Ellicott City	449.4750	–	O 156.7	K3CUJ	Col. ARA
Ellicott City	449.5250	–	O 100.0	N3EZD	N3EZD
Jessup	444.0000	146.1600	O 107.2l	WA3DZD	MFMA
Jessup	444.0000	+	O 107.2l	WA3DZD	MFMA

Location	Output	Input	Notes	Call	Sponsor
Jessup	444.0000	223.1600	O 107.2l	WA3DZD	MFMA
Millersville	442.4000	+	O 100.0e	KP4IP	KP4IP
NW Baltimore	443.3500	+	O(CA)	WB3DZO	BRATS
Towson	449.2750	–	O 107.2ael	N3CDY	N3CDY
Towson	449.6250	–	O 107.2ael r	W3FT	BARC
CENTRAL MD					
Glen Burnie	442.6000	+	O 127.3 (CA)	N3MIR	GBURG
CUMBERLAND					
Cumberland	442.3000	+	O 167.9 (CA)ersWX	AB3FE	AB3FE
Cumberland	444.0000	+	O 123.0el	KK3L	KK3L
Cumberland	444.5000	+	O 118.8	W3YMW	Mtn ARC
Midland	442.7500	+	O 167.9ers WX	AB3FE	AB3FE
FREDERICK					
Boonsboro	442.9500	+	O 94.8e	KD3SU	KD3SU
Frederick	442.8000	+	O 79.7 L(P25 NAC 797)	N3ITA	N3ITA
Frederick	443.4000	+	O 136.5l	WA3KOK	NERA
Frederick	444.1000	+	O 167.9ls	N3ST	N3ST
Frederick	448.1250	–	O 123.0e L(P25)	K3MAD	MADXRA
Frederick	448.4250	–	O 100.0e	K3ERM	Fdk ARC
Jefferson	443.3000	+	O 100.0	K3LMS	K3LMS
Myersville	447.1250	–	O 100.0	N3JDR	N3JDR
Thurmont	448.0250	–	O 103.5	K3KMA	K3KMA
HAGERSTOWN					
Clear Spring	442.6500	+	O 79.7eWX	N3UHD	N3UHD
Hagerstown	447.9750	–	Oe	W3CWC	Anttm RA
NORTH CENTRAL					
Manchester	447.6750	–	O 107.2	N3KZS	N3KZS
Westminster	449.8750	–	O 127.3el	K3PZN	CCARC
NORTH EASTERN SHORE					
Centreville	448.2250	–	O 107.2e	N8ADN	K.I. ARC
Chestertown	449.1750	–	O 156.7 (CA)rsWX	K3ARS	Kent ARS
St Michaels	449.9250	–	O 156.7	K3SVA	K3SVA
NORTHEAST MD					
Bel Air	449.7750	–	O 162.2aer	WBØEGR	HarfdCoRACES
Charlestown	442.9500	+	O 103.5a	N3RCN	+N3AJJ
Elkton	447.3250	–	O 131.8 (CA)lWX	W3BXW	BEARS
Elkton	447.7250	–	O 94.8r	N3XJT	Cecil Co. DES
HavreDeGrace	444.1500	+	O 131.8el	N3KZ	UPennARC
Jarrettsville	448.4750	–	O	N3UR	N3UR
Port Deposit	449.8250	–	O 167.9 L(222.92)	WA3SFJ	CBRA

Location	Output	Input	Notes	Call	Sponsor
Shawsville	449.3750	–	Ol	W3EHT	W3EHT
Whiteford	442.6500	+	O 107.2el RB WX	N3CDY	N3CDY
SOUTH EASTERN SHORE					
Ocean City	443.4500	+	O 151.4 WX	N3HF	N3HF
Salisbury	442.6500	+	O 156.7	N3HQJ	Muddy Hole
SOUTHERN MD					
Accokeek	444.5000	+	O	W3TOM	W3TOM
Aquasco	447.0750	–	O 167.9els	N3ARN	CMRG
Brandywine	443.6000	+	O 103.5	WA3YUV	WA3YUV
Golden Beach	447.1250	–	O 131.8	WX3SMD	W3SMD
Indian Head	442.4500	+	O	WB3IUT	WB3IUT
LaPlata	443.7000	+	Oa	KA3GRW	CCARC2
Lexington Park	443.0500	+	OaelsRBz	WA3UMY	WA3UMY
WASHINGTON AREA					
Ashton	443.1500	+	O 156.7a	K3WX	ARCS
Bethesda	447.9250	–	Oe	K3YGG	NIHRAC
Bowie	442.1500	+	O	W3XJ	W3XJ
Hyattsville	447.5750	–	O 156.7e	KB3KOU	KB3KOU
Jessup	444.0000	146.1600	O 107.2l	WA3DZD	MFMA
Jessup	444.0000	223.1600	O 107.2l	WA3DZD	MFMA
Jessup	444.0000	+	O 107.2l	WA3DZD	MFMA
Laurel	442.5000	+	O 156.7e	W3LRC	LARC
Laurel	444.7000	+	O 167.9els	WA3GPC	CMRG
Rockville	442.7500	+	O 156.7 (CA)r	KV3B	MARC
Rockville	443.9000	+	Or	WA3YOO	MontCoRACES
Silver Spring	443.4500	+	O 156.7 WX	N3HF	N3HF
Silver Spring	444.2500	+	Oa	WB3GXW	WB3GXW
Silver Spring	449.0250	–	O 156.7el	N3AUY	+KD3R
Silver Spring	449.0250	29.5600	O 141.3el	N3AUY	+KD3R
Suitland	448.9250	–	O 167.9ls	N3ST	CMRG
Upper Marlboro	444.6500	+	Oe L(MOTOTRBO CC6/TS1/TS2/ID-1)rs	N3LHD	N3LHD
WESTERN MD					
McHenry	444.4250	+	O 100.0	WJ8G	McARC
Oakland	444.2750	+	O 110.9e WX	KB3AVZ	KB3AVZ

MASSACHUSETTS

Location	Output	Input	Notes	Call	Sponsor
ALL AREAS					
Statewide	441.4500	+	OpEXP	SNP	NESMC
BLACKSTONE VALLEY					
Milford	446.8250	–	O 100.0e L(E3819 MMRA)s	WA1QGU	GMARG
Uxbridge	447.3250	–	ODCS(244) L(WESTBORO MA 448.775)	W1WNS	ATT

Location	Output	Input	Notes	Call	Sponsor
Northborough	441.6000	+	O 88.5	K1WPO	W1DXH
Southborough	448.3750	–	O 88.5er	W1EMC	EMC ARC
Southborough	449.5750	–	O 88.5 L(MMRA)	W1BRI	MMRA
Wellesley	444.6000	+	O 88.5e L(COLLOCATED WITH 147.030)	W1TKZ	WellslyARS
Westborough	448.7750	–	ODCS(244) L(927.6125)	W1WNS	ATT
Weston	442.7000	+	O 88.5 (CA) L(MMRA)	W1MRA	MMRA
NORTH SHORE					
Beverly	444.9500	+	O 100.0	N1GSC	N1GSC
Beverly	447.8500	–	O 88.5 E-SUNr	WA1PNW	BEMA
Danvers	442.8000	+	O 136.5 (CA)ersx	NS1RA	NSRA
Gloucester	443.7000	+	O	W1GLO	CAARA
Gloucester	447.5250	–	O 114.8e	W1RAB	W1RAB
Lynn	442.4000	+	O 88.5#	N1VGJ	UNCOORD
Lynn	443.9500	+	O 151.4 (CA)eL(NO)	W1SWR	PCD
Salem	446.6250	–	O 88.5	NS1RA	NSRA
Topsfield	447.4750	–	O 146.2e	WA1KAT	MAREX-NA
SOUTH COAST					
Assonet	442.5500	+	O 67.0 (CA)	WG1U	WG1U
East Freetown	449.7750	–	OtL(D*V)	KB1WUW	SAF ARC
Fall River	444.3500	+	O 88.5 (CA) ersx	W1ACT	FRARC
Fall River	449.5250	–	OteL(D*V) EXPx	NN1D	SEMARG
SOUTH SHORE					
Bridgewater	444.5500	+	O 88.5e	W1MV	MARA
Brockton	449.2750	–	OtL(D*V)	KB1YAC	OC D-Star
Norwell	443.6000	+	O 88.5 L(E25209 145.39 RMTBASE)	NS1N	NS1N
SPRINGFIELD/PIONEER VALLEY					
Belchertown	443.7000	+	O 71.9e	N1SIF	N1SIF
Feeding Hills	449.1750	–	OeL(D*V)x	W1KK	W1KK
Florence	449.5250	–	O 167.9 (CA) E-SUN E-WINDx	KA1OAN	KA1QFE
Granville	442.7500	+	O 77.0 L(KB1AEV LINK SYSTEM)	KB1AEV	KB1AEV
Granville	449.8250	–	O 107.2ex	N1PAH	N1PAH
Holyoke	443.2000	+	O 127.3s	W1TOM	MTARA
Holyoke	447.3750	–	OeL(D*V REF010C)	AA1KK	W1KK
THE BERKSHIRES					
Mt Greylock	449.4250	–	O 162.2ex	K1FFK	NBARC
Pittsfield	443.8500	+	O 162.2e L(I4101)	KE3HT	LTL

Location	Output	Input	Notes	Call	Sponsor
MICHIGAN					
LOWER PEN NORTHEAST					
Alpena	442.2750	+	O 131.8	KD8KUB	KD8KUB
Alpena	442.4750	+	O 100lrs WX	WB8ZIR	8BITRG
Bad Axe	443.5500	+	O 114.8 WXx	KA8WYN	KA8WYN
Bay City	444.5000	+	O 123eWX	KB8YUR	BAARC
Breckenridge	442.6500	+	O 103.5rs WX	W8QPO	W8QPO
Burt	442.2000	442.7000	O 103.5lrs WX	K8JSL	K8JSL
Cheboygan	444.8500	+	O 110.9ex	WB8DEL	WB8DEL
Farwell	443.0250	+	O 103.5rs	KG8XS	KG8XS
Harrison	442.8500	+	O 103.5e WX	KA8DCJ	KA8DCJ
Mackinaw City	444.3750	+	O 107.2r	W8AGB	CCECPSCO
Mayville	443.7750	+	O 100lx	KB8ZUZ	KB8ZUZ
Midland	443.3250	+	O 103.5elr sWX	W8QN	Midland County ARE
Midland	444.3500	+	O 131.8	WB8WNF	Phoenix Amateur Rad
Roscommon	443.1000	+	Ors	WF8R	CRARC
Saginaw	443.6000	+	O 103.5ers	KC8VOA	KC8VOA
Ubly	442.3250	+	O 103.5e	KC8KOD	KC8KOD
LOWER PEN NORTHWEST					
Big Rapids	443.9000	+	OarsWX	KB8QOI	BRAARC
Cadillac	442.2000	+	O 114.8l	WIØOK	KF8KK
Cadillac	444.8250	+	O	K8CAD	WEXARC
Edmore	444.7000	+	O 103.5	KC8LEQ	WD8NQB
Glen Arbor	444.7250	+	O 114.8el	WIØOK	N7LMJ
Hart	443.6750	+	O 94.8ers	W8VTM	OCARS
Holton	444.6750	+	O 94.8e	N8DWZ	WD8MKG
Kalkaska	444.9250	+	Oe	W8KAL	AA8ZV
Lake City	444.5250	+	O 100e	KA8ABM	KA8ABM
Mancelona	442.8000	+	Oe	K8WQK	Cherryland ARC
Morley	442.0750	+	O 103.5 (CA)elrsWXx	K8SN	K8SN
Mt Pleasant	442.8250	+	O 100rsWX	KC8RTU	KC8RTU
Pellston	444.9500	+	O 103.5	WA8EFE	WA8EFE
Stutsmanville	442.3750	+	O 107.2er WXx	N8DNX	N8DNX
Traverse City	442.5000	+	O 114.8rs	W8TCM	CARC
Traverse City	442.9000	+	O 94.8rs	W8QPO	Grand Traverse Emer
White Cloud	444.9750	+	O 94.8e	KB8IFE	KB8IFE
LOWER PEN SOUTHEAST					
Adrian	443.3750	+	O 107.2e WX	K8ADM	K8ADM
Ann Arbor	443.5000	+	O 100es	W8PGW	Arrow ARC
Ann Arbor	443.6500	+	O 100	N8AMX	Washtenaw Advance

Location	*Output*	*Input*	*Notes*	*Call*	*Sponsor*
Ann Arbor	444.0750	+	O 82.5	WR8DAR	RADAR
Ann Arbor	444.6750	+	●t(CA)lprs WXz	AA8B	AA8B
Ann Arbor	444.9750	+	O 107.2el	WD8DPA	WD8DPA
Beverly Hills	443.2250	+	O 107.2 (CA)rsx	W8HP	DART
Brooklyn	443.9000	+	●t(CA)	N8GY	N8GY
Chelsea	443.5750	+	O 100es WX	WD8IEL	CARC
Clio	444.3750	+	Oel	N8NJN	FAIR
Dansville	444.5750	+	O 107.2 (CA)elWXx	N8OBU	N8OBU
Dearborn	442.8000	+	O 107.2 (CA)ers	WR8DAR	RADAR
Dearborn	443.4250	+	O 107.2	K8UTT	Ford ARL
Dearborn	444.3500	+	O 82.5l	K8UH	K8UH / W2PUT
Detroit	442.1750	+	O 123elWX x	KC8LTS	KC8LTS
Detroit	442.4500	+	O 100 (CA) e	N8PYN	N8PYN
Detroit	443.0250	+	O 107.2e WX	KC8DCS	SpiritARC
Detroit	443.0750	+	O 123 (CA) elrsWXxz	WW8GM	GMARC
Detroit	443.4750	+	O 88.5ers WXx	WR8DAR	N8COP
Detroit	444.0000	+	O 100sx	WB8CQP	DRCG/Spirit of 7
Detroit	444.2250	+	O 107.2 DCS	N8XN	Ind Repeater Soc
Dundee	442.8250	+	O 100lrs WX	K8RPT	RRRA
Durand	442.6250	+	O 100lrs WX	N8IES	N8IES
Farmington Hills	442.7000	+	O 100	WA8SEL	FARC
Fenton	442.3500	+	O 107.2 (CA)elsWXx	W8FSM	W8FSM
Fenton	443.2000	+	O 151.4 (CA)lx	KC8YGT	KC8YGT
Fenton	443.9750	+	●t(CA) WX x	KB8PGF	KB8PGF
Flint	442.0000	+	O 107.2	N8UMW	N8UMW
Flint	443.6750	+	●t(CA)	WB8YWF	WB8YWF
Flint	444.2000	+	O 107.2	W8ACW	GCRC
Flint	444.4500	+	O 100 (CA)l	N8JYI	N8JYI
Flint	444.6000	+	Oel	W8JDE	FAIR
Frankenmuth	444.0250	+	O 100lrs WX	KB8SWR	KB8SWR
Garden City	444.7250	+	O 107.2 (CA)ers	KA8SPW	KA8SPW

Location	*Output*	*Input*	*Notes*	*Call*	*Sponsor*
Grosse Pointe Woods	446.5000	–	●taz	N8ZVZ	N8ZVZ
Holly	442.2500	+	O 100 WXz	KA8ZAU	KA8ZAU
Howell	444.5250	+	O 100ers	W8LRK	LARK
Ida	442.6500	+	O 100lrs WX	K8RPT	RRRA
Lapeer	442.7500	+	O 123ersx	W8LAP	LCARA
Luna Pier	444.5500	+	O 100e	N8OSC	N8OSC+RRRA
Mason	443.7000	+	O	WB8RJY	WB8RJY
Milan	444.1000	+	O 82.5el	W2PUT	W8PUT
Milford	442.1500	+	O 107.2als WX	WB8CRK	DRCG
Milford	444.4250	+	O 118.8	WR8DAR	N8PO
Millington	444.6500	+	O 100rsWX	KC8KGZ	Michigan Specialized
Mt Clemens	443.6250	+	O 151.4alr sWXx	KC8UMP	KC8UMP
Munith	442.3250	+	O 77e	KB8UB	KB8UB
New Hudson	442.7750	+	●tel	N8BK	N8BK
North Branch	443.4500	+	O 100elWX	W8ECG	KG8ID
Northville	443.1000	+	O 82.5er	WR8DAR	W8ICN
Novi	444.8000	+	O 110.9	WA8UMT	NARC
Ovid	444.0000	+	O 173.8	N8TSK	N8TSK
Owosso	442.4000	+	O 100 (CA) ersWX	N8DVH	N8DVH
Petersburg	442.2000	+	OlWX	K8OF	K8OF
Pinckney	442.6750	+	O(CA) DCS(047)elWX	W2GLD	W2GLD
Pontiac	443.8250	+	O	WN8G	WN8G
Pontiac	444.3250	+	O 107.2ers WX	W8OAK	Oakland Co EmerMg
Rankin	442.3000	+	O 91.5l	W8YUC	RARG
Rochester	443.7250	+	O 100	K8ZKJ	K8ZKJ
Romeo	442.5500	+	O 110.9e	WA1APX	WARTS
Romulus	442.2750	+	O 107.2	W8TX	W8TX
Romulus	445.5000	–	O 136.5elp	KD8NNY	KD8NNY
Roseville	440.5000	+	●talp	N8MET	N8MET
Saginaw	444.9500	+	O 100elrs WXx	KB8VGJ	KB8VGJ
Sterling Heights	442.9250	+	O 100e	N8LC	LCARC
Swartz Creek	444.1500	+	●tel	WD8JOF	RARG
Warren	443.5500	+	O 107.2 (CA)eWXx	KA8WYN	KA8WYN
Waterford	442.3750	+	●t(CA)el WX	N8EPL	N8EPL
Waterford	442.4750	+	●t(CA)el WXz	W8JIM	W8JIM
Wayne	443.1500	+	O 107.2ae	W8RIF	W8RIF
Westland	443.1250	+	O 107.2lrs	N8DJP	N8DJP
Westland	443.2750	+	O 107.2elr s	N8ISK	N8ISK

Location	*Output*	*Input*	*Notes*	*Call*	*Sponsor*
Yale	443.3000	+	O 100ers WX	N8ERV	N8ERV
LOWER PEN SOUTHWEST					
Allegan	442.3500	+	O 94.8ers WX	AC8RC	Allegan Amateur
Aurelius	443.8750	+	O 100 (CA) elWXx	KC8LMI	KC8LMI
Battle Creek	443.9500	+	O 94.8aelz	W8DF	SMARS
Berrien Springs	442.8250	+	O(CA)x	W8YKS	DOCRG
Bridgman	442.7750	+	O 88.5lrs WX	W8MAI	Blossomland Am
Buchanan	443.6500	+	O(CA)x	N8NIT	DOCRG
Cassopolis	443.5500	+	O 131.8ers WX	N8VPZ	N8VPZ
Cedar Springs	443.0750	+	O 94.8	NW8J	NW8J
Centreville	442.1500	+	O 94.8e	KC8BRO	ARPSA
Charlotte	443.6250	+	O 100 (CA) rsWX	N8HEE	EFFECT
Coldwater	443.3000	+	O 123rsWX	WD8KAF	BCARC
Crystal Lake	442.1250	+	O 107.2l	KB8LCY	KB8LCY
Dimondale	442.0500	+	O 100a	N9UV	N9UV
Eagle	443.3500	+	O 100 (CA) elrWX	K8VEB	EARS
Eaton Rapids	443.2500	+	O 100a	KD8JGN	KD8JGN
Edwardsburg	443.0750	+	O 131.8al WX	KD8BHP	KD8BHP
Fruitport	442.3000	+	O 94.8	KE8LZ	N8UKF
Glennwood	443.4000	+	O 94.8elrs WXx	W8GDS	W8GDS
Grand Haven	443.7750	+	●t	W8GVK	W8GVK
Grand Ledge	442.5250	+	O 107.2el	KC8QYW	KB8HWT
Grand Rapids	442.0000	+	●tex	K8EFK	K8EFK
Grand Rapids	443.8000	+	O 94.8ael WXxz	KA8YSM	IRA
Grand Rapids	444.1000	+	O 94.8 (CA) WX	N8NET	N8NET
Grand Rapids	444.3250	+	O 82.5	N8WKN	N8WKN
Grand Rapids	444.4000	+	O 94.8al	W8DC	GRARA
Grand Rapids	444.7750	+	O 94.8l	K8WM	K8WM
Holland	443.8250	+	O 94.8elrs WX	K8DAA	HARC
Holland	444.8000	+	O 103.5e	N8XPQ	N8XPQ
Holt	444.9250	+	Oae	KE8DR	KE8DR
Hudsonville	442.2500	449.2500	●t	K8TB	K8TB
Hudsonville	444.9000	+	O 94.8e	K8IHY	K8IHY
Jackson	443.1750	+	O 77ersWX x	WD8EEQ	WD8EEQ
Jackson	444.1750	+	O 100ersx	KA8YRL	KA8YRL
Kalamazoo	444.6500	+	●te	W8VY	KARC

Location	Output	Input	Notes	Call	Sponsor
Kalamazoo	444.8750	+	O	K8KZO	SMART
Lansing	442.4250	+	●teWX	KD8PA	KD8PA
Lansing	442.7250	+	O 100x	KB8SXK	KB8SXK
Lansing	444.1250	+	O 107.2er	N8DEF	WIRE
Lansing	444.7500	+	O 100	KC8BFK	KC8BFK
Lawton	444.4750	+	●t	N8GH	N8GH
Lowell	443.8500	+	O 94.8aers WXz	K8LHS	ARGYL
Moline	442.1750	+	●tersWXx	K8SN	K8SN
Muskegon	442.9500	+	O 94.8al	N8KQQ	N8KQQ
Muskegon	443.2000	+	O 94.8	N8UKF	N8UKF
Muskegon	444.5500	+	O 94.8e	W8ZHO	MAARC
Muskegon	444.9500	+	O 94.8r	K8WNJ	MCES (Muskegon Co
Niles	442.2250	+	O 94.8er WX	KC8OVZ	KC8OVZ
Niles	444.1250	+	O 94.8el	WB9WYR	BRRG
Ovid	445.5000	–	O 94.8lrs WX	KD8AGP	KD8AGP
Potterville	442.0250	+	O 173.8r WXx	N8JI	N8JI
Saranac	444.7250	+	O 94.8e	KC8SIV	Saranac Comm Sch
Saugatuck	442.7000	+	O 94.8e	AC8GN	AC8GN
St Johns	443.5250	+	O 100ers WX	W8CLI	Clinton County ARPS
St Johns	444.8500	+	O 141.3lrs WX	WC8CLI	CCARA
Whitehall	443.2500	+	O 94.8rs	K8COP	K8COP
Zeeland	445.5000	–	O 94.8	KD8CAO	KD8CAO
UPPER PEN CENT					
Escanaba	444.3000	+	O	WD8RTH	WD8RTH
Gladstone	444.4500	+	O	N8OYR	N8OYR
Iron Mountain	444.8500	+	O 100.0ae WX	WA8FXQ	MichACon
Marquette	443.4500	+	O 100.0e	K8LOD	HARA
Marquette	443.5000	+	O 100.0	KBØP	KBØP
Marquette	444.8000	+	Oe	KE8IL	MrquttRA
Menominee	444.0750	+	O 107.2e	W8PIF	M&MARC
UPPER PEN EAST					
Moran	444.6250	+	OeEXP	K8EUP	MADARC
Newberry	444.9000	+	O 131.8	W8ARS	EUPAR
SaultSte Marie	442.8500	+	Oe	KB8SKC	KB8SKC
UPPER PEN WEST					
Calumet	442.5500	+	O 100.0e	W8CDZ	CCRAA
Copper Harbor	444.1500	+	O 107.2e	K9SJ	K9SJ
Gaastra	444.1750	+	O 107.2e	N8LVQ	IRARC
Houghton	444.5000	+	Oe	W8YY	HuskyARC

Location	Output	Input	Notes	Call	Sponsor
MINNESOTA					
CENTRAL					
Avon	443.6500	+	O 85.4e	KGØCV	KGØCV
Becker	443.4750	+	O 85.4	KBØRRN	KBØRRN
Big Lake	443.6000	+	O 114.8e	NØJDH	SHERBCRG
Cambridge	443.9750	+	O 114.8e	WRØP	ICSES
Crown	442.9250	+	O 127.3	NØGEF	NØGEF
Hutchinson	443.4000	+	O 146.2e	KBØWJP	CRARC
Isanti	443.3250	+	O 146.2el	KBØQYC	LSAC
Litchfield	443.8000	+	O 146.2	KCØCAP	KCØCAP
Little Falls	443.0750	+	O 146.2	NØRND	NØRND
Little Falls	443.1250	+	O 123.0	KAØJSW	LKARRA
Morris	444.4000	+	O 103.5e	NGØW	NGØW
St Cloud	442.2250	+	O 85.4e	WØSV	STCLDARC
DULUTH					
Duluth	442.8000	+	O	KBØQYC	LSAC
Duluth	444.1000	+	Ol	WØGKP	ARAC
Duluth	444.2000	+	O 103.5e	KCØRTX	KCØRTX
Duluth	444.3000	+	O 103.5	NØEO	SVAMTRS
EAST CENTRAL					
Center City	443.6250	+	O 146.2a	KCØASX	CCARES
North Branch	443.8750	+	O 146.2e	KØDMF	KØDMF
METRO					
Arden Hills	442.0750	+	O 110.9l	WI9WIN	W.I.N.
Bloomington	444.3250	+	O 131.8	NØBVE	NØBVE
Burnsville	444.3000	+	O 114.8ae	WØBU	TCRC
Chaska	443.0000	+	O 100.0	KAØKMJ	KAØKMJ
Cologne	444.6000	+	Oe	NØKP	SCAN
Columbia Hts	444.5500	+	O 114.8e	NØFKM	NØFKM
Columbia Hts	444.7500	+	O 114.8l	NØFKM	NØFKM
Columbus	444.9750	+	O 94.8e	KØMSP	MIDWESTRA
Edina	444.1250	+	O 114.8	WØEF	TCFMCLUB
Edina	444.2000	+	O 127.3e	WCØHC	HC RACES
Edina	444.8500	+	O 114.8	KGØBP	HANDIHAM
Edina	444.9000	+	O 114.8	KGØSG	KGØSG
Falcon Heights	442.7000	+	O 167.9	KBØUPW	RAMCOES
Forest Lake	442.0500	+	O 114.8	NØODK	NØODK
Gem Lake	444.9500	+	O 114.8	KØLAV	KØLAV
Golden Valley	444.1750	+	O 127.3e	WCØHC	HENNRACES
Lino Lakes	443.2000	+	O 151.4e	WD8CBO	WD8CBO
Little Canada	444.7250	+	O 100.0a	KCØVOE	KCØVOE
Maple Grove	442.4000	+	O 100.0	KEØL	KEØL
Maplewood	442.6000	+	O 156.7	KCØMQW	SPEARS
Maplewood	444.8250	+	O 114.8e	WØMR	MINING ARC
Minneapolis	442.0000	+	O 114.8a	KØSEY	KØSEY
Minneapolis	442.7000	+	O 114.8	KBØYTU	KBØYTU
Minneapolis	443.0000	+	● 118.8	NØYNT	UofM ARC
Minneapolis	443.3000	+	O 114.8	NØNKI	NØNKI
Minneapolis	443.3750	+	O 179.9	KAØJQO	KAØJQO

Location	Output	Input	Notes	Call	Sponsor
Minneapolis	444.4250	+	O 100.0	WØYC	UOFM RC
Minneapolis	444.4250	+	O 114.8	KAØKMJ	KAØKMJ
Minneapolis	444.6500	+	O	NØBVE	MRHA
Minneapolis	444.8750	+	O	WBØMPE	WBØMPE
Moundsview	444.5250	+	O 114.8	WØMDT	BAKKEN ARS
New Brighton	443.4250	+	● 114.8e	NØYNT	+KØBEN
Oakdale	444.2750	+	O 67.0	KØLAV	KØLAV
Plymouth	444.3750	+	O 114.8	NØFWG	NØFWG
Plymouth	444.5000	+	O 127.3e	WØPZT	HC SHERIFF
Ramsey	444.9750	+	O 114.8e	KØMSP	MIDWESTRA
Richfield	444.4750	+	O 118.8e	WBØPWQ	RICHPSAF
Robbinsdale	444.7250	+	O 162.2	KØLTC	RARC
Robbinsdale	444.7750	+	O 114.8e	KØYTH	MNYARC
Rogers	442.9500	+	O 114.8	WØIDS	FARM RADIO
St Louis Park	444.1000	+	O 114.8	WØEF	TCFMCLUB
St Paul	443.1000	+	O 114.8ae	NØNKI	NØNKI
St Paul	444.0500	+	O 114.8l	NØGOI	MAGIC
St Paul	444.8000	+	O 114.8	WDØHWT	MARA
West St Paul	442.5500	+	O 100.0e	WØDCA	DCEC
White Bear Lake	444.2500	+	O 100.0	WDØHWT	MARA
NORTH CENTRAL					
Bemidji	444.0250	+	O 71.9	WØBJI	PBARC
Brainerd	444.9250	+	O	WØUJ	BAARC
Grand Rapids	444.5500	+	O 123.0ae	KØGPZ	NLARC
Nisswa	443.9250	+	O 123.0	WØUJ	BAARC
Pinewood	442.2250	+	O 118.8l	KCØFTV	KCØFTV
NORTH EAST					
Gilbert	443.5000	+	O 141.3	KBØQYC	LSAC
Grand Marais	444.2500	+	O 151.4	WØBBN	BWARC
Hinkley	444.5750	+	O 146.2e	KBØQYC	LSAC
Mcgregor	444.4500	+	O 151.4e	N4TGO	N4TGO
NORTH WEST					
Bemidji	444.9500	+	123.0e	NIØK	+KCØOQR
Fergus Falls	444.2000	+	O 151.4ae	KØQIK	LKREGARC
Karlstad	444.9750	+	O 100.0	KAØNWV	KAØNWV
Mahnomen	444.5000	+	O	WØBJI	PBARC
Thief River Falls	444.8000	+	OeWX	WBØWTI	WBØWTI
NORTHCENTRAL					
Cohasset	444.1500	+	O 114.8e	KBØCIM	KBOCIM
NORTHEAST					
Littlefork	444.9000	+	O 103.5s	KAØWRT	KARES
Tamarack	443.2000	+	O 114.8	NØBZZ	NØBZZ
NORTHWEST					
Moorhead	444.8750	+	O 123.0el	WØILO	WØILO
SOUTH CENTRAL					
Albert Lea	443.5250	+	O 100.0e	WAØRAX	ALARC
Fairmont	443.9250	+	O	K6ZC	CMARS
Fairmont	444.3500	+	O 136.5	NØPBA	PBANET
Faribault	444.5750	+	● 612er	NØPQK	NØPQK

Location	*Output*	*Input*	*Notes*	*Call*	*Sponsor*
Mankato	443.6500	+	O 114.8ae	WA2OFZ	WA2OFZ
Mankato	444.6750	+	O 100.0	WØWCL	MARC
St Peter	444.1500	+	O	WQØA	SCAN
Waseca	442.3000	+	O 141.3e WX	KBØUJL	WCEM
Waseca	443.7500	+	Oe	WAØCJU	VARS
SOUTH EAST					
Austin	443.5000	+	Oa	NØRZO	AUSTIN ARC
Ellendale	442.9250	+	O 114.8	KAØPQW	HANDIHAM
Owatonna	444.4500	+	O 100.0ael	WBØVAK	WBØVAK
Red Wing	442.2500	+	O 136.5	KCØLXM	HIWATVATC
Spring Valley	444.5250	+	Oae	NØZOD	BLUFLDSER
Winona	444.2250	+	Oae	WØNE	WINONARC
SOUTH SE					
Faribault	444.6250	+	O 100.0ae	WBØNKX	WBØNKX
SOUTH WEST					
Wabasso	444.5250	+	O 141.3ael	KBØCGJ	REDWARA
Worthington	444.8500	+	O 141.3es WX	WØDRK	NPRRC
SOUTHWEST					
Tyler	444.6750	+	O 136.5e	KBØNLY	KBØNLY
STATEWIDE					
Statewide	443.7000	+	O 186.2ep	KØYTH	MNYARC
Statewide	443.7000	+	167.9	WGØC	WGØC
Statewide	443.7000	+	O 173.8p	NØGEF	NOGEF
WEST CENTRAL					
Alexandria	442.0250	+	O 88.5e	WØALX	RUNESARC
Madison	444.9000	+	O 136.5e	NYØI	WCARC
Willmar	444.8000	+	O 146.2	KBØMNU	KCEM

MISSISSIPPI

Location	*Output*	*Input*	*Notes*	*Call*	*Sponsor*
Aberdeen	444.4500	+	O	KD5AHI	MONROE CTY A
Ackerman	443.6500	+	O	NM5D	------------
Ackerman	444.9000	+	O	NM5D	------------
Amory	444.8250	+	O	KB5DSN	------------
Biloxi	443.9250	+	O	W5OXA	W5OXA
Biloxi	444.2500	+	O	KB5CSQ	KB5CSQ
Biloxi	444.5500	+	O	KC5IF	KC5IF
Biloxi	444.9500	+	O	W5OXA	------------
Brandon	444.8250	+	O	K5RKN	KD4RWF
Brandon	444.9000	+	O	K5RKN	KD5RWF
Byhalia	444.3000	+	O	W5GWD	W5GWD
Clinton	444.0000	+	O	W5PFR	JARC INC
Columbus	444.3250	+	O	KB5ZZC	LOWNDES CO A
Columbus	444.9250	+	O	KC5ULN	KC5ULN
Corinth	441.8000	+	O	WB5CON	ALCORN CO AR
Corinth	443.9000	+	O	KJ5CO	KJ5CO
Derby	443.9750	+	O	KB5OXE	------------

Location	*Output*	*Input*	*Notes*	*Call*	*Sponsor*
Ellisville	442.2500	+	O	AA5SG	AA5SG/N5HOA
Ellisville	442.3250	+	O	N5DWU	------------
Ellisville	443.8750	+	O	N5EKR	N5EKR
Gautier	426.2500	439.2500	O	KA5NOJ	KA5NOJ
Gloster	443.8250	+	O	N5ZNS	N5ZNS
Greenville	444.6750	+	O	N5PS	G.R.A. INC.
Grenada	444.7000	+	O	AD5IT	AD5IT
Gulfport	444.1500	+	O	WD5BJT	WD5BJT
Gulfport	444.2500	+	O	KK5RK	HARRISON CO CD
Gulfport	444.3500	+	O	N5UCF	SCMSRC
Hattiesburg	442.7250	+	O	N5LRQ	------------
Hattiesburg	443.3500	+	O	W5CJR	W5CJR
Hattiesburg	443.7000	+	O	W5CJR	HATTIESBURG ARC
Hattiesburg	444.7750	+	O	K5IJX	K5IJX
Hazlehurst	443.9500	+	O	N5ZDF	------------
Heidelberg	444.3000	+	O	KC5RC	JONES CO ARC
Helena	443.4500	+	O	N4KMH	------------
Hernando	444.9250	+	O	N5PYQ	SRA
Hickory Flat	444.7250	+	O	W4ZCD	------------
Horn Lake	444.6500	+	O	KE5ST	------------
Horn Lake	444.6500	+	O	N5NBG	------------
Indianola	444.8500	+	O	AB5DU	AB5DU
Jackson	444.3250	+	O	KB5KGE	------------
Jackson	444.4500	+	O	KB5LCL	------------
Jackson	444.6000	+	O	KB5CO	JARC INC
Jackson	444.7000	+	O	NC5Y	NC5Y
Jackson	444.8000	+	O	KB5CO	------------
Jackson East	443.6250	+	O	AA5RZ	------------
Laurel	442.3750	+	O	WV5D	WV5D
Laurel	443.6500	+	O	W5NRU	AA5SG/N5HOA
Laurel	444.9750	+	O	KC5PIA	KB5AAB
Leakesville	444.2250	+	O	KE5WGF	GREEN CO EM COM
Mccomb	444.8750	+	O	W5WQ	SW MS ARC
Mchenry	444.7500	+	O	KK5RK	HARRISON CO CD
Meridian	443.8750	+	O	WD5HLD	LAUDERDALE REP
Meridian	444.1000	+	O	KB5BRZ	WB5AKR
Meridian	444.5000	+	O	W5LRG	LAUDERDALE RPT
Monticello	442.0750	+	O	N5DWU	------------
Natchez	443.8000	+	O	N5IAT	N5IAT
Nettleton	444.6250	+	O	AB5MU	AB5MU
New Albany	444.1500	+	O	WB5YCR	NEMARC
New Hebron	444.5250	+	O	N5NNI	N5MRS
O'Reilly	444.9750	+	O	N5PS	DELTA ARA/G.R.A.
Olive Branch	444.7000	+	O	W5OBM	W5OBM
Oxford	444.3500	+	O	W5LAF	W5UMS
Pascagoula	443.4500	+	O	KC5LCW	KC5LCW
Pearl	444.3750	+	O	KB5HAV	------------
Perkinston	442.4750	+	O	K5GVR	K5GVR
Philadelphia	444.9500	+	O	WB5YGI	NESHOBA ARC

Location	*Output*	*Input*	*Notes*	*Call*	*Sponsor*
Picayune	443.7250	+	O	KE5LT	KE5LT
Pinola	444.8500	+	O	KC5LXF	KC5LXF
Port Gibson	444.5750	+	O	KC5CLM	------------
Raymond	443.6000	+	O	W5PPB	K5HYE
Richton	444.6250	+	O	N5OCF	N5OCF
Ridgeland	443.7000	+	O	N5WDG	N5WDG
Rose Hill	442.8750	+	O	KB5ZCX	EMERGENCY C
Sataria	444.7750	+	O	N5PS	DELTA ARA/G.R
Soso	444.2750	+	O	WV5D	WV5D
Starkville	444.7500	+	O	KD5GVU	MAGNOLIA ARC
Stennis Space Cen	421.2500	439.2500	O	WB4FUR	NASA/SSC ARC
Stennis Space Cen	444.6500	+	O	WB4FUR	NASA/SSC ARC
Taylorsville	442.2000	+	O	AA5SG	AA5SG
Tishomingo	444.9750	+	O	KE5IPO	KE5IPO
Tupelo	444.9500	+	O	N5VGK	------------
Vicksburg	444.9250	+	O	WB5TTE	WB5TTE
Waynesboro	443.5000	+	O	W5SAR	W5SAR
Waynesboro	443.5500	+	O	W5SAR	W5SAR
Waynesboro	443.9000	+	O	N5DWU	EARS
West Point	443.4500	+	O	N5WXD	N5WXD
Wiggins	443.3000	+	O	KB5DZJ	KB5DZJ

MISSOURI

CAPE GIRARDEAU					
Cape Girardeau	444.2000	+	Ox	WØRMS	WØRMS
CENTRAL					
Barnett	442.9250	+	O 127.3	AAØIY	AAØIY
Boonville	442.7000	+	O 77/77el	KAØGFC	KAØGFC
Boonville	444.7000	+	O 77el	KAØGFC	KAØGFC
Camdenton	442.2000	+	O 100/100el	KB8KGU	------------
Centralia	444.8000	+	O 103.5a (CA)ers	AFØAM	------------
Freeburg	443.7000	+	O 77/77elx	KAØGFC	KAØGFC
Holts Summit	443.8000	+	O	KBØNXX	KBØNXX
Mexico	444.8250	+	Oax	AAØRC	AudrainARC
Moberly	443.9750	+	O	KØMOB	TriCtARC
Osage Beach	444.5000	+	O 127.3e LITZ	NØQVO	------------
Stover	444.9250	+	O	KBØQWQ	KBØQWQ
Warrensburg	442.8250	+	●x	KUØG	------------
Windsor	442.7250	+	O 107.2/107.2	WØOA	WØOA
Windsor	443.8750	+	O 107.2/107.2x	NØTLE	BYRG
COLUMBIA/JEFF CITY					
Ashland	444.1750	+	O 107.2/107.2elx	KAØGFC	KAØGFC

Location	Output	Input	Notes	Call	Sponsor
California	444.6250	+	O 127.3rsx	KØMCA	MOCtyARES
Centralia	443.0250	+	O 77/77ex	NØPBM	WØSMI
Columbia	444.4250	+	O 77/77lx	KØSI	CMRA
Columbia	444.9750	+	Oa(CA)erx	NØLBA	NØLBA
Holts Summit	444.8750	+	O	KB4VSP	KB4VSP
			127.3/127.3eL(147.42) RB		
Jefferson City	443.1750	+	O 77elsx	WØSMI	ShowMeINT
EAST CENTRAL					
Barnhart, Mo	443.7250	+	O	KØAMC	KØRWU
			192.8/192.8 RBx		
De Soto	442.8500	+	O	KØMGU	KØMGU
Defiance	443.5250	+	OTT	NØRVC	NØRVC
Foristell	444.4750	+	O 77/77els	WØECA	ECA OF STC
High Hill	444.0250	+	O 77/77l	WØSMI	ShowMeINT
Potosi	444.4000	+	O 100/100	NØWNC	NØWNC
Washington	444.1000	+	O 151.4	NØMFD	NØMFD
Washington	444.3500	+	O	WAØFYA	ZBARC
			141.3/141.3ex		
JOPLIN					
Joplin	443.4750	+	O	WBØUPB	4StARCP
Joplin	444.5000	+	O 100/100	WD6FIC	WD6FIC
KANSAS CITY METRO					
Belton	442.8000	+	O	KAØOXO	BARC
			151.4/151.4		
Blue Springs	444.9500	+	O 107.2e	KBØVBN	BluSprRPTR
			RBx		
Excelsior Spgs	443.3250	+	●	KØAMJ	KØBSJ
			141.3/141.3a(CA)elx		
Excelsior Spgs	444.6500	+	O 156.7	KØESM	RayClay RC
Holden	444.3750	+	O	NØNDP	NØNDP
			107.2/107.2x		
Hoover	442.0750	+	O 151.4	KAØFKL	------------
Independence	444.5750	+	O 186.2l	NØOEV	------------
Kansas City	442.5500	+	O	WBØYRG	BYRG
			186.2/186.2elRB WX		
Kansas City	442.9750	+	O	KØORB	SJMC ARC
			151.4/151.4x		
Kansas City	443.1000	+	O	NGØN	BYRG
Kansas City	443.1750	+	●x	WØWJB	------------
Kansas City	443.2500	+	O	WØOEM	WØOEM
			131.8/131.8esx		
Kansas City	443.3500	+	Oa(CA)	WVØT	SEIDKR
Kansas City	443.4500	+	Olx	WØWJB	WØWJB
Kansas City	443.7750	+	O	WAØNQA	ArtShrnRC
			110.9/110.9		
Kansas City	444.0250	+	O	WBØYRG	BYRG
			186.2/186.2aeL(433.8) RB		
Kansas City	444.1250	+	O 123/123	NØNKX	NØNKX
Kansas City	444.3500	+	O	NØAAP	NØAAP

Location	Output	Input	Notes	Call	Sponsor
Kearney	443.9000	+	O 127.3e	KBØEQV	KBØEQV
Kearney	444.2000	+	Oa(CA)e	KØKMO	MJARS
Lee's Summit	444.3000	+	O 131.8	KØMRR	------------
Lee's Summit	444.4500	+	O 151.4/151.4eL(PAOLA KS REPEATER 442.	NØNDP	NØNDP
Oak Grove	444.2750	+	O 123/123	KBØTHQ	PHRRL
Peculiar	442.0250	+	●eL(433.8) RB	WØMCJ	BYRG
Platte City	444.1500	+	O 88.5/88.5 e	WØUSI	WØUSI
Platte Woods	444.0500	+	O 151.4/151.4elsLITZx	KDØEAV	PlatteCoARG
Platte Woods	444.5500	+	O 151.4/151.4lLITZx	KDØEAV	KDØEAV
Smithville	443.6250	+	O 114.8	NØVER	NØVER
NORTHEAST					
Ewing	444.8750	+	O 100	KBØYKI	------------
Marceline	443.1500	+	O 110.9/110.9sx	KDØETV	------------
NORTHWEST					
Amity	443.1250	+	O 146.2	KBØALL	KBØALL
Bethany	443.0750	+	O 100/100x	N2OYJ	N2OYJ
Graham	444.4750	+	O 146.2	NØGGU	NØGGU
Kingston	444.6750	+	● 107.2/107.2x	NJØZ	------------
Osborn	442.6750	+	O 127.3/127.3	NØSWP	NØSWP
Rockport	444.7750	+	O 100/100x	N2OYJ	N2OYJ
ROLLA					
Rolla	443.8250	+	Oa(CA)l	WØEEE	UMR ARC
SOUTH CENTRAL					
Belle	442.6000	+	O 127.3	NØVHN	------------
Mountain Grove	444.9500	+	Oae	KØKNC	ToARC
Newberg	443.4250	+	O 100/100	KBØWD	------------
Rolla	443.6000	+	O 114.8/114.8l	WB9KHR	------------
Willow Spgs	443.9750	+	Ot	KC5DGC	------------
SOUTHEAST					
Dexter	443.9000	+	O 100x	NØDAN	NØDAN
Park Hills Mo	442.0500	+	O 100/100x	KDØKIB	KDØKIB
Poplar Bluff	444.9250	+	O 179.9/179.9x	ABØJW	SEMOARA
Southeast	444.5750	+	O 107.2/107.2	KCØLAT	KMS
SOUTHWEST					
Bolivar	443.6750	+	O 107.2/107.2x	WBØLVR	LksAraARA
Carthage	442.3250	+	O 103.5/103.5	WØLF	CARC

Location	Output	Input	Notes	Call	Sponsor
Crane	442.1500	+	O 162.2/162.2ex	KØNXA	Nixa ARC
Highlandville	442.1250	+	O 162.2/162.2ers	WA6JGM	CC ARC
Highlandville	444.8750	+	Oers	WA6JGM	CC ARC
Kimberling Cty	444.3000	+	O	NØNWP	NØNWP
Monett	444.6500	+	O 123	KØSQS	KØSQS
Neosho	444.5250	+	O 127.3/127.3esx	KCØNJZ	SWARG
Nevada	444.0000	+	O	KØCB	KØCB
Nevada	444.2250	+	O 127.3x	WØHL	WØHL
Nixa	442.2750	+	O 162.2/162.2elx	KØNXA	Nixa ARC
SPRINGFIELD					
Springfield	442.3750	+	Oex	WØPM	WØPM
Springfield	444.0500	+	O 77e	WBØQIR	------------
Springfield	444.4000	+	O 100a (CA)e	WØEBE	SW MO ARC
Springfield	444.6000	+	O 77e	W6OQS	EARS
Springfield	444.7250	+	O 136.5	WØYKE	SMSU ARC
ST JOSEPH					
St Joseph	443.9500	+	O 151.4/151.4ex	KMØHP	MULEBARN - KMØH
St Joseph	444.9250	+	O 100ex	WAØHBX	WAØHBX
ST LOUIS METRO					
Berkeley	443.6500	+	●	KBØPE	KBØPE
Bridgeton	443.4500	+	O 146.2e	WØKE	NWAR/EAsn
Clayton	442.1000	+	O 141.3ers	KBØMWG	SLSRC
Clayton	444.0000	+	O	KØCEH	------------
Crystal City	443.6250	+	O 100/100	WØWHW	WØWHW
High Ridge	444.5500	+	O 192.8/192.8eL(146.925)	KØAMC	AMARC
High Ridge	444.7500	+	O 192.8/192.8 RB	KØAMC	AMARC
High Ridge	444.8500	+	O 192.8/192.8 RB	KØAMC	AMARC
Imperial	442.5000	+	Oa(CA)e	KEØPE	KEØPE
New Haven	444.9000	+	O	KAØBWH	------------
Olivette	443.0750	+	O 141.3/141.3ers	WØSRC	SLSRC
St Charles	443.2500	+	O 151.4l	NØKQG	------------
St Charles	444.6500	+	Oar	WBØHSI	StChasARC
St Louis	442.8250	+	O 127.3el	KØGFM	SMARC
St Louis	442.8750	+	O 141.3/141.3a(CA)el	WØMA	BEARS-STL
St Louis	443.1500	+	Oe	NØFLC	NØFLC
St Louis	443.3000	+	O 123	KA9HNT	XEEARC
St Louis	443.4750	+	O 77elrs	WDØEFP	WDØEFP
St Louis	443.5500	+	O/141.3a (CA)ex	KØGOB	UHF ARA

Location	*Output*	*Input*	*Notes*	*Call*	*Sponsor*
St Louis	443.7750	+	OeEXP	WØXEU	------------
St Louis	444.0500	+	Oe	WØSLW	14739RPTR
St Louis	444.1500	+	Oa(CA)e	WBØQXW	#NAME?
St Louis	444.6250	+	O	K9GXU	StClairARC
St Paul	444.2000	+	Olr	KAØEJQ	KAØEJQ
St Peters	442.4750	+	O	NØFHN	------------
St Peters	444.2750	+	O 141.3/141.3es	KB3HF	KB3HF
Webster Groves	443.8500	+	O 141.3a (CA)es	NØUHJ	KCØVSJ
WEST CENTRAL					
Clinton	443.3000	+	O 107.2e L(147.195)	WØDR	RATS
Kingston	443.3750	+	O 192.8	WØBYU	WØBYU
Marshall Junction	442.1750	+	O 127.3/127.3ex	KMØHP	KMØHP - MO H
Richmond	442.0250	+	O	ACØJR	KCØVNB
Warrensburg	443.2000	+	O 107.2e	WØAU	WAARCI
MONTANA					
CENTRAL					
Lewistown	442.0000	+	O 100.0	K7VH	K7EC
EAST CENTRAL					
Sidney	444.5000	+	Ol	W7DXQ	LYARC
NORTH CENTRAL					
Cut Bank	441.2000	+	O	KE7QIP	KE7QIP
Cut Bank	443.3000	+	O	W7DPK	HARK
Cut Bank	443.3250	+	O 100.0	K7IQA	HARK
Cut Bank	443.3750	+	O 88.5eRB	W7DPK	HARK
Great Falls	444.3500	+	Oae	W7ECA	GFAARC
Great Falls	449.5000	–	O 100.0l	W7ECA	GFAARC
Havre	444.7000	+	O 114.8	KE7BBN	KE7BBN
Havre	447.1250	–	O 100.0	W7HAV	Hi-Line ARC
NORTHEAST					
Plentywood	444.0000	+	Ol	KB7QWG	KB7QWG
Plentywood	444.6000	+	Ol	KB7QWG	KB7QWG
Plentywood	448.3500	–	O	KD7ZEB	Sheridan County.
Scobey	443.5000	+	O	NØPL	NØPL
NORTHWEST					
Bigfork	442.0750	+	O 88.5ael RBxz	KA5LXG	FVRG
Bigfork	444.6000	+	O 103.5	KE7JI	KE7JI
Columbia Falls	444.4000	+	O	W7HGM	W7HGM
Eureka	443.8000	+	O 100.0	WR7DW	WR7DW
Eureka	444.1500	+	O	KU7R	KU7R
Eureka	444.2500	+	O 100.0	WR7DW	WR7DW
Kalispell	442.2000	+	O 100.0	N7ONV	N7ONV
Lakeside	442.6250	+	O 123.0l	KA7G	KA7G
Lakeside	444.3250	+	O	KA7G	NWMRG

Location	Output	Input	Notes	Call	Sponsor
Libby	444.3500	+	O	KB7SQE	KB7SQE
Libby	444.8250	+	O	KB7SQE	KB7SQE
Lookout Pass	444.2000	+	O 131.8	WR7HLN	WR7AGT
Somers	448.4500	–	O 100.0 RB	N7LT	N7LT
Whitefish	443.7750	+	O 100.0	K7LYY	FVARC
Whitefish	444.6500	+	O 100.0 E-SUN	WR7DW	WR7DW
Whitefish	444.7500	+	O 100.0e	K6KUS	K6KUS
Whitefish	444.9750	+	O 100.0	K7LYY	FVARC
Yaak	444.2250	+	O	W3YAK	N3AAW
SOUTH CENTRAL					
Bozeman	447.0000	–	O 162.2ae	KL7JGS	KL7JGS
Bozeman	447.7000	–	O 77.0a	KI7XF	ERA
Bozeman	447.9500	–	O 100.0	WA7U	WA7U
Bozeman	448.3500	–	O 100.0	KB7KB	KB7KB
Bozeman	449.9000	–	O 100.0l	KL7JGS	KL7JGS
SOUTHEAST					
Billings	449.2500	–	O 100.0	WB6EHV	WB6EHV
Billings	449.7000	–	O 103.5	KE7YDB	KE7YDB
Billings	449.7500	–	O	N7VR	N7VR
Billings	449.8000	–	O 100.0 E-SUN	KA7MHP	KA7MHP
Red Lodge	449.9000	–	O 100.0	KE7FEL	KE7FEL
Worden	447.9000	–	O	AE7V	AE7V
SOUTHWEST					
Boulder	449.2000	–	O 131.8l	WR7HLN	WR7AGT
Butte	449.4000	–	O 131.8	WR7HLN	KB8ML
Dillon	444.1000	+	O 100.0	WR7HLN	WR7AGT
Dillon	449.7750	–	Ol	K7IMM	DARC
Drummond	444.9000	+	O 146.2	W7KNT	W7KNT
Gold Creek	449.3000	–	O 131.8l	WR7HLN	WR7AGT
Helena	444.1000	+	O 131.8l	WR7HLN	WR7AGT
Helena	448.9000	–	O 131.8	WR7HLN	WR7AGT
Helena	449.5500	–	O 123.0	W7MRI	W7MRI
Toston	449.3000	–	O 131.8l	WR7HLN	WR7AGT
WEST CENTRAL					
Frenchtown	449.0500	–	O 146.2	N7DWB	N7DWB
Hamilton	447.5000	–	O 186.2l	W7FTX	BARC
Hamilton	448.3000	–	O 151.4	AE7OD	AE7OD
Missoula	444.8000	+	O 88.5	W7PX	HARC
Missoula	448.9000	–	O 131.8	WR7HLN	WR7AGT
Stevensville	442.2500	+	O 88.5	KE7WR	KE7WR
Stevensville	444.4250	+	O 203.5	KD7HP	KD7HP
Stevensville	447.7000	–	O 146.2	W7KNT	W7KNT

NEBRASKA

Location	Output	Input	Notes	Call	Sponsor
COLUMBUS					
Columbus	442.1750	+	Oe	WAØCOL	PAWNEE ARC

Location	Output	Input	Notes	Call	Sponsor
EAST					
Wahoo	443.6000	+	Os	KBØDYY	KBØDYY
FREMONT					
Fremont	444.1750	+	O	WØUVQ	WØUVQ
Fremont	444.3750	+	Oes	KFOMS	------------
HASTINGS					
Hastings	443.2000	+	Ols	WØWWV	ARAN
LINCOLN					
Lincoln	442.3000	+	Oe	KGØS	KGØS
Lincoln	443.0000	+	Oes	NØFER	------------
Lincoln	443.6750	+	Oes	WØMAO	NEMA
LINCOLN/OMAHA					
Gretna	444.9000	+	Oes	WØMAO	NE. GOVT
NORTH CENT					
O'Neill	444.8750	+	O	KBØGRP	------------
NORTH EAST					
Norfolk	444.2500	+	O	WØOFK	EVARC
OMAHA					
Bellevue	443.3500	+	O 179.9/179.9sz	WBØQQK	WBØQQK
Bellevue	443.8250	+	O 179.9/179.9 (CA)sz	WBØQQK	WBØQQK
Bellevue	444.8750	+	O 179.9/179.9eL(29.64)s	WBØQQK	WBØQQK
Omaha	442.3500	+	O	KF6SWL	KF6SWL
Omaha	442.9000	+	Oe	NØUP	NØUP
Omaha	442.9500	+	O 146.2/146.2	KCØYUR	KCØUAD
Omaha	443.1500	+	Oel	KØAWB	KØAWB
Omaha	443.4500	+	Oael	KBØSMX	PLATTSMOUTH
Omaha	443.7250	+	O	KF6SWL	KF6SWL
Omaha	443.7750	+	Os	WØEQU	ARC DIS SVC
Omaha	443.9250	+	Ol	KGØS	KGØS
Omaha	443.9750	+	O 146.2/146.2	KCØYUR	KCØUAD
Omaha/KPTM	444.9500	+	Ox	WBØCMC	WB0CMC
Valley	443.5500	+	Oels	KØAWB	K0AWB
Yutan	444.4250	+	Oel	NØYMJ	EWETAN ARC
SOUTH CENT					
Campbell	444.4750	+	Oels	WØWWV	ARAN
SOUTH EAST					
Beatrice	443.0750	+	Oes	KCØSWG	KCØSWG
Fairbury	444.2750	+	Oaels	WBØRMO	JCARS
Fairbury	444.4500	+	Oels	WBØRMO	JCARS
Falls City	443.7500	+	Oe	KBØFVP	KBØFVP
Humboldt	443.5750	+	Oels	KØHAM	NEKSUN
Julian	444.6250	+	Oes	WØMAO	NE. GOVT
Murray	443.2250	+	Oael	KBØSMX	PLATTSMOUTH
Wilber	443.4000	+	Oes	NØYNC	Saline EMA

Location	*Output*	*Input*	*Notes*	*Call*	*Sponsor*
WEST					
North Platte	444.4000	+	○e	NØIQ	------------
NEVADA					
CARLA					
Reno	440.7500	+	○ 127.3	K6LNK	CARLA
Reno	441.5500	+	○ 127.3	K6LNK	CARLA
Topaz	443.4750	+	○ 110.9	K6LNK	CARLA
CENTRAL					
Dyer	443.6000	+	○ 131.8el	W7WOW	W7WOW
Tonopah	444.3500	+	● 67l	KB7PPG	KB7PPG
Warm springs	444.8500	+	● 94.8l	WA6TLW	WA6TLW
E SIERRA/TAHOE					
Incline Village	443.2250	+	● 114.8	WA6OOU	WA6OOU
Lake Tahoe	442.4750	+	○el	WA6EWV	WA6EWV
S Lake Tahoe	443.7000	+	●l	WA6EWV	WA6EWV
South Lake Tahoe	442.8250	+	○ 88.5	W6SUV	W6SUV
South Lake Tahoe	444.1750	+	○ 146.2e	W6SUV	W6SUV
Tahoe City	444.9500	+	● 94.8l	WA6TLW	WA6TLW
EAST CENTRAL					
Ely	444.5750	+	○l	WB7WTS	WB7WTS
Ely	444.6500	+	○ 94.8l	WB7WTS	WB7WTS
EASTERN CLARK COUNTY					
Opal Mtn	448.8000	–	●	WB6TNP	TRISTATE
Red Mtn	449.1000	–	●	WA7HXO	LVRA
LAS VEGAS VALLEY					
Angel Peak	447.4750	–	○	N7OK	SDARC
			110.9/110.9		
Angel Peak	448.5750	–	●	WB6TNP	------------
Angel Peak	448.7750	–	●	WH6CYB	------------
Angel Peak	448.9250	–	○	WB6TNP	------------
Angel Peak	449.5000	–	●	N7TND	LVRA
			146.2/146.2 (CA)elx		
Angel Peak	449.6500	–	●	WR7NV	NARC
Angel Peak	449.8000	–	○	N6JFO	PINOYHAM
			131.8/131.8 Bl		
Apex Mtn	447.6250	–	○	N7YOR	HDRA
			114.8/114.8		
Apex Mtn	447.8500	–	○	KD5MSS	------------
Apex Mtn	449.8750	–	○	KC7TMC	------------
			127.3/127.3		
Black Mtn	447.7750	–	○	KP4UZ	ECHO/IRLP
			114.8/114.8		
Black Mtn	448.0000	–	●	KD8S	------------
Black Mtn	448.6250	–	○	NX7R	HDRA
			114.8/114.8		
Black Mtn	448.9500	–	○	WAØVJR	FARS
			146.2/146.2		

Location	*Output*	*Input*	*Notes*	*Call*	*Sponsor*
Blue Diamond Hill	446.2000	–	O 77/77	W7HTL	IRLP
			E-SUN WX		
Blue Diamond Hill	446.2250	–	O 85.4/85.4	W7HTL	------------
			E-SUN L(146.52)		
Blue Diamond Hill	447.0000	–	O 123/123	N7ARR	NARRI - IRLP
Blue Diamond Hill	447.0250	–	O	KI6VEJ	------------
Blue Diamond Hill	447.9500	–	O 100	K6JSI	WINS System
Blue Diamond Hill	448.1250	–	O	AK7DB	HELLDORADO
			127.3/127.3		
Henderson	447.3750	–	●	KH7R	------------
Henderson	447.6500	–	O 123/123	KE7OPJ	ECHO/IRLP
Henderson	447.6750	–	O 100/100e	K7FED	------------
			L(145.420) WXx		
Henderson	448.8750	–	O	K7RSW	HDRA - ECHOLI
			114.8/114.8		
Hi Potosi Mtn	449.0000	–	●	N6DD	Cactus
Hi Potosi Mtn	449.1750	–	●	WA7HXO	LVRA
Hi Potosi Mtn	449.9500	–	●	KB6CRE	------------
Hi Potosi Mtn	449.9750	–	O	KB6XN	------------
			203.5/203.5 L(146.790)		
Las Vegas	445.0000	–	O DCS(606)	WB6EGR	ALLSTAR
Las Vegas	446.6250	–	O	N7ARR	------------
Las Vegas	446.6750	–	O	KF7LVG	------------
			118.8/118.8		
Las Vegas	446.7250	–	O	K2RIC	------------
Las Vegas	446.7500	–	O	KB2ZHE	------------
Las Vegas	446.7750	–	O	AB8TN	------------
			114.8/114.8		
Las Vegas	447.0750	–	O 100/100	NK2V	------------
Las Vegas	447.1000	–	O	WR7NV	------------
Las Vegas	447.1500	–	O	N7LD	------------
Las Vegas	447.2750	–	O	KG7SS	------------
			110.9/110.9		
Las Vegas	447.3000	–	O	KG7SS	------------
			100.0/100.0		
Las Vegas	447.4250	–	O	WB9STH	ECHO/IRLP
			173.8/173.8 (CA) L(447.25)		
Las Vegas	448.0500	–	O	KF6QYX	------------
Las Vegas	448.0750	–	O	WN9ANF	------------
			127.3/127.3		
Las Vegas	448.2250	–	O 123/123	W7AOR	NARRI - IRLP
Las Vegas	448.3000	–	O	KE7KD	------------
Las Vegas	448.4500	–	O	WB6EGR	------------
Las Vegas	448.4750	–	O 100/100	WB6EGR	ALLSTAR
			RB		
Las Vegas	448.5000	–	O 100/100	K7UGE	LVRAC
Las Vegas	448.6750	–	O	N8DBM	------------
Las Vegas	448.7250	–	●	WB6TNP	------------
Las Vegas	449.0250	–		W7AOR	------------

NEVADA

Location	*Output*	*Input*	*Notes*	*Call*	*Sponsor*
Las Vegas	449.6750	–	○ 192.8/192.8	WA7CYC	------------
Las Vegas	449.9250	–	○	KE7OPJ	------------
Lo Potosi Mtn	447.2250	–	○ 151.4/151.4	N6LXX	------------
Lo Potosi Mtn	447.8750	–	○ 107.2/107.2	K6DLP	------------
Lo Potosi Mtn	447.9000	–	○	WB6ORK	------------
Lo Potosi Mtn	448.2750	–	○ 141.3/141.3	KF6FM	------------
Lo Potosi Mtn	448.5250	–	●	WR7BLU	SCRN
Lo Potosi Mtn	448.8250	–	●	KG6ALU	KARC
Lo Potosi Mtn	449.2500	–	●	WB6TNP	TRISTATE
Lo Potosi Mtn	449.4000	–	●	W7OQF	LVRA
Lo Potosi Mtn	449.4750	–	○ 151.4/151.4	N6LXX	------------
North Las Vegas	447.2500	–	○ 100/100 L(447.425)	WB9STH	ALLSTAR
Red Mountain	447.3250	–	○ 100/100 L(CC ARES/RACES)rs	N7SGV	CC ARES/RACES
Sunrise Mtn	447.8000	–	○ 100/100	K7IZA	ALLSTAR
Sunrise Mtn	448.9000	–	○	K7IZA	ALLSTAR
Sunrise Mtn	449.7250	–	○ 94.8/94.8	N7ARR	NARRI - IRLP
NORTH CENTRAL					
Battle Mountain	442.6500	+	○ 100	KE7LKO	KE7LKO
Battle Mountain	444.9750	+	○ 100el	KE7LKO	WB7BWV
Battle Mt	443.9000	+	○	KC7LCY	N7EV
Battle Mt	444.8500	+	○ 94.8l	WA6TLW	WA6TLW
Battle Mt	446.9750	–	○ 186.2#l	W7LKO	N7EV
Carlin	441.9750	+	○ 186.2	W7LKO	N7EV
Carlin	443.8500	+	○ 100	KE7LKO	KE7LKO
Carlin	444.3500	+	○ 100	KE7LKO	WV3LMA
Elko	443.3750	+	○ 100e	KE7LKO	WV3LMA
Elko	443.9500	+	○ 100e	KE7LKO	WB7BTS
Elko	444.1000	+	○ 100	KC7YNS	KC7YNS
Elko	444.7000	+	○l	W7LKO	WA7BWF
Elko	444.8000	+	○	W7LKO	WA7BWF
Elko	446.9750	–	○ 186.2#l	W7LKO	N7EV
Spring Creek	442.1250	+	● 127.3	NB9E	NB9E
Tuscarora	444.6500	+	● 94.8l	WA6TLW	WA6TLW
Winnemucca	442.3500	+	○ 100e	KH6QAI	KH6QAI
Winnemucca	442.8250	+	○ 141.3	WO7I	WO7I
Winnemucca	443.7000	+	○ 103.5	WA6MNM	WA6MNM
Winnemucca	444.9500	+	○ 94.8	KA7HQZ	KA7HQZ
NORTH EAST					
Wells	444.8500	+	● 94.8l	WA6TLW	WA6TLW
NORTH WEST					
Black Rock	444.2000	+	○ 100el	KF7EHY	KF7EHY
Empire	444.6750	+	○	KS2R	KS2R

Location	*Output*	*Input*	*Notes*	*Call*	*Sponsor*
Gerlach	440.1750	+	O 100	KD6KAC	KD6KAC
Gerlach	444.3250	+	O 107.2e	N9NPF	N9NPF
Portola	444.1000	+	O 100l	N7PLQ	N7PLQ
NORTHERN CLARK COUNTY					
Mesquite	448.0200	–	●	WA7HXO	LVRA
Mesquite	449.8250	–	O	N7ARR	IRLP---------
NVLLRC					
Gardnerville	440.3000	+	O 141.3	KD7FPK	KC7STW
Gardnerville	442.1500	+	O 123elx	KD7FPK	KD7FPK
Reno/Sparks	442.2000	+	O 123elx	N7ACL	N7ACL
Sun valley	440.3000	+	O 141.3	KC7STW	KC7STW
NYE COUNTY					
Pahrump	447.4000	–	O 100	K6JSI	WINS System
Pahrump	447.5000	–	O 123/123	W7NYE	------------
Pahrump	447.7000	–	O 123/123	W7NYE	------------
Pahrump	448.3500	–	O 103.5/103.5	N7MRN	ECHO/IRLP
Pahrump	448.8500	–	O 127.3/127.3	N7HYV	------------
Pahrump	449.2750	–	O 100/100	WB7DRJ	------------
Pahrump	449.7500	–	O 123/123	N7ARR	NARRI - IRLP
PORTABLE					
Gerlach	441.6750	+	O 123ep	KD7VMK	KD7VMK
Gerlach	442.8000	+	O 123p	KD7VMK	KD7VMK
Gerlach	443.4500	+	O 100p	KD6THY	KD6THY
Portable	440.8000	+	O 123ep	W7TA	K7JN
Portable	441.8000	+	● 100ep	KA7FOO	KA7FOO
Portable	442.4000	+	O 110.9ep	W7RHC	N7KP
RENO HAM RADIO CLUB					
Reno	442.3750	+	O 123	W7RHC	W7NIK
SOUTH					
Las Vegas	448.7750	–	● 131.8	WH6CYB	NH7M
Laughlin	448.7500	–	●e	K7RLW	K7RLW
SOUTHERN CLARK COUNTY					
Christmas Tree Pass	448.2000	–	●	WR7RED	SCRN
Christmas Tree Pass	448.7000	–	●	WB6TNP	TRISTATE
Christmas Tree Pass	449.3000	–	O	N6JFO	------------
Spirit Mtn	447.5250	+	O 141.3/141.3	KF6FM	------------
WEST					
Wells NV	449.7500	–	Olx	WA7BWF	EARC
WEST CENTRAL					
Carcon City	441.2500	+	O 123el	W7DI	K7VC
Carson	444.2000	+	O 110.9el	W7RHC	W7NIK
Carson City	441.9750	+	Ol	KB7MF	KB7MF
Carson City	443.3250	+	O 127.3	K6LNK	CARLA

NEVADA

Location	*Output*	*Input*	*Notes*	*Call*	*Sponsor*
Carson City	443.4500	+	● 131.8l	NH7M	NH7M
Carson City	444.4750	+	O 162.2	KI6SSF	KI6SSF
Carson City	444.5500	+	O 127.3	WA6JQV	WA6JQV
Cold Springs	443.6500	+	O 100lx	KE7DZZ	KE7DZZ
Dayton	441.9250	+	O 123eRB	K7DNV	K7DNV
Fallon	443.6500	+	O 126e	KE6UNR	KE6UNR
Fernley	443.5000	+	O 100l	N7PLQ	N7PLQ
Fernley	444.3000	+	O 88.5	KK7ECV	KK7ECV
Gardnerville	440.3000	+	O 141.3	KD7FPK	KC7STW
Gardnerville	442.1500	+	O 123elx	KD7FPK	KD7FPK
Gardnerville	442.1500	+	O 123el	KD7FPK	KD7FPK
Gardnerville	443.7750	+	● 131.8l	NH7M	NH7M
Gardnerville	443.9750	+	O 123e	KD7FPK	KD7FPK
Hawthorne	440.7250	+	O 127.3	K6LNK	CARLA
Hawthorne	444.8500	+	● 94.8lx	WA6TLW	WA6TLW
Lovelock	444.5000	+	● 94.8	WA6TLW	WA6TLW
Minden	442.7500	+	●	NV7CV	WA6EYD
Minden	443.7500	+	O 123el	W7DI	K7VC
New Washoe City	440.3750	+	O 97.4	NH7M	NH7M
Reno	440.2000	+	O 107.2	KB6TDJ	KB6TDJ
Reno	440.4250	+	● 123e	W7ROZ	K7JN
Reno	440.5500	+	O 110.9el	W7RHC	W7NIK
Reno	440.7250	+	O 123	KD7DTN	KD7DTN
Reno	440.7500	+	O 127.3	K6LNK	CARLA
Reno	441.3000	+	O 114.8l	KD7DTN	KD7DTN
Reno	441.4000	+	O 123	NV7L	NV7L
Reno	441.5500	+	O 127.3	K6LNK	CARLA
Reno	441.6500	+	O 123e	N7ARR	W7AOR
Reno	441.8500	+	O 123	W7UNR	NS9E
Reno	442.0250	+	O 156.7	W6KCS	W6KCS
Reno	442.1750	+	● 94.8l	WA6TLW	WA6TLW
Reno	442.3750	+	O 123	W7RHC	W7NIK
Reno	442.5500	+	O 110.9	W7NIK	W7NIK
Reno	442.8500	+	O 141.3	N7ACM	N7ACM
Reno	443.0250	+	● 114.8	K7JN	K7JN
Reno	443.0750	+	O 123e	W7TA	K7JN
Reno	443.4500	+	O 103.5	NH7M	NH7M
Reno	443.7750	+	● 131.8	NH7M	NH7M
Reno	444.0250	+	●	WA7RPS	WA7RPS
Reno	444.3500	+	O 123e	KE7R	NN7B
Reno	444.4000	+	● 118.8	K6ALT	KL2P
Reno	444.4250	+	O 131.8e	K7HVY	K7HVY
Reno	444.5250	+	Ol	N7PLQ	N7PLQ
Reno	444.6000	+	● 123	W9CI	W9CI
Reno	444.6500	+	● 94.8l	WA6TLW	WA6TLW
Reno	444.7000	+	● 110.9	W7RHC	W7NIK
Reno	444.7500	+	● 94.8l	WA6TLW	WA6TLW
Reno	444.7750	+	O 100e	KD7DPW	KK7RON
Reno	444.9000	+	O 123e	KD7DTN	KD7DTN

Location	*Output*	*Input*	*Notes*	*Call*	*Sponsor*
Reno	445.0000	–	○ 123	KB2LUC	KB2LUC
Reno	448.6250	–	○ 100#	KE7DZZ	KE7DZZ
Reno/Carson	444.8250	+	○ 123l	WA7DG	KK7SL
Reno/Sparks	440.9750	+	● 123lx	W7ACF	KK7RON
Reno/Sparks	442.2000	+	○ 123elx	N7ACL	N7ACL
Reno/Sparks	442.2000	+	○ 123el	N7ACL	N7ACL
Reno/Sparks	442.2500	+	○ 103.5	KK7RON	KK7RON
Reno/Sparks	443.4000	+	○ 88.5e	KD7DPW	KD7DPW
Reno/Sparks	443.6000	+	○ 103.5e	N7KP	N7KP
Reno/Sparks	444.9250	+	○ 100elx	WA7DG	KK7SL
Silver Springs	444.5000	+	○	KE7CRZ	KE7CRZ
Sparks	440.0000	+	○ 110.9l	W7NIK	W7NIK
Sparks	440.0500	+	○ 100l	N7PLQ	N7PLQ
Sparks	441.6500	+	○ 123e	N7ARR	W7AOR
Sparks	443.0500	+	○ 123	N7PLQ	N7PLQ
Sparks	443.6250	+	○ 103.5	N7KP	N7KP
Sparks	443.6750	+	○ 103.5	KK7RON	KK7RON
Sparks	443.8000	+	○ 103.5l	N7KP	N7KP
Sparks	443.9500	+	○ 100	AE7CW	AE7CW
Sparks	444.1750	+	○ 123l	KC5CZX	KC5CZX
Sparks	444.2500	+	○ 146.2	KR7EK	KR7EK
Sparks	444.2750	+	○ 123el	KY7Y	KY7Y
Sparks	444.3000	+	○ 88.5	KK7ECV	KK7ECV
Sparks	444.8000	+	○ 123	N7PLQ	N7PLQ
Sparks	444.9750	+	○ 123	N7PLQ	N7PLQ
Sun valley	440.3000	+	○ 141.3	KC7STW	KC7STW
Sun Valley	443.1750	+	○ 123	N7TGB	N7TGB
Sun Valley	444.1500	+	○ 146.2l	KR7EK	KR7EK
Topaz	443.4750	+	○ 110.9	K6LNK	CARLA
Verdi	440.0750	+	○ 123	N7PLQ	N7PLQ
Wellington	440.0500	+	○ 94.8	KD7NHC	KD7NHC
Yerington	444.8750	+	○ 100lx	W7DED	W7DED

NEW HAMPSHIRE

ALL AREAS					
Statewide	441.4500	+	○pEXP	SNP	NESMC
DARTMOUTH/LAKE SUNAPEE					
Claremont	443.9500	+	○ 103.5	KU1R	SCARG
Claremont	447.0750	–	○ 131.8	KA1UAG	KA1UAG
			L(KA1UAG UHF/ NEFMA UHF)		
Enfield	444.9000	+	○ 131.8	KA1UAG	KA1UAG
			L(KA1UAG UHF/ NEFMA UHF)		
Hanover	441.9500	+	○ 88.5	K1JY	K1JY
			L(K1JY)		
Hanover	443.5500	+	○ 136.5e	W1FN	TSRC
			L(E363356 KB1FDA 147.21 VT (AS NEEDEs		
Sunapee	442.3500	+	○ 88.5	K1JY	K1JY
			L(K1JY)		
Warner	447.6750	–	○ 88.5	K1JY	K1JY
			L(K1JY)		

Location	*Output*	*Input*	*Notes*	*Call*	*Sponsor*
West Lebanon	443.5000	+	O 131.8	KA1UAG	KA1UAG
			L(KA1UAG UHF/ NEFMA UHF)		
LAKES REGION					
Alton	444.0500	+	O 88.5	K1JEK	K1JEK
			L(146.700 NORTHWOOD)		
Center Barnstead	446.4750	–	O 88.5e	K1DED	K1DED
			L(E511025) WX		
Gilford	447.7750	–	O 88.5	W1VN	CNHARC
			L(K1JY)		
New Durham	442.0500	+	O 88.5e	N1EUN	N1EUN
			L(53.210/52.210)p		
Pittsfield	442.1500	+	O 88.5	N1IMO	N1IMO
			L(N1IMO-N1IMN)s		
Rochester	441.4000	+	O 88.5e	N1UBB	N1UBB
West Ossipee	442.6500	+	O 110.9e	K1LTM	Kencom
			L(D*V)sEXPx		
MERRIMACK VALLEY					
Bedford	441.7500	+	O 136.5	KB1MSY	KB1MSY
			DCS(65)p		
Bedford	444.1500	+	O 131.8	KD6LFW	Alcanet
			L(ALCANET)		
Bow	447.3250	–	O 127.3	KB1NX	KA1SU
			E-SUN		
Bow	448.6750	–	O	KB1IIT	KB1IIT
Bow	449.1750	–	O 167.9	N1IIC	WA2SLO
Candia	449.5250	–	O 88.5e	W1ASS	W1ASS
Chester	442.5500	+	O 88.5	K1JC	K1JC
Chester	443.2500	+	O 88.5	KA1LCR	KA1LCR
			L(E290466)		
Chester	449.3250	–	Oe	WA1DMV	WA1DMV
Deerfield	449.2250	–	O 88.5	K1JY	K1JY
			L(K1JY)		
Deerfield	449.4500	–	O 123.0	WA1ZYX	Saddlbk RA
Derry	441.3000	+	O 107.2e	KC2LT	KC2LT
			L(KC2LT 448.275 HUDSON NH)x		
Derry	441.5500	+	O 141.3	N1TEC	N1TEC
			L(I7220)		
Derry	446.3750	–	O 88.5ers	N1VQQ	N1VQQ
Derry	447.2250	–	OL(D*V)	NN1PA	NN1PA
Derry	447.3750	–	O 85.4	K1QVC	SNHDStrGrp
Derry	447.8250	–	O 88.5e	N1VQQ	N1VQQ
			L(WA1ZYX/CANNON)rsx		
Derry	448.9250	–	O 85.4	N1MWK	BRE
Derry	449.6250	–	● 85.4x	K1CA	IntrStRS
Epsom	443.8500	+	O 88.5ex	W1ASS	W1ASS
Goffstown	443.4000	+	O 203.5e	W1LO	W1LO
Goffstown	444.2000	+	O 186.2s	N1PA	EWARN
Goffstown	446.5750	–	OL(D*V)	NE1DV	EWARN
Hollis	443.5000	+	O 88.5e	N1IMO	N1IMON1IMN
			L(N1IMO-N1IMN)s		

Location	*Output*	*Input*	*Notes*	*Call*	*Sponsor*
Hollis	444.2500	+	O 88.5e	N1VQQ	N1VQQ
			L(447.825 53.97 449.875)rsx		
Hudson	447.7250	–	O 114.8	NE1B	RptRschAsn
			L(E15837)		
Hudson	448.2750	–	O 107.2e	KC2LT	KC2LT
			L(KC2LT 443.05 WALTHAM AND 441.8 GEO		
Hudson	448.4375	–	O	K1MOT	MARC-NE
			L(DMR-MARC)		
Hudson	449.9750	–	O 71.9 (CA)	WA1SOT	WA1SOT
			eL(E355114 222MHZ/440MHZ SEL LINKS)s		
Londonderry	442.0000	+	O 100.0e	K1DED	K1DED
			WX		
Loudon	443.7500	+	O 123.0e	N1WEB	W1DIO
			L(2M LINK)		
Manchester	441.8000	+	OL(D*V	K1COM	EWARN
			IRCDDB)		
Manchester	444.3000	+	O 136.5	KB1MSY	KB1MSY
Manchester	449.2750	–	O 141.3	N1OOL	N1OOL
Mont Vernon	447.1250	–	O 88.5	WA1HCO	WA1HCO
			L(I4881)		
Mont Vernon	448.4250	–	O 88.5	K3RQ	K3RQ
Nashua	444.8000	+	O 131.8e	K1SI	Alcanet
			L(ALCANET)		
Nashua	448.8250	–	O 88.5e	N1IMO	N1IMON1IMN
			L(N1IMO-N1IMN SYSTEM)s		
Northwood	443.2000	+	O 88.5e	N1QVS	FBG
Pelham	443.1500	+	O 88.5	K1SI	Alcanet
Pembroke	443.6500	+	O 131.8	KA1OKQ	NHRC
			L(NHRC NETWORK)		
Salem	444.3500	+	OL(D*V)	K1HRO	K1HRO ARC
Salem	448.3250	–	O 88.5	N1WPN	N1WPN
			L(53.65)		
Salem	449.7750	–	O	NY1Z	MtMRH RS
Windham	442.6000	+	O 88.5	N1WPN	N1WPN
			L(53.650 PL 71.9)		
MONADNOCK REGION					
Alstead	444.7500	+	O 110.9	WR1NH	NFMRA
			L(WRRC AND NFMRA)rs		
Greenfield	448.5250	–	O 123.0e	KA1BBG	KA1BBG
			L(HUB REPEATER FOR NH 2M REP. NET)x		
Keene	444.6500	+	O 141.3ex	WA1ZYX	HylandHill
Pack Monadnock	443.3500	+	O 110.9ers	KA1OKQ	KA1OKQ
			x		
Peterborough	449.3750	–	O 88.5	N1IMO	N1IMON1IMN
			L(N1IMO-N1IMN)s		
Temple	447.4250	–	O 141.3ex	WA1ZYX	Temple Mt
Walpole	443.8000	+	O 141.3	WA1ZYX	KA1QFA
			(CA)eL(STATEWIDE)		
Walpole	444.8500	+	O 110.9e	W2NH	WRRC
			L(WRRC AND NFMRA)rs		

Location	Output	Input	Notes	Call	Sponsor
SEACOAST					
East Kingston	446.7250	–	OL(D*V	KB1TIX	Seacoast
			TCP/IP LINK ONLY)		
Greenland	444.4000	+	O 100.0s	W1WQM	PCARC
Hampton	449.4750	–	OteL(D*V)	K1HBR	HBAR
Madbury	448.8750	–	OL(D*V	N1HIT	NE-RDS
			IRCDDB)		
WHITE MOUNTAINS					
Franconia	449.8750	–	O 123.0ex	WA1ZYX	Cannon Mtn
Mt Washington	448.9750	–	O 141.3es	W1NH	W1NH
Sargents Purchase	448.2250	–	O 88.5	WA1PBJ	NETARC
Whitefield	449.8250	–	O 82.5	N1PCE	N1PCE
			L(NNH REPEATER NETWORK)s		
NEW JERSEY					
ATLANTIC					
Absecon	442.9000	+	● 110.9	N2LXJ	N2LXK
			(CA)		
Atlantic City	444.3500	+	O 107.2	AA2BP	N2JVM
			(CA)		
Atlantic City	447.5750	–	O 156.7e	K2ACY	------------
Brigantine	445.23125	–	OtlEXP	K2ACY	------------
Brigantine	449.4250	–	O 131.8	KA2OOR	------------
			(CA) RB		
Egg Harbor Twp	448.7750	–	O 118.8	K2BR	SCARA
			(CA)er		
W Atlantic City	443.2500	+	O 146.2e	W2HRW	SPARC
BERGEN CO					
Alpine	442.7000	+		W2MR	------------
Alpine	442.9000	+	O	K2ETN	CRRC
			141.3/141.3aTT		
Englewood	448.9750	–	Oesz	W2LGY	ST BARNABAS
Fort Lee	441.3000	+	O 114.8a	W2IP	BCFMA
Fort Lee	442.9500	+	O 141.3	K2QW	------------
			(CA) TTelLITZ		
Fort Lee	443.9500	+	O 100r	W2MPX	METROPLX
Franklin Lakes	443.1000	+	O 141.3	K2GCL	BCFMA
Hasbrouck Hts	442.5000	+	● 141.3	K2OMP	------------
			(CA)e		
Little Ferry	441.8500	+	O 136.5	W2NIW	------------
Midland Park	444.9000	+	O 114.8	WA2CAI	------------
			(CA)		
Montvale	446.9750	–	O 141.3	K2ZD	------------
Paramus	441.7500	+	O	N2SMI	------------
			136.5/136.5lrsBI		
Paramus	444.1000	+	O 141.3	W2AKR	BCFMA
Paramus Park	441.9500	+	O 114.8e	KA2MRK	------------
WoodRidge	443.7500	+	O 141.3	W2RN	------------
			(CA)eL(442.950) RB LITZ		

Location	Output	Input	Notes	Call	Sponsor
BURLINGTON					
Bordentown	449.0250	–	O 203.5eBI LITZ	K2JZO	------------
Browns Mills	448.3250	–	● 127.3 (CA)ersWX	KC2QVT	BURLCO OEM
Browns Mills	449.6750	–	O 141.3 BI WX	K2JZO	------------
Burlington	447.6750	–	O 103.5e	WA2EHL	------------
Cinnaminson	445.6250	–	O 127.3e	K2CPD	CINNPDOEM
Willingboro	442.0500	+	O 118.8 (CA)e	WB2YGO	WARG Inc.
CAMDEN					
Blue Anchor	445.1250	–	O 91.5ers WX	KB2AYS	------------
Camden	442.1500	+	O 156.7e EXP	N2KDV	------------
Camden	444.3000	+	O 131.8eBI	WB3EHB	------------
Camden	448.0250	–	O 131.8es	N2HQX	DVRC
Cherry Hill	444.9000	+	O 131.8 (CA)elRB	K3RJC	------------
Gloucester City	447.7750	–	O 146.2ers	NJ2GC	GCARC
Pine Hill	442.3500	+	O 131.8 (CA)el	K2UK	CCAPRA
Sicklerville	446.3750	–	O 131.8e	N3PUU	------------
Waterford Wks	442.3000	+	O 131.8 (CA)elsRB WX	KA2PFL	------------
Waterford Wks	442.7000	+	O 131.8 (CA)el	N3KZ	UPenn ARC
Waterford Wks	444.4500	+	●teRB EXP	W2FLY	------------
CAPE MAY					
Cape May	449.8750	–	O 146.2ers	KC2JPP	------------
Cape May CH	447.4750	–	Oters	NJ2DS	------------
Ocean City	448.4250	–	O 131.8 (CA)lRB	N3KZ	UPenn ARC
Ocean City	448.6250	–	O 131.8	WA3UNG	------------
CUMBERLAND					
Centerton	448.1250	–	O 192.8e EXP	KE2CK	------------
Greenwich	443.7000	+	O 131.8 (CA)elRB	N3KZ	UPenn ARC
Vineland	447.4250	–	O 131.8 (CA)elrsRB WX	W3BXW	BEARS
Vineland	448.5250	–	O 156.7	N2EHS	------------
ESSEX CO					
Irvington	449.4750	–	O 114.8 (CA)eprsz	N2JGC	I-ART
Newark	446.1250	–	O 141.3 TT RB BIz	N2NSS	PARA

Location	Output	Input	Notes	Call	Sponsor
Newark	446.9000	–	O 141.3 (CA)elrz	N2BEI	SCJRA
Verona	448.8750	–	O 151.4/151.4 (CA)	W2UHF	MEARC
West Orange	440.0500	+	O 141.3	W2NJR	NJRA
West Orange	442.6000	+	O 141.3lRB	N2MH	------------
West Orange	445.0250	–	O 141.3/141.3 (CA) TTelrsLITZxz	W2NJR	NJRA
GLOUCESTER					
Franklinville	443.4500	+	O 162.2e	W2RM	------------
Mantua	449.9750	–	O 131.8 (CA) WX	W2FHO	------------
Pitman	442.1000	+	O 131.8	W2MMD	GCARC
Williamstown	445.2750	–	O 131.8eBI	AA2QD	------------
HUDSON CO					
Bayonne	446.6250	–	O 141.3 E-SUN BI WX	AA2QD	BARC
Cliffside Park	447.4250	–	● 127.3/127.3 BI	KB2OOJ	LARA
Guttenberg	441.7500	+	O 114.8elr sBI	N2SMI	------------
Hudson City	441.2000	+	O 192.8/192.8ez	N2DCS	------------
Jersey City	440.6250	+	O 141.3 (CA)eRB WX	WB2TAW	------------
Secaucus	441.5500	+	O 91.5 (CA) ersz	KC2IES	Secaucus RACES
HUNTERDON					
Bloomsbury	449.5750	–	O 151.4 (CA)elrRB WX	N3MSK	N3ODB
Cherryville	444.8500	+	O 141.3 (CA)e	W2CRA	------------
Frenchtown	448.1250	–	O 151.4el RB LITZ	K2PM	FrenchtownRG
Mt Kipp	446.4750	–	O 203.5eBI	W2CRA	------------
MERCER					
Princeton	442.8500	+	O 131.8 (CA)elRB	N3KZ	UPenn ARC
Trenton	442.2000	+	O 141.3	N2GBK	------------
West Trenton	442.6500	+	O 131.8 (CA)ersWX	W2ZQ	DVRA
MIDDLESEX CO					
Carteret	447.6750	–	O 136.5 TT	K2ZV	------------
New Brunswick	440.0500	445.4500	O 123.0/123.0lBIz	NE2E	------------
Old Bridge	446.1750	–	O 131.8/131.8 (CA)elrsz	W2CJA	PSARN
Sayerville	443.2000	+	O 141.3/141.3 (CA)eL(146.760)rsLITZx	K2GE	RBRA

Location	*Output*	*Input*	*Notes*	*Call*	*Sponsor*
Sayreville	444.2500	+	O 123.0/123.0lBlz	NE2E	------------
South Amboy	446.9000	–	O 118.8 (CA)elrz	N2BEI	SCJRA
South River	443.5000	+	O 141.3 (CA)eL(IRLP4287)rsLITZ	WB2SNN	South Rvr EM
MONMOUTH					
Tinton Falls	448.9250	–	O 094.8	K2EPD	------------
MONMOUTH CO					
Asbury Park	449.5250	–	O 141.3	W2NJR	NJRA
Brown Mills	440.4250	+	● 203.5 TT DCS(23) L(430.175)rsWXz	WR2MSN	Metro 70
Ellisdale	447.5250	–	O 131.8 (CA)	K2NI	HRG
Howell Twp	440.3000	+	O 141.3r	KB2RF	Howell TwpPD
Middletown	448.7250	–	O 151.4r	N2DR	MT RACSOEM
Ocean Twp	443.0000	+	O 127.3/127.3eL(IRLP)	WW2ARC	AERIALS
Union Beach	442.1500	+	O 192.8	KC2QVK	------------
Wall Township	444.3500	+	O(CA)r	WB2ANM	Wall Tsp EM
Wall Twp	448.1250	–	O 141.3	W2NJR	NJRA
MORRIS CO					
Boonton	449.7750	–	O 151.4/151.4eL(IRLP)	N2WNS	------------
Budd Lake	448.6750	–	O 136.5 (CA)elrRB LITZ WX	WS2V	------------
Budd Lake	448.9250	–	O 136.5r LITZ	N2VUG	------------
Butler	449.9250	–	O 151.4/151.4elrRB EXP	WB2FTX	Butler RACES
Chatham	449.1750	–	O 141.3/141.3er	WB2CMK	------------
Lk Hoptacong	441.6000	+	OL(INT)	NJ2MC	NNJDSA
Long Branch	440.8500	+	O 94.8 (CA) elRBz	WR2M	WR2M RC
Long Valley	444.0000	+	O 141.3/141.3ers	N2GS	CWRACES
Morris Twp	443.2500	+	O 141.3/141.3er	WS2Q	------------
Parsippany	440.1000	+	O 141.3/141.3er	WB2JTE	PTHOEM
Randolph	441.5000	+	O 141.3/141.3e	WA2SLH	------------
OCEAN					
Barnegat	449.4750	–	O 131.8 (CA)elrsLITZ WX	KA2PFL	------------
Beach Haven	448.5750	–	O 141.3er WX	WA2NEW	BeachHavEM
Eagleswood Twp	442.7500	+	O 131.8 (CA)elsWX	KA2PFL	------------

Location	Output	Input	Notes	Call	Sponsor
Lakehurst	443.3500	+	O 141.3e	W2DOR	JSARS
Lakehurst	447.2250	–	O 131.8 (CA)elrsRB WX	W3BXW	BEARS
Lakewood	449.3750	–	O 141.3 (CA)elBI LITZ	NE2E	------------
Lakewood	449.8250	–	O 103.5ers	W2RAP	EARS
Manahawkin	448.0750	–	O 131.8 (CA)elrsRB WX	W3BXW	BEARS
Toms River	444.0000	+	O 141.3	WA2OTP	------------
PASSAIC CO					
Garrett Mtn	440.9500	+	● 097.4/097.4 TTersz	WX2KEN	WX2KEN RG
Little Falls	443.0500	+	O 141.3/141.3 (CA)	WV2ZOW	A.R.R.L.
Little Falls	449.0750	–	O 141.3/141.3eL(927.8000)r	W2VER	VRACES
Paterson	444.6000	+	● 131.8/131.8ersWXz	KC2MDA	TECNJ
Wanaque	444.1500	+	O 141.3 (CA)ersWX	W2PQG	10-70 RA
Wanaque	446.1750	–	Oa	WA2SNA	RAMPO ARC
Wayne	446.8500	–	Oe	W2GT	Party Line
West Patterson	442.5500	+	O 141.3	W2FCL	Lnd Rovers
SOMERSET CO					
Bedminster	443.9000	+	O 151.4/151.4 (CA) RB	W2UHF	MEARC
Green Brook	442.2500	+	141.3	W2QW	RVRC
Green Brook	444.5000	+	O 131.8/141.3 (CA) L(444.2)rsWX	N2NSV	BEARS
Green Brook	447.1250	–	O 141.3e	N2IKJ	WATCHUNG
Somerville	448.7250	–	ODCS(205) s	KC2YOG	NJDHSS MCC
Warrensville	443.6500	+	O 131.8/131.8l	N3KZ	UPARC
SUSSEX					
Hopatcong	446.7750	–	O 136.5elr RB	WS2V	------------
Hopatcong	448.1750	–	O 151.4e	N2OZO	------------
Hopatcong Boro	440.8500	+	Ot(CA)el RB	WR2M	WR2M RC
Newton	443.0000	+	O 103.5rs	W2LV	SCARC
Vernon	449.0750	–	O 141.3er RB	W2VER	Vern RACES
Vernon	449.0750	–	O 141.3elr s	W2VER	VRACES
UNION CO					
Murray Hill	449.9750	–	O 141.3/141.3 (CA)rsWX	W2LI	TRI-CTY RA
Roselle Park	445.9750	–	141.3 (CA) TTelrsLITZ WX	NJ5R	------------

Location	Output	Input	Notes	Call	Sponsor
Springfield	446.3750	–	O 141.3 (CA) TTerz	W2FCC	RAHWAY VLY
Summit	440.0500	+	O 141.3/141.3 (CA)elrsLITZ WXz	W2NJR	NJRA
WARREN					
Mont Mt	444.3500	+	Ote	N3FHN	------------
Washington	443.8500	+	O 110.9r	W2SJT	PJARC
Washington	446.4250	–	O 162.2lRB WX	K2FN	------------
NEW MEXICO					
ALBUQUERQUE					
Albuquerque	442.0500	+	O 100.0e L(145.1600)rs	K5BIQ	BC-OEM
Albuquerque	442.6000	+	O 100.0 (CA)x	WA5YUE	------------
Albuquerque	443.5000	+	O 123.0	KB5XE	------------
Albuquerque	443.6500	+	O 100.0	K5LXP	------------
Albuquerque	444.0000	+	O 100e L(145.3300)x	W5CSY	ARCC
Albuquerque	449.5500	–	O 71.9e	K5FIQ	URFMSI
Bernalillo	442.6500	+	O 114.8/114.8	NØWJE	------------
Isleta Pueblo	442.1500	+	O 100.0/100.0ae	AB1Q	------------
Rio Rancho	442.3500	+	O 100a	WA5OLD	------------
Rio Rancho	443.0000	+	O 100.0e L(147.1000)rs	NM5RR	SCARES
Rio Rancho	443.7000	+	O 100.0 E-SUN	KC5IZR	KC5IZR
Rio Rancho	444.1800	+	O 100.0eprs	W5SCA	SCARES
Rio Rancho	444.7000	+	O 100.0e	K5CPU	Intel EARS
Sandia Crest	442.1000	+	O 162.2e L(147.38)x	KB5GAS	Albuq. Gas
Sandia Crest	442.7500	+	O 162.2ex	KC5IPK	------------
Sandia Peak	442.4750	+	O 100ex	WA5IHL	------------
Tijeras	444.1500	+	O 100.0 L(224.9400)x	W5AOX	------------
CENTRAL					
Belen	442.7000	+	O 100	KC5OUR	VCARA
Los Lunas	444.1750	+	O 100.0 (CA)e	WA5TSV	LLARA
Mountainair	444.0750	+	O 100.0	WB5NES	------------
Socorro	444.2750	+	O 100.0	WB5QZD	------------
EAST CENTRAL					
Clovis	443.4500	+	O 131.8 (CA)e	KA5B	ENM ARC
Clovis	444.4500	+	O 88.5/88.5 e	WS5D	------------

Location	Output	Input	Notes	Call	Sponsor
Clovis	444.9250	+	O 131.8ers	KA5B	ENMARC
McAlister	447.4000	–	Ors	W5DDR	------------
Texico	442.7500	+	O 162.2/162.2aers	KB5TZK	------------
Tucumcari	443.7500	+	O	WA5EMA	------------
MEGA-LINK					
Albuquerque	444.3250	+	O 100.0 (CA)exZ(123)	NM5ML	Mega-Link
Carlsbad	449.2750	–	O 67 (CA)lr sZ(123)	NM5ML	Mega-Link
Clovis	442.5250	+	O 67.0/67.0	NM5ML	MegaLink
Eagle Nest	444.3500	+	O 100.0 (CA)exZ(123)	NM5ML	Mega-Link
Ruidoso	444.3750	+	O 67.0 (CA) exZ(123)	NM5ML	Mega-Link
NORTH CENTRAL					
La Cueva	442.1250	+	O 107.2e	N9PGQ	------------
Los Alamos	442.0000	+	Oe L(224.040)	KA5BIW	KA5BIW
Los Alamos	444.7750	+	O 131.8e RB	WD9CMS	------------
Pajarito Peak	443.1000	+	O 100ers	NM5SC	SCARES
Santa Fe	442.8250	+	O 131.8a	KB5ZQE	------------
Santa Fe	449.2750	–	O 146.2/146.2ersLITZ	K9GAJ	------------
Taos	444.8750	+	O 123.0/123.0eL(147.34)	KF5PFO	Taos ARC
Taos Ski Valley	444.9750	+	O 123.0x	N5TSV	------------
NORTH EAST					
Des Moines	444.8000	+	O 77.0ex	N5BOP	SGRC
Wagon Mound	444.4000	+	O 100.0	N7JNI	Mora ARC
NORTH WEST					
Aztec	447.4500	–	O 107.2 E-SUN RB	KB5ITS	------------
Farmington	447.6250	–	O 100e L(448.675)rs	KA5DVI	------------
Huerfano	448.6500	–	O 127.3e	KB5ITS	------------
SOUTH CENTRAL					
Alamogordo	442.4100	+	O 100a	KC5OWL	------------
Alamogordo	442.9500	+	O 85.4/85.4 e	N6CID	------------
Alamogordo	444.7000	+	Oprs	N7DRB	ARES/RACES
Alamogordo	444.8250	+	O 67.0e	K5LRW	Alamo ARC
Alamogordo	444.9750	+	Oeprs	N7DRB	------------
Caballo	448.5000	–	O 100/100rs	NM5C	------------
Cloudcroft	444.0250	+	O 100.0/100.0eL(147.34)rsx	KE5MIQ	SMRC
Dona Ana	441.4250	446.9250	● 79.7s	KG5ES	KC5SJQ

Location	Output	Input	Notes	Call	Sponsor
High Rolls	442.8000	+	100.0 E-SUN	W5AKU	------------
Las Cruces	442.0000	+	O 203.5/203.5 L(443.850)	WA5JXY	------------
Las Cruces	447.5000	–	O	N5IAC	------------
Las Cruces	448.2000	–	O 100.0 (CA)e	N5BL	MVRC
Las Cruces	449.5750	–	Oe	KC5EVR	------------
Ruidoso	443.6000	+	O 85.4/85.4 e	N5SN	Greenville Rptr A
Ruidoso	443.8250	+	O 100.0e L(146.74)rsWXx	K5FBK	------------
Ruidoso	443.9250	+	O 162.2/162.2 (CA)eE-SUNlrsRB WXx	K5RIC	ARC
Ruidoso Downs	443.4000	+	O 100.0/100.0eprsWX	KE5MWM	ARC
San Patricio	442.7500	+	● 123.0e	WØZW	------------
SOUTH EAST					
Artesia	442.0000	+	O	KU5J	------------
Artesia	442.4500	+	O 162.2e L(147.36)sLITZx	K5CNM	Eddy Co ARES/S
Artesia	444.9750	+	O 156.7/156.7	W5COW	------------
Carlsbad	444.4500	+	O 127.3/127.3ae	N5MJ	------------
Hagerman	444.4250	+	● 179.9/179.9 (CA)elx	W5GNB	------------
Hagerman	444.5500	+	O 162.2/162.2 L(52.525) RB	W5GNB	------------
Hagerman	444.9500	+	O 179.9/179.9e	W5GNB	------------
Hobbs	442.5250	+	O 203.5	KM5BS	------------
HobbS	444.1500	+	O 203.5	AH2AZ	------------
Hobbs	444.2750	+	O 162.2e	AH2AZ	------------
Jal	444.2500	+	O 162.2/162.2 L(147.22)x	N5SOR	------------
SOUTH WEST					
Columbus	442.0500	+	rsx	KBØTYJ	------------
Deming	449.4750	–	O 77.0e	WA6RT	DARC
Deming	449.8500	–	O 100.0e	N5WSB	Luna Co.AR
Glenwood	448.7750	–	O 103.5e L(448.800)	WY5G	------------
Silver City	448.0500	–	O 100.0els x	K5GAR	Gila ARS
Silver City	448.8000	–	O 100.0 L(448.775)	WY5G	------------
Silver City	448.8750	–	O 100.0	WA7ACA	------------
Silver City	449.3000	–	O 114.8e	K5GTG	Delsa ARC

Location	Output	Input	Notes	Call	Sponsor
STATEWIDE					
Statewide	444.1800	+	Oprs		ARES/SAR
WEST CENTRAL					
Deza Bluff	448.2000	–	O 100.0/100.0ersRBx	KC5WDV	------------
Gallup	449.7500	–	O 100.0rs	KC5WDV	------------
Grants	444.9500	+	O 100.0x	WB5EKP	CARCUS

NEW YORK

Location	Output	Input	Notes	Call	Sponsor
ADIRONDACKS EAST					
Blue Mtn	442.7500	+	O 123lx	N2JKG	RACES
Lake Placid	449.6750	–	● 192.8	N2NGK	N2NGK
Long Lake	443.8500	+	● 162.2/162.2ex	KC2ZZO	Bear Bait Radio Club
Plattsburgh	448.0750	–	●tr	WA2LRE	Clin RACES
Plattsburgh	448.7750	–	●tl	WA2LRE	Clin RACES
Plattsburgh	449.8250	–	O 100.0	N2MMV	Interplex
Whiteface Mtn	447.7750	–	●telr	N2JKG	Clin RACES
ALBANY/CAPITAL REGION					
Albany	444.0000	+	O 100 (CA) elx	K2AD	MT Assoc
Albany	444.7000	+	O 82.5ersx	KB2SIY	KC2FCP
Austerlitz	442.8500	+	O 156.7 TT eRBx	WA2ZPX	WA2ZPX
Chatham	444.1000	+	Oe	WA2PVV	Col CRA
Cohoes	449.8250	–	O 136.5elrs	KG2BH	CohEddy Ct
Defreestville	444.3000	+	O 100l	K2CWW	RENSSELAER AMAT
Grafton	442.2000	+	Oel	N2LOD	N2LOD
Grafton	442.9500	+	O	K2CBA	GURU
Grafton	444.6000	+	O 136.5	N2ZQF	N2ZQF
Grafton	444.6500	+	Oe	K2RBR	K2RBR
Halfmoon	448.8750	–	O 203.5	W2GBO	W2GBO
Knox	444.3500	+	O	WB2QBQ	WB2QBQ
Knox	444.5000	+	O 127.3l	KB2IXT	HMARC
Schenectady	443.5500	+	O 203.5	W2EWY	W2EWY
Schenectady	443.7500	+	Oe	WZ2X	WZ2X
Schenectady	444.2000	+	Oal	K2AE	SCHENECTADY AM
Troy	443.0000	+	O	W2SZ	RPI AMATEUR RADI
Troy	444.8500	+	Ol	K2RBR	NiMo ARC
Troy	447.0750	–	O 127.3/127.3e	N2TY	TROY AMATEUR RA
Troy	447.2250	–	O 100 (CA)l	KD3NC	KD3NC
Troy	448.4250	–	Oel	W2GBO	Tel Pionrs
Troy	448.9750	–	O 100e	W2GBO	W2GBO
AUBURN					
Auburn	444.1500	+	O 71.9ae	W2QYT	W2QYT
Auburn	444.5000	+	O 100l	N2HLT	N2HLT
Auburn	444.6500	+	O 71.9	K2INH	K2INH

Location	Output	Input	Notes	Call	Sponsor
Poplar Ridge	449.9750	444.9250	O 71.9	W2FLW	W2FLW
Skaneateles	442.3000	+	Oae	W8JGP	W8JGP
BATH/HORNELL					
Alfred	444.8000	+	O 100	N2HLT	N2HLT
Bath	442.0500	+	O 131.8 (CA)l	N3KZ	UNIV OF PENNS
Bath	442.9500	+	Ol	KB2WXV	Keuka LARA
Branchport	422.6000	+	O 110.9	N2LSJ	N2LSJ
BINGHAMTON					
Binghamton	442.7000	+	O 100	K2ZG	K2ZG
Binghamton	444.1000	+	O 146.2	WA2QEL	Susquehanna Va
Endicott	444.3000	+	O 173.8e	N2YOW	N2YOW
Owego	444.7000	+	O 131.8 (CA)l	N3KZ	UNIV OF PENNS
Vestal	444.5500	+	O 88.5 (CA) l	AA2EQ	AA2EQ
CANANDAIGUA					
Bristol	443.6000	+	O 110.9	W2IMT	W2IMT
Bristol	444.5500	+	O 110.9l	WR2AHL	W2HYP
Hemlock	443.5000	+	O	K2BWK	SQUAW ISLAND
Middlesex	442.5000	+	Ol	W2CSA	W2CSA
South Bristol	442.2000	+	O 110.9e	W2ONT	ONTARIO COUN
South Bristol	442.9250	+	O 110.9alr s	N2HJD	RRRA
CATSKILLS NORTH					
Cooperstown	442.3500	+	Oer	NC2C	OTSEGO COUN
Schenevus	447.1250	–	O 100	KC2AWM	KC2AWM
Sharon Springs	449.2750	–	O 167.9	KF2JT	KF2JT
Stamford	448.7250	–	Opx	WA2MMX	WA2MMX
Summit	442.5000	+	O 100	KB2NSE	KB2NSE
Walton	443.0000	+	Oers	K2NK	Del Cty ES
CORTLAND/ITHACA					
Cortland	442.8500	+	Oe	KB2FAF	KB2FAF
Cortland	443.1500	+	O 127.3e	KB2FAF	KB2FAF
Cortland	444.4500	+	O	WA2VAM	FngrLksRA
Dryden	449.0250	–	O 103.5	AF2A	TOMPKINS COU
Norwich	442.6500	+	O	K2DAR	CHENANGO VA
Norwich	443.6000	+	O	K2DAR	ChngoARA
ELMIRA/CORNING					
Corning	444.3500	+	O(CA)elz	N2IED	CORNING AMAT
Elmira	443.5500	+	O 100	N2HLT	N2HLT
Elmira	444.2000	+	O(CA)erxz	KA3EVQ	ROOKIES
FRANKLIN					
Malone	444.6500	+	110.9a(CA) L(KW2F)	NG2C	------------
LONG ISLAND - NASSAU CO					
Carle Place	445.9750	–	O 123.0/123.0 DCS(073)eRB BI	N2YXZ	------------
Cedarhurst	445.6750	–	O 179.9/179.90ers	K2AAU	------------

Location	*Output*	*Input*	*Notes*	*Call*	*Sponsor*
East Meadow	443.3250	+	○ 136.5/136.5 TTelrs	K2CX	ROCK HILL RA
East Meadow	443.8000	+	○ 141.3er	AA2UC	N2TJV
East Meadow	444.7500	+	○ 110.9/110.9elrs	WB2ERS	INTERPLEX NETWO
East Meadow	444.8875	+	○ 179.9/179.9ers	NC2PD	NCPARC
Huntington	448.2250	–	● 156.7 L(147.33;147.93)	W2ATT	MIDDLE ISLNY
Mineola	441.3500	+	● 107.2e	W2EJ	PLAZA RPTR GROU
Mineola	443.2500	+	○ 123.0/123.0 RB BI	KC2DVQ	RC os Pirates
Oceanside	447.9250	–	○ 114.8lrs RB	N2ION	------------
Plainview	446.4250	–	○ 136.5/136.5 DCSes	WB2WAK	------------
Plainview	446.4750	–	○ 136.5 (CA)lsRB WX	WB2WAK	PHOENIX
Plainview	447.3500	–	○ 114.8	N2FLF	NCWA
Plainview	449.1250	–	○ 136.5 (CA)e	WB2NHO	LIMARC
Syosset	444.5500	+	○ 141.3/141.3e	W2MRK	------------
Syosset	447.9750	–	○ 136.5 (CA)lRB	WB2CYN	PHOENIX
Syosset	448.0250	–	○ 136.5/136.5el	N2HBA	NCAPD
Valley Stream	444.6500	+	○ 103.5 (CA)e	WB2IIQ	------------
Valley Stream	448.6250	–	○ 136.5 (CA)e	N2ZEI	------------
LONG ISLAND - SUFFOLK CO					
Babylon	446.7750	–	○ 114.8 (CA)ers	KB2UR	SSARC
Bay Shore	448.1750	–	○ 107.2	WA2RYY	------------
Bethpage	449.3000	–	○ 110.9 TT el	K2ATT	NYT PIONRS
Dix Hills	448.5000	–	○ 114.8 L(443.475)	W2RGM	------------
Dix Hills	448.5250	–	○ 114.8e L(443.5)	W2RGM	------------
Greenlawn	447.6250	–	○ 114.8	WA2AMX	------------
Greenport	440.0500	+	○ 107.2/107.2aersz	W2AMC	Peconic ARC
Hauppauge	448.4250	–	○ 136.5l	W2LRC	LARKFIELD ARC
Holtsville	442.0500	+	○ 114.8 (CA)	AG2I	Symbol Tech
Huntington	448.6750	–	○ 141.3 (CA)l	WR2ABA	LARKFIELD ARC

Location	*Output*	*Input*	*Notes*	*Call*	*Sponsor*
Islip Terrace	447.7750	–	● 114.8 (CA)elRB	WA2UMD	------------
Manorville	444.7000	+	● 114.8 RB	WR2UHF	GABAMFKRA
Mattituck	448.6750	–	● 141.3/141.3 (CA) TT(*911)sRBz	K1IMD	Radio Guys
Melville	442.9500	+	O 114.8e L(53.11)rs	WB2CIK	------------
Port Jefferson	449.5250	–	O 136.5 (CA)el	W2RC	RADIO CENTRL
Riverhead	449.0750	–	O 114.8lrs RB	N2ION	------------
Rocky Point	443.9000	+	O 136.5 WX	N2FXE	------------
Sag Harbor	449.6750	–	O 94.8/94.8	K1IMD	Radio Guys
Selden	445.7250	–	O 091.5/091.5 TTelrs	K2LI	------------
Selden	447.5250	–	●t(CA)el RB	WA2UMD	------------
Selden	447.8000	–	●t(CA)el RB	WA2UMD	------------
Selden	448.8250	–	O 114.8e L(146.76)	WA2VNV	SBRA
Setauket	449.1750	–	O 114.8er	W2SBL	Symbol Tch ARC
Upton	442.4000	+	O 114.8/114.8 (CA)	K2BNL	BNL RC
Wading River	442.3000	+	O 100.0 (CA)eL(447.3)rsz	N2NFI	------------
West Islip	440.8500	+	O 110.9/110.9elrsRB WXz	W2GSB	GSBARC
Woodbury	441.4000	+	O 151.4/151.4e	KC2AOY	LIRRARC
Yaphank	446.6250	–	O 110.9ers	W2DQ	SCRC
LOWER HUDSON - WESTCHESTER					
Briarcliff Manor	441.9000	+	O 114.8/114.8e	WI2RES	WIRES
Hastings	443.6000	+	O 110.9ls RB EXPz	N2ION	------------
Mt Vernon	446.7250	–	O 141.3/141.3 L(224.700)sRB	NY4Z	Alive Network
Valhalla	440.6500	+	Ot(CA)elr RB BI	WR2I	------------
Valhalla	447.4750	–	O 114.8elr sRB WX	WB2ZII	WECA
Yonkers	440.1500	+	Ot(CA)erBI WX	W2YRC	Yonkers ARC
Yonkers	440.4250	+	O 136.5/136.5e	N2QNB	------------
Yonkers	443.3500	+	● 179.7 TT DCS(23) L(430.175)rsz	WR2MSN	Metro 70

Location	*Output*	*Input*	*Notes*	*Call*	*Sponsor*
Yorktown Heights	443.1500	+	O 88.5	AF2C	YCDARC/MSARC
MID HUDSON					
Beacon	441.0500	+	O 114.8/114.8eL(147.27)x	W2ABC	BEARS, INC
Beacon	443.5500	+	O 156.7/156.7ersWX	KC2OUR	ORANGE CO. ARES
Carmel	447.5750	–	O 123.0	KC2ZPK	KC2ZPK
Clove Mountain	449.9750	444.9250	O 88.5e	N2CJ	DutchRACES
Cragsmoor	445.7250	–	O 100	WB2BQW	NORTHEAST CONN
Cragsmoor	448.6250	–	O 162.2	K2UG	HUDSON VALLEY C
Goshen	449.6750	–	O 162.2/162.2#ersWX	KC2OUR	ORANGE COUNTY A
Hudson	449.9250	–	Oes	K2RVW	Rip Van Winkle Amat
Kingston	442.0500	+	O 103.5	K2HVC	HUDSON VALLEY S
Lake Peekskill	449.9250	–	O 179.9es	KB2CQE	PEEKSKILL CORTLA
Livingston	449.0250	–	O 114.8l	N2LEN	N2LEN
Mahopac	448.9250	–	O 74.4al	K2HR	ALIVE NETWORK A
Marlboro	447.7250	–	O 100e	WA2BXK	WA2BXK
Middletown	442.8500	+	Ox	WA2ZPX	WA2ZPX
Middletown	443.3500	+	O 156.7ls	WR2MSN	METRO 70 CM NET
Middletown	449.5250	–	O 123rsWX x	WA2VDX	WA2VDX
Mohonk Lake	447.9250	–	O 118.8	K2MTB	K2MTB
Mount Beacon	449.5750	–	O 100 (CA) e	WA2GZW	MOUNT BEACON A
Newburgh	449.4750	–	O 71.9	N2HEP	N2HEP
Nyack	443.8500	+	O 114.8l	N2ACF	ROCKLAND REPEA
Pawling	448.1250	–	O 88.5	KA2NAX	KA2NAX
Pomona	444.4500	+	O 114.8l LITZx	N2ACF	ROCKLAND REPEA
Port Jervis	445.9250	–	O 114.8# TT(CALL INVALID - OPEN PAIR ?)ers	KB2TM	KB2TM
Putnam Valley	448.7250	–	O 107.2es	N2CBH	PCARA
Washingtonville	447.5250	–	O 82.5x	KQ2H	KQ2H
Woodstock	449.1750	–	O 82.5x	KQ2H	KQ2H
Wurtsburo	449.2250	–	O 107.2x	KQ2H	KQ2H
Wurtsburo	449.8750	–	O 114.8lx	N2ACF	N2ACF
MONROE COUNTY					
Churchville	443.1000	+	O 110.9e L(ECHOLINK)	KB2CHM	------------
Greece	444.8750	+	O 110.9 L(443.8) RB	N2KG	------------
Ogden	443.8000	+	O 110.9	K1NXG	------------
Rochester	443.9000	+	O 110.9e	KB2CHY	------------
Rochester	444.8500	+	O 110.9e L(ECHOLINK)x	WB2KAO	------------
NEW YORK CITY - BRONX					
Bronx	440.6000	+	O 141.3l	NY4Z	Alive Network
Bronx	440.8000	+	O 162.2/162.2	N2CUE	------------

Location	Output	Input	Notes	Call	Sponsor
Bronx	442.7500	+	O 77.0/77.0 (CA)rsBI	N2YN	------------
Bronx	442.7500	+	O 77.0	N2YN	------------
Bronx	443.3000	+	O 123.0/123.0sRB BIz	N2NSA	------------
Bronx	447.6250	–	O 136.5/136.5el	N2HBA	NCAPD
Bronx	447.7250	–	O 141.3/141.3eL(443.325;448.325)rs	WA2LYQ	------------
NEW YORK CITY - KINGS					
Brooklyn	440.2000	+	O 88.5/88.5	KB2NGU	------------
Brooklyn	440.5000	+	O 136.5/136.5 L(440.500;447.225) BI	N2XPK	------------
Brooklyn	441.1000	+	O 136.5/136.5 (CA) TTrsBI EXPz	N2ROW	------------
Brooklyn	445.4750	–	ODCSelWX	WG2MSK	KCRA
Brooklyn	446.6750	–	O 114.8es	WA2JNF	------------
Brooklyn	447.2250	–	114.8lBI	N2CHP	------------
Brooklyn	448.3750	–	O 162.2/162.2e	KB2NGU	------------
Brooklyn	448.9750	–	● 136.5/136.5 BI	KB2PRV	LARA
Brooklyn	449.3750	–	O 136.5rs	W2CXN	BTHS ARC
Brooklyn	449.7750	–	O 088.5/088.5 DCS(114)eBI	K2MAK	------------
NEW YORK CITY - MANHATTAN					
Manhattan	440.0000	+	O 114.8 (CA)lBI	N2KPK	MARC
Manhattan	440.4250	+	● 156.7 TT DCS(23) L(430.175)rsWXz	WR2MSN	Metro 70
Manhattan	441.4500	+	O 141.3/141.3 DCS(075)lRB BIz	NE2E	------------
Manhattan	441.7000	+	O 100.0	K2IRT	------------
Manhattan	442.0500	+	O 141.3	NY4Z	Alive Network
Manhattan	442.4500	+	179.9/179.9 BI	KB2RQE	LARA
Manhattan	443.7000	+	O 141.3 (CA)el	K2JRC	BEARS
Manhattan	444.2000	+	O 136.5/136.5es	WB2ZZO	HOSARC
Manhattan	445.0750	–	O 114.8 (CA)el	WA2CBS	BCARS
Manhattan	445.1750	–	O(CA)elr RBz	NB2A	LAW ENFCMT
Manhattan	445.9000	–	● 206.5el	KQ2H	------------
Manhattan	446.2750	–	O 74.4 (CA) lRB	NY4Z	Alive Netwrk
Manhattan	446.9000	–	O 136.5 (CA)elrz	N2BEI	SCJRA

Location	Output	Input	Notes	Call	Sponsor
Manhattan	446.9250	–	O	KF2GV	------------
Manhattan	447.1750	–	● 141.3el	WB2ZTH	ARCECS
Manhattan	447.8250	–	O 107.2er	WA2ZLB	MAARC
Manhattan	448.4750	–	O 127.3 L(443.5)	W2RGM	------------
Manhattan	448.5000	–	O 127.3	W2RGM	------------
Manhattan	449.0250	–	O 114.8/114.8z	N2JDW	Manh RS
Manhattan	449.3250	–	O 136.5 RB	W2ML	------------
New York	448.2750	–	O 088.5/088.5eBlz	K2MAK	------------

NEW YORK CITY - QUEENS

Location	Output	Input	Notes	Call	Sponsor
Flushing	449.7250	–	O 114.8 DCS(1DMR)eBI	KC2CQR	------------
Glen Oaks	447.0250	–	O 107.2/107.2 TTelrs	K2TC	NE NET
Maspeth	449.2750	–	O 88.5/88.5	KB2YHS	------------
Queens Village	442.6500	+	● 141.3e	WB2QBP	ARCECS
Whitestone	445.6750	–	O 179.9	K2AAU	------------
Whitestone	447.3250	–	O 107.2/107.2 L(223.650) BI	KC2EFN	HARA

NEW YORK CITY - RICHMOND

Location	Output	Input	Notes	Call	Sponsor
Staten Island	442.3000	+	141.3/141.3 es	KC2RQR	------------

NEW YORK CITY - STATEN ISLAND

Location	Output	Input	Notes	Call	Sponsor
Staten Island	440.5500	+	O 141.3 L(445.575)	KC2LEB	SIRS
Staten Island	445.1250	–	O 141.3/141.3	KC2GOW	------------
Staten Island	445.3250	–	O 156.7	W2CWW	SI ARA
Staten Island	445.8250	–	O 156.7/156.7 (CA) TTeL(146.880)sRB EXP	KA2PBT	SI UHF RA
Staten Island	445.8750	–	O 136.5/136.5 TTeL(927.2125)	N2BBO	------------
Staten Island	447.2250	–	O 192.8 DCS(2051-2510)eEXP	N2CBU	NBFFRC
Staten Island	447.3750	–	O 141.3/141.3 TTrsz	KC2CIG	NYCRA
Staten Island	447.7250	–	O 71.9/71.9 TT BI	KB2EA	------------

NIAGARA

Location	Output	Input	Notes	Call	Sponsor
Buffalo	442.6250	+	O 107.2e	KC2KOO	------------
Buffalo	443.5250	+	O 151.4 L(146.865)	WB2ECR	------------
Buffalo	444.0000	+	Oe L(BARRA ECHOLINK IRLP)x	WA2HKS	BARRA
Colden	442.1000	+	O 88.5e L(BARC) RB	W2IVB	BARC
Colden	442.3250	+	O 107.2	WB2ELW	STARS

Location	*Output*	*Input*	*Notes*	*Call*	*Sponsor*
Colden	444.9250	+	● 88.5	WB2FXY	------------
Eden	442.1500	+	O 107.2	W2BRW	------------
Eden	444.2000	+	O 88.5 L(IRLP)	WB2JPQ	ILS
Gasport	443.6875	+	O L(D-STAR)	KD2STR	FARC
Hamburg	443.4000	+	O 107.2 (CA)e	WB2DSS	------------
Kenmore	443.8750	+	O 107.2	KC2KOO	------------
Kenmore	444.7500	+	O 151.4	WB2DSS	BARRA
Lackawanna	444.1500	+	O 88.5e L(ILS IRLP)	WB2JPQ	ILS
Lancaster	443.8500	+	O 107.2e L(LARC IRLP)	W2SO	LARC
Lewiston	443.9250	+	O 151.4 L(224.420 ECHOLIONK)	N3AU	------------
Lockport	444.6250	+	Oer	W2OM	NCRACES
Newfane	444.8000	+	O 107.2 (CA)el	K2AER	NCARA
Orchard Park	443.9750	+	O 141.3e	WB2ECR	------------
Orchard Park	444.6750	+	O 88.5e L(IRLP)	N2XFX	------------
Royalton	443.4500	+	O 107.2e L(51.640) RB	KD2WA	------------
Sanborn	442.5750	+	O 107.2e	N3AU	------------
West Seneca	442.4000	+	O 100.0 (CA)e	WA2OLW	------------
OSWEGO/FULTON					
Hannibal	442.3500	+	O	K2QQY	ARES
QUEENS					
Far Rockaway	442.1000	+	O 074.4/074.4e	NY4Z	Alive Network
ROCHESTER					
Canadice	443.7500	+	O 100	N2HLT	N2HLT
Canandaigua	443.0750	+	O	KC2NFU	KC2NFU
Fairport	444.9000	+	O 110.9	N2BZX	N2BZX
Fairport	447.1750	−	O(CA)ep	WB2SSJ	WB2SSJ
Mendon	444.7000	+	O 110.9alr z	N2HJD	ROCHESTER R
Rochester	442.6500	+	Ol	K2SA	Genesee RA
Rochester	442.7000	+	O 110.9elr s	K2RRA	ROCHESTER R
Rochester	442.8000	+	O 110.9ael rz	N2HJD	ROCHESTER R
Rochester	442.9000	+	O 110.9alr z	N2HJD	RRRA
Rochester	443.0000	+	Or	N2WPB	ROCHESTER R
Rochester	443.7000	+	Oaz	K2SA	Genesee RA
Rochester	443.9000	+	O 110.9e	KB2CHY	ROCHESTER R

Location	Output	Input	Notes	Call	Sponsor
Rochester	444.4000	+	O	W2RFC	R F COMMUNICATIO
Rochester	444.8250	+	Oex	KE2MK	Xerox ARC
Rochester	444.8500	+	O 110.9 (CA)x	WB2KAO	WB2KAO
Rochester	444.9500	+	O	WR2AHL	GRIDD
SOUTHERN TIER					
Alma	444.1000	+	O 107.2e L(146.955 147.210 145.430 ECHOLINK) WX	KA2AJH	-----
Celeron	444.9750	+	O 127.3	AB2WL	------------
Delevan	444.1750	+	O 88.5	K2XZ	------------
Limestone	444.6500	+	O 88.5 L(442.750)	W3VG	------------
Mayville	444.4500	+	O 88.5 L(442.75)	WB2EDV	------------
Olean	442.1250	+	O 127.3e	N2XFX	------------
Olean	444.8500	+	O	K2XZ	------------
Perrysburg	443.0000	+	O 107.2 L(53.610)	WB2DSS	------------
Perrysburg	444.9000	+	O 107.2e	KC2DKP	------------
Pomfret	444.3500	+	O 88.5e L(442.750)rsx	W2SB	NCARC
Ripley	443.1250	+	O 127.3e	K2OAD	------------
Sherman	442.7500	+	O 88.5el	WB2EDV	------------
ST LAWRENCE					
Ogdensburg	443.5250	+		N2MX	------------
Parishville	444.8500	+	123.0	W2LCA	NCARC
Potsdam	443.3500	+	151.4 L(146.895) Z(*911)	K2CC	CUARC
SYRACUSE					
Camillus	444.7500	+	O 103.5e	KB2ZBI	KB2ZBI
Canastota	443.0000	+	O	N2UDF	N2UDF
Cayuga	444.8000	+	Owx	K2JMA	K2JMA
Cazenovia	444.0000	+	O 151.4ae	N2LZI	James I McHerron M
Clay	444.1000	+	O 110.9el	WA2U	WA2U
Dewitt	448.5750	–	O 141.3 (CA)	K2OOP	K2OOP
Liverpool	443.2000	+	O 103.5e	W2ISB	W2ISB
Pompey	442.5500	+	O 71.9e	W2JST	W2JST
Syracuse	442.2000	+	O	WA2VAM	WA2VAM
Syracuse	442.4000	+	O 123aesx z	W2QYT	W2QYT
Syracuse	442.7500	+	O 100	N2HLT	N2HLT
Syracuse	442.9000	+	O 103.5 TT(CALL CANCELLED)	N2NUP	N2NUP
Syracuse	443.1000	+	O 103.5	WA2AUL	WA2AUL
Syracuse	443.3000	+	O 103.5	KD2CJS	LARC
Syracuse	443.3500	+	O 103.5p	KA2CTN	KA2CTN
Syracuse	443.4000	+	O 103.5elz	KA2CTN	KA2CTN
Syracuse	443.4500	+	O 131.8	N2UQG	N2UQG

Location	Output	Input	Notes	Call	Sponsor
Syracuse	444.2000	+	Oa	K2IV	NiMo ARC
Syracuse	448.8750	–	O 141.3l	K2OOP	K2OOP
Syracuse	448.9250	–	O	K2OOP	K2OOP
UPPER HUDSON					
Corinth	448.1250	–	Oer	WA2UMX	SARATOGA CO
Lake George	443.4500	+	O 100r	KT2M	Warr RACES
Lake George	444.7500	+	O 110.9l	WA2DDQ	N.E. FM As
Saratoga Spr	448.2250	–	O 100elrz	WA2UMX	SARATOGA CO
UTICA/ROME					
Ilion	444.4000	+	O	KB3BIU	KB3BIU
Kirkland	443.8500	+	O 103.5r	KA2FWN	KA2FWN
Utica	442.1000	+	O 100elx	KR1TD	MT Assoc
Utica	444.8500	+	O	W2JIT	Deerfld RA
Verona	443.6500	+	Oael	KA2NIL	KA2NIL
WATERTOWN					
Dry Hill	442.5000	+	Oz	N2YQI	N2YQI
Watertown	442.4500	+	O 100	N2HLT	N2HLT
Watertown	443.1500	+	Oaelx	KE2UA	TIARA
Watertown	444.0500	+	Oz	KA2QJO	KA2QJO
WATKINS GLEN					
Branchport	442.6000	+	O 110.9	N2LSJ	N2LSJ
Penn Yan	442.2500	+	O 100alz	N2HLT	N2HLT
Watkins Glen	442.1500	+	O 123l	N2IED	CARA
WAYNE/NEWARK					
Clyde	449.0750	–	O	KA2NDW	KA2NDW
Palmyra	444.2500	+	Oe	W2RFM	GRID
Sodus Point	444.9500	+	Oa	WA2AAZ	DRUMLINS AMA
WEST					
Attica	442.8750	+	O 100.0 L(N2HLT)	N2HLT	------------
Attica	444.0500	+	O 88.5e L(443.600)	N2XFX	------------
Batavia	444.2750	+	O 141.3 (CA)e	W2SO	LARC
Wethersfield	442.0000	+	O 110.9e L(145.11) RBx	WR2AHL	BARRA
Wethersfield	443.6250	+	O 141.3e L(147.315)	WA2CAM	------------

NORTH CAROLINA

Location	Output	Input	Notes	Call	Sponsor
Ahoskie	444.2000	+	O 131.8/131.8l	WB4YNF	WB4YNF
Ahoskie	444.7500	+	O 131.8/131.8	WB4YNF	WB4YNF
Air Bellows Gap	442.1500	+	O	WA4PXV	WA4PXV
Air Bellows Gap	443.5750	+	O	WA4PXV	WA4PXV
Albemarle	444.9000	+	O	N4HRS	KD4ADL
Alexander	441.6500	+	O 100/100e l	KG4LGY	------------

Location	*Output*	*Input*	*Notes*	*Call*	*Sponsor*
Anderson Mt	444.0750	+	O TTl	WX4BRW	WX4BRW
Andrews	442.6000	+	O	WD4NWV	WD4NWV
Apex	442.0750	+	O	KD4PBS	KD4PBS
Asheville	442.5500	+	O	WA4TOG	WA4TOG
Asheville	442.6500	+	O	KD4GEU	------------
Asheville	443.2750	+	O	KF4TLA	KF4TLA
Asheville	443.9000	+	O	N4HRS	NC HEARS
Auburn	442.2750	+	O	N4ZCM	------------
Banner Elk	444.4000	+	O	K4DHT	K4NOW
Bath	442.5500	+	O 82.5es	N4JEH	Pamlico ARC
Bladenboro	444.7250	449.3250	O	N4DBM	N4DBM
Brevard	442.8500	+	O	AG4AZ	AG4AZ
Bryson City	443.4000	+	O	NØSU	NØSU&K4JAT
Bunn	444.2500	+	O	KC4WDI	N4EWS
Burgaw	444.0750	+	O	N4JDW	N4JDW
Burlington	443.0250	+	O	WB4IKY	WB4IKY
Burlington	443.6000	+	O	K4EG	K4EG
Burlington	444.3500	+	O	WB4IKY	WB4IKY
Burlington	444.8875	+	O	AK4EG	AI4UE
Burnsville	443.6500	+	O	KD4WAR	KD4WAR
Cane Mt	443.4500	+	O	KD4RAA	KD4RAA REPEATER
Canton	443.4750	+	O	KE4UIU	------------
Canton	444.8500	+	O	KI4GMA	KI4GMA
Cary	444.7750	+	O	K4JDR	CAROLINA 440
Castalia	444.9750	+	O	N4JEH	N4JEH
Chapel Hill	442.5375	+	O	KB4HG	KB4HG
Charlotte	441.6000	+	O	KD4ADL	N4HRS
Charlotte	441.9750	+	O	KD4ADL	KD4ADL
Charlotte	442.4125	+	O	W4ZO	W4ZO
Charlotte	442.6500	+	O	WØUNC	WA2EDN
Charlotte	442.7250	+	O	KD4ADL	KD4ADL
Charlotte	443.8625	+	O	KI4WXS	KI4WXS
Charlotte	444.1750	+	O	N4HRS	NC HEARS
Charlotte	444.3500	+	O 151.4/151.4e	K4KAY	K4KAY
Charlotte	444.4500	+	O	W4CQ	CHARLOTTE AR CO
Charlotte	444.4750	+	O	KI4PJL	KI4PJL
Charlotte	444.6000	+	O 118.8/118.8	W4BFB	W4BFB
Charlotte	444.6750	+	O	W4WBT	CHARLOTTE ARC W
Charlotte	444.8500	+	O	W4CQ	CHARLOTTE AR CO
Charlotte	444.9500	+	O 136.5/136.5s	WA1WXL	KQ1E
Cherry Mtn	442.5000	+	O	KG4JIA	KG4JIA
China Grove	441.5500	+	O	KQ1E	KQ1E
China Grove	443.2500	+	O	N4UH	KQ1E
Clayton	443.6750	+	O	N4TCP	N4TCP
Clayton	444.1500	+	O	K4JDR	CAROLINA 440
Cleveland	442.9250	+	O 127.3/127.3l	K4CH	N4TZD

Location	*Output*	*Input*	*Notes*	*Call*	*Sponsor*
Clinton	441.7000	+	O	K4ITL	K4ITL
Clinton	443.0750	+	O	N4JDW	N4JDW
Clyde	444.0500	+	O	KJ4VKD	KJ4VKD
Clyde	444.2750	+	O 94.8/94.8	KW4P	KW4P
Columbia	442.7250	+	O 131.8/131.8elsWX	K4OBX	W4HAT
Columbia	443.3000	+	O	KX4NC	COLUMBIA EME
Concord	442.5250	+	O 94.8/94.8	N2QJI	N2QJI
Concord	444.2500	+	O	W4ZO	W4ZO
Concord	444.3875	+	O	W4ZO	W4ZO
Concord	444.7750	+	O	KD4ADL	N4HRS
Crowder's Mt	443.6750	+	O	KD4FRP	------------
Dallas	444.2250	+	O	N4HRS	N4HRS
Denton	443.6500	+	O 127.3/127.3l	K4AE	------------
Dobson	444.5250	+	O 100/100s WX	W4DCA	W4DCA
Durham	444.1000	+	O	WR4AGC	DURHAM FM AS
Durham	444.5750	+	O	W4BAD	KG4GAL
Durham	444.9250	+	O	KB4WGA	KB4WGA
Earl	442.5750	+	O	KI4ZJI	KI4ZJI
Elizabeth City	443.3250	+	O 123/123e	W4UUU	KE4H
Elizabeth City	444.3000	+	O	WA4VTX	TAARS
Fayetteville	444.4000	+	O	K4MN	CAPE FEAR AR
Forest City	442.0000	+	O	AI4M	AI4M
Forest City	443.3000	+	O	AI4M	AI4M
Fountain	444.4250	+	Oe	N4HAJ	N4HAJ
Franklin	444.3750	+	O	K4KSS	K4KSS
Garner	443.8250	+	O	W1SMW	W1SMW
Gastonia	442.7000	+	O	KC4YOT	KC4YOT
Gastonia	442.7750	+	O	KG4LWG	KG4LWG
Gastonia	443.7500	+	O	KC4ZTI	KC4ZTI
Gastonia	443.9125	+	O	KA4YMZ	KA4YMZ
Gastonia	443.9875	+	O	KA4YMZ	KA4YMZ
Gastonia	444.1500	+	O	AG4EI	AG4EI
Gastonia	444.5500	+	O	N4GAS	GASTON CTY A
Gastonia	444.7500	+	O	K4GNC	KC4YOT
Graham	443.7250	+	O	K4GWH	K4GWH
Grantsboro	444.3500	+	O	KR4LO	KR4LO
Grantsboro	444.8750	+	O 85.4/85.4 e	KF4IXW	KF4IXW
Greensboro	444.2250	+	O	K4GWH	K4GWH
Greensboro	444.9500	+	O	KF4DWV	W4GG
Greenville	444.6250	+	O	KE4TZN	KE4TZN
Greenville	444.7250	+	Oe	N4HAJ	N4HAJ
Greenville	444.8000	+	O	WB4PMQ	WB4PMQ
Hatteras Island	444.9250	+	O	K4OBX	W4HAT
Henderson	442.1250	+	O	KG4IWI	KG4IWI
Henderson	444.3750	+	O	KB4WGA	KB4WGA

Location	*Output*	*Input*	*Notes*	*Call*	*Sponsor*
Hendersonville	442.4500	+	O	WA4TOG	WA4TOG
Hendersonville	444.2500	+	O	WA4KNI	WA4KNI
Hickory	442.3750	+	O	WA4PXV	WA4PXV
Hickory	444.0000	+	O	K4JEQ	K4JEQ
Hickory	444.3750	+	O	KC4FM	K4ICU
Hickory	444.8000	+	O	KF4LUC	KF4LUC
High Point	442.7750	+	O	N4ROZ	N4ROZ
High Point	443.9000	+	O	W4UA	HPARC
Hillsborough	444.4500	+	O	WR4AGC	DURHAM FM ASSN
Holly Ridge	442.0250	+	O	N4JDW	N4JDW
Holly Springs	444.3250	+	O	KF4AUF	K4JDR
Hubert	444.6750	+	Oe	N4HAJ	N4HAJ
Huntersville	443.2250	+	O 110.9/110.9l	WG8E	WG8E
Jefferson	443.0750	+	O	W4JWO	W4JWO
Jefferson	443.5250	+	O	W4YSB	ASHE COUNTY ARC
Johnsonville	444.2000	+	O 179.9/179.9l	N1RIK	N1RIK
Kannapolis	443.3500	+	O	N4JEX	W1WBT
Kernersville	444.6250	+	O 107.2/107.2	KF4OVA	KF4OVA
King	444.2000	+	O	KE4QEA	------------
Kinston	444.5750	+	O 88.5/88.5 e	N4HAJ	N4HAJ
Kornegay	444.1250	+	Oe	N4HAJ	N4HAJ
Lansing	444.3000	+	O 103.5/103.5ls	W4MLN	W4MLN
Laurinburg	443.8250	+	O	N4DBM	W4DEX & N4DBM
Level Cross	442.8250	+	O 82.5/82.5 a(CA)el	K4ITL	K4ITL
Level Cross	442.8875	+	O	K4ITL	PCRN
Lexington	442.2750	+	O	KO∅NTZ	KO∅NTZ
Lexington	442.5500	+	O 107.2/107.2	KJ4SPF	KJ4SPF
Lexington	444.5000	+	O	W4PAR	HSMVHF SOC
Lincolnton	442.3500	+	O 141.3/141.3e	WA4YGD	WA4YGD
Linville	442.1750	+	O	W4JJO	KC4UBR
Linville	444.5750	+	O	N4DBM	W4DEX & N4DBM
Locust	443.7000	+	O	WA4LBT	WM. GLENN PEARS
Lumberton	444.6250	+	O	WB4DVN	WB4DVN
Lumberton	444.6250	+	O	WB4DVN	WB4DVN
Margarettsville	442.3500	+	O	K4MJO	K4MJO
Mccain	442.2500	+	Oel	N1RIK	N1RIK
Mcleansville	444.1250	+	O	WB4GUG	WB4GUG
Middlesex	444.6500	+	O	NE4J	NE4J
Mills River	442.0250	+	O	W4ENC	W4ENC
Mint Hill	444.6375	+	O	W4ZO	W4ZO
Mint Hill	444.8250	+	O	KD4ADL	KD4ADL

Location	Output	Input	Notes	Call	Sponsor
Monroe	444.3000	+	O	W4ZO	W4ZO
Monroe	444.4250	+	O	NC4UC	UCARS
Mooresville	443.8250	+	Oel	WG8E	KD4ADL
Mooresville	443.8250	+	O	WG8E	KD4ADL
Moravian Falls	442.6750	+	O	KA2NAX	KA2NAX
Morg/Walker Top	442.3000	+	O	KC4QPR	KC4QPR
Morganton	443.8000	+	O	KC4QZL	KC4QZL
Morganton	444.6250	+	O	KD4ADL	KD4ADL
Morrisville	444.0750	+	O	KC4SCO	AG4BJ
Mount Gilead	442.2000	+	O	KI4DH	KI4DH
Mt Airy	443.4250	+	O	KD4ADL	N4HRS
Mt Airy	444.8250	+	O	KF4UY	KF4UY
Mt Mitchell	443.6000	+	O	N2GE	N2GE
Nashville	443.7000	+	O	N4JEH	N4JEH
Nashville	444.2250	+	O 107.2/107.2e	KB4CTS	KB4CTS
Needmore	444.5500	+	O	KT4WO	KT4WO
New Bern	442.0750	+	Oe	N4HAJ	N4HAJ
New Bern	444.9000	+	O	W4EWN	NBARC (NEW B
Newell	442.1250	+	O	WT4IX	WT4IX
Newport	444.9750	+	O	W4YMI	CCARS
Newton	442.6250	+	O	KE4KIV	KE4KIV
North Wilkesboro	443.7750	+	O	WB4SRV	WA4PXV
Oxford	444.6000	+	O	NO4EL	GRANVILLE AR
Pineview	444.2750	+	O	NC4BJ	CAROLINA 440
Piney Knob	443.8750	+	O	KC4KPW	KC4KPW
Pittsboro	444.1750	+	O	K4WDG	K4WDG
Polkville	444.9750	+	O	N4DWP	N4DWP
Powells Point	442.8500	+	O	W4PCN	OBRA
Raeford	442.1000	+	O	KG4HDV	KG4HDV
Raleigh	441.7250	+	O	K4JDR	CAROLINA 440
Raleigh	442.4500	+	O	N4LMR	N4LMR
Raleigh	442.5125	+	O	K4ITL	PCRN
Raleigh	442.5750	+	O	W4MLU	W4FAL
Raleigh	442.6750	+	O	NC4SU	NCSU ARC
Raleigh	442.9500	+	O	W4MLU	W4FAL
Raleigh	443.1000	+	O	W4RLH	K4JDR
Raleigh	443.1250	+	O	WA4NNA	WA4NNA
Raleigh	443.1750	+	O	W4BAD	W4BAD
Raleigh	443.2250	+	O	N4ZCM	N4ZCM
Raleigh	444.3000	+	O	W4FAL	W4FAL
Raleigh	444.5250	+	O	W4RNC	RALEIGH ARS
Raleigh	444.6750	+	O	KD4RAA	BNR/NT ARC
Raleigh	444.8250	+	O	K4GWH	K4GWH
Reidsville	443.9750	+	O	W4BJF	ROCKINGHAM
Reidsville	444.8000	+	O	K4YEC	K4YEC
Roanoke Rapids	444.5500	+	O	KA4BQM	KA4BQM
Rocky Mount	441.7500	+	O	NC4FM	N4JEH
Rocky Mount	444.7000	+	O	N4JEH	CARL H. BRILEY

Location	*Output*	*Input*	*Notes*	*Call*	*Sponsor*
Rocky Mount	444.8500	+	O	WN4Z	ROCKY MOUNT AR
Rolesville	444.9500	+	O	KF4HFQ	FCARC
Rougemont	443.2750	+	O	NC4CD	NC4CD
Roxboro	441.6750	+	O	W4BAD	W4BAD
Salisbury	443.1500	+	O	N4UH	WA4PVI
Sanford	441.9500	+	O	KB4HG	KB4HG
Sauratown Mtn	443.0500	+	O	KQ1E	KQ1E
Scotland Neck	444.0750	+	O	NC4FM	N4JEH
Shelby	444.1875	+	O	W4NYR	SHELBYARC
Shelby	444.2750	+	O	AE6JI	AE6JI
Shelby	444.3250	+	O	W4NYR	SHELBY ARC
Sophia	443.0750	+	O	WR4BEG	BROADCAST PKT &
Sophia	444.9750	+	O	KE4QAP	KB4TWG
Sparta	442.6000	+	O	WA4PXV	WA4PXV
Sparta	444.4250	+	O	KI4M	KI4M
Spruce Pine	443.9250	+	O 123/123es	KK4MAR	KK4MAR
Stacy	444.0000	+	O	KD4KTO	KD4KTO
Stanfield	443.2000	+	O	N4DBM	W4DEX & N4DBM
Statesville	443.2750	+	O	KI4UBG	KI4UBG
Statesville	443.4500	+	O	N4VOZ	N4VOZ
Statesville	444.7000	+	O	AE4GA	AE4II
Sylva	444.1500	+	O	KJ4VKD	KJ4VKD
Sylva	444.7000	+	O 131.8/131.8el	K4RCC	K4RCC
Tarboro	444.5000	+	O	NC4FM	N4JEH
Tarboro	444.9250	+	O	N4NTO	N4NTO
Taylorsville	441.6250	+	O	W4ERT	ALEXANDER ARA
Thomasville	441.8000	+	O 127.3/127.3l	W4TNC	------------
Thomasville	442.7500	+	O 118.8/118.8l	KD4LHP	KD4LHP
Thomasville	443.3250	+	Ol	KD4LHP	KD4LHP
Triangle Park	443.4250	+	O	WA1YYN	WA1YYN
Triangle Park	443.6250	+	O	W4EUS	ERICSSON ARC
Troy	443.4000	+	O	W4WAU	EFARG
Tryon	442.8750	+	O	K4SV	K4SV
Wade	443.9000	+	O 100/100	KN4ZZ	KN4ZZ
Waxhaw	444.5250	+	O	K4WBT	WBT ARC
Waynesville	443.8500	+	O	K4KGB	NC HEARS
Waynesville	444.4500	+	O	N4DTR	N4DTR
Waynesville	449.8750	–	O 131.8/131.8el	K4RCC	K4RCC
Wendell	444.8750	+	O	KD4RAA	CAROLINA 440
Wilkesboro	442.4750	+	O	KE4DGP	------------
Wilkesboro	443.5500	+	O 94.8/94.8	WB4PZA	------------
Williamston	444.2500	+	O	K4SER	ROANOKE ARS
Wilmington	442.1750	+	O	WA4US	WA4US
Wilmington	442.2000	+	O	WA4US	WA4US

Location	Output	Input	Notes	Call	Sponsor
Wilmington	442.5000	+	O	AC4RC	AZALEA COAST
Wilmington	443.4000	+	O	AD4DN	AD4DN
Wilmington	443.8500	+	O	WA4US	WA4US
Wilmington	443.9500	+	O	WA4US	WA4US
Wilmington	444.0500	+	O	N4JDW	N4JDW
Wilmington	444.1750	+	O	N4ILM	WILMINGTON V
Wilmington	444.2000	+	O	WA4US	WA4US
Wilmington	444.4500	+	O	WA4US	WA4US
Wilmington	444.6500	+	O	WA4US	WA4US
Wilmington	444.7750	+	O	N4PLY	N2QEW
Wilmington	444.8500	+	O	N4ILM	WILMINGTON V
Wilson	442.3250	+	O 88.5/88.5	WA4WAR	K4WLH
Wilson	444.9000	+	O	W4EJ	W4EJ
Wingate	444.8750	+	O	WB4U	WB4U
Winston-Salem	444.2750	+	O	W4NC	FORSYTH ARC
Winston-salem	444.7250	+	O	KD4MMP	------------
Yadkinville	442.0250	+	O	KD4KMK	KD4KMK
Yadkinville	442.8000	+	O	N4AAD	N4AAD
Youngsville	442.1750	+	O	N4TAB	K4ITL
Youngsville	442.3000	+	O	WB4IUY	WB4IUY
Youngsville	443.2000	+	O	KC4WDI	KD42LH & KC4
Zebulon	442.4000	+	O	WB4IUY	WB4IUY

NORTH DAKOTA

Location	Output	Input	Notes	Call	Sponsor
FREQUENCY USAGE					
Statewide	443.7000	+		SNP	
Statewide	444.3250	+		SNP	
Statewide	444.7250	+		SNP	
N E CENTRAL					
Maddock	442.2500	+	O 141.3	KFØHR	KFØHR
N W CENTRAL					
Minot	442.3000	+	O	KØAJW	SVARC
Minot	444.4000	+	O	WØCQ	WØCQ
Minot	444.8000	+	O	KØAJW	SVARC
NORTHWEST					
Williston	443.8500	+	Oe	KØWSN	WBARC
S E CENTRAL					
Jamestown	444.2500	+	O	NØHNM	NØHNM
Jamestown	444.9250	+	O	WBØTWN	WBØTWN
S W CENTRAL					
Bismarck	444.2000	+	Oae L(52.525)	NØFAZ	NØFAZ
Bismarck	444.6500	+	Oe	KCØAHL	Hillside A
Center	444.9000	+	O	KEØVF	KEØVF
SOUTHEAST					
Fargo	443.9000	+	O 100.0e	KEØVN	KEØVN
Horace	443.7500	+	O	WØZOK	WØZOK
Wahpeton	443.8000	+	O 107.2	WØEND	TRARC

Location	*Output*	*Input*	*Notes*	*Call*	*Sponsor*
SOUTHWEST					
Dickinson	442.6750	+	O	KØND	TRARC
Killdeer	444.6750	+	O	KØND	TRARC
Sentinel Butte	443.6750	+	O	KØND	TRARC
OHIO					
ADAMS					
Peebles	442.6750	+	O(CA)e	KJ8I	#NAME?
Peebles	444.0250	+	O	WD8LSN	WD8LSN
Seaman	444.5125	+	O(CA)e	KC8FBG	KC8FBG
ALLEN					
Bluffton	444.0000	+	O 107.2	W8AK	W8AK
Lima	444.0750	+	Oae	N8GCH	ShawneeRA
Lima	444.7750	+		WB8PJZ	WB8PJZ
ASHLAND					
Ashland	442.8000	+	O	W8IVG	KB8GF
Polk	442.1500	+	O 88.5	KG8FV	LLWA
Polk	443.3250	+	131.8 (CA)l	N8SIW	N8SIW
Polk	443.6250	+	O 2162.2a (CA)elrWXx	KA8VDW	SREL
Widowville	444.3250	+	O 131.8	KD8JBF	KD8JBF
ASHTABULA					
Geneva	443.6250	+	O 146.2	N8WPZ	N8WPZ
Kingsville	443.6500	+	O 103.5e	N8XUA	N8XUA
Orwell	444.2500	+	ael	KF8YF	KF8YF
ATHENS					
Athens	442.1000	+	O	K8LGN	HVARC
AUGLAIZE					
Cridersville	444.9250	+	O	W8EQ	LAARC
St Marys	444.2000	+	O 107.2el	K8QYL	Rsvr ARA
Wapakoneta	442.1500	+	107.2arWX	KD8CQL	A.C.E.M.A
BUTLER					
Fairfield	443.6500	+	Oae	W8PRH	FARA
Hamilton	442.6500	+	O	WD8KPU	FARA
Hamilton	443.3375	+	O 123.0	KD8OFL	KD8SES
Hamilton	444.1125	+	O 118.8	KD8EYB	BCAREC
Hamilton	444.6500	+	O 123.0	K8KY	K8KY
Middletown	443.5375	+	O 118.8e	W8MUM	MiamiUARC
Middletown	444.4750	+	O 100.0 TT el	AG8Y	AG8Y
Middletown	444.8250	+	O 77.0el	W8BLV	Dial ARC
Monroe	442.5500	+	O 118.8e	WA8MU	WA8MU
Monroe	443.0875	+	Oep	KC8ECK	KC8ECK
West Chester	442.3250	+	123	KC8RKM	KC8RKM
West Chester	442.7000	+	●l	W8VVL	QCEN
West Chester	444.9750	+	●prxz	K8CR	K8CR
CARROLL					
Carrollton	442.4000	+	Ot(CA)e	K8VPJ	K8VPJ
Carrollton	442.5875	+	Oe	N8RQU	N8RQU

Location	Output	Input	Notes	Call	Sponsor
Carrollton	442.6250	+	●(CA)e	K8VPJ	K8VPJ
Carrollton	443.2750	+	O	KC8RKA	KC8RKA
Carrollton	444.2125	+	Oe	NC8W	NC8W
Malvern	443.2000	+	aelRB LITZ	K8NNC	CC ARES
CHAMPAIGN					
Urbana	443.1750	+	O 123.0e	WB8UCD	WB8UCD
Urbana	443.3500	+	O	KA8HMJ	KA8HMJ
CLARK					
N Hampton	444.3750	+	O 127.3e	K8IRA	IndepndRA
Springfield	443.3000	+	O 146.2	W8BUZ	W8BUZ
Springfield	444.4125	+	●t(CA)elx	KA8HMJ	KA8HMJ
CLERMONT					
Batavia	444.3250	+	OaelrWXx	N8NKS	N8NKS
Cincinnati	444.0750	+	O 110.9	KB8SBN	KB8SBN
Cincinnati	444.9250	+	a	K8CF	K8CF
Goshen	443.4500	+	O 146.2	K8DV	K8DV
Loveland	442.7750	+	Oar	WD8KPU	WD8KPU
Loveland	444.5250	+	O 100.0	WU8S	WU8S
CLINTON					
Blanchester	442.0250	+	t	KB8CWC	KB8CWC
Wilmington	443.2375	+	O	AB8KD	AB8KD
Wilmington	443.2750	+	O	N8ASB	N8ASB
Wilmington	443.3750	+	O	K8IO	K8IO
Wilmington	444.5750	+	141.3er	WB8ZZR	WB8ZZR
COLUMBIANA					
E Liverpool	442.1750	+	O(CA)e	K8BLP	TrianglRC
Lisbon	442.5250	+	162.2ae	KD8XB	KD8XB
Lisbon	444.4625	+	O 162.2lp	KC8RPR	KC8RPR
Lisbon	444.9125	+	O 162.2 RB WXx	W8MMN	W8MMN
Minerva	442.9500	+	O	KC8PHW	KC8PHW
Salem	442.1000	+	O 88.5ael RB WXz	KB8MFV	KB8MFV
Salem	444.6750	+	O 156.7 (CA)eWXz	KA8OEB	KA8OEB
COSHOCTON					
Fresno	443.5375	+	O	KB9JSC	KB9JSC
CRAWFORD					
Bucyrus	442.5250	+	88.5ae	W8DZN	W8DZN
CUYAHOGA					
Brecksville	442.6500	+	Otaz	K8IIU	B.A.R.F.
Brook Park	442.0500	+	●	WB8ZQH	WB8ZQH
Brookpark	443.1250	+	O 131.8ez	N8LXM	N8LXM
Cleveland	442.7750	+	464 (CA)lp	KF8YK	KF8YK
Cleveland	444.1000	+	O(CA)el	NA8SA	NGARC
Cleveland	444.2750	+	●l	N8OND	N8OND
Cleveland	444.3500	+	131.8e	N8OOF	OBES
Cleveland	444.7000	+	O 131.8e	WR8ABC	LEARA
Euclid	442.8125	+	131.8	N8KXX	N8KXX

Location	Output	Input	Notes	Call	Sponsor
Euclid	444.4750	+	O 110.9	N8CHM	N8CHM
Highland Hill	444.9500	+	151.4	WB8APD	SMART
Highland Hils	442.1250	+	O 82.5 (CA) elRB WX	WX8CLE	CLEWARN
HighlandHills	444.4000	+	O 131.8	WR8ABC	LEARA
N Olmsted	444.0125	+	O 131.8	W8IZ	W8IZ
N Royalton	443.1500	+	O 131.8	K8SCI	N Cst ARC
N Royalton	443.9000	+	Ot(CA)l	WA8CEW	WA8CEW
N Royalton	444.0750	+	O 6563el	K8YSE	K8YSE
Parma	442.2250	+	O(CA)elRB	KB8WLW	KB8RST
Parma	442.4500	+	O 131.8 RB	KB8WLW	KB8RST
Parma	443.8250	+	O 131.8	K8ZFR	C.A.R.S.
Parma	444.0500	+	Otel	W8DRZ	W8DRZ
Parma	444.4500	+	131.8x	W8QV	ARSC
Parma	444.7750	+	●	WR8SS	SSARS
Parma	444.9000	+	131.8	W8CJB	WR RA
Shaker Hts	443.8000	+	●	KD8LDE	KD8LDE
Shaker Hts	444.7500	+	Oa	K8ZFR	C.A.R.S.
DARKE					
Greenville	444.1750	+	O(CA)	N8OBE	N8OBE
Greenville	444.3500	+	O	N8KPJ	N8KPJ
DEFIANCE					
Defiance	442.5750	+	O 107.2	K8VON	DCARC
DELAWARE					
Delaware	443.5500	+	O 4186lpr	W8SJV	W8SJV
Powell	443.6125	+	O 103.5elp r	KI4IVP	KI4IVP
Westerville	443.2125	+	O	K8MDM	K8MDM
ERIE					
Berlin Hts	443.3500	+	lRB	WD8OCS	WD8OCS
Sandusky	442.7250	+	O(CA)e	WA8VOE	N8BPE
Sandusky	444.3750	+	O 110.9e	W8LBZ	SREL
Vermilion	443.0500	+	O 131.8	W8DRZ	W8DRZ
Wakeman	443.5250	+	●	K8KXA	K8KXA
FAIRFIELD					
Lancaster	443.8750	+	O 71.9ael	K8QIK	LanFarARC
Pickerington	443.9500	+	O	W8LAD	W8LAD
Pickerington	444.2250	+	t	K8VKA	K8VKA
FAYETTE					
Greenfield	444.7750	+	O(CA)e	N8OOB	N8OOB
Washington CH	442.0750	+	O 77.0	N8QLA	N8QLA
Washington CH	444.6125	+	Ot(CA)	N8EMZ	FayetteRA
FRANKLIN					
CanalWinchstr	443.7000	+	elp	KA8ZNY	KB8LJL
Columbus	442.6000	+	114.8	W8LT	OSUARC
Columbus	442.8000	+	O 151.4ae WX	K8NIO	K8NIO
Columbus	443.4250	+		N8RQJ	N8RQJ
Columbus	443.5250	+	Ol	WB8YOJ	WB8YOJ

Location	*Output*	*Input*	*Notes*	*Call*	*Sponsor*
Columbus	443.5750	+	Ol	WB8YOJ	WB8YOJ
Columbus	443.8125	+	t	K8MK	K8MK
Columbus	444.1000	+	Oel	WB8MMR	WB8MMR
Columbus	444.1750	+	O 82.5e	WA8PYR	WA8PYR
Columbus	444.2000	+	151.4	W8RXX	CORC
Columbus	444.2750	+	O 94.8ae	K8DDG	COARES
Columbus	444.3000	+	Oal	WB8YOJ	WB8YOJ
Columbus	444.4000	+	O	W8RW	W8RW
Columbus	444.5250	+	O 179.9ael z	K8DRE	CCRA
Columbus	444.5500	+	O 123.0ael z	N8PVC	CCRA
Columbus	444.8000	+	Oae	K8DDG	COARES
Columbus	444.8500	+	●	N8EXT	N8EXT
Columbus	444.9000	+	O	N8ADL	N8ADL
Columbus	444.9750	+	O 131.8 TT	WR8ATV	ATCO
Gahanna	442.5000	+	O	KB8SXJ	CCRA
Galloway	443.4750	+	tRB	N8IHU	N8IHU
Groveport	442.5500	+	O(CA)	WA8DNI	WA8DNI
FULTON					
Delta	444.4500	+	O 4479lpr	K8LI	K8LI
Fayette	442.0750	+	Oe	AB8RC	AB8RC
Wauseon	443.4000	+	ae	KB8MDF	KB8MDF
GALLIA					
Gallipolis	442.0000	+	O 74.4	KC8ZAB	MOVARC
GEAUGA					
Bainbridge	444.2250	+	O 131.8e	KF8YK	KF8YK
Chardon	444.5625	+	(CA)	KF8YK	KF8YK
Chardon	444.8125	+	O 131.8ae	KF8YK	KF8YK
Chesterland	444.6000	+	O 131.8l	K9IC	K9IC
Middlefield	442.2500	+	O 131.8e	KC8IBR	WRARA
Montville	443.4500	+	●	N8XUA	N8XUA
Newbury	444.6250	+	O	WB8QGR	WB8QGR
Newbury	444.9750	+		K8SGX	K8SGX
GREENE					
Bellbrook	442.6750	+	O(CA)e	W8TOG	W8TOG
Bellbrook	442.7250	+	Oae	W8GCA	GCARES
Bellbrook	443.6750	+	Oe	W8DGN	BARC
Bellbrook	444.8750	+	●(CA)	N8NQH	N8NQH
Fairborn	442.3750	+	O 118.8	K8FBN	UpVlyARC
Fairborn	442.5750	+	127.3 (CA)z	N8QBS	N8QBS
Fairborn	442.8250	+	186.2	N8QBS	N8QBS
Xenia	443.1000	+	Oaelz	N8JFA	N8JFA
Xenia	444.4375	+	O 123.0	KC8QBL	KC8QBL
GUERNSEY					
Cambridge	444.3750	+	O 91.5e	KB8ZMI	KB8ZMI
HAMILTON					
Cincinnati	442.1250	+	●RB	W8MM	W8MM
Cincinnati	442.2000	+	O(CA)l	N8JRX	WhiprSnap

Location	Output	Input	Notes	Call	Sponsor
Cincinnati	442.4750	+	O 114.8elp	KD8TE	KD8TE
Cincinnati	443.4000	+	O 123.0e	WB8CRS	Cinci FMC
Cincinnati	443.7000	+	O(CA)	W8NWS	W.A.R.N.
Cincinnati	443.9000	+	O 123.0	WR8CRA	CRA
Cincinnati	444.2250	+	O 110.9l	W8ESS	E.S.S.
Cincinnati	444.3000	+	O 118.8	KD8EYB	BCAREC
Cincinnati	444.7500	+	O(CA)l	KB8BWE	CinciUHFG
Cincinnati	444.8625	+	O	K8YOJ	HCARPSC
Colerain Twp	443.5750	+	123.0 (CA)	K8CR	K8CR
Harrison	442.8000	+	O(CA) TTe	N8WYF	N8WYF
HANCOCK					
Findlay	442.8750	+	O 100.0	N8RTN	FndlyARTS
Findlay	444.1500	+	O 88.5	W8FT	FRC
Findlay	444.5750	+	O	WB8PBR	WB8PBR
HARDIN					
Kenton	442.4000	+	O	N8MTZ	N8MTZ
HENRY					
Deshler	444.9375	+	O	KC8QYH	KC8QYH
HIGHLAND					
Hillsboro	444.6750	+	Oe	WA8KFB	HlsboroRC
HOCKING					
Logan	443.1250	+	e	K8LGN	H.V.A.R.C
HOLMES					
Millersburg	444.8750	+	131.8	KD8QGQ	HARA
HURON					
Clarksfield	442.1750	+	71.9	AL7OP	AL7OP
Greenwich	442.9000	+	Oe	KA8LKN	KA8LKN
Norwalk	442.6750	+	O 162.2a (CA)elrWXxz	KA8VDW	SREL
JACKSON					
Jackson	442.2250	+	Ol	WB8LDB	WB8LDB
Oak Hill	444.1125	+	O	K8NDM	K8NDM
JEFFERSON					
Wintersville	443.7750	+	O	WD8IIJ	WD8IIJ
KNOX					
Fredericktown	442.3250	+	O(CA)	N8NMQ	N8NMQ
Mt Vernon	442.1000	+	O 71.9el	KD8EVR	KD8EVR
Mt Vernon	444.7500	+	O	KC8YED	KC8YED
LAKE					
Eastlake	443.7000	+	O(CA)	N8KT	CLARA
Mentor-O-T-Lk	444.1875	+	(CA) WX	KF8YK	KF8YK
Painesville	444.6500	+	131.8aelz	N8BC	LCARA
Painesville	444.8625	+	OteRB	W8SKG	W8SKG
Wickliffe	444.1500	+	O(CA)l	WA8PKB	WA8PKB
Wickliffe	444.7250	+	(CA) RB	WA8PKB	WA8PKB
LAWRENCE					
Willow Wood	444.6250	+	O	W8SOE	So OH ARA
LICKING					
Amsterdam	443.9250	+	91.5e	KB8ZMI	KB8ZMI

Location	*Output*	*Input*	*Notes*	*Call*	*Sponsor*
Johnstown	442.7750	+	O 151.4	W4TLB	COARES
Newark	442.0500	+	O(CA)	WD8RVK	WD8RVK
Newark	444.5000	+	O 141.3 (CA)l	W8WRP	NARA
LOGAN					
Bellefontaine	443.0250	+	O	KA8GRP	KA8GRP
Bellefontaine	443.2500	+	O 186.2	N8IID	N8IID
Bellefontaine	443.8250	+	O 186.2ael z	W8FTV	LognCoEMA
East Liberty	444.4500	+	O 127.3771 TTelz	KA7UUC	Honda-Ame
LORAIN					
Amherst	442.5000	+	Oe	NA8VY	NA8VY
Elyria	443.9875	+	O 162.2a (CA)elrWXxz	KA8VDW	SREL
Elyria	444.1750	+	O 11 RB	KC8BED	LCARA
Elyria	444.8000	+	O 131.8	K8KRG	NOARS
Lorain	443.6000	+	Oae	WA8CAE	WA8CAE
Lorain	444.1250	+	●l	WD8CHL	WD8CHL
Lorain	444.5875	+	O 131.8ae p	N8VUB	N8VUB
N Ridgeville	444.5000	+	O 131.8	K8IC	K8IC
Wellington	444.6625	+	O	K8TV	K8TV
LUCAS					
Maumee	444.7000	+	O 103.5	W8TER	W8TER
Oregon	443.3000	+	O 103.5e	N8UAS	N8UAS
Oregon	443.7500	+	O 103.5ae	KI8CY	KI8CY
Oregon	443.9750	+	●a	KG8EE	KG8EE
Oregon	444.9250	+	O 103.5	W8MTU	LCARES
Sylvania	443.7750	+	O 103.5	KC8GWH	KC8GWH
Toledo	442.8500	+	O 103.5123 aTTez	W8HHF	TMRA
Toledo	442.9500	+	O(CA)elr WX	WJ8E	WJ8E
Toledo	444.0250	+	taers	W8MTU	LucasARES
Toledo	444.2750	+	O 107.2	W8AK	W8AK
Toledo	444.8500	+	O 103.5	N8EFJ	N8EFJ
Toledo	444.9500	+	O 103.5	N8LPQ	N8LPQ
MAHONING					
Canfield	442.7500	+	O 131.8ael z	KC8WY	KC8WY
New Springfld	443.5250	+	O	KF8YF	KF8YF
Salem	444.7625	+	O 162.2	N8TPS	N8TPS
Youngstown	443.2250	+	O 156.7a	N8FAL	#NAME?
Youngstown	443.2500	+	O	W8IZC	W8IZC
MEDINA					
Brunswick	443.0250	+	O 131.8	N8OVW	N8OVW
Brunswick	444.9250	+	O 110.9	W8EOC	M2M
Hinckley Twp	443.4250	+	O 131.8e WX	W8WGD	B.A.R.C.

OHIO

Location	*Output*	*Input*	*Notes*	*Call*	*Sponsor*
Hinkley	443.3625	+	O 131.8l	KB8WLW	KB8WLW
Medina	444.2750	+	●l	N8OND	N8OND
Medina	444.9250	+	O 131.8	W8EOC	M2M GP.
Wadsworth	442.4750	+	O 131.8	AL7OP	AL7OP
Wadsworth	444.4250	+	OaeWXz	WA8DBW	WA8DBW
West Salem	443.3000	+	O 131.8	KE8X	KE8X
MEIGS					
Pomeroy	444.0500	+	OeWX	KC8KPD	BBARC
MERCER					
Celina	442.2250	+	O 107.2107.2	W8ARG	W8ARG
Celina	443.0750	+	O 107.2 WX	KC8KVO	ACARES
Ft Recovery	442.6750	+	O 107.2ae WX	KB8SCR	KB8SCR
MIAMI					
Piqua	442.1250	+	O 123.0	N8OWV	N8OWV
Piqua	444.7250	+	4267lpr	W8AK	W8AK
Piqua	444.8375	+	O	WF8M	MVRFG
Tipp City	444.5375	+	t	N8RVS	N8RVS
Troy	442.9750	+	(CA)z	WD8CMD	WB8CMD
Troy	443.6375	+	O	KB8MUV	KB8MUV
West Milton	444.5625	+	●	N8EIO	N8EIO
MONTGOMERY					
Clayton	442.1750	+	Ote	N8PS	N8PS
Dayton	442.0000	+	O	WB8HSV	WB8HSV
Dayton	442.1000	+	O	W8BI	DARA
Dayton	442.7500	+	O 77.0	W6CDR	W6CDR
Dayton	443.0000	+	O(CA)ez	WB8SMC	FaroutARC
Dayton	443.6000	+	Oe	KB8CSL	KB8GDE
Dayton	443.7250	+	O	WB8YXD	WB8YXD
Dayton	443.7500	+	O 123.0	W8AK	W8AK
Dayton	443.7750	+	O 4267lpr	WF8M	MVRFG
Dayton	444.0500	+	O 100.0l	KA8PGJ	NationalC
Dayton	444.2125	+	●lp	WB8TIA	M V HOSP
Dayton	444.2500	+	Oe	K8MCA	MVUS
Dayton	444.7625	+	77.0 (CA)e	W8NCI	KI8FT
Englewood	443.5000	+	O 103.5	KB8ZR	3Z
Englewood	444.6000	+	O	KC8QGP	K7DN
Fairborn	444.3125	+	●(CA)l	KI6SZ	KI6SZ
Huber Heights	442.9250	+	O 4523lpr RB	W8AK	W8AK
Huber Heights	442.9500	+	O 118.8l	NO8I	HHARC
Huber Hts	444.3375	+	O	KD8IVF	KD8IVF
Kettering	444.6625	+	● 123.0 (CA)	W8GUC	W8GUC
Miamisburg	442.3000	+	O 4235 (CA)lpr	WB8VSU	WB8YXD
Miamisburg	442.4500	+	123	NV8E	NV8E

Location	Output	Input	Notes	Call	Sponsor
Miamisburg	443.2250	+	77.0 (CA)e	WC8OH	WCOARA
Miamisburg	444.7000	+	O(CA)el	N8BYT	N8BYT
Trotwood	443.9250	+	O(CA)	W8ZOL	W8ZOL
Trotwood	443.9750	+	O	W8PB	W8PB
Union	442.8500	+	Oa	WA8ZWJ	Union RC
W Carrollton	443.8500	+	O	N8ZS	N8ZS
W Carrollton	444.5000	+	Oaelz	K8ZQ	WCARG
W Carrollton	444.7875	+	O	N8ZS	N8ZS
MUSKINGUM					
Roseville	442.1750	+	O 91.5	KA8GOO	TRI CO RC
Zanesville	442.2500	+	O 91.5e	KB8ZMI	KB8ZMI
Zanesville	444.9500	+	O 91.5aex	W8TJT	W8TJT
OTTAWA					
Oak Harbor	442.2500	+	Oe	K8VXH	OttawaARC
Oak Harbor	442.4250	+	●lRB WX	KI8CY	KI8CY
Oak Harbor	443.8500	+	eWX	WB8JLT	WB8JLT
PICKAWAY					
Circleville	442.7000	+	O	KD8HIJ	KC8ITN
PIKE					
Elm Grove	442.3500	+	O	KC8BBU	KC8BBU
Lucasville	443.2000	+	114.8	KB8SDC	KB8SDC
PORTAGE					
Kent	442.0250	+	131.8	N8BHU	N8BHU
Kent	444.3000	+	131.8	N8BHU	N8BHU
Ravenna	442.8750	+	O	KB8ZHP	PortageRC
PREBLE					
Eaton	442.9000	+	173.8	KB8RQD	KB8RQD
Eaton	444.0250	+	4106elpr	W8VFR	W8VFR
Eaton	444.9125	+		N8ZRD	N8ZRD
Eaton	444.9375	+	O 4106elpr	W8VFR	W8VFR
PUTNAM					
Miller City	443.5625	+	O 107.2	NO8C	NO8C
Ottawa	442.7000	+	O	N8PCO	N8PCO
Ottawa	443.8875	+	O 107.2e	N8PFM	N8PFM
RICHLAND					
Lexington	443.2250	+	O 146.242 TT	KD8KEK	MASER
Mansfield	443.0750	+	O 151.4a (CA)elrWXxz	KA8VDW	SREL
Mansfield	443.1000	+	O 71.9	AL7OP	AL7OP
Mansfield	444.0250	+	O 71.9	W8NW	W8NW
Mansfield	444.7000	+	O 971 RB	N8DPW	ICARC
ROSS					
Bainbridge	443.6250	+	O	KD8FJH	SE OH.NET
Chillicothe	444.4250	+	O	W8BAP	SciotoARC
Londonderry	444.3500	+	O	KD8EAD	KD8EAD
SANDUSKY					
Bellevue	442.6250	+	O 110.9ael rWX	NF8E	ClydeARS

Location	Output	Input	Notes	Call	Sponsor
Fremont	443.0000	+	O 164976e	N8FIS	N8FIS
Fremont	443.4500	+	O	KC8EPF	KC8EPF
Gibsonburg	443.1875	+	107.2	KC8RCI	WD8NFQ
SCIOTO					
McDermott	443.3250	+	a	KB8RBT	KB8RBT
SENECA					
Attica	443.6750	+	OeRB	NØCZV	NØCZV
Republic	444.4375	+	O 107.2	KC8RCI	WD8NFQ
Tiffin	443.8000	+	O 107.2	K8EMR	K8EMR
Tiffin	444.8250	+	O 188650a el	W8MTD	CTS
SHELBY					
Anna	442.3500	+	Otel	KC8CFI	Honda-Ame
Ft Loramie	444.9625	+	O	KC8OIG	KC8OIG
Sidney	442.4750	+	Oe	W8JSG	W8JSG
Sidney	443.2000	+	156.7ael WXz	AA8OF	SCARES
Sidney	443.9000	+	O 156.7	N8YFM	YFMRC
Sidney	444.8875	+	O 107.2	N6JSX	N6JSX
STARK					
Alliance	442.3500	+	Oaez	W8LKY	AARC
Canton	442.0750	+	O 131.8	N8GNO	N8GNO
Canton	442.3000	+	O 131.8lx	WØOZZ	WØOZZ
Canton	443.3750	+	Oae	KB8LWP	KB8LWP
Canton	443.8500	+	Oe	W8TUY	WD8PTW
Canton	444.5750	+	O 131.8a	N8EOO	KC8GL
Massillon	442.8500	+	O 131.8ae z	W8NP	MARC
Massillon	443.6750	+	O 131.8ae RBz	WA8GXM	WA8GXM
North Canton	443.9750	+	O(CA)e	WB8AVD	WB8AVD
Uniontown	442.0000	+	Ot	WB8OVQ	WB8OVQ
Waynesburg	442.2000	+	O	KC8ONY	K8SFD
SUMMIT					
Akron	442.6000	+	O	WD8MDF	WD8MDF
Akron	442.7000	+	Oael	WB8AZP	WB8AZP
Akron	443.1125	+	(CA)	W8UPD	U/AkrnRC
Akron	444.2000	+	O 131.8 TT elRBxz	WA8DBW	WA8DBW
Akron	444.4875	+	a	KC8MXW	KC8MXW
Akron	444.5125	+	●	WB8AVD	WB8AVD
Akron	444.5500	+	●arWX	W8ODJ	N8NOQ
Cuyahoga Fls	444.8500	+	t	K8EIW	K8EIW
CuyahogaFalls	443.7875	+	OaeWXz	W8DFA	W8DFA
Fairlawn	443.7500	+	O 131.8	N8NOQ	N8NOQ
Hudson	443.4750	+	Ot(CA)z	KD8DFL	WRARG
Macedonia	443.5500	+	O 131.8	K8ICV	NERTNORTH
Norton	442.5750	+		W8MBF	AmishNERT
Norton	444.0000	+	O	WD8KNL	WD8KNL

Location	*Output*	*Input*	*Notes*	*Call*	*Sponsor*
Richfield	442.5500	+	●	N8CPI	N8CPI
Richfield	443.9250	+	O 131.8e	KA8JOY	KA8JOY
Stow	442.4250	+	O 131.8	AF1K	AF1K
TRUMBULL					
Cortland	443.8750	+	Ot	WA8ILI	WA8ILI
Cortland	444.8375	+	Oelp	WA8ILI	WA8ILI
Fowler	443.5750	+	Oel	WD8PVC	WD8PVC
Girard	443.1000	+	O	W8IZC	W8IZC
Warren	442.8250	+	131.8aer WX	W8FBE	W8FBE
Warren	443.0000	+	O(CA)e	W8VTD	WarrenARA
Warren	443.7250	+	O 131.8	N8DOD	N8DOD
TUSCARAWAS					
Uhrichsville	443.5000	+	O	K8CQA	K8CQA
UNION					
Jerome	444.1250	+	192.8lp	N8IJV	W8RW
VAN WERT					
Delphos	443.1500	+	O 107.2	KB8UDX	KB8UDX
Van Wert	442.0250	+	O 156.7	N8IHP	N8IHP
Van Wert	444.8500	+	136.5	W8FY	VWARC
VINTON					
McArthur	442.5250	+	●t(CA)l	KB8TNN	KB8TNN
WARREN					
Franklin	442.4250	+	O 77.0a (CA)e	WE8N	BEARS
Franklin	443.1500	+	O 118.8 (CA)r	WB8ZVL	WB8ZVL
Lebanon	444.1875	+	Oar	WC8EMA	WCARES
Loveland	443.8000	+	●a	WB8BFS	WB8BFS
Mason	442.2750	+	O 110.9l	W8ESS	E.S.S.
Mason	444.1500	+	O	WB8WFG	WB8WFG
Mason	444.9500	+	O 131.8ae	W8SAI	W8SAI
Morrow	444.6250	+	O 123.0	N8GCI	N8GCI
WASHINGTON					
Constitution	444.1000	+	te	N8ILO	N8ILO
Marietta	442.6000	+	taRB	W8JL	KC8GF
Marietta	442.9000	+	●alp	W8JL	W8JL
Marietta	443.0500	+	O 186.2el RB	W8JTW	W8JTW
Marietta	443.4000	+	91.5al	W8HH	M.A.R.C.
Marietta	444.0000	+	Ol	WD8BRZ	WD8BRZ
Marietta	444.9250	+	O 146.2	N8MDG	N8MDG
WAYNE					
Doylestown	442.2750	+	O 110.9el	W8WKY	SlvrckARA
Rittman	442.3750	+	●	N8CD	SARTECH
Wooster	443.1750	+	O(CA)	W8WOO	WARC
Wooster	443.4000	+	Otlp	K8WAY	K8WAY
Wooster	444.2500	+	O 131.8e	WB8VPG	WAYNE ARG

Location	Output	Input	Notes	Call	Sponsor
WILLIAMS					
Bryan	444.4000	+	O 107.2	N8VO	N8VO
WOOD					
Bowling Green	442.1250	+	O 67.0	K8TIH	WoodCoARC
Bowling Green	443.5125	+	O 103.5	KD8BTI	WCARES
Bowling Green	444.4750	+	O 67.0ae	K8TIH	WCARC
Perrysburg	444.6500	+	Oa	KB8YVY	KA8WPC
OKLAHOMA					
LAWTON/ALTUS					
Altus	442.0500	+	O 100/100 E-SUN WX	WX5ASA	ALTUS SKYW
Headrick	444.1000	+	Ot	WD5BBN	------------
Hollis	442.0250	+	O 100/100 WX	WX5ASA	ALTYSA SKY
Lawton	443.6000	+	O 123/123	N5PLV	N5PLV
Lawton	443.8500	+	Ot	W5KS	LFSARC
Lawton	444.9000	+	O 118.8/118.8 E-SUN	K5VHF	K5VHF
Medicine Park	442.1750	+	● 123/123	WJ5G	WJ5G
Medicine Park	444.0750	+	O 123/123 E-SUN	WX5LAW	LIRA
NORTHEAST					
Bartlesville	442.1750	447.1720	O 88.5/88.5	W5RAB	W5RAB
Bartlesville	443.1250	+	O 88.5/88.5	KB5KZS	KB5KZS
Bartlesville	444.4250	+	O 88.5/88.5 L(443.850)sWX	W5IAS	W5RAB/TARC
Bartlesville	444.7750	+	O 88.5/88.5 E-SUNsLITZ WXx	W5NS	BARC
Blackwell	444.9500	+	OE-SUN	KD5MTT	OIDAR
Hichita	444.6000	+	O 88.5/88.5 WX	W5IAS	TULSA ARC
Ketchum	444.8750	+	O 88.5/88.5 WX	W5RAB	W5RAB
Muskogee	443.1000	+	O 88.5/88.5	W5IAS	WA5VMS/TAR
Okmulgee	444.8250	+	OtE-SUN	W5KO	W5KO
Pawhuska	444.9750	+	O 167.9/167.9	W5IRAB	W5RAB
Ponca City	444.6000	+	O	W5RAB	270 GROUP
Ponca City	444.7000	+	Ot	W5HZZ	KAY COUNTY
Pryor	444.6750	+	O 88.5/88.5 E-SUN	WB5Y	WB5Y
Skiatook	442.1750	+	Ot	W5RAB	W5RAB
Skiatook	444.7250	+	Ot	WA5LVT	TRO INC
Stillwater	442.6000	+	O 103.5/103.5	K5FVL	K5FVL
Stillwater	443.8750	+	OtE-SUN	W5YJ	OSU ARC
Stillwater	444.4750	+	O 100/100 E-SUN	K5FVL	K5FVL

Location	Output	Input	Notes	Call	Sponsor
Stillwater	444.5250	+	O 88.5/88.5 E-SUN WXx	K5FVL	K5FVL/TARC
Stillwater	444.9000	+	O 141.3/141.3 E-SUN WXx	K5FVL	K5FVL
Tahlequah	442.2250	+	O 88.5/88.5 WX	N5ROX	EMERG NET/
Vinita	444.3750	+	O 88.5/88.5 E-SUN	KC5VVT	NORA
NORTHWEST					
Alva	443.4500	+	O 103.5/103.5 WXx	KCØGEV	GSPARC
Alva	444.9000	+	O 103.5/103.5 WXx	W5ALZ	GSPARC
Blanchard	444.6250	+	O 127.3/127.3 E-SUN WX	W5LHG	------------
Buffalo	442.0750	+	O 131.8/131.8 E-SUN E-WIND WXx	W5HFZ	GBARG
Camp Houston	442.0500	+	O 131.8/131.8 E-SUN E-WINDsWXx	W5HFZ	GBARG
Enid	443.0000	+	Ot	WD5GUG	WD5GUG
Enid	443.2000	+	Ot	WD5GUG	WD5GUG
Enid	444.4000	+	Ot	WA5QYE	ENID ARC
Enid	444.8250	+	Ot	N5LWT	N5LWT
Fairview	444.7250	+	Ot	N5RHO	N5RHO
Guthrie	443.2500	+	O 88.5/88.5 WXx	W5IAS	TULSA ARC
Guymon	444.9750	+	O 88.5/88.5 E-SUNx	N5DFQ	DBARC
Kingfisher	444.9750	+	OtE-SUN WX	W5GLD	W5GLD
Lindsay	444.8750	+	O 131.8/131.8	N5RAK	KE5KK
Mooreland	444.2750	+	Ot	K5GUD	K5GUD
Mooreland	444.6750	+	O 103.5/103.5 E-SUNsWXx	K5GUD	TSARG
Perry	442.9250	+	O 141.3/141.3 E-SUN WX	KL7MA	NCRG
Pond Creek	442.3000	+	O 141.3/141.3 E-SUN	KW5FAA	MMACARC/SW
Seiling	444.9250	+	O 103.5/103.5 E-SUNsLITZx	W5OKT	TSARG
Seward	442.0750	+	O	KA5LSU	KA5LSU
Vici	444.9500	+	O 88.5/88.5 WX	N5WO	WX WATCH
Woodward	442.2000	+	O 88.5/88.5 WX	N5DFQ	DBARC
Woodward	444.8750	+	O 103.5/103.5 E-SUNsWXx	K5GUD	TSARG

Location	Output	Input	Notes	Call	Sponsor
OKLAHOMA CITY METRO					
Bethany	442.8500	+	O 103.5/103.5 E-SUN	N6USR	N5USR
Bethany	444.0500	+	O 192.8/192.8	WA5CZN	BOJIVE RN
Del City	443.3000	+	O 162.2/162.2	W5DEL	DEL CITY A
Del City	444.0000	+	O 141.3/141.3	KX5RW	WR5G
Edmond	442.2250	+	O 131.8/131.8 E-SUN	K5CPT	L & M RADI
Edmond	443.1500	+	O 179.9/179.9	N5TWC	KC5GEP
Edmond	443.4250	+	O 88.5/88.5	K5EOK	EARS
Elreno	442.2500	+	O 141.3/141.3	K5OL	K5OL
Elreno	444.2500	+	Ot	W5ELR	ERARC
Newcastle	444.6750	+	O 141.3/141.3 E-SUN	KB5LSB	KB5LSB
Norman	442.1250	+	O 107.2/107.2	WA5LKS	WA5LKS
Norman	443.7000	+	O 141.3/141.3	W5NOR	SCARS
Norman	444.3500	+	O 141.3/141.3 E-SUN	N5KUK	N5KUK
Oklahoma City	442.1500	+	O 141.3/141.3	KE5IOB	KOKH FOX
Oklahoma City	442.5000	+	● 203.5/203.5 E-SUN	N5KNU	N5KNU
Oklahoma City	442.5750	+	O 131.8/131.8	AD5RM	AD5RM
Oklahoma City	442.6250	+	O 146.2/146.2 EXP	WD5AII	EARC
Oklahoma City	442.7000	+	O 141.3/141.3	W5PAA	MMACARC
Oklahoma City	442.7750	+	O 141.3/141.3 E-SUN	KK5FM	------------
Oklahoma City	443.0500	+	O 100/100	W5RLW	W5RLW
Oklahoma City	443.1000	+	O/100	WN5J	WN5J
Oklahoma City	443.2750	+	O 141.3/141.3	W5MEL	OCAPA
Oklahoma City	444.1000	+	O 141.3/141.3 E-SUN	W5PAA	MMACARC
Oklahoma City	444.2000	+	O 167.9/167.9 E-SUN	WD5AII	EDMOND ARC
Oklahoma City	444.2250	+	O 141.3/141.3 E-SUN LITZ WX	WX5OKC	ODCEM
Oklahoma City	444.3000	+	O 141.3/141.3 E-SUN	W5MEL	OCAPA

Location	*Output*	*Input*	*Notes*	*Call*	*Sponsor*
Oklahoma City	444.6750	+	O	KB5LSB	KB5LSB
Seward	444.7750	+	O 141.3/141.3 E-SUN	KK5FM	KK5FM
The Village	443.4000	+	O 141.3/141.3	KB5QND	KB5QND
SOUTHEAST					
Ada	443.8000	+	O 114.8/114.8	WB5NBA	ADA ARC
Antlers	444.2000	+	O 88.5/88.5 E-SUNx	KD5DAR	KD5DAR
Antlers	444.9250	+	O 114.8/114.8 E-SUN	KI5KC	KI5KC
Cavanal Mtn	444.5000	+	O 88.5/88.5 E-SUNsLITZ WXx	W5ANR	FSAARC
Clarita	442.0250	+	O 114.8/114.8	KF5IUL	------------
Daisy	442.4000	+	O 88.5/88.5 WX	W5CUQ	PCARC/TARC
Durant	444.1250	+	O 114.8/114.8	AB5CC	AB5CC
Enterprise	442.1000	+	O 123/123 E-SUN	KA5HET	KA5HET
Enterprise	444.6250	+	O 88.5/88.5 WX	W5CUQ	PCARC/TARC
Kingston	443.4500	449.4500	O 127.3/127.3	N4SME	NTXRA
McAlester	444.9750	+	O 88.5/88.5 WXx	W5CUQ	PCARC/TARC
Nashoba	442.9000	+	O 114.8/114.8 E-SUN E-WIND	KM5VK	KM5VK
Pocola	444.0250	+	O	KB5SWA	KB5SWA
Purcell	444.5500	+	O 141.3/141.3	W5IF	W5IF
Seminole	444.8000	+	O 107.2/107.2	WJ5F	WJ5F
SOUTHWEST					
Arbuckle Mtns	443.0750	+	●tE-SUNs WXx	WG5B	WG5B
Ardmore	444.0750	+	OE-SUN WXx	KE5BAL	KE5BAL
Blanchard	442.0000	+	O 141.3/141.3	WØDXA	WØDXA
Bridge Creek	445.4700	445.4700	●t	WA7WNM	KS5B
Cement	444.4000	+	O 141.3/141.3 E-SUN	KW5FAA	MMACARC/SW
Cement	444.4500	+	O 123/123 E-SUN	WX5LAW	LIRA
Cyrill	442.2750	+	O 123/123 E-SUN WX	KB5LLI	SWIRA

Location	Output	Input	Notes	Call	Sponsor
Davis	443.0000	+	O 100/100	KC5LBP	KC5LBP
Duncan	444.8250	+	O 118.8/118.8 E-SUN	WD5IYF	CTARC
Grandfield	442.2000	+	O 123/123	WX5LAW	LIRA
Granite	442.0750	+	O 141.3/141.3 E-SUN	K5XTL	K5XTL
Granite	442.3000	+	O 162.2/162.2 DCS(712) E-SUN LITZ WX	K5GSM	K5GSM
Granite	444.6500	+	O 100/100 WX	WX5ASA	ALTUS SKYW
Headrick	443.3000	+	O 123/123	WX5LAW	LIRA
Lawton	444.6000	+	O 123/123	N5PLV	N5PLV
Lawton	444.7000	+	Ot	KD5IAE	SWAN
Oklahoma City	444.8500	+	O 141.3/141.3 E-SUN	KW5FAA	MMACARC/SW
TULSA METRO					
Broken Arrow	444.0000	+	OtE-SUN	W5DRZ	BAARC
Broken Arrow	444.5750	+	O	KC5JKU	KC5JKU 8 K
Claremore	442.0750	+	O 88.5/88.5 E-SUN	WB5Y	WB5Y
Claremore	444.3500	+	OE-SUN	KC5ARC	RCWA
Jenks	442.0500	+	O 88.5/88.5	NO5R	NO5R
Mannford	442.0000	+	O 88.5/88.5 eWX	W5IAS	TULSA ARC
Owasso	444.3000	+	Ot	K5LAD	K5LAD
Tulsa	443.8500	+	O 88.5/88.5 E-SUNrsWXx	W5IAS	TARC
Tulsa	444.9500	+	O 88.5/88.5 E-SUNr	WA5LVT	TRO INC

OREGON

Location	Output	Input	Notes	Call	Sponsor
CENTRAL WILLAMETTE VALLEY					
Albany	442.8500	+	O 167.9e	KA7ENW	ELRA
Albany	444.9750	+	O 100	KD6VLR	KD6VLR
Aumsville	440.7250	+	O 100e	WO7Z	WO7Z
Corvallis	440.4250	+	O 100e	K7TVL	K7TVL
Corvallis	442.3000	+	O 162.2e	N8GFO	BCARES
Cottage Grove	440.8750	+	O 293ael	WB7LCS	WB7LCS
Eagle Crest	442.5000	+	O 100e	KE7DLA	KE7DLA
Eugene	440.5750	+	O 293ael	WB7LCS	WB7LCS
Lyons	440.6000	+	O 100e	WO7Z	WO7Z
Myrtle Creek	444.1500	+	O 186.2e	KC7UAV	WA6KHG
Oakridge	441.6750	+	O 100ael	K7UND	K7UND
Roseburg	440.6250	+	O 114.8e	WA7JAW	WA7JAW
Salem	440.0750	+	Oel	N7PIR	N7PIR
Salem	440.2750	+	OTT	AC7RF	AC7RF
Salem	441.3750	+	O	AB7F	AB7F
Salem	441.7000	+	O 186.2	KC7NOS	KC7NOS
Salem	443.4500	+	Oe	KC7CFS	KC7CFS

Location	Output	Input	Notes	Call	Sponsor
Salem	444.9500	+	O 100els	K7LWV	WA7ABU
Silverton	444.2500	444.9500	O 100e	W7SAA	W7SAA
Sisters	441.6250	+	O 100el	K7UND	K7UND
Walton	443.0500	+	O 162.2e	W7SLA	W7SLA
CENTRAL-EAST					
Bend	442.1250	+	O 123el	K7UND	K7UND
Bend	443.0500	+	O 162.2ae	KB7LNR	KB7LNR
Bend	443.6500	+	O 162.2e	KB7LNR	KB7LNR
Bend	444.2500	+	O 103.5e	W7JVO	HIDARG
Bend	444.7500	+	O 156.7e	W7JVO	HIDARG
COAST-CENTRAL					
Florence	442.5750	+	O 100e	W7FLO	OCERI
Hebo	440.9000	+	O 118.8elr sWX	W7GC	OCRG
Lincoln City	443.7500	+	O 118.8e	W7CG	OCRG
Newport	444.7500	+	O 118.8elr sWX	W7CG	OCRG
COAST-NORTH					
Astoria	440.9250	+	O 100e	N7BAG	N7BAG
Hebo	441.2500	+	O	W7LI	W7LI
Hebo	441.3000	+	O	KD7YPY	KD7YPY
Manzanita	440.1750	+	O 100e	KD7YPY	KD7YPY
Manzanita	444.4250	+	O 107.2e	W7MOC	W7MOC
Rockaway Beach	442.7500	+	O 118.8e	W7GC	OCRG
Tillamook	440.5250	+	O 100e	KD7YPY	KD7YPY
COAST-SOUTH					
Brookings	444.0000	+	O 100e	K6JSI	K6JSI
Coos Bay	440.8000	+	O 103.5e	WA7JAW	WA7JAW
Coos Bay	442.0750	+	O 77ael	W7EXH	W7EXH
Coos Bay	443.1250	+	Ote	W7OC	SWORA
Florence	444.4000	+	O	W7OC	SWORA
Myrtle Point	444.1750	+	O	W7OC	SWORA
Port Orford	440.7250	+	O 114.8e	KD7IOP	WA7JAW
COLUMBIA RIVER GORGE					
Mosier	442.5750	+	Oe	KC7UNO	KC7UNO
The Dalles	444.7000	+	O 100e	KF7LN	KF7LN
NORTH CENTRAL					
Corvalis	441.9750	+	O 100e	W7CQZ	W7CQZ
NORTH COAST					
Astoria	444.5000	+	O 100e	N7BAG	N7BAG
NORTH EAST OREGON					
Huntington	444.1500	+	O 100 (CA) el	K7OJI	TVRA
NORTH WILLAMETTE VALLEY					
Boring	441.9500	+	O 100e	KD7TFZ	KD7TFZ
Canby	442.9000	+	O 123e	WB7QAZ	WB7QAZ
Cottage Grove	441.6500	+	O 100el	K7THO	K7THO
Estacada	440.8500	+	O 107.2l	KD7DEG	KD7DEG
Forest Grove	442.3250	+	O 100 (CA) e	K7RPT	ARRG

Location	Output	Input	Notes	Call	Sponsor
McMinnville	441.7250	+	O 127.3e	W7TRP	W7TRP
McMinnville	441.8000	+	O 100el	W7YAM	YCARES
Newberg	441.8750	+	O 100el	AH6LE	AH6LE
Newberg	442.7250	+	O	N7ASM	PMRA
Newberg	444.3000	+	O 127.3	K7WWG	K7WWG
Portland	443.5500	+	O 100e	KC7TP	K7GDS
Sandy	442.4250	+	O 100e	KD7TFZ	KD7TFZ
Sandy	442.7000	+	O 100	K7LTA	K7LTA
NORTHEAST					
Spout Springs	444.7250	+	O 100e	K7EI	K7EI
Vale	442.3500	+	O 110.9e	W7PAG	W7PAG
Weston	444.6500	+	O	N7DWC	N7DWC
NORTHWEST					
Banks	440.8750	+	O 103.5	KC7UQB	KC7UQB
NW OREGON & SW WASHINGTON					
Aloha	442.5250	+	O 107.2el	KA7OSM	WORC
Astoria	440.8250	+	O 118.8e	N7HQR	W7GC
Colton	442.9250	+	O 107.2ael sWX	WB7DZG	WORC
Colton	443.7000	+	O 103.5e	N7PIR	N/A
Newberg	443.4250	+	O 107.2el	KR7IS	WORC
Portland	440.2000	+	O 100e	N7BAR	N7BAR
Portland	443.0500	+	O 123e	WA7BND	WA7BND
Timber	441.8250	+	O 107.2ael sWX	KJ7IY	WORC
OREGON COAST-NORTH					
Seaside	443.8750	+	O 100l	N7PIR	N7PIR
OREGON COAST-SOUTH					
Brookings	444.9750	+	O 131.8e	KA7GNK	WA7JAW
Myrtle Point	444.5250	+	O 123e	WA7JAW	WA7JAW
PORTLAND METRO					
Aloha	442.0500	+	●	K7WWG	K7WWG
Aloha	443.0250	+	O 146.2	WN7VHF	WN7VHF
Aloha	443.3500	+	O 156.7	NM7B	NM7B
Beaver Creek	440.9500	+	O 100e	KE7AVI	KE7FBE
Beaverton	444.7500	+	O 123e	WB7CRT	WB7CRT
Gresham	441.6250	+	O 146.2e	KW7HAM	KD6KPC
Gresham	442.6250	+	O	WB7SKD	IRRA
Hillsboro	443.6500	+	Oel	K7AUO	TERAC
Hillsboro	444.9750	+	O 107.2e	K7CPU	IEARS
North Plains	442.8250	+	O 110.9e	NA7A	NA7A
Oregon City	440.0500	+	Oe	WB7QFD	HCARC
Oregon City	442.0750	+	O 103.5e	KD7LNB	OC RACES
Portland	440.3000	+	Oe	KC7MZM	KC7MZM
Portland	440.3500	+	127.3 (CA)z	KB7OYI	KB7OYI
Portland	440.4000	+	O 123elx	W7RAT	W7RAT
Portland	440.4500	+	O 103.5el	N7PIR	K7QDX
Portland	440.6250	+	O	KB7WIQ	KB7WIQ
Portland	440.8250	+	O 107.2e	KF7JJN	K7LHS

Location	*Output*	*Input*	*Notes*	*Call*	*Sponsor*
Portland	442.0250	+	O 100 (CA) ez	N7NLL	N7NLL
Portland	442.2250	+	O 100 (CA) ex	K7RPT	ARRG
Portland	442.8000	+	O 123e	W7EXH	W7EXH
Portland	443.1500	+	O 107.2ael sWX	KJ7IY	WORC
Portland	443.4750	+	O 167.9e	WB7QIW	HARC
Portland	443.8500	+	O 107.2e	KB7OYI	KB7OYI
Portland	444.5750	+	O 167.9	KGØD	KGØD
Sandy	442.8750	+	O 107.2ael sWX	KJ7IY	WORC
Sandy	443.2500	+	Oel	W7RY	W7RY
Scholls	442.1500	+	O	KB7PSM	IRRA
Sherwood	442.6750	+	O 100e	AH6LE	AH6LE
Tigard	440.1000	+	O 162.2e	K7ICY	K7ICY
Timberline	444.2250	+	O 100el	K7RPT	ARRG
West Linn	441.6500	+	O 107.2e	WA7DRO	WA7DRO
West Linn	443.0500	+	O 123e	WA7BND	WA7BND
Wilsonville	444.9000	+	O 100e	KD7OFU	WARES
SOUTH CENTRAL					
Ashland	442.3000	+	O 123el	K7VTL	K7TVL
Cave Junction	442.8250	+	O 203.5e	K7TVL	K7TVL
Central Point	443.1500	+	O 131.8e	KL7VK	KL7VK
Crescent	443.3750	+	O 100el	K7TVL	K7TVL
Keno	440.6750	+	O 173.8el	K7TVL	K7TVL
Klamath Falls	443.9000	+	O(CA)elz	KE7CSD	KBRA
Klamath Falls	444.0000	+	Oe	K7DXV	KA7DZI
Rogue River	440.8500	+	O 100e	K7TVL	K7TVL
Wolf Creek	444.5000	+	O 173.8e	K7TVL	K7TVL
SOUTH CENTRAL OREGON					
Keno	442.5250	+	esRBx	KD7TNG	KD7TNG
SOUTH WEST OREGON					
Colton	440.2500	+	Oe	W7OTV	N/A
Roseburg	440.3000	+	O 88.5e	WB6MFV	N/A
Roseburg	441.8750	+	O 186.2e	WB6MFV	WB6MFV
SOUTH WILLAMETTE VALLEY					
Blue River	442.0750	442.0750	O 100ael	W7EXH	W7EXH
Blue River	443.1000	+	O 100	K7SLA	W7ZQD
Cottage Grove	443.0250	+	O 156.7e	K7SLA	W7ZQE
Eugene	442.1250	+	O 100e	K7THO	K7THO
Eugene	442.9000	+	Oe	W7EXH	W7EXH
Eugene	443.2750	+	O 100	W7EXH	W7EXH
Eugene	443.5000	+	O 100e	W7EXH	W7EXH
Roseburg	441.8500	+	O 100e	K7TVL	K7TVL
Saginaw	440.1000	+	●	W7EXH	W7EXH
SOUTHEAST					
Applegate	444.9750	447.9750	O 100e	K7TVL	K7TVL
Gilbert Peak	444.5500	+	O 173.8e	K7TVL	K7TVL

Location	Output	Input	Notes	Call	Sponsor
Phoenix	444.7500	+	O 100e	K7TVL	K7TVL
SOUTHWEST					
Ashland	440.7000	+	O 162.2es	WX7MFR	NWSJAWS
Central Point	444.1000	+	Ol	W9PCI	W9PCI
Grants Pass	440.5500	+	O 173.8	K7TVL	RVLA
Jacksonville	444.2000	+	O	W9PCI	W9PCI
Jacksonville	444.3000	+	Oael	W9PCI	W9PCI
Rogue River	444.8250	+	O 100e	K7TVL	RVLA

PENNSYLVANIA

Location	Output	Input	Notes	Call	Sponsor
FREQUENCY USAGE - ALL WPA SECTION					
Mobile Repeaters	446.4000	446.4000		CROSS-BAND	
Mobile Repeaters	446.4250	446.4250		CROSS-BAND	
Mobile Repeaters	446.4500	446.4500		CROSS-BAND	
Mobile Repeaters	446.4750	446.4750		CROSS-BAND	
Mobile Repeaters	446.5000	446.5000		CROSS-BAND	
Mobile Repeaters	446.5250	446.5250		CROSS-BAND	
Mobile Repeaters	446.5500	446.5500		CROSS-BAND	
Mobile Repeaters	446.5750	446.5750		CROSS-BAND	
Mobile Repeaters	446.6000	446.6000		CROSS-BAND	
WPA SNP	442.0000	+		SNP	
WPA SNP	442.0250	+		SNP	
ADAMS					
BigFlatSoMt	443.0500	+	Ot	W3BD	KRAP
Biglerville	443.1000	+	O 103.5 (CA)elr	W3KGN	ACARS
ALTOONA 123.0					
Altoona	442.1000	+		NU3T	BKRA
Altoona	444.6000	+	O 123.0ae	W3VO	HARC
Carrolltown	443.5250	+	107.2l	KC3DES	CCDES
BEAVER 131.8					
Beaver	442.4500	+	ael	KA3IRT	KA3IRT
Beaver Falls	442.9750	+	100.0	W3SGJ	B.V.A.R.A.
Fombell	443.6250	+	O	N3ZJM	------------
Freedom	444.2500	+	O	N3TN	TAARA
Rochester	443.8250	+	O	KA3RFA	KA3RFA
BERKS					
Earlville	443.5500	+	O 131.8e	K3ZMC	PART
Pottstown	442.7500	+	O 141.3e	KI3I	------------
Reading	444.3500	+	O 114.8a	K3TI	DDXA
Reading	449.6250	–	O 114.8el	K3CX	------------
Texter Mt	449.0750	–	O 131.8e	N3SWH	SPARK
BRADFORD					
Sylvania	442.9000	+	O 131.8 (CA)elRB	N3KZ	UPenn ARC
Towanda	444.2500	+	O 151.4e	WA3GGS	------------
Troy	444.0500	+	O 100 (CA) LITZ WX	KB3DOL	------------

Location	Output	Input	Notes	Call	Sponsor
BUCKS					
Bensalem	444.2000	+	O 131.8 (CA)lrsRB WX	W3BXW	BEARS
Fairless Hills	447.1250	–	O(CA) DCS lrsRB WX	WA3BXW	BEARS
Hilltown	442.9000	+	O 123e	W3HJ	HighpointRA
Plumstead	449.7250	–	O 136.5ers	K3BUX	UpperBucksRC
Plumsteadville	447.9750	–	O 131.8 (CA)e	KB3AJF	------------
Quakertown	443.2000	+	O 114.8 (CA)e	WA3KEY	BLURA
Southampton	448.2250	–	O 131.8rs	W3SK	PWA
Springtown	442.9500	+	O 131.8 (CA)elrsRB WX	W3BXW	BEARS
Warminster	443.9500	+	O 131.8 (CA)ers	K3DN	WARC
CARBON					
Lake Harmony	442.1000	+	O 131.8 (CA)elRB	N3KZ	UPenn ARC
Nesquehoning	447.6250	–	O 103.5 (CA)	N3REA	------------
Palmerton	449.3750	–	O 100ers	W3EPE	EPAD2
White Bear	449.4750	–	O 103.5a	AA3TL	------------
CENTRAL 173.8/123.0					
Pennfield	442.3500	+	Oer	N3RZL	ElkOES
Philipsburg	444.7500	+	O 173.8e	W3PHB	PARA
Reedsville	443.5500	+	Oa	KA3ANJ	JMRA
Ridgway	442.2000	+	O	N3RZL	ElkOES
Rossiter	444.5750	+		N3FXN	N3FXN
State College	442.3000	+	O(CA)l	N3KZ	WN3A
State College	443.6500	+	O(CA)e	K3CR	PSARC
State College	444.7000	+	O	N3EB	N3EB
CHESTER					
Bucktown	446.1750	–	O 100aelrs LITZ WX	W3EOC	CCAR
Cochranville	449.6750	–	O 94.8 (CA) RB	WB3LGG	------------
Honeybrook	447.1250	–	O 131.8 (CA)elrsRB WX	W3BXW	BEARS
New London	448.9750	–	O 107.2	KB3DRX	------------
Oxford	448.8750	–	O 100aelrs WX	W3EOC	CCAR
Paoli	445.6750	–	O 131.8 (CA)el	WB3JOE	MARC
Thorndale	447.0750	–	O 123 (CA) LITZ	AA3VI	------------
Valley Forge	443.8000	+	O 131.8 (CA)elRB	N3KZ	UPenn ARC
Valley Forge	443.9000	+	O	W3PHL	PARA Group

Location	Output	Input	Notes	Call	Sponsor
West Chester	446.5250	–	O 100elrs LITZ WX	W3EOC	CCAR
CUMBERLAND					
Harrisburg	442.4500	+	O 131.8 (CA)elRB WX	W3BXW	BEARS
Mechanicsburg	443.3000	+	O 67ers	N3TWT	SMRA
Mt Holly Springs	444.3000	+	O 127.3e	KB3HJC	------------
Summerdale	442.2000	+	O 131.8 (CA)lRB	N3KZ	UPenn ARC
DAUPHIN					
Harrisburg	444.4500	+	O 123 (CA) r	W3ND	CPRA Inc
Harrisburg	448.0750	–	O 123er	W3ND	CPRA Inc.
Hershey	449.9250	–	O 123eWX	KA3RMP	------------
DELAWARE					
Darby	444.0500	+	O 131.8 (CA)elsRB	W3UER	DCARA
Deepwater	446.9250	–	O 173.8elr sEXP	KA3TWG	Penn-Del
Lawrence Park	447.3750	–	O 100lWX	W3DI	M-N ARC
Newtown Square	442.2500	+	O 131.8 (CA)l	W3DI	M-N ARC
Newtown Square	442.6000	+	O 131.8 (CA)l	WA3NNA	------------
ERIE 186.2					
Cherry Hill	444.9250	+	Oelx	N8XUA	N8XUA
Corry	444.8000	+	ar	W3YXE	RACorry
Erie	444.5000	+	O	KA3MJN	KA3MJN
Erie	444.8750	+	O 186.2aer s	W3ERC	RAE
Meadville	444.0750	+	O	W3MIE	C.A.R.S.
Union City	443.5000	+	O	N3UBZ	N3UBZ
JOHNSTOWN 123.0					
Johnstown	442.8250	+	110.9l	KC3DES	CCDES
LACKAWANNA					
Scranton	442.5500	+	O 100erWX	N3FCK	------------
Scranton	448.8250	–	O 136.5ar WX	N3EVW	------------
LANCASTER					
Cornwall	442.1500	+	O 131.8 (CA)elrsRB WX	W3BXW	BEARS
Cornwall	447.9250	–	O 82.5l	K3LV	LVSRA
Cornwall	449.0250	–	O 162.2	W3AD	LRTS
Ephrata	444.6500	+	O 131.8 (CA)eBI	W3XP	EphrataARS
Holtwood	448.6250	–	O 114.8el RB	N3TPL	------------
Lancaster	446.4750	–	O 94.8elrs EXP WX	N3FYI	RVARG

Location	*Output*	*Input*	*Notes*	*Call*	*Sponsor*
Lancaster	449.2250	–	O 131.8e LITZ	KA3CNT	R.H.R.A.
Lancaster	449.3250	–	O 173.8ael	KA3CNT	R.H.R. Assoc
Lancaster	449.5750	–	O 114.8e	W3RRR	R.R.R.A.
Manheim	443.2500	+	O 114.8aer sWX	K3IR	SPARC Inc.
Manheim	449.9750	–	O 114.8aer sWX	K3IR	SPARC Inc.
Quarryville	448.1750	–	O 94.8	N3EIO	KC3LE
LEBANON					
Eagles Peak	442.4000	+	O 131.8 (CA)lRB	N3KZ	UPenn ARC
Grantville	448.2250	–	O 192.8e	AA3RG	A.A.R.G.
Lebanon	447.6750	–	O 82.5ers RB	K3LV	LVSRA
Schaefferstown	448.9250	–	Ote	N3JOZ	------------
LEHIGH					
Allentown	443.3500	+	O 100ersBI LITZ	N3XG	EPA D2
Allentown	443.5000	+	O 156.7 (CA)e	N3HES	------------
Allentown	444.1000	+	O 151.4ers	KA3NRJ	KeystoneRG
Allentown	444.1500	+	O 131.8 (CA)elRB	N3KZ	UPenn ARC
Allentown	448.7750	–	O 131.8e RB	N3MFT	------------
Center Valley	444.3000	+	O 179.9a	W3LR	NLCRA
Coopersburg	443.5900	+	O 151.4e	W3LR	------------
Coopersburg	449.2750	–	O 151.4l	W3LR	NLCRA
Ironton	449.8750	–	O 131.8	KA3ZAT	------------
Slatington	447.7250	–	O 131.8 (CA)elrsRB WX	W3BXW	BEARS
LUZERNE					
Berwick	447.9250	–	O 74.4	N3OAP	BARS
Dallas	449.2750	–	O 151.4	W3LR	------------
Hazleton	449.4250	–	O 103.5e RB	W3HZL	A.R.A.
Jenkins Twp	443.6000	+	O 82.5	W3LR	------------
Wilkes-Barre	442.2000	+	O 131.8 (CA)lRB	N3KZ	UPenn ARC
Wilkes-Barre	443.4000	+	O 77 (CA)el	WX3N	------------
Wilkes-Barre	449.8250	–	O 82.5elrs WX	WB3FKQ	------------
LYCOMING					
Montoursville	443.5000	+	● 167.9ers WX	KB3DXU	LycCoEMA
Williamsport	443.0500	+	O 167.9 (CA)e	N3SSL	------------
Williamsport	443.2000	+	O 77 (CA)el	WX3N	------------

Location	*Output*	*Input*	*Notes*	*Call*	*Sponsor*
Williamsport	444.0000	+	O	W3AVK	WestBranch
MONROE					
Camelback Mtn	442.5000	+	O 131.8 (CA)elRB	N3KZ	UPenn ARC
Camelback Mtn	444.4500	+	O 131.8 (CA)elrsRB WX	W3BXW	BEARS
Long Pond	448.2750	–	O 131.8 (CA)e	N3BUB	------------
Long Pond	448.4750	–	O 123el LITZ	N3VAE	------------
Pohopoco Mtn	445.3750	–	O 131.8el WX	K4MTP	------------
Ross Twp	446.2250	–	O 131.8el	N3TXG	------------
Wooddale	448.3750	–	O 91.5 (CA) e	N3JNZ	------------
MONTGOMERY					
Eagleville	449.9250	–	O 100	K3CX	------------
Green Lane	449.1250	–	O 88.5elrs WX	AA3E	Montco OEP
Horsham	444.5500	+	O 100	WA3TSW	------------
Meadowbrook	443.1500	+	O 131.8 (CA)elWX	WA3UTI	HRH-ARC
Norristown	448.6750	–	O 131.8 (CA)	N3CB	------------
UpperPotsgrove	445.8250	–	O 156.7ael RB LITZ WX	W3PS	METRO-COMM
NORTH CENTRAL 173.8					
Bradford	444.4000	+	O 173.8e	KD3IJ	KD3IJ
Clearfield	444.6250	+	O	K3EDD	K3EDD
Coudersport	443.3000	+	O	KB3EAR	KB3EAR
Kane	443.0250	+		WB3IGM	------------
Ludlow	442.7750	+	Oel	WJ8G	------------
Rockton	443.4750	+	O	N5NWC	N5NWC
Russell	444.4750	+	Oe	W3GFD	W3GFD
Sigel	443.2750	+	Oe	N3GPM	N3GPM
St Marys	443.6750	+	O	WA8RZR	------------
NORTHAMPTON					
Bangor	447.2250	–	O 131.8 (CA)elLITZ	N3TXG	------------
Little Offset	448.5250	–	O 131.8e	KA2QEP	------------
Nazareth	443.4500	+	O 127.3	KB3KKZ	------------
Northampton	444.9000	+	O 151.4e	W3OK	DLARC
Wind Gap	443.7000	+	O 151.4el	KA3HJW	K3LZ
Wind Gap	447.5750	–	O 131.8 (CA)elrsRB WX	W3BXW	BEARS
NORTHWEST 186.2					
Clarion	442.6500	+		KE3EI	KE3EI
Clarion	444.3250	+	Oa	N3HZX	------------
Greenville	443.4250	+	O	KE3JP	KE3JP

Location	*Output*	*Input*	*Notes*	*Call*	*Sponsor*
New Bethlehem	444.4250	+		N3TNA	N3TNA
Oil City	444.1250	+	Oe	W3ZIC	FVMKC
Sheffield	442.7000	+	el	N3KZ	------------
Tionesta	442.4000	+	Oe	KE3EI	KE3EI
Utica	442.6000	+	O	KE3JP	KE3JP
Vowinkel	443.3750	+	O	N3GPM	N3GPM
Warren	442.9250	+		WJ8G	------------
Warren	443.9000	+	O	N3DDY	------------
Waterford	443.9500	+	100.0el	KF8YF	KF8YF
PERRY					
Newport	444.5500	+	O 123elWX	W3ND	CPRA Inc.
PHILADELPHIA					
Center City	443.1000	+	O 131.8eBI	K3QFP	CCRG
Philadelphia	440.1500	+	O 151.4el	K3CX	------------
Philadelphia	441.7000	+	O 74.4 (CA) l	W3WAN	WAN-RS
Philadelphia	442.4000	+	O 131.8 (CA)lRB	N3KZ	UPenn ARC
Philadelphia	442.5500	+	O 91.5e	W3SBE	SBE Ch. 18
Philadelphia	442.8000	+	O 131.8 (CA)elRB	K3TU	TUARC
Philadelphia	446.8750	–	O 131.8e	KD3WT	OARA
Philadelphia	449.7750	–	O 141.3 RB	WBØCPR	------------
Roxborough	444.8000	+	O 186.2 (CA)el	W3QV	Phil-Mont
PIKE					
Bushkill	449.7750	–	O 156.7 (CA)l	KC2UFO	Skywatchers
Greentown	444.6500	+	O 114.8 (CA)	WA2AHF	------------
Lake Wallenpaupack	442.3500	+	●tl	WA2ZPX	------------
PITTSBURGH 131.8					
Apollo	444.9000	+	O 131.8aer xz	N1RS	SARA
Apollo	444.9250	+	O 131.8elr	N1RS	SARA
Bridgeville	442.5000	+	O(CA)z	KS3R	SHARC
Canonsburg	443.6500	+	O 131.8el	N3FB	N3FB
Carnegie	444.4500	+	O 103.5e	W3KWH	SCARC
Clinton	443.0000	+	●tE-WIND	K3KEM	K3KEM
Clinton	444.8500	+	O 131.8 E-WINDl	K3KEM	K3KEM
Coraopolis	444.1500	+	Oalx	KA3IRT	KA3IRT
Irwin	442.2500	+	O 131.8e	W3OC	TRARC
Leechburg	442.8000	+	O 131.8elr	N1RS	SARA
Leechburg	442.8000	29.5800	O 141.3elr	N1RS	SARA
Monroeville	444.0000	+	Oe	K3CFY	Dot0RG
Mt Lebanon	442.5500	+	O 131.8	N3SH	WA3SH
Murrysville	443.5000	+	O	W3GKE	W3GKE

Location	Output	Input	Notes	Call	Sponsor
N Huntingdon	444.7750	+	Ol	K3CFY	K3CFY
New Kensington	442.8000	+	O 131.8elr	N1RS	SARA
New Kensington	442.8000	29.5800	O 141.3elr	N1RS	SARA
Pittsburgh/Carrick	444.9500	+	Oaelz	W3PGH	GPVHFS
Pittsburgh Downtown	442.6250	+	Otal	K3DUQ	DUARC
Pittsburgh Hazelwood	443.1000	+	O	WA3PBD	GtwyFM
Pittsburgh Hazelwood	444.0500	+	O	KA3IDK	------------
Pittsburgh Homestead	444.1000	+	Oaex	KB3CNN	GtwyFM
Pittsburgh/N Hills	444.4000	+	O 88.5 (CA) er	W3EXW	NHARC-RPT
Pittsburgh Oakland	443.4500	+	100.0 (CA)e	W3YJ	U of Pitt
Pittsburgh Oakland	443.5500	+	O(CA)	WA3YOA	NHARC
Pittsburgh Oakland	444.3500	+	Oer	W3EXW	NHARC-RPT
Pittsburgh Oakland	444.6500	+	O(CA)e	W3VC	CMUARC
Pittsburgh/W Mifflin	444.5000	+	Oae	KA3IDK	KA3IDK
Pittsburgh/W Mifflin	444.5250	+	Oae	KA3IDK	GtwyFM
Pittsburgh/W Mifflin	444.5500	+	O	KA3IDK	------------
SCHUYLKILL					
Pottsville	443.0000	+	O 77 (CA)el	WX3N	------------
Snyders	447.1750	–	O 131.8 (CA)elsRB	W3BXW WX	BEARS
SOMERSET 123.0					
Central City	443.5750	+	Ot	KE3UC	W3KKC
Jennerstown	444.4750	+	O 123.0r	NJ3T	------------
Meyersdale	442.2000	+	O 131.8 (CA)l	N3KZ	------------
Meyersdale	444.3750	+	O 107.2l	WJ8G	NET.ENG.
Mt Davis	443.7250	+	O 103.5lrz	WA3P	SMST-EMA
Seven Springs	443.9250	+	O 123.0lrz	KB9WCX	SMST-EMA
Somerset	443.2500	+		K3SMT	SCARC
Somerset	443.9500	+	O 88.5 (CA) lrz	N3VFG	SMST-EMA
Windber	443.1500	+	O 123.0r	N3LZV	------------
SOUTH CENTRAL 123.0					
Bedford	444.2000	+	O	K3NQT	BCARS
Chambersburg	443.7000	+	O 131.8 (CA)elx	N3KZ	UofPA ARC
Huntingdon	442.6000	+		WO3T	WO3T

Location	Output	Input	Notes	Call	Sponsor
SOUTHWEST 131.8					
Bentleyville	443.8000	+	O(CA)e	KA3GIR	MARC
Cherry Valley	442.3250	+		KC8PHW	KC8PHW
Connellsville	444.8250	+	O 151.4 TTl	N3LGY	SWPDA
Derry	442.2750	+	O 131.8r	KE3PO	KE3PO
E Monongahela	442.4250	+	O(CA)	W3CSL	MARC
E Monongahela	443.3500	+	O(CA)l	W3CDU	MARC
Georgeville	442.8500	+	O	KB3CNS	KA3SXQ
Greensburg	442.1500	+	Oelr	WC3PS	KE3PO
Hopwood	443.7500	+	O	W3PIE	UARC
Indiana	444.9750	+	O	W3BMD	ICARC
Laurel Mtn	442.3750	+	Ot(CA)elx	KA3JSD	KA3JSD
Long Branch	443.1250	+	O(CA)e	W3RON	W3RON
Mt Pleasant	444.8750	+	O(CA)l	KA3JSD	KA3JSD
New Stanton	442.5750	+	Ot(CA)	N3HOM	N3HOM
Perryopolis	444.6250	+		K3MI	K3MI
PGH/Brentwood	443.6000	+	O 131.8e	AB3PJ	S.W.Y.A.N.
Washington	442.1250	+	O 131.8	W3PLP	W3PLP
Washington	443.3000	+	O	W3CYO	W3CYO
West Newton	442.7000	+	O(CA)elp	N3OVP	N3OVP
SULLIVAN					
Laporte	446.9250	–	O 82.5 (CA) elrsRB LITZ WX	W3NOD	SCDES
Laporte	449.9250	–	O 82.5 (CA) elrsRB LITZ WX	W3NOD	SCDES
SUSQUEHANNA					
Elk Mountain	440.1000	+	O 131.8 (CA)el	N3KZ	UPenn ARC
Elk Mountain	447.3750	–	O 131.8 (CA)elsLITZ WX	N3HPY	B&B
TIOGA					
Jackson Summit	443.1000	+	O 127.3 (CA)e	N3FE	------------
Wellsboro	444.6000	+	O 127.3e	N3FE	------------
Wellsboro	447.3250	–	O 103.5 (CA)eRB	KB3EAR	N.T.R.S.
WARREN					
Grand Valley	443.0500	+		W3GFD	------------
WAYNE					
Waymart	448.8750	–	O 146.2aer sWX	WB3KGD	------------
WEST CENTRAL					
Sandy Lake	443.1750	+		WA3NSM	WA3NSM
WEST CENTRAL 131.8/186.2					
Brookville	444.2750	+	elr	N3GPM	JCEMARS
Butler	442.3000	+	Or	KA3HUK	KA3HUK
Butler	443.3250	+	O	KV3N	KV3N
Butler	443.9000	+	Oaer	N3LEZ	BCEMA
Cowansville	444.3000	+	O 131.8elr x	N1RS	SARA

Location	Output	Input	Notes	Call	Sponsor
Evans City	442.6750	+	Oar	N3XCD	N3XCD
Ford City	443.9750	+	O	K3TTK	FAWA
Mars	443.7000	+	Or	K3SAL	K3SAL
N Washington	442.9000	+	O(CA)er	K3PGS	MRG
New Bethlehem	442.7250	+		N3TNA	N3TNA
New Castle	444.0250	+	O	KA3UEX	KA3UEX
New Castle	444.7250	+	O(CA)el	N3ETV	N3ETV
Punxsutawney	442.4750	+	elr	N3GPM	JCEMARS
Saxonburg	443.2000	+	elr	K3PSG	Butler Co
Sharpsville	444.3750	+	Oaelz	KE3JP	KE3JP
Strattanville	444.2250	+	ar	N3HZV	N3HZV
Vandergrift	444.3000	+	O 131.8elr	N1RS	SARA
WYOMING					
Forkston	442.0000	+	O 131.8 (CA)elRB	N3KZ	UPenn ARC
YORK					
Hellam	444.5000	+	O 146.2el	W3SBA	SRC
Peach Bottom Twp	444.9000	+	O 100ers	W3FJD	YARS
Red Lion	444.2500	+	O 146.2elr	W3SBA	SRC
Red Lion	449.4250	–	O 123e	N3NRN	------------
Reesers Summit	446.4250	–	O 123elWX	W3ND	CPRA Inc.
Shrewsbury	449.7250	–	O 123es	K3AE	SoPaCommGp
York	442.0500	+	O 131.8 (CA)el	N3KZ	UPenn ARC
York	447.2750	–	O(CA)e	W3HZU	Keystone

PUERTO RICO

Location	Output	Input	Notes	Call	Sponsor
E					
Ceiba	448.5500	–	O	WP4DE	RODE
Fajardo	448.2500	–	O	NP3H	------------
Fajardo	448.7250	–	O	WP4NGX	------------
Juncos	447.4750	–	O	WP4NGX	------------
Luquillo	447.8250	–	O	KH2RU	------------
Luquillo	447.9000	–	● 100	N2JBM	------------
Luquillo	449.5500	–	O	WP4KER	NV
Luquillo	449.7500	–	O	NP3EF	------------
Patillas	447.1500	–	O 107.2	KP4KGZ	------------
Rio Grande	448.1500	–	● 100	KB9EZX	------------
Rio Grande	448.6750	–	● 100.0	KP4IP	------------
Rio Grande	449.7500	–	O 100	NP3EF	------------
San Lorenzo	447.5500	–	O 100	WP4LTR	------------
Yabucoa	447.6250	–	O 100	KP4MCR	------------
Yabucoa	447.6750	–	● 100	KP4DDF	------------
Yabucoa	448.3500	–	O	WP4BV	------------
N					
Aguas Buenas	447.1750	–	● 136.5	WP4YF	------------
Aguas Buenas	447.2250	–	77.0	KP3BR	------------
Aguas Buenas	449.1250	–	O	KP4PQ	PRARL

Location	*Output*	*Input*	*Notes*	*Call*	*Sponsor*
Arecibo	449.2500	–	○ 100	WP4DCB	NV
Bayamón	447.1000	–	○	WP4CIE	
Bayamón	447.1250	–		WP4IWJ	
Bayamón	447.3500	–	○	KP4DH	
Bayamon	448.2750	–	○ 136.5	NP3HD	
Bayamón	448.4500	–	○	KP3CB	
Bayamon	449.6000	–	○#	KP4ILG	
Bayamon	449.6250	–	○#	WP4KMB	
Bayamon	449.6500	–	● 67.0a (CA)	KP4KSL	
Bayamon	449.6750	–	○	KP4XC	NV
Corozal	447.5000	–	○ 94.8	WP4AIX	
Corozal	447.7000	–	● 151.4	KP3I	NV
Corozal	447.9500	–	○	KP4AOB	NV
Corozal	448.2250	–	○	WP4F	
Corozal	449.2000	–	○	KP3AV	NV
Guaynabo	447.8500	–	○	KP4GA	
Gurabo	448.9000	–	○a	WP4WC	
Gurabo	449.0000	–	○e	WP4KAG	
Naranjito	449.9250	–	○	WP4FUI	
San Juan	449.1750	–	○EXP	NP3A	NV
San Juan	449.9500	–	○	N1TKK	
Toa Baja	447.2750	–	● 100	WP3TM	NV
Toa Baja	448.0750	–	○e	WP3ZQ	NV
Utuado	448.6250	–	100#	KP4IP	HOLD
Vega Baja	448.3750	–	○	KP3JD	
NORTH					
Corozal	448.4750	–	○	KP3CB	
Gurabo	449.9000	–	○	WP4YF	
S					
Adjuntas	448.8250	–	○ 127.3	WP4NQR	NV
Barranquitas	447.2500	–	○	KP4LP	NV
Barranquitas	447.6500	–	● 127.3e	WP4YF	
Barranquitas	448.7750	–	67	NP3EF	
Barranquitas	449.4250	–	○a(CA)	NP4UG	NV
Barranquitas	449.5750	–	● 100.0ae	KP3JD	
Cayey	447.2000	–	○ 127.3	WP4MXB	
Cayey	449.9750	–	○	KP3AB	
Jayuya	447.0500	–	●	WP4AZT	
Jayuya	447.7250	442.7260	○	WP4CBC	
Jayuya	447.8000	–	○#	WP4IT	NV
Jayuya	448.1000	–	○	KP3AB	
Jayuya	448.5000	–	○	WP4AZT	
Jayuya	448.7000	–	○	KP4QY	NV
Jayuya	449.1000	–	○	KP4GBF	
Orocovis	447.3250	–	○ 136.5	NP4TX	
Orocovis	447.5250	–	○ 136.5	KP4FRE	NV
Ponce	449.2250	–	a	NP3MQ	NV
Villalba	448.0250	443.0025	○ 173.8	WP4NVY	

Location	Output	Input	Notes	Call	Sponsor
Villalba	448.6000	–	O	KP4IP	------------
SOUTH					
Cayey	447.3750	–	O 127.3e	WP4MXB	NONE
Coamo	448.9250	–	O	KP4VY	------------
Jayuya	448.9500	–	O	KP3IV	------------
Jayuya, PR	448.5250	–	O#	KP4IS	NONE
Orocovis	449.3500	–	O	KP4JLQ	------------
Orocovis	449.7750	–	O	KP4NIN	------------
			127.3/127.3		
Ponce	448.1750	–	O	WP3KI	NONE
Salinas	448.8500	–	O	WP4NWR	------------
Villalba	448.4000	–	O	KP4QI	FRA
W					
Aguada	447.7750	–	O	KP4KJU	NV
Aguada	447.9250	–	O	WP4MJP	------------
Aguada	448.5750	–	● 100.0	KP4IP	------------
Aguadilla	447.4250	–	O	WP4KZN	------------
Aguadilla	447.9750	–	O	WP4IR	CDXC
Isabela	447.4000	–	Oe	WP4MMR	------------
Maricao	448.6500	–	O	KP4IP	------------
Maricao	449.1500	–	O	KP4KJU	NV
Maricao	449.9750	–	O	KP3AB	------------
Sabana Grande	449.8500	–	O	WP4MJP	------------
San German	448.3250	–	O 100	WP4GAV	------------
San Sebastian	448.2000	–	O	WP4KJI	------------
San Sebastian	449.4500	–	O	WP4HVS	PepinoRG
X					
Temp/Emerg	447.0000	–	O	EMERG.	PR/VI
Temp/Emerg	448.0000	–		EMERG.	PR/VI

RHODE ISLAND

Location	Output	Input	Notes	Call	Sponsor
ALL AREAS					
Statewide	441.4500	+	OpEXP	SNP	NESMC
EAST BAY					
Bristol	443.1500	+	O 94.8	K1CW	K1CW
Little Compton	446.3750	–	O 67.0 (CA)	KA1RCI	KA1RCI
			E-SUN E-WIND L(KA1RCI NETWORK)rEXP		
Newport	448.3250	–	O 67.0e	KC2GDF	KC2GDF
			L(N1JBC NET)		
Portsmouth	442.3500	+	O 103.5	WG1U	WG1U
Portsmouth	447.5250	–	O 88.5e	WA1TAQ	WA1TAQ
			L(QRN)		
NORTHERN					
Coventry	443.6500	+	O 167.9	N1JL	N1JL
			E-SUN		
Cranston	448.9250	–	O 127.3e	K1CR	K1CR
East Providence	441.7500	+	O 192.8e	W1AQ	ARASNE
Greenville	448.0750	–	O 146.2	N1MIX	S.E.M.A
Johnston	441.5500	+	O 88.5	NN1U	NN1U

Location	*Output*	*Input*	*Notes*	*Call*	*Sponsor*
Johnston	449.3250	–	O 127.3 (CA)eL(KA1RCI)x	KA1RCI	KA1RCI
Lincoln	444.5000	+	O 67.0 (CA) eL(KA1RCI NETWORK)rEXP	KA1RCI	KA1RCI
Lincoln	447.7750	–	O 67.0 (CA) eL(KA1RCI)	KA1RCI	KA1RCI
North Providence	449.2250	–	O 141.3e L(QRN)	N1JBC	N1JBC
Providence	441.3500	+	O 103.5 (CA)eL(KA1RCI)x	KA1RCI	KA1RCI
Providence	444.2000	+	O 88.5 L(E524936)	N1RWX	N1RWX
Providence	446.4750	–	O 146.2e WX	N1MIX	N1MIX
Providence	448.5250	–	O 88.5e	N1MIW	N1MIW
Scituate	447.4250	–	Oe L(443.85)sWXx	AA1PL	RIAFMRS
Smithfield	446.4250	–	OL(DMR)	KB1ISZ	KB1ISZ
Warwick	447.0250	–	O 67.0 L(N1JBC NET)	WA1ABC	N1JBC
West Warwick	444.8500	+	O 88.5e	WW1EMA	WWEMA
West Warwick	446.7250	–	O 100.0e	K1WYC	K1WYC
SOUTH COUNTY					
Exeter	443.8500	+	O 141.3	AA1PL	RIAFMRS
West Greenwich	449.9375	–	ODCS(244) eL(WESTBORO MA 448.775)	W1WNS	ATT
Westerly	449.6750	–	O 127.3	N1LMA	N1LMA

SOUTH CAROLINA

Location	*Output*	*Input*	*Notes*	*Call*	*Sponsor*
Aiken	441.5250	+	O 91.5/91.5 TT(*58)elrs	WR4SC	SCHEART.US
Aiken	443.4000	+	O	AC4WW	AC4WW
Anderson	441.5250	+	O 203.5/203.5er	KN4SWB	KN4SWB
Anderson	442.8250	+	O 127.3/127.3el	KJ4VLT	KJ4VLT
Augusta	444.9500	+	O	W4DV	W4DV
Awendaw	441.7250	+	O 123.0/123.0 TT(*51)elrs	WR4SC	SCHEART.US
Aynor	441.6750	+	O 162.2/162.2 TT(*50)elrs	WR4SC	SCHEART.US
Barnwell	442.0000	+	O 91.5/91.5 TT(*65)elrs	WR4SC	SCHEART.US
Barnwell	449.2500	–	O	KK4BQ	KK4BQ
Beaufort	443.8500	+	O 123/123e	W4BFT	W4BFT
Beech Island	443.1250	+	O 91.5/91.5 TT(*62)elrs	WR4SC	SCHEART.US
Bennettsville	443.0000	+	O 123/123e	KG4HIE	KG4HIE

Location	*Output*	*Input*	*Notes*	*Call*	*Sponsor*
Bluffton	442.6750	+	O	W4IAR	I.A.R.A.
Calhoun Falls	444.0000	+	O	KI4CCZ	KI4CCZ
			118.8/118.8		
Calhoun Falls	444.5750	+	O	KI4CCZ	KI4CCZ
			103.5/103.5		
Ceasers Head	443.1250	+	O 123/123	K4ECG	Greenville CountyEG/
			TT(*56)elrs		
Charleston	441.5750	+	O	WR4SC	SCHEART.US
			123.0/123.0 TT(*53)elrs		
Charleston	442.1500	+	O	W4HRS	HEART
			123.0/123.0l		
Charleston	444.3000	+	O	N4MNH	N4MNH
Charleston	444.6000	+	O	KT4YW	KC4OOZ
Charleston	444.7750	+	O	W4HRS	HEART
			123.0/123.0l		
Clemson	444.6250	+	O	WD4EOG	KC2TGD
			156.7/156.7l		
Clover	443.7250	+	O	KC4KPJ	KC4KPJ
Columbia	441.7250	+	O 91.5/91.5	WR4SC	SCHEART.US
			TT(*52)elrs		
Columbia	442.2000	+	O	N7GZT	N7GZT
Columbia	444.2000	+	Oe	N5CWH	N5CWH
Conway	442.7875	+	O	NE4SC	K4SHP
Cowpens	443.6250	+	O	KE4EAN	KE4EAN
Darlington	444.6000	+	O	KJ4OEF	KJ4GSI
Dillon	443.9750	+	O	NE4SC	K4SHP
Dillon	444.9500	+	O	KJ4OEF	KI4WHZ
Donalds	442.6000	+	O	WJ4X	WJ4X
			107.2/107.2		
Easley	444.9250	+	O	AC4RZ	AC4RZ
Florence	441.5750	+	O 91.5/91.5	WR4SC	SCHEART.US
			TT(*55)elrs		
Florence	441.8750	+	O	WD4CHS	WD4CHS
Florence	442.0500	+	O 123/123e	W4APE	W4APE
			lWX		
Florence	444.0000	+	O	W4ULH	W4ULH
Florence	444.8500	+	O	KJ4OEF	KJ4DIA
Fort Mill	443.4750	+	O	K4YS	SUGAR CREEK ARS
Gaffney	443.0000	+	O	KG4JIA	KG4JIA
Gaffney	444.9000	+	O	KU4ZS	KU4ZS
Georgetown	444.9250	+	O	NE4SC	K4SHP
Greeleyville	444.7500	+	O 123/123e	KG4AQH	W4APE
			l		
Greenville	441.6750	+	O 91.5/91.5	WR4SC	SCHEART.US
			TT(*57)elrs		
Greenville	442.1750	+	O	KU4ZS	KU4ZS
Greenville	442.2500	+	O 123/123	KB4PQA	KB4PQA
Greenville	443.3500	+	O	W4IQQ	GREER ARC
Greenwood	443.9000	+	O	W4GWD	GREENWOOD ARS-

Location	*Output*	*Input*	*Notes*	*Call*	*Sponsor*
Greenwood	444.8250	+	O	KK4SM	KK4SM
Hilton Head	444.3500	+	O	W4IAR	I.A.R.A.
Inman	442.3250	+	O	N4ULE	N4ULE
Iva	443.2500	+	O	AI4JE	AI4JE
Knightsville	441.3500	+	O	WA4USN	WA4USN
Lake Murray	444.6500	+	O	N4UHF	N4UHF
Lake Wylie	444.0500	+	O	KQ1E	KQ1E
Lancaster	444.1000	+	O	W4PAX	LANCASTER CI
Laurens	443.7750	+	O	KF4Y	KB4YF
Leesville	443.3250	+	O	N5CWH	N5CWH
Leesville	443.5000	+	O	N5CWH	N5CWH
Lexington	421.2500	439.2500	O	N4GUP	N4GUP
Lexington	441.8500	+	O	N4ULE	N4ULE
Liberty	443.9750	+	O	N4VDE	N4VDE
Mountain Rest	442.7750	+	O 127.3/127.3l	N4LRD	N4LRD
Mountain Rest	443.5250	+	O 162.2/162.2	KJ4YLP	------------
Mountain Rest	443.7000	+	O 91.5/91.5 e	KJ4YLO	------------
Mt Pleasant	441.4500	+	O	WA4USN	WA4USN
Myrtle Beach	441.7750	+	O	NE4SC	K4SHP
Myrtle Beach	442.1000	+	O	NE4SC	K4SHP
Myrtle Beach	443.0000	+	O 162.2/162.2e	W2SOC	W2SOC
Myrtle Beach	444.6750	+	O	W4GS	GSARC (GRAND
Myrtle Beach	444.9000	+	O	NE4SC	K4SHP
Myrtle Beach	444.9750	+	O	NE4SC	K4SHP
Newberry	442.4250	+	O	WD4CWY	WD4CWY
North Augusta	444.8000	+	O	KE4RAP	KE4RAP
Orangeburg	441.7500	+	O 123/123 TT(*59)elrs	WR4SC	SCHEART.US
Orangeburg	444.9750	+	O	AD4U	EARS (EDISTO
Pacolet	441.9000	+	O	AG4VT	AG4VT
Palmetto	444.8000	+	O 91.5/91.5	KB4RRC	KO4L
Pelzer	442.9250	+	O	AC4RZ	AC4RZ
Pendleton	443.0250	+	O 127.3/127.3l	N4LRD	N4LRD
Pickens	442.1250	+	O	WT4F	WT4F
Pickens	442.4000	+	O	WR4XM	PICKENS CO C
Pickens	443.4500	+	O	AC4RZ	AC4RZ
Pickens	444.3500	+	O 127.3/127.3elr	KN4SWB	KN4SWB
Pickins	421.2500	1253.2500	O	N4VDE	N4VDE
Rock Hill	441.5250	+	O 162.2/162.2 TT(*60)elrs	WR4SC	SCHEART.US
Rock Hill	443.3750	+	O	KD4ADL	]KD4ADL
Rock Hill	444.7250	+	O	KC4KPJ	WC4ABD
Six Mile	441.8000	+	O	W4TWX	W4TWX

Location	Output	Input	Notes	Call	Sponsor
Six Mile	441.8750	+	O	KK4SM	WA4SSJ
Six Mile	441.8750	+	O	W4TWX	W4TWX
Spartanburg	441.9500	+	O 162.2/162.2 TT(*67)elrs	WR4SC	SCHEART.US
Spartanburg	442.0750	+	O	K4II	K4II
Spartanburg	442.8000	+	O	KI4WVC	KI4WVC
St George	444.8250	+	O 103.5/103.5	K4ILT	------------
Summerville	441.2500	+	O	KC4ED	KE2D
Summerville	441.3375	+	O	KC4ED	KE2D
Summerville	442.3000	+	O	KC4ED	KC4OOZ
Sumter	421.2500	439.2500	O	WZ4O	WZ4O
Sumter	441.6250	+	O 123/123 TT(*64)elrs	WR4SC	SCHEART.US
Sumter	444.1500	+	O	W4GL	SARA
Union	442.1000	+	O	K4USC	K4USC
Wallace	444.3750	+	O 91.5/91.5 e	KG4HIE	KG4HIE
Walterboro	444.5500	+	O	KG4BZN	KG4BZN
Waltersboro	444.8500	448.8500	O 123.0/123.0l	W4HRS	HEART
Ware Shoals	441.6250	+	O 91.5/91.5 TT(*63)elrs	WR4SC	SCHEART.US
Whitehall	441.6750	+	O 123.0/123.0 TT(*54)elrs	WR4SC	SCHEART.US

SOUTH DAKOTA

Location	Output	Input	Notes	Call	Sponsor
FREQUENCY USAGE					
Statewide	443.3250	+		SNP	
Statewide	443.7000	+		SNP	
CENTRAL					
Huron	443.8500	+		WØNOZ	Huron ARC
Sioux Falls	444.8250	+	O 146.2ae L(SDLINK 146.2) RB	KDØZP	SDARC
EAST					
Bruce	444.2500	+	O	KCØFLK`	KCØFLK
Madison SD	440.1750	+	131.8#	KBØMRG	KBØMRG
EAST CENTRAL					
Brookings	444.0500	+	O 136.5	NØVEK	NØVEK
Brookings	444.7000	+	O 103.5	KGØXM	KGØXM
Clear Lake {E}	444.3000	+	136.5/136.5 #L(446.325)	WØBXO	NØVEK
NORTH CENTRAL					
Bath	443.4000	+	O	WBØJZZ	HubCtyARC
NORTHEAST					
Clear Lake {W}	444.9500	+	O 136.5 L(446.325)	WØGC	DCARC
Watertown	442.0000	+	O 146.2/146.2 L(SD LINK SYSTEM)	KØTY	KØTY

Location	*Output*	*Input*	*Notes*	*Call*	*Sponsor*
Webster	442.1000	+	O 88.5/88.5 e	KCØMYX	KCØMYX
SOUTHEAST					
Sioux Falls	444.2000	+	O 82.5a	WØZWY	SEARC
Sioux Falls	444.9000	+	#	KDØZP	KDØZP
SOUTHWEST					
Martin	444.7250	+	O	N3NTV	N3NTV
WEST CENTRAL					
Rapid City	444.5750	+	146.2 RB	WØBLK	BlkHills ARC
Rapid City	444.8250	+	O 146.2	WØBLK	NQØF

TENNESSEE

Alamo	443.7500	+	O	K4WWV	STARNET
Algood	444.4250	+	O	N2BR	N2BR
Arlington	442.7750	+	O	N4GMT	N4GMT
Arnold AFB	443.9500	+	O	N4HAP	WARC
Athens	442.2750	+	O	KG4FZR	KC4KUZ
Athens	443.2750	+	O	KG4FZR	KC4KUZ
Bean Station	443.4500	+	O	W2IQ	LAKEWAY ARC
Benton	444.8000	+	O	KA4ELN	KA4ELN
Bluff City	442.2000	+	O	KE4CCB	KE4CCB
Brownsville	443.9000	+	O	KB4YTU	LARRY FORSYT
Brownsville	444.2000	+	O	KB4YTU	KB4YTU
Brownsville	444.5250	+	O	KI4BXI	KI4BXI
Brunswick	443.7000	+	O	KF4BB	BELLEVUE BAP
Camden	443.3000	+	O	KA4BNI	TEMA
Camden	444.5000	+	O	N4QDE	N4QDE
Carthage	442.5750	+	O	WT4X	WT4X
Caryville	444.6500	+	O 77/77el	KB4PNG	------------
Centerville	442.5500	+	O 107.2/107.2	KI4DAD	KI4DAD
Centerville	443.7000	+	O	N4XW	N4XW
Chattanooga	442.1500	+	O	KG4OVQ	KG4OVQ
Chattanooga	442.4250	+	Ol	W4YI	W4YI
Chattanooga	442.9000	+	O	N4YH	N4YH
Chattanooga	443.1250	+	O	KT4OL	KT4OL
Chattanooga	443.1250	+	Oe	K4VCM	KA4EMA
Chattanooga	443.5500	+	O	WB4LRD	KA4WFB
Chattanooga	443.9000	+	O	N4AFB	KA4WFB
Chattanooga	444.1000	+	Oe	W4AM	W4AM
Chattanooga	444.2000	+	O	N4AFB	KA4WFB
Chattanooga	444.4500	+	O	WJ9J	WJ9J
Chattanooga	444.8750	+	O	N4YH	N4YH
Chattanooga	444.9000	+	Ol	W4YI	W4YI
Clarksville	442.9000	+	O	W4CHM	N3ORX
Clarksville	443.5500	+	O	K4ORE	K2LAW
Clarksville	444.3250	+	O	WA4BZU	------------
Cleveland	442.2500	+	O	WD4DES	WD4DES

Location	Output	Input	Notes	Call	Sponsor
Cleveland	442.4000	+	O	KA4ELN	KA4ELN
Cleveland	442.4500	+	O	KD4NED	KD4NED
Cleveland	442.9250	+	Oel	W4OAR	OCOEE ARS
Cleveland	444.2750	+	O	W4GZX	CARC
Clinton	442.1500	+	O	WX4RP	WX4RP
Collegedale	443.5750	+	O	KA6UHV	KA6UHV
Collierville	442.6250	+	O	WB4EPG	WB4EPG
Collierville	443.3000	+	O	KA7UEC	KA7UEC
Collierville	443.6250	+	O	KA7UEC	KA7UEC
Collierville	444.1250	+	O	NU5O	KJ4FYA
Collierville	444.6250	+	O	WT4E	WT4E
Collinwood	443.9500	+	O	KF4AKV	KF4AKV
Columbia	442.7250	+	O	KG4LUY	W4RDM
Columbia	443.1750	+	Olwx	W4GGM	W4GGM
Columbia	444.9250	+	O	WA4AKM	K2GJY
Cookeville	442.3000	+	O	WA4UCE	WA4UCE
Cookeville	443.1750	+	O	KB4TEN	KB4TEN
Cookeville	443.2000	+	O	N4ECW	N4ECW
Cookeville	444.5000	+	O	K4DAV	K4DAV
Cookeville	444.6000	+	O	WA4PPL	COOKVL/PUTNAM C
Cross Plains	443.9000	+	O	AG4QK	AG4QK
Crossville	443.8750	+	O	WM4RB	WE4MB
Crossville	444.9500	+	O	W4EYJ	CUMBERLAND RPT
Cumberland Furnace	444.4750	+	O 85.4/85.4 el	N4FOX	N4FOX
Dayton	442.0750	+	O	KJ4BJ	KJ4BJ
Deason	443.3500	+	O	WA4AWI	WA4AWI
Decaturville	443.3250	+	O	KA4P	DECATUR CO GEN
Dover	444.9250	+	O	N4VIH	N4VIH
Dresden	442.1500	+	O	KA4BNI	KA4BNI
Dripping Spring	443.9250	+	O	N4PYI	W4BZU
Dunlap	442.6000	+	O	KB4ACS	W4HP
Dyersburg	444.4750	+	O	K4DYR	K4DYR
Elizabethon	441.8000	+	O	WM4T	WM4T
Elizabethton	442.2500	+	O 88.5/88.5 e	KN4E	KN4E
Elizabethton	442.7500	+	O 88.5/88.5	KN4E	KN4E
Etowah	442.3250	+	O	KG4FZR	KC4KUZ
Eva	443.6250	+	O	AD4QG	KF4GCB
Fisherville	443.1250	+	O	W4RSG	KA4JXT
Franklin	444.0250	+	O	WC4EOC	K4COM
Franklin	444.7250	+	O	WA4AKM	K2GJY
Gallatin	443.3000	+	O 107.2/107.2elrsWX	W4LKZ	W4LKZ
Gallatin	443.6000	+	O	WC4EOC	K4COM
Gallatin	444.3500	+	O	W4LKZ	SUMNER CO ARA
Gallatin	444.4500	+	O 107.2/107.2elsWX	W4CAT	CATS
Gallatin	444.7750	+	O	WA4AKM	K2GJY

Location	Output	Input	Notes	Call	Sponsor
Gatlinburg	443.1500	+	O	KD4PBC	KD4PBC
Gatlinburg	443.3000	+	O	WA4KJH	------------
Gatlinburg	444.9000	+	O	W4KEV	W4KEV
Georgetown	442.0250	+	O	WE4MB	WM4RB
Gladeville	443.3750	+	O	KG4SFI	KG4SFI
Goodspring	444.0500	+	O	K4CRS	K4CRS
Greenback	443.0500	+	O	KM4H	LOUDON CO E
Greenbrier	444.2500	+	O	WQ4E	WQ4E
Greeneville	441.8500	+	O	KI4OTQ	KI4OTQ
Greeneville	443.2000	+	O	W4WC	W4WC
Greeneville	444.2000	+	O	K4MFD	K4MFD
Greeneville	444.6500	+	O	WB4NKL	WB4NKL
Greeneville	444.7500	+	O	WD2E	WD2E
Greenville	442.7000	+	O	KF4FTD	N4FV
Harriman	442.8750	+	O	KC4WHL	KC4WHL
Henderson	442.2750	+	O	KE4PFW	KE4PFW
Henderson	442.5750	+	O	KU4RT	KU4RT
Henderson	444.7500	+	O	K4TC	CHESTER COU
Hendersonville	444.0000	+	O	W4LKZ	WD4BKY
Hohenwald	442.0000	+	O	K4TTC	TTC-ARCH
Hohenwald	444.8500	+	O	K4YN	K4YN
Hornbeak	442.4000	+	O	KA4BNI	KA4BNI
Huntingdon	444.3750	+	O	KB4YTM	CARROLL CO A
Indian Mound	442.6250	+	O	AA4TA	TEMA
Jackson	442.9000	+	O	WF4Q	WEST TN ARS
Jackson	443.8250	+	O	KE4OVN	KE4OVN
Jackson	444.4500	+	O 123/123e lrsWX	NE4MA	WA4VVX
Jackson	444.5500	+	O	WF4Q	WF4Q
Jackson	444.7250	+	O	WBØTMC	WBØTMC
Jackson	444.8750	+	O	KA4BNI	KA4BNI
Jamestown	443.6250	+	O	KC4MJN	ARC OF FENTR
Jasper	442.0500	+	O	KD4XV	SEQUACHIE VA
Jasper	443.1000	+	O 88.5/88.5 a(CA)eWX	KD4ATW	KD4ATW
Jefferson City	444.6250	+	O	KD4TUD	KD4TUD
Jefferson City	444.9500	+	O	KG4GVX	KG4GVX
Joelton	442.9500	+	O 167.9/167.9elrsWX	KF4TNP	KF4TNP
Johnson City	421.2500	434.0000	O	WD4ATV	------------
Johnson City	443.2500	+	O	W4BUC	KT4TD
Johnson City	444.1000	+	O 103.5/103.5e	K4LNS	K4LNS
Jonesborough	442.0500	+	O	K4DWQ	------------
Joyner	444.4000	+	O	K4EAJ	K4EAJ
Keith Springs	444.9500	+	O 107.2/107.2el	KF4TNP	KF4TNP
Kirkland	443.8750	+	O	WC4EOC	K4COM
Knoxville	442.5000	+	O	W4KEV	W4KEV

Location	*Output*	*Input*	*Notes*	*Call*	*Sponsor*
Knoxville	443.0000	+	ODCS	AA4UT	AA4UT
Knoxville	443.2500	+	O	WA4FLH	WA4FLH
Knoxville	443.5000	+	O	KD4CWB	------------
Knoxville	443.8000	+	O	KD4CWB	KA4AZQ
Knoxville	444.0000	+	O	KD4CWB	KD4CWB
Knoxville	444.1750	+	O	KN4QB	KN4QB
Knoxville	444.2250	+	O	AJ4NO	AJ4NO
Knoxville	444.3000	+	O	WB4GBI	WB4GBI
Knoxville	444.3250	+	O	N4KFI	N4KFI
Knoxville	444.4250	+	O	KC4NNN	KC4NNN
Knoxville	444.5000	+	O 100/100e l	W4KEV	W4KEV
Knoxville	444.5250	+	O	KB4REC	KB4REC
Knoxville	444.5750	+	O	W4BBB	W4BBB
Knoxville	444.9250	+	O	KD4TZD	KD4TZD
Lafayette	444.1250	+	O	KC4ECD	KC4ECD
Lafollette	443.7000	+	O	KB4OTK	KB4OTK
Lake City	442.8000	+	O	WD4LUR	WD4LUR
Laneview	443.8500	+	O	KE4OVN	KE4OVN
Lawrenceburg	443.4000	+	O	KF4AKV	KF4AKV
Lebanon	443.0000	+	O	KW4LS	KW4LS
Lebanon	443.2750	+	O	WA4AWI	WA4AWI
Lebanon	443.5750	+	O	W4LYR	WILSON AMATEUR
Lebanon	444.2750	+	O	W4RYR	WA4AXH
Lenior City	444.2500	+	O	KF4VDX	KI4RRI
Lewisburg	442.1000	+	O 107.2/107.2elrsWX	KF4TNP	KF4TNP
Lexington	442.0750	+	O	KA4BNI	KA4BNI
Linden	443.5000	+	O	WA4RNN	K4TTC
Lobelville	442.8500	+	O 107.2/107.2elrsWX	WA4VVX	WA4VVX
Loretto	442.8750	+	O	KF4OCK	KF4OCK
Lyles	443.8500	+	O 123/123	KI4DAD	KI4DAD
Madisonville	443.6000	+	Oes	KJ4OOY	KJ4OOY
Manchester	443.2250	+	O 107.2/107.2e	KF4TNP	KF4TNP
Manchester	444.0750	+	O 127.3/127.3elrsWX	KF4TNP	KF4TNP
Maryville	441.8250	+	O	W1BEW	W1BEW
Maryville	444.0750	+	O	KC4PDQ	KC4PDQ
Maryville	444.3500	+	O	KD4CLA	KD4CLA
Maryville	444.7000	+	O	KJ4JNO	KJ4JNO
Maryville	444.7750	+	O	KF4VDX	KF4VDX
Maryville	444.8250	+	Oes	KE4FGW	KE4FGW
Mason	442.7500	+	O	N4GMT	N4GMT
Mcewen	443.9250	+	O	KE4KNZ	------------
Mckenzie	443.8750	+	O	KD4KPV	KD4KPV
Mcminnville	444.3000	+	O	WB4CWS	WB4CWS
Mcminnville	444.8500	+	O	WD4MWQ	WD4MWQ

Location	*Output*	*Input*	*Notes*	*Call*	*Sponsor*
Medina	442.0500	+	O	WA4BJY	A R ECHO SYST
Memphis	441.6000	441.6000	O	KB4LJV	KB4LJV
Memphis	441.8875	+	O	KK4BWF	NS4B
Memphis	441.9500	441.9500	O	N4WAH	N4WAH
Memphis	441.9750	441.9750	O	N4WAH	N4WAH
Memphis	442.1750	+	Oer	W4GMM	W4GMM
Memphis	442.8250	+	O	WF4G	WF4G
Memphis	443.1000	+	O	W4RSG	MEGA SYSTEM
Memphis	443.2000	+	O	W4BS	DELTA ARC
Memphis	443.2500	+	O	W4EM	W4EM
Memphis	443.9500	+	O	N4ER	W4XF/WD4T
Memphis	443.9875	+	O	WA4MQQ	LEADING EDGE
Memphis	444.0750	+	O	KF4ATY	LEARC
Memphis	444.1000	+	O	W4RSG	MEGA SYSTEM
Memphis	444.1750	+	O	W4EM	W4EM
Memphis	444.5000	+	O	N4WAH	N4WAH
Memphis	444.7750	+	O	W5KUB	W5KUB
Memphis	444.8250	+	O	K5FE	FEDEX ARC
Memphis	444.8500	+	O	K7AG	------------
Milan	442.1000	+	O	WD4PAX	------------
Milan	442.6750	+	O	KA4BNI	KA4BNI
Monteagle	442.2000	+	O	NQ4Y	NQ4Y
Monteagle Mt	441.2500	+	O	NQ4Y	NQ4Y
Morristown	442.9500	+	O	AK4EZ	------------
Morristown	444.6000	+	O	KG4GVX	KG4GVX
Morristown	444.8000	+	O	WB4OAH	WB4OAH
Morristown	444.9750	+	O	KQ4E	KQ4E
Mountain City	441.6000	+	O	K4DHT	------------
Mountain City	443.9250	+	O	K4DHT	------------
Mt Juliet	444.4000	+	O	N4PYI	N4PYI
Mt Juliet	444.7500	+	O	N4PYI	N4PYI
Murfreesboro	441.8750	+	O	KD4TZZ	KD4TZZ
Murfreesboro	442.1750	+	O	KA4VFD	KA4VFD
Nashville	442.7500	+	OelsWX	WA4RCW	WA4RCW
Nashville	442.8000	+	O 107.2/107.2elrsWX	NE4MA	WA4VVX
Nashville	443.4500	+	O	KE4PJW	KE4PJW
Nashville	443.7250	+	O	W1ARN	MTEARS / TEMA
Nashville	443.8000	+	O	KG4NRC	KG4NRC
Nashville	444.0500	+	O	N4PYI	N4PYI
Nashville	444.1500	+	O	AF4TZ	RPT SOC OF MI
Nashville	444.2000	+	O	N4ARK	------------
Nashville	444.2250	+	O	N4ARK	N4ARK
Nashville	444.3000	+	O	WA4BZU	------------
Nashville	444.5250	+	O	WA4BGK	WA4BGK
Nashville	444.5500	+	O	WA4PCD	WA4PCD
Nashville	444.5750	+	O	WA4WCK	WA4WCK
Nashville	444.6250	+	O	WA4TOA	NASHVILLE FM
Nashville	444.6750	+	O	WA4PCD	WA4PCD

Location	Output	Input	Notes	Call	Sponsor
Nashville	444.8000	+	O	N4PYI	N4PYI
Nashville	444.8750	+	O	WA4AKM	K2GJY
Nashville	444.9750	+	O	WA4AKM	K2GJY
Newport	442.9000	+	OTTesWX	N2UGA	N2UGA
Newport	443.7500	+	O 203.5/203.5	KG4LHC	KG4LDK
Nolensville	443.6500	+	O	W4RYR	WA4AXH
Nunnely	444.0750	+	O	KG4UHH	KG4UHH
Oakfield	442.2000	+	O	WA4BJY	WAYNE MURLEY
Oneida	442.8250	+	O	KT4PN	KE4QQF
Paris	443.6750	+	O	KB4TKM	KB4TKM
Paris	444.9000	+	O	N4ZKR	N4ZKR
Paris Landing	443.2000	+	O	KA4BNI	KA4BNI
Pasquo	443.9750	+	O	W4CAT	TEMA
Piperton	444.0750	+	O	WA4MJM	WA4MJM
Prospect	444.6000	+	O	WA4AUX	WA4AUX
Pulaski	442.1500	+	O	WD4RBJ	WD4RBJ
Pulaski	443.5500	+	O	K4NVX	K4NVX
Ripley	443.6000	+	O	KA4BNI	KA4BNI
Rockwood	443.9750	+	O	KE4RX	ROANE CO ARC
Selmer	442.8000	+	O	KA4BNI	KA4BNI
Seviereville	442.3000	+	O	W4SRT	AE4SC
Sevierville	443.2250	+	O	KJ4HPM	KJ4HPM
Sevierville	443.6750	+	O	K4IBW	K4IBW
Sevierville	444.7250	+	O	N4CKB	N4CKB
Seymour	444.4750	+	O	K4ARO	K4ARO
Shelbyville	442.7000	+	O	NQ4U	BCARS
Shelbyville	443.8250	+	O	KC4KRM	KC4RSR
Short Mtn	444.6500	+	O	W4CAT	CATS
Signal Mountain	444.7000	+	O	KB4ACS	------------
Smithville	442.0000	+	O	AB4ZB	AB4ZB
Smithville	444.8250	+	O	N4PYI	K2GJY
Sneedville	442.4500	+	O 100/100s	KE4KQI	KJ4TKV
Sparta	444.3750	+	O	KD4WX	KD4WX
Spencer	443.7750	+	O	KA4MHJ	KA4MHJ
Tallassee	443.5750	+	O	WB4TVW	KJ4ZXW
Tellico Plains	442.5500	+	O	K4EZK	K4EZK
Thompsons Sta	443.0750	+	O	WC4EOC	K4COM
Thompsons Sta	443.4750	+	O	W4BZU	W4BZU
Troy	444.5750	+	O	W4RB	W4RB
Walden	443.3750	+	O	W4WQS	W4WQS
Walland	443.5500	+	O	AC4JF	AC4JF
Watertown	444.9000	+	O	W4LYR	W4LYR
Waynesboro	443.1000	+	OelrsWX	KF4TNP	KF4TNP
White Bluff	442.2250	+	OeWX	KG4HDZ	KG4HDZ
White Bluff	442.3750	+	Oe	KG4HDZ	KG4HDZ
Williston	442.4250	+	O	KA4BNI	IND - KA4BNI
Williston	444.4000	+	O	WB4KOG	WB4LHD
Woodbury	442.8250	+	O	KA4VFD	KA4VFD

Location	Output	Input	Notes	Call	Sponsor
TEXAS					
Abernathy	444.0000	+	O 118.8r	WB5BRY	CRRC
Abilene	443.5000	+	●	AI5TX	------------
Abilene	444.0000	+	O 167.9 WX	KD5YCY	BCARN
Abilene	444.1750	+	O 100lWX	WX5TX	CPARC
Abilene	444.2500	+	O 88.5lWX	N5TEQ	CPARC
Abilene	444.5000	+	O 91.5a	KD5EFB	------------
Abilene	444.7500	+	●	KB5GAR	------------
Abilene	444.8750	+	O 114.8	KE5OGP	------------
Adkins	444.7750	+	O 123e	KK5LA	------------
Albany	444.9000	+	O 114.8l	N5TEQ	CPARC
Aledo	443.2000	+	O 110.9l	KA5HND	------------
Allen	441.5000	+	O	N5LTN	ESIARC
Allen	441.5750	+	Oaer	K5PRK	Plano Amateur R
Allen	442.5500	+	Ox	WB5WPA	------------
Allen	444.2500	+	O	K5PRK	PARK
Alpine	443.9250	+	●	WX5II	INTERTIE
Alvin	442.2000	+	O 103.5	KA5QDG	------------
Alvin	442.7750	+	O 141.3 (CA)	KA9JLM	AARC
Alvin	443.9250	+	●	AI5TX	------------
Alvin	444.0500	+	O 103.5	W5ITI	------------
Alvin	444.7500	+	●	KA5AXV	------------
Amarillo	443.5000	+	●	N5LTZ	ARMADILLO
Amarillo	444.0500	+	O 88.5l	KC5EZO	------------
Amarillo	444.2000	+	O 88.5	N5LTZ	CRI
Amarillo	444.4750	+	O 88.5	W5WX	PARC
Amarillo	444.5250	+	O 146.2lx	WR5FM	CARE WTX
Anahuac	442.1000	+	O 103.5	KB5FLX	ARCDCT
Anahuac	443.5000	+	●	AI5TX	------------
Anahuac	444.8750	+	O 103.5l	WB5UGT	SALTGRASS
Andrews	442.1250	+	O 146.2l	KB5MBK	------------
Angleton	442.3000	+	O 127.3	KE5WFD	------------
Angleton	444.4250	+	O 103.5l	WB5UGT	SALTGRASS
Anhalt	442.6750	+	O 131.8l	W5DK	------------
Anthony	442.9500	+	O 67l	N5ZRF	AMIGO
Anton	441.6750	+	O 100	K5KTM	------------
Argyle	443.2250	+	O	KAØBRN	------------
Argyle	443.5500	+	O 110.9	WB5NDJ	------------
Arlington	441.3500	+	●	NR5E	ALERT
Arlington	443.4000	+	O 110.9l	WD5DBB	MCRG
Arlington	443.6750	+	●	AI5TX	------------
Arlington	443.8500	+	●	WA5VHU	------------
Arlington	444.2000	+	O 100	K5SLD	AARC
Arlington	444.5500	+	●	W5PSB	------------
Athens	441.7250	+	O 100	KF5WT	BSA CAMP
Athens	443.3000	+	O 100	KF5WT	------------
Athens	443.7000	+	●	AI5TX	------------

Location	Output	Input	Notes	Call	Sponsor
Austin	441.5250	+	O 107.2	K5TRA	------------
Austin	441.7750	+	O 131.8 (CA)	W5JWB	------------
Austin	441.8000	+	O 100	W5AAF	------------
Austin	441.8750	+	O 100	N5JGX	------------
Austin	441.9250	+	O 88.5	WA6KGI	------------
Austin	441.9750	+	O 97.4ae	KA9LAY	------------
Austin	442.0250	+	O 114.8	W5TRI	ATT LABS
Austin	442.1500	+	O 186.2e	AA5BT	------------
Austin	442.2750	+	O 110.9	KN5X	------------
Austin	442.4000	+	O	K5FX	------------
Austin	442.4500	+	O 141.3el	WB5UGT	SALTGRASS
Austin	442.4750	+	O 127.3	KE3D	------------
Austin	442.5000	+	O 162.2ls WX	W5LNX	SW LYNX SYS
Austin	442.6000	+	O 141.3	K5TCR	TCREACT
Austin	443.0750	+	O 123	K5TRA	------------
Austin	443.9500	+	●	AI5TX	------------
Austin	444.0000	+	O 107.2l	WB5PCV	------------
Austin	444.1000	+	O 103.5	W5KA	AARC
Austin	444.2000	+	O 107.2	W5KA	Austin Amateur Radio
Austin	444.6000	+	Oael	W3MRC	3M ARC
Austin	444.7750	+	O 110.9 (CA)	AA5R	HELPS
Austin	444.9500	+	O 110.9x	N5RVD	------------
Azle	442.1500	+	O 110.9	WB5IDM	------------
Baird	443.8500	+	O 88.5	NZ5V	BCARN
Bangs	440.6750	+	O	K5BRC	Burleson ARC
Bastrop	441.9500	+	●	WB6ARE	------------
Bastrop	442.7250	+	O 114.8	WB6ARE	------------
Bastrop	443.1750	+	O 114.8e	WB6ARE	------------
Bastrop	443.7500	+	O 114.8	KE5FKS	BCARC
Baytown	443.8000	+	O 123	K5BAY	BAARC
Baytown	443.8750	+	O 173.8	N5XUV	HCTA
Beaumont	444.5000	+	O 100 (CA) elWXx	WB5ITT	Triangle Repeater As
Beaumont	444.7000	+	O 107.2l	W5RIN	BARC
Beaumont	444.9000	+	O 103.5	W5XOM	EXOMERC
Bedford	442.3000	+	O	KA5SYL	------------
Bedford	442.8250	+	O 110.9e	N5VAV	TRAIN
Bee Cave	443.6250	+	●	AI5TX	------------
Bee Cave	443.9250	+	●	K5GJ	------------
Beeville	443.5250	+	O 141.3el	WD5IEH	------------
Bellare	441.8250	+	Oael	AK5G	------------
Benbrook	441.6250	+	●	K5SXK	BBRC
Big Lake	442.3000	+	O 162.2	N5SOR	------------
Big Lake	442.6500	+	O 146.2l	KB5MBK	------------
Big Spring	442.1000	+	O 162.2el	KE5PL	WTXC
Big Spring	442.6250	+	O 146.2l	KB5MBK	------------

Location	*Output*	*Input*	*Notes*	*Call*	*Sponsor*
Big Spring	443.3500	+	O 156.7	N5BTJ	------------
Big Spring	443.9500	+	●	KE5PL	ARMADILLO
Big Spring	444.4750	+	Oel	KK5MV	------------
Black	444.4250	+	●	N5LTZ	CRI
Blanco	443.9750	+	●	WA5JEC	INTERTIE
Bluffton	444.8000	+	O 100	W5KFT	BARC
Boerne	444.7500	+	O 162.2l	W5VEO	SWLS
Boerne	444.9000	+	O 123e	W5VEO	------------
Bonham	443.7500	+	O	K5FRC	FCARC
Boonsville	443.9000	+	O 100	K5RHV	------------
Borger	444.6000	+	O 141.3	WB5ZDK	------------
Boyd	444.8250	+	O 110.9	W5OYS	------------
Brackettville	443.6250	+	●	WB5TZJ	INTERTIE
Brady	444.8750	+	O 162.2ael WX	WA5HOT	HOT-HOG
Brenham	443.2500	+	O 103.5l	W5AUM	BRENHAM ARC
Brownfield	442.2250	+	O 146.2lx	WR5FM	C.A.R.E.
Brownfield	444.8250	+	O 118.8	W5HFT	------------
Brownsville	441.3000	+	O 151.4	N5XWO	------------
Brownsville	444.3750	+	O 114.8l	KC5MAH	------------
Brownsville	444.6000	+	O 114.8	W5RGV	STARS
Brownwood	443.9250	+	●	AI5TX	------------
Brownwood	444.7000	+	O 94.8	K5BWD	BARC
Bruceville	440.6250	+	O	W5HAT	DIGTRX AMATE
Bruceville	444.4750	+	O	W5NCD	------------
Bryan	443.4000	+	Oaelrs	W5AC	TAMU ARC
Bryan	443.4500	+	O 127.3ex	KD5DLW	------------
Buchanan Dam	444.2750	+	O	WA5PJE	------------
Bulverde	443.2500	+	O 103.5l	WA5KBQ	------------
Bulverde	444.3500	+	O 131.8	W5DK	------------
Buna	442.4250	+	O 118.8	W5JAS	LAREAARC
Burkburnett	444.0250	+	O 192.8r WX	N5JDD	Witchita Falls Re
Burkburnett	444.5000	+	O 192.8	W5DAD	BURKRGR
Burnet	444.8250	+	O 114.8	KB5YKJ	------------
Caddo	444.7250	+	O 110.9e WX	KB5WB	------------
Canadian	443.7500	+	●	N5LTZ	------------
Canton	443.2000	+	●	N4RAP	------------
Canyon	443.6500	+	O 88.5l	N5LTZ	CRI
Canyon Lake	444.4500	+	O 114.8	W5ERX	------------
Carrollton	441.6250	+	●	K5JG	------------
Carrollton	441.8250	+	●	K5GWF	------------
Carrollton	442.4750	+	●	WO5E	------------
Carrollton	442.6500	+	O 110.9r	N5MJQ	METROCARC
Carrollton	444.4500	+	O 110.9l	K5AB	------------
Carrollton	444.8750	+	●	K5MOT	MORTOROLA
Carthage	444.8000	+	O 151.4	KA5HSA	------------
Cat Spring	444.8750	+	O 103.5el	W5SFA	SFARC

Location	*Output*	*Input*	*Notes*	*Call*	*Sponsor*
Cat Spring	444.9500	+	O 103.5el	WB5UGT	Salt Grass
Cedar Creek	444.0500	+	O 141.3	W5CTX	------------
Cedar Hill	442.1000	+	O 100rs	N5IUF	TRS
Cedar Hill	442.3250	+	●	KM5R	------------
Cedar Hill	442.4000	+	O 110.9	W5MAY	SBE
Cedar Hill	443.5000	+	●	AI5TX	------------
Cedar Hill	443.7250	+	●	W5AHN	ASHCRAFT REPEAT
Cedar Hill	443.9750	+	●	N5UN	FW 440
Cedar Hill	444.5000	+	O	W5AUY	SWDCARC
Cedar Hill	444.9500	+	O 110.9	N5DRP	Texas Disaster Resp
Cedar Park	441.5000	+	O 162.2	W5CGU	------------
Cedar Park	442.6500	+	O 114	KE5ZW	------------
Celina	444.0000	+	O	K5XG	------------
Celina	444.5125	+	O 123e	KE5UT	------------
Centerville	441.6500	+	O 103.5e	WA5GED	------------
Centerville	442.7750	+	●	K3WIV	------------
Centerville	442.9750	+	●	K3WIV	GULLS
Centerville	443.6750	+	●	AI5TX	------------
Channel View	442.8500	+	O 100	N5LUY	------------
Channelview	441.6000	+	O 203.5e WX	KC5TCT	CVFDRC
Channelview	443.6000	+	O 103.5el	KC5TCT	------------
Choate	443.6500	+	●	K5ZZT	INTERTIE
Christine	443.7750	+	O 141.3el	WD5IEH	------------
Clarendon	444.2750	+	O 127.3	KE5NCA	------------
Clear Lake	442.7500	+	O 103.5ael	K5HOU	CLARC
Cleburne	444.0000	+	O 136.5 WX	KY5O	------------
Cleveland	444.6500	+	O	N5AK	SHARK
Clifton	444.4000	+	O 123e	W5BCR	BOSQUECOARC
Clute	444.7250	+	O 103.5l	KB5HII	SALTGRASS
Coleman	444.3000	+	O 94.8e	N5RMO	CARC
College Station	443.0500	+	O 88.5	W5AC	TAMU ARC
College Station	443.6250	+	●	W6TRO	------------
College Station	444.5500	+	O 127.3	N1WP	------------
Colleyville	441.9000	+	O 110.9e WX	W5RV	------------
Colleyville	442.9500	+	O 110.9	N5SVZ	------------
Colorado City	444.8500	+	O 162.2l	K5WTC	WTXC
Columbus	442.7500	+	O 141.3l WX	WB5UGT	SALTGRASS
Commerce	444.5250	+	O 103.5e	W5AMC	TAMUC
Conroe	441.7500	+	O 123el	KE5PTZ	------------
Conroe	442.1250	+	O 123e	WM5E	------------
Conroe	442.1500	+	O 192.8e	WD5CFJ	------------
Conroe	442.1750	+	O 192.8e	WD5CFJ	------------
Conroe	442.2500	+	O 103.5	WB5DGR	------------
Conroe	442.5250	+	O 127.3	W5DCW	------------
Conroe	442.9000	+	O 151.4	WB5DGR	------------

Location	*Output*	*Input*	*Notes*	*Call*	*Sponsor*
Conroe	443.4250	+	○ 203.5l	KCØEJX	NSLS
Conroe	444.4250	+	○ 203.5	KB5HII	------------
Conroe	444.5750	+	○ 103.5l	KB5LS	LSARC
Conroe	444.8000	+	○ 100 (CA) el	WB5ITT	TRA
Coppell	441.8000	+	○ 107.2aer	KD5OEW	Coppell ARC
Coppell	444.2250	+	○ 110.9er	K5CFD	------------
Copperas Cove	443.3250	+	○ 88.5	K5CRA	CRA
Corpus Christi	442.6000	+	○ 162.2	N5IUT	LYNX
Corpus Christi	443.5000	+	●	N5HN	INTERTIE
Corpus Christi	443.7000	+	●	WA2MCT	------------
Corpus Christi	443.9500	+	●	WA5MPA	INTERTIE
Corpus Christi	444.3500	+	●	WD5FJX	------------
Corpus Christi	444.6000	+	○ 114.8e	K5GGB	NONE
Corpus Christi	444.9000	+	○ 107.2	K5GGB	NONE
Corsicana	442.7250	+	○ 110.9l	KE5CDK	Navarro ARC
Corsicana	442.9250	+	○	W5NFL	Navarro ARC
Corsicana	444.7750	+	○	N5ZUA	------------
Crockett	443.6000	+	○ 100e	WA5FCL	HCARC
Crockett	444.2250	+	○ 107.2l	WB5UGT	SALTGRASS
Crosby	441.5500	+	●	KB5OVJ	------------
Crosby	442.0500	+	○ 103.5e	KB5IJF	------------
Crosby	442.4000	+	●	KB5OVJ	------------
Crosby	443.7000	+	●	AI5TX	------------
Crosby	444.1250	+	○ 103.5	KB5NNP	------------
Crosby	444.7750	+	○ 103.5e	W5TWO	Two Two Club of
Crosbyton	442.2750	+	○ 107.2	KC5MVZ	------------
Cypress	442.6500	+	○ 156.7al	N5LUY	------------
Dale	443.0000	+	○ 114.8	KE5AMB	------------
Dallas	440.5750	+	○ar	W5FC	(DARC) Dallas A
Dallas	440.6375	+	○r	W5EBQ	------------
Dallas	441.9250	+	○ 110.9elr	W5EBQ	------------
Dallas	441.9500	+	○ 162.2er	AB5U	------------
Dallas	442.0250	+	○ 127.3	K5TIT	K5TIT
Dallas	442.0750	+	○ 110.9 (CA)er	N5IAG	DCREACT
Dallas	442.2750	+	○ 110.9	N5ZW	------------
Dallas	442.4250	+	○ 110.9 (CA)erWX	W5FC	DARC
Dallas	443.3500	+	○ 110.9 (CA)	WD5EEH	------------
Dallas	443.4750	+	●	K5TIT	K5TIT
Dallas	443.8250	+	○ 103.5	K5XG	------------
Dallas	443.9500	+	●	AI5TX	------------
Dallas	444.0750	+	○ 110.9er	K5MET	------------
Dallas	444.1500	+	○ 100rs	N5IUF	TRS
Dallas	444.6500	+	●	W5DS	DART
Davy	443.1250	+	○ 141.3el	WD5IEH	------------
Decatur	442.6000	+	○	WB5TYE	NTWG

Location	Output	Input	Notes	Call	Sponsor
Decatur	444.4000	+	O 156.7l WX	KA5PQK	------------
Del Rio	443.5000	+	●	WB5TZJ	INTERTIE
Del Rio	443.7250	+	O 100	KD5HAM	BARS
Denton	440.7125	+	Oar	KE5YAP	------------
Denton	441.3000	+	O 146.2e	N5API	NONE
Denton	441.3250	+	O 88.5e	W5NGU	DCARA
Denton	442.7250	+	O 100	N5IUF	TRS
Denton	443.5250	+	O 118.8	WA5LIE	4SQR
Denton	444.0500	+	O 110.9ar	W5NGU	DCARA
Devers	442.5750	+	O 103.5	KA5QDG	------------
Devers	444.8500	+	O 151.4 (CA)el	N6LXX	------------
Devine	443.9000	+	●	WB5LJZ	------------
Dickens	444.3250	+	O 162.2 WX	WX5LBB	SPSST
Doss	442.3000	+	O 162.2l	W5RP	HOTROCS
Double Mountain	443.7000	+	●	AI5TX	------------
Dripping Springs	444.3250	+	O 186.2 (CA)	W5MOT	CMARC
Dumas	444.3500	+	O 88.5	N5LTZ	CRI
Duncanville	441.3500	+	O 114.8	W5GSR	------------
Duncanville	441.5500	+	O 110.9	KG5LL	------------
Eagle Pass	442.1000	+	O 100	N5UMJ	------------
Eastland	444.8000	+	O 107.2e WX	KB5WB	------------
Eden	443.9750	+	●	AI5TX	------------
Edgewood	444.2000	+	O 136.5	W5EEY	------------
Egan	443.7500	+	O 110.9el	KB5YBI	Johnson Co. ARC
El Campo	442.1250	+	O 103.5l	K5SOI	------------
El Campo	442.2750	+	O 103.5l WX	WB5UGT	------------
El Paso	441.7000	+	O 100a	N5ZFF	------------
El Paso	442.0000	+	Ol	K5KKO	EPDIG
El Paso	442.1000	+	O 123l	N5FAZ	EPDIG
El Paso	442.1250	+	O 103.5l	N5FAZ	RAVE RADIO
El Paso	442.2500	+	O 100l	K5WPH	SCARC MEGALINK
El Paso	442.5500	+	O 100	K5JAL	JPARA
El Paso	442.6000	+	●	KJ5EO	EPACS
El Paso	442.8250	+	O 100l	K5ELP	------------
El Paso	443.0000	+	●	KJ5EO	RACES
El Paso	443.3750	+	O 100 (CA)	N6TOC	------------
El Paso	443.4000	+	O 100l	K5WPH	SCARC
El Paso	443.6500	+	●	W5DPD	MARIE
El Paso	443.7000	+	●	WB5LJO	JACKS PK
El Paso	443.9250	+	●	KA5CDJ	MARIE
El Paso	444.2000	+	O 100al	K5ELP	WTRA
El Paso	444.3250	+	O 103.5l	NB5O	ROCKET BOX
Elgin	442.8000	+	O 114.8	KC5WXT	Bastrop ARES

Location	*Output*	*Input*	*Notes*	*Call*	*Sponsor*
Emory	443.6250	+	O 151.4	W5ENT	Rains Amateur R
Euless	441.3250	+	O	KC5GVN	------------
Euless	442.9000	+	O	W5EUL	------------
Everman	441.5250	+	O 110.9	AB5XD	------------
Fabens	442.4500	+	O 203.5	W5PDC	NONE
Flatonia	443.8250	+	O 141.3	WB5UGT	SALTGRASS
Florence	442.9000	+	O 100	K5AB	------------
Floresville	441.8500	+	O 179.9	WB5LOP	------------
Flower Mound	444.8500	+	O 110.9er	N5ERS	EMERGENCY R
Floydata	444.7750	+	O 162.2l	WA5OEO	------------
Fort Davis	443.6750	+	●	AI5TX	------------
Fort Davis	444.6250	+	O 146.2 (CA)elr	AD5BB	BIGBEND ARC
Fort Davis	444.9000	+	O 146.2l	N5HYD	------------
Fort Stockton	443.6500	+	●	N5SOR	INTERTIE
Fort Stockton	444.8000	+	O 162.2	N5SOR	------------
Fort Worth	423.9750	+	●	N5UN	FW440
Fort Worth	440.5500	+	O	KB5DRP	TEXAS DISAST
Fort Worth	440.5875	+	O	KF5LOG	NTX DEG
Fort Worth	441.3000	+	●	W7YC	------------
Fort Worth	441.3250	+	Oar	KE5DPN	------------
Fort Worth	441.3750	+	O 110.9	KB5ZMY	HANDLEY AMAT
Fort Worth	441.6000	+	O 100100a es	W5FWS	------------
Fort Worth	441.6750	+	O	K5AMM	GBARC
Fort Worth	442.1250	+	O 156.7l WX	KA5GFH	------------
Fort Worth	442.2000	+	O 110.9 (CA)	W5SJZ	LMRARC
Fort Worth	442.2250	+	●	K5HIT	SWAUARC
Fort Worth	443.0500	+	O 88.5	WD5GIC	NTARA
Fort Worth	443.1500	+	O 110.9	N5PMB	------------
Fort Worth	443.4500	+	●	N4MSE	NTXRA
Fort Worth	443.9250	+	●	K5SXK	INTERTIE
Fort Worth	443.9750	+	●	N5UN	FW440
Fort Worth	443.9750	+	●	N5UN	FW 440
Fort Worth	444.1000	+	O 110.9	K5FTW	FWTX VHFFM
Fort Worth	444.3000	+	O 110.9	K5MOT	------------
Fort Worth	444.5250	+	●	WB5JHR	------------
Fort Worth	444.6000	+	●	N5HKA	------------
Fort Worth	444.9000	+	O 110.9	W5NRV	NGARC
Fredericksburg	443.7000	+	●	AI5TX	------------
Fredericksburg	444.1750	+	O 162.2	W5FJD	------------
Freeport	444.9000	+	O 141.3el	KA5VZM	BCARS
Freestone	441.8250	+	O 123	AK5G	------------
Ft Davis	442.0250	+	O 100	W5RHN	------------
Ft Worth	442.9750	+	O	N5UA	DFW Remote Ba
Gail	443.7500	+	O 162.2l	KK5MV	------------
Gail	444.6000	+	O 100l	N5SVF	------------

Location	*Output*	*Input*	*Notes*	*Call*	*Sponsor*
Gainesville	442.7750	+	○ 100	WB5FHI	CCOARC
Gainesville	443.1250	+	○ 100	K5AGG	------------
Galveston	443.1250	+	●	N5KIT	GULL
Galveston	443.2750	+	○ 103.5	N5FOG	GCATS
Galveston	443.9500	+	●	AI5TX	------------
Galveston	444.9500	+	●	WB5BMB	------------
Gardendale	442.1500	+	●	WD5MOT	MOTOWTX
Gardendale	444.4000	+	○ 88.5l	N5LTZ	------------
Gardendale	444.5250	+	○ 146.2lx	WR5FM	CARE WTX
Gardendale	444.8375	+	○ 1lx	WD5MOT	Motorola ARC
Garland	441.3500	+	○	AB6ST	------------
Garland	442.7000	+	○ 110.9	K5QHD	GARC
			(CA)er		
George West	443.6750	+	●	KD5FVZ	INTERTIE
George West	444.2375	+	○	WD5FJX	------------
George West	444.9250	+	○ 233.6	KC5QPP	------------
Georgetown	441.5750	+	○ 100ae	N5KF	------------
Georgetown	441.6250	+	○ 103.5ae	K5SCT	SCARS
Georgetown	442.2000	+	○ 100	K5AB	------------
Georgetown	443.7750	+	○ 131.8	KE5ZW	------------
Giddings	442.5750	+	○ 114.8	NE5DX	------------
Goldthwaite	441.9000	+	○	K5AB	------------
Goldthwaite	442.6000	+	○ 100	K5AB	------------
Granbury	440.6500	+	○	K1DRP	TXDRP_Granbury
Granbury	441.3500	+	○	W5HCT	------------
Granbury	442.0250	+	○ 88.5 (CA)	WD5GIC	NTARA
Granbury	443.6250	+	●	AI5TX	------------
Grangerland	444.7000	+	○ 100 (CA)	KC5DAQ	HARS
Grapevine	443.8750	+	○ 110.9	N5EOC	NETARC
Greenville	441.6000	+	○ 100	N5SN	GREENVILLE RPT A
Greenville	443.9000	+	○ 71.9	N5SN	GREENVILLE REPE
Harlingen	443.6000	+	○ 114.8er	K5VCG	AK5Z
Harlingen	444.9750	+	○ 114.8els	W5RGV	STARS
			WX		
Haslet	444.3250	+	○ 110.9	K9MK	------------
Haslet	444.4750	+	●	N5GRK	------------
Heath	441.3750	+	○ 141.3	KK5PP	------------
Helotes	442.0000	+	○ 123ae	W5ROS	ROOST
Henly	444.6750	+	○	W5IZN	------------
Henrietta	444.7250	+	○ 192.8	K5REJ	CCARC
Henrietta	444.8500	+	○ 192.8	KA5WLR	------------
			(CA)		
Hillsboro	443.2750	+	○ 123ae	WB5YFX	------------
			WX		
Hollowood Park	442.2000	+	○ 162.2	K5AWK	------------
Hondo	443.3500	+	○ 141.3e	KD5DX	MCARC
Houston	441.5000	+	○ 100	N5BET	RDL
Houston	441.5250	+	○ 103.5	KD5HKQ	TARMA
Houston	441.5750	+	○ 88.5	KF5AHR	------------

Location	*Output*	*Input*	*Notes*	*Call*	*Sponsor*
Houston	441.6750	+	O 88.5	W5INP	------------
Houston	441.7000	+	O	W5OMR	------------
Houston	441.7750	+	●	KD5DFB	------------
Houston	441.8750	+	O 114.8	W5ICF	------------
Houston	442.0000	+	O 103.5	K5DX	TDXS
Houston	442.0750	+	O 100	KG4BON	------------
Houston	442.4500	+	O 103.5l	WB5UGT	SALTGRASS
Houston	442.5000	+	O 123 (CA)	WA5F	RACFE
Houston	442.6000	+	O 156.7	KD5DFB	------------
Houston	442.8250	+	O 103.5al	KC5UIB	------------
Houston	442.9250	+	O 103.5	KB5IAM	HCTA
Houston	443.0750	+	O 88.5	KC5AWF	BRA
Houston	443.1000	+	O 123	K5IHK	TMBLRPTCRP
Houston	443.1750	+	O 103.5	KB5IAM	HCTA
Houston	443.2000	+	O 123 (CA) e	W5QV	------------
Houston	443.3250	+	O 103.5l	KB5FLX	ARCDCT
Houston	443.5250	+	O 136.5	AD5OU	------------
Houston	443.5750	+	O 103.5	KB5IAM	HCTA
Houston	443.6500	+	●	N5TZ	------------
Houston	443.6750	+	O 103.5	N5TRS	Transtar
Houston	443.7250	+	O 146.2	KB5TFE	------------
Houston	443.7500	+	O 94.8	KB5TFE	------------
Houston	443.8250	+	O 103.5l WX	WB5UGT	SALTGRASS
Houston	443.9000	+	O 114.8	K1BDX	------------
Houston	443.9000	+	O 77	K1BDX	------------
Houston	444.0250	+	O 156.7l	W5JSC	------------
Houston	444.2000	+	O 114.8e	W5AVI	------------
Houston	444.2250	+	O 103.5	KR5K	------------
Houston	444.2500	+	●	WD5X	------------
Houston	444.3000	+	O 100l	N5XWD	TRS
Houston	444.3250	+	●	KB5OVJ	------------
Houston	444.3750	+	O 103.5	KA5AKG	------------
Houston	444.4000	+	O 103.5	WD5BQN	ECHO
Houston	444.4500	+	O 103.5 (CA)	K5WH	COMPAQ
Houston	444.5000	+	O 103.5	WB5CEM	------------
Houston	444.5500	+	O 123	W5RPT	MERA
Houston	444.6000	+	O 71.9lWX	WR5AAA	HRRC
Houston	444.6250	+	●	WB5ZMV	------------
Houston	444.7250	+	O 103.5203.5	WB5UGT	------------
Houston (West)	444.2500	+	●	W5TMR	------------
Hubbard	442.6000	+	O	KE5YPH	------------
Humble	443.5500	+	O 103.5el	W5SI	TEAC
Huntsville	442.8500	+	O 127.3e	W5SAM	W.C. ARES
Huntsville	443.9750	+	●	AI5TX	------------
Hurst	442.8500	+	O 110.9	KM5HT	Hurst ARC

Location	Output	Input	Notes	Call	Sponsor
Hurst	443.5750	+	○ 110.9l	WB5TCD	------------
Idalou	443.0000	+	○ 67ae	N5TYI	------------
Idalou	443.2750	+	○ 107.2	KC5MVZ	------------
Ingram	443.9250	+	●	AI5TX	------------
Iraan	443.9500	+	●	AI5TX	------------
Irving	442.3750	+	○ 110.9	WA5CKF	Irving ARC
Irving	442.6750	+	○ 110.9	WA5CKF	IRVINGARC INC.
Irving	444.8000	+	○ 110.9er WX	AL7HH	------------
Jacksonville	444.5250	+	○ 136.5	K5JVL	CCARC
Jasper	442.2000	+	○ 192.8l	W5JAS	LAARC
Jasper	444.5500	+	○ 118.8	W5JAS	LAARC
Johnson City	440.6250	+	○ 146.213	KR4K	------------
Joshua	444.1250	+	○ 88.5e	KB5YBI	JCARC
Junction	443.6500	+	●	AI5TX	------------
Katy	441.9750	+	○ 123	W5EMR	------------
Katy	442.3250	+	○ 103.5	KB5FLX	ARCDT
Katy	442.3500	+	○ 131.8e	WD8RZA	------------
Katy	444.0750	+	○ 103.5l	WB5UGT	SALTGRASS
Katy	444.9250	+	○ 123	K5ILS	------------
Kaufman	440.6500	+	○	KA5DRP	Texas Disaster Resp
Keene	443.1250	+	○ 110.9e	KC5PWQ	------------
Kempner	444.3750	+	○ 88.5	KD5CO	------------
Kent	443.9250	+	●	KE5PL	ARMADILLO
Kent	444.0250	+	○ 146.2lx	WR5FM	CARE WTX
Kerrville	443.6250	+	●	K5ZZT	INTERTIE
King Mountain	444.9250	+	○ 146.2l	KB5MBK	------------
Kingsville	444.2250	+	○ 107.2el	WA5SWC	------------
Kingwood	444.8250	+	○ 103.5	W5SI	TEAC
La Grange	443.7000	+	●	AI5TX	------------
La Grange	444.7250	+	○ 141.3l WX	WB5UGT	SALTGRASS
La Marque	442.0250	+	○ 103.5e	K5BS	TARS
Lago Vista	444.8500	+	○ 103.5	KC5WLF	------------
Lakeway	444.4000	+	○ 103.5	WB5PCV	------------
Lamesa	443.5000	+	●	KE5PL	------------
Lamesa	444.7500	+	○ 162.2l	K5WTC	WTXC
Lamesa	444.9500	+	○ 100	N5SVF	------------
Lampasas	443.6500	+	●	KE5ZW	ARMADILLO
Lampasas County	444.4250	+	○E-SUN	K6STU	------------
Laredo	440.6000	+	○	KE5WFB	DCC
Laredo	441.6625	+	●	KE5WFB	D-STAR COMM CLU
Laredo	442.1000	+	○ 100	W5EVH	------------
Laredo	442.3000	+	●	N5LNU	------------
Laredo	442.7000	+	○ 88.5ax	N5LNU	RRGRC
Laredo	444.0000	+	○ 100elr WX	W5EVH	------------
Laredo	444.2000	+	●	KE5WFB	DSTAR COMM CLUB

Location	*Output*	*Input*	*Notes*	*Call*	*Sponsor*
League City	442.2250	+	O 131.8ex	WR5GC	GCECG
Leander	441.6000	+	O 100e	KE5RS	------------
Levelland	441.5000	+	O 67a	KB5STL	------------
Levelland	442.0000	+	O 67a	N5SOU	------------
Levelland	443.1250	+	O 103.5e	W5CP	EDXS
Levelland	443.1500	+	O 136.5 (CA)	KC5TAF	------------
Levelland	444.3750	+	O 162.2l	WA5OEO	------------
Little Elm	444.3500	+	O	WA5YST	------------
Littlefield	444.8500	+	O 162.2l	WA5OEO	------------
Live Oak	444.9750	+	O 100e	KE5BWO	------------
Livingston	442.3000	+	O 146.2	WA5QLE	------------
Livingston	443.1250	+	O 103.5l WX	WB5UGT	SALTGRASS
Llano	443.5000	+	●	AI5TX	------------
Lockhart	444.3000	+	O 203.5l	WB5UGT	SALTGRASS
Longfellow	443.9750	+	●	WX5II	INTERTIE
Longview	444.7250	+	O 136.5 WX	KD5UVB	GCEC
Los Fresnos	444.5000	+	●	K5RGV	K5RGV
Los Fresnos	444.7750	+	O 114.8e	KF5INZ	------------
Lubbock	441.6750	+	O 97.4	W5WAT	------------
Lubbock	441.9750	+	O 97.4	W5WAT	------------
Lubbock	442.1750	+	O 97.4	W5WAT	------------
Lubbock	442.4750	+	O 97.4	K5WAT	------------
Lubbock	443.0750	+	O 88.5	K5LIB	LARC
Lubbock	443.9250	+	●	AI5TX	------------
Lubbock	444.0000	+	O 118.8r	WB5BRY	CRRC
Lubbock	444.0250	+	O 146.2lx	WR5FM	CARE WTX
Lubbock	444.1000	+	O 146.2	K5TTU	TTARC
Lubbock	444.4500	+	O 114.8	KZ5JOE	------------
Lubbock	444.5000	+	O 118.8e	WB5BRY	CRRC
Lubbock	444.6250	+	O 118.8e	KC5OBX	------------
Lubbock	444.8750	+	O 162.2elr x	N5UQF	------------
Lubbock	444.9000	+	O 162.2	KA5ETX	CERT
Lubbock	444.9750	+	O 162.2l	WA5OEO	------------
Lufkin	444.1000	+	O 91.5	KD5NWH	------------
Lufkin	444.4250	+	O 203.5l	WB5UGT	SALTGRASS
Lufkin	444.5750	+	O 107.2el	KB5LS	LSARC
Lufkin	444.9000	+	O 107.2	KD5TD	------------
Lufkin	444.9750	+	O 107.2ers	W5IRP	DETARC
Magnolia	441.6000	+	O 127.3 (CA)	KB5FLX	------------
Magnolia	442.9500	+	O 123	W5JON	------------
Magnolia	443.0250	+	O 103.5	KB5FLX	ARCDT
Magnolia	443.8500	+	O 156.7	W5JSC	------------
Magnolia	444.6750	+	O 192.8	KDØRW	------------
Manchaca	442.3250	+	O 167.9	KE5AST	------------

Location	Output	Input	Notes	Call	Sponsor
Manor	442.4250	+	O 100e	KI4MS	------------
Marathon	443.5000	+	●	AI5TX	------------
Marathon	448.0000	–	Oelr	AD5BB	BIGBENDARC
Marble Falls	442.8500	+	O 103.5	K5WGR	------------
Markham	444.7000	+	O 146.2	WA5SNL	MCARC
Marshal	443.1750	+	O	KB5TSY	------------
Marshall	444.1500	+	O	KB5MAR	Marshal ARC
Mcallen	444.3000	+	O 114.8ls WX	W5RGV	STARS
Mccamey	443.4750	+	Ol	KK5MV	------------
Mccamey	444.7000	+	●	N5SOR	------------
Mcelroy Mt	443.9500	+	●	N5HYD	INTERTIE
Mckinney	442.3500	+	O 100	KF5TU	PAGER
Mckinney	442.5750	+	O 127.3elx	N5GI	N. Texas Repeater A
Melissa	443.2000	+	O 100e	W5MRA	MERA
Mercedes	441.6000	+	O	KR4ZAN	------------
Mesquite	441.3000	+	O 110.9 (CA)r	AK5DX	------------
Mesquite	442.6250	+	O 110.9 (CA)	AK5DX	------------
Mesquite	443.3750	+	O 162.2er WX	N5AIB	------------
Mesquite	444.4250	+	O 156.7l WX	KA5PQK	------------
Miami	444.8500	+	O 88.5l	N5LTZ	CRI
Midland	441.7000	+	O	W5QGG	MARC
Midland	441.9250	+	O 162.2	W5MDS	ARES
Midland	442.0250	+	O 162.2	N5MXE	------------
Midland	442.2000	+	O 162.2l	W5LNX	SWLS
Midland	442.9750	+	O 162.2e	K5PSA	PSARAPB
Midland	443.2750	+	O 162.2	N5XXO	------------
Midland	443.3000	+	O 123	W5WRL	------------
Midland	443.5750	+	●	KE5PL	------------
Midland	443.6500	+	●	KE5PL	ARMADILLO
Midland	443.7250	+	●	N5SOR	INTERTIE
Midland	443.8000	+	O 162.2e	KK5MV	NONE
Midland	443.9750	+	●	KE5PL	ARMADILLO
Midland	444.2000	+	O 162.2	W5QGG	MARC
Midland	444.6000	+	O 146.2l	KB5MBK	------------
Midland	444.7750	+	O 88.5	W5UA	WTDXA
Mineral Wells	442.7000	+	O 85.4	WB5TTS	------------
Missouri City	444.0000	+	O	W5XC	------------
Missouri City	444.1500	+	O 103.5	W5XC	CYPRESS
Mont Belvieu	441.8000	+	O 103.5	KK5XQ	CCOEM
Montgomery	441.7250	+	O 103.5	WA5AIR	SALTGRASS
Moody	442.3000	+	O 123	AA5RT	SV70RC
Moody	443.9250	+	●	AI5TX	------------
Mound Creek	441.9250	+	●	WD5IEH	------------
Mount Pleasant	442.1000	+	O 173.8l	KA5FGJ	RAILS

Location	*Output*	*Input*	*Notes*	*Call*	*Sponsor*
Mount Pleasant	444.9500	+	O 151.4l	W5XK	ETXARC
Murphy	441.7000	+	●	AA5BS	------------
Nacogdoches	443.9500	+	●	KD5MBZ	------------
Nacogdoches	444.0500	+	O 141.3e	W5NAC	NARC
Nassau Bay	442.4750	+	O	NB5F	BAARC
New Braunfels	443.5000	+	O 146.2l	WD5IEH	------------
New Braunfels	443.8500	+	O 103.5	WB5LVI	------------
New Waverly	442.2750	+	●	NA5SA	------------
New Waverly	442.7250	+	O 103.5l	WA5AIR	SALTGRASS
North Richland Hills	441.7500	+	O 100	K5NRH	N. Richland Hills
North Richland Hills	443.6000	+	O 110.9	W5URH	------------
Notrees	442.5000	+	O 162.2l	N5SOR	WTC
Notrees	442.6000	+	O 146.2l	KB5MBK	------------
Notrees	443.7000	+	●	AI5TX	------------
Notrees	444.6750	+	O 162.2l	N5XXO	SWLS
Oak Ridge North	441.3250	+	O 123	KW5O	------------
Odessa	441.9000	+	O 173.8	N5MW	------------
Odessa	443.6250	+	●	KE5PL	Armadillo
Odessa	444.1000	+	O 162.2el	W5CDM	WTC
Odessa	444.2375	+	O 71	KA3IDN	------------
Odessa	444.4250	+	O 162.2	WT5ARC	WTARC
Odessa	444.9750	+	O 179.9el	K5PSA	PSARAPB
Onalaska	443.0250	+	O 67	WB5HBU	------------
Ovalo	444.9750	+	O 103.5e	KD5YCY	------------
Ozona	443.6250	+	●	KE5PL	------------
Palestine	442.3750	+	O 136.5	KR5Q	------------
Palestine	444.6000	+	O 103.5e	K5PAL	PACARC
Pampa	444.4000	+	O 88.5l	N5LTZ	CRI
Pandale	443.9250	+	●	WB5TZJ	------------
Paradise	441.9250	+	O 173.8	KJ5HO	------------
Paris	442.1250	+	O 151.4e	N4RAP	RRVARC
Paris	444.4750	+	O	KI5DX	------------
Paris	444.5000	+	●	W5KJC	RAILS
Pasadena	441.6250	+	O 103.5 (CA)	KD5HKQ	TARMA
Pasadena	442.3750	+	●	WA5LQR	------------
Pasadena	443.3750	+	O 123	KD5HKQ	TARMA
Pasadena	443.4500	+	O 114.8	WB5ZMY	PASADENA OE
Pasadena	444.2750	+	O 103.5ae WX	W5PAS	PECG
Pearland	441.9250	+	●	N5KJN	------------
Pearland	443.0500	+	O 167.9	K5PLD	PARC
Penwell	443.6750	+	●	N5SOR	INTERTIE,INC
Penwell	444.5750	+	O 146.2lx	WR5FM	------------
Pflugerville	441.8250	+	O 114.8	KC5CFU	------------
Pflugerville	444.3500	+	●	K5UUT	------------
Pine Springs	444.0500	+	O	N5SOR	ZIA

Location	*Output*	*Input*	*Notes*	*Call*	*Sponsor*
Pipe Creek	442.3750	+	O 141.3 (CA)	WD5FWP	BARK
Plainview	441.5750	+	O 156.7l	WR5FM	CARE WTX
Plainview	443.9500	+	●	AI5TX	------------
Plano	441.3000	+	O 179.9 WX	N5UIG	------------
Plano	443.6500	+	●	AI5TX	------------
Plano	444.1750	+	●	W5SUF	------------
Plantersville	444.9000	+	O 100	KF5GXZ	------------
Pleasanton	443.9750	+	●	NU5P	INTERTIE, INC.
Plum Grove	444.1750	+	O 103.5el	WB5UGT	SALTGRASS
Port Aransas	444.1000	+	O 107.2l	KG5BZ	------------
Port Arthur	444.8000	+	O 118.8e	KC5YSM	------------
Port Lavaca	442.6750	+	O 103.5	W5KTC	PLARC
Portable	440.6000	+	Oar	K5MIJ	ROCKWALL DIGITAL
Potosi	443.1000	+	O 88.5e	KD5YCY	------------
Prosper	442.0500	+	O	N5TPS	------------
Ranger	443.6750	+	●	AI5TX	------------
Ranger	444.9500	+	O 88.5	K6DBR	------------
Rankin	443.9250	+	●	KE5PL	ARMADILLO
Refugio	443.0500	+	O 103.5ex	K5WAG	RCARC
Refugio	443.8750	+	O 103.5	AD5TD	------------
Richardson	441.8750	+	O 131.8a	W5ROK	RCARC
Richardson	442.8000	+	O 110.9	W5VV	ALCATEL
Richardson	443.3250	+	O 110.9 (CA)e	NT5NT	NNARC
Richardson	444.0250	+	O 110.9l	WX5O	------------
Richardson	444.3750	+	O	N5GI	------------
Richardson	444.6750	+	O	N5UA	DFW Remote Base A
Richland Hills	441.8500	+	O 110.9elr	N5VAV	------------
Richmond	444.5250	+	O 123erWX	KD5HAL	FBCOEM
Riesel	444.6750	+	O 5	W5BCR	Bosque County ARC
Rio Medina	443.0000	+	●	W5TSE	------------
Rockwall	440.6750	+	Oar	W5MIJ	TEXAS INTERCONN
Rockwall	441.5250	+	O 141.3er	KK5PP	------------
Rockwall	442.2500	+	O	N5MIJ	------------
Rockwall	443.5500	+	O 162.2e	K5GCW	------------
Rosenberg	442.5500	+	●	WB5TUF	------------
Rosharon	441.9500	+	O 167.9e WX	N5QJE	------------
Round Rock	441.7000	+	O 110.9	KM5MQ	RRARE
Round Rock	442.8250	+	O 114.8	W5TEY	------------
Round Rock	443.1000	+	O 110.9	N5ECG	------------
Round Rock	443.6750	+	●	AI5TX	------------
Rowlett	441.3125	+	O	KR5EOC	------------
Rowlett	441.3250	+	O 162.2er WX	AB5U	------------
Rowlett	441.9500	+	O 110.9elr	AB5U	------------
Sachse	444.7625	+	O	AC5BC	------------

Location	Output	Input	Notes	Call	Sponsor
Saginaw	441.9750	+	○	N5GMJ	------------
Saint Hedwig	444.0750	+	○ 123	WA5FSR	SHARC
San Angelo	441.7500	+	○ 162.2l WX	KC5EZZ	------------
San Angelo	442.2500	+	○ 162.2	W5RP	------------
San Angelo	443.7000	+	●	AI5TX	------------
San Angelo	444.1250	+	○ 71.9l	KC5EZZ	------------
San Angelo	444.2250	+	○ 162.2el WX	KC5EZZ	------------
San Angelo	444.3500	+	○ 162.2e	N5SVK	------------
San Antonio	441.5500	+	○	KD5GDC	------------
San Antonio	441.9000	+	○ 103.5	KE5HBB	------------
San Antonio	442.0750	+	○ 100	W5SC	SARC
San Antonio	442.1250	+	○ 127.3 (CA)	KD5GSS	------------
San Antonio	442.3500	+	○	KB5UJM	------------
San Antonio	442.3750	+	○ 141.3 (CA)	WD5FWP	------------
San Antonio	442.6250	+	○ 127.3	KB5ZPZ	------------
San Antonio	442.8750	+	○ 82.5	K5RTO	PERSONAL
San Antonio	443.0250	+	○ 82.5	N5XO	------------
San Antonio	443.4750	+	○ 162.2l	WB5FNZ	------------
San Antonio	443.5500	+	○ 141.3	WA5LNL	------------
San Antonio	443.5750	+	○ 141.3 E-SUNl	WD5IEH	------------
San Antonio	443.6750	+	●	AI5TX	------------
San Antonio	443.7000	+	●	W5FQA	INTERTIE
San Antonio	443.7250	+	●	WX5II	Intertie, Inc.
San Antonio	443.8750	+	○ 162.2l	AA5RO	AARO
San Antonio	443.9000	+	●	WB5LJZ	------------
San Antonio	443.9500	+	●	WX5II	INTERTIE
San Antonio	444.0250	+	○	K5DSF	------------
San Antonio	444.1000	+	○ 179.9ae	WB5FWI	SARO
San Antonio	444.1250	+	○	K5SUZ	SARO
San Antonio	444.2000	+	●	WR5Q	------------
San Antonio	444.2500	+	○(CA)	KJ5UU	SAARMI
San Antonio	444.3250	+	●	W5DKK	------------
San Antonio	444.5750	+	○ 141.3l	WB5UGT	SALTGRASS
San Antonio	444.6000	+	○ 141.3	AB5QW	------------
San Antonio	444.6250	+	○ 141.3el	WD5IEH	------------
San Antonio	444.9500	+	○ 103.5l	WA5KBQ	------------
San Marcos	443.6500	+	●	AI5TX	------------
Santa Anna	444.0250	+	○ 94.8	KE5NYB	------------
Santa Anna	444.4500	+	○ 94.8	N5RMO	COLEMAN ARC
Santa Fe	443.4750	+	●	N5NWK	------------
Santa Maria	444.2750	+	○ 114.8els WX	W5RGV	STARS
Schertz	443.3250	+	○ 118.8	K9CTF	------------
Schertz	444.8750	+	○ 100 (CA)	KB5MXO	SCTA

Location	*Output*	*Input*	*Notes*	*Call*	*Sponsor*
Seabrook	443.2500	+	O 127.3e	KE5VJH	------------
Seguin	441.7250	+	O 156.7e	K5RGD	------------
Seguin	442.2250	+	O 141.3alx	W5CTX	------------
Seguin	444.4000	+	O	W5WD	CRC
Seminole	444.0500	+	O 146.2lx	WR5FM	CARE WTX
Seymour	444.9250	+	O 192.8	N5LEZ	------------
Sheffield	443.5000	+	●	N5SOR	INTERTIE
Sherman	444.7500	+	O 100	W5RVT	SHERMAN
Shiner	443.4500	+	O 141.3el	WD5IEH	------------
Shiner	444.2750	+	O 141.3	W5CTX	------------
Slidell	442.9250	+	O 110.9 WX	W5FKN	LTARC
Smyer	442.0750	+	O 146.2	KB5MBK	HTI
Snook	441.5000	+	O 103.5	W5FFP	------------
Snyder	443.6250	+	●	AI5TX	------------
Sonora	443.9750	+	●	N5SOR	INTERTIE
South Padra Island	444.8750	+	O 114.8	W5RGV	SOUTH TEXAS REP
Southlake	442.1750	+	O	N1OZ	------------
Southlake	443.0750	+	O	N5LLH	------------
Southlake	444.7000	+	O 110.9	N5EOC	NETARC
Speaks	442.5250	+	O	K5SOI	------------
Spearman	442.0000	+	O 88.5el WX	N5DFQ	DUST BOWL LINK S
Spring	441.3750	+	O 100	KC2EE	------------
Spring	441.5250	+	O 151.4 (CA)	KC5DAQ	HARS
Spring	442.6750	+	O 103.5l	KB5FLX	ARCDCT
Spring	442.7000	+	O 103.5l WX	WA5AIR	SALTGRASS
Spring	442.8000	+	O 88.5e	K5JLK	SMCARC
Spring	444.3500	+	O 103.5	KA2EEU	------------
Stephenville	444.7750	+	O 88.5	AB5BX	RAILS
Sterling City	441.5750	+	O 156.7lx	WR5FM	CARE
Sterling City	443.6750	+	●	AI5TX	------------
Stinnett	443.2000	+	O 88.5el WX	N5DFQ	DUST BOWL LINK S
Sugarland	443.0000	+	●	KC5EVE	------------
Sugarland	444.4750	+	O 173.8e	W5KDE	------------
Sulphur Springs	444.2750	+	O	K5SST	------------
Sulphur Springs	444.8250	+	●	K5SST	------------
Sundown	444.7250	+	●	KD5SHB	------------
Sweet Home	442.0500	+	O 103.5	K5SOI	K5SOI
Sweet Home	443.8250	+	O 203.5	WB5UGT	------------
Sweetwater	443.6500	+	●	AI5TX	------------
Sweetwater	444.7750	+	O 162.2el	KE5YF	NCARA
Tabor	443.5250	+	O 127.3e	KD5DLW	------------
Taft	444.2000	+	O 103.5	W5CRP	W5CRP
Taft	444.8000	+	O 107.2ex	K5YZZ	------------

Location	*Output*	*Input*	*Notes*	*Call*	*Sponsor*
Temple	444.7000	+	O 123	W5LM	TARC
Terrell	441.6750	+	O 110.9	K5RCP	------------
Texas City	443.8500	+	O 156.7	W5JSC	------------
Texas City	444.9250	+	●	WB5BMB	------------
The Woodlands	443.2250	+	O 203.5	KCØEJX	NSLS
The Woodlands	443.3000	+	O 203.5l	KCØEJX	NSLS
Timpson	444.6750	+	O 107.2e	KK5XM	------------
Tom Bean	441.6500	+	●	N5MRG	NTRS
Trinity	444.9250	+	O 103.5	N5ESP	------------
Trophy Club	441.3500	+	O	KA5R	Alliance ARC
Tuxedo	442.0250	+	O 88.5	KD5YCY	BCARN
Tyler	444.4000	+	O 110.9elr x	K5TYR	TYLER ARC
Tyler	444.7500	+	O 110.9e	WB5UOM	------------
Tyler	444.8500	+	O	W5ETX	ETECS
Van Alstyne	443.8000	+	O 103.5e	W5VAL	VARC
Vanhorn	444.9500	+	O 162.2l	N5SOR	------------
Venus	443.7750	+	O 110.9l	WS5J	JARS
Vernon	444.1500	+	O 192.8	NC5Z	------------
Victoria	443.2250	+	O 141.3el	WD5IEH	------------
Victoria	443.5500	+	O 103.5ax	KC5WUA	------------
Victoria	443.8000	+	O 103.5e	W5DSC	VARC
Victoria	443.9750	+	●	WD5IEH	INTERTIE
Victoria	444.6500	+	O 103.5	K5SOI	K5SOI
Victoria	444.6750	+	O 162.2	WB5MCT	------------
Vidor	443.6750	+	●	AI5TX	------------
Waco	442.4500	+	Oa	WA5BU	BARC
Waco	442.8750	+	O 123	W5ZDN	HOTARC
Waco	444.1500	+	O 123	AA5RT	SV70RC
Waco	444.7250	+	O 123	AA5RT	------------
Walburg	443.3000	+	O 88.5	K5AB	------------
Watauga	444.5750	+	O 110.9	W7YC	------------
Watauga	444.6250	+	O	W5URH	------------
Waxahachie	441.6500	+	O 110.9	N5OUW	------------
Wayside	442.3250	+	O 146.2lx	WR5FM	C.A.R.E.
Wayside	443.4000	+	O 146.2lx	WR5FM	C.A.R.E.
Wayside	443.9750	+	●	N5LTZ	ARMADILLO
Wayside	444.5750	+	O 88.5l	N5LTZ	CRI
Weatherford	440.6125	+	Oar	KT5DRP	TXDRP
Weatherford	442.4500	+	O 156.7l WX	KA5PQK	------------
Weatherford	443.2500	+	O 110.9l	W5URH	------------
Weatherford	443.7000	+	●	AI5TX	------------
Weatherford	443.8000	+	O 110.9	W5URH	------------
Weatherford	444.1750	+	●	W5SUF	------------
Weatherford	444.2750	+	O 103.5	WØBOE	------------
Weatherford	444.7500	+	O 110.9ae	K5RNB	------------
Webster	442.8750	+	●	N5JJY	------------
Webster	442.9750	+	●	KE5LYY	GULLS

Location	Output	Input	Notes	Call	Sponsor
Weslaco	444.2000	+	O 114.8	KC5WBG	------------
West Columbia	443.6250	+	●	AI5TX	------------
Wharton	444.1250	+	O 167.9	W5DUQ	Golden Crescent AR
Wharton	444.6500	+	O 203.5l	WB5UGT	SALTGRASS
Whitney	442.2000	+	O 103.5	W5WK	------------
Wichita Falls	442.5250	+	O 192.8	W5DAD	------------
Wichita Falls	444.0000	+	O 192.8 (CA)	N5WF	Morton
Wichita Falls	444.2000	+	O 118.8	WB5ALR	TFR GROUP
Wichita Falls	444.3250	+	O 192.8	K5WFT	------------
Wichita Falls	444.7500	+	O 192.8	KD5INN	------------
Wichita Falls	444.7750	+	O 173.8	K5HRO	------------
Wichita Falls	444.8000	+	O 192.8 WX	W5GPO	------------
Wichita Falls	444.9750	+	O 192.8	N5LEZ	------------
Willis	442.6250	+	O 156.7	W5JSC	------------
Wimberley	442.5500	+	O 141.3el	W5CTX	WARS
Wimberley	444.1500	+	O 114.8 (CA)	WA5PAX	------------
Woodlands, The	444.1000	+	O 136.5el	W5WFD	TWARC
Wortham	443.9000	+	O 136.5	KE5DFY	------------

UTAH

Location	Output	Input	Notes	Call	Sponsor
FREQUENCY USAGE					
Statewide	446.0000	446.0000	O	SIMPLEX	
Statewide	446.5000	446.5000	O	SIMPLEX	
Statewide	447.8000	447.8000	O	SIMPLEX	
Statewide	447.8500	447.8500	O	SIMPLEX	
Statewide	449.2500	–	O	SHARED	
CENTRAL					
East of Holden	449.3000	–	O 88.5 RBx	WB7REL	W7DHH
Fairview	449.0250	–	Oex	WA7X	------------
High Top	449.2500	–	O 131.8 L(145.29)x	WB7REL	------------
Horseshoe	447.3000	–	O 131.8 L(223.92)x	WB7REL	------------
Manti	448.2750	–	O 107.2a L(146.66)	WB7REL	------------
Manti	448.9750	–	●lx	WA7FFM	DARS
Manti	449.7500	–	O 131.8a (CA)	N7YFZ	------------
Marysvale	449.8000	–	Ox	N7ZSJ	------------
Richfield	447.4500	–	O 114.8 L(146.72)x	W7DHH	------------
Salina	447.1500	–	ORBx	KD7YE	WB7REL
Sterling	447.8500	–	O 131.8	WB7REL	------------
NORTH					
Bear Lake	448.4500	–	O 123.0	K7OGM	BEARS
Bear Lake	448.9750	–	●l	K7OGM	DARS

Location	Output	Input	Notes	Call	Sponsor
Bear Lake	449.7000	–	○ 100	K7OGM	------------
Logan	447.0000	–	○	WA7MXZ	------------
Logan	449.3250	–	○ 156.7 A(*007/#)	N7RRZ	------------
Logan	449.6250	–	○ 103.5a (CA) L(147.26/145.31/146.72)X	AC7O	BARC
Preston ID	448.7500	–	○ 88.5	KE7EYY	------------
Riverside	449.5750	–	○L(449.8) RB	WA7KMF	BARC
Thiokol	448.3000	–	○ 123a L(145.29/145.43 123)	KK7DO	GSARC
Wellsville	449.8000	–	○ 103.5	WA7KMF	BARC
NORTHEAST					
Vernal	449.7000	–	○ 136.5	W7BYU	W7BYU
PRICE					
Castledale	447.6250	–	○ 100lx	K7YI	------------
Castledale	447.7000	–	○ 88.5a (CA)x	WX7Y	------------
Castledale	448.5500	–	○ 88.5 RBx	WX7Y	N7QLO
Cedar Mtn	447.1250	–	● 100lx	K7YI	------------
Helper	447.0250	–	○ 88.5lx	K7SDC	N7TAG
Indian Canyon	447.3250	–	○ 114.8	N7KYY	------------
Price	448.3000	–	○ 88.5	W7CEU	------------
Price	449.3500	–	○	KA7LEG	------------
Scofield	448.9000	–	○L(147.34) x	KF7OY	------------
Sunnyside	449.0500	–	○ 88.5a (CA) L(147.32) RBx	K7SDC	SDARC
SOUTH					
Kanab	449.8500	–	○	W7NRC	------------
Kanab	449.8750	–	○	WI7M	------------
Page AZ	448.7500	–	○x	NA7DB	------------
Page, Az	449.9250	–	○x	W7CWI	LPARG
SOUTH EAST					
Mexican Hat	449.9000	–	○ 123 E-SUN	KD7HLL	------------
Moab	449.1000	–	●lx	K7QEQ	GMRA
Monticello	447.1000	–	○ 107.2lx	NØNHJ	------------
Monticello	447.4000	–	●lx	K7QEQ	GMRA
SOUTH WEST					
Black Hill	449.9750	–	○a	NR7K	------------
Cedar City	448.1000	–	○	N7DZP	------------
Cedar City	448.4000	–	○ 100eRBx	WA7GTU	------------
Cedar City	448.6500	–	●lRBx	KB6BOB	DARS
Cedar City	449.5000	–	○ 100 RB	WA7GTU	------------
Cedar City	449.9000	–	○ 100 RB	WA7GTU	------------
Kolob Peak	448.5000	–	○	K7WS	------------
Milford	448.6750	–	●elx	K7JL	DARS
Seegmiller	449.3250	–	○x	NR7K	------------

UTAH

Location	Output	Input	Notes	Call	Sponsor
St George	446.7000	446.7000	○a	KA7STK	------------
St George	448.6250	–	●	KD7YK	DARS
St George	448.7250	–	○	WB6TNP	------------
ST George	449.3500	–	○s	KI2U	------------
St George	449.4250	–	○ 203.5a (CA)	KA7STK	------------
St George	449.5250	–	● 100 A(*123) (CA)	KA7STK	------------
St George	449.7000	–	○ 100	K7SG	------------
St George	449.7250	–	○a	KD7YK	------------
St George	449.7500	–	○ 123	W7AOR	N7ARR
Webb Hill	449.9500	–	○	NR7K	------------
STATEWIDE					
Statewide	447.5750	–	○p	WA7GTU	------------
WASATCH FRONT					
Alpine	449.3750	–	○	N7XHO	------------
Antelope Is	447.2000	–	○ 127.3x	K7DAV	DCARC
Bountiful	447.2250	–	● 156.7	N7TDT	------------
Bountiful	447.4250	–	○ 192.8	KD7RTO	------------
Bountiful	447.6500	–	○ 123p	W7CWK	------------
Bountiful	448.8000	–	● 88.5 RB	KA7SLC	RMRA
Bountiful	449.3500	–	○ 123	W7CWK	------------
Bountiful	449.9250	–	○ 100eRBx	K7DAV	DCARC
Brighton	449.5250	–	○ 131.8e L(147.2)x	K7JL	------------
Clearfield	447.1500	–	○ 114.8	KR7K	------------
Clearfield	447.3250	–	○ 118.8	W7UTA	------------
Clearfield	447.3500	–	○	N7CRG	CSERG
Clearfield	448.8250	–	○ 123e	KØNOD	CSERG
Clearfield	449.9500	–	○ 123	NJ7J	------------
Clinton	447.0500	–	○ 114.8a RB	KK7AV	------------
Coalville	448.6500	–	●x	WA7GIE	DARS
Coalville	448.9000	–	○RBx	WB7TSQ	------------
Coalville	449.5500	–	○ 100x	WA7GIE	------------
Draper	447.0000	–	○ 123.0	KE7QGT	------------
Draper	447.3750	–	○	AA7XY	------------
Draper	448.3500	–	○e	N7GAD	------------
Eden	447.6000	–	○	KJ7YE	------------
Erda	447.3000	–	○ 88.5	N7SLC	------------
Eureka	448.2250	–	○ 146.2ax	KC7MVI	UVCC
Farmington	449.7000	–	○ 100	K7DOU	DCARC
Grantsville	447.4750	–	○ 114.8	KK7AV	------------
Huntsville	448.0250	–	○ 123	W7DBA	------------
Kamas	448.7500	–	● 100l	WA7GIE	DARS
Lake Mtn	449.9750	–	○ 131.8ex	K7UCS	UTCOARES
Layton	449.2500	–	○ 100	AI7J	SNP
Layton	449.8750	–	○ 167.9x	W7MVK	------------
Lehi	447.6000	–	○ 162.2	KD7RBR	------------

Location	*Output*	*Input*	*Notes*	*Call*	*Sponsor*
Lehi	448.2000	–	O 123	KB7M	------------
			L(224.560 HF)sx		
Lehi	448.7000	–	O 114.8e	N7IMF	------------
Lehi	448.8750	–	O 100x	WB7RPF	ERC
Midway	449.9500	–	O	N7ZOI	------------
Murray	447.0250	–	O 100	WØHU	SLCO ARES
Murray	447.2500	–	O 100.0es	KE7LMG	SLCO ARES
Murray	448.1250	–	O 192.8a	N7HIW	------------
			(CA)		
Murray	448.8250	–	O	N7TGX	------------
Ogden	448.2750	–	O 107.2x	WB7TSQ	------------
Ogden	448.5750	–	O 100	W7SU	OARC
Ogden	448.6000	–	O 123	W7SU	OARC
Ogden	449.6000	–	O 136.5	AI7J	------------
			E-SUNx		
Ogden	449.7750	–	OE-SUN	N7TOP	------------
			L(447.775) RB		
Orem	447.2750	–	O 100e	K7UCA	UTCOARES
Orem	449.5750	–	Op	N7FOC	------------
Park City	447.5000	–	Oe	NZ6Z	------------
			L(145.23)		
Park City	448.4750	–	O	KB7HAF	------------
Payson	447.0000	–	O	NV7V	------------
Payson	447.1250	–	O 100es	K7UCA	UTCOARES
Payson	448.0250	–	O 131.8 RB	N7HMF	------------
Payson	448.9500	–	O	WA7FFM	------------
Payson	449.2250	–	O 100e	K7MLA	ERRS
Pleasant Grove	449.3250	–	O 114.8	N7UEO	------------
Powder Mtn	447.7750	–	O 123	N7TOP	------------
			L(449.775)X		
Provo	447.4250	–	O	N7EVC	------------
Provo	448.3250	–	● 103.5ex	K7UCS	UTCOARES
Provo	448.9000	–	Op	KF7OY	------------
Provo	449.1750	–	O 131.8	KA7EGC	------------
Provo	449.2000	–	Oep	WA7FFM	------------
Provo	449.4750	–	O 100	WA7GIE	------------
			L(449.425)X		
Provo	449.6750	–	● 173.8ae	K7UCS	UTCOARES
			L(147.28/448.325)		
Provo	449.8250	–	O 167.9	KB7YOT	------------
Provo	449.8500	–	O	WA7FFM	UVRMC
Provo BYU	449.0750	–	O 167.9	N7BYU	KI7TD
Riverdale	449.0750	–	O 123l	W7RSS	------------
Salem	447.0750	–	O 131.8	N7FQ	------------
Salt Lake	433.6000	423.6000	O 100	WA7GIE	------------
Salt Lake	445.1000	445.1000	OaelRBxz	WB6CDN	IREAN
Salt Lake	447.1750	–	Op	W7SAR	------------
Salt Lake	447.5250	–	O 107.2	K2NWS	------------
			WXx		

Location	Output	Input	Notes	Call	Sponsor
Salt Lake	447.9000	–	O 114.8e RBx	WD7SL	OLRC So Jordan
Salt Lake	448.0000	–	O 127.3p	K7SLC	SLCOARES
Salt Lake	448.0000	–	O 100	W7DES	------------
Salt Lake	448.0500	–	O 100	K7CSW	SLPEAKARC
Salt Lake	448.1500	–	O 127.3 L(53.15)x	KI7DX	WA7X
Salt Lake	448.1750	–	O 203.5x	N7HIW	------------
Salt Lake	448.4000	–	Ox	W7IHC	------------
Salt Lake	448.4250	–	O 100	WD7SL	ERC
Salt Lake	448.4500	–	O 100e	K6TUG	SLCOARES
Salt Lake	448.5250	–	O	N7GXT	------------
Salt Lake	448.5500	–	O 100	W7IHC	------------
Salt Lake	448.6250	–	●lRBx	WA7GIE	DARS
Salt Lake	448.8500	–	●x	KD7PB	------------
Salt Lake	449.0000	–	●lRBx	WA7GIE	DARS
Salt Lake	449.0250	–	O 146.2ae x	WA7X	YOUARK
Salt Lake	449.1000	–	O 146.2ae x	WA7X	YOUARK
Salt Lake	449.2500	–	Op	K7MLA	SNP
Salt Lake	449.2500	–	O 88.5	W7XDX	------------
Salt Lake	449.2750	–	O 88.5x	K7OJU	------------
Salt Lake	449.3000	–	Op	K7DOU	------------
Salt Lake	449.4250	–	O 100 L(449.475)x	WA7GIE	------------
Salt Lake	449.5000	–	O 100ex	K7JL	------------
Salt Lake	449.5250	–	O 100lx	K7JL	------------
Salt Lake	449.6500	–	O 167.9l	W7YDO	------------
Salt Lake	449.7250	–	O 151.4ex	WA7UAH	ERC
Salt Lake	449.7500	–	O	KA7OEI	------------
Salt Lake	449.9000	–	O 100	KDØJ	SLCOARES
Sandy	447.6250	–	O	KD7IMR	------------
Sandy	448.3750	–	O 100.0	W7ROY	------------
Sandy	449.1500	–	O 100ex	K7JL	------------
Sandy	449.4000	–	O 100ae	K7JL	------------
Spanish Fork	447.4000	–	O 100x	K7DSN	------------
Springville	447.3250	–	O 114.8e	N7KYY	------------
Springville	447.4750	–	O 186.2	WD7N	------------
Statewide	449.2500	–	O 100	W7DES	SNP
U of U Hospital	448.1000	–	O 114.8	KD7NX	------------
West Haven	448.7750	–	O 123 L(449.775)	N7TOP	------------
West Jordan	447.5750	–	O 114.8	K7LNP	------------
West Mtn	448.2500	–	O 100.0x	N6QWU	------------
West Point	447.0750	–	O 123.0# L(E401462)	W7WPC	KE7OJJ
WEST					
Tooele	449.3500	–	O 100	W7EO	------------

Location	Output	Input	Notes	Call	Sponsor
Vernon	448.9750	–	●lx	WA7GIE	DARS
Vernon	449.9500	–	O 100	W7EO	TCARES
Wendover	448.6750	–	●lRBx	WA7GIE	DARS
Wendover	449.5500	–	O 123 L(449.425)X	WA7GIE	------------
VERMONT					
BURLINGTON					
Bolton	445.0250	–	●tel	WB1GQR	RANV
Burlington	443.1500	+	O 100.0	W1FP	NETARC
Monkton	444.6500	+	O 110.9el	W1AAK	NFMRA
Mt Mansfield	447.1750	–	O 110.9l	W1IMD	Brlngtn ARC
CENTRAL					
Killington	444.5500	+	O 110.9el	W1ABI	NFMRA
Pico Peak	444.5000	+	O 71.9l	KA1UAG	KA1UAG
EAST CENTRAL					
Cabot	449.6250	–	O 67.0	K1US	K1US
Corinth	443.9000	+	O 131.8l	KA1UAG	KA1UAG
White River Jct	444.0000	+	O 141.3	N1DAS	N1DAS
Williamstown	444.6000	+	O 110.9l	W1JTB	NFMRA
Williamstown	447.8750	–	O 100.0l	N1IOE	N1IOE
NORTHEAST					
Burke	449.1250	–	O 110.9l	W1AAK	NFMRA
Jay Peak	447.2250	–	O 100.0	K1JAY	StAlbansRC
NORTHWEST					
St Albans	443.4000	+	O 162.2	N1STA	StAlbansRC
SOUTHEAST					
Grafton	441.7000	+	O 110.9l	KB1PIH	W River RC
Mt Ascutney	448.1250	–	O 110.9l	W1IMD	NFMRA
Newfane	444.7000	+	O 110.9l	WA1KFX	NFMRA
SOUTHWEST					
Mt Equinox	444.0500	+	O 100.0l	K1EQX	NFMRA
WEST CENTRAL					
Rutland	449.1750	–	O 100.0e	WA1ZMS	WA1ZMS
VIRGINIA					
Abingdon	442.9750	+	O	KB8KSP	ARA-SOUTH
Accomack	444.3000	+	O	K4BW	K4BW
Alexandria	420.0250	223.1200	O	WD4KHP	NOVA6MGP
Alexandria	421.0000	146.1900	O	W4LBL	NVFMA
Alexandria	421.2000	146.3100	O	WA2RIA	NVFMA
Alexandria	434.3250	52.1300	O	WA4CCF	ALEX RC
Alexandria	439.2500	426.2500	O	WA9GVK	------------
Alexandria	444.6000	+	O	W4HFH	------------
Altavista	444.4250	+	O	WA4ISI	WA4ISI
Amelia	443.2000	+	O	KB4YKV	KB4YKV
Annandale	445.6250	147.8100	O	WD4IWG	AMRAD
Arlington	444.1500	+	O	KI4MB	------------

Location	*Output*	*Input*	*Notes*	*Call*	*Sponsor*
Arlington	446.1250	144.8700	O	WB4MJF	R&R RG
Arlington	446.1250	144.8700	O	WB4MJF	R&R RG
Arlington	446.1500	144.8700	O	WB4MJF	R&R RG
Arlington	449.8750	–	O	KA4DCS	------------
Ashburn	442.1000	+	O	KQ4CI	KQ4CI
Ashburn	448.8250	–	O	KQ4CI	KQ4CI
Bald Knob	441.9500	+	O	KD4BNQ	KD4BNQ
Bassett	442.7250	+	O	KF4RMT	KF4RMT
Bedford	420.0500	433.0500	O	WA1ZMS	MTN TOP ASSOC
Bedford	444.3500	+	O	N4CH	N4CH
Bedfrd/apl Orch	442.6500	+	O	WA1ZMS	MTN TOP ASSOC
Bedfrd/apl Orch	443.8000	+	O	WA1ZMS	MTN TOP ASSOC
Big A Mtn	444.8750	+	O	KB4WTP	KB4WTP
Blacksburg	444.6500	+	O	N4NRV	KC5EJR
Blackstone	442.2500	+	O	W2CPB	W2CPB
Blackstone	446.8250	–	O	KC4NSE	------------
Bland	443.8500	+	O	KD8DZP	KD8DZP
Bluefield	442.4500	+	O	W8MOP	W8MOP
Bluefield	443.6250	+	O	WZ8E	ARA-SOUTH
Bluefield	444.6250	+	O	WZ8E	ARA-SOUTH
Bluemont	445.7500	52.2500	O	N3AGB	MCNRC
Bluemont	449.9250	–	O	WA4TSC	------------
Boyton	444.7250	+	O	K4MMS	K4MMS
Broadway	444.4000	+	O	KC4TJY	------------
Buckingham	444.9500	+	O	WW4GW	WW4GW
Bull Run Mtn	420.4000	222.7400	O	KM4OI	#NAME?
Bull Run Mtn	434.0500	29.5600	O	N3AUY	#NAME?
Bull Run Mtn	434.0500	444.0250	O	N3AUY	#NAME?
Bull Run Mtn	446.7250	146.1150	O	WA4TXE	WA4TXE
Chantilly	448.3750	–	O	K4HTA	------------
Charlottesville	442.0750	+	O	KF4UCI	KF4UCI
Charlottesville	443.0000	+	O 151.4/151.4	W4UVA	W4UVA
Charlottesville	444.0000	+	O	WA4TFZ	WA4TFZ/ABBEMARL
Charlottesville	444.2500	+	O	WA4TFZ	K4RKA
Check	443.3500	+	O	KG4MAV	KG4MAV
Chesapeake	443.1000	+	O	KB4NKO	KB4NKO
Chesapeake	443.9000	+	O	N4EVG	N4EVG
Chesapeake	444.0000	+	O	W4CAR	W4CAR
Chester	444.2000	+	O	KD4KWP	KD4KWP
Chesterfield	433.0750	438.7750	O	WA3KOK	NERA
Chesterfield	442.1500	+	O	KA4CBB	KA4CBB
Chesterfield	442.4500	+	O	WA3KOK	(NERA)
Christiansburg	444.6500	+	O	WD4BSB	WD4BSB
Clifton Forge	444.3750	+	O	K4IJ	------------
Coeburn	444.2250	+	O	KC4UBU	KC4UBU
Copper Ridge	444.5500	+	O	KB4WTP	KB4WTP
Covington	442.2500	+	O	WA4PGI	VHF COMM ASSOC
Dale City	440.2250	448.1000	O	N4LJZ	LRRC

Location	*Output*	*Input*	*Notes*	*Call*	*Sponsor*
Dale City	440.2500	448.1000	O	N4LJZ	LRRC
Dale City	446.4250	448.1000	O	N4LJZ	LRRC
Daleville	444.4750	+	O	K4IJ	K4IJ
Danvile/wht Oak	444.7000	+	O	K4AU	K4AU
Danville	443.8500	+	O	KQ4I	KQ4I
Fairfax	449.7750	–	O	WD4KHP	------------
Falls Church	433.2000	444.9750	O	WA3KOK	NERA
Falls Church	444.3000	+	O	N4EFK	------------
Falls Church	444.4500	+	O	K8ZOA	------------
Falls Church	446.1750	144.8700	O	WB4MFJ	R&R RG
Fancy Gap	433.2000	438.8000	O	WD4ICX	REISENWEAVE
Fancy Gap	442.4250	+	O 107.2/107.2el	KF4OVA	KF4OVA
Fancy Gap	442.4250	+	O	K4AE	N4TZD
Fancy Gap	442.5750	+	O	K4IL	K4GW
Fancy Gap	444.9000	+	O	WA4CQK	WA4CQK
Fancy Gap	444.9250	+	O	KD4FWS	KD4FWS
Forest	443.6000	+	O	W8CXD	W8CXD
Forest	444.7500	+	O	WD4KQI	WD4KQI
Fork Mountain	443.1750	+	O	KD4TMB	KD4TMB
Franklin	444.8250	+	O	WT4FP	FRANKLIN PD
Fredricksburg	442.8500	+	O	K4SPT	SPOTSYLVANIA
Front Royal	434.3750	444.2250	O	N4MKH	CARS
Galax	443.1250	+	O 100/100l	KI4AVS	KI4AVS
Gasburg	442.0000	+	O	W4LG	W4LG
Gate City	441.9000	+	O	K4GV	K4GV
Gate City	444.7000	+	O	N4WWB	SCOTT CO ARC
Gloucester	421.2500	439.2500	O	N4XND	MIDDLE PENINS
Great Falls	444.0500	+	O	N3AVA	------------
Greenbay	443.1750	+	O	K4ARO	K4ARO
Gretna	443.0000	+	O	WA4ISI	WA4ISI
Gretna/smith Mt	444.0750	+	O	KD4TBC	KD4TBC
Gum Spring	442.8000	+	O	KB4MIC	KB4MIC
Hampton	443.5000	+	O	W4HPT	KC4F
Hampton	443.6500	+	O	KG4NJA	WB5POJ
Hampton	443.7500	+	O	WA4OHX	WA4OHX
Hampton	444.5500	+	O	W4QR	SPARK
Haymarket	420.5250	52.3700	O	KB4CVL	KB4CVL
Haymarket	420.5500	449.7500	O	KB4CVL	NVFMA
Haymarket	420.5750	146.3100	O	KB4NRU	NVFMA
Haymarket	420.6250	146.1900	O	KB4NRU	NVFMA
Henry	442.1000	+	O	KG4UAV	KG4UAV
Herndon	433.9500	222.8200	O	WD4KHP	WD4KHP
Herndon	433.9500	444.7750	O	WD4KHP	NOVA6MGP
Hillsville	442.1250	+	O	KK4EJ	KK4EJ
Hillsville	442.3250	+	O	KB4GHT	KB4GHT
Independence	443.3750	+	O	KI4URL	KI4URL
Independnce Hill	443.8000	+	O	AA4VA	------------
Indepndnthill	420.6000	146.3100	O	WB4FMD	NVFMA

VIRGINIA

Location	*Output*	*Input*	*Notes*	*Call*	*Sponsor*
Indepndnthill	420.8000	146.1900	O	W4LBL	NVFMA
Itinerant	440.7500	+	O	N4NSP	N4NSP
Jonesville	442.5750	+	O	WB4IVB	WM4MD
Keysville	443.5250	+	O	KB4TLZ	KB4TLZ
King George	448.4750	–	O	KG4SCP	SPOTSYLVANIA AR
Lexington	444.1500	+	O	KI4ZR	ROCKBRIDGE ARC
Lexington	444.3000	+	O	KI4ZR	RARC
Lorton	424.9000	444.7250	O	WD4KHP	NOVA6MGP
Lorton	449.7250	–	O	WD4KHP	------------
Louisa	442.2250	+	O	KD4OUZ	KD4OUZ
Lynchbg/jack Mt	442.4000	+	O	KF4YI	KF4YI
Lynchburg	420.0500	426.0500	O	K4CQ	K4CQ
Lynchburg	420.0500	426.0500	O 136.5/136.5s	NN4RB	NN4RB
Lynchburg	442.3500	+	O	KE4VNN	------------
Lynchburg	442.9500	+	O	AB4FU	AB4FU
Lynchburg	443.4500	+	O	KC4RBA	KC4RBA
Lynchburg	443.5000	+	O	K4IJ	K4IJ
Lynchburg	444.0000	+	O	N4TZE	N4TZE
Lynchburg	444.5000	+	O	K4CQ	K4CQ
Lynchburg/trow	442.2000	+	O	N4IFC	N4IFC
Madison	438.6500	449.4000	O	N8HON	#NAME?
Manassas	449.2250	–	O	WD4JCE	------------
Mappsville	444.3000	+	O	KD4NVM	KD4NVM
Martinsville	442.1000	+	O	N4FU	KB4ZGO
Martinsville	442.1750	+	O	KD4CRM	KD4CRM
Martinsville	442.2250	+	O	KB4ZGO	KB4ZGO
Martinsville	443.3000	+	O	K4IJ	MARTINSVILLE/MH
Martinsville	443.7500	+	O	W4DLW	W4DLW
Martinsville	443.8250	+	O	KF4RMT	KF4RMT
Mclean	434.1000	448.4500	O	AA3HA	AA3HA
Meadows Of Dan	444.2500	+	O	WG4R	WG4R
Mt Vernon	444.5000	+	O	WA5ZAI	WA5ZAI
Newport News	442.9000	+	O	W4MT	PARC
Newport News	444.7750	+	Oe	KI4LAO	------------
Norfolk	442.9500	+	O	W4VB	K4DA
Norfolk	444.4750	+	O	W4VB	W4NMH
Norfolk	444.6750	+	O	WD4MIZ	WD4MIZ
North Chesterfield	441.6000	+	O 100/100e I	WA4AYB	WA4AYB
Norton	444.8500	+	O	WA4NDQ	WA4NDQ
Nw Arlington	445.5000	144.8700	O	WB4MJF	R&R RG
Oilville	444.8000	+	O	KB4MIC	KB4MIC
Patrick Springs	443.1750	+	O	WG8S	WB8POC
Patrick Springs	443.7500	+	O	KC3FB	KC3FB
Pearisburg	444.6750	+	O	K4WCH	K4IJ
Pearisburg	444.9750	+	O	N4AZJ	DISMAL PEAK ARS
Pennington Gap	443.8500	+	O	W4NFR	W4NFR
Petersburg	442.6000	+	O	K4ARO	K4ARO

Location	*Output*	*Input*	*Notes*	*Call*	*Sponsor*
Petersburg	443.5875	+	O	WA4FC	KD4BPZ
Petersburg	443.8250	+	O	WB4KZI	WB4KZI
Petersburg	444.9000	+	O	K4SRM	WC4VAA
Poor Mtn	442.3000	+	O	K5JCT	K5JCT
Pops Peak	441.7000	+	O	N4JNE	N4JNE
Portsmouth	443.8000	+	O	W4POX	PORTSMOUTH
Portsmouth	443.9625	446.9625	O	KI4KWR	KI4KWR
Pound	444.8500	+	O	KF4VDF	KF4VDF
Powhatan	443.1000	+	O	KN4YM	AC4QG
Prince George	444.2750	+	O	KG4YJB	KG4YJB
Pulaski	442.0750	+	O	K4XE	K4XE
Richmnd	444.6500	+	O	W4FEG	W4FEG
Richmond	442.3000	+	O	KC4VDZ	WB4YMA
Richmond	442.5500	+	O	W4RAT	W4RAT
Richmond	443.3500	+	O	N4LFU	N4LFU
Richmond	443.7125	+	O	W4FJ	K4YEF
Richmond	444.8500	+	O	AB4SF	------------
Richmond	444.9750	+	O	W4VCU	WC4VAA
Roanoke	439.2500	426.2500	O	N4FHL	LEE MCDANIEL
Roanoke	441.7750	+	O	K4IJ	K4IJ
Roanoke	442.5000	+	O	W4CA	ROANOKE VALL
Roanoke	442.6000	+	O	K4ARO	K4ARO
Roanoke	442.7000	+	O	W7CP	W7CP/K1GG/N4
Roanoke	443.6500	+	O	WB8BON	ROBERT BRUC
Roanoke	443.7500	+	O	WD4KZK	KD4EG
Roanoke	443.8000	+	O	K4ARO	------------
Roanoke	444.1750	+	O	K4IJ	K4IJ
Roanoke	444.2750	+	O	K4IJ	K4IJ
Roanoke	444.9250	+	O	WB8BON	WB8BON
Roanoke	446.6500	446.6500	O	N4CH	N4CH
Roanoke/mill Mt	442.7500	+	O	W4KZK	W4KZK
Roanoke/poor Mt	442.8500	+	O	N3ZE	ARA-SOUTH
Roanoke/poor Mtn	443.6750	+	O	K5JCT	K5JCT
Roanoke sugarloa	444.8500	+	O	W4KZK	W4KZK
Rustburg	443.3250	+	O	N4UTN	N4UTN
Seaford	441.8125	446.8145	O	W4MT	W4MT
Singers Glen	444.6000	+	O	K4SAD	------------
Slings Gap	444.7750	+	O	W4KZK	W4KZK
South Boston	443.9250	+	O	KF4AGO	PIEDMONT ARC
South Boston	444.6250	+	O	W4HCH	W4HCH
South Hill	443.5250	+	O	K4MJO	KD4MJO
South Hill	444.1250	+	O	W4CMH	WC4VAA
Spoon Mtn	443.4000	+	O	WD4KZK	K4RCA
Springfield	449.8250	–	O	WD4KHP	WD4KHP
Stafford	443.8500	+	O	KB4OB	S.A.R.A.
Standardsville	443.9000	+	O	KF4UCI	KF4UCI
Staunton	444.8250	+	O	WA4ZBP	TEL PIO OF AM

Location	*Output*	*Input*	*Notes*	*Call*	*Sponsor*
Staunton	444.9500	+	O	W4WRN	ROY SILLING
Staunton/el Knob	444.1000	+	O	KE4CKJ	EKRA
Sterling	442.1000	+	O	WA4TXE	WA4TXE
Sterling	442.2000	+	O	WA4TXE	------------
Sterling	446.3000	29.6800	O	KD4DN	KD4DN
Stuarts Draft	444.0500	+	O	KB4OLM	KB4OLM
The Pentagon	444.5500	+	O	K4AF	PENTAGONRC
Tysons Corner	424.8500	52.6200	O	WD4KHP	NOVA6MGP
Tysons Corner	424.8500	222.8200	O	WD4KHP	NOVA6MGP
Tysons Corner	425.0250	223.1200	O	WD4KHP	NOVA6MGP
Tysons Corner	425.1750	146.1900	O	KM4OI	NVFMA
Tysons Corner	443.5000	+	O	KM4FI	FI ASSOC.
Tysons Corner	444.7500	+	O	K4JYF	NVFMA
Tysons Corner	446.6250	146.1150	O	WA4TXE	WA4TXE
Vienna	434.4250	146.0850	O	K4HTA	VWS
Vienna	444.8500	+	O	N4KOU	RMRG
Virginia Beach	441.9000	+	O	W4BBR	W4RVN
Virginia Beach	444.4000	+	O	W4BBR	W4RVN
Virginia Beach	444.9500	+	O	W4KXV	VBEARS
Warrenton	420.1250	144.7500	O	KA3TQD	XTRA104
Warrenton	445.5500	147.8100	O	WD4IWG	AMRAD
Waynesboro	426.2500	439.2500	O	N3XA	WA4ZBP
Waynesboro	444.7750	+	O	KF4UCI	KF4UCI
Whitetop Mt	443.0000	+	O 103.5/103.5e	KM4X	KI4PAY
Williamsburg	443.5500	+	O	N4ARI	N4ARI
Williamsburg	443.9500	+	O	W4NTG	WAARC
Williamsburg	444.1000	+	O	KB4ZIN	KC4CMR
Willis	442.9000	+	O	N4USA	KG4MAV
Willis	443.8750	+	O	W4DUM	W4DUM
Winchester	420.1750	144.7500	O	KA3TQD	XTRA104
Winchester	442.0000	+	O	W3CSG	------------
Winchester	448.7750	–	O	W4RKC	SHEN.VAL ARC
Winchester	449.1750	–	O	NB3O	------------
Wintergreen	444.5500	+	O 136.5/136.5	K4CQ	K4CQ
Woodbridge	443.1000	+	O	N4LJZ	LRRC
Woodbridge	444.9000	+	O	WB4FQR	ALLEN JOHNSON
Woodbridge	449.8750	–	O	KA4DCS	------------
Woodford	448.9750	–	O	WA4SDE	------------
Wytheville	442.0000	+	O	W4VSP	K4EZ
Wytheville	442.5250	+	O	W4VSP	K4EZ
ALL OF TMARC AREA					
SNP	442.9000	+	O		------------
SNP	447.8750	–	O		------------
CULPEPER					
Banco	443.2500	+	O 107.2l	WA3KOK	NERA
Gordensville	444.4000	–	O 151.4ers	KF4UCI	KF4UCI

Location	Output	Input	Notes	Call	Sponsor
DAHLGREN					
King George	448.4750	–	O 79.7e	KJ4KQB	KGARO
FREDERICKSBURG					
Quantico	443.5500	+	O 167.9	K3FBI	FBI ARA
Stafford County	444.4500	+	O 79.7 (CA) eWX	WW4VA	SARA
FRONT ROYAL					
Front Royal	442.7250	+	O 107.2el	NO4N	K4QJZ +NERA
Linden	442.3500	+	Oa	N3UR	N3UR
HARRISONBURG					
Bayse	444.6000	+	O 131.8rs	K4MRA	MARA
New Market	443.3500	+	O 203.5es	KQ4D	KQ4D
Penn Laird	443.1500	+	O	N4DSL	N4DSL
SPOTSYLVANIA					
Fredericksburg	442.8500	+	O 107.2el	K4MQF	K4MQF
Spotsylvania	442.7000	+	O 114.8 WX	KD4QNA	KD4QNA
Spotsylvania	447.8750	–	Ot	N2XHZ	N2XHZ
WARRENTON					
Warrenton	442.2500	+	O 167.9	W4VA	Fauquier ARA
WASHINGTON AREA					
Alexandria	443.1000	+	O 107.2	KI4PIW	TJHSST
Alexandria	444.6000	+	O 107.2l	W4HFH	Alex RC
Alexandria	444.6000	147.9150	O 107.2l	W4HFH	Alex RC
Arlington	443.2000	+	Oe L(ICOM IDAS)	AB4YP	AB4YP
Arlington	444.5500	+	O 88.5	K4AF	Pentagon
Arlington	448.6250	–	O 107.2er	W4AVA	ARPSC
Arlington	449.3250	–	O 151.4	W8HNT	W8HNT
Ashburn	448.8250	–	O 77.0	KQ4CI	KQ4CI
Bull Run Mtn	447.7750	–	O 67.0	WA3KOK	NERA
Burke	448.6750	–	O 100.0e	WA3TOL	NARC
Dulles	444.7500	+	O 100.0e	K4IAD	E-Star
Fairfax	448.3750	–	O	K4XY	VWS
Falls Church	447.4250	–	O 91.5e	KC1AD	KC1AD
Falls Church	447.6250	–	O 107.2er	W4AVA	ARPSC
Haymarket	448.2250	–	O 77.0el	W4BRM	BRM ARA
Haymarket	448.3250	–	O 77.0el	K8GP	DVMS
Haymarket	448.9750	–	Oe L(MOTOTRBO CC6 TS 1/ID-1 TS2/ID-2)	W4YP	W4YP
Haymarket	449.0250	–	O 156.7el	N3AUY	+KD3R
Herndon	443.0000	+	O 88.5	N2LEE	N2LEE
Loudoun	442.1000	+	O 77.0al WX	WA4TXE	WA4TXE
Manassas	442.2000	+	O 100.0e	W4OVH	OVHARC
Manassas	443.5000	+	O 110.9els RB	K4GVT	K4GVT
Nokesville	442.6000	+	O 100.0elr s	WC4J	PWC ARES

Location	Output	Input	Notes	Call	Sponsor
Reagan Airport	444.7500	+	O 203.5e	K4DCA	E-Star
Tysons Corner	447.0250	–	O 100.0 (CA)ez	NV4FM	NVFMA
Woodbridge	444.9000	+	O 127.3 (CA)e	W4IY	WWI
WINCHESTER					
Bluemont	443.6500	+	O 77.0el	K8GP	DVMS
Bluemont	449.9250	–	O 146.2	WA4TSC	WA4TSC
Maurertown	442.4750	+	O 77.0lWX	N3UHD	N3UHD
Winchester	442.0000	+	O 146.2	W3IF	W3IF
Winchester	448.7750	–	O 146.2	W4RKC	SVARC
Winchester	449.1750	–	O 141.3 A(888)erWX	WA4RS	WinchesterARS
WASHINGTON					
FREQUENCY USAGE - EAST WASH LINK					
Spokane	430.0750	439.0750		AK2O	
Spokane	430.1750	439.1750		AK2O	
Spokane	439.0750	430.0750		AK2O	
Spokane	441.2500			AK2O	
Spokane	446.2250	–		AK2O	
Spokane	446.2500	446.2500		AK2O	
Wenatchee	430.0250			AK2O	
Wenatchee	430.1000			KB7TYR	
Wenatchee	430.3500			KB7TYR	
Wenatchee	439.0250	430.0250		AK2O	
Wenatchee	439.1000			KB7TYR	
Wenatchee	439.1750	430.1750		AK2O	
Wenatchee	439.3500			KB7TYR	
Wenatchee	440.8750			WA7PUD	
Wenatchee	441.2250	+		AK2O	
Yakima	442.6250	+	●	WA7SAR	
FREQUENCY USAGE - IACC AREAS					
Snp	443.0000	+	t		
W WA - FREQUENCY USAGE					
Crossband	440.0250	440.0250			
Data - Nat'l Simplex	441.0000	441.0000			
Data - Rptr Output	440.7000	440.7750			
Data -Simplex	440.8000	440.9000			
Data Rptr Input	445.7000	445.7750			
Nat'l Calling Freq'y	446.0000	446.0000			
Rptr Inputs	445.0000	445.6750			
Rptr Inputs	446.0500	449.8750			
Rptr Outputs	440.0500	440.6750			
Rptr Outputs	440.9250	444.9750			
Simplex - Voice	445.8000	445.9000			

Location	Output	Input	Notes	Call	Sponsor
Simplex - Voice	445.9750	446.0250			
SNP #1 Input	445.0000	445.0000			
SNP #1 Output	440.0000	440.0000			
SNP #2 Input	448.0000	448.0000			
SNP #2 Output	443.0000	443.0000			
COLUMBIA RIVER GORGE					
Hood River Mountain	443.1750	+	O 88.5	NB7M	KA7JNU
E WA - CHELAN					
McNeal Canyon	444.5250	+	O 94.8	K7SMX	K7SMX
E WA - CHEWELAH					
Chewelah	443.7250	+	110.9	W7GHJ	NE WA ARC
E WA - CLARKSTON					
Clarkston	444.3750	+	O 131.8ez	N7SAU	N7SAU
E WA - CLE ELUM					
Cle Elum	444.9250	+	O 131.8ez	W7HNH	W7HNH
Sky Meadows	442.2000	+	O 131.8l	WR7KCR	KCRA
E WA - DAVENPORT					
Link Only	443.0750	+	●l	N7YPT	LCRG
E WA - DAYTON					
Skyline Rd Tower	444.4750	+	● 123.0el	N7LZM	N7LZM
E WA - DEER PARK					
Scoop	444.6500	+	123.0	KA7ENA	KA7ENA
Scoop Link Only	444.9500	+	O 110.9l	WA7UJO	WA7UJO
E WA - ELLENSBURG					
Ellensburg	444.8250	+	100.0	K7RMR	K7RMR
E WA - EPHRATA					
Beezley Hill	443.9000	+	Or	W7TT	CWARC
Beezley Hill	444.9000	+	O 103.5	W7DTS	W7DTS
E WA - GOLDENDALE					
Juniper Point	443.3500	+	82.5el	KF7LN	KF7LN
E WA - LIND					
Lind Hill Link Only	443.7000	+	● 123.0l	N7HZS	N7HZS
E WA - MABTON					
Missouri Falls	443.8250	+	O 100.0	KB7CSP	KB7CSP
E WA - MEDICAL					
Medical Lake	443.6000	+	100.0	WA7RVV	WA7RVV
E WA - MOSES LAKE					
Moses Lake	444.4250	+	100.0	W7KX	W7KX
Moses Lake	444.6750	+	100.0	N7BHB	N7BHB
E WA - NEWPORT					
Cooks Mtn	444.5750	+	O 100.0	KB7TBN	PCARC
E WA - OKANOGAN					
Pitcher Mtn	443.5500	+	100.0	W7GSN	ORA
E WA - PROSSER					
Prosser	442.3000	+	O 103.5#e	N7QNM	N7QNM
Prosser	444.8750	+	141.3	WB7WHF	WB7WHF
E WA - PULLMAN					
Pullman	444.3000	+	103.5	KC7AUI	KC7AUI

Location	Output	Input	Notes	Call	Sponsor
E WA - RICHLAND					
Banton Co	442.8750	+	● 203.5	WA7BCA	BCARES
E WA - SPOKANE					
Foothills	443.9250	+	O 100.0	K7MMA	K7MMA
Hwy 27	444.4250	+	O 100.0	N7FM	N7FM
Lookout Mtn	444.1500	+	114.8	N7BFS	N7BFS
Lookout Mtn	444.1750	+	84.5	N7BFS	N7BFS
Mica Peak	444.3500	+	192.8	N1NG	N1NG
Riblets	444.9000	+	123.0	WR7VHF	IEVHF
Spo Vly Link Only	443.6500	+	●l	W7TRF	SHRC
Spokane	442.0250	+	O	W6LNB	W6LNB
Spokane	444.7000	+	141.3l	AK2O	SpRptGrp
Spokane Co Emer	443.4000	+	100.0	AD7FO	AD7FO
Spokane Vly	442.4250	+	O	K7HRT	K7HRT
Spokane Vly	443.4750	+	88.5l	W7TRF	SHRC
Tower Mtn	443.8000	+	123.0	KA7ENA	KA7ENA
E WA - TRI-CITIES					
Kennewick	443.7750	+	O 203.5	W7JWC	W7JWC
Kennewick	443.9500	+	123.0 (CA)l	W7UPS	W7UPS
Rattlesnake	444.1000	+	100.0	W7AZ	TCARC
E WA - TWISP					
McClure Mtn	444.8000	+	110.9lRB	KB7SVP	KB7SVP
E WA - WALLA WALLA					
Walla Walla	444.2500	+	O	KL7NA	KL7NA
E WA - WENATCHEE					
Badger Mtn	444.7500	+	O 100.0ael	N7RHT	N7RHT
Link Only	442.2500	+	●	N7RHT	N7RHT
Wenatchee	443.6500	+	O	KB7MWF	KB7MVF
E WA - WINTHROP					
Mazama	444.8500	+	127.3	WB6WUI	WB6WUI
E WA - YAKIMA					
Bethel Ridge	444.6000	+	123.0	WA7SAR	YakSO
Moxee Link Only	442.6250	+	●	WA7SAR	YAKSO
Selah	444.2750	+	O 110.9	W7HAR	W7HAR
Tieton Orchard	444.2250	+	123.0	AB7XQ	NHRA
Tieton Site B	442.7250	+	123.0	W7YKM	NHRA
Yakima Link Only	444.6250	+	●	WA7SAR	yAKIMA S&R
E WA-MEDICAL					
Medical Lake	444.8500	+	100.0l	K7EI	K7EI
E WA-SPOKANE					
Spokane	444.0500	+	123.0	KG7SD	WA6HSL
IACC					
E WA-Kennewick	444.0500	+	100.0	W7UPS	W7UPS
NW OREGON & SW WASHINGTON					
Vancouver	442.3750	+	O 123ael	AB7F	AB7F
Vancouver	444.5500	+	O 131.8e	N7XMT	WB7DFV
Woodland	440.5750	+	O 100el	N8VJP	N8VJP

Location	Output	Input	Notes	Call	Sponsor
PORTLAND METRO					
Camas	444.5250	+	○ 103.5	KD7TFZ	KD7TFZ
Vancouver	440.1500	+	○	KB7PSM	KB7PSM
Vancouver WA	443.6750	+	○ 107.2	KE7FUW	KE7FUW
Vancouver WA	443.9000	+	○ 179.9	KE7FBE	KE7FBE
SOUTHWEST WASHINGTON					
Battle Ground	444.6500	+	○ 118.8	N7QXO	N7QXO
Hazel Dell	443.8000	+	○ 100	KC7QPD	KC7QPD
LaCenter	444.9250	+	○ 94.8	K7ABL	K7ABL
Longview	440.3750	+	○ 123el	AB7F	AB7F
Vancouver	443.9750	+	○ 123el	KB7APU	KB7APU
Yacolt	440.3250	+	○	W7RY	W7RY
SW WASHINGTON					
Vancouver WA	443.9250	+	○ 94.8e	W7AIA	CCARC
Yacolt	443.1250	+	○ 94.8s	W7AIA	CCARC
W WA - NORTH					
Anacortes	441.7250	+	○ 103.5el	W7PSE	PSE ARG
Arlington	440.4000	+	○ 123ae	N7XCG	------------
Bellingham	440.4750	+	○ 103.5	WC7SO	------------
Bellingham	441.9250	+	○ 103.5e	N7FYU	N7FYU
Bellingham	442.7500	+	○ 103.5el	W7UMH	5cecg
Camano Island	441.0500	+	○ 103.5	W7MBY	5 CNTY ERG
Cultus Mtn	444.3500	+	○ 100e	K7OET	------------
Darrington	442.6750	+	○ 127.3ael	W7MB	------------
Ferndale	442.8250	+	○ 156.7ael z	W7SSO	Whatcom Co
King Mtn	443.6500	+	○ 103.5l	W7SKW	MT. BAKER
Lookout Mtn	442.2500	+	○ 156.7e	W7SSO	W7SSO
Lookout Mtn	443.7500	+	○ 103.5e	WA7ZWG	MT. BAKER
Lyman Hill	442.4000	+	○ 107.2e	W7UMH	Mt Baker A
Lyman Hill	442.8000	+	○ 123.0e	N7NFY	N7NFY
Lyman Hill	444.5000	+	○ 103.5	WA7ZUS	MIKE OLDS
Matts Matts	442.5250	+	○ 103.5a	WR7V	MARK MC KI
Maynard Hill	441.1250	+	○ 123l	WBØCZA	WBØCZA
Maynard Hill	442.4250	+	○ 103.5e	W7UDI	PSE ARG
Mt Constitution	442.0000	+	○ 110.9e	K7SKW	MT. BAKER
Mt Constitution	444.0500	+	○ 103.5 (CA)elz	K7SKW	MT BAKER A
Roche Harbor	441.6000	+	● 131.8 (CA)e	W6QC	------------
Roche Harbor	443.4500	+	○ 103.5e	W6QC	SAN JUAN CNT
Sumas Mtn	440.3750	+	○ 131.8el	W7MBY	SUMAS MT R
W WA - NORTH COAST					
Neilton	444.7000	+	○ 118.8aer LITZ	W7EOC	AUX EMERGE
Pt Angeles	443.7000	+	○ 103.5e	WA7EBH	CHARLES ST
Sequim	442.0500	+	○ 103.5 (CA)el	KO6I	------------
Sequim	442.1000	+	○ 100e	KC7EQO	------------

Location	*Output*	*Input*	*Notes*	*Call*	*Sponsor*
Sequim	442.1250	+	O 123el	KC7LGT	------------
Sequim	444.2750	+	O 100 (CA) e	AF7DX	------------
Sequim	444.9000	+	O 131.8e	K6MBY	------------
W WA - SEATTLE-TACOMA					
Bainbridge Island	444.4750	+	O 103.5	W7NPC	BAINBRIDGE
Baldi Mtn	441.6250	+	O 100	KE7KKA	KE7KKA
Baldi Mtn	441.7000	+	O 103.5el	W7PSE	PSE AMATEU
Baldi Mtn	442.3250	+	● 107.2l	K7MMI	Cougar ARG
Baldi Mtn	442.6250	+	O 103.5	K7EK	GARY KOHTA
Baldi Mtn	444.8000	+	O 141.8	K7OET	------------
Bellevue	441.1000	+	O 156.7	KC7IYE	KC7IYE
Bothell	442.5500	+	O 103.5	WA7HJR	PSRRG
Bremerton	442.2500	+	O 127.3l	K7OET	EMERALD CI
Buck Mtn	441.2000	+	●DCSe L(147.2)	K7PP	K7PP
Buckley	442.8500	+	● 141.3l	K7MYR	------------
Cougar Mtn	441.5500	+	O 103.5e	W7GLB	------------
Cougar Mtn	442.3250	+	O 131.8	K7MMI	COUGAR MT
Cougar Mtn	443.4000	+	O 123 (CA) el	K7PP	K7PP
Cougar Mtn	443.7000	+	O 103.5e	WA7EBH	------------
Cougar Mtn	444.3250	+	O 100 (CA)	K7OET	EMERALD CI
Dash Point	443.9500	+	O 131.8	N7QOR	N7QOR
Dupont	442.9250	+	O 110.9e	W7CPU	IEARS
Duvall	441.8500	+	O 203.5e	N6TJQ	Mark Mille
Edmonds	440.3750	+	O 103.5	NU7Z	5-Cnty Eme
Edmonds	444.0250	+	O 103.5l	NU7Z	------------
Enumclaw	443.1750	+	O 107.2	N7OEP	N7OEP
Everett	441.6500	+	O 123.0	N7NFY	------------
Everett	441.8750	+	O 103.5e	W7EAR	Ev'grn ARS
Everett	443.9250	+	O 100lLITZ	W7FLY	BEARS
Everett	444.5750	+	O 103.5a (CA)l	WA7LAW	WA7LAW
Federal Way	442.9500	+	O 103.5ae	WA7FW	DAVID SWAR
Federal Way	443.5750	+	O 100	KSØF	KSØF
Federal Way	444.3000	+	O 103.5e	WA7WKT	ARNE W SKOOG
Fort Lawton	444.1500	+	O 100a	W7GVJ	MONTE MUEL
Gold Bar	442.1750	+	O 103.5	W7EAR	EVERGREEN
Gold Mtn	441.2000	+	O 123	K7PP	K7PP
Gold Mtn	442.6500	+	O 103.5 (CA)ez	WW7RA	W WASH RPT
Green Mtn	441.7500	+	O 103.5el	W7PSE	PSE ARG
Haystack Mtn	444.9750	+	O 114.8e	KD7GWM	------------
Haystack Ridge	443.8750	+	O 127.3e	N7NFY	SNOHOMISH
Highline	443.3750	+	O 103.5	N7IO	------------
Kingston	442.2250	+	O 100e	W7KWS	------------
Kirkland	441.0750	+	O 103.5el	K7LWH	Lake Washi
Kirkland	443.2000	+	O 103.5	K7PAR	PUGET AMAT

Location	Output	Input	Notes	Call	Sponsor
Lake Forest Park	442.0000	+	O 141.3	NU7Z	------------
Lakewood	441.3750	+	O 103.5l	K7EK	K7EK
Mercer Island	440.1500	+	O 103.5e	W7MIR	MERCER IS
Monroe	443.1250	+	O 110.9	K7SLB	------------
Monroe	443.2250	+	O 103.5e	K7MJ	------------
Mountlake Terrace	443.7250	+	O 103.5	WE7SCA	ESCA RACES
North Bend	440.2500	+	O 123	N9VW	------------
North Bend	442.7250	+	O 123e	W7EFR	EFR ARC
Olalla	440.2250	+	O 103.5 (CA)lz	WR7HE	HERMAN ENT
Port Ludlow	441.5750	+	O 103.5a (CA)ez	N7PL	PORT LUDLO
Port Orchard	444.1000	+	O 100 (CA) z	K7BTZ	ERNEST BEE
Poulsbo	442.2000	+	O 103.5el	WA6PMX	WA6PMX
Quilcene	443.4250	+	O 103.5e	WO7O	------------
Rattlesnake Mtn	441.7750	+	O 103.5el	W7PSE	PSE ARC
Rattlesnake Mtn	442.3000	+	O 123	W7SRG	W7SRG
Redmond	440.6750	+	O 103.5el	N6OBY	REDMOND AR
Renton	443.6000	+	O 103.5	K7FDF	City of Re
Roosevelt Hill	443.6500	+	O 141.3e	W7ACS	Seattle AC
Sammamish	440.2500	+	O 123	W7SRG	------------
Seatac	441.4500	+	O 186.2l	KF6VTA	------------
Seatac	443.1000	+	O 103.5	KE7WMH	SeaTac FD
Seattle	440.5250	+	O 141.3	WA7UHF	WA7UHF
Seattle	441.8000	+	O 141.3e	W7AW	West Seatt
Seattle	442.8750	+	O 141.3	WA7UHF	Seattle UH
Seattle	442.9000	+	ODCS	WA7LZO	Sea Amat Radio
Seattle	443.0000	+	O 141.3e	W7ACS	Seattle AC
Seattle	443.5500	+	O 103.5el	W7SRZ	WW MST
Seattle	444.0000	+	O 103.5	K7SPG	------------
Seattle	444.2250	+	O 123e	KC7LFW	NWFACARA
Seattle	444.3750	+	O 88.5	AJ7JA	------------
Seattle	444.5500	+	O 141.3	WW7SEA	COLUMBIA C
Seattle	444.7000	+	O 103.5e	WW7SEA	WW7SEA
Seattle	444.7750	+	O 173.9	KB7FHQ	CHILDRENS
Seattle	444.8250	+	O 103.5el	W7SRZ	ARES DISTR
Shelton	443.2500	+	O 100e	N7SK	MASON COUN
Shoreline	440.3000	+	O 103.5	KC7ONX	Shoreline
Shoreline	442.8250	+	O 103.5	K7UW	SHORELINE
Shoreline	444.7250	+	O 103.5	WB7UFR	K7CHN
Snohomish	442.9750	+	O 103.5e	W7ERH	Bill Rourk
Snoqualmie	444.9250	+	O 85.4e	N7SNO	------------
Squak Mtn	444.5250	+	O 103.5e	N7KGJ	Joe Basta
Sultan	444.1250	+	O 103.5e	W7SKY	SKY VALLEY
Sumner	443.6250	+	O 103.5e	W7PSE	PSE ARG
Tacoma	440.6250	+	O 103.5e	W7DK	Radio Club
Tacoma	442.4500	+	O 103.5 (CA)lz	NB7N	STARS

Location	Output	Input	Notes	Call	Sponsor
Tacoma	443.6750	+	○ 103.5el	WW7MST	WWMST
Tacoma	444.1750	+	○ 103.5a (CA)ez	K7HW	------------
Tacoma	444.7500	+	○ 192.8ael	KB7CNN	KB7CNN
Three Sisters	444.6750	+	○ 136.5e	N7BUW	BOB MIZENE
Tiger Mtn East	442.0250	+	○ 103.5	W7GLB	------------
Tiger Mtn East	442.3000	+	○ 123.0e	W7SRG	Samm ARES
Tiger Mtn East	442.6000	+	● 127.3e	K7TGU	------------
Tiger Mtn East	443.3250	+	○ 103.5#	N6OBY	REDMOND AR
Tiger Mtn East	444.6500	+	○ 131.8	WA7HTJ	------------
Tiger Mtn West	441.1250	+	○ 123l	WBØCZA	WBØCZA
Tiger Mtn West	442.0750	+	○ 110.9e	K7NWS	BEARS
University Place	442.3750	+	○ 103.5e	K7NP	U.P. Rptr
University Place	443.1500	+	○ 173.8e	N7EHP	------------
Vashon Island	443.5000	+	○ 103.5	W7VMI	W7VMI
Woodinville	442.7750	+	○ 100e	WA7TZY	WA7TZY&K6R
W WA - SOUTH					
Ashford	442.5750	+	○ 141.3e	K7DNR	WADNR ARC
Capitol Peak	440.5000	+	○ 110.9ae	K5IN	K5IN
Capitol Peak	443.5250	+	○ 173.8	WB7DPF	------------
Capitol Peak	444.9500	+	○ 118.8	W7EOC	GRAYS HARB
Chehalis	443.2750	+	○ 123l	AB7F	AB7F
Chehalis	443.4500	+	○ 110.9e	K7KFM	------------
Crawford Mtn	441.4000	+	○ 103.5ael z	NT7H	OLYMPIA AR
Eatonville	442.7250	+	○ 103.5	WW7CH	------------
Eatonville	443.9750	+	○ 103.5e	W7PFR	Gobblers Knob ARC
Electron	444.2500	+	○ 103.5el	W7PSE	PSE ARG
Graham	442.3500	+	○ 141.3l	K7EK	K7EK
Graham	444.6750	+	○ 127.3e	N7BUW	BOB MIZENE
Kalama	442.8250	+	○ 131.8 TTl	WB7DFV	R.F. ASSOC
Lacey	440.5500	+	○ 103.5el	W6TOZ	WW7MST
Lacey	442.4750	+	○ 100ae	WC7I	------------
Longview	442.1250	+	○ 114.8el	N3EG	------------
Longview	444.9000	+	○ 114.8e	W7DG	Lower Colu
Olympia	440.7250	+	○	NT7H	OARS 9600 packet
Olympia	443.0750	+	○ 103.5	KC7CKO	------------
Olympia	443.8000	+	○ 146.2el	W7USJ	W7USJ
Randle	444.8750	+	○ 100	AB7F	AB7F
Rooster Rock	444.9750	+	○ 110.9e	KB7WVX	MICHAEL DA
South Mtn	440.6500	+	○ 100l	K7CH	------------
South Mtn	441.9250	+	○ 100e	W7UVH	W7UVH
South Mtn	444.4500	+	○ 100	KD7HTE	K7CH
Woodland	444.4750	+	○ 100l	K7LJ	K7LJ
W WA - SOUTH COAST					
Aberdeen	444.6000	+	○ 100e	KA7DNK	KA7DNK
Aberdeen	444.8250	+	○ 118.8er LITZ	N7UJK	------------
Chinook	444.9250	+	○ 82.5el	NM7R	Beachnet

Location	Output	Input	Notes	Call	Sponsor
Cosmopolis	444.3750	+	O 100l	WA7ARC	NDCRT
Ko Peak	441.6750	+	O 118.8e	N7XAC	NM7R&N7XAC
Long Beach	444.8000	+	O 118.8el	NM7R	PACIFIC CO
Minot Peak	444.0500	+	O 118.8ers	N7UJK	------------
Naselle Ridge	440.6750	+	O 118.8	NM7R	Beachnet
Pacific	444.4000	+	O 118.8l	NM7R	PACIFIC CO
Raymond	441.3000	+	Ol	K7PP	K7PP
Raymond	442.1500	+	O 127.3 TTl	KB7IEU	KB7IEU
Raymond	443.8250	+	O 103.5 (CA)	KA7DNK	KA7DNK
South Bend	442.6750	+	O 118.8ael	NM7R	BEACH-NET

WEST VIRGINIA

Location	Output	Input	Notes	Call	Sponsor
Alderson	444.4000	+	O	KC8IT	N8LVE
Beckley	441.5750	+	O	N8FWL	N8FWL
Beckley	443.0500	+	O	N8FWL	N8FWL 222 RAD
Beckley	443.2250	+	O	W8LG	------------
Beckley	444.1250	+	O	N8LVE	------------
Beckley	444.5250	+	O	WB8YST	WB8YST
Beckley	444.8000	+	O	WV8B	ARA NORTH
Beckley	446.4500	–	O	WV8B	ARA
Beckley	446.7250	–	O	KE4QOX	KE4QOX
Beckly	443.1000	+	O	KE4QOX	KE4QOX
Belington	443.4500	+	O	W8BS	W8BS
Belington	444.9000	+	O	N8SCS	N8SCS
Belle	444.8250	+	O	N8RKU	N8RKU
Berkeley Springs	433.2500	0	O	WA3KOK	NERA
Berkeley Springs	440.0000	146.1450	O	KK3L	KK3L
Birch River	444.2750	+	O	N8FMD	N8FMD
Blfd-windmillgap	444.4500	+	O	W8MOP	------------
Bolt	444.2500	+	O	AB8DY	AB8DY
Bolt	444.4250	+	O	KC8AFH	KC8AFH
Buckhannon	442.6750	+	O	W8LD	WV WESLEYAN
Buckhannon	443.1000	+	O	N8FHE	N8FHE
Buckhannon	444.2500	+	O	N8ZAR	N8ZAR
Buckhannon	444.4750	+	O	K8VE	K8VE
Buckhannon	444.5000	+	O	WV8Y	WV8Y
Chapmanville	442.4750	+	O	W8CH	W8CH
Chapmanville	442.4750	+	O	W8CH	W8CH
Charleston	442.9250	+	O	KB8QKM	------------
Charleston	443.3000	+	O	WS8L	HUNT KNOB RP
Charleston	444.3500	+	O	WB8YST	WB8YST
Charleston	444.7500	+	O	WS8L	GR. KANAWHA
Clarksburg	441.4375	+	O	N8FMD	N8FMD
Clarksburg	444.1750	+	O	N8FMD	N8FMD
Craigsville	443.6500	+	O	KC8SDN	KC8SDN
Crawford	443.9750	+	O 103.5/103.5er	W8DDW	W8DDW

WEST VIRGINIA

Location	Output	Input	Notes	Call	Sponsor
Cross Lanes	444.4000	+	O	KC8RRI	KC8RRI
Cross Lanes	444.5000	+	O	AB8DY	AB8DY
Dunmore	444.2750	+	O	KC8CSE	KC8CSE
Elkins	442.1000	+	O	KD8JCS	WV8ZH
Elkins	444.8500	+	O	WJ8G	N8FMD
Fairmont	443.8750	+	O	W8SP	MOUNTAINEER ARA
Flat Top	441.3500	+	O	WV8B	ARA
Flatwoods	443.0750	+	O	KC8SDN	KC8SDN
Flatwoods	444.2000	+	O	W8FES	N8ZVK
Gassaway	444.6750	+	O	AB8WB	K8WGB
Gilbert	442.7250	+	O	KB8PCW	KB8PCW
Glenville	444.3250	+	O	KA8ZXP	KA8ZXP
Grafton	444.7500	+	O	W8SLH	WD8LNB
Hamlin	443.9500	+	O	N8IKT	N8IKT & LINCOLN
Harper's Ferry	420.1500	144.7500	O	KA3TQD	XTRA104
Hartmansville	444.7500	+	O	KC7OSZ	KC7OSZ
Harts	443.7500	+	O	N8IKT	LINCOLN CO COMM
Hernshaw	444.7000	+	O	WB8CQV	WB8CQV
Hinton	443.9000	+	O	KC8CNL	BLUESTONE ARC
Huntington	421.2500	434.0000	O	WA4GSS	OHIO VALLEY WIRE
Huntington	442.5750	+	O	KB8EHJ	------------
Huntington	443.0000	+	O	N8HZ	WPBY-TV RPTR GR
Huntington	444.8500	+	O	WB8ZER	WB8ZER
Hurricane	444.0750	+	O	K8WRF	------------
Hurricane	444.5000	+	O	W8HYX	W8HYX
Kenova	443.6000	+	O	KC8PFI	KC8PFI
Keyser	444.1250	+	O	N8RCG	N8RCG
Lewisburg	444.7250	+	O	KF8FO	KF8FO
Logan	444.9000	+	O	NV8H	------------
Madison	443.0500	+	O	K8WVA	K8WVA
Morgantown	444.7000	+	O	W8MWA	MWA
Morgantown	444.8000	+	O	W8CUL	WVU ARC
Moundsville	444.0750	+	O	KC8FZH	KC8FZH
Mount Hope	444.0250	+	O	K2BSA	K2BSA
Mullens	444.0000	+	O	KC8IT	KC8IT
Oak Hill	443.8000	+	O	KA8OTX	KA8OTX
Parkersburg	441.8500	+	O	AB8WV	AB8WV
Parkersburg	443.0500	+	O	W8VT	W8VT
Parkersburg	444.1000	+	O	N8ILO	N8ILO
Parsons	444.6750	+	O	AC8HQ	AC8HQ
Pennsboro	442.8500	+	O	WB8NSL	WB8NSL
Princeton	443.7000	+	O	KB8UJG	KB8UJG
Red House	444.2250	+	O	WV8AR	WV AMATEUR RADI
Richwood	442.2750	+	O	K8VKB	WA8YWO
Richwood	443.3750	+	O	KC8SDN	KC8SDN
Richwood	443.4750	+	O	KB8YDD	WA8YWO
Richwood	443.5750	+	O	KC8AUY	WA8YWO
Richwood	443.6250	+	O	KC8SDN	KC8SDN
Ripley	444.1500	+	O	KC8AOF	KC8AOF

Location	Output	Input	Notes	Call	Sponsor
Rockport	443.3500	+	O	N8LHL	N8LHL
Shirley	444.4250	+	O	KB8TJH	KB8TJH
Snowshoe	441.6500	+	O	KC8CSE	KC8CSE
So Charleston	444.9500	+	O	WB8CQV	WB8CQV
Spruce Knob	433.6500	147.8850	O	N8HON	MARA
St Albans	443.1500	+	O	K8MHR	------------
St Joseph	444.8750	+	O	KC8FZH	KC8FZH
Stonewood	443.2750	+	O	KD8TC	KD8TC
Welch	443.7250	+	O	N8SNY	N8SNY
Weston	444.6000	+	O	KA8TCF	KA8TCF
Wheeling	421.2500	434.0000	O	KB8QHO	KB8QHO
Wheeling	441.9500	+	O	N8EKT	N8EKT
Wheeling	443.0250	+	O	KA8YEZ	KA8YEZ
Wheeling	444.5750	+	O	W8MSD	W8MSD
Wheeling	444.9750	+	O	N8EKT	N8EKT
ALL OF TMARC AREA					
SNP	442.9000	+	O		------------
SNP	447.8750	–	O		------------
BERKELEY SPRINGS					
Berkeley Springs	442.4500	+	O 107.2al	WA3KOK	N.E.R.A.
Berkeley Springs	443.8500	+	O 123.0l	KK3L	KK3L
Berkeley Springs	444.7500	+	O 127.3	K7SOB	K7SOB
CHARLES TOWN					
Charles Town	444.3500	+	O 123.0 L(P25 NAC 734)	N3EAQ	N3EAQ
MARTINSBURG					
Martinsburg	442.8500	+	O 100.0e	N8RAT	N8RAT
MOOREFIELD					
Moorefield	442.4000	+	O 127.3a	K7SOB	K7SOB
Moorefield	444.4000	+	O 103.5e	KD8IFP	PHARC
Moorefiled	447.3250	–	O 103.5e	KD8AZC	KD8AZC
ROMNEY					
Romney	443.2000	+	O 127.3l	K7SOB	K7SOB

WISCONSIN

Location	Output	Input	Notes	Call	Sponsor
WAR					
Allenton	442.3500	+	O 127.3aes	N9GMT	FM38
Amberg	443.7000	+	O 114.8aelr	WI9WIN	W.I.N.
Appleton	442.1750	+	O 100.0aers	W9RIC	W9RIC
Appleton	443.6500	+	O 100.0aers	W9ZL	FCARC
Arlington	443.3500	+	O 123.0aelrs	KC9HEA	KC9HEA
Baraboo	443.5750	+	O 123.0aelrs	N9BDR	Empire Twr
Baraboo	443.7250	+	O 123.0aelrs	KØVSC	KØVSC

Location	*Output*	*Input*	*Notes*	*Call*	*Sponsor*
Baraboo	443.9000	+	O 123.0aelrs	WI9WIN	W.I.N.
Baraboo	444.5000	+	O 123.0aelrs	N9GMT	FM38
Beldenville	443.2250	+	O 110.9ers	NØNIC	B.A.T.S.
Berlin	444.9500	+	O 123.0aelrs	N9GMT	FM38
Big Flats	444.7250	+	O 123.0aelrs	N9WYQ	N9WYQ
Brookfield	444.2000	+	O 127.3aes	KB9YQU	KB9YQU
Burlington	442.8500	+	O 127.3aes	WB9COW	COWFAR
Cedarburg	442.1000	+	O 127.3aes	K9QLP	CFD/WERA
Chaffey	444.9500	+	O 110.9ers	KC9AEG	AB9AC
Chilton	444.8000	+	O 100.0aers	KD9TZ	KD9TZ
Chippewa Falls	442.3000	+	O 110.9ers	WD9HFT	WD9HFT
Chippewa Falls	444.0000	+	O 110.9ers	WD9HFT	WD9HFT
Clinton	443.1750	+	O 123.0aelrs	WB9SHS	RCRA
Colfax	442.8000	+	O 110.9ers	WI9WIN	W.I.N.
Colfax	444.3500	+	O 110.9ers	W9RMA	W9RMA
Coloma	442.6750	+	O 123.0aelrs	W9LTA	W9LTA
Delafield	444.1250	+	O 127.3aes	K9ABC	SEWFARS
East Troy	440.7750	+	O 123.0aelrs	N9WMN	N9WMN
Eau Claire	443.3000	+	O 110.9ers	KB9R	KB9R
Edgerton	442.3000	+	O 123.0aelrs	WI9WIN	W.I.N.
Elkhorn	443.7000	+	O 123.0aelrs	N9LOH	LAARC
Fitchburg	444.0000	+	O 123.0aelrs	KA9VDU	KA9VDU
Fond Du Lac	442.4000	+	O 100.0aers	WI9WIN	W.I.N.
Fond Du Lac	443.8750	+	O 100.0aers	N9WQ	NFDL ARS
Fond Du Lac	444.6000	+	O 100.0aers	N9GMT	FM38
Galesville	442.5000	+	O 131.8es	WI9WIN	W.I.N.
Germantown	442.8750	+	O 127.3aes	W9CQ	WARC, Inc
Germantown	444.5250	+	O 127.3aes	WD9IEV	WD9IEV
Gillett	444.2250	+	O 114.8aelr	WØLFE	WØLFE

Location	*Output*	*Input*	*Notes*	*Call*	*Sponsor*
Granton	444.0500	+	O 114.8aelr	W9EYN	N9RRF
Green Bay	443.4000	+	O 100.0aers	WI9WIN	W.I.N.
Green Bay	443.5000	+	O 100.0aers	KB9AMM	TEARUG
Green Bay	444.5500	+	O 100.0aers	KB9GKC	KB9GKC
Green Bay	444.7500	+	O 100.0aers	W9OSL	W9HAM
Green Bay	444.7750	+	O 100.0aers	K9EAM	G B M&K
Hancock	442.7250	+	O 123.0aelrs	WI9WIN	W.I.N.
Holcombe	444.5250	+	O 110.9ers	N9LIE	N9LIE
Hollandale	444.5500	+	O 123.0aelrs	WI9WIN	W.I.N.
Irma	442.7750	+	O 114.8aelr	KB9QJN	M.A.R.G.
Ixonia	442.0250	+	O 123.0aelrs	WA9YVE	WARC
Janesville	443.2250	+	O 123.0aelrs	KC9KUM	KC9KUM
Janesville	444.7500	+	O 123.0aelrs	WB9SHS	RCRA
Jefferson	444.9000	+	O 123.0aelrs	AB9KL	AB9KL
Kaukauna	444.4500	+	O 100.0aers	ND9Z	ND9Z
Kewaskum	444.2750	+	O 127.3aes	N9NLU	KMCG
La Crosse	444.4750	+	O 131.8es	AB9TS	AB9TS
La Crosse	444.7500	+	O 131.8es	NØEXE	NØEXE
Madison	441.4000	+	O 123.0aelrs	WI9WIN	W.I.N.
Madison	442.5750	+	O 123.0aelrs	KØVSC	KØVSC
Madison	443.4000	+	O 123.0aelrs	N9KAN	SWRG
Madison	443.6000	+	O 123.0aelrs	W9YT	UW BARS
Madison	443.7750	+	O 123.0aelrs	WI9HF	UWHC
Madison	444.2000	+	O 123.0aelrs	WD8DAS	NERT
Madison	444.3750	+	O 123.0aelrs	N9BDR	Empire Twr
Madison	444.5750	+	O 123.0aelrs	KB9DRZ	Empire Twr

Location	Output	Input	Notes	Call	Sponsor
Madison	444.7750	+	O 123.0aelrs	NG9V	NG9V
Manitowoc	443.1500	+	O 100.0aers	W9RES	W9RES
Marinette	444.5000	+	O 114.8aelr	AB9PJ	AB9PJ
Marshfield	444.8500	+	O 114.8aelr	WI9WIN	WIN
Mauston	442.2750	+	O 123.0aelrs	K9TD	K9UGJ
Medford	444.8250	+	O 114.8aelr	N9LIE	N9LIE
Merton	444.6250	+	O 127.3aes	W9JPE	W9JPE
Milwaukee	442.0500	+	O 127.3aes	K9MAR	R.A.M.W.L.
Milwaukee	442.4250	+	O 127.3aes	N9UUR	N9UUR
Milwaukee	443.0250	+	O 127.3aes	W9HHX	MSOE ARC
Milwaukee	443.2750	+	O 127.3aes	WI9WIN	W.I.N.
Milwaukee	443.5500	+	O 127.3aes	N9LKH	N9LKH
Milwaukee	443.8000	+	O 127.3aes	N9GMT	FM38
Milwaukee	443.9500	+	O 127.3aes	AA9JR	AA9JR
Milwaukee	444.4500	+	O 127.3aes	W9EFJ	W9EFJ
Milwaukee	444.8500	+	O 127.3aes	W9DHI	WERA
Necedah	444.1250	+	O 123.0aelrs	K9UJH	K9UJH
New Berlin	442.6750	+	O 127.3aes	WA9AOL	WA9AOL
New Berlin	443.3000	+	O 127.3aes	W9LR	WERA
New Richmond	444.6750	+	O 110.9ers	N9LIE	N9LIE
North Freedom	443.6750	+	O 123.0aelrs	KD9UU	SWRG
Northfield	443.5500	+	O 131.8es	WI9WIN	W.I.N.
Oshkosh	442.0750	+	O 100.0aers	N9GDY	N9GDY
Oshkosh	443.6250	+	O 100.0aers	N9GMT	FM38
Osseo	444.2000	+	O 131.8es	N9LIE	N9LIE
Park Falls	444.7500	+	O 110.9ers	W9PFP	PCRA
Platteville	444.3250	+	O 131.8es	KC9KQ	HVARC

Location	*Output*	*Input*	*Notes*	*Call*	*Sponsor*
Plover	442.0500	+	O 114.8aelr	W9SM	WVRA
Plymouth	443.2250	+	O 100.0aers	KD9TZ	S CTY 440
Plymouth	444.3500	+	O 100.0aers	WE9R	WERA
Port Washington	443.5250	+	O 127.3aes	WB9RQR	OZARES
Port Washington	443.7500	+	O 127.3aes	W9CQO	O.R.C.
Porterfield	444.4000	+	O 100.0aers	W4IJR	W4IJR
Pound	442.0000	+	O 114.8aelr	WI9WIN	W.I.N.
Prairie Du Chien	444.4500	+	O 131.8es	WI9WIN	W.I.N.
Prairie Du Sac	444.2500	+	O 123.0aelrs	N9KXX	N9KXX
Racine	442.0000	+	O 127.3aes	KR9RK	LRA Racine
Racine	444.0500	+	O 127.3aes	KA9LOK	KA9LOK
Rice Lake	442.1000	+	O 110.9ers	WI9WIN	W.I.N.
Rice Lake	443.6500	+	O 110.9ers	W9GDH	ARC2
Richland Center	442.7000	+	O 131.8es	W9PVR	WIN / PVR
River Falls	443.0250	+	O 110.9ers	WI9WIN	W.I.N.
Rudolph	444.3250	+	O 114.8aelr	WD9GFY	WERA
Sayner	444.4000	+	O 114.8aelr	WI9WIN	W.I.N.
Slinger	442.6500	+	O 127.3aes	WB9BVB	WB9BVB
Slinger	443.8250	+	O 127.3aes	KC9PVD	KC9PVD
Spooner/Hertel	443.5000	+	O 110.9ers	KB9OHN	BARS
Stevens Point	444.7000	+	O 114.8aelr	KC9NW	KC9NW
Sturgeon Bay	444.0000	+	O 100.0aers	K9KJM	K9KJM
Suring	442.5500	+	O 114.8aelr	AB9PJ	AB9PJ
Tomah	444.8000	+	O 131.8es	WI9WIN	W.I.N.
Tomahawk	444.5750	+	O 114.8aelr	N9CLE	TOM RPT A
Town Of Lisbon	444.2250	+	O 127.3aes	KC9HBO	N9AAO
Trevor	442.6000	+	O 127.3aes	KA9VZD	KA9VZD
Union Grove	442.2500	+	O 127.3aes	N9OIG	N9OIG

Location	Output	Input	Notes	Call	Sponsor
Watertown	440.1500	+	O 123.0aelrs	WI9WIN	W.I.N.
Waupaca	444.6750	+	O 114.8aelr	AA9NV	AA9NV
Waupaca	444.9000	+	O 114.8aelr	N5IIA	N5IIA
Wausau	442.2000	+	O 114.8aelr	WI9WIN	W.I.N.
Wausau	443.3250	+	O 114.8aelr	KA9HQE	KA9HQE
Wausau	443.5250	+	O 114.8aelr	W9SM	WVRA
Wausau	443.7500	+	O 114.8aelr	KC9NW	KC9NW
Wausau	444.1000	+	O 114.8aelr	W9SM	W.V.R.A.
Wausau	444.3000	+	O 114.8aelr	W9BCC	RMRA
Wausau	444.4250	+	O 114.8aelr	W9SM	W.V.R.A.
West Allis	444.4250	+	O 127.3aes	N9MKX	R.R.A.R.C.
Wisconsin Dells	443.8500	+	O 123.0aelrs	N9ROY	N9ROY

WYOMING

CENTRAL

Location	Output	Input	Notes	Call	Sponsor
Casper	449.5000	–	O	NB7I	NB7I
Casper	449.7500	–	OeE-SUN	N7EUE	N7EUE
Casper	449.9250	–	O	W7TOY	W7BLM
Casper Mountain	447.5000	–	Ox	KD7AGA	CARC
Casper Mountain	449.5750	–	Ot L(146.640)	KD7AGA	CDK Net
Casper Mountain	449.9000	–	O 100.0 L(IRLP)	K7YE	CDK Net
Lander	449.9000	–	Ol	N7HYF	WYAME
Riverton	448.2000	–	Oe	KD7BN	KD7BN
Riverton	449.2000	–	Ol	KD7BN	W7PAW
Riverton - Griffy Hill	449.9750	–	● DCS(DCS261N)elsWX	N7HYF	WYAME
Shoshoni	449.4500	–	O	KB7PLA	KB7PLA
Shoshoni - Copper Mtn	449.0000	–	O 100.0 L(HERC)x	KD7BN	KD7BN
Thermopolis	449.6750	–	O 114.8 L(52.525)	WA7JRF	WA7JRF
Worland	449.6000	–	O	KB7PLA	KB7PLA

EAST CENTRAL

Location	Output	Input	Notes	Call	Sponsor
Douglas	449.7000	–	O	NX7Z	NX7Z

Location	Output	Input	Notes	Call	Sponsor
HERC - STATEWIDE					
Copper Mountain	449.0000	–	O 100.0lx	KD7BN	KD7BN
Rawlins - Nine Mile Hill	449.8000	–	O 146.2e L(HERC)x	N7RON	N7RON
Wright - Pumpkin Butte	449.2000	–	O 100.0l	KD7BN	------------
NORTH CENTRAL					
Shell	449.6500	–	O	WB7QQA	CMARC
Sheridan	449.7000	–	O	W7GUX	SRAL
Sheridan	449.8500	–	O	N7KEO	N7KEO
NORTH EAST					
Gillette	448.0000	–	O	K7VU	K7VU
Gillette	449.7500	–	O 123.0e L(IRLP NODE 3307)	WR7CW	K7RDC
Gillette	449.9500	–	O	KJ7UG	KJ7UG
NORTH WEST					
Cody	448.3500	–	O 42.0l	KC7NP	KC7NP
Jackson - Snow King West	447.7000	–	O 123.0e L(IRLP 3464)rWXx	W7TAR	TARRA
Worland	448.2500	–	O 42.0l	KC7NP	KC7NP
NORTHEAST					
Evanston WY	449.3250	–	Ox	N7LMN	------------
SOUTH CENTRAL					
Rawlins	448.3000	–	O	KD7SU	KD7SU
Rawlins	449.4000	–	O 147.5l	KJ7AZ	HAMS
Rawlins - Nine Mile Hill	449.8000	–	O 146.2e L(HERC)x	N7RON	N7RON
SOUTH EAST					
Cheyenne	447.0250	–	O 131.8	N7DEN	N7DEN
Cheyenne - Archer Tower	449.9750	–	O L(MOTOTRBO)rsx	WY7EOC	Laramie Co Eme
Cheyenne - Chalk Bluffs	449.3000	–	O 131.8 (CA)xz	WU7G	WU7G
Cheyenne - Crystal Lake	448.1500	–	O 100.0x	KB7SWR	KB7SWR
Laramie	447.1000	–	O 114.8	N7QJL	N7CTM
Laramie	449.0750	–	O	WB7CJO	WB7CJO
Torrington	448.6000	–	O	N7CFR	N7CFR
Wheatland	449.6000	–	O	WA7SNU	WA7SNU
Wheatland	449.6250	–	O	WA7SNU	GPARA
Wheatland	449.7750	–	100.0	N7UCL	N7UCL
SOUTH WEST					
Evanston	448.1500	–	O	N7LMN	N7LMN
Evanston	449.3250	–	O	N7LMN	N7LMN
Evanston - Runge Hill	448.8000	–	● 131.8l	K6JR	K6JR
Fort Bridger	449.7250	–	O 123.0	KF7ELU	KF7ELU
Kemmerer	449.0750	–	123.0	KC7FDO	KC7FDO
Kemmerer	449.8250	–	O	N7HCH	ORARC

Location	Output	Input	Notes	Call	Sponsor
WEST CENTRAL					
Bedford - Lone Star Ranch	447.0000	–	● 100.0rs	W7UY	W7UY
Pinedale - Mt Airy	448.1000	–	O 100.0e L(146.775)rx	KC7BJY	SCARC

ALBERTA

Location	Output	Input	Notes	Call	Sponsor
CALGARY					
Calgary	444.0000	+	Ox	VE6RYC	CARA
Calgary	444.0750	+	OE-SUN	VE6AQK	VE6AQK
Calgary	444.1250	+	O	VE6WRT	VE6CPT
Calgary	444.2750	+	O 110.9	VE6ZV	VE6AQK
Calgary	444.3500	+	O	VE6EHX	CARA
Calgary	444.4000	+	Ol	VE6NOV	CARA
Calgary	444.4750	+	O	VE6DDC	VE6FH
Calgary	444.4750	+	O	VE6GAB	VE6GAD
Calgary	444.5750	+	O 110.9	VE6RY	CARA
Calgary	444.6500	+	O	VE6RPN	VE6DNY
Calgary	444.6750	+	O	VE6FIL	FARS
Calgary	444.7500	+	Ol	VE6KQ	VE6KQ
Calgary	444.9000	+	Olx	VE6WRT	WRN
Calgary	444.9250	+	O	VE6CPT	VE6CPT
Calgary	449.4500	–	O	VE6SPR	VE6NZ
CENTRAL EAST					
Hardisty	444.0250	+	O	VE6TDW	VE6TDW
Legal	444.6500	+	O	VE6DFW	VE6DFW
Legal	444.7250	+	O	VE6DFW	VE6DFW
CENTRAL NORTH					
Pigeon Lake	443.1500	+	O	VE6LPR	------------
EDMONTON					
Beaumont	444.9750	+	O	VE6SBE	VE6AVK
Edmonton	444.1000	+		VE6HM	VE6NC
Edmonton	444.4000	+	O	VE6GPS	VE6JTM
Edmonton	444.8000	+	O	VE6SBR	VE6SBS
Edmonton	444.9750	+		VE6EAR	VE6ETU
Ft Saskatchewan	444.4500	+	O	VE6TCK	VE6TCK
Sherwood Park	444.3000	+	O	VE6DXX	VE6DXX
Sherwood Park	448.2500	–	O	VE6SBR	VE6SBS
LETHBRIDGE					
Lethbridge	444.0500	+	O	VE6HDO	VE6HDO
Lethbridge	444.1000	+	O	VE6IRL	VE6COM
Lethbridge	444.6750	+	O	VE6COM	VE6COM
Lethbridge	444.7000	+	Op	VE6DES	VE6DES
Lethbridge	444.8500	+	Ol	VE6XA	VE6XA
Lethbridge	449.7500	–	Ol	VE6CAM	SARC
MEDICINE HAT					
Medicine Hat	444.0750	+	O	VE6MHU	VE6MLD
Medicine Hat	444.4750	+	O	VE6MLT	------------
Medicine Hat	444.8000	+	O	VE6GLF	VE6GLF

Location	*Output*	*Input*	*Notes*	*Call*	*Sponsor*
Medicine Hat	449.9250	–	O	VE6VOA	VE6MLD
NORTH					
Slave Lake	444.3500	+	O	VE6AMY	VE6AMY
NORTH EAST					
Ashmont	444.1500	+	Ol	VE6TTL	VE6ARJ
Cold Lake	442.2000	+	O	VE6TAR	CLARC
Elk Island	444.3750	+	O	VE6REI	VE6REI
Glendon	444.9750	+	O	VE6COW	VE6XLR
Lloydminster	444.7250	+	Oa	VE5FD	VE6FF
St Paul	444.5000	+	O	VE6SB	------------
PEACE RIVER					
Peace River/Tangent	444.6000	+	O	VE6AAF	------------
RED DEER					
Alix/Bashaw	448.9750	–	O	VE6PAT	VE6ZH
Red Deer	443.3750	+	O	VE6ONE	VE6ONE
Red Deer	444.5500	+		VE6SCR	VE6AQK
Red Deer	444.5500	+	O	VE6YX	VE6CIA
SOUTH					
Claresholm	444.4750	+	O	VE6CC	VE6CC
High River	444.1500	+	O	VE6HRB	FARS
High River	444.7250	+	O	VE6HRB	FARS
YELLOWHEAD					
Hinton	447.8250	–	O	VE6YAR	YARC

BRITISH COLUMBIA

FRASER VALLEY					
Abbotsford	442.0250	+	110.9el	VE7RVA	FVERESS
Chilliwack	442.8000	+	O 110.9	VA7RSH	Cheam Repe
Chilliwack	444.7000	+	Oel	VE7RAD	VE7IHR & V
Langley	441.3750	+	Oe	VE7RMH	VE7AVM
Langley	443.9750	+	O	VE7RLY	Langley AR
Langley	444.1250	+	127.3	VE7NPN	VE7NPN
Maple Ridge	443.6250	+	156.7	VE7RMR	Maple Ridg
GREATER VANCOUVER					
Burnaby	442.2000	+	110.9el	VA7LNK	VE7KED
Burnaby	442.4750	+	e	VA7PRE	VE7RMY
Burnaby	442.8500	+	O	VE7RBY	Burnaby AR
Burnaby	443.6750	+	O	VE7CBN	VE7XL
Burnaby	444.7500	+	123.0l	VE7ROX	VE7ROX
Delta	443.3500	+	127.3e	VE7EPP	VA7NY
Delta	444.4250	+	107.2	VE7RDE	Delta ARS
New Westminster	442.3750	+	110.9	VA7HPS	VE7ISV
North Vancouver	430.9500	439.9500	O	VE7RYZ	VE7PSA
Port Coquitlam	443.1000	+	94.8	VE7UDX	VE7ZZX
Richmond	442.3750	+	203.5	VE7RMD	Richmond A
Surrey	442.3500	+	O	VE7RUK	WestCoastU
Surrey	443.6000	+		VE7MAN	VE7MAN
Surrey	443.7750	+	110.9e	VE7RSC	Surrey ARC

BRITISH COLUMBIA

Location	Output	Input	Notes	Call	Sponsor
Vancouver	441.9750	+	O	VE7RHS	UBC ARS
Vancouver	442.2250	+	O	VE7RPS	VE7MMA
Vancouver	442.3250	+	100	VE7VHF	VE7CIM
Vancouver	442.5750	+	O	VE7ZIT	Radio Fili
Vancouver	442.9500	+	el	VE7AAU	RADIO ATS
Vancouver	443.1500	+	e	VE7NYE	VA7NY
Vancouver	443.2000	+	Ol	VE7NSR	VE7CHU
Vancouver	443.2500	+	O	VE7RCH	Cheam Repe
Vancouver	443.2750	+	O	VE7RCI	Cheam Repe
Vancouver	443.4000	+	el	VE7RAG	BCFMCA
Vancouver	443.5250	+	●e	VE7RPT	BCFMCA
Vancouver	443.5500	+		VA7RPA	Radio Pino
Vancouver	443.7250	+	O	VE7RDJ	VE7AOV
Vancouver	443.8000	+	●t	VE7UHF	VE7MQ
Vancouver	444.0000	+	156.7	VE7URG	VE7DBK
Vancouver	444.0750	+	O	VE7TOK	VE7MBG
Vancouver	444.1000	+		VE7ROY	VE7COT
Vancouver	444.2250	+	O	VE7RFI	Rogers Cab
Vancouver	444.4000	+	103.5	VE7BAS	VE7BAS
Vancouver	444.4750	+	O	VE7PRA	Pacific Ri
Vancouver	444.6750	+	O	VE7CDN	Can. Airli
Vancouver	444.8250	+	156.7	VE7VYL	BCFMCA
Vancouver	444.9500	+		VE7RNV	VE7CHU
Vancouver	444.9750	+	Ot	VE7SKY	VE7WF
NORTH COAST					
Terrace	444.9750	+	O	VE7RDD	Doug Davie
NORTH INTERIOR					
Nimpo Lake	444.8250	+	88.5	VA7SPY	VE7EWS
Quesnel	444.8000	+	100	VE7RES	PGARC
Williams Lake	444.1000	+	O	VE7ZIG	VE7IG
SOUTH CENTRAL					
Barriere	442.6500	+	l	VA7RTN	VE7MOB
Barriere	442.8750	+	l	VE7RTN	VE7PW
Blackpool	444.0000	+	O	VE7RBP	WELLS GRAY
Clinton	442.6500	+		VE7LMR	VE7PW
Clinton	442.8250	+		VE7LMR	VE7PW
Edgewood Nakusp	449.2500	–	O	VE7SMT	NORAC
Falkland	442.4500	+	O	VE7RAM	VE7EHL
Kamloops	432.4750	+	l	VE7TSI	Kamloops A
Kamloops	442.0500	+	103.5	VE7CRW	VE7NI
Kamloops	442.1500	147.9200	e	VE7RLO	Kamloops A
Kamloops	442.1750	147.9200	e	VE7RLO	Kamloops A
Kamloops	447.5000	–	156.7	VE7RXD	VE7EJE
Kamloops	449.2500	–	O	VE7RLO	Kamloops A
Kamloops	449.3000	–	O	VE7RHM	VE7LDM
Kamloops	449.5000	–	O	VE7KIG	IPARN
Kelowna	439.2500	2410.0000	te	VE7KTV	VA7UN
Kelowna	443.7750	+	l	VE7HWY	OCARC

Location	Output	Input	Notes	Call	Sponsor
Kelowna	444.3000	+	el	VE7KTV	VA7UN
Kelowna	444.8250	+	88.5	VA7KEL	OCARC
Kelowna	447.3000	–	88.5	VA7UN	VA7UN
Kelowna	447.7750	–	O	VE7KEL	OCARC
Kelowna	449.1250	–	O	VE7ROW	OCARC
Oliver	444.6000	+	100	VE7RSO	VA7WCN
Peachland	447.2250	–	88.5	VA7OKV	OCARC
Penticton	444.5000	+	O	VE7RPC	Penticton
Sorrento	444.1000	+	O	VE7SPG	Shuswap AR
Vernon	441.1500	147.5550	l	VA7NWS	VA7JMP
Vernon	444.3500	+	100	VE7RFM	VE7DQ
Vernon	447.4250	–		VE7RVP	NORAC
SOUTH EAST					
Cranbrook	443.6250	+	O	VE7CAP	EKARC
Nelson	444.5500	+		VE7RCT	WKARC
VANC ISLAND CENTRAL					
Chemainus	442.6000	+	141.3	VE7RNA	Cowichan A
Gibsons	442.6500	+	O 123.0e	VE7RXZ	VE7ALT
Ladysmith	444.8000	+	156.7e	VE7RNX	VA7DN
Lund	444.3500	+	100	VA7LND	Powell Riv
Nanaimo	442.5250	+	O	VA7ZSU	Mount Bens
Nanaimo	443.9000	+	141.3l	VE7DJA	NARA
Nanoose Bay	444.3000	+	O 141.3	VA7LPG	VE7IT
Parksville	442.2750	+	136.5	VA7JPS	VE7PI
Parksville	444.2000	+	Oael	VE7PQD	ORCA
Port Alberni	444.4500	+	O	VE7KU	Arrowsmith
Port Alberni	444.7500	+	O	VE7RTE	Arrowsmith
Port Alberni	449.4500	–	O	VE7KU	Arrowsmith
Powell River	444.5000	+	e	VE7PRR	Powell Riv
Qualicum Beach	445.0000	144.7700	O	VE7RQR	Mid Island
Saanich	449.4500	–	100	VE7SLC	Saanich Em
Texada Island	444.0250	+	141.3	VE7TIR	Powell Riv
VANC ISLAND NORTH					
Campbell River	442.4500	+	O	VE7NVI	VE7JZ
Campbell River	443.6500	+	l	VE7CRC	CRARS
Comox Valley	447.5750	–	O	VE7RAP	Comox Vall
Courtenay	443.7000	+	141.3	VE7NIR	North Isla
Sayward	443.7000	+	O	VE7RNC	North Isla
VANC ISLAND SOUTH					
Duncan	442.1500	+	141.3	VA7CDH	Cowichan V
Langford	442.7250	+	e	VE7FRF	VE7DAT
Nanaimo	444.7250	+	141.3e	VE7ITS	NARA
Saanich	443.0750	+	Oe	VA7XMR	CERT-BC
Saturna Island	444.5500	+	97.4	VA7RMI	VE7MIA, VE
Survey Mountain	444.9250	+	100	VE7RWS	VE7ED
Victoria	442.7000	+	e	VE7RFR	VE7DAT
Victoria	442.7750	+	O	VA7CRT	CERT-BC
Victoria	443.0250	+	100	VE7RWS	CRERCC
Victoria	443.5750	+	O	VE7RAA	VE7CCD

Location	*Output*	*Input*	*Notes*	*Call*	*Sponsor*
Victoria	443.8250	+	100.0e	VE7VOP	Victoria E
Victoria	443.9000	+	141.3el	VE7RFR	VE7DAT
Victoria	443.9500	+	123.0	VE7RTC	WARA
Victoria	444.1500	+	103.5e	VE7US	CRERCC
Victoria	444.2500	+	O	VE7IA	VE7IA
Victoria	444.4500	+	100	VE7SLC	Saanich Em
Victoria	444.5500	+	O	VE7RGP	Rogers Cab
Victoria	444.8750	+		VE7VIC	WARA
Victoria	449.8750	146.2400	l	VE7XIC	WARA
MANITOBA					
INTERLAKE					
Selkirk	444.1500	+	Oe	VE4SLK	E Selkirk
NORTHWEST					
Dauphin	448.4000	–	O	VE4BMR	DARC
Swan River	443.4000	+	O	VE4SRR	SwanRivARC
SOUTHWEST					
Killarney	449.5000	–	O 127.3	VE4KIL	------------
WINNIPEG					
Winnipeg	433.7500	+	O 5.0/5.0	VE4KEG	------------
Winnipeg	434.0000	1253.2500	O	VE4EDU	------------
Winnipeg	443.5000	+	Olrsx	VE4VJ	------------
Winnipeg	444.0000	+	127.3/127.3	VE4UHF	------------
Winnipeg	444.5000	+	O	VE4AGA	VE4AGA
Winnipeg	444.7500	+	O 127.3	VE4PAR	------------
NEW BRUNSWICK					
DALHOUSIE					
Dalhousie	444.6000	+	O	VE9FMG	VE9DEN
FREDERICTON					
Fredericton	448.7000	–	O 141.3e	VE9ARZ	VE9MP
Fredericton	449.2500	–	O	VE9ZC	FARC
MACES BAY					
Maces Bay	444.8750	+	Ol	VE9MBY	IRG
MONCTON					
Moncton	432.2500	+	O 141.3lRB	VE9UDM	VE9MDB
Moncton	442.2500	+	O 141.3l	VE9UDM	VE9MDB
Moncton	442.6000	+	O	VE9MER	VE9MCD
Moncton	443.3500	+	Ol	VE9LNK	------------
Moncton	444.9750	+	O	VE1PJX	VE1XW
Moncton	449.3250	–	Ol	VE9SHM	TCARC
SAINT JOHN					
Spruce Lake	443.6000	+	O 141.3 L(HUB)	VE9SJW	LCARC
ST ANDREWS					
St Andrews	448.1000	–	O 141.3	VE1IE	VE9NZ

Location	Output	Input	Notes	Call	Sponsor
NEWFOUNDLAND AND LABRADOR					
AVALON EAST					
St John's	444.9000	+	Oae	VO1RCR	AVRAC
St John's	447.1000	–	L(EIRLP)	VO1KEN	VO1ST
AVALON WEST					
Marystown	448.8500	–	OTTlr	VO1MST	VO1EE
Placentia	447.1250	–	O	VO1SEP	VO1SO
WESTERN NF					
Corner Brook	444.4000	+	O	VO1MO	HUMBARS
NOVA SCOTIA					
AMHERST					
Amherst	442.4250	+	OL(IRLP)	VE1WRC	WCARC
ANTIGONISH					
Antigonish	443.5000	+	OL(HUB)	VE1RTI	NSARA
BARRINGTON					
French Lake	443.8000	+	O	VE1KDE	BAARS
DARTMOUTH					
Dartmouth	444.6000	+	O	VE1DAR	DARC
GORE					
Gore	449.9000	–	OL(HUB)	VE1NSC	NSARA
GREENWOOD					
Greenwood	449.0500	–	O	VE1VLY	GARC
HALIFAX					
Halifax	444.2500	+	Ol	VE1PSR	HARC
Halifax	444.3500	+	Oel	VE1PSR	HARC
Halifax	444.4500	+	OeL(LINK)	VE1PSR	HARC
Halifax	444.5500	+	OeL(LINK)	VE1PSR	HARC
Halifax	444.6500	+	OeL(LINK)	VE1PSR	HARC
Halifax-All NS	449.1500	–	Oep	VE1HRM	VE1AJP
HFX Airport	444.0000	+	OeL(HUB)	VE1CDN	VE1YZ
INVERNESS					
Kiltarlity	444.9000	+	Oel	VE1KIL	SARC
LIVERPOOL					
Middlefield	444.3000	+	O	VE1AVA	------------
MUSQUODOBOIT					
Musquodoboit Hbr	449.4250	–	OeL(LINK)	VE1MHR	ESARC
Musquodoboit Hbr	449.4500	–	OeL(LINK)	VE1MHR	ESARC
NEW GLASGOW					
New Glasgow	448.5000	–	OeL(LINK)	VE1HR	PCARC
PARRSBORO					
Kirkhill	443.4500	+	OE-SUNl	VE1PAR	VE1BXK
SHEET HARBOUR					
Sheet Harbour	444.4250	+	Oel	VE1ESR	ESARC
Sheet Harbour	444.8750	+	Oel	VE1ESR	ESARC
SHELBURNE					
Shelburne	444.2750	+	OeL(HUB)	VE1BBC	EOC

Location	Output	Input	Notes	Call	Sponsor
SHERBROOKE					
Sherbrooke	449.8750	–	Oel	VE1SAB	ESARC
SPRINGFIELD					
Springfield	444.8500	+	OeL(HUB)	VE1LCA	LCARC
SPRINGHILL					
Lynn Mtn	444.2000	+	OeL(HUB)	VE1SPR	VE1ZX
Sugarloaf	448.9250	–	OL(HUB)	VE1BHS	VE1ZX
SYDNEY					
Boisdale	449.9000	–	OeL(HUB)	VE1HAM	SARC
TRURO					
Nuttby	444.7500	+	OeL(LINK)	VE1XK	TARC
Nuttby	444.9000	+	OeL(LINK)	VE1XK	TARC
YARMOUTH					
Yarmouth	442.7000	+	Ols	VE1LN	YARC
Yarmouth	444.7000	+	Oel	VE1YAR	VE1IC

ONTARIO

Location	Output	Input	Notes	Call	Sponsor
CENTRAL					
Berkeley	444.7500	+	O 156.7e	VA3CAX	RARC
Collingwood	442.6000	+	O 156.7	VE3BMR	------------
Collingwood	443.8000	+	O 156.7e L(IRLP)	VE3RMT	CARC
Dwight	444.7000	+	O 156.7 L(IRLP ECHOLINK)	VE3MUS	VE3MUS
Edgar	442.8750	+	O 156.7	VA3NLS	------------
Goodwood	442.0750	+	O 103.5e L(GTU)	VE3GTU	------------
Goring	444.4250	+	O 156.7 L(WIK SED SNM WAJ)	VA3NEG	ERA
Hillsburgh	443.8750	+	O 88.5e L(VE3ZAP)	VE3ZAP	------------
Huntsville	443.1250	+	O 156.7e L(IRLP ECHOLINK)	VE3MUS	VE3MUS
Huntsville	444.9500	+	O 103.5 L(LINK7)	VE3UHN	------------
Moonstone	444.2750	+	O 103.5 L(IRLP ALLSTAR)	VA3BNI	------------
Orangeville	444.0250	+	O 156.7e L(IRLP ECHOLINK)	VE3ORX	OAREX
Orillia	442.5750	+	O 103.5 L(LINK7)	VE3UOR	------------
Orillia	444.5500	+	O	VE3ORC	OARC
Parry Sound	443.5750	+	O	VE3RPL	PARRA
Parry Sound	444.8000	+	O 103.5 L(ECHOLINK)	VE3UPS	------------
Sarnia	442.3500	+	O(CA)e L(IRLP)	VE3WHO	------------
Shelburne	443.6250	+	Oe	VE3DRC	------------
Singhampton	444.9000	+	O 156.7e L(ERA)	VA3WIK	ERA

Location	Output	Input	Notes	Call	Sponsor
CENTRAL EAST					
Baltimore	444.9750	+	O 103.5 L(VE3YYZ)	VE3MXR	YYZ GROUP
Colborne	443.3750	+	O 162.2 RB	VE3RTY	------------
Kawartha Lakes	444.6500	+	O 156.7	VE3CKL	------------
Omemee	444.9000	+	O 162.2e L(IRLP)	VA3OME	OCR
Oshawa	443.0000	+	O 136.5	VE3NAA	NSARC
Oshawa	443.8000	+	O 136.5	VA3NSR	NSARC
Peterborough	444.5750	+	O 162.2	VA3PBO	PARC
CENTRAL WEST					
Dundalk	442.9250	+	O 131.8	VA3WWM	------------
Owen Sound	442.3500	+	O 156.7e L(VE3OSR)	VE3OSR	------------
FRONTENAC/LEEDS-ADDINGTON					
Kingston	434.8000	434.8000	203.5/203.5 #	VE3FRG	FRONTENAC A
FRONTENAC/LENNOX-ADDINGTON					
Kingston	443.3000	+	s	VE3KTO	Kingston ARES
HAMILTON-WENTWORTH					
Hamilton	444.6500	+	O 67.0	VE3GIV	------------
HASTINGS/PRINCE EDWARD					
Belleville	444.4750	+	118.8/118.8	VE3QAR	QARC
Marmora	443.4750	+	OA(1* #) L(I 2176)	VE3OUR	VE3LIZ
LANARK/LEEDS-GRENVILLE					
Almonte	444.3000	+	O 100.0/100.0 L(I 2220)	VA3AAR	Almonte ARC
Brockville	444.0000	+	100.0/100.0	VE3IWJ	Brockville PG
Lavant	444.8500	+		VE3DVQ	WCARC
Rideau Ferry	442.2000	+	O#	VE3REX	LNLARES
Smiths Falls	444.7500	+	136.5 A(* OPEN # DROP)	VE3WDP	------------
METRO TORONTO					
Acton	442.8250	+	O 103.5	VA3GTU	------------
Aurora	442.0250	+	O 141.3e L(CANWARN)	VE3ULR	VE3ULR RA
Aurora	444.1000	+	O 103.5 L(SSPBD)	VE3WDX	SSPBD
Ballantrae	442.4750	+	O 103.5 L(IRLP ALLSTAR)	VA3URU	GTARS
Ballantrae	442.8500	+	O 136.5 L(VE3WIK WAJ SED)	VE3SNM	ERA
Ballantrae	443.7000	+	O 103.5 (CA) L(IRLP COARC)	VA3BAL	COARC
Brampton	443.5500	+	O(CA)eWX z	VE3PRC	PARC
Brampton	444.9500	+	O 103.5	VA3OPR	------------
Brougham	444.6000	+	O	VE3DAX	SPARC

Location	*Output*	*Input*	*Notes*	*Call*	*Sponsor*
Caledon	444.1750	+	O 103.5	VE3WOO	------------
Etobicoke	442.7750	+	O 103.5e	VA3GTU	------------
Etobicoke	442.8000	+	O 103.5e L(GTU)	VA3GTU	------------
Etobicoke	443.1000	+	O	VE3SKI	SARC
King City	443.7750	+	O 103.5 L(IRLP ECHOLINK)	VE3JOP	VE3JOP
King City	444.3000	+	O 103.5	VE3TSU	YRPARC
Mississauga	444.2500	+	O 103.5ae L(147.540 IRLP) WX	VA3PMO	------------
Mississauga	444.5750	+	O 103.5 (CA)e	VE3MIS	MARC
Newmarket	442.6000	+	O 103.5e	VE3CAY	RARC
Newmarket	443.2750	+	O 103.5 (CA) L(ILP ECHOLINK)	VA3PWR	------------
Raglan	444.5250	+	OL(SSPBD ECHOLINK)	VE3OBI	SSPBD
S Richmond Hill	444.2250	+	O 118.8e L(VE3MOT)	VE3YRC	YRARC
Scarborough	443.3500	+	O 131.8	VE3RTC	------------
Scarborough	443.7500	+	O 103.5e L(GTU)	VA3GTU	------------
Scarborough	443.8250	+	O 88.5e	VATVB	------------
Toronto	442.1750	+	O 136.5	VA3UKW	------------
Toronto	442.3375	+	O L(DMR MOTOTRBO)	VA3XPR	------------
Toronto	442.3750	+	O 103.5e L(GTU)	VA3GTU	------------
Toronto	442.6500	+	O 100.0e	VA3GTU	------------
Toronto	442.7500	+	O 82.5 L(SSBPD)	VE3WOO	------------
Toronto	442.9750	+	O 103.5 L(ECHOLINK)	VA3GTU	------------
Toronto	443.0500	+	O 103.5e L(IRLP ECHOLINK YYZ)	VE3YYZ	TARCS
Toronto	443.3250	+	O 103.5 (CA)	VE3VOP	MARC
Toronto	443.5000	+	O 103.5/103.5eL(IRLP)	VE3NIB	------------
Toronto	443.6500	+	O 103.5 L(IRLP)	VE3NOR	NARC
Toronto	443.9000	+	O 127.3l	VE3OBN	SSPBD
Toronto	444.4000	+	O 103.5e L(TFM IRLP)	VE3TWR	TFMCS
Toronto	444.4750	+	O 103.5 L(IRLP ALLSTAR)	VE3URU	GTARS
Toronto	444.5125	+	O L(D-STAR)	VE3YRC	YRARC
Toronto	444.7750	+	O 103.5 (CA)e	VE3ATL	ALTARC

Location	*Output*	*Input*	*Notes*	*Call*	*Sponsor*
Toronto	444.8500	+	O 136.5	VE3UKW	------------
Unionville	442.2750	+	O 103.5 L(ECHOLINK)	VA3CTR	CCARS
Uxbridge	442.1000	+	O 103.5e L(TFM IRLP)z	VE3RPT	TFMCS
Vaughan	444.4500	+	O 103.5	VA3BMI	GTARC
Whitby	443.4750	+	O 103.5e	VE3WOM	WARC
Whitby	444.3750	+	O 103.5e	VE3WOQ	WARC
NATIONAL CAPITOL REGION					
Cumberland	444.3500	+	O 100.0/100.0	VA3RCB	VE3CVG
Ottawa	443.8000	+	O 136.5	VE3OCE	EMRG
Ottawa	444.1250	+	136.5/136.5 L(I 2210)x	VE3TST	VE3HXP
Ottawa	444.2000	+	A(*123/#) L(147.3/53.03)	VE3TWO	OVMRC
Ottawa	444.4000	+	/100al	VE3MPC	CPCARC
Ottawa	444.4750	+	O 100.0/100.0	VE3URU	Greater Toronto
Ottawa	444.5000	+	123.0/123.0	VA3LGP	VE3JGL
Ottawa	444.5500	+	O 151.4/152.3	VE3ORF	VA3MPM
Ottawa	444.5500	+	151.4/151.4	VA3KPT	VA3WHS
Ottawa	444.9500	+	/136.5s	VA3EMV	EMRG
NIAGARA					
Campden	443.5750	+	O 107.2e	VE3ALS	------------
Fonthill	443.1750	+	O 107.2e	VE3RNR	NPARC
Fonthill	444.7250	+	O 107.2 L(IRLP) RB	VE3PLF	COBRA
Niagara Falls	442.4250	+	O 107.2 L(ERA IRLP)	VA3WAJ	------------
Niagara Falls	442.9000	+	O 107.2 (CA)e	VE3GRW	------------
Thorold	442.2500	+	O/107.2 L(VE3RAF)	VE3RAF	RAFMARC
Thorold	443.7250	+	O 107.2	VA3RFM	RAFMARC
NORTHEASTERN ONTARIO					
Echo Bay	444.4750	+	O 100.0/100.0 E-WINDI	VE3SNT	SN CLUSTER
Little current	444.3000	+		VE3RQQ	------------
Sault Ste Marie	442.6500	+	aL(VE3SJI) Z(Y)	VE3SSM	------------
Searchmont	444.4500	+	O 100.0/100.0 E-WINDI	VE3SNB	SN CLUSTER
Timmins	444.9000	+	I	VE3AA	------------
NORTHWESTERN ONTARIO					
Thunder bay	443.8500	+	●	VE3TBU	------------
Thunderbay	442.0750	+	O 100.0/100.0	VE3TBR	LARC

Location	*Output*	*Input*	*Notes*	*Call*	*Sponsor*
Thunderbay	442.8250	+	O	VE3BGA	VE3OJ
RENFREW					
Arnprior	443.2000	+	O 136.5/136.5 A(*/#)eL(I 2910)s	VE3YYX	Arnprior FD
Pembroke	448.0250	–	/100.0 A(*22/#) L(ZBC/I 2520)sx	VE3NRR	RCARC
SOUTH					
Acton	442.1250	+	O 136.5e L(224.720)	VE3PAQ	PRO-ARA
Ancaster	442.5000	+	O 136.5e L(ECHOLINK)	VE3RDM	HPESS
Brantford	443.0250	+	OL(IRLP)	VE3TCR	BARC
Burlington	443.1500	+	Oe L(442.450)	VE3BUR	------------
Burlington	443.2000	+	O	VA3BUR	------------
Burlington	444.8250	+	O 131.8e	VE3RSB	BARC
Carlisle	443.6375	+	O L(ERA D-STAR)	VE3WIK	Rick Reemeyer
Carlisle	443.6750	+	O 131.8e L(ERA)	VE3WIK	------------
Grassie	442.7250	+	O 131.8 L(ECHOLINK)	VE3BQQ	TECHNET
Halton Hills	443.4250	+	O 131.8ae L(ECHOLINK)	VA3HR	HARC
Halton Hills	443.9500	+	O 131.8 (CA)eL(ECHOLINK ASTERISK IRLP 146.580)	VE3ZRB	------------
Halton Hills	444.1250	+	O 131.8 (CA)eL(ECHOLINK ASTERISK IRLP 146.580)	VE3ADT	------------
Hamilton	442.5250	+	O 103.5 L(LINK7)	VE3UHM	------------
Hamilton	442.5500	+	O 136.5e	VE3ESM	HPESS
Hamilton	443.0750	+	O	VE3ZOE	------------
Hamilton	444.0750	+	O 131.8ae L(IRLP)	VE3NCF	HARC
Kitchener	442.2000	+	O 131.8e L(ERA)	VE3SED	------------
Kitchener	442.3500	+	O 131.8e	VE3BAY	KWARC
Kitchener	444.5375	+	O L(MOTOTRBO)	VE3NXS	------------
Kitchener	444.8750	+	O 131.8e L(IRLP ECHOLINK)	VE3RBM	KWARC
Milton	442.3000	+	O	VE3HAL	------------
Oakville	442.2250	+	O 131.8 L(ECHOLINK)	VA3ODX	ODXA
Oakville	442.4500	+	Oe L(443.150)	VE3OKR	OKR RG
Oakville	444.3250	+	Oe	VE3OAK	OARC
Simcoe	442.0500	+	O 131.8e	VE3BIC	------------
Waterford	444.5500	+	O 131.8e RB	VE3HJ	------------

Location	Output	Input	Notes	Call	Sponsor
Woodstock	442.8750	+	O 131.8	VA3OHR	TCERG
SOUTHWEST					
Grand Bend	442.0500	+	O 114.8e L(VE3SUE)	VE3SRT	SORT
Ingersoll	443.4500	+	O 114.8	VE3OHR	------------
London	444.2000	+	O 88.5ae L(OEG)	VE3IWR	OEG
London	444.4000	+	O 114.8e L(IRLP 442.200)	VE3SUE	SORT
London	444.6125	+	Oe L(IPSC MOTOTRBO DIGITAL)	VE3RGM	SARC
Milverton	444.9250	+	O 114.8 L(IRLP)	VE3NMN	------------
Richmond	443.2250	+	O 131.8e	VE3XXL	------------
Sarnia	442.3500	+	O 118.8 (CA)eL(146.955 IRLP)	VE3WHO	------------
Sarnia	444.7000	+	O 114.8	VA3LAM	------------
St Mary's	444.3750	+	O 114.8e L(VE3RFC)	VA3SMX	FCARC
St Marys	444.5250	+	O 114.8	VE3SDF	SMARC
St Thomas	443.8250	+	O 114.8	VE3STR	EARS
Stratford	444.9750	+	O 114.8e L(IRLP)	VE3FCG	FCARC
Windsor	444.3000	+	O 118.8ae	VE3RRR	WARC
Windsor	444.4000	+	Oe	VE3UUU	------------
Windsor	444.5000	+	O 118.8ae L(145.470)	VE3III	SPRARC
Woodstock	443.9250	+	O 131.8	VE3WHR	TCERG
STORMON-DUNDAS-GLENGARRY					
Cornwall	443.6500	+	O 110.9/110.9	VE3MTA	SVARC
STORMONT-DUNDAS-GLENGARRY					
Lancaster	444.1500	+	O 110.9/110.9 (CA)eL(I 2018)	VE2REH	ARAI
Moose creek	443.0500	+	151.4/151.4	VE3TYF	------------
Williamsburg	443.1500	+	O 110.9/110.9	VA3ESD	SDEG

PRINCE EDWARD ISLAND

Location	Output	Input	Notes	Call	Sponsor
CENTRAL					
Glen Valley	444.6750	+	Ol	VE1UHF	VE1AIC
CHARLOTTETOWN					
Charlottetown	443.3000	+	Oael	VE1AIC	VE1AIC
Charlottetown	443.8500	+	Oel	VY2UHF	VY2ROB
Charlottetown	444.4000	+	Oae L(IRLP)	VE1AIC	VE1AIC
Charlottetown	449.1000	–	OaeL(X)	VE1CRA	VE1AIC
SUMMERSIDE					
Summerside	444.5000	+	Oae L(HUB)	VE1CFR	SPARC

Location	*Output*	*Input*	*Notes*	*Call*	*Sponsor*
QUEBEC					
Acton Vale	443.9500	+	O 110.9	VE2RBY	VE2GKE
Alma	449.4200	–	O	VE2RIU	VE2DIA
Alma	449.6200	–	O	VA2RIU	VE2TMR
Anjou	440.4400	440.4400	O	VA2GGR	VA2GGR
Baie-Comeau	442.3500	+	O 131.8e	VE2RBG	VE2FVV
Baie-Comeau	442.6200	+	O	VE2RUU	VE2RUU
Baie-Comeau	443.8500	+	Oex	VE2RMH	VE2FAZ
Baie-Comeau	444.0000	+	O 123	VA2RLP	VE2TPE
Baie-Comeau	447.6200	–	Oe	VE2RBC	VE2FAJ
Baie-Comeau	449.6000	–	O	VE2RBD	VE2RBD
Bedford	443.8000	+	O 103.5	VE2RSN	VE2TUA
Blainville	443.1000	+	O 141.3ae	VE2RMR	VE2DJE
Blainville	444.6000	+	O 131.8e	VE2REG	VE2ZVL
Blainville	444.9800	+	e	VE2PCQ	VE2PCQ
Blainville	449.7200	–	O 103.5	VE2RVV	VE2SMB
Blainville Nord	442.6000	+	O 136.5	VE2RNO	VE2THE
Boucherville	449.8200	–	O 103.5	VE2MRQ	VE2MRI
centre ville Québec	444.4500	+	O 100	VA2MB	VE2MBK
Charny	444.6000	+	Oe	VE2RDB	VE2FTO
Chicoutimi	449.0200	–	Oex	VE2RKA	VA2NA
Chicoutimi	449.7000	–	O	VE2RDH	VE2MDH
Coaticook	440.5000	+	118.8e	VE2RDM	VE2DPD
Coaticook	444.8500	+	O 118.8	VE2RDM	VE2DPD
Coaticook	449.2700	–	O 118.8	VE2RJV	VE2GNN
Coaticook	449.8500	–	118.8x	VE2RDM	VE2DPD
Colline Poudrier	449.7200	–	O 100	VE2GPA	VE2GPA
Contrecoeur	443.6500	+	O 141.3	VE2CKC	VE2AN
Covey Hill	440.0000	440.0000	Oex	VA2REX	VE2JT
Cowansville	447.6700	–	O 118.8	VE2RCZ	VE2CAF
Delson	442.1500	+	O	VE2LHF	VE2LHF
Drummondville	442.9500	+	O 110.9	VE2RBU	VE2YLA
Drummondville	444.0500	+	O 110.9	VE2RBZ	VE2ZBR
Drummondville	444.1500	+	O 110.9e	VE2RDL	VE2CRD
Fleurimont	442.9200	+	O	VE2RLX	VE2LGX
Gatineau	444.2500	+	O 110.9	VA2UHF	VE2GUY
Gatineau	444.6000	+	O 110.9e	VE2REH	VE2ZVL
Gatineau	444.7000	+	O 123	VA2CMB	VA2CMB
Granby	448.6200	–	O 118.8	VE2RGJ	VE2JRG
Grand-Mere	449.5200	–	O	VE2RLM	VE2CM
Grand-Mere	449.6700	–	O 110.9	VE2RGM	VE2GM
Grand-Mere	449.9200	–	O	VA2RTI	VE2JTR
Grand-Mere	449.9700	–	O 110.9ex	VA2RDX	VE2PWP
Grenville	443.8500	+	O 123ex	VE2RCS	VE2HMA
Hull	443.3000	+	O 100	VE2CRA	VE2CRA
Hull	443.9500	+	O 123e	VE2RAO	VE2CRO
Iberville	449.7500	–	O 103.5	VE2RJE	VE2MCJ

Location	*Output*	*Input*	*Notes*	*Call*	*Sponsor*
Joliette	444.6200	+	O 103.5e	VE2RLJ	VE2EML
Joliette	444.8000	+	O 103.5ep	VE2RIA	VE2MCM
Joliette	449.1200	–	Oe	VE2RHO	VE2BFK
Jonquière	440.0700	440.0700	O	VE2RNU	VE2JHG
Jonquière	449.0000	–	O	VE2RPA	VE2SV
Jonquière	449.1000	–	Oe	VE2RFL	VE2EFL
L'Anse-St-Jean	449.9000	–	Oe	VE2RME	VE2XIT
La Baie	444.9500	+	O	VE2RCX	VA2BCA
La Pocatière	448.9700	–	Oe	VE2RIP	VE2XIT
Lac Daran	442.1000	+	O	VE2RLD	VE2CSQ
Lac Daran	442.2000	+	x	VE2RLD	VE2CSQ
Lac Larouche	449.6200	–	O	VE2RPV	VE2RPV
Lac-a-la-Tortue	443.2000	+	O	VE2RBR	VE2GM
Laval	444.9500	+	O 107.2e	VE2OCZ	VE2JKA
Laval	447.5200	–	141.3p	VE2VK	VE2VK
laval	448.1700	–	O 107.2	VE2JKA	VE2JKA
Legardeur	442.3000	+	O 103.5	VE2CZX	VE2BFK
Levis-Lauzon	444.1000	+	O 100	VE2RHD	VE2CQ
Longueuil	442.4000	+	O 103.5e	VE2HPB	VE2UF
Longueuil	445.2200	445.2200	O	VE2RSM	VE2AZX
Magog	444.2500	+	O 118.8e	VE2RZZ	VE2CGM
Mascouche	443.8000	+	Oe	VE2RTM	VE2KAR
Mascouche	448.8200	–	Ox	VE2RTM	VE2KAR
Mercier	442.1000	+	O	VE2RTF	VE2BCM
Mercier	444.5000	+	O	VE2RTS	VE2BCM
Mont Bélair	444.2000	+	Oe	VE2RAX	VE2EZZ
Mont Bélair	444.9000	+	O 100	VA2TEL	VE2OSQ
Mont Bélair	448.6200	–	O 100	VE2UCD	------------
Mont Bélair (Québec)	448.6200	–	O 100e	VE2UCD	VE2JTX
Mont Orford	444.5500	+	100e	VE2RMO	VE2HR
Mont Rougemont	444.3200	+	O 103.5e	VE2RAW	VE2AW
Mont St-Bruno	449.1000	–	Oe	VE2RST	VE2CLM
Mont Sutton	447.2000	–	Oe	VE2RTC	VE2DIW
Mont-Carmel	447.0700	–	O 110.9ex	VE2RIR	VE2EX
Mont-Carmel	447.6700	–	O 100ex	VA2RES	VA2OMU
Mont-Cosmos	449.8700	–	O 156.7	VA2III	VE2WP
Mont-Gladys	442.4000	+	O	VE2RMG	VE2CQ
Mont-Laurier	444.6200	+	O	VE2RMC	VE2RMC
Mont-Orford	442.0000	+	O 118.8e	VE2RTO	VE2EKL
Mont-St-Bruno	444.1000	+	O 103.5e	VE2RSP	VE2GGY
Mont-St-Grégoire	444.2000	+	Oe	VE2RKL	VE2EKL
Mont-Ste-Anne	447.3700	–	O 110.9	VE2RAA	VE2CQ
Mont-Yamaska	442.3500	+	O 103.5ex	VA2RMY	VA2LRT
Mont-Yamaska	443.3000	+	O 103.5	VE2RMV	VE2ULU
Montréal	442.2500	+	O 141.3el	VE2RXM	VE2XM
Montréal	442.4500	+	O 103.5	VA2CVM	VE2LPN
Montréal	442.5000	+	O 141.3ex	VE2RCW	VE2WCC
Montréal	442.6000	+	103.5x	VE2RNO	VE2THE

Location	*Output*	*Input*	*Notes*	*Call*	*Sponsor*
Montréal	442.6500	+	O 103.5e	VE2ETS	VE2ETS
Montréal	442.8000	+	O	VE2JGA	VE2JGA
Montréal	442.9000	+	O 103.5	VE2REZ	VE2EZ
Montreal	443.0500	+	O 141.3ex	VE2RWI	VE2CWI
Montreal	443.7000	+	O 100	VE2RHH	MTL220
Montreal	444.2500	+	O 88.5x	VE2RVH	VE2VNH
Montréal	444.3700	+	O 103.5e	VE2LLL	VE2AAS
Montréal	444.4000	+	Oe	VE2REM	UMS
Montréal	444.9000	+	O 107.2e	VA2RDG	VE2JKA
Montréal	447.0200	–	O 103.5	VE2RJX	VE2JX
Montréal	447.9700	–	O 103.5	VA2RJX	VA2JX
Montréal	448.7200	–	O 103.5	VA2CME	VA2CBL
Montréal	449.3000	–	O	VE2AIF	VE2ACG
Montréal	449.4700	–	O	VE2WM	VE2WM
Montréal	449.9200	–	O 103.5	VE2RIO	RAQI
Montréal	449.9700	–	O 77e	VE2RJS	VE2ARC
Montreal-Nord	448.6500	–	O	VE2RPT	VE2FMK
Mt-Orford	446.5000	446.5000	O 71.9 E-SUNx	VE2DCR	VE2DCR
Parc des Laurentides	442.3700	+	O 110.9x	VE2RMG	VE2CQ
Parc des Laurentides	442.5000	+	O	VE2RMG	VE2CQ
Pointe-Claire	448.6500	–	O	VE2RHI	VE2RHI
Québec	444.3000	+	Oe	VE2RXR	VE2XR
Québec	444.5000	+	O 100	VE2REA	VE2TPE
Québec	444.5000	+	O 100	VE2RTB	VE2TEP
Québec	445.1000	445.1000	O 100	VA2MD	VE2TSO
Richmond	443.7500	+	O 123	VE2RHP	VE2LBN
Rigaud	442.2500	+	Ox	VE2RM	VE2RM
Rigaud	442.6200	449.7200	O 100	VE2RM	MTL220
Rigaud	444.0000	+	O 100ex	VE2RM	VE2RM
Rimouski	442.6200	+	O 123	VE2RWM	VE2CSL
Rock Forest	442.5000	+	O 123	VE2RVO	VE2VF
Rock Forest	448.3700	–	O 123	VA2CAV	VE2MKJ
Rosemere	445.1500	445.1500	O	VE2RXZ	VE2GXZ
Saint-Lin Laurentides	444.6500	+	O 103.5e	VE2RFO	VE2BFK
Salaberry-de Valleyfield	444.3500	+	Oe	VE2RVF	VE2BYB
Sherbrooke	441.1700	441.1700	O	VE2PAK	VE2SBK
Sherbrooke	444.7500	+	O	VE2RQM	VE2KIT
Sorel	442.1500	+	O 103.5	VE2RBS	VE2GGF
Sorel	446.2500	144.7700	O 103.5e	VE2CBS	VE2GFF
St-Antoine-sur Richelieu	447.1200	–	O	VE2RSO	VE2WA
St-Calixte	432.0100	432.0100	O	VE2RVK	VE2VK
St-Calixte	434.8000	432.4000	141.3e	VE2RVK	VE2VK
St-Calixte	434.8000	440.8000	141.3e	VE2RVK	VE2VK

Location	*Output*	*Input*	*Notes*	*Call*	*Sponsor*
St-Calixte	434.8000	432.4000	141.3e	VE2RVK	VE2VK
St-Calixte	442.6000	+	103.5x	VA2RLD	VA2DU
St-Calixte	442.7200	+	O 103.5e	VA2RLD	VA2DLU
St-Calixte	443.5500	+	O 141.3	VE2RVK	VE2VK
St-Calixte	443.5500	+	O 141.3	VE2RVK	VE2VK
St-Calixte	443.6000	+	O 141.3	VE2RVK	VE2VK
St-Calixte	444.0000	+	O 103.5ex	VA2 RLD	VA2 DU
St-Calixte	444.9000	+	O 1072	VA2RDG	VE2JKA
St-Calixte	447.1200	–	O 103.5ex	VE2PCQ	VE2PCQ
St-Calixte	449.9800	–	e	VE2PCQ	VE2PCQ
St-Charles de Bourget	444.2000	+	O	VE2RCR	VE2CRS
St-Constant	442.2000	+	O	VE2APO	VE2AFP
St-Donat	444.6000	+	O 103.5 E-SUN	VE2RRA	VE2BFK
St-Donat	444.8000	+	O 103.5 E-SUN	VA2RIA	VE2MCM
St-Eleuthere	442.3700	+	O 110.9x	VE2NY	VE2TC
St-Eleuthere	442.6200	+	O 123	VE2NY	VE2TC
St-Hubert	449.0200	–	O	VA2ASC	VA2ASC
St-Hyacinthe	444.4500	+	Oe	VE2RBE	VE2GGM
St-Jean-de-Matha	447.8200	–	O	VE2RHR	VE2JHR
St-Jean-sur Richelieu	442.8500	+	O 141.3	VE2RVR	VE2CVR
St-Jérome	449.7500	–	O	VE2RJE	VE2MCJ
St-Joseph-de Beauce	445.0500	445.0500	O	VE2RSJ	VE2BDP
St-Joseph-de Sorel	446.5200	144.7700	O 103.5	VE2CBS	VE2CBS
St-Joseph-du-Lac	449.8700	–	O 123	VE2RST	VE2GSB
St-Michel-Des Saints	443.8500	+	O 103.5	VE2ESN	VE2ESN
St-Nazaire	447.1200	–	x	VA2RAU	VA2NA
ST-Pamphile	447.7700	–	O 100x	VA2LLL	VE2SG
St-Pascal-de Kamouraska	449.5700	–	Ox	VE2RQA	VE2MEL
St-Simon-les Mines	449.9700	–	O 100	VE2RSG	VE2BPD
St-Tite-des-Caps	447.2000	–	Oe	VE2RSB	VE2BPU
St-Ubalde	442.3000	+	O	VE2RZT	VE2TRZ
Ste-Agathe	448.2700	–	Ox	VE2RLO	VE2LLA
Ste-Foy	442.7000	+	O	VE2RCH	VE2MER
Ste-Foy	444.7000	+	O	VE2RSX	VE2VEM
Ste-Foy	444.8000	+	O	VA2ROY	VE2LRI
Ste-Marcelline	444.7000	+	O 103.5e	VE2RMS	VE2BFK
Ste-Sophie D'Halifax	448.9200	–	O	VE2RNB	VE2NBE
Ste-Therese	448.4200	–	O 103.5	VE2RWW	VA2MAC
Ste-Victoire de Sorel	446.5000	144.7700	O 103.5	VE2RBS	VE2GFF

Location	*Output*	*Input*	*Notes*	*Call*	*Sponsor*
Taché	449.0200	–	O	VE2RTX	VE2SV
Thetford Mines	448.1700	–	Oe	VE2CVA	VE2LES
Trois-Rivières	442.7500	+	O	VE2VIP	VE2ZZ
Trois-Rivières	448.6700	–	O 136.5e	VE2RBN	VE2MTE
Trois-Rivières	449.1700	–	O 110.9x	VE2RTZ	VE2TRZ
Val-Belair	447.6200	–	O	VE2RGG	VE2TEB
Varennes	448.2700	–	O	VE2REQ	VE2ESM
Victoriaville	442.8500	+	Ox	VE2RMD	VE2MF
Victoriaville	443.5000	+	O	VE2RBF	VE2FQG
Victoriaville	444.6000	+	O 110.9	VE2RHY	VE2HY
Waterloo	443.9000	+	Oe	VE2ESM	VE2ESM
ARGENTEUIL					
Brownsburg	442.3500	+	O 100.9/100.9	VE2RWC	BARC
Grenville	443.8500	+	123.0/123.0l	VE2RCS	VE2HMA
GATINEAU					
Aylmer	444.0000	444.9000	O 123.0/123.0	VE2AAR	VE2AAR
Aylmer	445.0250	–	O 100.0/100.0	VE2AAR	VE2AAR
LAURENTIDES					
Rigaud	444.0000	+		VE2RM	------------
OUTAOUAIS					
Cantley	444.6000	+	110.9/110.9 (CA) L(I 2018)	VE2REH	ARAI
Cantley	444.7000	+	● 123.0/123.0 (CA)e	VA2CMB	VA2CMB
Chelsea	443.3000	+	/100x	VE2CRA	OARC
Chelsea	444.5000	+	O 146.2/146.2	VE2GFV	VE2GFV
Gatineau	433.1000	+	L(9600B RPTR)	VE2UQH	CRAO
Gatineau	443.9500	+	123.0/123.0 A(*/ #)eL(VHF)	VE2RAO	CRAO
Gatineau	444.2500	+	/110.9l	VA2UHF	GRAC
Gatineau	444.9000	+	● 162.2/162.2 (CA)e	VA2XAD	VA2XAD

SASKATCHEWAN

Location	*Output*	*Input*	*Notes*	*Call*	*Sponsor*
REGINA					
Avonlea	444.1500	+	O	VE5AHR	------------
Regina	444.2500	+	O	VE5UHF	------------
Regina	447.2500	–	O	VE5BBZ	------------
SASKATOON					
Saskatoon	441.0000	+	O	VE5RPH	------------
Saskatoon	443.9750	+	O	VE5PJH	VE5PJH
Saskatoon	448.0000	–	O	VE5HG	VE5HG
SOUTHEAST					
Estevan	444.8000	+	O	VA5EST	VE5AJ

Location	Output	Input	Notes	Call	Sponsor
YUKON TERRITORY					
YUKON					
Beaver Creek	449.9000	–	**O**I	VY1RHH	YARA

902-928 MHz

Location	Output	Input	Notes	Call	Sponsor
ALABAMA					
Huntsville	927.5875	902.5875	O 100.0	W4XE	W4XE
Huntsville/ MonteSano	927.5000	902.5000	O 100.0	W4XE	W4XE
ARIZONA					
CENTRAL					
Pinal Peak	927.4125	902.4125	O 151.4elx	W7ARA	ARA
Pinal Peak	927.8375	902.8375	●t	N7TWW	FHART
EAST CENTRAL					
Greens Peak	927.2875	902.2875	O 151.4ael RBx	N9CZV	N9CZV
Porter Mtn	927.3375	902.3375	O 151.4ax	N9CZV	N9CZV
NORTH CENTRAL					
Bill Williams Mtn	927.0750	902.0750	O 218.1lx	WB7BYV	Steve Crumley
Maricopa	927.0250	902.0250	O 151.4	KE7JVX	Ed Buelow
Maricopa	927.6500	902.6500	O 151.4 RB	KE7JVX	Monty Dana
Mingus Mtn	927.0875	902.0875	O 151.4lx	WB7BYV	WB7BYV
Mingus Mtn	927.2625	902.2625	O 141.3x	WA7JC	WA7JC
Mt Elden	927.8375	902.8375	●t	N7TWW	FHART
Prescott	927.3875	902.3875	O 151.4x	WB7BYV	Steve Crumley
Prescott	927.5875	902.5875	O 131.8el	WB7BYV	WB7BYV
Towers Mountain	927.2875	902.2875	O 151.4x	KF7EZ	KF7EZ
NORTH WEST					
Kingman	927.6125	902.6125	●	K7RLW	K7RLW
NORTHEASTERN					
Greens Peak	927.1625	902.1625	O 151.4elx	W7ARA	ARA
NORTHWEST					
Dolan Springs	927.9125	902.9125	ODCS(606) e	KC7UJL	KC7UJL
PHOENIX					
Chandler	927.4375	902.4375	O 151.4e	W7MOT	MARCA
Phoenix	927.0125	902.0125	O 151.4	KQ7DX	Scott Willard
Phoenix	927.7125	902.7125	O 151.4e	NØFPE	NØFPE
Scottsdale	927.1625	902.1625	O 151.4	W7ARA	ARA
Scottsdale	927.3875	902.3875	O 151.4ael	W7MOT	M.A.R.C.A.
Scottsdale	927.6875	902.6875	O 151.4l	KØNL	Gregory Banks
Shaw Butte	927.1875	902.1875	O 151.4x	W7ATV	AATV
Shaw Butte	927.5375	902.5375	O 151.4x	KF7EZ	KF7EZ
SMnt	927.2125	902.2125	O 151.4elx	W7MOT	M.A.R.C.A.
Tempe Butte	927.0375	902.0375	ODCS(023) x	KE7EJF	Dennis Bietry
White Tank	927.3375	902.3375	O 151.4lx	W7ARA	ARA

Location	Output	Input	Notes	Call	Sponsor
White Tank	927.3625	902.3625	O 151.4x	WW7B	Morgan E. Hoaglin
PHX METRO					
Usery Pass	927.4625	902.4625	●t	N7MK	FHART
SOUTH CENTRAL					
Mnt Lemmon	927.3125	902.3125	ODCS(606) eRBx	N7OEM	Tom Long
SOUTHEAST					
Sierra Vista	927.9125	902.9125	O 100ael	NØNBH	NØNBH
SOUTHWEST					
Yuma	927.4625	902.4625	● 88.5	W7DIN	George Strickrogh
TUCSON					
Oracle	927.3750	902.3750	●DCS(156) x	WA7ELN	Troy Hall
Tumamoc Hill	927.9750	902.9750	ODCS(606) RBx	N7OEM	Tom Long
Vail	927.8875	902.8875	ODCS(606)	WB4LDS	Don Stiver
WEST CENTRAL					
Lake Havasu	927.4375	902.4375	ODCS(532) elx	K7GDM	KA3IDN

ARKANSAS

Location	Output	Input	Notes	Call	Sponsor
NORTHWEST					
Aurora	927.5625	902.5625	ODCS(143)	W4GYV	W4GYV
Fayetteville	927.5125	902.5125	ODCS(143)	W4GYV	W4GYV

CALIFORNIA

Location	Output	Input	Notes	Call	Sponsor
FREQUENCY USAGE - SOUTHERN CALIFORNIA					
So Cal	927.6000			SIMPLEX	
So Cal	927.7000	902.7000		TEST PAIR	
So Cal	927.8000			SIMPLEX	
E SIERRA/TAHOE					
Meyers	927.6750	902.6750	O 107.2el	NC9RS	KJ6KO
Tahoe City	927.0250	902.0250	● 432e	WA6JQV	WA6JQV
Tahoe City	927.0375	902.0375	O 100	WA6JQV	WA6JQV
Tahoe City	927.8750	902.8750	●l	WA6TLW	WA6TLW
EASTERN SIERRAS					
Bishop	927.0125	902.0125	O 100l	NC9RS	KJ6KO
NORCAL-CENTRAL COAST					
Felton	927.9250	–	O 123e	W6MOW	W6MOW
Monterey	927.2875	–	Oelrsx	W6JSO	W6JSO
Monterey	927.9750	–	●DCSelrs	WE6R	WE6R
Salinas	927.6375	–	O 123elx	NC9RS	nc9rs.com
Salinas	927.9500	–	ODCSelx	KG6UYZ	KG6UYZ
NORCAL-EAST BAY					
Berkeley	927.9875	–	O 127.3lx	WI6H	WI6H
Clayton	927.1125	–	●lx	N6AMG	ERG
Columbia	927.5250	–	O 74.4e	K6LPG	MCAR
Hayward	927.6250	–	O 162.2	KB6LED	KB6LED
Moraga	927.3250	–	O 127.3#l	K6SJH	K6SJH

Location	Output	Input	Notes	Call	Sponsor
Newark	927.5500	–	O 103.5el	N3EL	N3EL
Oakland	927.0250	–	●DCSelx	WA6JQV	WA6JQV
Oakland	927.0375	–	●#DCSlx	WA6JQV	wa6jqv
Oakland	927.1750	–	O 100el	K6LNK	CARLA
Oakland	927.4250	–	●DCSelx	WA6JQV	WA6JQV
Oakland	927.4750	–	●DCSelx	WA6JQV	WA6JQV
Oakland	927.5750	–	O 100ers	N6SSB	BA900UG
Oakland	927.6500	–	O 131.8elx	NC9RS	NC9RS.COM
Oakland	927.9375	–	●DCSl	WA6JQV	WA6JQV
Palo Alto	927.9625	–	O 141.3lx	WI6H	WI6H
Pleasanton	927.1875	–	O 94.8ersx	W6SRR	Sunol Ridg
Pleasanton	927.3750	–	O 88.5#elx	N6QL	N6QL
San Pablo	927.0250	–	●DCSelx	WA6JQV	WA6JQV
San Pablo	927.4500	–	●DCSelx	WA6JQV	WA6JQV
Walnut Creek	927.8250	–	O 127.3ex	WU7Q	WU7Q
NORCAL-NORTH BAY					
American Canyo	927.4000	–	O 192.8el	K6ZRX	HAMSEXY
Napa	927.5250	–	O 173.8elx	K6ZRX	K6ZRX
Novato	927.3500	–	O 131.8#	KM6PA	KM6PA
Santa Rosa	927.5250	–	O 173.8elx	K6ZRX	K6ZRX
NORCAL-NORTH COAST					
Willits	927.7500	–	O 103.5#el rsx	K7WWA	K7WWA
NORCAL-NORTH EAST					
Corning	927.6375	–	O 123elx	NC9RS	NC9RS.COM
Redding	927.1250	–	O 107.2ex	KK6JP	WR6TV
NORCAL-SACRAMENTO VALLEY					
Auburn	927.1500	–	●	N6NMZ	N6NMZ
Auburn	927.3625	–	Oelrsx	KI6SSF	KI6SSF
Auburn	927.7750	–	O 77	NA6DF	SHARK
Auburn	927.7750	–	O 77lx	N6NMZ	N6NMZ
Chico	927.0750	–	O 88.5x	KI6ND	KI6ND
Chico	927.9625	–	O 141.3l	WI6H	WI6H
Dixon	927.8000	–	O 103.5#l	K6JWN	K6JWN
El Dorado	927.0250	–	●DCSlx	WA6JQV	WA6JQV
El Dorado	927.1625	–	O 131.8lx	N6UG	N6UG
El Dorado	927.4750	–	●DCSlx	WA6JQV	WA6JQV
ElDorado Hills	927.0125	–	O 100elx	NC9RS	NC9RS.COM
Elverta	927.9500	–	●elrsx	N6ICW	N6ICW
Folsom	927.2750	–	O 127.3	K6ZWZ	K6ZWZ
Georgetown	927.8500	–	O 123e	K6YC	K6YC
Grass Valley	927.1375	–	O 77elx	N6NMZ	N6NMZ
Grass Valley	927.1875	–	O 131.8lx	KF6GLZ	KF6GLZ
Grass Valley	927.2500	–	●	WB4YJT	WB4YJT
Livermore	927.0250	–	●DCSlx	WA6JQV	WA6JQV
Livermore	927.4375	–	●DCSelx	WA6JQV	WA6JQV
Lodi	927.1000	–	O 100el	N6GKJ	N6GKJ
Modesto	927.0250	–	●DCSlx	WA6JQV	WA6JQV
Modesto	927.0375	–	O 100lx	WA6JQV	WA6JQV

Location	Output	Input	Notes	Call	Sponsor
Placerville	927.1750	–	O 114.8el	K6LNK	CARLA
Rescue	927.2375	–	O 127.3x	K6ZWZ	K6ZWZK6KRD
Sacramento	927.2000	–	O 100e	K6YC	K6YC
Sacramento	927.2125	–	●elrx	N6ICW	N6ICW
Stockton	927.6125	–	O 107.2el	NC9RS	NC9RS
Sunol	927.6875	–	O 77elx	NC9RS	NC9RS.COM
Vacaville	927.0250	–	●DCSelx	WA6JQV	WA6JQV
Vacaville	927.0375	–	O 100e	WA6JQV	WA6JQV
Vacaville	927.0500	–	O 77aelrsx	N6ICW	N6ICW
Vacaville	927.0625	–	O 167.9x	W6KCS	Steve Dold
Vacaville	927.1250	–	O 131.8elx	W6NQJ	N6ZN
Vacaville	927.2625	–	●el	KI6SSF	KI6SSF
Vacaville	927.3375	–	O 162.2el	KI6SSF	KI6SSF
Vacaville	927.4750	–	●DCSelx	WA6JQV	WA6JQV
Vacaville	927.9375	–	●DCSl	WA6JQV	WA6JQV
Volcano	927.9000	–	O 127.3#x	W6KAP	W6KAP
Walnut Grove	927.3000	–	O 100elx	K6YC	K6YC
NORCAL-SAN JOAQUIN VALLEY					
Auberry/Fresno	927.0625	–	O 141.3e	K6VAU	K6VAU
Bakersfield	927.1250	–	ODCSe	K6RET	K6RET
Clovis	927.0375	–	O 100ex	W6JPU	W6NCG
Coalinga	927.6625	–	O 146.2elx	NC9RS	NC9RS.COM
Columbia	927.4000	–	O 107.2#a elx	K6NOX	K6NOX
Fresno	927.0250	–	●#DCSelx	WA6JQV	WA6JQV
Fresno	927.0375	–	O 100#elx	WA6JQV	WA6JQV
Fresno	927.0500	–	O 141.3#a elx	N6VRC	CVRC
Livermore	927.4750	–	●DCSelx	WA6JQV	WA6JQV
Lodi	927.0750	–	O 100elrsx	WB6ASU	WB6ASU
Lodi	927.0875	–	O 100ex	N6GKJ	N6GKJ
Mount Bullion	927.1500	–	O 100#elx	K6RDJ	WB6PBN
Patterson	927.6250	–	O 100#	KK6AT	KK6AT
Reedley	927.4000	–	O 114.8#a elx	K6NOX	K6NOX
Ridgecrest	927.0125	–	O 88.5l	NC9RS	NC9RS.COM
San Andreas	927.0750	–	O 100el	N6GKJ	N6GKJ
Stockton	927.4125	–	O 107.2#a elx	K6NOX	K6NOX
Westley	927.1000	–	O 100elx	W6RD	WB6PBN
NORCAL-SOUTH BAY					
Cupertino	927.1375	–	O#DCSelr sx	WA6FUL	WA6FUL
Cupertino	927.2125	–	O#DCSers x	WA6FUL	WA6FUL
Los Gatos	927.0250	–	●DCSelx	WA6JQV	WA6JQV
Los Gatos	927.0500	–	ODCSel	K6DND	K6DND
Los Gatos	927.1500	–	O 156.7l	N6NMZ	N6NMZ
Los Gatos	927.2500	–	O 114.8elx	K6INC	KD6YYJ

Location	Output	Input	Notes	Call	Sponsor
Los Gatos	927.4625	–	●DCSelx	WA6JQV	WA6JQV
Los Gatos	927.4750	–	●DCSelx	WA6JQV	WA6JQV
Los Gatos	927.9125	–	O 167.9ael x	K6DND	K6DND
Palo Alto	927.8625	–	ODCSelx	WW6BAY	Bay-Net
San Jose	927.8125	–	O 123l	N6SPB	N6SPB
San Jose	927.9000	–	ODCSl	N6TBQ	LPRC
Santa Clara	927.7375	–	O 100elrs	K6SNC	K6WAR
Santa Clara	927.8375	–	O 100#rs	N6MEF	N6MEF
NORCAL-TAHOE					
Meyers	927.6750	–	O 156.7elx	NC9RS	NC9RS.COM
Reno/Tahoe	927.0125	–	O 88.5elx	NC9RS	NC9RS.COM
NORCAL-WEST BAY					
Half Moon Bay	927.7000	–	●#e	N6IMS	N6IMS
Pacifica	927.4000	–	O 114.8e	WB6JKV	WB6JKV
Vacaville	927.0875	–	O 127.3ael rsx	WV6F	WV6F
SOCAL-#COASTAL					
Catalina	927.9375	902.9375	ODCS(311)	KR6AL	------------
SOCAL-#KE,LA,OR,SBER					
Blue Ridge	927.2250	902.2250	O 123.0l	N6LXX	------------
Tehachapi	927.7250	902.7250	ODCS(411)	WA6CGR	SCEARA
SOCAL-#LA CENTRAL					
Mt Harvard	927.5625	902.5625	O 123.0l	N6LXX	------------
Mt Lukens	927.9750	902.9750	O 103.5	N6VGU	------------
Mt Wilson	927.2500	902.2500	O 114.8 L(224.940)	WA6DVG	------------
Pasadena	927.9625	902.9625	O 100.0	W6DMV	------------
Santa Anita Ridge	927.6250	902.6250	ODCS(411)	WA6CGR	SCEARA
SOCAL-#LA EAST					
Sunset	927.1625	902.1625	● DCS(131N)l	N6RTR	------------
Sunset	927.5500	902.5500	O 123.0l	N6LXX	------------
Sunset	927.6125	902.6125	O 151.4	K6DLP	------------
SOCAL-#LA NORTH					
Contractors	927.6875	902.6875	O# DCS(606)	K6LRB	------------
Oat Mtn	927.5875	902.5875	O 131.8l	N6LXX	------------
SOCAL-#LA SOUTH					
Palos Verdes	927.6625	902.6625	ODCS(606)	K6LRB	------------
SOCAL-#LA WEST					
Woodland Hills	927.8375	902.8375	O 162.2	WS6RG	WSRG
SOCAL-#LA,OR					
Hollywood Hills	927.2750	902.2750	O 103.5	W6DEK	------------
Signal Peak	927.1375	902.1375	ODCS(411)	N6EX	SCEARA
SOCAL-#PALMDALE					
Hauser Mtn	927.3750	902.3750	O 114.8	WB6FYR	------------
Phelan	927.4750	902.4750	ODCS(532) l	N6LXX	------------

Location	Output	Input	Notes	Call	Sponsor
Pinon Hills	927.3500	902.3500	O 88.5	KA6YTT	------------
SOCAL-#SAN BERNARDINO					
Crestline	927.4875	902.4875	ODCS(411)	K6LRB	------------
Crestline	927.6750	902.6750	● DCS(131N)l	N6RTR	------------
SOCAL-#SAN DIEGO					
Black Mtn	927.3875	902.3875	O 151.4	K6XI	------------
Mt Otay	927.3375	902.3375	O 151.4	WA6OSB	------------
Mt San Miguel	927.5750	902.5750	O 151.4l	N6LXX	------------
Palomar Mtn	927.5375	902.5375	ODCS(606)	KE6YRU	------------
Palomar Mtn	927.9750	902.9750	100.0	W6NWG	PARC
SOCAL-#SANTA BARBARA					
Santa Barbara	927.4625	902.4625	O 131.8	KG6MNB	UCSB
SOCAL-#VENTURA					
Red Mtn	927.8750	902.8750	O 103.5	WB6ZTQ	SMRA
SOCAL-LA,OR					
Covers Area	927.9500	902.9500	●	KA6RWW	------------
SOCAL-LA,OR,RIV,SBER,SD					
Covers Area	927.1250	902.1250	●	KD6WLY	------------
Covers Area	927.4000	902.4000	●	WA6FDG	------------
Covers Area	927.6500	902.6500	●DCS(411)	N6CA	SBMS
Covers Area	927.9000	902.9000	●	KD6WLY	------------
SOCAL-RIV,SBER					
Covers Area	927.4125	902.4125	●	K6DLP	------------
SOCAL-SD					
Covers Area	927.1500	902.1500	●	K6MOT	MARC

COLORADO

Location	Output	Input	Notes	Call	Sponsor
BOULDER COUNTY					
Boulder	927.7500	902.7500	O 91.5/91.5 l	NØSZ	RMHR
CENTRAL					
El Jabel	927.7375	902.7375	Oa DCS(411) RB	KØVQ	RFARC
COLORADO SPRINGS					
Colorado Springs	927.7250	902.7250	ODCS(144) eRBx	WA6IFI	WA6IFI
Colorado Springs	927.8000	902.8000	ODCS(116)	WØMOG	WØMOG
Colorado Springs	927.8500	902.8500	ODCS(114) e	KCØCVU	CMRG
DENVER METRO					
Denver	927.7125	902.7125	O 107.2/107.2l	WRØAEN	CARN
Woodland Park	927.9000	902.9000	O(CA) DCS(205)e	KAØWUC	MARC
NORTH FRONT RANGE					
Fort Collins	927.8250	902.8250	O 100/100	ABØSF	ABØSF
Fort Collins	927.8750	902.8750	ODCS(114)	NØZUQ	NØZUQ
Fort Collins	927.9500	902.9500	O 100/100e	K1TJ	K1TJ

Location	*Output*	*Input*	*Notes*	*Call*	*Sponsor*
PUEBLO					
Canon City	927.7000	902.7000	O DCS(114) e	WBØWDF	WBØWDF
Pueblo	927.9125	902.9125	O (CA) DCS(250)	KFØKR	KFØKR
Westcliffe	919.1000	–	O 88.5/88.5 lx	NDØQ	PuebloHC
SOUTH CENTRAL					
Salida	927.9625	902.9625	O DCS(114) lx	KCØCVU	CMRG
Silvercliff	927.7750	902.7750	O DCS(116) el	KBØTUC	RGARC
CONNECTICUT					
NEW HAVEN & S CENTRAL					
Branford	927.8125	902.8125	O DCS(311) e	N1HUI	BFD OEM
Hamden	927.4125	902.4125	O /100.0 DCS(311)	WA1MIK	------------
N Guilford	927.4875	902.4875	O /192.8 DCS(311)e	NI1U	Guilford Radio S
NEW LONDON & SOUTHEAST					
Norwich	927.4375	902.4375	O 156.7/156.7	N1NW	Rason
DELAWARE					
ALL					
SNP	920.0000	–	O		------------
SNP	927.7000	902.7000	O		------------
DISTRICT OF COLUMBIA					
SNP	920.0000	–	O		------------
SNP	927.7000	902.7000	O		------------
FLORIDA					
CENTRAL - ORLANDO					
Kissimmee	927.7000	902.7000	O 103.5/103.5 DCS(411)eL(147.2100 444.450	N4GUS	ARRGUS
Orlando	927.0500	902.0500	O a(CA) DCS(411)eL(443.95)x	KAØOXH	KAØOXH
EAST CENTRAL					
Ft Pierce	927.7000	902.7000	O 100/100e lrsWXxz	K4NRG	NRG
Port St Lucie	927.6625	902.6625	O 100/100e L(444.000 146.985 927.700)rsWXxz	K4NRG	NRG
NORTH CENTRAL					
Trenton	921.2000	–	O e	N4TSV	N4TSV
NORTH EAST					
Daytona Beach	927.6500	902.6500	O l	KE4NZG	KE4NZG

Location	Output	Input	Notes	Call	Sponsor
Daytona Beach	927.6500	446.9000	O 103.5/103.5l	KE4NZG	KE4NZG
Daytona Beach	927.6500	145.7700	O 103.5/103.5l	KE4NZG	KE4NZG
NORTH WEST					
Perry	927.6500	902.6500	ODCS(411) eL(444.3)x	K4III	K4III
SOUTH EAST					
Boca Raton	927.6250	902.6250	O 100/100x	KI4LJM	KI4LJM
Ft Pierce	927.6000	902.6000	O 100/100 L(444)	K4NRG	NRG
Ft Pierce	927.6125	902.6125	O 100/100 L(444)	K4NRG	NRG
SOUTH EAST - MIAMI/FT LAUD					
Coral Gables	927.6875	902.6875	● 110.9/110.9er	WA4PHG	Teletrol
Ft Lauderdale	927.6750	902.6750	●DCS(25)e	KB2TZ	KB2TZ
Ft Lauderdale	927.7000	902.7000	O 110.9/110.9eL(224.4) LITZ	KF4LZA	KF4LZA
Miami	923.0000	–	O	WB4TWQ	WB4TWQ
Riviera Beach	927.5250	902.5250	O 100/100e L(443.925 443.900)x	KF4ACN	KF4ACN
WEST CENTRAL - TAMPA/ST PETE					
Tampa	927.5500	902.5500	O 141.3/141.3	N2MFT	N2MFT

GEORGIA

Location	Output	Input	Notes	Call	Sponsor
Atlanta	927.0625	902.0625	O	K5TEX	K5TEX
Atlanta	927.5125	902.5125	O	KD4GPI	TARA
Buford	927.6250	902.6250	O	N4GJF	N4GJF
Cumming	927.0375	902.0375	O	W4OO	W4OO
Cumming	927.6875	902.6875	O	W4FRT	W4PX
Grayson	927.5250	902.5250	O	K7TMD	K7TMD
Jasper	927.6625	902.6625	O	W4MAA	M&M 10-10 CHAPTE
Lawrenceville	927.5500	902.5500	OesWX	WX4NET	WX4NET
Marietta	927.0875	902.0875	O 151.4/151.4	K5TEX	K5TEX
Marietta	927.5750	902.5750	O	N4YCI	N4NEQ
Milton	927.6500	902.6500	O	K5TEX	SPYDER RADIO GR
Moultrie	927.0125	902.0125	O 100/100e	N4JMD	N4JMD
Savannah	923.0000	910.2500	O	WA4VHP	------------
Stone Mountain	927.7125	902.7125	O	KG4LMT	KG4LMT
Sweat Mt	927.0125	902.0125	O 146.2/146.2l	NF4GA	NF4GA
Valdosta	927.4875	902.4875	O	WR4SG	KBØY

Location	*Output*	*Input*	*Notes*	*Call*	*Sponsor*
HAWAII					
HAWAII					
Kona	927.1375	902.1375	O# DCS(411)	WB6EGR	WB6EGR
Kona	927.2125	902.2125	O# DCS(411)	WB6EGR	WB6EGR
OAHU					
Honolulu	925.6000	922.0000	O#eRB	AH6CP	AH6CP
IDAHO					
SW IDAHO					
Boise	927.8375	902.8375	●DCSI	N7CVR	N7CVR
Emmett	927.7375	902.7375	Ot DCS(412)	NB7C	NB7C
ILLINOIS					
EAST CENTRAL					
Danville	927.6250	902.6250	100.0 (CA)e	KC9USH	KC9USH
NORTH CENTRAL					
Joliet	927.5250	902.5250	151.4e	N9WYS	N9WYS
NORTHEAST					
Huntley	927.7250	902.7250	114.8	AB9OU	AB9OU
Lake Zurich	927.6875	902.6875	151.4	W9JEM	W9JEM
Lockport	927.5875	902.5875	411e	N9OWR	N9OWR
West Chicago	927.7000	902.7000	114.8aelz	W9DMW	MOOSEFAR
INDIANA					
EAST CENTRAL					
Lynn	927.0125	902.0125	O 131.8e WX	K9NZF	K9NZF
Lynn	927.5750	902.5750	O 131.8e WX	K9NZF	K9NZF
Muncie	927.7125	902.7125	O 151.4	N9CZV	N9CZV
Winchester	927.6875	902.6875	O 151.4	N9CZV	N9CZV
INDIANAPOLIS					
Indianapolis	927.4875	902.0375	O 131.8el	W9ICE	ICE
Indianapolis	927.9875	902.0625	O 77.0el	W9ICE	ICE
Noblesville	927.0875	902.0875	O 131.8e	K3HTK	K3HTK
NORTH CENTRAL					
Elkhart	927.6500	902.6500	O 131.8l WX	KC9GMH	KC9GMH
Elkhart	927.9750	902.9750	O 131.8ael rWX	N8AES	N8AES
NORTHEAST					
Roanoke	927.5125	902.5125	O 131.8	WB9VLE	WB9VLE
SOUTH CENTRAL					
Floyds Knob	927.5250	902.5250	O 67.0e	N9CVA	N9CVA
Floyds Knob	927.8750	902.8750	O 67.0e	N9CVA	N9CVA

Location	Output	Input	Notes	Call	Sponsor
WEST CENTRAL					
Otterbein	927.5625	902.5625	O 88.5ae	W9CBA	W9CBA
IOWA					
Mo Vab===	927.3250	902.3250			------------
KANSAS					
KANSAS CITY METRO					
Kansas City	927.0125	902.0125	O 186.2/186.2el	WBØYRG	BYRG
Kansas City	927.5875	902.5875	O	WBØKIA	------------
Kansas City	927.5875	902.5875	O 151.4/151.4e	WBØYRG	BYRG
Kansas City	927.9125	902.9125	O 186.2/186.2lx	WBØYRG	BYRG
Merriam	927.7125	902.7125	O 151.4/151.4a(CA)el	KØKN	SMMC
Merriam	927.7125	902.7125	O 151.4/151.4a(CA)eL(ECHOLINK#307578)	KØKN	SMMC
WEST CENTRAL					
Victoria	927.9750	902.9750	O 162.2/162.2	KDØEZQ	------------
KENTUCKY					
Lexington	923.2500	439.2500	O	KY4ATV	BLUEGRASS ARS
LOUISIANA					
REG 8 MONROE					
West Monroe	927.9750	902.9750	O	KB5TLB	KB5TLB
STATEWIDE					
Shared	920.0000	–		SNP	------------
MARYLAND					
ALL					
SNP	920.0000	–	O		------------
SNP	927.7000	902.7000	O		------------
BALTIMORE					
Dayton	927.5375	902.5375	156.7e	W3YVV	W3YVV
Owings Mills	927.5125	902.5125	O 156.7	N3CDY	N3CDY
Towson	927.4875	902.4875	O 156.7er	N3CDY	N3CDY
WASHINGTON AREA					
Ashton	927.7250	902.7250	O 156.7	K3WX	WA3KOK
MASSACHUSETTS					
BOSTON METRO					
Boston	927.0625	902.0625	ODCS(244) L(I4977)x	K1RJZ	MMRA

Location	Output	Input	Notes	Call	Sponsor
Cambridge	927.6625	902.6625	O 88.5e L(444.75)	N1OMJ	N1OMJ
Waltham	927.1375	902.1375	O 131.8/100	W1MHL	WARA
Woburn	927.4375	902.4375	O 131.8/100eL(449.825)	N1OMJ	N1OMJ
BOSTON SOUTH					
North Attleborough	927.7875	902.7875	O 127.3ers	N1SEC	N1SEC
Norton	927.7125	902.7125	O 131.8/100	KB1HTO	KB1HTO
Taunton	927.6875	902.6875	O/131.8e	KA1DTA	KA1DTA
Wrentham	927.4875	902.4875	O 131.8	N1UEC	N1UEC
CENTRAL					
Fitchburg	927.5625	902.5625	O 74.4	W1HFN	W1HFN
Worcester	927.7375	902.7375	ODCS(244) e	WE1CT	WorcECTeam
MERRIMACK VALLEY					
Pepperell	927.4625	902.4625	O 88.5/.0e L(224.64 RPT 1270.40 AUX.)x	WA1VVH	H Chase
METROWEST					
Framingham	927.0125	902.0125	O 131.8	WA1NVC	WA1NVC
Framingham	927.5875	902.5875	O 131.8/100p	WA1NVC	WA1NVC
Hopkinton	927.8875	902.8875	O 131.8 L(E551833 I4624)	N3HFK	N3HFK
Marlborough	927.7000	902.7000	ODCS(244)	W1MRA	MMRA
NORTH SHORE					
Georgetown	927.7250	902.7250	O 100e	W1ASS	W1ASS
Peabody	927.9375	902.9375	O 131.8/100eL(W1WNS 448.775)x	W1WNS	W1WNS
Salem	927.7500	902.7500	O/131.8	NS1RA	NSRA
SOUTH COAST					
Assonet	927.4625	902.4625	O/103.5e	WG1U	WG1U
Dartmouth	927.6500	902.6500	O 67	W1SMA	SCMARG
Dartmouth	927.8375	902.8375	O 67 L(I8884 NEAR-900)	W1AEC	SEMARA
Fall River	927.0375	902.0375	ODCS(31)e x	NN1D	NN1D
Rehoboth	927.5750	902.5750	O/131.8e	N1UMJ	N1UMJ
SOUTH SHORE					
Abington	927.4500	902.4500	Oe	WG1U	WG1U
Bridgewater	927.4250	902.4250	O/131.8e	W1WCF	PAWA
Hingham	927.8250	902.8250	O 131.8 L(E465199 I4335 NEAR-900)	NS1N	NS1N
Marshfield	927.4750	902.4750	O 131.8/100eL(E465188 I4571 NEAR-900)	W1ATD	N1ZZN
Pembroke	927.6250	902.6250	O 131.8/100e	W1EHT	SSBG

Location	Output	Input	Notes	Call	Sponsor
Plymouth	927.4125	902.4125	O 67ex	N1OTY	N1OTY
SPRINGFIELD/PIONEER VALLEY					
Feeding Hills	927.8000	902.8000	ODCS(244) ex	W1KK	W1KK
Holyoke	927.8375	902.8375	ODCS(244) ex	AA1KK	W1KK
THE BERKSHIRES					
Adams	927.8750	902.8750	O/100x	K1FFK	NoBARC
MICHIGAN					
LOWER PEN SOUTHEAST					
Auburn Hills	927.2125	902.2125	●tex	WB8ROI	WB8ROI
Dansville	927.5250	902.5250	O 131.8 (CA)el	KB8FUN	N8OBU
Dearborn	927.1250	902.1250	Ors	WR8DAR	RADAR
Fenton	927.5375	902.5375	O 131.8elx	N8VDS	N8VDS
Fenton	927.6875	902.6875	O 131.8 (CA)	W8FSM	W8FSM
Holly	927.2625	902.2625	O 131.8 (CA)x	W8FSM	W8FSM
Mt Clemens	927.2500	902.2500	O 131.8 (CA)lWXx	W8FSM	W8FSM
Pontiac	927.5125	902.5125	O 131.8e	N8NM	N8NM
Riverview	927.4875	902.4875	O 131.8	KC8LTS	KC8LTS
LOWER PEN SOUTHWEST					
Battle Creek	927.5500	903.5500	●t	WD8BVL	WD8BVL
Grand Rapids	927.2625	902.2625	●te	N8WKM	N8WKM
Greenville	927.4875	902.4875	O 131.8e WX	KB8ZGL	KB8ZGL
Jackson	927.2250	902.2250	O 131.8 (CA)elWXxz	N8URW	KC8LMI
Lowell	927.6875	902.6875	O 131.8e	KB8ZGL	KB8ZGL
MINNESOTA					
DULUTH					
Duluth	927.4875	902.4875	O 103.5	KBØQYC	LSAC
Duluth	927.6000	902.6000	O 114.8	KBØQYC	LSAC
METRO					
White Bear Lake	919.1000	–	Ol	KØLAV	KØLAV
MISSISSIPPI					
Gautier	911.2500	439.2500	O	KA5NOJ	------------
MISSOURI					
SOUTHWEST					
Nixa	927.5375	902.5375	O 162.2/162.2ex	KØNXA	Nixa ARC

Location	*Output*	*Input*	*Notes*	*Call*	*Sponsor*
NEW MEXICO					
NORTH CENTRAL					
Los Alamos	927.1125	902.1125	O DCS(432)	K4KIY	------------
Los Alamos	927.9000	902.9000	O 131.8e	WD9CMS	------------
NEW YORK					
ALBANY/SCHENECTADY					
Albany	920.8000	–	O (CA)l	KD3NC	KD3NC
New Scotland	921.0000	–	O 100 (CA) elx	K2AD	MountTop A
Schenectady	921.3000	–	O 100 (CA) el	K2AD	MountTop A
BATH/HORNELL					
Hornell	927.4750	902.4750	●	KD2WA	KD2WA
ELMIRA/CORNING					
Elmira	923.2500	434.0000	O	KB3APR	ARAST
LONG ISLAND - SUFFOLK CO					
Bohemia	927.9625	902.3125	O 151.4/151.4eL(446.100)rsBI	N2HBA	NCAPD
Old Bethpage	927.3125	902.3125	O 192.8/192.8 (CA) DCS(031)elrsWX	W2YMM	------------
LOWER HUDSON - WESTCHESTER					
Valhalla	927.9875	902.9875	O 114.8/114.8ers	WB2ZII	WECA
MID HUDSON					
Mount Beacon	921.2000	–	O 100 (CA) e	N2HPA	MOUNT BEACO
Nyack	927.8500	902.3750	O 114.8l	N2ACF	ROCKLAND RE
NEW YORK CITY - KINGS					
Brooklyn	927.5875	902.5875	O 151.4s	N2UOL	------------
Brooklyn	927.9625	902.3125	O 151.4/151.4eL(446.100)rsBI	N2HBA	PSARN
NEW YORK CITY - MANHATTAN					
New York	927.9375	902.9375	O 151.4 (CA)l	KQ2H	------------
NEW YORK CITY - QUEENS					
Kew Gardens	927.6000	902.6000	O 151.4	N2EZZ	------------
NIAGARA					
Buffalo	927.3250	902.3250	O 88.5 L(IRLP)	N2LYJ	------------
Cheektowaga	927.9250	902.9250	O 88.5 L(IRLP)	N2LYJ	------------
Colden	927.2500	902.2500	O 107.2 DCSeL(BARC)	W2IVB	BARC
Colden	927.5250	902.5250	O 107.2	W2ERD	------------
Eden	927.2000	902.2000	O DCS(411)	W2BRW	------------
Royalton	927.4500	902.4500	O 107.2	K2DWA	------------
Springville	927.6250	902.6250	O 88.5	K2PMS	------------

Location	Output	Input	Notes	Call	Sponsor
ROCHESTER					
Rochester	919.0250	–	Oel	W2RFM	GRID
SOUTHERN TIER					
Delevan	927.4000	902.4000	O 88.5	K2XZ	------------
NORTH CAROLINA					
Angier	927.5375	902.5375	O	NC4RA	NC4RA
Charlotte	927.6125	902.6125	Oe	K4KAY	K4KAY
Gastonia	927.0125	902.0125	O	KA4YMZ	KA4YMZ
Gastonia	927.0375	902.0375	O	KC4IRA	KC4IRA
Gastonia	927.7125	902.7125	O	KG4DNC	KG4DNC
Hendersonville	927.5625	902.5625	O	N4KOX	N4KOX
Waynesville	927.6625	902.6625	O	N4DTR	N4DTR
OHIO					
CUYAHOGA					
Parma	927.5875	902.5875	Ot(CA)	KD8B	KD8B
Parma	927.6125	902.6125	O 131.8l	KB8WLW	KB8RST
FRANKLIN					
Groveport	927.4875	902.4875	131.8 (CA)e	KA8ZNY	KA8ZNY
HAMILTON					
Cincinnati	902.5500	927.5500	O 110.9er	W8ESS	E.S.S.
MEDINA					
Medina	927.6375	902.6375	131.8	W8CJB	W8CJB
Wadsworth	927.6625	902.6625	O 131.8	WB8UTW	NERT
PORTAGE					
Mantua	927.7125	902.7125	O 131.8	K8ICV	K8ICV
STARK					
Uniontown	919.0250	–	Ot	WB8OVQ	WB8OVQ
SUMMIT					
Akron	927.5375	902.5375	OaTTelRB XZ	WA8DBW	WA8DBW
WARREN					
Mason	927.6625	902.6625	O	W8SAI	W8SAI
WAYNE					
Wooster	927.4875	902.4875	Ote	KD8B	KD8B
OREGON					
CENTRAL WILLAMETTE VALLEY					
Monmouth	927.0000	902.7000	O 162.2e	KE7AAJ	KE7AAJ
NORTH WILLAMETTE VALLEY					
Estacada	927.1750	902.1750	O 123e	K7KSN	K7KSN
NW OREGON & SW WASHINGTON					
Gales Creek	927.1125	902.1125	O 107.2e	KJ7IY	WORC
Hood River	927.1625	902.1625	O 151.4e	KF7LN	KF7LN
Portland	927.1250	902.1250	O 103.5e	K7QDX	K7QDX
PORTLAND METRO					
Portland	927.1875	902.1875	O 151.4l WX	KB7APU	KB7APU

Location	*Output*	*Input*	*Notes*	*Call*	*Sponsor*
PENNSYLVANIA					
FREQUENCY USAGE - ALL WPA SECTION					
WPA SNP	920.0000	–		SNP	
BERKS					
Earlville	927.5250	902.5250	O 131.8l	N3KKL	------------
BUCKS					
Hilltown	927.3125	902.3125	ODCS(131) ers	K3BUX	UBRC
Morrisville	927.6500	902.6500	O 141.3el	WBØYLE	------------
West Rockhill	927.8625	902.8625	O 131.8e	KS3Z	------------
LANCASTER					
Cornwall	927.5875	902.5875	O 114.8s	N3TUQ	LRTS
LUZERNE					
Wilkes-Barre	927.8125	902.8125	O 82.5elrs WX	WB3FKQ	------------
PHILADELPHIA					
Philadelphia	927.8875	902.8875	O 91.5l	W3SBE	SBE Ch. 18
PITTSBURGH 131.8					
Pittsburgh Homestead	920.5000	–	O	KA3IDK	KA3IDK
SOMERSET 123.0					
Central City	921.0000	–	O 123.0lp	KE3UC	WJ8G
PUERTO RICO					
E					
San Lorenzo	918.1000	–	O	WP4LTR	------------
N					
Caguas	927.1000	927.1000	●E-SUN	KP3AB	------------
RHODE ISLAND					
NORTHERN					
Cumberland	927.6750	902.6750	ODCS(244) EXP	N3LEE	TSARA
Johnston	921.7000	–	O	W1OP	ProvRA
Lincoln	927.6125	902.6125	O(CA)e L(KA1RCI)	KA1RCI	KA1RCI
North Providence	927.7625	902.7625	O 67	KA1EZH	KA1EZH
Providence	921.9000	–	O	WA1TAQ	WA1TAQ
SOUTH CAROLINA					
Little Mountain	927.6375	902.6375	O	N5CWH	N5CWH
Pickens	927.5125	902.5125	ODCS	WB4LZT	WB4LZT
Pickens	927.5125	902.5125	O	KE4PAB	KE4PAB
TENNESSEE					
Collierville	927.5370	902.5370	O	WB4EPG	WB4EPG
Collierville	927.5375	902.5375	O	WB4EPG	WB4EPG
Elizabethton	927.9875	902.9875	O	K4TMM	------------

Location	Output	Input	Notes	Call	Sponsor
Greeneville	927.5125	902.5125	O	N4FV	N4FV
Knoxville	927.0125	902.0125	O	W4KEV	W4KEV
Louisville	927.0375	902.0375	O 100/100e l	W4KEV	W4KEV
Memphis	927.6125	902.6125	O	W4EM	MID SOUTH ARA
Mooresburg	927.6125	902.6125	O 114.8/114.8s	KE4KQI	KE4KQI
Morristown	920.8000	–	O	KQ4E	KQ4E
Newbern	920.0000	–	O	K4DYR	DYER CO ARA
Newport	927.7000	902.7000	O 203.5/203.5	KG4LHC	KG4LDK
Sevierville	927.0625	902.0625	O	WB4GBI	WB4GBI
Troy	927.6000	902.6000	O	W4RB	W4RB
TEXAS					
Amarillo	927.1625	902.1625	O 151.4lx	N5TBD	------------
Arlington	927.7375	902.7375	O	W5PSB	------------
Austin	927.1125	902.1125	O 432lx	K5TRA	------------
Austin	927.1250	902.1250	O 103.5lx	K5TRA	------------
Austin	927.1375	902.1375	O 131.8lx	K5TRA	------------
Austin	927.1625	902.1625	O 151.4lx	WA6UFQ	------------
Big Spring	927.7250	902.0125	O 146.2lx	KA3IDN	------------
Corpus Christi	927.3125	902.3125	O 82.5e	W5DCH	W5DCH
Duncanville	927.0375	902.0375	O 110.9	KD5OBX	------------
Gardendale	927.0625	902.0625	O 203.5lx	WR5FM	CARE WTX
Gardendale	927.1250	902.1250	O 103.5lx	KA3IDN	------------
Grapevine	927.8750	902.8750	O 103.5ls	N5ERS	Emergency Repeater
Lubbock	927.0125	902.0125	O 225.7lx	KA3IDN	------------
Midland	927.0375	902.0375	O 141.3lx	KA3IDN	------------
Midland	927.0500	902.0500	O 411lx	KE5PL	------------
Midland	927.1375	902.1375	O 411l	KA3IDN	------------
Notrees	927.0875	902.0875	O 151.4l	KA3IDN	------------
Odessa	927.0250	902.0250	O 532l	KD4LXC	------------
Odessa	927.1875	902.1875	O 151.4l	KA3IDN	------------
Penwell	927.1125	902.1125	O 432lx	WR5FM	902 HUB
Port Aransas	927.0750	902.0750	O 218.1e	KG5BZ	------------
Rose Hill	927.2000	922.2000	O 123	KC5PCB	------------
Sterling City	927.1625	902.1625	O 151.4lx	KA3IDN	------------
Sweetwater	927.1125	902.1125	O 432el	KC5NOX	NCARA
UTAH					
CENTRAL					
Richfield	927.9375	902.9375	Ox	K1ENT	------------
NORTH					
Wellsville	927.5125	902.5125	O 103.5	WB7ASQ	BARC
WASATCH FRONT					
Murray	920.0000	–	O	K7JL	------------
Salt Lake	927.1125	902.1125	O 432 DCS(432)	W7XDX	------------

Location	Output	Input	Notes	Call	Sponsor
Salt Lake	927.3875	902.3875	O	N7SLC	------------
Salt Lake	927.4125	902.4125	O	AA7J	------------
Salt Lake	927.4875	902.4875	Ox	K7JL	------------
Salt Lake	927.5875	902.5875	O 432 DCS(432)	W7XDX	------------
Salt Lake	927.6125	902.6125	O 151.4ex	KE7WKS	------------
Saratoga Springs	927.3125	902.3125	O 151.4	KE7WKS	------------
VERMONT					
EAST CENTRAL					
Williamstown	927.4875	–	O 131.8l	N1IOE	N1IOE
WEST CENTRAL					
Rutland	921.2000	–	O 100.0l	W1AD	W1AD
VIRGINIA					
Alexandria	911.2500	426.2500	O	WA9GVK	------------
Alexandria	919.6000	–	O	WA4CCF	------------
Bedfrd/apl Orch	921.1000	–	O	WA1ZMS	MTN TOP ASSO
Charlottesville	927.0125	902.0125	O 151.4/151.4l	KA3NXN	KA3NXN
Fancy Gap	927.4875	902.4875	O	N4JNE	N4JNE
Leesburg	906.3500	222.4200	O	KC3BM	KC3BM
Lynchburg	921.0000	–	O 100/100	K4CQ	K4CQ
Lynchburg	921.2000	–	O	K2AD	K2AD
Lynchburg	923.2500	426.2500	O	K4CQ	K4CQ
Pearisburg	927.5375	902.5375	O	K4GWC	K4GWC
Poor Mtn	927.5125	902.5125	O	KE4NYV	KE4NYV
Roanoke	920.9000	–	O	KM4TT	KM4TT
Roanoke/poor Mt	919.5000	–	O	W4KZK	W4KZK
Slings Gap	927.6000	902.6000	O	W4KZK	W4KZK
Sterling	918.3500	146.1150	O	KC3BM	KC3BM
ALL OF TMARC AREA					
SNP	920.0000	–	O		------------
SNP	927.7000	902.7000	O		------------
CENTRAL					
Richmond	927.0500	902.0500	O 100/100l	WA4FC	KD4BPZ
FREDERICKSBURG					
Fredericksburg	927.5250	902.5250	O 192.8	W1ZFB	W1ZFB
FRONT ROYAL					
Linden	927.5875	902.5875	O 156.7e	KD8DWU	KD8DWU
WASHINGTON AREA					
Alexandria	919.6000	–	O 107.2l	W4HFH	Alex RC
Alexandria	927.6000	902.6000	O 107.2l	W4HFH	Alex RC
Haymarket	927.6250	902.6250	O 77.0el	W4BRM	BRM ARA
WASHINGTON					
W WA - FREQUENCY USAGE					
Rptr Inputs	902.3000	903.0000			

Location	Output	Input	Notes	Call	Sponsor
Rptr Outputs	927.3000	928.0000		RPTR OUTPUTS (25KHZ SPACI	
E WA - KENNEWICK					
Kennewick	903.3000	+	●EXP	WI7B	W7IB
E WA - PROSSER					
Prosser Tower	927.9875	902.9875	114.8	KB7CSP	KB7CSP
E WA - SPOKANE					
Krell	927.2500	902.2500	114.8	W7IF	W7IF
NW OREGON & SW WASHINGTON					
Camas	927.1375	902.1375	O 131.8l WX	KB7APU	KB7APU
W WA - NORTH					
Blaine	927.3750	902.3750	O 114.8e	W7BPD	Blaine PD
Cultus Mtn	927.5500	902.5500	O 114.8e	K7OET	------------
Lookout Mtn	927.4875	902.4875	O 114.8e	WA7ZWG	WA7ZWG
Lyman Mtn	927.6875	902.6875	O 114.8e	W7UMH	W7UMH
W WA - SEATTLE-TACOMA					
Baldi Mtn	927.9500	902.9500	O 114.8el	K7EK	K7EK
Buck Mtn	927.4000	–	123l	WBØCZA	WBØCZA
Cougr Mtn	927.4250	902.4250	123	N9VW	N9VW
Gold Mtn	927.4125	902.4125	O 114.8	N7NFY	N7NFY
Lk Forest Park	927.3500	902.3500	O 114.8	NU7Z	NU7Z
Rattlesnake Mtn	927.8875	902.8875	O 114.8e	N7NFY	N7NFY
Shoreline	927.6375	902.6375	O 114.8e	NU7Z	NU7Z
Tacoma	927.8000	902.8000	O 114.8e	K7HW	K7HW
Tiger Mtn East	927.4500	902.4500	O 114.8	K7KG	Ch1 Rptr G
Tiger Mtn West	927.4000	–	O 123	WBØCZA	WBØCZA
University Place	927.6000	902.6000	O 114.8	K7NP	UNIV PL. RPTR GRP
W WA - SOUTH					
Ashford	927.5250	902.5250	O 114.8	K7DNR	WADNR ARC
Baw Faw Peak	927.9250	902.9250	O 114.8	K7CH	K7CH
Capitol Peak	927.3000	902.3000	O 114.8	W7SIX	W7SIX
Kalama	927.2750	902.2750	O 114.8	W7UVH	W7UVH
South Mtn	927.2500	902.2500	O 114.8	W7UVH	W7UVH
Tumwater	927.7500	902.7500	O 114.8e	KD7HTE	KD7HTE

WEST VIRGINIA

Location	Output	Input	Notes	Call	Sponsor
Flat Top	927.5250	902.5250	O	WV8B	WV8B
ALL OF TMARC AREA					
SNP	920.0000	–	O		------------
SNP	927.7000	902.7000	O		------------

WISCONSIN

Location	Output	Input	Notes	Call	Sponsor
WAR					
Eau Claire	927.6000	902.6000	O 110.9ers	N9QWH	N9QWH
Green Bay	927.5125	902.5125	O 100.0aers	KB9MWR	ATC
Kenosha	927.6125	902.6125	O 127.3aes	K9KEA	K9KEA

Location	Output	Input	Notes	Call	Sponsor
Sturgeon Bay	920.0000	–	O 100.0aers	K9KJM	K9KJM

NEW BRUNSWICK

FREDERICTON

Location	Output	Input	Notes	Call	Sponsor
	927.6875	902.6875	O 100.00/100.00 L(444.700)	VE9CBZ	VE9GLN

QUEBEC

Location	Output	Input	Notes	Call	Sponsor
Blainville	904.9000	920.9000	O	VE2THE	VE2THE
Mont-Belair	919.1000	–	O	VE2RPQ	APQ
Mont-Belair	919.2000	–	O	VE2GPQ	APQ
Montreal	920.0000	–	Oe	VE2RHH	MTL220
Quebec	921.1200	–	Oe	VA2OLM	VE2OLM
Ste-Marcelline	920.0000	910.0000	OE-SUN	VE2RVQ	VE2BFK
Ste-Marcelline	920.0000	915.0000	OE-SUN	VE2RVQ	VE2BFK
Ste-Marcelline	923.2500	910.2500	OE-SUN	VE2RVQ	VE2BFK
Ste-Marcelline	923.2500	–	OE-SUN	VE2RVQ	VE2BFK
Ste-Marcelline	923.2500	913.2500	OE-SUN	VE2RVQ	VE2BFK
Ste-Marcelline	923.2500	919.2500	OE-SUN	VE2RVQ	VE2BFK
Ste-Marcelline	923.2500	919.2500	OE-SUN	VE2RVQ	VE2BFK
Ste-Marcelline	923.2500	439.2500	OeE-SUN	VE2RVQ	VE2BFK

1240 MHz and Above

Location	Output	Input	Notes	Call	Sponsor
ALABAMA					
Birmingham	1291.0000	1271.0000	O 100.0	N4PHP	N4PHP
ALASKA					
SOUTH CENTRAL					
Nikiski	9999.9999	445.4500	O 103.5 TTl RB	KL7UW	KL7UW
ARIZONA					
CENTRAL					
Pinal Peak	1283.6500	–	O 100lx	KD7DR	SARBA
Usery Mt	1284.6500	–	O 107.2lx	N7TWY	CHRIS RADICK
NORTHWEST					
Hayden Peak	1286.7000	–	Otlx	N6RHZ	CAL.MICROWA
SOUTHEAST					
Haystack Mt	1284.7000	–	O 131.8lx	K7SPV	SAN PEDRO VA
Sierra Vista	1282.5000	–	O 100al	NØNBH	PAUL HERRMA
TUCSON					
Tucson	1283.5000	–	O 110.9lRB	KG7KV	CHRIS BORDEN
CALIFORNIA					
FREQUENCY USAGE - SOUTHERN CALIFORNIA					
So Cal	1260.0000			OSCAR	
So Cal	1287.0000	–		TESTPAIR	
So Cal	1294.1000			PACKET	
So Cal	1294.2500			DIGITAL	
So Cal	1294.3000			D-STAR NARROW VOICE	
So Cal	1294.5000			FM SPLX	
So Cal	1294.7000			RMT BASE	
So Cal	1294.9000			NOV SSB	
So Cal	1296.0000			WEAK SIG	
So Cal	1296.1000			SSB CALL	
NORCAL-CENTRAL COAST					
Monterey	1286.7000	–	O 162.2#es	K6LY	NPSARC
Watsonville	1286.2000	–	O 110.9e	N6NAC	N6NAC
NORCAL-EAST BAY					
Berkeley	1285.3000	–	O 88.5#	KK6PH	23 CM Club
Berkeley	1285.5500	–	O 114.8ers	N6BRK	NALCO ARES
Fremont	10369.1500	–	O 100#ex	AD6FP	50MHzAndUp
Livermore	1282.2250	–	O 88.5lx	W6RLW	ARRC
Oakland	1284.4500	–	●#	KD6GLT	KD6GLT
Pinole	1286.6000	–	O 114.8el	N6PBC	N6PBC

CALIFORNIA

Location	Output	Input	Notes	Call	Sponsor
Pleasanton	1284.7250	–	O 88.5#elx	N6QL	N6QL
Pleasanton	1284.7500	–	O 88.5#elx	N6QL	N6QL
Pleasanton	1287.6250	–	O 88.5#el	K6LRG	L.A.R.G.E.
NORCAL-NORTH BAY					
American Canyo	1285.7000	–	O 173.8#el	W6FMG	W6FMG
AmericanCanyon	1287.4000	–	O 88.5el	WZ6X	WZ6X
Calistoga	1283.9000	–	O 88.5el	WZ6X	WZ6X
Cordelia	1282.4000	–	O 88.5e	WZ6X	WZ6X
Corte Madera	1287.9000	–	O 88.5lx	W6RLW	ARRC
Guerneville	1285.1000	–	O 88.5l	W6GHZ	NMG
Mill Valley	1285.0500	–	O 88.5el	W6GHZ	NMG
Petaluma	1286.2500	–	O 88.5aelx	W6GHZ	NMG
Santa Rosa	1283.2000	–	O 88.5#elx	KC6REK	KC6REK
Vallejo	1284.3500	–	O 131.8#l	KC6PGV	NCRG
NORCAL-SACRAMENTO VALLEY					
Auburn	1282.7000	–	O 162.2	AA6LK	AA6LK
Folsom	1283.7500	–	O 88.5el	W6YDD	YDD 1.2
Georgetown	1285.7500	–	O 88.5elx	K6RTL	NCAA
Paradise	1287.1000	–	O 88.5l	KE6IIV	WZ6X
Red Bluff	1286.9000	–	O 100el	K6JDS	K6JDS
Rescue	1284.8000	–	O 107.2#x	W6OIU	HAWK
Roseville	1282.6500	–	O 100l	KA6OIJ	KA6OIJ
Sacramento	1284.8500	–	O 88.5#	KD6GFZ	KD6GFZ
Vacaville	1282.9000	–	O 88.5er	K6SOL	Solano/ACS
Vacaville	1285.8500	–	O 100lx	W6YDD	YDD 1.2
Vacaville	1285.9000	–	O 156.7#x	KD6ZNG	HARC
Vacaville	1291.9000	–	O 127.3#	WV6F	Western Va
NORCAL-SAN JOAQUIN VALLEY					
Bakersfield	1283.3000	–	O 88.5#e	N6UPH	N6UPH
Bakersfield	1285.4500	–	O 103.5elx	WC6MRA	CMRA
Clovis	1286.3000	–	O 141.3#el x	N6JXL	CARP
Fresno	1283.4500	–	O 100#ex	W6YEP	W6YEP
Mariposa	1284.3000	–	O 88.5x	W6BXN	TurlockARC
Mariposa	1287.6000	–	O 88.5lx	W6RLW	ARRC
Visalia	1286.3000	–	O 103.5elx	N6VYT	TCARC
Westley	1282.8000	–	● elx	K6RDJ	KF6EQR
NORCAL-SOUTH BAY					
Campbell	1284.8500	–	O 100#s	K6KMT	K6KMT
Cupertino	1284.0000	–	O 100#	N6MBB	N6MBB
Cupertino	1285.6500	–	O 110.9l	W6MOW	MARG
Cupertino	1292.5200	–	O #e	KW6KW	KW6KW
Los Altos	1283.1500	–	O 100ex	W6SRI	SRI INT
Los Altos	1286.4000	–	O 88.5#	AA6IW	AA6IW
Mountain View	1284.2500	–	O 88.5#e	N6SGI	SGIARC
Palo Alto	1282.5000	–	O 88.5elx	W6YX	SUARC
Palo Alto	1284.9500	–	O 88.5ex	K6BAM	BAMA
Palo Alto	1292.5500	–	O 88.5#	WA6ITV	WA6ITV
San Jose	1282.0000	–	O 88.5l	W6RLW	ARRC

Location	Output	Input	Notes	Call	Sponsor
San Jose	1282.2000	–	○ 88.5lx	W6RLW	ARRC
San Jose	1283.1000	–	○ 88.5#ael	N6AKK	CarJack
San Jose	1283.4000	–	○ 94.8al	N6EEZ	N6EEZ
San Jose	1283.5500	–	○ 88.5#ael	N6AKK	CarJack
San Jose	1283.7000	–	○ 100ex	WA6GFY	LMERA ARC
San Jose	1284.3000	–	○ 100#e	N6AKB	N6AKB
San Jose	1285.0000	–	○ 88.5lx	W6RLW	ARRC
San Jose	1285.8000	–	○ 127.3#	KD6AOG	KD6AOG
San Jose	1285.9500	–	○ 100aelx	KU6V	KU6V
San Jose	1286.0000	–	○ 110.9elx	N6NAC	N6NAC
San Jose	1286.0750	–	○ 88.5#aex	WB6OCD	WB6OCD
San Jose	1286.1500	–	○ 127.3#x	KD6AOG	KD6AOG
San Jose	1286.2000	–	○ 100aels	W6PIY	WVARA
San Jose	1286.3250	–	○ 88.5l	N6SPB	N6SPB
San Jose	1286.4500	–	●el	K6MF	K6MF
San Jose	1286.5000	–	○ 173.8elrsx	W7AFG	AREA-Amate
San Jose	1287.2000	–	○ 88.5a	KE6STH	KE6STH
San Jose	1287.7000	–	○ 88.5lx	W6RLW	ARRC
Santa Clara	1286.8500	–	○ 88.5#	K6GDS	K6GDS
Santa Clara	1287.0000	–	○ 88.5#e	K6CPU	IEARS
Saratoga	1283.0000	–	○ 88.5l	W6RLW	ARRC
Saratoga	1287.5000	–	○ 88.5el	K6UB	K6UB
NORCAL-TAHOE					
So Lake Tahoe	1285.0000	–	○ 123#e	N3KD	N3KD
Tahoe City	1287.8000	–	○ 88.5lx	W6RLW	ARRC
NORCAL-WEST BAY					
Daly City	1285.1000	–	○ 131.8#lx	KC6PGV	NCRG
Los Altos Hill	1282.6000	–	○ 100er	K6AIR	K6AIR
Redwood City	1284.7000	–	○ 114.8#el	WD6GGW	WD6GGW
Redwood City	1285.2500	–	○ 88.5#el	KE6UIE	KE6UIE
San Bruno	1286.0500	–	○ 123#lrs	KM6EF	GSARC
San Francisco	1284.9000	–	○ 67e	KA6TGI	KA6TGI
SOCAL LA,OR					
Verdugo Peak	1286.6000	–	●	K6VGP	DARN
SOCAL-#LA CENTRAL					
Mt Disappointment	1285.3000	–	○ 100.0	K6CPT	LA RACES
Mt Harvard	1287.1250	–	○ 114.8	WA6TFD	BHARC
Mt Lukens	1287.0750	–	○ 100.0	KO6TD	------------
Mt Lukens	1287.4750	–	○ 77.0	WA6DPB	------------
Mt Wilson	1287.2500	–	○ 127.3	WD8CIK	PAPA
SOCAL-#LA EAST					
West Covina	1282.8750	–	○ 103.5	WB6QZK	------------
SOCAL-#LA NORTH					
Canyon Country	1285.6250	–	○ 100.0	KI6JL	------------
Contractors Pt	1285.9000	–	○ 123.0	W6CPA	IRC
Frazier Peak	1285.1500	–	○ 88.5	W6RLW	ARRC

Location	Output	Input	Notes	Call	Sponsor
Oat Mountain	1286.5000	–	○ 67.0	KF6HHV	Baykitty ARC
SOCAL-#LA SOUTH					
Rancho Palos Verdes	1287.1500	–	○ 114.8	WA6MDJ	------------
Rolling Hills	1287.9250	–	○ 127.3	K6RH	RHRC
Signal Hill	1286.3000	–	○ 156.7	K6CHE	LBRACES
SOCAL-#LA WEST					
Hollywood Hills	1286.7500	–	○ 103.5	N6VGU	------------
Los Angeles	1287.1750	–	○ 103.5	K6PYP	------------
SOCAL-#ORANGE					
Anaheim	1283.1000	–	○ 114.8	KB6ZDB	------------
Bolero Pk	1287.7250	–	○ 88.5	W6KRW	OCCC
Fountain Valley	1287.5000	–	○ 100.0	W6RLW	ARRC
Orange	1283.1500	–	○ 85.4	W6OPD	------------
Santiago Peak	1287.6500	–	○ 88.5	W6KRW	OCCC
Sierra Peak	1287.6750	–	○ 88.5	W6KRW	OCCC
Signal Pk	1287.7000	–	○ 88.5	W6KRW	OCCC
SOCAL-#ORANGE SOUTH					
San Clemente	1282.7500	–	○ 88.5	W6KRW	OCCC
SOCAL-#SAN DIEGO					
El Cajon	1285.4000	–	○ 88.5	WA6ZFT	ECRA
Otay Mtn	1282.3000	–	○ 103.5	WB6WLV	SANDRA
Otay Mtn	1285.8000	–	○ 88.5	WA6ZFT	ECRA
SOCAL-#VENTURA					
Red Mtn	1287.1000	–	○ 127.3	K6ERN	SMRA-ERN
SOCAL-LA,OR					
Canyon Country	1285.6500	–	●	KI6JL	ESSN
Contractors PT	1286.0250	–	●	W6WAX	------------
Flint Peak	1286.0500	–	●	KA6VHA	------------
Mt Disappointment	1286.7000	–	●	K6VGP	DARN
Mt Lukens	1286.3250	–	●	KC6MQP	------------
Palos Verdes	1283.5500	–	●	N6UL	------------
Palos Verdes	1286.9000	–	●	K6VGP	DARN
Saddle Peak	1287.2000	–	●	K6VGP	DARN
Santa Anita Rg	1286.0750	–	●	WA6CGR	SCEARA
Torrance	1284.0750	–	●	KE6LDM	------------
Tujunga	1285.2500	–	●	NW6B	------------
SOCAL-LA,OR,RIV,SBER					
Heaps Peak	1287.3500	–	●	AF6HP	MARC
Keller Peak	1285.2000	–	●	WC6MRA	CMRA
Keller Peak	1286.2500	–	●	KG6YS	MARA
Mt Wilson	1286.2000	–	●	K6JP	SCJHC
Running Spr	1286.0000	–	●	KA6RWW	------------
Sierra Peak	1287.3500	–	●	AF6HP	METS
Sunset Ridge	1284.0500	–	●	WC6MRA	CMRA
Sunset Ridge	1285.2750	–	●	WH6NZ	------------
SOCAL-LA,OR,RIV,SBER,SD					
Santiago Peak	1286.1500	–	●	WA6SVT	ATN

Location	*Output*	*Input*	*Notes*	*Call*	*Sponsor*
Santiago Peak	1286.3750	–	●	AF6HP	MARC
Santiago Peak	1286.4500	–	●	N6SLD	CLARA
SOCAL-LA,OR,SBAR,VE					
Saddle Peak	1283.5000	–	●	WB6FOD	CMRA
SOCAL-LA,OR,VE					
Oat Mtn	1283.8250	–	●	KC6WTL	SCARA
SOCAL-OR					
Fountain Valley	1286.1250	–	●	W6TMB	FOCUS
Loma Ridge	1287.7750	–	●	W6KRW	OCCC
Mission Viejo	1283.4500	–	●	KM6NP	SCARA
SOCAL-RIV,SBER					
Chuckwalla	1283.3000	–	●	WC6MRA	CMRA
SOCAL-SBAR					
Santa Ynez	1284.0500	–	●	K6RCL	CMRA
SOCAL-SD					
San Miguel	1284.3000	–	●	WV6H	CARE
SOCAL-VE					
Oxnard	1285.7500	–	●	W6KGB	------------
COLORADO					
DENVER METRO					
Denver	1287.9000	–	O	WØCRA	CRA
NORTH FRONT RANGE					
Fort Collins	1283.5500	–	O 100/100	K1TJ	K1TJ
SOUTH CENTRAL					
Cripple Creek	1287.7000	–	O 67 E-SUN	WBØWDF	WBØWDF
DELAWARE					
ALL					
SNP	1283.0000	–	O		------------
DISTRICT OF COLUMBIA					
SNP	1283.0000	–	O		------------
FLORIDA					
CENTRAL					
The Villages	1292.1500	1272.1500	O 91.5/91.5 e	WA1UTQ	WA1UTQ
SOUTH EAST - MIAMI/FT LAUD					
Hialeah	1291.1000	1271.1000	O 110.9/110.9a(CA)ersBIx	WB4IVM	WB4IVM
Miami	1293.0000	1273.0000	Oe	WB4TWQ	WB4TWQ
WEST CENTRAL - TAMPA/ST PETE					
Dunedin	1285.5000	–	O 103.5/103.5 L(146.970 224.940 444.150 4	KJ4JBO	CARS
Tampa	1291.5000	1271.5000	O 88.5/88.5 a(CA) DCS(33)eL(444.000 444.675 443.42	W4AQR	W4AQR

Location	*Output*	*Input*	*Notes*	*Call*	*Sponsor*
GEORGIA					
Atlanta	1292.0000	1272.0000	O	KB4KIN	MATPARC
Morrow	1292.1000	1272.1000	O	K4USD	W2XAB
ILLINOIS					
CHICAGO					
Chicago	1292.2000	1272.2000	e	NS9RC	NSRC
NORTHEAST					
Batavia	1291.9000	1271.9000	l	W9NE	W9XA
Batavia	1292.0000	1272.0000	88.5l	W9XA	W9XA
Lisle	1293.1000	1273.1000	114.8 (CA)e LITZ	WA9AEK	WA9AEK
Wayne	1292.6000	1272.6000	esWX	W9DPA	DCERA
PEORIA					
Peoria	1292.4000	1272.4000		W9PIA	PAARC
SPRINGFIELD					
Springfield	1293.2500	1273.2500	103.5ers WXxz	WS9V	MR DX
INDIANA					
INDIANAPOLIS					
Indianapolis	1293.5000	1273.5000	O 77.0	W9ICE	ICE
NORTHEAST					
Roanoke	1286.3500	–	O 131.8	WB9VLE	WB9VLE
NORTHWEST					
Valparaiso	1292.0000	1272.0000	O 88.5e	KB9KRI	Duneland
KANSAS					
KANSAS CITY METRO					
Shawnee Msn	1285.0000	–	Oe	KØGXL	SMMC
Shawnee Msn	1285.0000	–	Oe	KØGXL	SMMC
WICHITA					
Valley Center	1288.0000	1275.0000	O 88.5/88.5 e	KØPY	------------
LOUISIANA					
STATEWIDE					
Shared	1283.0000	–		SNP	------------
MAINE					
PORTLAND/SOUTH COAST					
Brunswick	1284.0000	–	Oesx	KS1R	MARA
MARYLAND					
ALL					
SNP	1283.0000	–	O		------------

Location	Output	Input	Notes	Call	Sponsor
MASSACHUSETTS					
SPRINGFIELD/PIONEER VALLEY					
Feeding Hills	1282.5000	–	Oex	W1KK	W1KK
THE BERKSHIRES					
Adams	1283.9000	–	O	K1FFK	NoBARC
MICHIGAN					
LOWER PEN SOUTHEAST					
Hell	1280.2000	1270.2000	OelrsWX	K8LCD	W8SS
LOWER PEN SOUTHWEST					
Berrien Springs	1282.0000	–	O(CA)	W8YKS	DOCRG
Berrien Springs	2410.0000	2306.0000	O(CA)x	W8YKS	DOCRG
NEVADA					
LAS VEGAS VALLEY					
High Potosi Mtn	1265.0000	913.0000	#	KB7BY	------------
Las Vegas	1293.6250	–	O 114.8/114.8	NX7R	------------
NORTH CENTRAL					
Elko	1283.1000	–	O 100	KE7LKO	WV3LMA
WEST CENTRAL					
Carson City	1253.0000	1253.0000	O	KB7MF	KB7MF
Carson City	1293.0000	1283.0000	O	KB7MF	KB7MF
Gardnerville	1273.0000	+	O 88.5e	N7KD	N7KD
Reno	1250.0000	1250.0000	●e	KD7EOC	KD7BQX
Reno	1255.0000	1255.0000	Oel	WA6DDF	WA6DDF
Reno	1286.5000	–	O 88.5lx	W6CYX	W6CYX
Reno	2430.0000	2430.0000	O	WA6DDF	WA6DDF
Reno/Sparks	2441.2500	2441.2500	O	WA6DDF	WA6DDF
NEW HAMPSHIRE					
MERRIMACK VALLEY					
Goffstown	1285.0000	–	e L(D-STAR)sWXx	N1HIT	NHIT
Goffstown	1290.1000	1270.1000	O	K1GHZ	NHMRA
NEW JERSEY					
MORRIS CO					
Butler	1282.0500	–	O 151.4elr s	WB2FTX	Butler RACES/O
Parsippany	1287.5000	–	O 141.3	WA2UEM	WA2UEM
OCEAN					
Lakewood	1295.0000	1275.0000	O 127.3el	N2AYM	------------
NEW MEXICO					
SOUTH CENTRAL					
Organ	1293.9000	1273.9000	Osx	KC5SJQ	KC5SJQ

Location	Output	Input	Notes	Call	Sponsor
NEW YORK					
LONG ISLAND - SUFFOLK CO					
Islandia	1286.0000	–	●L(449.65) RB	WR2UHF	GABAMFKRA
NEW YORK CITY - QUEENS					
Glen Oaks	1288.0000	–	O 136.5 (CA)e	W2VL	Long Island Mobile A
NIAGARA					
Royalton	1283.4500	–	O 107.2e L(443.500) RB	KD2WA	------------
ROCHESTER					
Rochester	1288.0000	1268.0000	Ol	N2HJD	ROCHESTER RADIO
NORTH CAROLINA					
Burlington	1284.4000	–	O	AK4EG	AI4UE
Burlington	1299.4000	1299.4000	O	AK4EG	AI4UE
Gastonia	1292.0000	1272.0000	O	KA4YMZ	KA4YMZ
OHIO					
FRANKLIN					
Columbus	1292.3000	1272.3000	Ol	WB8YOJ	WB8YOJ
LUCAS					
Toledo	1285.0000	–	O	WJ8E	WJ8E
Toledo	1287.0000	–	O	WJ8E	WJ8E
MIAMI					
Ludlow Falls	1292.0800	1272.0800	Otl	WD8JPP	WD8JPP
SUMMIT					
Akron	1292.2000	1272.2000	OaTTelRB xz	WA8DBW	WA8DBW
OKLAHOMA					
OKLAHOMA CITY METRO					
Oklahoma City	1283.1000	–	Ot	WN5J	WN5J
OREGON					
PORTLAND METRO					
Clackamas	1291.0000	1271.0000	O 107.2ael	KB7WUK	WORC
Hillsboro	1291.5000	1271.5000	Oel	K7AUO	TERAC
PENNSYLVANIA					
FREQUENCY USAGE - ALL WPA SECTION					
WPA SNP	1283.0000	–		SNP	
CHESTER					
Glen Mills	1295.8000	1280.8000	O 94.8e	W3LW	------------
LYCOMING					
Williamsport	1285.0000	–	●t(CA)e	N3PFC	------------
NORTHAMPTON					
Easton	1294.0000	1274.0000	OlLITZ	N2ZAV	------------

Location	Output	Input	Notes	Call	Sponsor
PHILADELPHIA					
Philadelphia	1294.1000	1274.1000	O 127.3el	K3PHL	------------
PITTSBURGH 131.8					
Pittsburgh/W Mifflin	1285.0000	–	O	KA3IDK	KA3IDK
PUERTO RICO					
E					
Luquillo	1285.0000	–	●	WP4KER	------------
RHODE ISLAND					
NORTHERN					
Cranston	1291.5000	–	O	KA1BRJ	KA1BRJ
SOUTH CAROLINA					
Greenville	1250.0000	1280.0000	Ol	WA4MWC	KB4PQA
TENNESSEE					
Bartlett	1284.2500	–	O 107.2/107.2	N4GMT	N4GMT
Memphis	1292.0000	1272.0000	O	N4HKS	MID SOUTH MIC
Nashville	1284.4000	–	O	WA4AKM	------------
TEXAS					
Austin	1292.4000	1272.4000	O 88.5	W5NFC	------------
Dallas	1292.3000	1272.3000	O 100	AD5KZ	------------
Dallas	1292.6000	1272.6000	●	N5MIJ	------------
Dallas	1295.0000	1275.0000	Ors	W5FC	Dallas ARC
Fort Worth	1292.7800	1272.7800	O 110.9	N5UN	FW1200
Houston	1292.1000	1272.1000	O	WA5KXG	------------
Mesquite	1292.0000	1272.0000	O 156.7 (CA)	AK5DX	------------
San Antonio	1292.0000	1272.0000	O	KB5BI	------------
San Antonio	1292.3000	1272.3000	●	W5DKK	------------
San Antonio	1293.3000	1273.3000	O	WD5STR	SANANTONIOD
Temple	1292.1000	1272.1000	O	K5CTX	------------
Venus	1292.9800	1278.9800	OerWX	WA5FWC	------------
UTAH					
FREQUENCY USAGE					
Statewide	1283.0000	–	O	SHARED	
WASATCH FRONT					
Salt Lake	1284.0000	–	Ox	WA7GIE	------------
Salt Lake	1285.0000	–	O 88.5 L(448.4)X	K7OJU	------------
Salt Lake	1286.0000	–	O	AA7XY	------------

Location	Output	Input	Notes	Call	Sponsor
VIRGINIA					
Alexandria	1282.6000	–	O	WA4CCF	------------
Bedford	2411.6000	2441.6000	O	WA1ZMS	WA1ZMS
Bedfrd/apl Orch	1283.1000	–	O	WA1ZMS	MTN TOP ASSOC/W
Mclean	1292.1000	1272.1000	O	K6LEW	K6LEW
Roanoke/poor Mt	1291.0200	1271.0200	O	N4CH	N4CH
Tysons Corner	1292.0000	1272.0000	O	WR4S	WB5MMB
Virginia Beach	1284.6000	–	O	W4BBR	W4RVN
ALL OF TMARC AREA					
SNP	1283.0000	–	O		------------
WASHINGTON AREA					
Alexandria	1282.6000	–	O 107.2l	W4HFH	Alex RC
Bull Run Mtn	1286.1000	–	O	N3KL	N3KL
WASHINGTON					
W WA - FREQUENCY USAGE					
Crossband	1292.0000	1292.0000			
Digital	1248.0000	1252.0000			
Fm Links	1282.0000	1288.0000			
Nb Fm Links	1246.0000	1248.0000			
Nb Fm Links	1275.0000	1276.0000			
Rptr Inputs	1268.0000	1275.0000			
Rptr Outputs	1288.0000	1295.0000			
SW WASHINGTON					
Vancouver	1292.5000	1272.5000	O 94.8e	W7AIA	CCARC
W WA - NORTH					
Bellingham	1290.9500	1270.9500	O 103.5	N7FYU	N7FYU
W WA - SEATTLE-TACOMA					
Baldi Mtn	1292.3000	1272.3000	O 103.5el	N7FSP	N7FSP
Tacoma	1292.4000	1272.4000	O 103.5el	KB7CNN	------------
Tiger Mtn East	1292.2000	1272.2000	O 103.5el	KB7CNN	------------
WEST VIRGINIA					
ALL OF TMARC AREA					
SNP	1283.0000	–	O		------------
WISCONSIN					
WAR					
Sturgeon Bay	1282.1000	–	O 100.0aers	K9KJM	K9KJM
BRITISH COLUMBIA					
GREATER VANCOUVER					
Vancouver	1291.9400	1271.9400	el	VE7RAG	BCFMCA
MANITOBA					
WINNIPEG					
Winnipeg	1280.5000	–	O	VE4KEG	------------

Location	Output	Input	Notes	Call	Sponsor
Winnipeg	1289.2500	915.0000	O	VE4EDU	------------
Winnipeg	1292.0000	1272.0000	O	VE4AGA	------------

ONTARIO

Location	Output	Input	Notes	Call	Sponsor
CENTRAL					
New Tecumseth	1285.0000	–	O	VE3VGA	------------
METRO TORONTO					
Toronto	1250.0000	1250.0000	O 103.5 L(D-STAR)	VE3YYZ	TARCS
Toronto	1284.0000	–	O	VA3GTU	------------
Toronto	1287.5000	–	O 103.5 L(D-STAR)	VE3YYZ	TARCS
Uxbridge	1286.0000	–	O 103.5e L(IRLP TFMCS)	VE3RPT	TFMCS
NIAGARA					
Niagara On The Lake	1282.5000	–	O L(D-STAR)	VA3NAG	------------
Niagara On The Lake	1299.1500	1299.1500	Oe L(D-STAR DATA)	VA3NAG	------------

QUEBEC

Location	Output	Input	Notes	Call	Sponsor
Joliette	1284.0000	–	O 103.5e	VE2RHO	VE2BFK
Montreal	1283.0000	–	O 103.5e	VE2RIO	RAQI
Montreal	2310.1000	448.6000	O	VE2RVK	VE2VK
Saint-Lin Laurentides	1284.0000	–	O 141.3e	VE2RFO	VE2BFK
St-Adolphe d'Howard	2310.1500	448.6000	O	VE2RVK	VE2VK
St-Calixte	1283.6000	–	O 141.3	VE2RVK	VE2VK
St-Calixte	1296.0700	2310.0000	O	VE2RVK	VE2VK
Ste-Marcelline	1280.0000	1252.0000	OE-SUN	VE2RVQ	VE2BFK
Ste-Marcelline	1280.0000	1255.0000	OE-SUN	VE2RVQ	VE2BFK
Ste-Marcelline	1280.0000	1265.0000	OE-SUN	VE2RVQ	VE2BFK
Ste-Marcelline	1289.2500	1241.2500	OE-SUN	VE2RVQ	VE2BFK
Ste-Marcelline	1289.2500	1253.2500	OE-SUN	VE2RVQ	VE2BFK
Ste-Marcelline	1289.2500	1265.2500	OE-SUN	VE2RVQ	VE2BFK
Ste-Marcelline	1289.2500	–	OE-SUN	VE2RVQ	VE2BFK
Ste-Marcelline	2442.0000	1255.0000	OE-SUN	VE2RVQ	VE2BFK
Ste-Marcelline	2442.0000	2398.0000	OE-SUN	VE2RVQ	VE2BFK
Ste-Marcelline	2442.0000	2412.0000	OE-SUN	VE2RVQ	VE2BFK
Ste-Marcelline	2442.0000	2428.0000	OE-SUN	VE2RVQ	VE2BFK

Amateur Television (ATV)

Location	*Output*	*Input*	*Notes*	*Call*	*Sponsor*
ALABAMA					
Gadsden	421.2500	439.2500	O	N5XNQ	N5XNQ
Gadsden	421.2500	1255.0000	O	N5XNQ	N5XNQ
Huntsville	421.2500	439.2500	O	W4ATV	TVATV
ARIZONA					
CENTRAL					
Shaw Butte	1241.2500	1265.0000	Olx	W7ATV	ARIZONA AMAT
White Tanks	1253.2500	2441.5000	Olx	WA6SVT	Amateur TV Net
White Tanks	1289.2500	421.2500	Olx	W7ATV	ARIZONA AMAT
TUCSON					
Mt Lemmon	1277.2500	2441.5000	Olx	W7ATN	ARIZONA ATN
ARKANSAS					
CENTRAL					
Little Rock	421.2500	439.2500	O	N5AT	ARES
Pine Bluff	426.2500	439.2500	Oer	K5DAK	PinBlufARC
NORTH					
Harrison	421.2500	439.2500	O	K5YWL	K5YWL
CALIFORNIA					
FREQUENCY USAGE - SOUTHERN CALIFORNIA					
So Cal Atv	144.3450			ATV-SPLX VOICE	
So Cal Atv	146.4300		100.0	ATV-RPT VOICE	
So Cal Atv	426.2500			ATV-SPLX	
So Cal Atv	434.0000			ATV-RPT INPUT-H SYNC A	
So Cal Atv	913.2500			ATV	
So Cal Atv	915.0000			ATV	
So Cal Atv	919.2500			RPT OUT	
So Cal Atv	1241.2500			ATV-RPT OUT	
So Cal Atv	1253.2500			ATV-RPT OUT	
So Cal Atv	1265.2500		EXP	ATV-SPLX	
So Cal Atv	1277.2500			ATV-RPT OUT	
So Cal Atv	1289.2500			ATV	
So Cal Atv	2398.0000			ATV-FM-SPLX	
So Cal Atv	2417.0000			ATV-FM-LINKS	
So Cal Atv	2441.5000			ATV-FM-RPT INPUT, H-SY	
So Cal Atv	3380.0000			ATV-WFM-RPT OUTPUT	
So Cal Atv	3480.0000			ATV-WFM-RPT OUTPUT	
So Cal Atv	5910.0000			ATV-FM-RPT OUTPUT	
So Cal Atv	10400.0000			ATV	
NORCAL-EAST BAY					
Concord	427.2500	1289.2500	Oersx	W6CX	MDARC

Location	*Output*	*Input*	*Notes*	*Call*	*Sponsor*
Concord	1241.2500	1289.2500	Oersx	W6CX	MDARC
NORCAL-SAN JOAQUIN VALLEY					
Lodi	1252.0000	915.0000	Oelrsx	WB6ASU	WB6ASU
Springville	427.2500	910.2500	O#x	N6BYH	N6BYH
NORCAL-SOUTH BAY					
Palo Alto	2433.7500	1255.0000	O#es	W6YX	SUARC
San Jose	923.2500	427.2500	●#aerx	W2NYC	W2NYC
SanJose	427.2500	1255.2500	O 123#ers	K6BEN	K6BEN
SOCAL-#LA CENTRAL					
Mt Wilson	1241.2500	434.0000	OL(NTSC)	W6ATN	ATN analog
Mt Wilson	1241.2500	2441.5000	Ol	W6ATN	ATN
Mt Wilson	1243.0000	434.0000	OL(QAM64)	W6ATN	ATN DATV
SOCAL-#LA NORTH					
Oat Mtn	919.2500	434.0000	Ol	W6ATN	ATN
Oat Mtn	919.2500	2441.5000	Ol	W6ATN	ATN
Oat Mtn	3380.0000	2441.5000	Ol	W6ATN	ATN
Oat Mtn	3380.0000	434.0000	Ol	W6ATN	ATN
SOCAL-#ORANGE					
Santiago Peak	1253.2500	434.0000	Ol	W6ATN	ATN hub
Santiago Peak	1253.2500	2441.5000	Ol	W6ATN	ATN hub
Santiago Peak	3480.0000	10400.0000	O	AF6HP	METS
Santiago Peak	5910.0000	434.0000	Ol	W6ATN	ATN
Santiago Peak	5910.0000	2441.5000	Ol	W6ATN	ATN
Sierra Peak	3380.0000	10400.0000	Ol	AF6HP	METS
Sierra Peak	3380.0000	2441.5000	Ol	AF6HP	METS
Sierra Peak	3380.0000	434.0000	Ol	AF6HP	METS
SOCAL-#SAN BERNARDINO					
Heaps Peak	3380.0000	2441.5000	O	AF6HP	METS
Heaps Peak	3380.0000	10400.0000	O	AF6HP	METS
Snow Peak	1241.2500	434.0000	Ol	W6ATN	ATN
Snow Peak	1241.2500	2441.5000	Ol	W6ATN	ATN
SOCAL-#SAN DIEGO					
Mt Palomar	1241.2500	2441.5000	O	W6WNG	Palomar ARC
Mt Palomar	1241.2500	915.0000	O	W6NWG	Palomar ARC
Pt Loma	1277.2500	434.0000	Ol	W6ATN	ATN
Pt Loma	1277.2500	2441.5000	Ol	W6ATN	ATN
SOCAL-#SANTA BARBARA					
Santa Barbara	1289.2500	434.0000	Ol	WB9KMO	ATN
Santa Barbara	1289.2500	2441.5000	Ol	WB9KMO	ATN
SOCAL-#VICTORVILLE					
Blue Ridge	919.2500	434.0000	Ol	W6ATN	ATN
Blue Ridge	919.2500	2441.5000	Ol	W6ATN	ATN

COLORADO

BOULDER COUNTY					
Boulder	421.2500	1277.2500	Os	WØBCR	BCARES
DENVER METRO					
Aurora	420.0250	433.0250	●	NØZUQ	NØZUQ

Location	Output	Input	Notes	Call	Sponsor
FLORIDA					
SOUTH EAST - MIAMI/FT LAUD					
Miami	435.0000	910.2500	Oe	KC4JHS	KC4JHS
SOUTH WEST - FT MYERS					
Cape Coral	421.2500	439.2500	O	W1RP	W1RP
WEST CENTRAL - SARASOTA					
Laurel	421.2500	434.0000	Oers	N4SER	SERC
GEORGIA					
Dalton	421.2500	1265.0000	O	N4BZJ	N4BZJ
IDAHO					
SW-ID					
Burley	434.0000	1253.2500	O	K6ZVA	ISRA MHCH
ILLINOIS					
ROCKFORD					
Rockford	421.2500	1253.2500	Oe	W9ATN	RARA-ATV
INDIANA					
INDIANAPOLIS					
Indianapolis	425.2500	439.2500	Oe	K9LPW	CentIN RA
NORTHEAST					
Fort Wayne	910.2500	427.2500	O	W9TE	FWRC
Fort Wayne	910.2500	439.2500	O	W9TE	FWRC
SOUTHWEST					
Evansville	421.2500	434.0000	OersWX	W9KXP	W9KXP
KANSAS					
KANSAS CITY METRO					
Kansas City	426.2500	439.2500	Oer	WRØATV	KC ATV Gp
Kansas City	426.2500	439.2500	Oer	WRØATV	KC ATV Gp
SOUTHEAST					
Pittsburg	426.2500	1252.0000	O	KØPRO	PRO ATV
TOPEKA					
Topeka	427.2500	1252.0000	O	WAØVRS	911 Top
WICHITA					
Wichita	421.2500	439.2500	O	KAØTV	ICUC-UHF-T
KENTUCKY					
Bowling Green	421.2500	439.2500	O	KY4TV	KY4TV
Bowling Green	1280.0000	439.2500	O	KY4TV	KY4ATV
LOUISIANA					
REG 1 NEW ORLEANS					
New Orleans	421.2500	439.2500	O	WDØGIV	WDØGIV

Location	Output	Input	Notes	Call	Sponsor
MARYLAND					
BALTIMORE					
Baltimore	439.2500	426.2500	O L(AUDIO 430.75)	W3WCQ	BRATS
Baltimore	439.2500	1253.2500	O L(AUDIO 1293.75)	W3WCQ	BRATS
Baltimore	911.2500	426.2500	O L(AUDIO 915.75)	W3WCQ	BRATS
Baltimore	1289.2500	426.2500	Ol	W3WCQ	BRATS
WASHINGTON AREA					
Laurel	923.2500	1265.2500	O L(AUDIO 147.495)	K3UQQ	CATS
Rockville	923.2500	1277.2500	O	K3ATV	MACS
MICHIGAN					
LOWER PEN SOUTHEAST					
Flint	1253.2500	439.2500	O 100lrs	KC8KGZ	Michigan Specialized
LOWER PEN SOUTHWEST					
Grand Rapids	421.2500	439.2500	Oex	K8DMR	K8DMR
MINNESOTA					
METRO					
New Brighton	910.2500	426.2500	Ol	NØNMB	RCES
New Brighton	1253.2500	426.2500	Ol	NØNMB	RCES
SOUTH EAST					
Wabasha	421.2500	439.2500	Oe	WAØUNB	WAØUNB
NEBRASKA					
OMAHA					
Omaha/KPTM	421.2500	434.0000	OH SYNC	WBØCMC	GOATS
Omaha/KPTM	1248.2500	434.0000	OH SYNC	WBØCMC	------------
NEVADA					
LAS VEGAS VALLEY					
Black Mtn	2410.7500	–	O	KD8S	------------
Black Mtn	2433.7500	–	O	KD8S	------------
Hi Potosi Mtn	913.0000	2442.0000	O	N7ZEV	------------
Hi Potosi Mtn	1265.0000	2417.0000	O L(SOUTHERN CALIFORNIA)	N7ZEV	------------
Hi Potosi Mtn	1265.0000	434.0000	O L(SOUTHERN CALIFORNIA)	N7ZEV	------------
NEW JERSEY					
SUSSEX					
Vernon	5665.0000	5885.0000	Oters	W2VER	VRACES
NEW MEXICO					
NORTHWEST					
Farmington	421.2500	439.2500	O	NO3Y	NO3Y

Location	Output	Input	Notes	Call	Sponsor
NEW YORK					
CORTLAND/ITHACA					
Ithaca	421.2500	439.2500	O	AF2A	TOMPKINS COU
ELMIRA/CORNING					
Elmira	421.2500	434.0000	O	KB3APR	ARAST
OHIO					
ALLEN					
Lima	421.2500	439.2500	O	WB8ULC	NWOhioARC
COLUMBIANA					
Lisbon	421.2500	434.0000	O	KC8PHW	KC8PHW
FRANKLIN					
Columbus	10.3500	10.4500		WR8ATV	ATCO
Columbus	427.2500	439.2500		WR8ATV	ATCO
Columbus	1258.0000	1280.0000		WR8ATV	ATCO
Columbus	1268.0000	+		WR8ATV	ATCO
Columbus	2433.0000	2398.0000		WR8ATV	ATCO
VAN WERT					
Van Wert	434.0000	923.2500		W8FY	VWARC
OKLAHOMA					
TULSA METRO					
Tulsa	913.2500	434.0000	OWX	W5IAS	TULSA ARC
OREGON					
CENTRAL WILLAMETTE VALLEY					
Salem	910.0000	426.2500	O	K7ATV	SATVA
PORTLAND METRO					
Portland	426.2500	910.2500	Ol	WB2QHS	WB2QHS
PENNSYLVANIA					
LANCASTER					
Manheim	923.2500	910.2500	OersWX	K3IR	SPARC Inc.
PHILADELPHIA					
Philadelphia	421.2500	439.2500	Or	W3PHL	PARA Group
Philadelphia	923.2500	910.2500	Or	W3PHL	PARA Group
PITTSBURGH					
Carnegie	426.2500	439.2500	O	W3KWH	SCARC
Pittsburgh Hazelwood	421.2500	910.2500	O	WA3PBD	GFMA
Pittsburgh Hazelwood	923.2500	910.2500	O	WA3PBD	GFMA
SOUTHWEST					
Acme	421.2500	439.2500	O	W3NBN	LHVHFS
YORK					
Dover	439.2500	426.2500	Otel	W3HZU	Keystone

Location	Output	Input	Notes	Call	Sponsor
PUERTO RICO					
N					
Aguas Buenas	426.2500	1252.0000	O	KP4IA	M/Vision
TEXAS					
Beaumont	421.2500	439.2500	O	KE5O	------------
Houston	421.2500	1255.0000	O	W5GFP	HATS
Marshall	421.2500	439.2500	O	K5FBI	------------
Mesquite	421.2500	1248.0000	O	AK5DX	NTSC
Waco	421.2500	439.2500	O	W5ZDN	HOTARC
UTAH					
FREQUENCY USAGE					
ATV Intercomm	145.7300	145.7300	Oe	SIMPLEX	
WASATCH FRONT					
Salt Lake	1248.0000	439.2500	O	KA7OEI	------------
Salt Lake	1252.0000	2416.0000	Oex	WA7GIE	------------
WASHINGTON					
E WA-SUNNYSIDE					
Rattlesnake	421.2500	439.2500		N7IWA	N7IWA
E WA-YAKIMA					
Eagle Peak	1253.2500	434.0000		N7IWA	N7IWA
Little Bald Mtn	923.2500	426.2500		N7IWA	N7IWA
SEATTLE/TACOMA					
Cougar Mtn	1253.2500	434.0000	O	KF7BQH	WWATS
Federal Way	1290.1000	1270.1000	O	WA7FW	FWARC
Seattle	1277.2500	434.0000	O	WW7ATS	WWATS
WISCONSIN					
WAR					
Wausau	421.2500	1250.0000	Otaelr	AD9W	RMATS
ALBERTA					
CALGARY					
Calgary	910.2500	439.2500	Osx	VE6RTV	CARA
Calgary	923.2500	439.2500	O	VE6TVR	VE6CDU
Calgary	1276.0000	1282.0000	O	VE6CDU	VE6CDU
BRITISH COLUMBIA					
FRASER VALLEY					
Abbotsford	1289.0000	1246.0000	O	VE7RVA	FVARESS
GREATER VANCOUVER					
Vancouver	915.0000	147.5250	O	VE7VHF	VE7CIM
Vancouver	1246.0000	2410.0000	O	VE7VHF	VE7CIM
Vancouver	1289.0000	2434.0000	O	VE7VHF	VE7CIM
Vancouver	2310.0000	147.5250	O	VE7VHF	VE7CIM

Location	*Output*	*Input*	*Notes*	*Call*	*Sponsor*
SOUTH CENTRAL					
Vernon	1289.0000	1246.0000	O	VE7VTV	VE7VVW
MANITOBA					
WINNIPEG					
Winnipeg	1253.2500	434.0000		VE4EDU	------------
Winnipeg	1289.2500	915.0000		VE4EDU	------------
Winnipeg	1292.0000	1272.0000	O	VE4AGA	------------
ONTARIO					
NATIONAL CAPITOL REGION					
Ottawa	439.2500	1246.0000	eL(914.000)	VE3TVA	VE3CZO
Ottawa	914.0000	1246.0000	L(439.250)	VE3TVA	VE3CZO
QUEBEC					
Joliette	439.2500	910.0000		VA2ATV	VE2BFK
Saint-Lin Laurentides	439.2500	1255.0000		VE2RFO	VE2BFK
Ste-Foy	1257.7500	438.5000		VE2RQT	CRAQ
Ste-Foy	1278.7500	434.0000		VE2RQT	CRAQ
Ste-Marcelline	439.2500	910.0000		VE2RVQ	VE2BFK

APCO 25

Location	*Output*	*Input*	*Notes*	*Call*	*Sponsor*
ARIZONA					
PHOENIX					
Usery Mtn	448.7250	–	OtxZ(N)	KE7JFH	F.H.A.R.T.
CALIFORNIA					
NORCAL-EAST BAY					
San Jose	444.0375	+	Oel	K6HLE	AREA Repea
NORCAL-NORTH COAST					
Willits	442.1000	+	ODCSlx	K7WWA	WI6H
NORCAL-SACRAMENTO VALLEY					
Magalia	147.1500	+	O 110.9lrs	KB6FEC	AREA
NORCAL-SAN JOAQUIN VALLEY					
Fresno	443.6000	+	O 114.8ex	N6LYE	N6LYE
Madera	443.6000	+	O 186.2e	N6LYE	N6LYE
Merced	440.8000	+	O 114.8ex	N6LYE	N6LYE
NORCAL-SOUTH BAY					
San Jose	444.0250	+	Oelsx	K6HLE	AREA
SOCAL-LA,OR,RIV,SBER					
Covers Area	445.3800	–	●	K6CCC	------------
FLORIDA					
CENTRAL - ORLANDO					
Eustis	146.8950	–	O 293/293	W4ALR	LCSO
			(CA)eL(147.390 (APCO25) 147.345 (APCO2		
Groveland	147.3450	+	O 293/293	KD4MBN	LCPS
			(CA)eL(146.895 (APCO25) 147.390 (APCO		
Orange City	442.8750	+	O 55/55	W4ORL	W4ORL
			DCS(411)e		
Orlando	442.0750	+	O 55/55x	W4LOV	KD4JYD
Orlando	927.0500	902.0500	Oa(CA)	KAØOXH	KAØOXH
			DCS(411)eL(443.95)x		
Tavares	147.3900	+	O 293/293e	K4AUS	LCSO
			L(147.345 (APCO25) 146.895 (APCO25))rs		
DEEP SOUTH					
Big Pine Key	442.3750	+	● 6/6	NQ2Z	N2GKG
			A(220-111-110) TT(*05ON/#05OFF)eL(EC-9		
NORTH EAST					
Crescent City	145.1900	–	O 49/49e	KJ4UOP	KJ4UOP
			WX		
NORTH EAST - JACKSONVILLE					
Jacksonville	147.3150	+	O 293/293	W4RNG	Jax Range
Jacksonville	444.2000	+	O 55/55e	K4QHR	K4QHR
			L(EC-444200 442.100 444.900 442.900)		

Location	Output	Input	Notes	Call	Sponsor
NORTH WEST					
Wacissa	147.0000	+	Ot L(147.375)x	K4TLH	TARS
NORTH WEST - TALLAHASSEE					
Tallahassee	146.9100	–	Otaer	K4TLH	TARS
SOUTH EAST					
Boca Raton	147.3900	+	O 293/293e rsx	KS4VT	KS4VT
Boca Raton	442.0000	+	O 293/293e r	KS4VT	KS4VT
Palm Beach Gardens	146.6250	–	O 293/293a (CA)ers	W4JUP	JTRG
Riviera Beach	146.8800	–	O 293/293e rs	W4PBC	PBCRACES
West Palm Beach	145.2300	–	O 293/293e rsx	N4QPM	N4QPM
West Palm Beach	145.3900	–	O 293/293e rs	W4PBC	PBCRACES
West Palm Beach	147.3600	+	O 293/293e rs	W4PBC	PBCRACES
West Palm Beach	444.2750	+	Oter	W4PBC	PBCRACES
SOUTH EAST - MIAMI/FT LAUD					
Ft Lauderdale	146.7900	–	O 293/293e sx	N4MOT	MARC
Ft Lauderdale	443.0000	+	O 293/293e sx	N4MOT	MARC
Ft Lauderdale	443.4000	+	●teWX	N4BIF	N4BIF
Hollywood	442.7750	+	Ot L(EC-329701) BI WX(99*)	K4ABB	K4ABB
Plantation	146.7900	–	O 293/293e sx	W4MOT	MARC
WEST CENTRAL - TAMPA/ST PETE					
Plant City	147.2000	+	O 293/293	W4CLL	PCDC

HAWAII

Location	Output	Input	Notes	Call	Sponsor
HAWAII					
Hilo	443.8250	+	O 103.5elr RBx	KH6HPZ	HCDA
Hilo	444.7250	+	O 123.0l	WH6FM	WH6FM
Hilo	444.9000	+	O 100.0l	WH6FM	WH6FM
OAHU					
Honolulu	444.7250	+	O/123.0l	WH6FM	WH6FM

ILLINOIS

Location	Output	Input	Notes	Call	Sponsor
CHICAGO					
Chicago	145.1100	–	107.2	W9GN	UFDA
Chicago	443.6750	+	114.8 (CA) WX	KC9DFK	CHI-TOWN
Chicago	443.7500	+	114.8 (CA)	WA9ORC	CFMC

Location	Output	Input	Notes	Call	Sponsor
NORTH CENTRAL					
Marseilles	146.7450	–	114.8elWX	KA9FER	KA9FER
Marseilles	442.6000	+	023elWX	KA9FER	KA9FER
NORTHEAST					
Batavia	444.1000	+	100.0ex	KA9LFU	ELFAR
Crystal Lake	145.2700	–	107.2	W9DWP	W9DWP/KAPS
East Dundee	443.0250	+	114.8	W9DWP	W9DWP
Gurnee	443.1500	+	114.8e	N9OZB	ARG
Morris	146.7150	–	94.8	KC9KKO	JP WATTERS
Morris	147.2700	+	107.2eWX	KB9SZK	GCARC
Morris	442.0000	+	94.8	KC9KKO	JP WATTERS
Morris	442.3250	+	114.8eWX	KB9SZK	GCARC
Schaumburg	145.3700	–	107.2	K9SO	AMA
Schaumburg	442.9000	+	114.8 (CA)l WXx	WA9VGI	FISHFAR
Schaumburg	443.5750	+	114.8	N9KNS	MOTO ARC
Schaumburg	443.7250	+	114.8	N9KNS	MOTO ARC
WEST CENTRAL					
Quincy	146.8200	–	100.0l	WA9VGI	FISHNET
Quincy	442.9000	+	114.8l	WA9VGI	FISHNET
MARYLAND					
FREDERICK					
Frederick	442.8000	+	**O** L(NAC 797)	N3ITA	N3ITA
Frederick	448.1250	–	**O** L(NAC ???)	K3MAD	MADXRA
WASHINGTON AREA					
Germantown	147.2700	+	**O** L(NAC 293)	WA3KOK	NERA
MASSACHUSETTS					
BLACKSTONE VALLEY					
Uxbridge	447.3250	–	**O**t L(P25:NAC353 WESTBORO MA 448.775)	W1WNS	ATT
BOSTON METRO					
Boston	448.7250	–	**O**t L(P25:NAC444)	W1NAU	W1NAU
Waltham	146.6400	–	**O**t L(P25:NAC293 E490278)	W1MHL	WalthamARA
CENTRAL					
Worcester	146.9250	–	**O**t L(P25:NAC293)	W1YK	WPIWA
Worcester	449.8750	–	**O**t L(P25:NAC250)	N1PFC	WECT
METROWEST					
Westborough	448.7750	–	**O**t L(P25:NAC353 927.6125)	W1WNS	ATT

Location	Output	Input	Notes	Call	Sponsor
MICHIGAN					
LOWER PEN SOUTHEAST					
Detroit	147.3300	+	O 151.4ex	KC8LTS	KC8LTS
MINNESOTA					
METRO					
Minneapolis	146.7000	–	O 293e	WCØHC	HC RACES
NEBRASKA					
OMAHA					
Omaha	442.6500	+	Ol	KØBOY	KØBOY
NEW HAMPSHIRE					
MERRIMACK VALLEY					
Hudson	448.4375	–	Ot L(DMR-MARC)	K1MOT	MARC-NE
NEW MEXICO					
NORTH CENTRAL					
Los Alamos	444.7750	–	ODCS(311) eRB	WD9CMS	------------
Los Alamos	927.9000	902.9000	ODCS(293) e	WD9CMS	------------
OHIO					
CUYAHOGA					
Brooklyn	442.9250	+	O 293a	K5BLS	NOHP25GRP
FRANKLIN					
Columbus	443.6500	+	Otx	W8DIG	W8KHW
OREGON					
CENTRAL WILLAMETTE VALLEY					
Eugene	145.3900	–	O 293ael	WB7LCS	WB7LCS
TENNESSEE					
Benton	144.9400	147.4400	O	K4AJM	K4AJM
TEXAS					
Austin	146.6800	–	O 123	KE5ZW	------------
Austin	146.8600	–	●	NØGSZ	------------
Cedar Park	442.6500	+	O 114	KE5ZW	------------
WEST VIRGINIA					
CHARLES TOWN					
Charles Town	444.3500	+	O L(NAC 734)	N3EAQ	N3EAQ

Location	*Output*	*Input*	*Notes*	*Call*	*Sponsor*
WISCONSIN					
WAR					
Milwaukee	146.9400	–	O 127.3aes	N9PAY	GFD/EOC
Milwaukee	443.3250	+	O 127.3aes	N9PAY	ATC
Milwaukee	927.5125	902.5125	O 127.3aes	N9PAY	ATC/MATC
New Berlin	443.0500	+	O 127.3aes	KT9AC	KT9AC
Wausau	145.3700	–	O 114.8aelr	KB9KST	KB9KST
BRITISH COLUMBIA					
FRASER VALLEY					
Chilliwack	444.6250	+	O	VE7RCK	VE7BHG
GREATER VANCOUVER					
Delta	440.7250	+	O	VE7SUN	VE7DID
New Westminster	444.6000	+	O	VE7NWR	VE7KA
Whistler	443.8500	+	O	VE7SLV	VA7BC
SOUTH CENTRAL					
Kelowna, Winfield	440.9500	+	O	VA7DIG	OCARC
VANC ISLAND CENTRAL					
Ladysmith	440.7000	+	O	VA7DXH	VA7DN
VANC ISLAND SOUTH					
Ganges	444.8500	+	O	VE7XNR	VA7DN
Saltspring Island	440.8500	+	O	VE7MDD	VA7DN
Saltspring Island	440.9500	+	O	VE7MDN	VA7DN
Saltspring Island	443.8500	+	O	VE7MDN	VA7DN

D-Star

Location	Output	Input	Notes	Call	Sponsor
ALABAMA					
Alabaster	146.7300	–	/DV EXP	N4RON	AARC
Alabaster	442.0750	+	/DV	N4RON	AARC
Alabaster	1248.6000	1248.6000	/DD	N4RON	AARC
Alabaster	1293.0000	1273.0000	/DV	N4RON	AARC
Anniston / Oak Mtn	145.2800	–	OEXP	KJ4JGK	EMA / DHS
Anniston / Oak Mtn	443.3500	+	OEXP	KJ4JGK	EMA / DHS
Anniston/Cheaha Mt	145.3000	–	O/D-STAR	WB4GNA	Mentone Ed.
Anniston/Cheaha Mt	442.4250	+	O/D-STAR	WB4GNA	Mentone Ed.
Anniston/Cheaha Mt	1251.0000	1251.0000	/DD	WB4GNA	Mentone Ed.
Anniston/Cheaha Mt	1285.0000	–	/DV	WB4GNA	Mentone Ed.
Argo/Trussville	145.2600	–	O/DV EXP	K4YNZ	K4YNZ
Birmingham	145.4100	–	O/D-STAR	K4DSO	BARC
Birmingham	443.2000	+	/DV	K4DSO	BARC
Birmingham	443.9750	+	O/DV	KI4SBB	Mentone Ed
Birmingham	1250.0000	1250.0000	/DD	K4DSO	BARC
Birmingham	1251.0000	1251.0000	O/D-D	KI4SBB	Mentone Ed
Birmingham	1282.5000	1270.0000	O/DV	KI4SBB	Mentone Ed
Birmingham	1283.4000	–	/DV	K4DSO	BARC
Birmingham	1285.5000	1270.5000	O/DV	KI4SBB	Mentone Ed
Clanton	145.1800	–	O/DV L(GATEWAY)	KF4LQK	AEMA ARC
Clanton	444.3750	+	O/D-STAR L(GATEWAY)	KF4LQK	AEMA ARC
Clanton	1285.5000	–	O/DV L(GATEWAY)	KF4LQK	AEMA ARC
Enterprise	145.1300	–	Oe	KJ4OTP	Coffee Co. EMA
Enterprise	442.6500	+	Oe	KJ4OTP	Coffee Co. EMA
Fort Payne	145.4400	–	O/D-STAR	KI4SAY	Mentone Ed.
Fort Payne	1285.0000	–	/DV	KI4SAY	Mentone Ed.
Greenville	145.1900	–	O/DV	K4TNS	Jim Bell Wireless
Greenville	442.2250	+	O/D-STAR elWX	K4TNS	Jim Bell Wireless
Guntersville	145.1400	–	OeWX	KI4RYX	MCEARS
Huntsville	145.3600	–	O/DV EXP	W4WBC	Mentone Ed.
Huntsville	145.4300	–	/DV	KI4PPF	HIT
Huntsville	443.3750	+	●/D-STAR	KI4PPF	HIT

Location	Output	Input	Notes	Call	Sponsor
Huntsville	443.3750	+	/DV	KI4PPF	HIT
Huntsville	443.4250	+	/DV	W4WBC	Mentone Ed.
Huntsville	1251.8000	1251.8000	/DD	KI4PPF	HIT
Huntsville	1253.5000	1253.5000	/DD	W4WBC	Mentone Ed.
Huntsville	1282.5000	–	O/DV	W4WBC	Mentone Ed.
Huntsville	1284.0000	–	/DV	KI4PPF	HIT
Magnolia Springs	145.3100	–	O/D-STAR	KI4SAZ	Mentone Ed.
Magnolia Springs	444.3000	+	O/D-STAR	KI4SAZ	Mentone Ed.
Magnolia Springs	1251.0000	1251.0000	/DD	KI4SAZ	Mentone Ed.
Magnolia Springs	1285.0000	–	/DV	KI4SAZ	Mentone Ed.
Mentone	443.3250	+	/DV	KI4SAY	Mentone Ed.
Mentone	1251.0000	1251.0000	/DD	KI4SAY	Mentone Ed.
Mobile	145.3900	–	/DV	W4IAX	MARC
Mobile	444.9000	+	/DV	W4IAX	MARC
Mobile	444.9000	+	O/D-STAR	W4IAX	Mobile ARC
Montgomery	146.9200	–	O/DV	W4AP	MARC
Roanoke	145.4000	–	O/DV	KJ4JNX	Pike ARC
Roanoke	145.4000	–	O/D-STAR	KI4JNX	Pike ARC
Roanoke	444.9000	+	O/D-STAR	KJ4JNX	Pike ARC
Roanoke	1251.6000	1251.6000	O/DD	KJ4JNX	Pike ARC
Roanoke	1283.0000	–	O/DV	KJ4JNX	Pike ARC
Talladega / Bald Mtn	145.1600	–	OeEXP	N4WNL	TRAC
Tuscaloosa	146.6050	–	/DV	W4KCQ	TARC
Tuscaloosa	147.5800	146.4800		W4TTR	Tall Twr RC
Tuscaloosa	442.9000	+	/DV	W4TTR	Tall Twr RC
Tuscaloosa	444.0750	+	O/D-STAR	W4KCQ	TARC
Tuscaloosa	1248.2000	1248.2000	/DD	W4TTR	Tall Twr RC
Tuscaloosa	1249.0000	1249.0000	/DD	W4KCQ	TARC
Tuscaloosa	1249.0000	1249.0000	/DD	W4KCQ	TARC
Tuscaloosa	1284.4000	–	/DV	W4KCQ	TARC
Tuscaloosa	1284.4000	–	O/DV	W4KCQ	TARC
Tuscaloosa	1287.9500	–	/DV	W4TTR	Tall Twr RC

ARIZONA

CENTRAL

Location	Output	Input	Notes	Call	Sponsor
Usery Mt	1285.6500	–	Olx	KE7JFH	Fountain Hills Am Ra
Usery Mt	1297.5000	1297.5000	Olx	KE7JFH	Fountain Hills Am Ra
Usery Pass	145.1250	–	Olx	KE7JFH	FOUNTAIN HILLS A
White Tanks	1283.8500	–	Olx	K7PNX	City of Phoenix
White Tanks	1283.9000	–	Olx	W7MOT	MARCA
White Tanks	1298.0000	1298.0000	Olx	K7PNX	City of Phoenix
White Tanks	1299.5000	1299.5000	Olx	W7MOT	MARCA

KINGMAN

Location	Output	Input	Notes	Call	Sponsor
Kingman	1284.0000	–	Ol	W7KDS	Northern AZ Digital R
Kingman	1299.0000	1299.0000	Ol	W7KDS	Northern AZ Digital R

NORTHEASTERN

Location	Output	Input	Notes	Call	Sponsor
Kingman	145.1350	–	O	W7KDS	N.AZ DIGITAL REPE

Location	Output	Input	Notes	Call	Sponsor
PHOENIX					
Scottsdale	445.9500	–	O	KF7CUF	SPRC-SW
Usery Mtn	445.9750	–	Olx	KE7JFH	F.H.A.R.T.
White Tanks	145.1350	–	Oelx	W7MOT	MOTOROLA AM
White Tanks	145.1350	–	Oelx	W7MOT	ARIZONA REPE
White Tanks Mid Peak	440.8125	+	Oelx	W7MOT	A.R.A.
SOUTHEAST					
Pinal Peak	445.8500	–	Ox	N7CI	F.H.A.R.T.
SOUTHERN					
Mt Lemmon	147.4100	146.4100	Oex	K7RST	RADIO SOCIET
SOUTHWEST					
Yuma	445.9750	–	O	N7YDX	Yuma DX Associ
TUCSON					
Mt Lemmon	445.9000	–	Ox	K7RST	R.S. of T.
Mt Lemmon	1284.2500	–	Olx	K7RST	RADIO SOC OF
Mt Lemmon	1298.2500	1298.2500	Olx	K7RST	RADIO SOC OF
Tucson	145.1150	–	O	KR7ST	RADIO SOCIET
Tucson	445.9500	–	O	KR7ST	R.S. of T.
Tucson Bank Of Am	1284.7500	–	Oal	KR7ST	RADIO SOC OF
Tucson Bank Of Am	1298.7500	1298.7500	Oal	KR7ST	RADIO SOC OF
WEST CENTRAL					
Kingman	445.9000	–	O	W7KDS	N.A.D.R.S.

CALIFORNIA

Location	Output	Input	Notes	Call	Sponsor
FREQUENCY USAGE - SOUTHERN CALIFORNIA					
SO CAL	1283.0000	–		DVOICE TEST PAIR	
SO CAL	1294.3000			DVOICE SIMPLEX	
SO CAL	1299.1000			DDATA TEST	
LOS ANGELES COUNTY					
Blueridge	147.5400	144.9850	Ot	W6CPA	IRC
Contractor's Point	147.5600	145.0050	Ot	WA6IRC	IRC
HRO Burbank	147.5700	145.0150	Otl	KB6HRO	------------
NORCAL-EAST BAY					
Concord	144.9750	147.4750	O#elrsx	K6MDD	K6MDD
Concord	147.4250	146.4250	O#ersx	W6CX	MDARC
Concord	1284.2000	–	Oelrsx	K6MDD	K6MDD
Fremont	444.6875	+	O#x	K6LRG	K6LRG
Fremont	1286.6250	–	Ox	K6LRG	K6LRG
Livermore	444.6125	+	O#el	W6UUU	N6LDJ
Oakland	440.0375	+	O#l	W6YYY	N6LDJ
NORCAL-NORTH BAY					
Santa Rosa	145.0400	144.6400	O#r	K6ACS	KD6RC
Santa Rosa	442.1125	+	O#er	K6ACS	K6ACS
NORCAL-SACRAMENTO VALLEY					
Chico	1286.5250	–	Olsx	K6CHO	AREA
Folsom	147.6750	–	Oex	KS6HRP	SHARP

CALIFORNIA

Location	Output	Input	Notes	Call	Sponsor
Folsom	1284.5000	–	O#el	KD6SAC	K6HLE
Oroville	444.2750	+	Olr	KJ6LVV	LOARN
Volcano	144.9600	144.5600	O#elrx	W6DHS	N6RDE
Volcano	440.6000	+	Oelrsx	W6DHS	N6RDE
NORCAL-SAN JOAQUIN VALLEY					
Dunlap	443.8500	+	O#ex	WD6SJV	DCTS
Dunlap	1285.3000	–	O#ex	WD6SJV	DCTS
Mariposa	145.1300	–	Oelsx	W6HHD	W6HHD
Mariposa	444.8000	+	Oelsx	W6HHD	W6HHD
Mariposa	1284.1000	–	Oelsx	W6HHD	W6HHD
Visalia	145.4500	–	Oelrsx	K6VIS	TCARC
Visalia	440.0500	+	Oelrsx	K6VIS	TCARC
Visalia	1286.3250	–	Oelrsx	K6VIS	TCARC
NORCAL-SOUTH BAY					
Palo Alto	444.0750	+	Oelx	WW6BAY	Bay Net
San Jose	440.3000	+	Oel	W6IOS	CARC-SJ
San Jose	1286.5250	–	Oersx	K6HLE	AREA
NORCAL-WEST BAY					
Menlo Park	144.9625	147.4625	O#el	W6OTX	PAARA
Menlo Park	444.4750	+	Oel	W6OTX	PAARA
Menlo Park	1284.1500	–	Oel	W6OTX	PAARA
San Francisco	147.1050	+	Oersx	W6PW	SFARC
ORANGE COUNTY					
HRO Anaheim	147.5700	145.0150	Otl	W6HRO	------------
Laguna Beach	146.1150	+	Oter	K6SOA	SOARA
SAN BERNARDINO COUNTY					
Keller Peak	147.5500	144.9950	Ote	KI6WZX	------------
SAN DIEGO COUNTY					
Palomar Mtn	147.5700	145.0150	Ot	KI6MGN	PAPA System
SOCAL-#LA NORTH					
Burbank	1287.8000	–	O	KB6HRO	HRO DVoice
Burbank	1299.3000	1299.3000	O	KB6HRO	HRO DData
Contractors Pt	1286.1000	–	O	WA6IRC	IRC DVoice
Contractors Pt	1299.7000	1299.7000	O	WA6IRC	IRC DData
SOCAL-#ORANGE					
Anaheim	1287.8250	–	O	W6HRO	HRO DVoice
Anaheim	1299.5000	1299.5000	O	W6HRO	HRO DData
Laguna Beach	1282.6000	–	O	K6SOA	SOARA DVoice
Laguna Beach	1299.9000	1299.9000	O	K6SOA	SOARA DData
SOCAL-#SAN DIEGO					
Pauma Valley	1287.0500	–	O	KI6MGN	PAPA DVoice
Pauma Valley	1298.5000	1298.5000	O	KI6MGN	PAPA DData
SOCAL-LA CENTRAL					
Topanga	1286.8000	–	●	KJ6BWR	PAPA DVoice
Topanga	1298.9000	1298.9000	●	KJ6BWR	PAPA DData
SOCAL-SAN DIEGO					
Mt Otay	1286.8000	–	●	KW6HRO	PAPA DVoice
Mt Otay	1298.7000	1298.7000	●	KW6HRO	PAPA DData

Location	*Output*	*Input*	*Notes*	*Call*	*Sponsor*
COLORADO					
BOULDER COUNTY					
Boulder	145.3875	–	O	WØDK	BCARES
			DCS(D-STAR)es		
Boulder	1283.8625	–	ODCSes	WØDK	BCARES
Boulder	1299.5000	1299.5000	ODCSes	WØDK	BCARES
CENTRAL					
Salida	446.9750	–	O	KDØQPG	CARES
COLORADO SPRINGS					
Monument	446.8875	–	ODCSel	WØTLM	TLMFRA
Monument	1299.1000	1299.1000	ODCSelr	WØTLM	TLMFRA
DENVER METRO					
Boulder	446.8625	–	ODCSes	WØDK	BCARES
Castle Rock	446.8250	–	ODCSers	WØDTF	ARESD22
			WX		
Colorado Springs	446.9125	–	ODCS	KCØCVU	CMRG
Denver	145.2500	–	ODCSelrsx	WØCDS	CO DSTAR
Denver	446.9625	–	ODCSelrsx	WØCDS	CO DSTAR
Denver	1283.9625	–	ODCSelrsx	WØCDS	CO DSTAR
Denver	1299.9000	1299.9000	ODCSelrsx	WØCDS	CO DSTAR
GRAND JUNCTION					
Grand Jct	446.7750	–	Oe	KDØRED	GMRA
Parachute	446.7500	–	Oe	KDØREE	GMRA
NORTH FRONT RANGE					
Fort Collins	446.8125	–	O	WØBFD	KI6MPA
SOUTH CENTRAL					
Trinidad	446.7750	–	Ox	KCØCVU	CMRG
CONNECTICUT					
FAIRFIELD & SOUTHWEST					
Norwalk	441.6000	+	O	W1NLK	GNARC
HARTFORD & N CENTRAL					
Bristol	145.1400	–	Oe	W1IXU	WA1IXU
Bristol	448.3750	–	Oe	W1IXU	WA1IXU
Newington	147.3900	+	O	W1HQ	ARRL OPS
Newington	442.1000	+	O	W1HQ	ARRL OPS
Newington	1284.1250	–	O	W1HQ	ARRL OPS
Rocky Hill	145.2700	–	Oe	W1VLA	WB1EXV
Rocky Hill	444.1500	+	Oe	W1VLA	WB1EXV
Vernon	145.2600	–	Oe	AA1HD	PVRA
Vernon	442.1500	+	Oe	AA1HD	PVRA
LITCHFIELD & NORTHWEST					
Torrington	444.1000	+	O	N1GAU	CT Dstar Group
NEW HAVEN & S CENTRAL					
Haddam	444.5500	+	O	KB1UHS	CT Dstar Group
Meriden	145.4900	–	Oe	W1ECV	SARA
Meriden	444.2500	+	Oe	W1ECV	SARA
Westbrook	444.0000	+	O	W1BCG	SARC

Location	Output	Input	Notes	Call	Sponsor
NEW LONDON & SOUTHEAST					
Salem	443.4000	+		KD1STR	CT Dstar Group
DISTRICT OF COLUMBIA					
WASHINGTON AREA					
Washington	147.3600	+	Oel	W3AGB	AlexGrahamBell
Washington	444.1625	+	Oel	W3AGB	AlexGrahamBell
Washington	1283.1000	–	Oel	W3AGB	AlexGrahamBell
FLORIDA					
CENTRAL - ORLANDO					
Altamonte Springs	442.3000	+	OL(145.15)	W4PLB	OARC
Lake Buena Vista	442.0000	+	O 103.5/103.5	WD4WDW	DEARS
Leesburg	444.5000	+	Oe	KJ4TJD	LADG
Orlando	145.2900	–	OL(442.025 1291.3000)	KJ4MMC	AESOARC
Orlando	146.8200	–	O L(443.2750 1285.0000)	K1XC	OARC
Orlando	443.1375	+	Oex	KJ4OVA	1KDA
Orlando	443.2750	+	O L(146.8200 1285.0000)	K1XC	OARC
Orlando	443.6250	+	Oex	W4AES	AESOARC
Orlando	1285.0000	–	O L(146.8200 443.2750)	K1XC	OARC
Sanford	145.1500	–	OL(442.3)	W4PLB	OARC
Wildwood	443.7000	+	Os	W4VLG	W4VLG
EAST CENTRAL					
Ft Pierce	444.5000	+	Oex	W4AKH	FPARC
Melbourne	442.0250	+	O	K4RPT	OMRA
NORTH CENTRAL					
Ocala	146.7900	–	Oers	KK4DFC	MERT
NORTH EAST - JACKSONVILLE					
Jacksonville	146.8800	–	Oa(CA)e	W4RNG	Jax Range
NORTH WEST					
Greensboro	444.1250	+	Oe	K4GFD	K4GFD
NORTH WEST - PENSACOLA					
Crestview	1291.3000	1271.3000	O	K4FWB	N4GXX
NORTH WEST - TALLAHASSEE					
Monticello	444.0500	+	Oes	KA3FZO	KA3FZO
Tallahassee	146.8350	–	Oe L(443.4500 1293.0000)s	NF4DG	NFDG
Tallahassee	443.4500	+	Oe L(146.8350)s	NF4DG	NFDG
Tallahassee	444.1500	+	Oe	KJ4PYE	SHDA
Tallahassee	1293.0000	1273.0000	Oe L(146.8350 443.4500)s	NF4DG	NFDG

Location	Output	Input	Notes	Call	Sponsor
SOUTH EAST					
West Palm Beach	145.3200	–	O	K4WPB	WPBARC
SOUTH EAST - MIAMI/FT LAUD					
Ft Lauderdale	442.4500	+	Oel	W4AB	BARC
Miami	145.2800	–	OBI	KB4AIL	KB4AIL
Pompano Beach	145.3400	–	Oe	W4BUG	GCARA
			L(442.2000 1291.6000)		
Pompano Beach	442.2000	+	Oa(CA)e	W4BUG	GCARA
			L(145.340 1291.600)		
SOUTH WEST					
Naples	145.4900	–	Oe	AA4PP	NCC
Naples	442.1000	+	O	AA4PP	NCC
SOUTH WEST - FT MYERS					
Naples	443.8000	+	O	AB4FL	CDG
WEST CENTRAL					
New Port Richey	147.1500	+	O	W4PEM	PCEM
			146.2/146.2esx		
Wesley Chapel	442.3250	+	O	W4SRT	SERT
Wesley Chapel	1291.4000	1271.4000	O	W4SRT	SERT
WEST CENTRAL - TAMPA/ST PETE					
Dunedin	444.0750	+	●I	KA9RIX	Homey HC
Largo	444.5000	+	●I	KA9RIX	Homey HC
Palm Harbor	444.3500	+	O	KJ4ZWW	UPARC
Safety Harbor	1292.0000	1272.0000	Oe	KJ4ARB	FDWS
			L(1293.000 1253.000)rs		
St Petersburg	145.3900	–	●I	KA9RIX	Homey HC
St Petersburg	442.7500	+	Oe	W4ICY	CRNC
St Petersburg	444.0625	+	ODCS(546)	KA9RIX	KA9RIX
			L(145.110 444.725)		
St Petersburg	444.1750	+	O 88.5/88.5	KA9RIX	BEARS
			aeL(444.000 444.725 145.390) RBz		
St Petersburg	444.7250	+	OtaTT(*)	KA9RIX	Homey HC
			E-SUN L(145.390 444.175 444.275 444.07		
Tampa	147.0100	+	OE-SUN	KJ4ARB	FDWS
			L(1293.0000 444.6750 1292.0000 1252.00		
Tampa	443.9875	+	O 88.5/88.5	KJ4ARB	FDWS
			E-SUN L(444.0000 443.4250 1291.500 14		
Tampa	444.6750	+	OE-SUN	KJ4ARB	FDWS
			L(147.0100 1293.0000 1253.0000 1292.00		
Tampa	444.8125	+	OL(442.725	W4RNT	RANT
			444.250)		
Tampa	1293.0000	1273.0000	OE-SUN	KJ4ARB	FDWS
			L(147.0100 444.6750 1292.0000 1252.000		

GEORGIA

Location	Output	Input	Notes	Call	Sponsor
Albany	440.7000	+	OesWX	KJ4KLD	KJ4KLD
Appling	145.0800	146.4800	OesWX	KJ4PYA	KJ4PYA
Appling	445.6500	–	OesWX	KJ4PYA	KJ4PYA

Location	Output	Input	Notes	Call	Sponsor
Athens	144.9800	147.4800	OesWX	KJ4PXY	KJ4PXY
Athens	440.6375	+	OesWX	KJ4PXY	KJ4PXY
Atlanta	145.3500	–	OsWX	W4DOC	W4DOC
Atlanta	440.6000	+	OlsWX	W4DOC	W4DOC
Atlanta	1282.6000	–	OlsWX	W4DOC	W4DOC
Braselton	440.5875	+	OsWX	WJ4FD	K4DPW
Brunswick	440.5625	+	Ols	K3RCB	K4KAH
Buford	440.7250	+	OsWX	KJ4BDF	KJ4BDF
Carrollton	444.0750	+	Ol	W4FWD	W4FWD
Chatsworth	145.0800	146.4800	OesWX	KJ4KLF	KJ4KLF
Cumming	145.2000	–	Oes	NA4MB	W4TL
Cumming	444.3500	+	Oes	NA4MB	NA4MB
Cumming	1284.4000	–	Oes	NA4MB	NA4MB
Dawson	144.9600	147.0600	OesWX	KJ4KLD	KJ4KLD
Doraville	440.7125	+	O	WB4HRO	WB4HRO
Dublin	145.1800	–	O	KJ4YNR	KD4IEZ
Dublin	440.5250	+	O	KJ4YNR	KD4IEZ
Dublin	1282.8500	–	O	KJ4YNR	KD4IEZ
Ellijay	443.9875	+	O	W4HHH	W4HHH
Fort Mountain	440.6500	+	OesWX	KJ4KLF	KJ4KLF
Gainesville	145.1200	–	OesWX	KJ4ZLL	KJ4ZLL
Gainesville	441.8625	+	OlsWX	KJ4ZLL	KJ4ZLL
Lawrenceville	145.0600	146.4600	OesWX	WD4STR	WD4STR
Lawrenceville	1282.5500	–	OesWX	WD4STR	WD4STR
Marietta	440.6875	+	OsWX	W4BTI	W4BTI
Pelham	145.0800	146.4800	OesWX	KJ4PYB	KJ4PYB
Pelham	440.6500	+	OesWX	KJ4PYB	KJ4PYB
Pembroke	145.2800	–	OesWX	KJ4GGV	KJ4GGV
Pembroke	440.7000	+	OesWX	KJ4GGV	KJ4GGV
Pembroke	1282.7000	–	OelsWX	KJ4GGV	KJ4GGV
Pine Mountain	144.9200	147.4200	OesWX	KJ4KLE	KJ4KLE
Stone Mountain	144.9600	147.4600	OelsWX	WX4GPB	W4DOC
Stone Mountain	440.7000	+	OelsWX	WX4GPB	W4DOC
Stone Mountain	1282.7000	–	OelsWX	WX4GPB	W4DOC
Tifton	444.5625	+	O	W4PVW	W4PVW
Tifton	1282.6500	–	OlsWX	W4PVW	W4PVW
Valdosta	443.7125	+	O	W4VLD	W4VLD
Valdosta	1282.8250	–	O	W4VLD	W4VLD
Warm Springs	440.6750	+	OesWX	KJ4KLE	KJ4KLE

HAWAII

Location	Output	Input	Notes	Call	Sponsor
HAWAII					
Hilo	444.7250	+	O 123.0l	WH6FM	WH6FM
OAHU					
Honolulu	147.1800	+	O#	WH6DIG	NH7QH
Honolulu	444.9250	+	O#	WH6DIG	NH7QH
Leeward	145.4500	–	O#	WH6DHT	NH7QH
Leeward	442.7000	+	O#p	WH6DHT	NH7QH
Leeward	1293.0000	1273.0000	●#	WH6DHT	NH7QH

Location	Output	Input	Notes	Call	Sponsor
IDAHO					
N ID - MOYIE					
Moyie Springs	145.1250	–		KF7MJA	NSDA
SW ID					
Boise	145.5000	–	O	W7VOI	VOIARC
Boise	444.3500	448.3500	O	W7VOI	VOIARC
ILLINOIS					
CHAMPAIGN					
Champaign	443.48125	+		W9YR	Synton ARC
CHICAGO					
Chicago	441.90625	+		WA9ORC	CFMC
Chicago	442.09375	+	e	NS9RC	NSRC
Chicago	1292.2000	1272.2000	e	NS9RC	NSRC
DECATUR					
Cadwell	145.1950	–	e	W9BIL	MARK
Cadwell	440.64375	+	e	W9BIL	MARK
EAST CENTRAL					
Danville	443.7250	+	100	NE9RD	NERD
NORTHEAST					
Batavia	147.2250	+		W9CEQ	FRRL
Batavia	442.10625	+		W9CEQ	FRRL
Batavia	1291.9000	1271.9000	l	W9NE	W9XA
Glendale Heigh	440.10625	+		KC9PWC	SPRAG-SWC
Lake Zurich	440.74375	+		KC9OKW	SUHFARS
Rolling Meadow	442.8000	+		KC9RBB	SPRAG-N9EP
Wayne	440.26875	+	esWX	W9DPA	DPA EMCOMM
Wayne	1292.6000	1272.6000	esWX	W9DPA	DCERA
PEORIA					
Peoria	145.1050	–		W9PIA	PAARC
Peoria	443.46875	+		W9PIA	PAARC
Peoria	1292.4000	1272.4000		W9PIA	PAARC
SOUTH					
Carbondale	442.65625	+		W9UIH	SIU ARC
SPRINGFIELD					
Springfield	443.78125	+	e	W9DUA	SVRC
WEST CENTRAL					
Quincy	147.1950	+		W9AWE	WIARC
INDIANA					
D-STAR					
Anderson	441.7500	+	OeWX	WA9EOC	ChfAndARC
Bloomington	147.1800	+	O	K9IU	IU ARC
Bloomington	444.9000	+	O	K9IU	IU ARC
Fishers	441.4500	+		WR9AND	HamCoAG
Fort Wayne	442.99375	+	O	W9TE	FWRC
Indianapolis	147.3900	+	O	W9ICE	ICE
Indianapolis	444.1250	+	O	W9ICE	ICE
Marion	443.4000	+	O 131.8er	W9EBN	GrantARC

Location	*Output*	*Input*	*Notes*	*Call*	*Sponsor*
Muncie	145.4900	–	O	W9DUK	DelawrARC
Plainfield	442.7750	+	O	KA9ZYL	KA9ZYL
West Lafayette	146.7300	–	Oe	W9ARP	WARP
West Lafayette	444.3000	+	O	W9ARP	WARP
KANSAS					
KANSAS CITY METRO					
Kansas City	443.4000	+	Oa(CA)el	WØCW	BYRG
Kansas City	1285.0500	–	Oe	WØCW	BYRG
Louisburg	145.1200	–	●	KØHAM	NEKSUN
Louisburg	145.1200	–	O	KØHAM	NEKSUN
Louisburg	442.1250	+	●	KØHAM	NEKSUN
Louisburg	442.1250	+	O	KØHAM	NEKSUN
Louisburg	1257.0000	1257.0000	O	KØHAM	NEKSUN
Louisburg	1287.0000	–	O	KØHAM	NEKSUN
Louisburg	1287.0000	–	O	KØHAM	NEKSUN
NORTHEAST					
Topeka	442.0250	+	Ors	WØSIK	NEKSUN
NORTHWEST					
Colby	444.6500	+	Oe	NWØK	TARC
WEST CENTRAL					
Scott City	444.7000	+	O	WØMI	SHARC
KENTUCKY					
Lexington	145.4600	–	O	W4DSI	W4DSI
Lexington	441.8125	+	O	W4DSI	W4DSI
Louisville	144.9600	147.4600	Oe	KK4CZ	KK4CZ
Lynch	145.4000	–	O	AJ4G	AJ4G
Lynch	444.4625	+	O	AJ4G	AJ4G
Lynch	1284.5000	–	O	AJ4G	AJ4G
Middlesboro	145.3000	–	O	AJ4G	AJ4G
Middlesboro	443.4625	+	O	AJ4G	AJ4G
Middlesboro	1282.4000	–	O	AJ4G	AJ4G
Richmond	442.8125	+	Oers	KE4YVD	KE4YVD
LOUISIANA					
REG 1 NEW ORLEANS					
Jefferson	146.9250	–	Oel	W5GAD	JARC
Jefferson	444.9250	+	Oel	W5GAD	JARC
Jefferson	1251.0000	1251.0000	Oel	W5GAD	JARC
Jefferson	1285.0000	1265.0000	Oel	W5GAD	JARC
REG 2 BATON ROUGE					
Baton Rouge	146.8800	–	Oelr	KD5CQB	EBR RACES
REG 4 LAFAYETTE					
Carencro	147.0000	+	Oe	W5NB	DRCC
REG 6 ALEXANDRIA					
Leesville	147.3450	+	Ol	KE5PFA	W5JZQ
Many	146.8050	–	Ol	N5MNY	KC5UCV

Location	Output	Input	Notes	Call	Sponsor
REG 7 SHREVEPORT					
Minden	147.4200	144.9200	OI	N5MAD	KC5UCV
Shreveport	147.3600	+	OI	W5SHV	SDT
Shreveport	442.0000	+	OI	W5SHV	SDT
Shreveport	1253.0000	1253.0000	OI	W5SHV	SDT
Shreveport	1293.0000	1273.0000	OI	W5SHV	SDT
REG 8 MONROE					
Ruston	145.1400	–	OI	N5APB	N5APB
West Monroe	442.0000	+	OI	WA5WX	W5CFI
REG 9 HAMMOND					
Franklinton	147.4400	144.9000	Oelrs	KF5BSZ	WPWIN
Franklinton	444.5875	+	Oelrs	KF5BSZ	WPWIN
Franklinton	1253.0000	1253.0000	Oelrs	KF5BSZ	WPWIN
Franklinton	1293.0000	–	Oelrs	KF5BSZ	WPWIN
MAINE					
MID-COAST					
Knox	145.4100	–	Oters	W1EMA	WCARA
Knox	444.3000	+	Otrs	W1EMA	WCARA
PORTLAND/SOUTH COAST					
Brunswick	447.5750	–	OtE-WINDs x	KS1R	MARA
Cornish	441.5000	+	Ote L(CCS NETWORK) EXPx	N1KMA	CLEOSYS
Sanford	146.8050	–	Otae L(CCS SYSTEM)x	N1KMA	CLEOSYS
Sanford	147.1800	+	Ote L(KQ1L NETWORK)x	K1PHF	KQ1L
Sanford	441.5000	+	Ote L(CCS NETWORK)x	N1KMA	CLEOSYS
West Newfield	146.6700	–	Ote L(CCS NETWORK) EXPx	N1KMA	CLEOSYS
West Newfield	441.7000	+	Ote L(CCS NETWORK)sEXPx	N1KMA	CLEOSYS
MARYLAND					
BALTIMORE					
Towson	145.1400	–	OelWX	W3DHS	BCACS
Towson	442.1125	+	OelWX	W3DHS	BCACS
Towson	1282.7000	–	OelWX	W3DHS	BCACS
FREDERICK					
Frederick	444.8000	+	OI	KB3YBH	FARG
NORTHEAST MD					
Bel Air	447.9875	–	O	KB3TOG	HarfdCoRACES
Bel Air	1282.3000	–	O	KB3TOG	HarfdCoRACES
SOUTH EASTERN SHORE					
Salisbury	444.2000	+	O	W3PRO	K3RIC
WASHINGTON AREA					
Germantown	444.2000	+	OI	KV3B	MARC

Location	Output	Input	Notes	Call	Sponsor
MASSACHUSETTS					
ALL AREAS					
East Freetown	449.7750	–	Ot L(GATEWAY)	KB1WUW	SAF ARC
MERRIMACK VALLEY					
Westford	145.3300	–	Ot L(GATEWAY)	WB1GOF	PART
Westford	442.4500	+	Ot L(GATEWAY)	WB1GOF	PART
METROWEST					
Holliston	145.1400	–	Ot L(GATEWAY)	W1DSR	DigitalARC
SOUTH COAST					
Dartmouth	145.2200	–	Ot	K1RFI	SEMARG
Fall River	145.4200	–	Ot L(GATEWAY)	K1RFI	SEMARG
Fall River	449.5250	–	OteEXPx	NN1D	SEMARG
SOUTH SHORE					
Brockton	449.2750	–	Ot	KB1YAC	OC D-Star
Norwell	145.2500	–	Ote	W1QWT	W1QWT
SPRINGFIELD/PIONEER VALLEY					
Feeding Hills	145.1500	–	Otex	W1KK	W1KK
Feeding Hills	449.1750	–	Otex	W1KK	W1KK
Feeding Hills	1248.5000	1248.5000	Ote L(D*DATA)x	W1KK	W1KK
Feeding Hills	1282.5000	–	Otex	W1KK	W1KK
Holyoke	447.3750	–	Ote L(REF010C)	AA1KK	W1KK
MICHIGAN					
LOWER PEN NORTHEAST					
Gaylord	444.0375	+	OWXx	KD8QCC	CCECPSCO
LOWER PEN NORTHWEST					
Elmira	145.3200	–	Oers	NM8ES	NMARES
Elmira	444.1125	+	Oers	NM8ES	NMARES
Holton	145.3600	–	O	WD8MKG	WD8MKG
Stutsmanville	443.3750	+	OlrWXx	W8CCE	N8DNX
Traverse City	145.3600	–	Oel	WIØOK	KF8KK
Traverse City	443.3125	+	OlrsWXz	KD8OXV	Traverse Bay Amateu
LOWER PEN SOUTHEAST					
Adrian	145.2800	–	Oe	N8TTH	Southeastern Michiga
Adrian	443.3375	+	Ors	N8TTH	Southeastern Michiga
Auburn Hills	444.2625	+	O	K8DXA	Tri-County D-Star Gro
Hell	147.2100	+	OlrsWX	K8LCD	Livingston County D-
Hell	444.0625	+	OlrsWX	K8LCD	Livingston County D-
Hell	1280.2000	1270.2000	OlrsWX	K8LCD	W8SS
Holly	444.1125	+	Ox	W8CMN	Central Michigan Em
Howell	145.3200	–	Ors	W8LIV	Livingston County AR
Howell	444.0375	+	Ors	W8LIV	Livingston County AR

Location	*Output*	*Input*	*Notes*	*Call*	*Sponsor*
Lansing	443.7375	+	Ors	KD8IEG	Lansing/Ingham
Norton Shores	444.0875	+	O	N8DWY	N8DWY
Owosso	145.2400	–	OelWX	W8SHI	Shiawassee Cou
Owosso	444.3000	+	OelsWX	W8SHI	N8DVH
Port Huron	146.6900	–	Oel	K8ARC	ARCARS
LOWER PEN SOUTHWEST					
Charlotte	145.2000	–	Olrs	K8ETN	ECARC
Charlotte	443.4375	+	Olrs	K8ETN	ECARC
Coldwater	146.7300	–	OerWXz	KD8JGF	Branch County A
East Lansing	446.5000	–	Ol	W8MSU	MSU Alumni Ass
Grand Rapids	147.2900	+	●	WX8GRR	N8WKM
Hillsdale	145.4200	–	OelrsWX	KD8IFO	Hillsdale County
Hillsdale	442.2375	+	Oelrs	KD8IFO	Hillsdale County
Holton	444.0125	+	Oe	KC8LBZ	KC8LBZ
Ithaca	147.1500	+	OrsWX	KD8IEK	GCARA
Ithaca	443.1375	+	Olrs	KD8IEK	Gratiot County A
Jackson	145.1200	–	Oel	K8JXN	CARS
Jackson	443.4625	+	Olrs	K8JXN	CARS
Lowell	147.3500	+	OrsWXx	W8LRC	Lowell Amateur
Lowell	443.1125	+	O	W8LRC	Lowell Amateur
Moline	442.5500	+	Oelx	WX8GRR	N8WKM
Sister Lakes	442.2750	+	OrsWX	W8MAI	Blossomland Am
St Johns	145.4400	–	O	KD8IEI	CCARPSC
St Johns	442.9375	+	Oelrs	KD8IEI	Clinton County A
UPPER PEN EAST					
Moran	146.9850	–	Oe	K8EUP	MADARC
Moran	444.6250	+	Oe	K8EUP	MADARC

MINNESOTA

Location	*Output*	*Input*	*Notes*	*Call*	*Sponsor*
CENTRAL					
Little Falls	444.0000	+	Oe	WØREA	LARA
DULUTH					
Duluth	442.2000	+	Oe	NØEO	SVAMTRS
METRO					
Chaska	147.2700	+	O 127.3	KDØJOS	WBØZKB
Chaska	442.1250	+	O 114.8	KDØJOS	WBØZKB
Chaska	1283.5000	–	O	KDØJOS	WBØZKB
Golden Valley	145.1500	–	O	KØFVF	KØTI
Golden Valley	442.9000	+	O	KØFVF	KØTI
Minneapolis	1283.3000	–	O	KDØJOU	WBØZKB
Moundsview	145.4050	–	Ors	WØANA	ANOKA ARES
Moundsview	443.7750	+	Ors	WØANA	ANOKA ARES
Moundsview	1287.0000	–	Ors	WØANA	ANOKA ARES
White Bear Lake	444.0000	+	e	KCØWLB	EMETDSTAR
White Bear Lake	1285.5000	–	Oe	KCØWLB	14567.ORG
NORTHWEST					
Bemidji	145.2450	–	O	WØBJI	PBARC
SOUTH EAST					
Rochester	443.8500	+	O	WØMXW	ROCHARC

Location	Output	Input	Notes	Call	Sponsor
SOUTH WEST					
Slayton	146.7900	–	OesWX	WØDRK	NPRRC
SOUTHWEST					
Wanda	444.0250	+	O	KDØIAI	RAARA

MISSOURI

Location	Output	Input	Notes	Call	Sponsor
COLUMBIA/JEFF CITY					
Columbia	442.3250	+	Olsx	WXØBC	WXØBC
JOPLIN					
Joplin	146.4500	147.4500	●x	NØCSW	NØCSW
Joplin	444.6250	+	OtLITZx	NOCSW	NØCSW
KANSAS CITY METRO					
Kansas City	443.4000	+	OeL(344.8)	WØCW	BYRG / KCDXC
Kansas City	1285.0500	–	Oe	WØCW	BYRG
SPRINGFIELD					
Ozark	146.7750	–	Oersx	WØOMD	WØOMD
Ozark	442.2250	+	Otersx	WØOMD	WØOMD
ST LOUIS METRO					
St Louis	147.0150	+	Oelx	KØMDG	MODigGRP
St Louis	442.5750	+	Oelx	KØMDG	MODigGRP
St Louis	1285.0000	–	Oel	KØMDG	MODigGRP

MONTANA

Location	Output	Input	Notes	Call	Sponsor
SOUTHEAST					
Billings	449.0000	–	O 100.0	K7EFA	YRC

NEBRASKA

Location	Output	Input	Notes	Call	Sponsor
COLUMBUS					
Columbus	146.9950	–	Oe	WAØCOL	PAWNEE ARC
Columbus	442.1750	+	Oe	WAØCOL	PAWNEE ARC
GRAND ISLAND					
Grand Island	146.6650	–	Oels	WØMAO	NEMA
KEARNEY					
Kearney	147.0300	+	Oels	WØMAO	NEMA
LINCOLN					
Lincoln	145.2500	–	Oes	WØMAO	NEMA
Lincoln	442.1500	+	Oes	WØMAO	NEMA
OMAHA					
Omaha	145.1750	–	Oel	KDØCGR	ODCGr
Omaha	442.1250	+	O DCS(DSTAR)e	KDØCGR	------------

NEVADA

Location	Output	Input	Notes	Call	Sponsor
LAS VEGAS VALLEY					
Las Vegas	145.1750	–	ODCS(C)	N7ARR	NARRI
Las Vegas	147.9750	–	ODCS(C)	W7AES	LVRA
Las Vegas	446.8000	–	ODCS(B)	N7ARR	NARRI
Las Vegas	449.5750	–	ODCS(B)	W7AES	LVRA
Las Vegas	1251.0000	1251.0000	ODCS(DD)	N7ARR	NARRI

Location	*Output*	*Input*	*Notes*	*Call*	*Sponsor*
Las Vegas	1282.3900	–	**O**DCS(A)	W7AES	LVRA
Las Vegas	1293.9000	–	**O**DCS(A)	N7ARR	NARRI
Las Vegas	1299.3900	1299.3900	**O**DCS(DD)	W7AES	LVRA
NEW HAMPSHIRE					
ALL AREAS					
West Ossipee	442.6500	+	**O**tesEXPx	K1LTM	Kencom
LAKES REGION					
West Ossipee	147.0750	+	**O**teEXPx	K1LTM	Whittier
MERRIMACK VALLEY					
Derry	447.2250	–	**O**t	NN1PA	NN1PA
Goffstown	145.4800	–	**O**t	NE1DV	EWARN
Goffstown	446.5750	–	**O**t	NE1DV	EWARN
Goffstown	1285.0000	–	tesWXx	N1HIT	NHIT
Manchester	441.8000	+	**O**t L(IRCDDB)	K1COM	EWARN
Salem	145.3200	–	**O**t L(GATEWAY)	K1HRO	K1HRO ARC
Salem	444.3500	+	**O**t	K1HRO	K1HRO ARC
SEACOAST					
East Kingston	446.7250	–	**O**t L(TCP/IP LINK ONLY)	KB1TIX	Seacoast
Hampton	145.4400	–	**O**te	K1HBR	HBAR
Hampton	449.4750	–	**O**te	K1HBR	HBAR
Kensington	145.4000	–	**O**t L(GATEWAY)	KB1TIX	SeacoastDA
Madbury	145.3800	–	**O**t L(IRCDDB)	N1HIT	NE-RDS
Madbury	448.8750	–	**O**t L(IRCDDB)	N1HIT	NE-RDS
NEW JERSEY					
ATLANTIC					
Atlantic City	444.65625	+	**O**el	KC2TGB	------------
Egg Harbor Twp	445.16875	–	**O**er	KC2VAC	DSTAR Grp
BURLINGTON					
Burlington	445.33125	–	**O**elrsWX	KC2QVT	BurlCo OEM
CAMDEN					
Lindenwold	440.24375	+	**O**ers	K2EOC	CCOEM
CAPE MAY					
Cape May Ct Hse	146.7750	–	**O**ers	NJ2DS	JCDUG
Cape May Ct Hse	1255.3000	+	**O**ers	NJ2DS	JCDUG
Ocean View	440.09375	+	**O**ers	NJ2CM	RACES/ARES
CUMBERLAND					
Bridgeton	445.31875	–	**O**ersWX	KC2TXB	CumbEmOpCl
Hopewell	146.4750	147.4750	**O**elrsWX	KC2WJE	CumbEmcomm
GLOUCESTER					
Glassboro	440.10625	+	**O**ersWX	KC2TXX	G.C.E.G.

Location	*Output*	*Input*	*Notes*	*Call*	*Sponsor*
SALEM					
Woodstown	445.03125	–	OlrsWX	NJ2SC	Salem Co.
SOMMERSET CO					
Martinsville	441.6500	+	Oe	NJ2DG	CNJDG
Martinsville	1284.0000	–	Oe	NJ2DG	CNJDG
NEW MEXICO					
ALBUQUERQUE					
Albuquerque	146.8600	–	Oel	K5URR	URFMSI
Sandia Crest	443.8000	+	Oelx	W5MPZ	SNLARC
CENTRAL					
Socorro	444.5000	+	Oe	W5AQA	Socorro ARA
NORTH CENTRAL					
Belen	444.5250	+	Oel	W5URD	URFMSI
Los Alamos	442.4250	+	Ors	NM5WR	LADSRA
Santa Fe	444.5750	+	Os	W5SF	SFARC
SOUTH CENTRAL					
Las Cruces	146.8400	–	O#	W5GB	NMSU
NEW YORK					
ALBANY/CAPITAL REGION					
Voorheesville	443.3000	+	Oe	K2DLL	Saratoga County RA
			L(OTHER D-STAR SYSTEMS)rx		
MID HUDSON					
Carmel	445.8750	–	O 114.8r	K2PUT	PUTNAM EMERGEN
NEW YORK CITY - MANHATTAN					
Manhattan	445.2750	–	ODSTARe	K2DIG	DigIntGrp
			L(INT)		
Manhattan	1253.0000	1233.0000	ODSTARe	K2DIG	DigIntGrp
			L(INT)		
Manhattan	1293.0000	1273.0000	ODSTARe	K2DIG	DigIntGrp
			L(INT)		
NIAGARA					
Royalton	443.6875	+	O	K2DWA	------------
			L(D-STAR)		
SOUTHERN TIER					
Gerry	444.5000	+	O 88.5e	AC2JC	------------
			L(WB2EDV)		
ST LAWRENCE					
Potsdam	443.3500	+	O	K2CC	K2CC ARC
Potsdam	1272.0000	+	O	K2CC	K2CC ARC
Potsdam	1298.0000	1298.0000	O	K2CC	K2CC ARC
NORTH CAROLINA					
Greensboro	442.8625	+	Oe	W4GSO	W4GSO
Kannapolis	442.0625	+	O	N3DMS	N4JEX
Mount Airy	444.5625	+	O	KJ4HFV	W4DCA
Raleigh	442.2125	+	Oe	K4ITL	WB4UBU

Location	Output	Input	Notes	Call	Sponsor
OHIO					
ALLEN					
Lima	443.6250	+		KT8APR	LimaDARTS
BUTLER					
Hamilton	145.1500	–		W8RNL	R&L ELECT
Hamilton	442.6250	+		W8RNL	R&L ELECT
Hamilton	1293.0000	1273.0000		W8RNL	R&L ELECT
CLINTON					
Wilmington	442.1500	+		W8GO	ClintonRA
CUYAHOGA					
Cleveland	145.3500	–		WB8THD	WB8APD
Cleveland	442.3250	+		WB8THD	WB8APD
FAIRFIELD					
Stoutsville	443.0625	+		KD8FJH	KD8FJH
FRANKLIN					
Columbus	145.3900	–		W8DIG	CODIG
Columbus	145.4900	–		W8CMH	K8NIO
Columbus	442.6500	+		W8DIG	CODIG
Columbus	444.0000	+		W8CMH	K8NIO
Columbus	1285.0000	–		W8DIG	CODIG
HAMILTON					
Cincinnati	145.3500	–		K8BIG	K8CLA
Cincinnati	147.1500	+		K8CLA	K8CLA
Cincinnati	444.0000	+		K8BIG	K8CLA
HIGHLAND					
Hillsboro	443.0750	+		KD8RWK	HILSBUHFC
LORAIN					
Elyria	443.4375	+		WA8DIG	NODIG
Elyria	444.5250	+		WD8OCS	WD8OCS
Lorain	444.3125	+		KB8O	KB8O
LUCAS					
Oregon	444.2500	+		KD8QOF	WJ8E
Toledo	442.7500	+		W8HHF	TMRA
MAHONING					
Youngstown	442.7250	+	tars	K8WGR	DORG
MONTGOMERY					
Dayton	147.1050	+		W8RTL	DARA
Dayton	443.0500	+		W8RTL	DARA
Huber Hts	145.2700	–		W8HEQ	DARA
Huber Hts	444.0875	+		W8HEQ	DARA
TUSCARAWAS					
PortWashinton	444.8250	+		W8ZX	TUSC ARC
OKLAHOMA					
NORTHWEST					
Elk City	146.6850	–	**O**	KC9VF	KC9VF
Elk City	443.0250	+	**O**	KC9VF	KC9VF
Mooreland	444.2750	+	**O**E-SUNs WXx	W5OKT	TSARG

OKLAHOMA-PENNSYLVANIA

Location	Output	Input	Notes	Call	Sponsor
Sharon	147.3150	+	O 88.5/88.5	K5GUD	K5GUD
Woodward	444.4750	+	OE-SUN	WW5EM	WCEM
OKLAHOMA CITY METRO					
Norman	444.7500	+	O 141.3/141.3 E-SUN	W5TC	OUARC
Oklahoma City	147.3450	+	OtEXP	WD5AII	EARC
Oklahoma City	444.2125	+	O	WD5AII	EARC
TULSA METRO					
Tulsa	443.0000	+	Ot	W5IAS	TULSA ARC
Tulsa	443.0250	+	O	N5XP	TULSA D-ST
OREGON					
NORTH WILLAMETTE VALLEY					
Sherwood	1292.0000	1272.0000	O	WB7DZG	WORC
NW OREGON & SW WASHINGTON					
Gaston	146.6100	146.0150	O	KJ7IY	WORC
Gaston	444.3125	+	O	WB7DZG	WORC
PORTLAND METRO					
Hillsboro	440.5500	+	O	KD7REX	N7QQU
Sherwood	1248.7500	1248.7500	O	WB7DZG	WORC
PENNSYLVANIA					
CENTRAL					
Kylertown	147.2550	+		W3PHB	N3SPW
CHESTER					
Bucktown	445.08125	–	Oelrs	KB3SLR	CCAR
Bucktown	1255.6000	+	Oelrs	KB3SLR	CCAR
Devault	440.00625	+	OelrsWX	KB3SLS	CCAR
Devault	1255.7000	+	OelrsWX	KB3SLS	CCAR
Pocopson	146.4900	147.4900	OelBI	W3EOC	CCAR
Pocopson	445.06875	–	OelrsBI	W3EOC	CCAR
Pocopson	1255.5000	+	OelBI	W3EOC	CCAR
DELAWARE					
Drexel Hill	440.04375	+	Oelrs	N3AEC	Delco ARES
Drexel Hill	1255.5250	+	Oelrs	N3AEC	Delco ARES
Media	440.05625	+	Oelrs	W3AEC	Delco ARES
Media	1255.5500	+	Oelrs	W3AEC	Delco ARES
MONTGOMERY					
Eagleville	440.01875	+	OtelrsWX	AA3E	MontcoRACES
Eagleville	1255.5750	+	OtelrsWX	AA3E	MontcoRACES
Wyndmoor	146.6100	–	Otelrs	K3PDR	PDRA
Wyndmoor	445.18125	–	OtelrsWX	K3PDR	PDRA
NORTHWEST 186.2					
Atlantic	147.1500	+		K3AWS	AWS
PITTSBURGH					
Pittsburgh Oakland	444.3500	+	Oer	W3EXW	NHARC-RPT
PITTSBURGH 131.8					
Pittsburgh	146.8200	–		W3EXW	NHARC

Location	*Output*	*Input*	*Notes*	*Call*	*Sponsor*
SOUTHWEST					
Greensburg	442.1500	+	Oelr	WC3PS	KE3PO
WEST CENTRAL	131.8/186.2				
New Castle	443.0750	+	Oes	KB3YBB	------------
RHODE ISLAND					
EAST BAY					
Portsmouth	145.3000	–	Ot	W1AAD	NCRC
NORTHERN					
West Warwick	147.0450	+	Ot	W1HDN	PVRA
SOUTH CAROLINA					
Aiken	145.1600	–	Oelrs	KR4AIK	Aiken D-Star Clu
Aiken	443.4125	+	Oelrs	KR4AIK	Aiken D-Star Clu
Awendaw	145.1200	–	Oelrs	KR4CHS	SC HEART
Columbia	145.3800	–	Oel	KJ4FCS	MJ ARC
Columbia	145.4000	–	Oel	KJ4BWK	MJ ARC
Columbia	442.7750	+	Oel	KJ4FCS	MJ ARC
Columbia	443.2000	+	Oel	KJ4BWK	MJ ARC
Conway	144.9800	147.4800	Oel	NE4SC	Beach & Inland
Dillon-Floyd Dale	145.3400	–	Oel	W4PDE	Greater Pee Dee
Dillon-Floyd Dale	443.8875	+	Oel	W4PDE	Greater Pee Dee
Elgin	1284.0000	–	Oel	KJ4FCS	MJ ARC
Greenwood	145.3600	–	Oes	W4GWM	Greenwood Cou
Little Mountain	145.2400	–	Oel	KJ4MKV	MJ ARC
Whitehall	145.4800	–	Oel	KJ4LNJ	Beaufort Radio D
TENNESSEE					
Chattanooga	145.2900	–	O	W4PL	K4VCM
Chattanooga	443.1500	+	O	W4PL	K4VCM
Chattanooga	1291.0000	1271.0000	O	W4PL	K4VCM
Cleveland	145.4800	–	Oe	KK4BXE	KK4BXE
Cleveland	440.5250	+	O	KK4BXE	------------
Gallatin	443.7500	+	Oe	WD4BKY	W4LKZ
Morristown	144.9200	147.4200	O	W4LDG	------------
Morristown	444.4750	+	OesWX	W4LDG	N4FNB
TEXAS					
Austin	440.6500	+	O	W5KA	AUSTIN ARC
Austin	1293.1000	1273.1000	O	W5KA	AUSTIN ARC
Bangs	440.6750	+	Oar	K5BRC	Burleson ARC
Bryan	443.4000	+	Oaelrs	W5AC	TAMU ARC
Burleson	440.7000	+	O	K5JCR	JOHNSON COU
Corsicana	147.3400	+	OrWX	K5NEM	Navarro County
Dallas	147.3600	+	O	K5TIT	TEXAS INTERC
Dallas	440.5750	+	Oar	W5FC	(DARC) Dallas A
Dallas	442.0000	+	O	K5TIT	K5TIT
Dallas	443.0000	+	O	N5DA	NTRN

Location	*Output*	*Input*	*Notes*	*Call*	*Sponsor*
Dallas	443.0250	+	Oe	NT5RN	------------
Dallas	1293.0000	1273.0000	O	N5MIJ	------------
Fort Worth	440.5500	+	O	KB5DRP	TEXAS DISASTER R
Fort Worth	440.5875	+	O	KF5LOG	NTX DEG
Granbury	440.6500	+	Oar	K1DRP	TXDRP_Granbury
Granbury	441.3500	+	O	W5HCT	------------
Houston	145.1300	144.8300	O	N5HDS	HDSTAR
Houston	440.6000	+	Oe	W5HDR	HDEARC
Houston	1293.0000	1273.0000	Oe	W5HDR	HDEARC
Houston	1293.2000	1273.2000	Oe	W5HDT	HD1200EMCOMMAR
Kaufman	440.6500	+	O	KA5DRP	Texas Disaster Resp
Laredo	147.3600	+	O	KE5WFB	D-STAR Comm Club
Lindale	147.1200	+	Ors	W5ETX	ETX Emergency Com
Magnolia	440.7125	+	O	N5MDS	MDSTAR.ORG
Magnolia	1291.0000	1271.0000	O	N5MDS	MDSTAR.ORG
Mesquite	145.1500	–	Ors	N5DA	------------
Rockwall	440.6000	+	O	K5TIT	Texas Interconnect T
Rockwall	440.6750	+	Oar	W5MIJ	TEXAS INTERCONN
Rockwall	1292.7000	1272.7000	O	N5MIJ	------------
San Antonio	440.6000	+	O	WD5STR	SANANTONIODSTA
San Antonio	440.7000	+	O	WA5UNH	SARO
Spring	145.3400	–	O	KF5KHM	------------
Spring	1292.2000	1272.2000	O	KF5KHM	------------
Sulphur Springs	444.2750	+	O	K5SST	------------
Temple	440.5250	+	O	K5CTX	------------
Temple	1292.1000	1272.1000	O	K5CTX	------------
Tyler	444.8500	+	Oar	W5ETX	ETECS
Walburg	145.1300	–	O	KE5RCS	HOTERA
Walburg	440.5750	+	O	KE5RCS	HOTERA
Walburg	1293.2000	1273.2000	O	KE5RCS	HOTERA
Weatherford	440.6125	+	Oar	KT5DRP	TXDRP

UTAH

NORTH

Logan	145.1500	–	O	AC7O	BARC
Logan	447.9750	–	O	AC7O	BARC
Logan	1299.7500	1299.7500	O	AC7O	BARC
Wellsville	449.5750	–	O	NU7TS	BARC

PRICE

Castledale	448.0750	–	Ox	K7YI	------------

SOUTH WEST

Cedar City	145.1500	–	O	WR7AAA	------------
Cedar City	447.9500	–	O	WR7AAA	------------
Cedar City	1299.2500	1299.2500	O	WR7AAA	------------
Toquerville	145.1500	–	O	KF7YIX	Washington County A
Toquerville	447.9500	–	O	KF7YIX	Washington County A
Toquerville	1299.2500	1299.2500	#s	KF7YX	Washington County A

WASATCH FRONT

Murray	145.1500	–	Oes	KO7SLC	SLCO ARES ARRL

Location	Output	Input	Notes	Call	Sponsor
Murray	447.9500	–	Os	KO7SLC	SLCO ARES AR
Murray	1298.7500	1298.7500	Oes	KO7SLC	SLCO ARES AR
Ogden	145.1125	–	Oesz	KE7EGG	------------
Ogden	447.9500	–	Oesz	KE7EGG	------------
Ogden	1284.4000	–	Oesz	KE7EGG	------------
Ogden	1298.7500	1298.7500	Oesz	KE7EGG	------------
Provo	1284.5000	–	O	W7OAD	------------
Salt Lake	145.1250	–	Oelx	KF6RAL	------------
Salt Lake	147.3800	+	Oelx	WA7GIE	------------
Salt Lake	448.0750	–	Oelx	KF6RAL	------------
Salt Lake	448.7250	–	Oelx	WA7GIE	------------
Salt Lake	1250.0000	1250.0000	Oex	KF6RAL	------------
Salt Lake	1287.0000	–	Oex	KF6RAL	------------
Salt Lake	1299.2500	1299.2500	Oex	KF6RAL	------------
VIRGINIA					
FREDERICKSBURG					
Stafford	145.3200	–	Ol	WS4VA	SARA
Stafford	447.2750	–	O	WS4VA	SARA
Stafford	1282.2000	–	Ol	WS4VA	SARA
WASHINGTON AREA					
Alexandria	145.3800	–	O	W4HFH	Alex RC
Alexandria	442.0600	+	Ol	W4HFH	Alex RC
Alexandria	1284.6000	–	Ol	W4HFH	Alex RC
Haymarket	145.4500	–	O	N4USI	AO-27 Ctl Op
Haymarket	442.4125	+	Ol	N4USI	AO-27 Ctrl Op
Manassas	146.8650	–	O	W4OVH	OVHARC
Manassas	442.5125	+	Oes	W4OVH	OVHARC
Reagan Airport	443.5125	+	Ol	K4DCA	E-Star
Reagan Airport	1283.2000	–	Ol	K4DCA	E-Star
Tysons Corner	145.3400	–	O	NV4FM	NVFMA
Tysons Corner	448.0350	–	Ol	NV4FM	NVFMA
Tysons Corner	1282.8000	–	Ol	NV4FM	NVFMA
WASHINGTON					
NW OREGON & SW WASHINGTON					
Vancouver	440.0125	+		K7CLL	CCARES
Vancouver	440.4625	+	O	K7CLL	K7CLL
Vancouver	1248.9500	1248.9500	O	K7CLL	CCARES
Vancouver	1292.5250	1272.5250	O	K7CLL	K7CLL
W WA - NORTH					
Bellingham	146.7000	–	O	W7CDC	W7CDC
Mt Pilchuck	440.3250	+	O	NR7SS	N7SS
Mt Pilchuck	1251.6500	1251.6500	O	NR7SS	N7SS
W WA - SEATTLE-TACOMA					
Burien	443.4250	+	O	KF7CLD	HI LINE RP
Edmonds	440.0125	+	O	NM7DR	NW DIgital Radio
Federal Way	146.8400	–	Oe	WA7FW	Federal Wa
Federal Way	443.8500	+	O	WA7FW	FWARC

Location	Output	Input	Notes	Call	Sponsor
Seattle	442.9000	+	Oe	WA7LZO	SARS
W WA -SEATTLE-TACOMA					
Federal Way	1249.2500	1249.2500	Oe	WA7FW	Federal Wa

WISCONSIN

Location	Output	Input	Notes	Call	Sponsor
WAR					
Baraboo	145.3150	–	O 123.0aelrs	WB9FDZ	YTARC
Grafton	145.2250	–	O 127.3aes	W9FRG	LEFROG
Grafton	442.81875	+	O 127.3aes	W9FRG	LEFROG
Madison	145.3050	–	O 123.0aelrs	W9HSY	M A R A
Milwaukee	145.2350	–	O 127.3aes	K9AES	AES
Milwaukee	145.2450	–	O 127.3aes	KC9LKZ	MADOG
Milwaukee	442.46875	+	O 127.3aes	KC9LKZ	MADOG
Milwaukee	1290.0500	1270.0500	O 127.3aes	KC9LKZ	MADOG
Mount Pleasant	441.81875	+	O 127.3aes	WI9RAC	RCARES
Park Falls	145.3450	–	O 110.9ers	W9PFP	PCRA
Park Falls	442.48125	+	O 110.9ers	W9PFP	PCRA
Sheboygan	442.48125	+	O 100.0aers	N9YLS	N9YLS
Wausau	442.46875	+	O 114.8aelr	W9BCC	RMRA
Wausau	1282.1000	–	O 114.8aelr	W9BCC	RMRA

WYOMING

Location	Output	Input	Notes	Call	Sponsor
EAST CENTRAL					
Gillette - Antelope Butte	145.3400	–	O	NE7WY	NEWARA
SOUTH EAST					
Cheyenne	447.2250	–	O	KC7SNO	SHYWY

ALBERTA

Location	Output	Input	Notes	Call	Sponsor
BANFF					
Banff	147.0300	+	O	VE6WRO	WW
CALGARY					
Calgary	146.8050	145.6050	O	VE6CPT	VE6CPT
Calgary	147.0900	+	O	VE6GHZ	VE6DDE
Calgary	147.2850	+	O	VE6IPG	CARA
Calgary	443.9500	+	O	VE6IPG	CARA
Calgary	444.9500	+	O	VE6GHZ	VE6DD

Location	Output	Input	Notes	Call	Sponsor
Calgary	1275.9500	+	O	VE6IPG	CARA
EDMONTON					
Edmonton	449.9000	+	O	VE6KM	NARC
Edmonton	1275.5000	+	O	VE6KM	NARC
EDMONTON/SHERWOOD PARK					
Edmonton/ SherwoodPark	440.8500	+	Os	VE6DXX	VE6DXD
Edmonton/ SherwoodPark	440.9000	+	Os	VE6DXP	VE6DXX
BRITISH COLUMBIA					
GREATER VANCOUVER					
Surrey	145.0400	+	O	VA7ICM	ICOM
Surrey	442.0000	+	O	VA7ICM	ICOM
Surrey	1247.0000	+	O	VA7ICM	ICOM
Vancouver	147.0200	+	O	VE7RAG	BCFMCA
SOUTH CENTRAL					
Kelowna	1247.0000	+	O	VA7DIG	OCARC
Kelowna, Winfield	145.0300	+	O	VA7DIG	OCARC
VANC ISLAND SOUTH					
Victoria	145.0800	+	O	VE7VIC	WARA
Victoria	442.0000	+	O	VE7VIC	WARA
Victoria	1291.5000	1271.5000	O	VE7VIC	WARA
NEWFOUNDLAND AND LABRADOR					
AVALON EAST					
St John	145.0900	+	TTl	VO1ILP	VO1PX
St John	443.4000	449.4000	TTl	VO1ILP	VO1PX
St John	1251.0000	1251.9400	TTl	VO1ILP	VO1PX
St John	1291.0000	1271.9400		VO1ILP	VO1PX
NOVA SCOTIA					
NEW GERMANY					
Church Lake	145.2900	–	O	VE1DSR	------------
ONTARIO					
CENTRAL					
Edgar	145.1900	–	Oe L(D-STAR) WX	VE3LSR	LSRA
Edgar	444.3500	+	O 156.7e L(D-STAR)	VE3LSR	LSRA
LANARK/LEEDS GRENVILLE					
Almonte/Union Hall	145.5500	–	O	VA3AAR	ALMONTE ARC
Almonte/Union Hall	444.1000	+	O	VA3AAR	ALMONTE ARC
LANARK/NORTH LEEDS					
Almonte/Union Hall	1281.0000	–	O	VA3AAR	ALMONTE ARC

ONTARIO

Location	Output	Input	Notes	Call	Sponsor
Almonte/Union Hall	1299.3000	1299.3000	O	VA3AAR	ALMONTE ARC
METRO TORONTO					
Mississauga	443.8125	+	Oe L(PMO/TNK D-STAR)	VA3PMO	------------
Toronto	442.7000	+	O L(D-STAR)	VE3YYZ	TARCS
Toronto	444.6375	+	OL(P-25 D-STAR NAC 293 L YYZ)	VE3YYZ	TARCS
Toronto	1250.0000	1250.0000	O 103.5e L(D-STAR)	VE3YYZ	TARCS
Toronto	1287.5000	–	O 103.5e L(D-STAR)	VE3YYZ	TARCS
Uxbridge	443.2250	+	O 103.5e L(TFM IRLP D-STAR)	VE3RPT	TFMCS
NATIONAL CAPITOL REGION					
Ottawa	145.5300	–	O	VA3ODG	OARDG
Ottawa	444.8500	–	O	VA3ODG	OARDG
Ottawa	1282.0000	–	O	VA3ODG	OARDG
Ottawa	1299.2000	1299.2000	O	VA3ODG	OARDG
Stittsville	443.6000	+	O	VE3BFH	ALMONTE ARC
SOUTHWEST					
London	442.3000	+	Oe L(D-STAR)	VE3TTT	SORT
STORMONT-DUNDAS-GLENGARRY					
Cornwall	145.5700	–	O	VA3SDG	John Vining
Cornwall	444.4500	+	O	VA3SDG	John Vining

IRLP Repeaters

The following is a list of repeaters in the US and Canada that are interconnected through the Internet Radio Linking Project (IRLP). For more information, see **irlp.net**.

Our thanks to Dave Cameron, VE7LTD, for providing this information.

United States

State	*City*	*Call Sign*	*Repeater Output Frequency (MHz)*	*CTCSS*	*Node*
AK	Bethel	AL7YK	444.1	100	3465
AL	Tuscaloosa	W4UAL	145.21	103.5	4719
AL	Moulton	KN4CI	146.96	107.2	8003
AL	Huntsville	W4VM	147.18	100	4950
AL	Huntsville	KB4CRG	444.575	100	4641
AR	Desha	K5NES	147.225	107.2	3956
AR	Springdale	AD5ZX	442.525	100	3298
AR	Maumelle	K6MFM	442.7	114.8	3511
AR	Springdale	NX5V	443.65	97.4	3953
AR	Harrison	AJ5C	442.175	123	4311
AR	Berryville	N6WI	443.8	100	4671
AR	Little Rock	K5DTE	443.2	114.8	7492
AZ	Tolleson	AJ9Y	448.075	100	3423
AZ	Phoenix	KC7GHT	447.575	151.4	3820
AZ	West Chandler	WW7CPU	448.95	100	5430
AZ	Kingman	KC8UQP	449.75	79.7	7359
AZ	Phoenix	N7TWB	447.95	100	7460
AZ	Lake Havasu	WA6YZF	447.54	136.5	7537
AZ	Phoenix	K0NL	449.425	100	7570
AZ	Tucson	K7IOU	224.74	136.5	3033
AZ	Tucson	N6DGT	146.7	127.3	3300
AZ	Green Valley	WE7GV	145.27		3826
AZ	Tucson	WD7F	146.94	110.9	3892
AZ	Safford	K7EAR	146.9	141.3	7787
AZ	Phoenix	WK7B	145.23	94.5	7893
AZ	Prescott	N7NGM	52.56	100	3301
AZ	Tucson	N7HOR	147.3	110.9	3924
AZ	Tonopah	WT9S	440.475	123	3107
AZ	Maricopa	W9LEO	449.125	136.5	3354
AZ	Pinnacle Peak	W0NWA	441.1	103.5	4243
AZ	Sun City West	KA7G	442.45	91.5	8383
AZ	Tucson	W7FDF	927.85	114.8	3850
CA	San Gabriel Valley	WB6DAO	447.6	107.2	3910
CA	San Jose	K6MF	1286.45	123	3900
CA	San Jose	K6MF	1206.45	123	3930
CA	San Jose	W6RLW	1285	88.5	7670

State	*City*	*Call Sign*	*Repeater Output Frequency (MHz)*	*CTCSS*	*Node*
CA	Santa Barbara	W6MV	445.22	131.8	3013
CA	Perris	KC6ORG	445.86	103.5	3051
CA	Barstow	N6TAP	449.08	100	3077
CA	Cloverdale	WB6QAZ	449.7	88.5	3183
CA	Hollywood	WD8CIK	445.14	127.3	3190
CA	Hemet	KB6JAG	446.88	74.4	3204
CA	Los Angeles	W6DVI	445.16	103.5	3339
CA	Palm Springs	K6IFR	445.64	131.8	3540
CA	Mount Disappointment		K6VGP	446.24	100
3556					
CA	Los Angeles	KE6PCV	447.72	100	3650
CA	Santa Barbara	K6TZ	446.4	131.8	3673
CA	Intertie	K6JSI	440	100	3727
CA	Thousand Oaks	W6AMG	449.44	131.8	3785
CA	Los Angeles	WB5EKU	446.58	127.3	3830
CA	Hemet	K6JRM	446.86	100	3912
CA	Hemet	W6COH	446.88	74.4	3987
CA	Fullerton	KI6DXN	449.46	123	4036
CA	Palmdale	KJ6W	445.6	100	5850
CA	Edom Hill	K6IFR	445.86	100	7097
CA	Arcadia	K6TEM	445.48	131.8	7729
CA	Bakersfield	W2MGM	447.04	136.5	7814
CA	Palomar Mtn	KA6UAI	449.3	100	7870
CA	Hollywood	K6CBS	224.56	77	3125
CA	Pasadena	WR6JPL	224.08	156.7	3340
CA	Auburn	W7FAT	224.02	100	3373
CA	Palos Verdes	WA6LA	223.78	100	3460
CA	San Francisco	KU6V	224.18	94.8	3620
CA	Santa Rosa	WX6ZZ	223.9	88.5	3927
CA	Sunnyvale	KB6BA	223.9		7425
CA	Napa	WA7G	224.16	100	7584
CA	Morgan Hill	KU6V	223.92	110.8	7607
CA	Palos Verdes	W6RE	224.66	100	7840
CA	Oxnard	W6KGB	1285.75	136.5	3141
CA	Santiago Peak	WD6AWP	145.14	110.9	3170
CA	Palm Springs	W6DRA	145.48	107.2	3180
CA	Los Angeles	KC6PXL	145.12	103.5	3278
CA	Laguna Beach	K6SOA	147.645	110.9	3287
CA	Santa Cruz	K6BJ	146.79	94.8	3318
CA	Hemet	N7OD	145.42	88.5	3341
CA	Poway	KF6HPG	145.18	107.2	3505
CA	Saratoga	K6SA	146.655	114.8	3671
CA	Claremont	N6USO	145.44	136.5	3718
CA	San Ardo	N6SPD	145.37	100	3796
CA	Santa Rosa	KD6RC	146.79	88.5	3856
CA	Orangevale	K6RTL	146.625	151.4	3880
CA	Sacramento	K6MVR	147	136.5	3895
CA	Woodland Hills	KD6GDB	445.04	107.3	7211

State	*City*	*Call Sign*	*Repeater Output Frequency (MHz)*	*CTCSS*	*Node*
CA	Sacramento	K6IS	145.19	162.2	7457
CA	Willits	K7WWA	145.13	103.5	7628
CA	Visalia	WA6BAI	146.88	103.5	8120
CA	Rio Dell	N7HQZ	51.84	114.8	3572
CA	Lompoc	WA6VPL	52.88	82.5	3640
CA	Lone Pine	N6BKL	52.9	100	7867
CA	San Pedro	N6RJA	446.525		7421
CA	Barstow	WD6BNG	147.03		7190
CA	Walnut Creek	K6MFM	442.525	88.5	3206
CA	Santa Rosa	KK6JAB	444.9	88.5	3331
CA	Los Angeles	N6EW	445.32		3884
CA	San Francisco	K6KYA	444.85	114.8	8730
CA	Bakersfield	WA6LVX	52.56	82.5	3100
CA	Sacramento	N6ICW	927.05	77	3470
CA	Templeton	W6SMV	443.525	100	3946
CA	Coalinga	N6DL	147.33	100	3004
CA	Mt. Diablo	W6CX	147.06	100	3057
CA	Sacramento	N6FR	147.39	146.2	3172
CA	San Bernardino	KE6TZG	146.385	146.2	3216
CA	Santa Cruz	W6WLS	147.18	94.8	3228
CA	Duarte	KA6AMR	146.085	110.9	3686
CA	Redding	W6REB	147.3	100	3812
CA	Hollister	N6SBC	147.315	94.8	7464
CA	Sacramento	N6ICW	147.195	123	7650
CA	Morgan Hill	K7DAA	147.33	103.5	7662
CA	Oakland	WB6TCS	147.21	100	8410
CA	Eureka	WB6HII	147.445	103.5	3560
CA	Sacramento	KJ6JD	224.82		7797
CA	San Dimas	AE6TV	449.16	77	3012
CA	Oakland	WB6NDJ	442.4	77	3115
CA	Nipomo	KB6Q	444.7	100	3139
CA	Oceanside	W6YJ	446.86	151.4	3160
CA	Smith River	K6SLS	443.1	100	3165
CA	Willits	K7WWA	444.925	100	3219
CA	Monterey	N6SPD	441.65	94.8	3234
CA	San Jose	WB6KHP	444.7	127.3	3246
CA	Livermore	K7FED	444.125	100	3319
CA	Sacramento	W6YDD	443.9	136.5	3367
CA	Sylmar	K6HOG	445.04	107.3	3410
CA	Sunnyvale	AF6EQ	0		3497
CA	Monterey	N6SPD	444.275	100	3589
CA	Pleasanton	WB6BDD	441.825	114.8	3667
CA	San Jose	KJ6VU	443.225	100	3802
CA	Atwater	K6IXA	443.075	107.2	3840
CA	Fresno	K6JSI	444.25	100	3847
CA	Bakersfield	KG6FOS	444.75	141.3	3901
CA	Santa Barbara	K6MF	440.12	85.4	3920
CA	Susanville	K6LRC	443.9	91.5	5060

State	*City*	*Call Sign*	*Repeater Output Frequency (MHz)*	*CTCSS*	*Node*
CA	San Luis Obispo	W6FM	444.525	127.3	5570
CA	Stockton	W6KAP	440.45	127.3	5750
CA	Redondo Beach	W6TRW	447	100	7067
CA	San Carlos	W6CBS	441.6125	100	7540
CA	Sacramento	K6MFM	442.525	77	7990
CA	San Carlos	KR6WP	440.075	114.8	8240
CA	Pittsburg	K6BIV	440.125	127.3	8420
CO	Grand Junction	KE0TY	448.15	100	3467
CO	Colorado Springs	N0PWZ	449.725	100	3043
CO	Denver	W0CRA	447.575	107.2	3291
CO	Boulder	N0SZ	447.75	141.3	3450
CO	Colorado Springs	WD0C	447.1	107.2	3621
CO	Westminster	N1UPS	449.3	100	3699
CO	Grand Junction	WA4HND	449.3	107.2	3710
CO	Lamar	KC0HH	449.5	123	3774
CO	Fort Lupton	AC0KC	447.3	107.2	3887
CO	Springfield	KZ0DEM	449.2	118.8	7142
CO	Grand Junction	KB0YNA	449.65	151.4	7279
CO	Denver	WR0AEN	449.675	107.2	7708
CO	Denver	N0PQV	145.34	103.5	3350
CO	Breckenridge	WB0QMR	146.7	107.2	3972
CO	Estes Park	N0FH	146.685	123	7268
CO	Rifle	N0SWE	146.88	107.2	7287
CO	Vail	N0AFO	146.61	107.2	7772
CO	Denver	W ├ÿMTZ	145.43	103.5	7981
CO	Canon City	WD0EKR	447.75	103.5	3081
CO	Centennial	W0CBI	449.6	100	3345
CO	Golden	W0KU	449.625	141.3	3750
CO	Carbondale	K0ELK	449.725	179.9	3722
CO	Limon	KC0VJD	147.06	103.5	3794
CO	Greeley	KC0KWD	147	100	3839
CO	Colorado Springs	KC0CVU	147.345	107.2	3854
CO	Denver	W0CRA	147.225	107.2	3990
CO	Colorado	N0SZ	449.225	141.3	3015
CT	Norwalk	K1RFD	448.075	114.8	4579
CT	Niantic	N1BOW	446.75	77	5960
CT	West Haven	K1SOX	147.505	77	7505
CT	Tolland	W1GPO	53.15	162.2	8088
CT	Vernon	W1HDN	146.79	82.5	4159
CT	Branford	N1HUI	449.325	103.5	4344
CT	Vernon	KB1AEV	147.345	77	4395
CT	Danbury	K1RFD	147.3	100	4593
CT	Bristol	KB1AEV	224.16	77	4096
CT	Woodbridge	W1WPD	442.5		4663
DC	Washington	WA3KOK	449.975	107.2	4000
FL	Naples	KC1AR	147.505	67	8127
FL	Flagler County	N2TDI	145.41	123	4246
FL	Clearwater	N4BSA	146.97	146.2	4647

State	City	Call Sign	Repeater Output Frequency (MHz)	CTCSS	Node
FL	Orlando	K4UCF	146.64	103.5	4775
FL	Delray Beach	W2GGI	145.5	110.9	8847
FL	Venice	KB2WVY	442.05	100	4434
FL	Bartow	WC4PEM	146.985	127.3	4128
FL	Kissimmee	N4ARG	147.21	103.5	4338
FL	Key Largo	KC4SFA	147.165		5520
FL	Wellington	WB2NBU	147.285		7830
FL	Port Charlotte	K4VMS	442.2	100	4021
FL	West Palm	W2WDW	443.875	110.9	4111
FL	Bartow	WC4PEM	444.95	127.3	4156
FL	Merritt Island	KC2UFO	444.775	107.2	4227
FL	Fort Pierce	W4AKH	444.8	107.2	4545
FL	Boynton Beach	NR4P	444.65	127.3	4667
FL	Ft. Lauderdale	KI4VFB	443.75	110.9	4787
FL	Valkaria	K4HV	444.7	77	4853
FL	Ft. Lauderdale	KF4LZA	443.625	110.9	4864
FL	Tampa	N4TCP	443.675	146.2	4880
FL	Deerfield Beach	KA4EPS	442.75	110.9	4887
FL	Orlando	K4ZPZ	443.1	103.5	4949
FL	Cocoa	W4JAZ	444.4	103.5	7710
FL	Port Charlotte	N4FOB	442.7	136.5	8317
FL	Miami	KF4LZA	443.425	94.8	8369
FL	Orlando	KW4GT	443.65	103.5	8566
FL	Lake Worth	W2WDW	444.475	110.9	8641
FL	Melbourne	K4RPT	444.825		8709
FL	Beverly Hills	KC0MPD	444.6	146.2	8717
FL	St. Petersburg	K4LX	443.2	100	8910
GA	Atlanta	W4DOC	146.82	146.2	4550
GA	Jesup	N4PJR	146.925	141.3	5030
GA	Cumming	WB4GQX	441.9	141.3	4065
GA	Gray	WA7RZW	444	67	4522
HI	Pearl Harbor	KH6FV-6	443.55	114.8	3217
HI	Keaau	AH6HN	147.28		3277
HI	Honolulu	KH6FV-2	443.425	114.8	3080
HI	Kailua-Oahu	KH6FV-4	444.375	114.8	3197
HI	Wailuku Heights	AH6GR	442.75	136.5	3440
HI	Kaanapali	KH6RS	442.35	136.5	7001
HI	Wailuku	KH6RS	443.225	110.9	7018
HI	Mt. Haleakala	KH6RS	442.1	136.5	7020
HI	Honolulu	AH7GK	443.95	203.5	7309
IA	Gilman	NF0T	444.15	151.4	3162
IA	Mondamin	K0BVC	444.925	136.5	3328
IA	Honey Creek	AB0VX	444.8	97.4	3548
IA	Des Moines	K0PCG	444.575	151.4	4110
ID	Idaho Falls	W7RUG	447.62	88.5	3754
ID	Payette	NB7C	443.05	114.8	3417
ID	Boise	KB7SYE	443.2	100	7339
ID	Fruitland	KC7BSA	443.65	100	3130

State	City	Call Sign	Repeater Output Frequency (MHz)	CTCSS	Node
ID	Twin Falls	W7CTH	442.6	146.2	3541
ID	Lewiston	W7TRO	444.4	162.2	7510
ID	Rathdrum	KC7TIG	444.25	110.9	8350
IL	Downers Grove	W9DUP	145.43	107.2	5370
IL	Chicago	KP4EOP	443.975	114.8	4134
IL	Hanover Park	WA6TMJ	223.78	100	7970
IL	Dixon	W9DXN	444.8	114.8	4350
IL	Chicago	N9VMR	440.9	100	4512
IL	Barrington	N9EP	442.8	114.8	4630
IL	Danville	N9UWE	443.45	88.5	4670
IL	Aurora	W9CEQ	444.3	114.8	4850
IL	Belleville	K9GXU	444.625	127.3	4979
IL	Deer Park	KP4EOP	444	114.8	7040
IN	West Lafayette	W9YB	146.76	88.5	4315
IN	Fort Wayne	W9FEZ	145.33		8380
IN	Goshen	W9BIF	224.82	146.2	4927
IN	Kirksville	WB9TLH	443.05	136.5	4187
IN	Culver	N9GPY	443.925	131.8	4961
IN	Plymouth	K9WZ	147.285	131.8	4330
IN	Indianapolis	K9DC	147.315	94.8	4735
IN	Anderson	KB9VE	147.09	110.9	4834
IN	Indianapolis	N9ILS	224.58	127.3	8912
IN	Williams	N9UMJ	442.25	136.5	4253
IN	Indianapolis	K9IP	443.425	94.8	4730
IN	Culver	N9GPY	444.925	131.8	4960
IN	Terre Haute	NS9M	443.025		7810
KS	Colby	NW0K	146.82	156.7	3608
KS	Goodland	KS0GLD	147.03	88.5	3769
KS	Hays	N7JYS	147.045	131.8	3917
KS	Ottawa	KX0N	147.39	151.4	7989
KS	Wallace	WA0VJR	444.525	146.2	3148
KS	Olathe	KE5BR	442.2	151.4	3534
KS	Russell	N7JYS	442.475	131.8	3913
KY	Somerset	N4AI	224.3		4458
KY	Nancy	AC4DM	146.88	77	8321
KY	Williamsburg	KB4PTJ	444.05	100	4076
KY	Nancy	AC4DM	443.6	100	4209
KY	Bowling Green	W4WSM	444.1		4678
KY	Henderson	KY4K	444.725	82.5	4945
LA	New Orleans	W5MCC	146.86	114.8	3914
LA	Houma	W5YL	147.3	114.8	8402
LA	De Ridder	WB5UGT	443.25	173.8	3486
LA	Alexandria	N5ZUA	444.975	173.8	3517
LA	Lafayette	W5NB	443.8	103.5	7221
LA	Baton Rouge	WB5LHS	444.625	156.7	8266
MA	Wrentham	N1UEC	927.4875	131.8	4486
MA	Hopkinton	N3HFK	927.8875	131.8	4624
MA	Boston	K1RJZ	927.0625	DPL244	4977

State	*City*	*Call Sign*	*Repeater Output Frequency (MHz)*	*CTCSS*	*Node*
MA	Marlborough	W1MRA	927.7	DPL244	4978
MA	Salem	NS1RA	927.75	131.8	8682
MA	Marlborough	W1MRA	449.925	88.5	4133
MA	Framingham	WA1NVC	448.175	88.5	4610
MA	Brookline	W1CLA	446.325	146.2	4942
MA	Boston	KB1GXW	223.86	100	4314
MA	New Bedford	NB1MA	145.11	67	4245
MA	Scituate	W1QWT	145.39		4320
MA	Springfield	W1TOM	146.67	127.3	4322
MA	Danvers	NS1RA	145.47	136.5	4427
MA	Fairhaven	W1SMA	145.49	67	4617
MA	Canton	K1BFD	146.745	146.2	4632
MA	Norwood	W1JLI	147.21	100	4393
MA	Framingham	W1FY	147.15	100	4355
MA	Bridgewater	W1MV	147.18	67	4388
MA	Wrentham	N1UEC	147.09	146.2	4751
MA	Whitman	WA1NPO	147.225	67	8691
MA	Marshfield	N1ZZN	927.475	131.8	4571
MA	Braintree	AE1TH	442.5	118.8	4086
MD	Clarksville	WA3KOK	448.725	107.2	4542
MD	Ocean City	N3KZS	147.015	156.7	4234
MD	Manchester	WA0OJS	146.895	107.2	7070
MD	Baltimore	W3YT	146.865	123	8676
MD	Baltimore	N3CDY	440	100	4040
MD	Ocean City	N3HF	443.45	151.4	4291
MD	Silver Spring	N3HF	443.45	156.7	4712
MD	Severn	KP4IP	442.4	100	7192
MD	Boonsboro	KD3SU	442.95	94.8	8657
MD	Ashton	WA3KOK	927.725	156.7	4088
MI	Pinckney	W2GLD	446.425	131.8	4615
MI	Grand Rapids	N8JPR	223.92	94.8	4167
MI	Lowell	W8LRC	145.27	94.8	4635
MI	Hudsonville	K8TB	440.5	94.8	4835
MI	Beverly Hills	W8HP	443.225	107.2	4502
MI	Bangor	K8BRC	147.36	94.8	4642
MI	Grand Rapids	K8SN	442.175	103.5	4168
MI	Holland	K8DAA	443.825	94.8	4373
MI	Muskegon	N8KQQ	442.95	94.8	4391
MI	Milan	W2PUT	444.1	82.5	4428
MI	Stutsmanville	N8DNX	442.375	107.2	4450
MI	Maybee	K8RPT	442.825	100	4529
MI	Charlotte	N8HEE	443.625	100	7930
MI	Ishpeming	KB0P	443.5	100	8993
MN	Minnetonka	N0BVE	145.45		3590
MN	Mankato	N0PBA	147.24	136.5	3239
MN	Fairmont	N0PBA	444.35	136.5	3945
MN	Shoreview	K9EQ	444.075	114.8	4779
MN	North Branch	K0DMF	443.875	146.2	8193

State	City	Call Sign	Repeater Output Frequency (MHz)	CTCSS	Node
MO	Kansas City	N0NDP	444.45		3309
MO	Kansas City	KD0EAV	444.05	151.4	3759
MO	Kansas City	K0AMJ	443.325	141.3	3849
MO	Nixa	K0NXA	442.275	162.2	3995
MO	St. Louis	KB5YZY	146.85	141.3	3453
MO	St. Louis	KB0TUD	443.45		3591
MO	St. Louis	W0MA	442.875	127.3	3934
MO	St. Louis	K0GFM	442.825	127.3	3616
MO	Holden	N0NDP	444.375	107.2	7894
MT	Billings	N7VR	449.75	100	3398
MT	Bozeman	KB7KB	448.35	100	3692
MT	Eureka	KC7CUE	145.43	100	3363
MT	Libby	KB7SQE	444.35	100	3056
MT	Lakeside	KA7G	442.625	123	7068
NC	Hendersonville	W4FOT	146.64	91.5	4686
NC	Newport	K4GRW	145.45		4903
NC	Wilmington	N4JDW	145.17	88.5	7480
NC	Clayton	N4TCP	443.675	146.2	4637
NC	Buxton	K4OBX	442.425	100	8536
NC	Raleigh	KD4RAA	146.775	100	4260
NC	Raleigh	KD4RAA-2	441.725	100	4270
NC	Waynesville	K4RCC	444.875	131.8	4397
NC	Hendersonville	N2CKH	443	127.3	7280
ND	Fargo	KB0IXM	145.49	82.5	4549
ND	Wheatland	KC0SHM	444.375	123	7478
NE	Lincoln	K0RPT	145.145	123	3915
NE	Ainsworth	WM0L	147.36	131.8	3142
NE	Hastings	W0WWV	443.2		3258
NE	Omaha	KG0S	443.925	103.5	7536
NE	Grand Island	KC0MWM	439.7	162.2	7479
NH	Derry	K1CA	146.85	85.4	4561
NH	Derry	N1TEC	441.55	127.3	7220
NJ	Blue Anchor	KB2AYS	445.125	131.8	4449
NJ	Brigantine	K2ACY	447.575	156.7	4466
NJ	Asbury Park	W2NJR	449.525	141.3	4935
NJ	Brick	N2QKV	224.76	131.8	8929
NJ	Springfield	W2OEM	147.505	123	4377
NJ	Camden	WB3EHB	444.3	203.5	4546
NJ	Freehold	KB2RF	440.3	141.3	4665
NJ	West Orange	WA2JSB	146.415	85.4	4469
NJ	Westampton	KC2QVT	448.325	127.3	3740
NJ	South River	WB2SNN	443.55	141.3	4287
NJ	Lyndhurst	KC2JES	441.25	127.3	4329
NJ	West Orange	N2MH	442.6	141.3	4740
NJ	Sayreville	K2GE	443.2	141.3	4789
NJ	Wood-Ridge	W2RN	443.75	141.3	7290
NM	Santa Fe	K9GAJ	449.275	146.2	3939
NM	Lordsburg	WB5QHS	145.25	88.5	3093

State	*City*	*Call Sign*	*Repeater Output Frequency (MHz)*	*CTCSS*	*Node*
NM	Albuquerque	KB5GAS	147.38	162.2	3676
NM	Albuquerque	NM5HD	145.37	162.2	7706
NM	Albuquerque	K6LIE	224.48		3285
NM	Clovis	WS5D	444.45	88.5	3713
NM	Albuquerque	NO5DE	442.475	100	3979
NM	Rio Rancho	KC5IPK	442.75	162.2	7855
NV	Las Vegas	N3TOY	927.1125		3418
NV	Las Vegas	WB9STH	927.425	82.5	3088
NV	Las Vegas	W7HTL	446.2	77	3166
NV	Las Vegas	N7ARR	447.725	107.2	3194
NV	Henderson	KE7OPJ	447.65	123	3336
NV	Las Vegas	KP4UZ	447.775	114.8	3395
NV	Pahrump	N7ARR	449.75	123	3491
NV	Pahrump	N7MRN	448.35	103.5	3571
NV	Las Vegas	WB9STH	447.425	173.8	3629
NV	Las Vegas	N7ARR	447	123	3641
NV	Mesquite	N7ARR	449.75	123	3705
NV	Henderson	K7IZA	447.8	100	3724
NV	Las Vegas	KF6QYX	447.4	100	3911
NV	Las Vegas	NK2V	447.075	100	7918
NV	Las Vegas	N7ARR	145.37	123	3290
NV	Tonopah	N7ARR	146.64	123	3396
NV	Amargosa Valley	N7ARR	146.91	123	7337
NV	Las Vegas	N7ARR	147	123	3260
NV	Clark County	N7SGV	147.18		3376
NV	Pioche	N7ARR	147.12	123	7244
NV	Reno	N7ARR	441.65	123	3082
NV	Las Vegas	WO3B	449.45	100	3632
NV	Las Vegas	W7AOR	448.225	123	3646
NV	Elko	W7LKO	444.95	100	3806
NV	Reno	N7TGB	443.175	123	5560
NV	Gerlach	KD6KAC	444.175	100	7249
NV	Reno	N7ACM	442.85	141.3	7397
NY	Buffalo	N2LYJ	927.325	88.5	4844
NY	Plainview	KE2EJ	447.2	136.5	4016
NY	Bayshore	WA2RYY	448.175	107.2	4148
NY	Bethpage	W2YMM	449.3	156.7	4265
NY	Eastern Long Island	K1IMD	449.975	94.8	4480
NY	Manhatten	WA2ZLB	447.825	107.2	4551
NY	Sag Harbor	K2GLP	448.675	141.3	4878
NY	Selden	K2TC	445.725	91.5	8186
NY	New York	WA2CBS	445.075	114.8	8232
NY	Staten Island	KC2GOW	445.125	141.3	8327
NY	West Islip	KK2NY	223.86	156.7	7737
NY	New Windsor	WB2BQW	145.25	100	3390
NY	Albany	K2ALB	147.12	100	3499
NY	Malverne	NC2EC	146.67	136.5	4223
NY	Manorville	N2NFI	145.37	136.5	4411

State	City	Call Sign	Repeater Output Frequency (MHz)	CTCSS	Node
NY	Eden	WB2JPQ	146.835	88.5	4715
NY	Potsdam	K2CC	146.895	151.4	4747
NY	East Hampton	N2NEI	145.27	136.5	4819
NY	New Hyde Park	WA2GUG	145.41	114.8	4827
NY	Long Island	W2RGM	147.075	136.5	4951
NY	S. Bristol	WR2AHL	145.11	110.9	8058
NY	New Paltz	K2MTB	447.925	118.8	4666
NY	GlenOaks	W2VL	146.85	136.5	4438
NY	Rochester	WR2ROC	146.79	110.9	4252
NY	Chatham	WA2PVV	444.1	100	3387
NY	New York City	N2VYS	51.11	136.5	4204
NY	Wellsville	KC2VUX	147.21	123	4025
NY	Cortland	KB2FAF	147.18	71.9	4090
NY	Middletown	WA2ZPX	147.39	123	4130
NY	East Windham	N2LEN	147.15	114.8	4207
NY	Selden	W2KPQ	147.375	136.5	4478
NY	Lancaster	W2SO	147.255	107.2	4908
NY	Rochester	K2GXT	147.075	110.9	5800
NY	Nyack	WB2RRA	147.165	114.8	5930
NY	Buffalo	WB2JPQ	444.15	88.5	4068
NY	Macedon	KB2SOZ	444.925	88.5	4222
NY	Rochester	WR2ROC	444.25	110.9	4250
NY	Flushing	WB2JSM	444.2	136.5	4277
NY	Ithaca	AF2A	449.025	103.5	4306
NY	Buffalo	K2ILH	444		4591
NY	Hauppauge	WR2UHF	444.7	114.8	4700
NY	Brooklyn	K2RMX	446.825	141.3	4915
NY	Branchport	N2HLT	434.05	100	7720
NY	New York City	WB2HWW	440.7	114.8	7820
NY	Staten Island	KC2RQR	442.3	141.3	8643
OH	Cleveland	WR8ABC	146.88	110.9	4282
OH	Lima	KT8APR	145.37	107.2	4370
OH	Toledo	WJ8E	147.345	103.5	4071
OH	Cleveland	KB8ENV	147.52	123	3425
OH	Delta	K8LI	147.285	103.5	4479
OH	Akron	WB8CXO	147.33	110.9	4710
OH	Pataskala	W8NBA	147.33	123	8094
OH	Kettering	W8KMC	147.075		8131
OH	Archbold	WD8IEJ	145.41		8866
OH	Sandusky	KL0AD	444.2	103.5	3468
OH	Eaton	W8VFR	444.9375	67	4106
OH	Columbus	K8EHB	443.55		4186
OH	Chardon	KF8YK	444.8125	131.8	4203
OH	Dayton	WB8VSU	442.3	123	4235
OH	Dayton	WF8M	443.775	131.8	4267
OH	Dayton	W8AK	442.925	123	4523
OH	Columbus	W8DIG	443.65	179.9	4694
OH	Pleasant Plain	NG8Y	444.4375		4718

State	*City*	*Call Sign*	*Repeater Output Frequency (MHz)*	*CTCSS*	*Node*
OH	Warren County	WE8N	442.425	77	5690
OH	Marietta	K8KHW	444.125	103.5	8322
OH	Bellbrook	N8NQH	444.875	94.8	8421
OH	Mason	W8SAI	444.95	131.8	8577
OK	Oklahoma City	W5PAA	146.85	141.3	3761
OK	Oklahoma City	W5DEL	145.25	103.5	3867
OK	Bartlesville	W5NS	146.76	88.5	7764
OK	Bartlesville	KB5KZS	443.125	88.5	3050
OK	Lawton	WX5LAW	444.075	123	3704
OK	Altus	WX5ASA	442.05	100	8115
OK	Oklahoma City	W5DEL	443.3	162.2	8440
OR	Portland	AH6LE	146.92	107.2	3000
OR	Eugene	KC7RJK	145.5	100	3543
OR	Medford	W9PCI	145.33	100	7700
OR	Portland	W7RAT	440.4	123	3039
OR	Lake Oswego	K7RPT	147.12		3231
OR	Portland	N7PIR	440.45	103.5	3420
OR	Portland	WA7BND	443.05	123	3916
OR	Salem	WA7ABU	444.95	100	7638
OR	Buxton	W7RY	444.025	77	7951
OR	Portland	K7QDX	927.125	103.5	5050
PA	Philadelphia	WB0CPR	449.775	141.3	4882
PA	Cochranville	WB3LGG	449.675	94.8	7340
PA	Laporte	N3XXH	145.31	167.9	4038
PA	Hummelstown	KF3EM	146.925	114.8	4354
PA	Harrisburg	W3ND	145.29	88.5	7060
PA	Mountville	KA0JQO	147.105	94.8	4288
PA	Media	K3TAT	147.195		4790
PA	Pottsville	W3SC	147.345	131.8	4867
PA	Pottstown	K3ZMC	443.55	131.8	4317
PR	Aguadilla	WP4LHN	448.575	100	7675
PR	Rio Grande	KP4EOP	448.15	100	7777
PR	Maricao	KP4IP	147.13	100	7008
PR	Hatillo	WP3HY	447.575	100	7578
RI	Cumberland	K1TSR	927.675		4335
SC	Simpsonville	AA4LB	146.73	100	4200
SC	Charleston	N4SJW	145.45	123	4557
SC	Columbia	N7GZT	442.2	82.5	3220
SD	Aberdeen	N0AHL	147.03	146.2	7046
SD	Mina	KC0QJZ	443	141.3	3868
SD	Sioux Falls	K9VKG	444.2	82.5	3908
SD	Watertown	KB0LCR	443.725	146.2	3263
TN	Gleason	KA4BNI	145.47	100	4364
TN	Nashville	W4RPT	145.37		4660
TN	Nashville	AF4TZ	147.015	114.8	4900
TN	Collegedale	KA6UHV	443.575	131.8	4169
TN	Hohenwald	K4TTC	442	100	4705
TN	Chattanooga	W4YI	442.425		7520

State	City	Call Sign	Repeater Output Frequency (MHz)	CTCSS	Node
TX	Eagle Pass	W5EVH	146.64	100	3338
TX	Laredo	W5EVH	146.94	100	3378
TX	Port Aransas	KG5BZ	145.29	110.9	3456
TX	Bonham	K5FRC	145.47		3602
TX	Aubrey	K5RNB	145.27	100	3751
TX	Victoria	K5COD	145.19	103.5	3951
TX	Odessa	N5XXO	444.1	162.2	3035
TX	Fort Worth	N5VAV	441.85	110.9	3832
TX	Arlington	K5SLD	444.2	100	3412
TX	Austin	K5VPW	147.32	114.8	3364
TX	Commerce	WB5MQP	147.02	167.9	3711
TX	Bayou Vista	N5ZUA	147.04	100	3753
TX	Loving/Graham	K7KAB	147	110.9	3969
TX	Laredo	W5EVH	147.12	100	5380
TX	Corpus Christi	W5DCH	147.1	107.2	5841
TX	Groves	N5BZM	147.2	118.8	7645
TX	Houston	N5XWD	444.3	123	3018
TX	McKinney	N5GI	0		3079
TX	El Paso	N5FAZ	442.125	103.5	3097
TX	College Station	W5AC	443.05	88.5	3127
TX	Houston	KE5HTA	441.875	114.8	3283
TX	Port Lavaca	W5KTC	442.675	103.5	3299
TX	Pedernales Falls	N5ZTW	444.325	114.8	3357
TX	Georgetown	NA6M	444.525	100	3402
TX	Wimberly	KE5FGY	444.15	114.8	3539
TX	Beeville	W5LOS	444.925	136.5	3639
TX	Pharr	N5SIM	440.6	82.5	3657
TX	Dallas	N5GI	442	127.3	3695
TX	Bastrop	WB5UGT	444.3	203.5	3696
TX	Fort Worth	K5MOT	444.3	110.9	3747
TX	San Antonio	WD5IEH	443.575	141.3	3795
TX	Lufkin	WB5UGT	444.425	203.5	3829
TX	Houston	AD5OU	443.525	136.5	3843
TX	Houston	WA5DTR	444.25	192.8	3869
TX	Plum Grove	WB5UGT	444.175	103.5	3962
TX	Gonzales	WD5IEH	443.125	141.3	3986
TX	Houston	K5DX	442	103.5	3989
TX	Wichita Falls	N5LEZ	444.975	192.8	4640
TX	Canyon Lake	W5ERX	444.45	114.8	7149
TX	Bonham	K5FRC	443.75	100	7901
TX	Harlingen	K5VCG	443.6	114.8	3600
UT	Ameican Fork	KB7TEB	449.175	131.8	3065
UT	Big Water	W7WAC	145.51		3362
UT	Castle Dale	K7SDC	449.05	88.5	3270
UT	Castle Dale	WX7Y	448.55	88.5	3280
UT	Cedar City	WA7GTU	449.9	100	3574
UT	Clearfield	NJ7J	449.95	123	3876
UT	Clearfield	K0NOD	448.825	123	4654

State	City	Call Sign	Repeater Output Frequency (MHz)	CTCSS	Node
UT	Clearfield	N7SWW	147.52		7401
UT	Huntsville	W7DBA	448.025	123	3211
UT	Salt Lake City	N7GTE	448.425	100	3837
UT	Layton	K7NEL	445.5		7232
UT	Layton	K7NEL	145.67		7517
UT	Logan	W7BOZ	449.3	103.5	7576
UT	Magna	KD7KQG	438.025	123	3584
UT	Manti	WB7REL	146.66	100	3576
UT	Monroe	AC7OD	147.5		3771
UT	Provo/Salt Lake City	W7SP	146.76		3352
UT	Salt Lake City	K7MLA	147.14	127.3	3215
UT	Salt Lake City	WA7GIE	449.425	100	5620
UT	Salt Lake City	W7DES	146.44		3578
UT	St George	W7DRC	146.64	100	7935
UT	Winchester Hills	KA7STK	449.425	203.5	3310
UT	Logan	AC7O	147.2	103.5	3381
VA	Lynchburg	WA1ZMS	224.18	100	5330
VA	Charlottesville	KG4HOT	224.6	151.4	8478
VA	Richmond	W4MEV	224.42	74.4	8635
VA	Hillsville	K4EZ	146.895	103.5	3569
VA	Charlottesville	K4DND	145.45	151.4	4703
VA	Petersburg	KE4SCS	146.985	127.3	4769
VA	Cumberland	WW4GW	146.79	110.9	8134
VA	Front Royal	K4QJZ	51.94	141.3	4331
VA	Richmond	W4RAT	146.88	74.4	4424
VA	Richmond	W4RAT	442.55	74.4	4995
VA	Hampton	KA4VXR	147.225	136.5	4183
VA	McLean	W4CIA	147.21		4721
VA	Williamsburg	KB4ZIN	147.105		4943
VA	Isle of Wight	WT4RA	147.195	100	8373
VA	Petersburg	KG4YJB	444.275	103.5	4055
VA	Roanoke	KS4BO	443.675	110.9	4208
VA	Richmond	KC4VDZ	442.3	114.8	5770
VA	Muck Cross	KB2AHZ	442	100	8187
VA	Roanoke	K4IJ	444.175	103.5	8226
VI	St. Thomas	KP2O	146.81	100	8784
VT	Bolton	WB1GQR	145.15	100	7230
WA	Spokane	N7BFS	224.98	107.2	3250
WA	Kennewick	W7UPS	145.39	103.5	3223
WA	Whidbey Island	W7AVM	146.86	127.3	3333
WA	Spokane Valley	KE7PG	145.33	100	3502
WA	Spokane	N7FM	146.66	100	3507
WA	Seattle	K7LWH	145.49	103.5	3978
WA	Spokane	KD7DMP	444.15	114.8	3255
WA	Bellingham	K7SKW	147.16	103.5	3276
WA	Oroville	KD7ITP	147.14	103.5	3377
WA	Maple Valley	KF7NPL	147.26	103.5	3615
WA	Spokane	N1NG	147.36		3957

State	*City*	*Call Sign*	*Repeater Output Frequency (MHz)*	*CTCSS*	*Node*
WA	Tacoma	W7DK	147.28	103.5	7110
WA	Otis Orchards	AD7DD	147.14		7205
WA	Issaquah	KF7BIG	442.125	103.5	3067
WA	Chinook	NM7R	444.925	82.5	3105
WA	Kennewick	W7JWC	443.775	203.5	3122
WA	Sequim	AF7DX	444.275	100	3311
WA	Battle Ground	N7QXO	444.65	100	3329
WA	Sequim	KC7LGT	442.125	123	3529
WA	Yacolt	KC7NQU	441.2	107.2	3599
WA	Vancouver	AB7F	442.375	123	3652
WA	Medical Lake	WA7RVV	443.6	100	3755
WA	Seattle	K7SPG	444	103.5	5860
WA	Olympia	K5IN	440.5	110.9	7217
WA	Seattle	W7TWA	441.625	100	7377
WA	Seattle	WW7SEA	444.7	103.5	7378
WA	Seattle	AJ7JA	444.375	88.5	7784
WA	Seattle	WW7SEA	444.55	141.3	7795
WI	Ogdensburg	W9GAP	146.925	118.8	4294
WI	Milwaukee	N9LKH	145.13	127.3	5590
WI	Hubertus	K9JAC	146.85	127.3	7550
WI	Merrill	KB9QJN	146.64	114.8	4618
WI	Green Bay	N9DKH	147.075	107.2	4619
WI	Wausau	W9BCC	146.82	114.8	4709
WI	Wausau	W9BCC	444.3	114.8	4380
WI	La Crosse	W9UUM	444.75	131.8	4994
WV	Hillsboro	KC8LRN	224.22	91.5	4126
WV	Buckhannon	AA8CC	146.925	103.5	8550
WV	Elkins	AB8E	442.1	162.2	4737
WY	Gillette	K7RDC	449.75	123	3307
WY	Jackson	W7TAR	447.7	123	3464
WY	Sinclair	KD7SU	448.3	100	7102
WY	Casper	KD7AGA	449.575	173.8	7707
WY	Rawlins	N7RON	146.7	162.2	7045
WY	Rock Springs	N7ABC	444.5	123	7955
Canada					
AB	Edmonton	VE6HM	147.06	100	1068
AB	Lethbridge	VA6IRL	146.97		1270
AB	Red Deer	VE6QE	147.15		1353
AB	Porcupine Hills Lookout	VE6AAH	145.21	103.5	1890
AB	Edmonton	VE6RES	147.12	100	1909
AB	Edmonton	VE6AFP	147.21		1919
BC	Vancouver	VE7RHS	145.27	100	1000
BC	Nanaimo	VE7ISC	146.64		1003
BC	Vancouver	VE7RHS	441.975	100	1010
BC	Birken	VA7IP	145.49		1011

State	City	Call Sign	Repeater Output Frequency (MHz)	CTCSS	Node
BC	North Vancouver	VE7RNV	444.95		1015
BC	Chemainus	VE7RNA	146.68		1020
BC	Victoria	VE7VIC	146.84	100	1030
BC	Vernon	VE7RVN	444.275		1050
BC	Coquitlam	VE7MFS	145.31		1070
BC	Chilliwack	VE7RAD	444.7		1073
BC	Kamloops	VE7TSI	146.96		1080
BC	Port Alberni	VE7KU	147.24		1120
BC	Nanoose Bay	VA7LPG	444.3	141.3	1130
BC	Squamish	VE7SQR	147		1147
BC	Parksville	VA7RFR	147.08	141.3	1179
BC	Parksville	VE7PQA	147.28	141.3	1180
BC	Richmond	VE7UHF	443.8	100	1190
BC	Vancouver	VA7SCA	444.4	100	1269
BC	Vancouver	VE7RPS	442.225	107.2	1396
BC	Abbotsford / Chilliwack	VE7RVA	146.61	110.9	1461
BC	Kelowna	VE7KTV	147.3	88.5	1473
BC	Chilliwack	VE7VCR	147.22	88.5	1503
BC	Vernon	VE7NOR	444.275		1524
BC	Osoyoos	VE7RSO	146.66		1567
BC	Cranbrook	VE7CAP	146.94		1660
BC	Vancouver	VE7RPT	146.94		1694
BC	Abbotsford	VE7ASM	147.28	110.9	1705
BC	Nanaimo	VE7BSM	444.725	141.3	1755
BC	Nakusp	VE7EDA	146.94		1811
BC	Pitt Meadows	VE7MTY	443.625	156.7	1849
BC	Maple Ridge	VE7RMR	146.8	156.7	1910
BC	Surrey	VE7RSC	147.36	110.9	1980
BC	Whistler	VE7WHR	147.06		2010
MB	Winnipeg	VE4WRS	145.45		1066
MB	Winnipeg	VA4FIL	443.6		1205
MB	Winnipeg	VE4KEY	444.975	664	1553
MB	Swan River	VE4SRR	146.94		1700
MB	Flin Flon	VE4FFR	146.94		1750
NB	Saint John	VE9SJN	147.27		2009
NB	Moncton	VE9TCR	147.345		2133
NB	Fredericton	VE9ZC	147.3		2780
NB	Moncton	VE9SHM	449.325		2805
NL	Grand Falls-Windsor	VO1HHR	146.6		2350
NL	Marystown	VO1MST	146.85		2390
NS	Halifax	VE1NSG	146.94		2050
NS	Beechville	VE1PS	449.25		2064
NS	Greenwood	VE1WN	147.24		2080
NS	Sugarloaf	VE1BHS	145.35		2109
NS	Maitland Bridge	VE1KEJ	147.195		2268
NS	Truro	VE1HAR	147.135		2370
NS	Yarmouth	VE1YAR	146.73		2952

State	*City*	*Call Sign*	*Repeater Output Frequency (MHz)*	*CTCSS*	*Node*
NS	Bridgewater	VE1KIN	147.12		2973
ON	Pickering	VE3SPA	147.375		1404
ON	Ottawa	VE2CRA	146.94	100	2040
ON	Ottawa	VE3RIX	145.45		2596
ON	Vaughan	VE3JOP	443.775	103.5	2069
ON	Toronto	VA3URU	442.475	103.5	2075
ON	Belleville	VE3BIP	146.985	118.8	2090
ON	Hammond	VE3PRV	147.33	110.9	2115
ON	Marmora	VE3OUR	443.475		2176
ON	Ingersoll	VE3OHR	147.27	114.8	2184
ON	Toronto	VE3SKY	146.985		2195
ON	Georgetown	VE3OD	147.135	131.8	2200
ON	Windsor	VE3III	147.06	118.8	2202
ON	Huntsville	VE3MUS	145.27	156.7	2203
ON	Ottawa	VE3TST	444.125	136.5	2210
ON	Edgar	VA3NLS	442.875	156.7	2236
ON	Niagara Region	VE3WCR	147.3	107.2	2248
ON	Whitby	VE3WOM	146.97	156.7	2255
ON	Toronto	VE3NIB	443.5	103.5	2271
ON	Almonte	VA3UW	147.24		2280
ON	Lavent	VE3KJG	146.64		2947
ON	Hamilton	VE3NCF	444.075	131.8	2313
ON	London	VE3SUE	444.4	114.8	2400
ON	Simcoe	VE3SME	146.925	131.8	2405
ON	Kitchener	VE3RBM	444.875	131.8	2410
ON	Ignace	VA3IGN	147.18	123	2414
ON	Waterloo	VE3WFM	147.09	131.8	2430
ON	Toronto	VE3RAK	444.7	103.5	2450
ON	Ballantrae	VA3BAL	147.33	103.5	2461
ON	Parry Sound	VE3RPL	145.49	118.8	2480
ON	Perth	VA3TEL	145.23		2947
ON	Sarnia	VE3WHO	146.955		2524
ON	Omemee	VA3OME	147.09	162.2	2650
ON	Mississauga	VE3RSD	224.62	103.5	2651
ON	Burlington	VE3RSB	147.21	131.8	2680
ON	Barrie	VE3LSR	147.315	156.7	2688
ON	Orangeville	VE3ORX	444.025	103.5	2700
ON	Brampton	VA3OPR	444.95	103.5	2718
ON	Kingston	VE3KBR	146.94	151.4	2750
ON	Kingston	VE3FRG	146.805	203.5	2088
ON	Kingston	VE3FRG	434.8	203.5	2088
ON	Windsor	VE3EOW	145.41	118.8	2759
ON	Atikokan	VE3RIB	147.12		2768
ON	Leamington	VE3TOM	147.3	118.8	2803
ON	Stratford	VE3FCG	444.975	114.8	2843
ON	Little Current	VE3RQQ	444.3		2860
ON	Newmarket	VA3PWR	443.275	103.5	2871
ON	London	VE3NMN	444.925	114.8	2874

State	*City*	*Call Sign*	*Repeater Output Frequency (MHz)*	*CTCSS*	*Node*
ON	Toledo	VE3HTN	146.865		2947
ON	Newmarket	VE3YRC	147.225	118.8	2920
ON	Tweed	VE3RNU	145.37		2947
ON	Mississauga	VE3MIS	145.43	103.5	2998
ON	Mt Pakenham	VE2REH	145.33	110.9	2018
ON	Williamsburg	VE3ESD	443.15	110.9	2141
ON	Pembroke	VE3NRR	146.76		2520
PE	Charlottetown	VE1CRA	146.67		2030
PE	Summerside	VE1CFR	146.85		2363
QC	Cantley	VE2REH	147.105	110.9	2018
QC	Chelsea	VE2CRA	146.94	100	2040
QC	St. Jerome	VA2RMP	443.55	103.5	2006
QC	Gatineau	VE2REH	147.105	110.9	2018
QC	Gatineau	VE2RAO	443.95	123	2332
QC	Quebec City	VE2RAX	146.79	100	2125
QC	Gatineau	VE2RAO	443.95	123	2332
SK	Saskatoon	VE5CMR	443.15		1330
SK	The Battlefords	VE5BRC	147.24		1340
SK	Saskatoon	VE5CC	449.975		1360
SK	Prince Albert	VE5LAK	146.61		1370
SK	Meadow Lake	VE5MLR	147.33		1380
SK	Regina	VE5YQR	147.12		1550
SK	Yorkton	VA5PAR	145.49		1710
SK	Preeceville	VE5SS	146.61		1858
SK	Nipawin	VE5NIP	146.79		2820
YT	Whitehorse	VY1IRL	146.88	100	1500
YT	Haines Junction	VY1RPM	146.88	100	1662

EchoLink Repeaters

The following is a list of repeaters in the United States and Canada that provide EchoLink capability. For more information about EchoLink, see **www.echolink.org**.

Our thanks to Jonathan Taylor, K1RFD, for providing this information.

United States

State	*City*	*Call Sign*	*Repeater Output Frequency (MHz)*	*CTCSS*	*Node*
AK	Bethel	AL7YK	146.1	114.8	14610
AL	Gadsden	K4JMC	147.16	100	242727
AL	Birmingham	K4TQR	146.76	88.5	146760
AL	Brewton	KI4GGH	444.65		373450
AL	Moulton	KN4CI	146.96	107.2	523154
AL	Dothan	N3FU	444.025	107.2	587877
AL	Roanoke	N4BCB	147.22		47197
AL	Opelika	WB4BYQ	147.06	123	392108
AL	Montgomery	WD4JRB	444.45	100	212144
AR	Hot Springs Village	K5UBM	444.725		474900
AR	Nashville	KE5DJC	147.045	94.8	586886
AR	Harrison	KF0PB	224.56		596930
AR	Texarkana	N5MFI	146.62	100	628287
AR	Malvern	W5BXJ	147.36	136.5	147360
AZ	Green Valley	AA7RP	449.225	107.2	1029
AZ	Tucson	K7IOU	224.74	136.5	22474
AZ	Clarkdale	K9FUN	441.775	156.7	282931
AZ	Phoenix	KC7GHT	447.575	151.4	173098
AZ	Sacaton Peak	KE7JVX	444.275	100	422112
AZ	Overard	N7QVU	446.6	100	530421
AZ	Mingus Mt	WB7BYV	927.087	151.4	204752
AZ	Tonopah	WT9S	440.475	123	505324
CA	Selma	AB6MJ	441.525	67	10191
CA	Thousand Oaks	K0AKS	147.15	127.3	5874
CA	Big Bear Lake	K6BB	147.33	131.8	335272
CA	Santa Cruz	K6BJ	146.79	94.8	354814
CA	Sacramento	K6MVR	147	136.5	38951
CA	Los Banos	K6TJS	147.21	123	126601
CA	Livermore	K7FED	442.125	100	6778

State	*City*	*Call Sign*	*Repeater Output Frequency (MHz)*	*CTCSS*	*Node*
CA	San Francisco	KA6TGI	224.52	67	68042
CA	Hemet	KB6JAG	446.88	74.4	416226
CA	Sierra Peak	KD6DDM	146.61	103.5	497278
CA	Madera	KD6FW	146.7	141.3	88988
CA	Redding	KE6CHO	145.11	94.8	390402
CA	Rohnert Park	KE6ZQH	146.52		63213
CA	San Francisco	KF6REK	442.475	114.8	64372
CA	Bakersfield	KG6FOS	444.675	107.2	74416
CA	Fallbrook	KG6HSQ	446.8	127.3	65043
CA	Bakersfield	KG6KKV	147.15	100	56555
CA	Los Altos	KH6N	440.875	100	96932
CA	Adelanto	KI6IES	146.025	91.5	362175
CA	Mountain House	KJ6OBV	146.655	100	587482
CA	Chino Hills	KJ6RAY	445.15	127.3	530401
CA	Adelanto	KR1IS	445.68	100	487258
CA	San Francisco	KR6DD	145.23	100	271122
CA	San Diego	N6DCR	445.68	123	117645
CA	Montebello	N6PMG	449.14		629585
CA	Monterey	N6SPD	441.65	94.8	202044
CA	Escondido	N6WB	146.88	107.2	2846
CA	Hemet	N7OD	145.42	88.5	3341
CA	Covina	N7YMM	449.675	100	123069
CA	San Diego	W1CDM	449.98	88.5	1314
CA	Napa Valley	W6CO	144.8	151.4	70359
CA	Hemet	W6COH	446.88	74.4	39871
CA	Mt Aukum	W6HMT	52.64	88.5	198910
CA	San Jose	W6NSA	441.775	100	67113
CA	Salinas	W6RTF	145.49	100	184524
CA	S Lake Tahoe	WA6EWV	147.24	123	279922
CA	Huntington Beach	WD6AWP	145.14	110.9	448040
CO	Denver	K0GUR	448.325	210.7	24340
CO	Pueblo	KA0SWT	147.48		481174
CO	Fort Collins	KC0RBT	447.45	123	447450
CO	Denver	N0OBA	145.19	131.8	10079
CO	Glenwood Springs	N0SWE	146.88	107.2	243117
CO	Boulder	W0IA	449.55	100	217336
CO	Denver	W0TX	449.35	100	4140
CO	Fort Collins	W0UPS	145.115	100	4236
CO	Winter Park	WA4CCC	447.45	103.5	468062
CT	Salem	K1IKE	440.8	110.9	44080
CT	West Haven	K1SOX	147.505	77	7505
CT	Norwich	KA1CQR	146.73	156.7	638282
CT	Durham	KB1MMR	446.925	77	313834

State	City	Call Sign	Repeater Output Frequency (MHz)	CTCSS	Node
CT	Shelton	N1BDF	146.985	141.3	387772
CT	Norwalk	ND1L	448.075	114.8	610081
CT	New Canaan	W1FSM	146.775	100	107213
CT	Vernon	W1HDN	145.41	141.3	146790
CT	Norwalk	W1NLK	448.075	114.8	46272
CT	Danbury	W1QI	147.3	100	1037
CT	Woodbridge	W1WPD	442.5	77	46633
FL	Durbin	AJ4FR	444.575	127.3	422890
FL	Hollywood	K4ABB	442.9	88.5	329701
FL	Ft Lauderdale	K4FK	147.33	103.5	581415
FL	West Palm Beach	K4LJP	146.97	77	314823
FL	Kissimmee	K4SLB	444.45	103.5	6457
FL	Orlando	K4ZPZ	443.1	103.5	44310
FL	Ocala	KA2MBE	145.43	141.3	161986
FL	Miami	KB4ELI	442.65	94.8	44891
FL	Naples	KC1AR	147.505	100	81270
FL	Merritt Island	KC2UFO	444.775	107.2	302025
FL	St Petersburg	KE4CGL	145.39	203.5	188923
FL	Sun City	KE4ZIP	147.225	146.2	587115
FL	Ft Lauderdale	KF4LZA	443.625	110.9	48646
FL	Balm	KF4MM	145.21	77	342674
FL	Palm Coast	KG4IDD	145.47	123	24216
FL	Dunnellon	KI4LOB	147.36	123	317405
FL	Melbourne	KI4SWB	442.4	107.2	44342
FL	Orange Park	KI4UWC	146.925	156.7	465626
FL	Ft Lauderdale	KI4VFB	443.75	110.9	47873
FL	Freeport	KJ4EZZ	145.23	100	564764
FL	Lake Wales	KJ4IDH	147.33	127.3	429535
FL	Cape Coral	KN2R	444.725	136.5	41712
FL	Palm Coast	N2TDI	145.41	123	102826
FL	Kissimmee	N4ARG	147.21	103.5	47210
FL	Stuart	N4BG	444.9	107.2	315546
FL	Port Charlotte	N4FOB	442.7	136.5	495622
FL	Orlando	N4HHA	443.4	103.5	390721
FL	Panama City	N4JTC	145.21		322151
FL	Boynton Beach	NR4P	444.65	127.3	237703
FL	Delray Beach	W2GGI	147.075	110.9	88477
FL	West Palm Beach	W2WDW	443.875	110.9	41119
FL	Sun City Center	W4KPR	147.09	162.2	311633
FL	Titusville	W4REN	146.91		350095
FL	Port St Joe	W4WEB	147.3	103.5	495353
FL	Milton	W5CL	145.49	100	629156
FL	New Port Richey	WA4GDN	146.67		46670

State	City	Call Sign	Repeater Output Frequency (MHz)	CTCSS	Node
FL	Naples	WB2QLP	146.67	136.5	389568
GA	Newport Beach	AK6TT	449.28	127.3	589232
GA	Hinesville	KF4MND	145.47		406496
GA	Brunswick	KG4PXG	146.685		8345
GA	Lafayette	KJ4ILK	442.3	94.8	416775
GA	Warner Robins	N4CI	146.85		311671
GA	Toccoa	N4DME	147.33	127.3	505625
GA	Dahlonega	N4KHQ	146.835	100	137890
GA	Savannah	W4SGA	146.97	123	416682
GA	Lawrenceville	WB4QDX	444	127.3	23551
GA	Dallas	WD4LUQ	444.7	77	204551
GA	Cochran	WM4B	145.11		292763
HI	Hilo	AH6JA	145.31		471133
IA	Denison	KD0JZS	144		501320
IA	Ottumwa	KE0BX	146.97	100	13213
IA	Clarion	N0AGE	146.955	103.5	617318
IA	Grimes	N0INX	444.725	151.4	460526
IA	Mt Pleasant	WB0VHB	147.165	156.7	339174
ID	Meridian	K7WIR	224.88	100	477476
ID	Middleton	KD7QAS	443.85	100	410789
ID	Boise	N7WTF	145.29	100	517296
IL	Northbrook	AA9VI	442.725	114.8	7641
IL	Champaign-Urbana	K9CU	146.76	162.2	8231
IL	Alton	K9HAM	145.23	79.7	204755
IL	Downers Grove	W9DUP	145.43	107.2	5370
IL	Clinton	KB9GIG	146.985		509749
IL	Dallas City	KC9JIC	145.33	82.5	506709
IL	Tuscola	KC9PXI	444.45	123	548372
IL	Lake Zurich	KD9GY	443.85	114.8	78073
IL	Peoria	KT9Y	444.05	103.5	473545
IL	New Lenox	N2BJ	444.4	141.3	27022
IL	Oak Forest	N9ZD	443.275	114.8	161122
IL	Greenville	W9KXQ	147.165	103.5	228190
IL	Winbago	W9TMW	442.35	88.5	280970
IL	Peoria	W9UFF	146.76		97114
IL	Orland Park	WD9HGO	444.85	71.9	55233
IL	Peoria	WX9PIA	444.05	103.5	629244
IN	Decatur	AB9SO	443.725		16145
IN	Lawrenceburg	K9GPS	443.875	146.2	110888
IN	Wolf Lake	N9MTF	147.27	131.8	147270
IN	Bloomington	W9AML	146.94	103.5	576672
IN	Kokomo	W9KRC	147.375		529155

State	City	Call Sign	Repeater Output Frequency (MHz)	CTCSS	Node
IN	Michigan City	W9LY	146.97	131.8	193001
IN	Ft Wayne	W9VD	444.3	131.8	37585
KS	Merriam	K0KN	927.712	151.4	307578
KS	Hutchinson	KB0FJI	147.12		105011
KS	Wichita	W0VFW	145.27		358668
KY	Murray	K4MSU	443.8	91.5	207370
KY	Corbin	KF4IFC	444.275	79.7	16883
KY	Richmond	KF4REN	146.865	192.8	451988
KY	Benton	KI4HUS	145.39	118.8	328811
KY	Columbia	KY4TF	147.195	136.5	499695
KY	Louisville	N4KWT	443.975	100	600977
KY	Louisville	W4CN	147.18	79.7	425970
KY	Paducah	W4NJA	147.06		458276
LA	W Orleans	KB5AVY	444.975	118.8	7052
LA	Shreveport	KC5XR	146.7		520478
LA	Pineville	KD5DFL	144		169091
LA	Morgan City	W5BMC	146.44		507010
LA	Kinder	W5ELM	146.925	203.5	92225
LA	Lafayette	W5EXI	147.04		370324
MA	Worcester	N1OHZ	443.3	100	421904
MA	Milford	W1BRI	446.825	100	3819
MA	Marlborough	W1MRA	449.925	88.5	4133
MA	Martha's Vineyard	W1FC	147.345	88.5	242147
MA	Gloucester	W1GLO	145.13		480139
MA	Springfield	W1TOM	146.67	127.3	21095
MA	Brewster	WA1YFV	147.255	67	403358
MA	Westford	WB1GOF	146.955	74.4	380799
MD	Chestertown	K3ARS	147.375	156.7	249466
MD	Annapolis	KA2JAI	442.3	107.2	90911
MD	Silver Spring	N3HF	443.45	156.7	84345
MD	Hagerstown	N3UHD	442.65	79.7	481682
MD	Frederick	N3WZ	144	167.9	635158
MD	Frederick	W3ICF	146.73	141.3	14613
MD	Greenbelt	WA3NAN	146.835		40045
MD	Silver Spring	WB3GXW	147.225	156.7	147225
ME	Augusta	W1PIG	145.29	100	15061
MI	Ironwood	K8DLM	146.76		573763
MI	Big Rapids	K8FSU	443.9		389477
MI	West Branch	K8OAR	146.94	103.5	457206
MI	Rockwood	K8UH	927.687	411	74379
MI	Newberry	KC8QZG	146.61		240336
MI	Calumet	KD8JAM	147.315	100	405654
MI	New Hudson	N8BK	442.775	107.2	331551

State	City	Call Sign	Repeater Output Frequency (MHz)	CTCSS	Node
MI	Grosse Pointe	N8BNA	146.74	100	540557
MI	Grand Haven	N8FQ	145.49	94.8	469574
MI	Lansing	NE8K	146.94	100	620311
MI	Battle Creek	W8DF	224.24		360014
MI	Menominee	W8PIF	147	107.2	481872
MI	Traverse City	W8TVC	145.27	114.8	56464
MI	Ann Arbor	W8UM	145.23	100	301138
MI	Roscommon	WF8R	145.45		205097
MI	Detroit	WW8GM	443.075	123	99846
MN	Brainerd	W0UJ	145.13		233515
MN	North Branch	K0DMF	443.875	146.2	23958
MN	Madison	K0LQP	146.73		275196
MN	Chaska	KA0KMJ	443	100	150438
MN	Ellendale	KA0PQW	224.64	110.9	267582
MN	Ellendale	KA0PQW	442.925	114.8	267582
MN	Hampton	K0JTA	147.36	136.5	9636
MN	Hutchinson	KB0WJP	147.375	146.2	252922
MN	Karlstad	KA0NWV	145.47	77	23832
MN	Knife River	KC0MKS	443.85		239444
MN	Litchfield	KC0CAP	443.8	146.2	72238
MN	Blue Earth	KC0NPJ	147	100	484492
MN	Edina	KG0BP	444.85	110.9	320484
MN	Minneapolis	KA0KMJ	444.425	114.8	192344
MN	Avon	KG0CV	443.65		619724
MN	New Brighton	N0FKM	145.29	114.8	268460
MN	Glenville	NX0P	444.975	100	513917
MN	Ramsey	K0MSP	145.37	107.2	4655
MN	Ramsey	K0MSP	444.975	114.8	9644
MN	Redwood Falls	KB0CGJ	146.865	141.3	29141
MN	Maple Lake	W0EQO	145.23	114.8	309436
MN	Minnetonka	N0BVE	145.45		89680
MN	Pinewood	KC0FTV	442.225	118.8	414532
MN	Rochester	W0STV	146.625	100	420993
MN	Wabasso	KB0CGJ	444.525	141.3	29141
MN	Wyoming	N0VOW	146.895	82.5	342623
MN	St Louis Park	W0EF	146.76		77598
MN	West St Paul	W0DCA	147.39	77	255364
MO	Ava	N0RFI	146.625	110.9	280629
MO	Ballwin	WD0FNS	1282.6	141.3	87622
MO	Boonvle	KA0GFC	442.7	77	239712
MO	Chillicothe	K0MPT	147.225		408916
MO	Holts Summit	KB4VSP	444.875	127.3	471579
MO	Joplin	N0CSW	145.35	91.5	543723

State	City	Call Sign	Repeater Output Frequency (MHz)	CTCSS	Node
MO	Independence	N0OEV	444.575	186.2	50031
MO	Lamoni	W0YO	146.73		127303
MO	Kansas City	KD0EAV	444.05	151.4	422327
MO	Laurie	KA0RFO	146.955	192.8	154449
MO	Mansfield	K5HEZ	147.09	162.2	65704
MO	Mexico	AA0RC	147.255		296997
MO	Nixa	K0NXA	145.27	162.2	113667
MO	Raytown	K0GQ	145.17	151.4	403841
MO	Rolla	WB9KHR	443.6	114.8	231270
MO	Springfield	W0PM	147.225	162.2	231270
MO	St Charles	N0KQG	443.25	151.4	84139
MO	St Louis	K0AMC	146.925	192.8	185485
MO	St Louis	W0SLW	147.39	100	4527
MO	St Louis	N0OBG	147.39	100	4527
MO	St Louis	WB0QXW	145.21	123	466277
MO	Rolla	WB9KHR	443.6	114.8	231270
MS	Hattiesburg	N5LRQ	147.315	136.5	410934
MS	Wiggins	N5UDK	147.51	136.5	385237
MS	Clinton	W5PFR	444	100	112793
MS	Sharon	W5PPB	145.45	77	39154
MT	Butte	KB8ML	449.4	131.8	449400
MT	Havre	KF7CNW	447.125	100	606109
MT	Bozeman	KL7JGS	449.9	100	207198
MT	Billings	N7YHE	147.2	100	104664
MT	Toston	WR7AGT	449.3	131.8	449300
MT	Macdonald Pass	WR7HLN	444.1	131.8	111730
NC	Shelby	AI4RF	147.045	127.3	603431
NC	Franklin	K2BHQ	145.49	151.4	400632
NC	Raleigh	K4JDR	441.725	100	42704
NC	Waxhaw	K4WBT	146.865	94.8	84335
NC	Bakersvle	KC4TVO	146.5		469253
NC	Burnsvle	N2EMD	146.895	123	611482
NC	Greensboro	N5ODE	145.15	100	590301
NC	Wilmington	NI4SR	147.375	67	559874
NC	Winston Salem	W4NC	146.64	100	384157
NC	Greensboro	W8JFQ	145.25	88.5	249694
NC	Elizabeth City	WA4VTX	444.3	131.8	312941
NC	Ahoskie	WB4YNF	444.2	131.8	219598
NC	Greenville	WD4JPQ	145.35	131.8	73724
ND	Fargo	KK7AV	438.2	114.8	201723
ND	Valier	N0CAV	147.15		331011
NE	Lincoln	K0SIL	147.195		393355
NE	Mccook	KD0MTI	446.925		557714

State	City	Call Sign	Repeater Output Frequency (MHz)	CTCSS	Node
NE	Omaha	KG0S	443.925	103.5	572977
NE	Neligh	N0NNE	146.835	131.8	225896
NE	Tucson	WD7F	146.94	110.9	1125
NH	Henniker	K1PDY	146.895	100	321904
NH	Derry	NM1D	146.745	114.8	501047
NH	Goffstown	W1AKS	147.135		600646
NH	Hanover	W1FN	145.33	100	363356
NJ	Hillsdale	K2ZD	446.975	141.3	350129
NJ	Forked River	KC2GUM	146.445	131.8	548032
NJ	Clifton	KB2N	224.36		336643
NJ	Tinton Falls	WB2ABT	147.045	67	562568
NJ	Fair Lawn	W2NPT	145.47	107.2	300501
NJ	Greenbrook	W2QW	442.25	141.3	311438
NJ	Morristown	WS2Q	145.37	151.4	330007
NM	Farngton	KB5ITS	146.76	100	249880
NM	Belen	KC5OUR	146.7		632009
NM	Gallup	KC5WDV	449.75	100	6810
NM	Albuquerque	KC7YWB	146.7		617907
NM	Ruidoso	KR5NM	146.92	100	346920
NM	Alamogordo	N6CID	442.95	85.4	474106
NM	Rio Raho	NM5RR	443	100	6748
NM	Roswell	W5GNB	444.55		383142
NV	Pahrump	AD7DP	146.85	173.8	331480
NV	Henderson	K7RSW	448.875	114.8	7745
NV	Reno-Sparks	KA7ZAU	146.895	123	357948
NV	Reno	KC5CZX	444.175	123	512874
NV	Reno	N7MLF	224.7		419865
NV	Sun Valley	N7TGB	443.175	123	
NV	Gerlach	W7BRD	440.175	100	7238
NV	Las Vegas	WR7NV	145.35	100	5069
NY	Lowville	AB2XN	146.955		427886
NY	Cortland	K2IWR	147.18	71.9	614766
NY	Johnstown	K2JJI	146.7		510372
NY	Brooklyn	K2RMX	446.825	141.3	255375
NY	Ghent	K2RVW	147.21		372818
NY	Farmingville	K2SPD	145.31	118.8	45717
NY	Napanoch	KC2FBI	147.535	100	461132
NY	East Greenbush	KC2IVI	147.33	146.2	48899
NY	Niagara Falls	N3AU	224.42	107.2	8718
NY	East Aurora	W2DXA	147.39	88.5	421912
NY	Staten Island	W2RJR	223.84	141.3	168188
NY	Troy	W2SZ	146.82		428054
NY	Bethpage	W2YMM	449.3	156.7	1224

State	City	Call Sign	Repeater Output Frequency (MHz)	CTCSS	Node
NY	Pompey	WW2N	145.27	103.5	64224
OH	East Liverpool	K8BLP	146.7	162.2	30022
OH	Delaware	K8EHB	443.55		262738
OH	Delta	K8LI	147.285	103.5	43515
OH	Lancaster	K8QIK	147.03	71.9	405426
OH	Kent	K8SRR	146.895	110.9	508081
OH	Defiance	K8VON	147.09		215376
OH	N Royalton	K8YSE	444.075	131.8	6563
OH	Independence	K8ZFR	146.82	110.9	343470
OH	Keen	KB8HEA	147.045		52824
OH	Salem	KB8MFV	147.285	88.5	43358
OH	Cleveland	KB8WLW	145.41	110.9	146520
OH	New Matamoras	KD8LXJ	145.5	103.5	480098
OH	Chardon	KF8YK	444.813	131.8	44024
OH	Polk	KG8FV	442.15	88.5	353296
OH	Middletown	W8BLV	146.61	77	323719
OH	Hamilton	W8CCI	146.97	118.8	369045
OH	Columbus	W8DIG	443.65	179.9	443650
OH	Van Wert	W8FY	146.7	107.2	315705
OH	Vandalia	W8GUC	444.662	123	296027
OH	North Olmsted	W8IZ	444.012	131.8	3049
OH	Dayton	WB8SMC	147.135		43988
OK	Enid	N5UBY	147.375		255318
OK	Blanchard	W5LHG	444.625	127.3	212302
OR	Medford	K7RVM	444.45		572479
OR	Joseph	KB7DZR	147	103.5	323569
OR	Bend	KB7LNR	146.36		211222
OR	Tlamook	KD7YPY	442.975		266640
OR	Mt Defiance	KF7LN	927.162	151.4	97040
OR	Washington Cty	KJ7IY	145.27	107.2	82962
OR	Portland	KW7HAM	927.137	131.8	335671
OR	Umatilla	W6NMR	147.02	103.5	200848
OR	Central Point	W9PCI	145.33	100	385956
OR	Salem	WA7ABU	444.95	100	592473
OR	Canby	WB7QAZ	442.9	123	429797
PA	Eagleville	AA3E	146.835	88.5	570945
PA	Pine Grove	AA3RG	146.64	82.5	149493
PA	Somerset	AK3J	147.195	123	506066
PA	Erie	K3WWA	147.315		380167
PA	Coraopolis	KA3IRT	444.15	100	176150
PA	Reading	KA3KDL	445.715	100	41809
PA	Derry	KE3PO	145.15	131.8	314685
PA	Lancaster	N3FYI	446.475	114.8	24905

State	City	Call Sign	Repeater Output Frequency (MHz)	CTCSS	Node
PA	Ridgway	N3RZL	144.39		391112
PA	Beaver	N3TN	146.85	131.8	286427
PA	Yeadon	N3UXQ	444.5	151.4	610840
PA	Matamoras	W2TAO	145.57	100	278703
PA	Illiamsport	W3AHS	147.3	151.4	277377
PA	Easton	W3IFI	145.27	151.4	346074
PA	Pittsburgh	W3KWH	147.03	123	147030
PA	Center Valley	W3LR	443.59	151.4	230150
PA	Meadville	W3MIE	147.03	186.2	349977
PA	Newtown Square	WA3NNA	442.6	131.8	480581
PA	Philadelphia	WB0CPR	449.775	141.3	403147
PA	Mohnton	WB3FPL	147.18	110.9	570686
PR	Humcaco	KP4MCR	147.19	71.9	78470
PR	Juncos	WP4SE	146.87		128413
SC	Union	K4USC	146.685		264598
SC	Aiken	N2ZZ	145.35	100	5764
SC	Myrtle Beach	NE4SC	145.4	123	376627
SC	Greenwood	W4GWD	147.165	107.2	584003
SC	Greenville	W4NYK	146.61		545072
SC	Liberty	WA4SSJ	443.45	110.9	7226
SC	Union	K4USC	146.685		264598
SC	Pickens	WX4PG	442.4	127.3	4031
SD	Sioux Falls	KD0ZP	444.9	146.2	74079
SD	Clear Lake	W0GC	444.3	136.5	578534
TN	Memphis	KA7UEC	443.3	107.2	236040
TN	Oakland	KE7UA	146.94		194927
TN	Athens	KG4FZR	442.275	141.3	608045
TN	Monteagle	NQ4Y	145.41	114.8	2043
TN	Memphis	W4RSG	443.1	107.2	299408
TX	Fort Worth	K5AMM	441.675		463758
TX	Austin	K5AXW	442.15	186.2	136958
TX	Rowlett	K5FER	441.325	162.2	394576
TX	Harlingen	K5RAV	146.7	114.8	67509
TX	Austin	K5TRA	927.125		242585
TX	Humble	KB5WAQ	147.28	100	302646
TX	Amarillo	KC5EZO	444.05	88.5	307304
TX	San Angelo	KC5EZZ	441.75	162.2	76362
TX	Sweetwater	KC5NOX	145.25	162.2	252137
TX	Yorktown	KD5BXV	146.64	103.5	237915
TX	Coppell	KD5OEW	441.8	107.2	484806
TX	Corsicana	KD5OXM	145.29	146.2	502586
TX	Richmond	KD5YOU	145.49	123	6709
TX	Leander	KE5RS	441.6	100	8327

State	*City*	*Call Sign*	*Repeater Output Frequency (MHz)*	*CTCSS*	*Node*
TX	Cedar Park	KE5TNO	145.37	103.5	4735
TX	Denison	KF5AUD	147	100	550670
TX	Midland	KK5MV	444.525	156.7	79706
TX	Cleburne	KY5O	444	136.5	100032
TX	Austin	N0GSZ	146.86	146.2	608525
TX	Port Arthur	N5BZM	147.2	118.8	458549
TX	Austin	N5JGX	441.875	100	341697
TX	Longview	N5REO	145.35	136.5	62763
TX	Austin	N5SMN	146.94		43388
TX	Dallas	N5UA	444.675	110.9	257890
TX	Temple	N5ZXJ	145.31	123	1947
TX	Georgetown	NA6M	147.08	100	147080
TX	Nash	NG5U	146.62	100	617912
TX	Cedar Park	W2DB	441.35	114.8	424532
TX	Belton	W5BEC	147.14	123	99000
TX	Jasper	W5JAS	147	118.8	480827
TX	Austin	W5JWB	441.775	131.8	366882
TX	Port Lavaca	W5KTC	147.02	103.5	463336
TX	Denton	W5NGU	444.05	110.9	165165
TX	Humble	W5OMR	441.7	23	4817
TX	Borger	W5RAW	147.06		387265
TX	San Antonio	W5ROS	147.34	123	294707
TX	Austin	WA5YZD	444.1		43010
TX	San Angelo	WB5VRM	444.35	162.2	412402
TX	Conroe	WD5CFJ	224.24	103.5	50073
TX	San Antonio	WD5IEH	443.575	141.3	3763
UT	Castle Dale	K7SDC	449.05	88.5	64264
UT	West Point	KE7OJJ	447.075	123	401462
UT	Provo	N7BYU	145.33	100	96806
UT	Panguitch	N7NKK	147.16	100	551925
UT	Logan	W7BOZ	449.3	103.5	558836
UT	Sandy	N7GAD	448.35		132045
UT	Provo	N7MKP	449.975	131.8	42450
UT	Orem	KD7LRJ	145.47	100	44866
UT	Cedar City	N7AKK	147.06		91510
UT	St. George	KA7STK	146.91	100	88660
UT	Clearfield	K0NOD	448.825	123	332144
UT	Price	K7SDC	449.05	88.5	6426
UT	Castledale	WX7Y	448.55	88.5	69883
UT	West Point	KE7OJJ	447.05	123	401462
UT	Provo BYU	N7BYU	145.33	100	96806
UT	Logan	W7BOZ	449.3	103.5	558836
UT	Cedar City	WA7GTU	449.9	100	193065

State	*City*	*Call Sign*	*Repeater Output Frequency (MHz)*	*CTCSS*	*Node*
UT	Manti	WB7REL	146.66	100	212338
WA	Lakewood	KB7IOG	446.05		342398
WA	Winthrop	KB7SVP	147.22	100	354157
WA	Issaquah	KF7BIG	442.125	103.5	529661
WA	Apple Valley	KF7NPL	147.26	103.5	566369
WA	Tacoma	N3KPU	147.22	146.2	561264
WA	Spokane	W7TRF	443.475	88.5	282039
WA	Seattle	WA7HJR	444.65	131.8	482474
WA	Ephrata	WB7WSP	444.9	103.5	411928
WI	Green Bay	K9JQE	223.94	107.2	69044
WI	Iola	N5IIA	444.9	114.8	273426
WI	Ogdensburg	W9GAP	146.925	118.8	409257
WI	Westby	W9HQ	146.715	131.8	455438
WI	Park Falls	W9PFP	444.75	110.9	590359
WI	Germantown	WD9IEV	444.525	114.8	222430
WV	Petersburgva-	K7SOB	442.15	127.3	140739
WV	Salt Rock	K8SA	145.11	110.9	2175
WV	Huntington	KB8TGK	443.85	162.2	150734
WV	Hillsboro	KC8LRN	224.22	91.5	1266
WV	Beckley	W8VT	443.8	141.3	606945

State	City	Call Sign	Repeater Output Frequency (MHz)	CTCSS	Node
Canada					
AB	Calgary	VA6RP	444.75		287151
AB	Lethbridge	VE6ROT	146.79		113371
BC	Delta	VA7DEP	444.425		168180
BC	Sooke	VE7RAH	145.43	100	49290
BC	Richmond	VE7RMD	147.14	79.7	526129
BC	Prie George	VE7SDE	147.12		638952
BC	Mcleod Lake	VE7ZBK	147.33		373776
NB	Miramichi	VE1NWC	146.73		128650
NB	Fredericton	VE9DGP	147.36		237401
NB	Woodstock	VE9DKS	147.18		288465
NB	Saint John	VE9SJN	147.27		285237
NS	West Chezzetcook	VE1ESC	147.03		94232
NS	Harmony	VE1HAR	147.135		161248
ON	Brockville	VE3IWJ	146.82	100	158695
ON	Cornwall	VE3PGC	443.65	110.9	463095
ON	Kapuskasing	VA3NKP	146.93		524524
ON	Hearst	VA3YHF	146.7		534843
ON	Timmins	VE3AA	147.06		122823
ON	Huntsville	VE3KR	446.55	156.7	184398
ON	Mississauga	VE3MIS	145.43	103.5	404792
ON	Huntsville	VE3MUS	146.775	156.7	150444
ON	Toronto	VE3RAK	444.7	103.5	2068
ON	Hamilton	VE3RFI	443.25	151.4	327534
ON	Burlington	VE3RSB	147.21	131.8	417869
ON	London	VE3TTT	147.18	114.8	10741
ON	Whitby	VE3WOM	146.97	156.7	484101
ON	Mississauga	VE3YPL	145.45	85.4	414510
ON	Smiths Falls	VE3RLR	147.21		525543
ON	Toronto	VE3YYZ	443.05	103.5	223557
QC	St-Calixte	VE2OCZ	146.85	123	4796
QC	Jonquière	VE2RHJ	145.17		148167
QC	Mascouche	VE2RHL	147.345	103.5	107300
QC	Quebec	VE2RIG	146.88	100	39339
QC	Montreal	VE2RVL	147.075	103.5	613838
SK	Rocanville	VE5LCM	146.31		425463
SK	Preecevle	VE5SS	146.61		581167

Index of Advertisers